FOREWORD

THE ROOTS OF ORGANIC CHEMISTRY lie deep in man's curiosity about life and his desire to understand more fully the complex chemical processes that occur in living organisms. Before a rational attack could be made on these and related problems of molecular structure, however, it became necessary, through exploratory researches, to identify the chemical transformations exhibited by particular atomic groupings under specified experimental conditions. As a result of this effort, there had evolved, by 1920, a massive but beautifully organized body of knowledge often referred to as the chemistry of "functional groups." In the course of these studies, the organic chemist learned a great deal about the geometry of complex molecules and formulated many useful generalizations relating molecular structure to chemical reactivity and physical properties.

By 1930, a new trend was under way. The quantum and wave mechanics were providing a more precise picture of chemical bonds, and the English school of organic chemists had made remarkable progress toward formulating a unified electronic theory of organic chemistry. At the same time, the old collision theory of reaction kinetics — which made little reference to molecular structure and thus was never popular with organic chemists — was falling into disrepute. By contrast, the newer transition-state theory, which regarded the "activated complex" as a discrete molecular entity, was quickly adopted.

The application of these new physico-chemical concepts to the systematic study of the general transformations which organic molecules undergo really ushered in the era of modern organic chemistry, and the exciting field of reaction mechanisms was born. On the experimental side, the introduction of new techniques, the availability of isotopes for tracer studies, and the accessibility of modern spectrometers and other instruments greatly facilitated the whole effort.

The author of a modern textbook of organic chemistry attempts to explain "why" organic compounds react as they do, and is not satisfied with a qualitative description of "how" they react. Where possible, he wishes to give a more exact and quantitative explanation for these phenomena.

Attempts to modernize classical descriptive textbooks, by inserting into them in a piecemeal fashion some of the newer concepts, have not been very successful. Professors Morrison and Boyd, on the other hand, have written a unified book that incorporates all of the major theoretical concepts and modern techniques used by the organic chemist, and have shown how these can be used to "explain" the chemistry of carbon compounds. In so doing, they demonstrate clearly — even to the beginning student — that organic chemistry, in spite of its inherent complexities, has become a relatively exact science and is no longer a mere empirical collection of experimental facts. Many of the most brilliant recent advances in the elucidation of the chemistry of natural products have been made by those who understand and can apply these modern physico-chemical concepts.

RICHARD T. ARNOLD
Alfred P. Sloan Foundation

4-6 1150

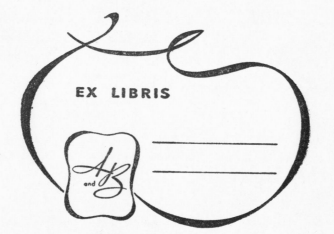

EX LIBRIS

ORGANIC CHEMISTRY

FIGURE 7.5. Scale models of (*a*) cyclohexane in chair conformation, on left, and in boat conformation, on right, (*b*) cyclopentane, (*c*) cyclodecane, and (*d*) bromocyclohexane with equatorial bromine, on left, and with axial bromine, on right.

ORGANIC CHEMISTRY

Robert Thornton Morrison and Robert Neilson Boyd

Associate Professors of Chemistry
New York University

Foreword by Richard T. Arnold
of the Alfred P. Sloan Foundation

ALLYN AND BACON, INC.

Boston

First printing..............July, 1959
Second printing............June, 1960
Third printing........September, 1960
Fourth printing........February, 1961
Fifth printing............August, 1961
Sixth printing..............May, 1962
Seventh printing.........October, 1962

Library of Congress catalog card number: 59–10054

PRINTED IN THE UNITED STATES OF AMERICA

OUR PRIMARY AIM in writing this book was to present organic chemistry as it actually is today: a vigorous science based on a well developed theory. We intended this book to develop in the student an understanding of the principles of organic chemistry that would serve equally well as the basis for further study of chemistry or as background in such related fields as biology, medicine, dentistry, and engineering. We aimed to treat basic concepts fully and clearly, in a way that could be followed by the average student, and yet also to stimulate and challenge the better student.

Is our primary aim reasonable and proper? *Can* one and *should* one teach modern organic chemical theory to beginning students? Our experience, in teaching the basic content of this book for a number of years to both chemistry majors and pre-professional students, has shown us that beginning students can grasp the principles underlying organic chemistry about as well as graduate students. We have found that students taught in this way are not deprived of the traditional kind of training, and actually do *better* with the classical problems of the organic chemist: synthesis and analysis. As in any field of science, the student needs a framework of ideas to support and hold together the multitude of individual facts. In addition — and this factor must not be underrated — the enthusiasm kindled by *ideas* acts as a powerful stimulus to fruitful study.

When we speak of "organic chemical theory," we mean the *structural theory*, which is founded on the principle that the properties of a compound arise from the structure of its molecules — the principle that has guided the development of organic chemistry since the days when chemists first wrote formulas as letters joined by dashes, and divided compounds into families on the basis of these formulas. Today, structure has come to mean not only the sequence of atoms in a molecule, but also their arrangement in space, the strength of the forces holding the atoms together, and the distribution of electrons over them. The theory links structure to properties by such bridges as acidity and basicity, reaction rate and equilibrium, transition state and activation energy, configuration and conformation. The theory deals with reaction mechanism, since the dependence of behavior on structure can often be seen only when one looks beneath the surface and examines the path taken by the reaction.

It attempts to account not only for the way in which variations in structure cause variations in reactivity, but also — much more important — for the fact that a particular compound undergoes a particular reaction at all.

In presenting this theory, we show how the shapes of atomic orbitals can be considered to give rise, in a simple way, to the shapes of molecules and the distribution of electrons over them, and how these in turn give rise to the characteristic properties of a compound. As practicing chemists do, we make use of both simple orbital theory and resonance among valence-bond structures, and point out the equivalence of the two methods of representation.

We discuss reactivity and orientation from the standpoint of relative rates of competing reactions or, where appropriate, from the standpoint of competing equilibria. We interpret relative rates in terms of the transition state, since this interpretation is not only more rigorous, but also much more easily understood than that based on the resting molecule; furthermore, it permits a more unified treatment of reactivity and orientation. Thus *ortho,para* (or *meta*) orientation can be seen to stem directly from the structure of the transition state, and to have little to do with the particular way — via resonance or inductive effect — in which we consider a substituent group to release (or withdraw) electrons. Nitration of an aromatic ring, addition of hydrogen iodide to an alkene, and dehydration of an alcohol come down to the same thing — how well and at which positions the molecule can accommodate a developing positive charge; falling into the same pattern are quite analogous reactions controlled by the accommodation of a negative charge or an odd electron.

Finally, the energy considerations implicit in *any* discussion of reactivity and orientation — no matter how qualitative — are discussed in detail, and the simplifying assumptions that the organic chemist must make are pointed out.

From the standpoint of organization, the book is the kind called *integrated:* that is, aliphatic and aromatic compounds are taken up together. This integration avoids compartmentalization and over-emphasis of the differences between the two classes of compounds. It permits the interplay between various parts of the molecule to be illustrated more strikingly. Synthetic operations of practical importance can be introduced early, and laboratory work can be started with easily handled aromatic compounds.

We have deliberately retained the traditional organization by family, because it emphasizes the dependence of properties on molecular structure. As the student gradually becomes acquainted with different kinds of structures, he becomes acquainted with different kinds of chemical and physical properties.

We have not isolated such concepts as stereochemistry, rate and equilibrium, acidity and basicity, and reaction mechanism in chapters of their own. Instead these basic tools are introduced whenever they are first needed to account for the facts, and then are used throughout.

The sequence of chapters is by and large the usual one for integrated textbooks. The chemistry of carbonyl compounds is so extensive and important that they are taken up, as a family, last among the monofunctional compounds; the aldol condensation is a logical bridge to the carbanion chemistry that makes up a large part of the chapters on dicarboxylic acids, keto acids, and unsaturated carbonyl compounds. The last ten chapters, devoted to polyfunctional compounds, emphasize the interaction between functional groups, and at the same time provide a review, through *use*, of the chemistry studied earlier.

Bearing in mind that this was to be a textbook, we put into each chapter the amount of material that, in our experience, a student can be expected to learn. To keep this vast, rapidly growing subject within the limits of a one-year course, we had to pick sparingly from new material and to prune out much that has been traditional.

We carefully screened methods of synthesis, and kept only those actually used widely by chemists. A realistic grasp of organic synthesis must surely include some understanding of the limitations of "general" methods; for this reason we have included discussion of such matters as the competition between substitution and elimination, the dangers of rearrangement, and the problem of isomer separation. We were obliged to omit many important aspects of theory to make room for proper discussion of those we retained.

To the average student, then, we aimed to present as much chemistry as he could cover, in language that he could understand. At the same time, we wanted to give the better student an opportunity to try himself: to learn more chemistry and, especially, to use this chemistry in the way a practicing organic chemist does. We have tried to achieve this flexibility in two ways: through optional chapters and through problems.

The usual one-year course will probably cover only two or three of the last six chapters, leaving several chapters that the student — if he wishes — can try on his own.

Of the thousand-odd problems in the book, most are intended as study guides and check-points. Many, however, are designed to let the student extend the scope of the book in facts and in theory. Some of these problems are inserted in the body of the text, at points where questions might naturally arise in the curious mind. Wherever feasible we have used actual experimental data as the basis for problems; proof of structure of natural products, for example, is handled almost entirely in this way.

We believe that the aims of our book are good ones; we hope that we have in some measure achieved them. Whatever the merits of this particular book, its existence may at least help bring into focus the growing feeling among organic chemists: that a change is long overdue. The science of organic chemistry has come of age, and needs to be taught on that basis.

ROBERT THORNTON MORRISON
ROBERT NEILSON BOYD

Washington Square
New York City

ACKNOWLEDGMENTS

WE GRATEFULLY ACKNOWLEDGE indebtedness to our students for their stimulating response during the development of this book; to our colleagues for helpful discussions; to Felix Cooper for many fine illustrations; to Richard T. Arnold for critical reading of the entire manuscript; and, most of all, to our wives, Joan and Carol, for their encouragement, understanding, and unfailing patience.

R. T. M.
R. N. B.

CONTENTS

ORGANIC CHEMISTRY

_____

Chapter one

STRUCTURE AND PROPERTIES

1.1 Organic chemistry

Organic chemistry is the chemistry of the **compounds of carbon.**

The misleading name "organic" is a relic of the days when chemical compounds were divided into two classes, inorganic and organic, depending upon where they had come from. Inorganic compounds were those obtained from minerals; organic compounds were those obtained from vegetable or animal sources, that is, from material produced by living organisms. Indeed, until about 1850, many chemists believed that organic compounds *must* have their origin in living organisms, and consequently could never be synthesized from inorganic material.

These compounds from organic sources had this in common: they all contained the element carbon. Even after it had become clear that these compounds did not have to come from living sources but could be made in the laboratory, it was convenient to keep the name *organic* to describe them and compounds like them. The division between inorganic and organic compounds has been retained to this day.

Today, although many compounds of carbon are still most conveniently isolated from plant and animal sources, most of them are synthesized. They are sometimes synthesized from inorganic substances like carbonates or cyanides, but more often from other organic compounds. There are two large reservoirs of organic material from which simple organic compounds can be obtained: *petroleum* and *coal*. (Both of these are "organic" in the old sense, being products of the decay of plants and animals.) These simple compounds are used as building blocks from which larger and more complicated compounds can be made.

What is so special about the compounds of carbon that they should be separated from compounds of all the other hundred-odd elements of the Periodic Table? In part, at least, the answer seems to be this: there are so very many compounds of carbon, and their molecules can be so large and complex.

The number of compounds that contain carbon is many times greater than the number of compounds that do not contain carbon. These organic compounds have been divided into families, which generally have no counterparts among the inorganic compounds.

Organic molecules containing thousands of atoms are known, and the arrangement of atoms in even relatively small molecules can be very complicated. One of the major problems in organic chemistry is to find out how the atoms are arranged in molecules, that is, to determine the structures of compounds.

There are many ways in which these complicated molecules can break apart, or rearrange themselves, to form new molecules; there are many ways in which atoms can be added to these molecules, or new atoms substituted for old ones. Much of organic chemistry is devoted to finding out what these reactions are, how they take place, and how they can be used to synthesize compounds we want.

What is so special about carbon, that it should form so many compounds? Carbon atoms can attach themselves to one another to an extent not possible for atoms of any other element. Carbon atoms can form chains thousands of atoms long, or rings of all sizes; the chains and rings can have branches and cross-links. To the carbon atoms of these chains and rings there are attached other atoms, chiefly hydrogen, but also fluorine, chlorine, bromine, iodine, oxygen, nitrogen, sulfur, phosphorus, and many others. (Look, for example, at cellulose on page 797, chlorophyll on page 836, and oxytocin on page 867.)

Each different arrangement of atoms corresponds to a different compound, and each compound has its own characteristic set of chemical and physical properties. It is not surprising that close to a million compounds of carbon are known today and that thousands of new ones are being made each year. It is not surprising that the study of their chemistry is a special field.

It is a field of immense importance to technology: organic chemistry is the chemistry of dyes and drugs, paper and ink, paints and plastics, gasoline and rubber tires; of the food we eat and the clothing we wear. It is a field that is fundamental to medicine and biology: aside from water, living organisms are made up chiefly of organic compounds, and biological processes are ultimately a matter of organic chemistry.

1.2 The structural theory

The basis of the science of organic chemistry is the **structural theory.** It is the basis upon which millions of facts about hundreds of thousands of individual compounds have been brought together and arranged in a systematic way. It is the basis upon which these facts can best be accounted for and understood.

The structural theory is the framework of ideas about how atoms are put together to make molecules. The structural theory has to do with the order in which atoms are attached to each other, and with the electrons that hold them together. It has to do with the shapes and sizes of the molecules that these atoms form, and with the way that electrons are distributed over them.

A molecule is often represented by a picture or a model — sometimes by several pictures or several models. The atomic nuclei are represented by letters or wooden balls, and the electrons that join them by lines or dots or wooden pegs. These crude pictures and models are useful to us only if we understand what they are intended to mean. Interpreted in terms of the structural theory, they tell us a good deal about the compound whose molecules they represent: how to go about making it; what physical properties to expect of it — melting point, boiling point, specific gravity, the kind of solvents the compound will dissolve in, even whether it will be colored or not; what kind of chemical behavior to expect — the kind of reagents the compound will react with and the kind of products that will be formed, whether it will react rapidly or slowly. We would know all this about a compound that we had never encountered before, simply on the basis of its structural formula and what we understand its structural formula to mean.

1.3   The chemical bond before 1926

Any consideration of the structure of molecules must begin with a discussion of *chemical bonds*, the forces that hold atoms together in a molecule.

We shall discuss chemical bonds first in terms of the theory as it had developed prior to 1926, and then in terms of the theory of today. The introduction of quantum mechanics in 1926 caused a tremendous change in ideas about how molecules are formed. For convenience, the older, simpler language and pictorial representations are often still used, although the words and pictures are given a modern interpretation.

In 1916 two kinds of chemical bond were described: the *ionic bond* by Walther Kossel (in Germany) and the *covalent bond* by G. N. Lewis (of the University of California). Both Kossel and Lewis based their ideas on the following concept of the atom.

A positively charged nucleus is surrounded by electrons arranged in concentric shells or energy levels. There is a maximum number of electrons that can be accommodated in each shell: two in the first shell, eight in the second shell, eight or eighteen in the third shell, and so on. The greatest stability is reached when the outer shell is full, as in the inert gases. Both ionic and covalent bonds arise from the tendency of atoms to attain this stable configuration of electrons.

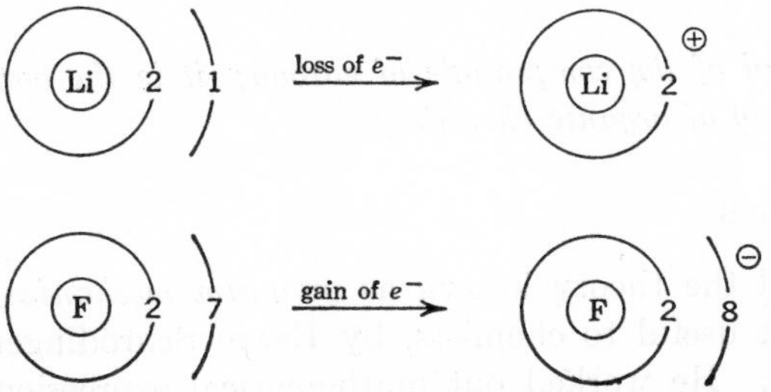

The **ionic bond** results from **transfer of electrons,** as, for example, in the formation of lithium fluoride. A lithium atom has two electrons in its inner shell and one electron in its outer or valence shell; the loss of one electron would leave lithium with a full outer shell of two electrons. A fluorine atom has two electrons in its inner shell and seven electrons in its valence shell; the gain of one electron would give fluorine a full outer shell of eight. Lithium fluoride is formed by the transfer of one electron from lithium to fluorine; lithium now bears a positive charge and fluorine bears a negative charge. The electrostatic attraction between the oppositely charged ions is called an ionic bond. Such ionic bonds are typical of the salts formed by combination of the metallic elements (electropositive elements) on the far left side of the Periodic Table with the non-metallic elements (electronegative elements) on the far right side.

The **covalent bond** results from **sharing of electrons**, as, for example, in the formation of the hydrogen molecule. Each hydrogen atom has a single electron; by sharing a pair of electrons both hydrogens can complete their shells of two. Two fluorine atoms, each with seven electrons in the valence shell, can complete their octets by sharing a pair of electrons. In a similar way we can visualize the formation of HF, H_2O, NH_3, CH_4, and CF_4.

$$H\cdot \ + \ \cdot H \ \longrightarrow \ H\!:\!H$$

$$:\!\overset{..}{\underset{..}{F}}\!\cdot \ + \ \cdot\overset{..}{\underset{..}{F}}\!: \ \longrightarrow \ :\!\overset{..}{\underset{..}{F}}\!:\!\overset{..}{\underset{..}{F}}\!:$$

$$H\cdot \ + \ \cdot\overset{..}{\underset{..}{F}}\!: \ \longrightarrow \ H\!:\!\overset{..}{\underset{..}{F}}\!:$$

$$2H\cdot \ + \ \cdot\overset{..}{\underset{..}{O}}\!: \ \longrightarrow \ H\!:\!\overset{..}{\underset{..}{O}}\!:\ \overset{\textstyle H}{}$$

$$3H\cdot \ + \ \cdot\overset{..}{N}\!: \ \longrightarrow \ H\!:\!\overset{\textstyle H}{\underset{\textstyle H}{N}}\!:$$

$$4H\cdot \ + \ \cdot\overset{.}{\underset{.}{C}}\!\cdot \ \longrightarrow \ H\!:\!\overset{\textstyle H}{\underset{\textstyle H}{C}}\!:\!H$$

$$4:\!\overset{..}{\underset{..}{F}}\!\cdot \ + \ \cdot\overset{.}{\underset{.}{C}}\!\cdot \ \longrightarrow \ :\!\overset{\textstyle :\overset{..}{\underset{..}{F}}:}{\underset{\textstyle :\overset{..}{\underset{..}{F}}:}{F}}\!:\!C\!:\!\overset{..}{\underset{..}{F}}\!:$$

The covalent bond is typical of the compounds of carbon; it is the bond of chief importance in the study of organic chemistry.

1.4 Quantum mechanics

In 1926 there emerged the theory known as *quantum mechanics*, developed, in the form most useful to chemists, by Erwin Schrödinger (of the University of Zürich). He worked out mathematical expressions to describe the motion of an electron in terms of its energy. These mathematical expressions are called *wave equations,* since they are based upon the concept that electrons show properties not only of particles but also of waves.

These wave equations are so complicated that they cannot be solved in an exact way. It has therefore been necessary to work out methods of obtaining approximate solutions called *wave functions.* The nature of the equations is such that the lower the energy value given by a wave function, the more nearly correct the wave function is. Despite the approximate nature of these solutions, quantum mechanics gives answers agreeing so well with the facts that it is accepted today as the most fruitful approach to an understanding of atomic and molecular structure.

1.5 Atomic orbitals

A wave equation cannot tell us exactly where an electron is at any particular moment, or how fast it is moving; it does not permit us to plot a precise orbit about the nucleus. Instead, it tells us the *probability* of finding the electron at any particular place.

The region in space where an electron is likely to be found is called an **orbital.** There are different kinds of orbitals, which have different sizes and different shapes. The particular kind of orbital that an electron occupies depends upon the energy of the electron. It is the shapes of these orbitals that we are particularly interested in, since these shapes determine the arrangement in space of the atoms of a molecule, and even help determine its chemical behavior.

It is convenient to picture an electron as being smeared out to form a cloud. We might think of this cloud as a sort of blurred photograph of the rapidly moving electron. The shape of this cloud is the shape of the orbital. The cloud is not uniform, but is densest in those regions where the probability of finding the electron is highest, that is, in those regions where the average negative charge, or *electron density,* is greatest. Such an electron cloud is said to show the *distribution of charge.*

Let us see what the shapes of some of the atomic orbitals are. The

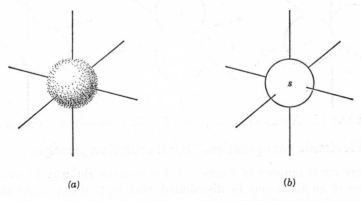

(a)   (b)

FIGURE 1.1. Atomic orbitals: *s* orbital. Nucleus at center.

orbital at the lowest energy level is called the 1s orbital. It is a sphere with its center at the nucleus of the atom, as represented in Figure 1.1. An orbital has no definite boundary since there is a probability, although very small, of finding the electron essentially separated from the atom — or even on some other atom! However, the probability decreases very rapidly beyond a certain distance from the nucleus, so that the distribution of charge is fairly well represented by the electron cloud in Figure 1.1a. For sake of simplicity, we may even represent an orbital as in Figure 1.1b where the solid line encloses the region where the electron spends most (say 95%) of its time.

At the next higher energy level there is the 2s orbital. This, too, is a sphere with its center at the atomic nucleus; it is larger than the 1s orbital.

Next there are three orbitals of equal energy called 2p orbitals, shown in Figure 1.2. Each 2p orbital is dumbbell-shaped. It consists of two lobes with the atomic nucleus lying between them. The axis of each 2p orbital is perpendicular to the axes of the other two. They are differentiated by the names $2p_x$, $2p_y$, and $2p_z$ where the x, y, and z refer to the corresponding axes.

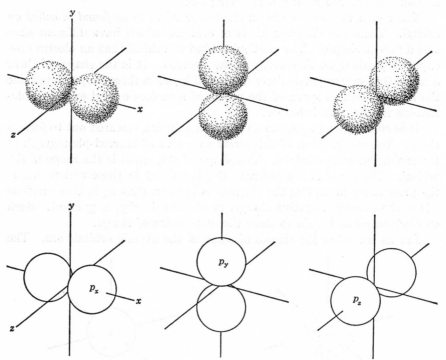

FIGURE 1.2. Atomic orbitals: p orbitals. Axes mutually perpendicular.

1.6 Electronic configuration. Pauli exclusion principle

There are a number of "rules" that determine the way in which the electrons of an atom may be distributed, that is, that determine the *electronic configuration* of an atom.

The most fundamental of these rules is the **Pauli exclusion principle:** *only two electrons can occupy any atomic orbital, and to do so these two must have* **opposite** *spins.* These electrons of opposite spins are said to be *paired.* *Electrons of* **like** *spin tend to get as far from each other as possible.* This tendency is the most important of all the factors that determine the shapes and properties of molecules.

The exclusion principle, advanced in 1925 by Wolfgang Pauli, Jr., of the Institute for Theoretical Physics in Hamburg, Germany, has been called the cornerstone of chemistry.

The first ten elements of the Periodic Table have the electronic configurations shown in Table 1.1.

TABLE 1.1

ELECTRONIC CONFIGURATIONS

	1s	2s	2p		
H	⊙				
He	⊙⊙				
Li	⊙⊙	⊙	○	○	○
Be	⊙⊙	⊙⊙	○	○	○
B	⊙⊙	⊙⊙	⊙	○	○
C	⊙⊙	⊙⊙	⊙	⊙	○
N	⊙⊙	⊙⊙	⊙	⊙	⊙
O	⊙⊙	⊙⊙	⊙⊙	⊙	⊙
F	⊙⊙	⊙⊙	⊙⊙	⊙⊙	⊙
Ne	⊙⊙	⊙⊙	⊙⊙	⊙⊙	⊙⊙

We see that an orbital becomes occupied only if the orbitals of lower energy are filled (e.g., 2s after 1s, 2p after 2s). We see that an orbital is not occupied by a pair of electrons until other orbitals of equal energy are each occupied by one electron (e.g., the 2p orbitals). The 1s electrons make up the first shell of two, and the 2s and 2p electrons make up the second shell of eight. For elements beyond the first ten, there is a third shell containing a 3s orbital, 3p orbitals, and so on.

Problem 1.1 (a) Show the electronic configurations for the next eight elements in the Periodic Table (from sodium through argon). (b) What relationship is there between electronic configuration and periodic family? (c) Between electronic configuration and chemical properties of the elements?

1.7 The covalent bond: bond length and bond strength

The orbitals described in the last section are the ones that are occupied by the electrons of an isolated atom. Now let us see how these atomic orbitals are related to the covalent bonds that an atom makes with other atoms. For convenience we shall picture the molecule being formed by the coming together of the individual atoms, although most molecules are not actually formed this way.

For a bond to form, two atoms must be located so that an orbital of one *overlaps* an orbital of the other; each orbital must contain a single electron. When this happens the two atomic orbitals merge to form a single *bond orbital* which is occupied by both electrons. The two electrons that occupy a bond orbital must have opposite spins, that is, must be paired. Each electron has available to it the entire bond orbital, and thus may be considered to "belong to" both atomic nuclei.

This arrangement of electrons and nuclei contains less energy — that is, is more stable — than the arrangement in the isolated atoms; as a result, formation of a bond is accompanied by evolution of energy. The amount of energy (per mole) that is given off when a bond is formed (or the amount that must be put in to break the bond) is called the **bond strength,** or **bond dissociation energy.** For a given pair of atoms, the greater the overlapping of atomic orbitals, the stronger the bond.

The principle of *maximum overlap*, first stated in 1931 by Linus Pauling of the California Institute of Technology, has been ranked only slightly below the exclusion principle in importance to the understanding of molecular structure.

As our first example let us consider the formation of the hydrogen molecule, H_2, from two hydrogen atoms. Each hydrogen atom has one electron, which occupies the $1s$ orbital. As we have seen, this $1s$ orbital is a sphere with its center at the atomic nucleus. For a bond to form, the two nuclei must be brought closely enough together for overlapping of the atomic orbitals to occur (Figure 1.3). For hydrogen, the system is most stable when the distance between the nuclei is 0.74 A; this distance is called the **bond length.** At this distance the stabilizing effect of overlapping is exactly balanced by repulsion between the similarly charged nuclei. The resulting hydrogen molecule contains 103 kcal/mole less energy than the hydrogen atoms from which it was made. We say that the hydrogen–hydrogen bond has a length of 0.74 A and a strength of 103 kcal.

This bond orbital has roughly the shape we would expect from the merging of two s orbitals. As shown in Figure 1.3, it is sausage-shaped,

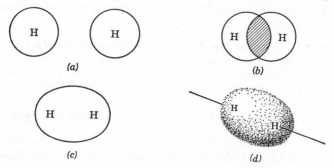

FIGURE 1.3. Bond formation: H_2 molecule. (*a*) Separate s orbitals. (*b*) Overlapping s orbitals. (*c*) and (*d*) The σ bond orbital.

with its long axis lying along the line joining the nuclei. It is cylindrically symmetrical about this long axis; that is, a slice of the sausage is circular. Bond orbitals having this shape are called σ *orbitals* (σ = sigma) and the bonds are called σ *bonds*. We may visualize the hydrogen molecule as two nuclei embedded in a single sausage-shaped electron cloud. This cloud is densest in the region between the two nuclei, where the negative charge is attracted most strongly by the two positive charges.

What factor causes the hydrogen molecule to be more stable than two hydrogen atoms, that is, what gives the covalent bond its strength? It is the increase in electrostatic attraction. In the atom, each electron is attracted by — and attracts — one positive nucleus; in the molecule, each electron is attracted by *two* positive nuclei.

Next, let us consider the formation of the fluorine molecule, F_2, from two fluorine atoms. As we can see from our table of electronic configurations (Table 1.1), a fluorine atom has two electrons in the $1s$ orbital, two electrons in the $2s$ orbital, and two electrons in each of two $2p$ orbitals. In the third $2p$ orbital there is a single electron which is unpaired and available for bond formation. Overlapping of this p orbital with a similar p orbital of another fluorine atom permits electrons to pair and the bond to form (Figure 1.4). The electronic charge is concentrated between the two nuclei, so that the back lobe of each of the overlapping orbitals shrinks to a comparatively small size. Although formed by overlapping of atomic

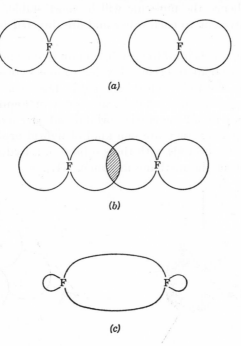

FIGURE 1.4. Bond formation: F_2 molecule. (*a*) Separate p orbitals. (*b*) Overlapping p orbitals. (*c*) The σ bond orbital.

orbitals of a different kind, the fluorine–fluorine bond has the same general shape as the hydrogen–hydrogen bond, being cylindrically symmetrical about a line joining the nuclei; it, too, is given the designation of σ bond. The fluorine–fluorine bond has a length of 1.42 A and a strength of about 38 kcal.

As the examples show, a covalent bond results from the overlapping of two atomic orbitals to form a bond orbital occupied by a pair of electrons. *Each kind of covalent bond has a characteristic length and strength.*

1.8   The covalent bond: bond angle.   Hybrid orbitals

Now let us consider the simplest of organic molecules, *methane*, CH_4. Carbon (Table 1.1) has an unpaired electron in each of two p orbitals, and on this basis might be expected to combine with two hydrogen atoms to form the compound CH_2.   But bond formation is an energy-releasing process, and the tendency is to form as many bonds as possible.   Actually, carbon combines with four hydrogen atoms, which requires four unpaired electrons.   These can be provided if one of the $2s$ electrons is "promoted" to the empty $2p$ orbital.

Judging from our previous discussion, we might now expect carbon to form three bonds of one kind, using the p orbitals, and one bond of another kind, using the s orbital.   But calculations show that the bonds will be strongest, and hence the molecule will be most stable, if the four bonds are exactly equivalent to each other and are directed to the corners of a tetrahedron.

At this stage, it is helpful to visualize a purely imaginary kind of carbon atom, one that is about to become bonded to four hydrogen atoms.   Such a carbon atom is said to be in a *valence state*.   This imaginary carbon atom has four equivalent atomic orbitals, as shown in Figure 1.5.   They are considered to arise by mixing of *one s* orbital and *three p* orbitals, and hence are called *sp³ orbitals;* they are one kind of **hybrid orbital.**   Overlapping of each of these sp^3 orbitals with the s orbital of a hydrogen atom results in the formation of the methane molecule, CH_4.

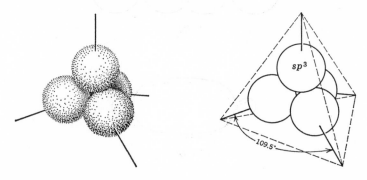

FIGURE 1.5. Atomic orbitals: hybrid sp^3 orbitals.   Axes directed toward corners of tetrahedron.

An extremely important concept emerges here: **bond angle.** The four sp^3 orbitals available for bond formation are directed to the corners of a tetrahedron. Of all arrangements it is the tetrahedral arrangement that permits four orbitals to get as far away from each other as possible. The angle between any two orbitals is the tetrahedral angle 109.5°. For each of these orbitals to overlap most effectively the s orbital of a hydrogen atom, and thus to form the strongest bond, the four hydrogen nuclei must be located at the corners of a tetrahedron (Figure 1.6). The angle between any two carbon–hydrogen bonds must therefore be the tetrahedral angle 109.5°.

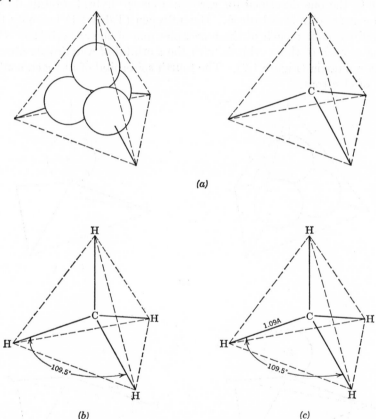

FIGURE 1.6. Bond formation: CH_4 molecule. (*a*) Tetrahedral sp^3 orbitals. (*b*) Predicted shape: H nuclei located for maximum overlap. (*c*) Shape and size.

Experiment has shown that, as calculated, methane has a tetrahedral structure. Each carbon–hydrogen bond has exactly the same length, 1.09 A; the angle between any pair of bonds is the tetrahedral angle 109.5°. It takes 101 kcal/mole to break one of the bonds of methane.

Thus we see that there are associated with covalent bonds not only characteristic bond lengths and bond strengths but also characteristic bond *angles*. These bond angles are determined by the arrangement of the atomic orbitals involved in bond formation, and ultimately go back to the Pauli exclusion principle and the tendency for unpaired electrons to get as far from each other as possible.

Unlike the ionic bond, which is equally strong in all directions, *the covalent bond is a directed bond.* We can begin to see how it is that the chemistry of the covalent bond deals much with molecular size and shape.

1.9 Unshared pairs of electrons

Next let us turn to ammonia, NH_3. Here nitrogen has a valence state similar to the one described for carbon: four sp^3 hybrid orbitals directed to the corners of a tetrahedron. But nitrogen (Table 1.1) has only three unpaired electrons; each of these occupies one of the sp^3 orbitals. Overlapping of each of these orbitals with the *s* orbital of a hydrogen atom results in ammonia (Figure 1.7). The fourth sp^3 orbital of nitrogen contains a pair of electrons.

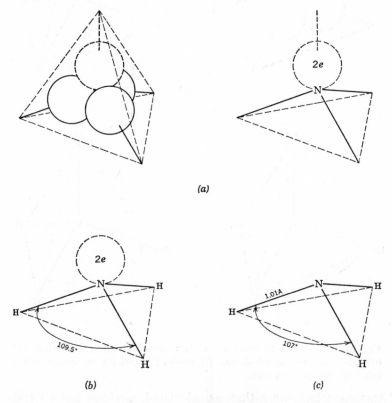

(a)

(b)   (c)

FIGURE 1.7. Bond formation: NH_3 molecule. (*a*) Tetrahedral sp^3 orbitals. (*b*) Predicted shape, showing unshared pair: H nuclei located for maximum overlap. (*c*) Shape and size.

If there is to be maximum overlapping and hence maximum bond strength, the hydrogen nuclei must be located at three corners of a tetrahedron; the fourth corner is occupied by an unshared pair of electrons.

Considering only atomic nuclei, we would expect ammonia to be shaped like a pyramid with nitrogen at the apex and hydrogen at the corners of a triangular base. Each bond angle should be the tetrahedral angle 109.5°.

Experimentally, ammonia is found to have the pyramidal shape calculated by quantum mechanics. The bond angles are 107°, slightly smaller than the predicted value; it has been suggested that the unshared pair of electrons occupies more space than any of the hydrogen atoms, and hence tends to compress the bond angles slightly. The nitrogen–hydrogen bond length is 1.01 A; it takes 111 kcal/mole to break one of the bonds of ammonia.

The sp^3 orbital occupied by the unshared pair of electrons is a region of high electron density. This region is a source of electrons for electron-seeking atoms and molecules, and thus gives ammonia its basic properties (Sec. 1.17).

Problem 1.2 What shape would you expect the ammonium ion, NH_4^+, to have?

Finally, let us consider water, H_2O. The situation is similar to that for ammonia, except that oxygen has only two unpaired electrons, and hence it bonds with only two hydrogen atoms, which occupy two corners

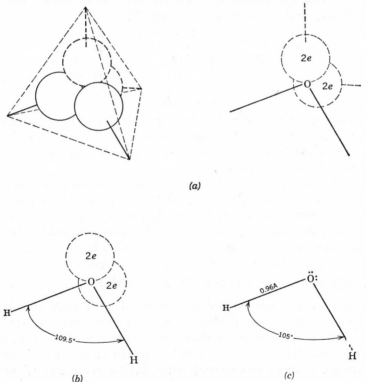

FIGURE 1.8. Bond formation: H_2O molecule. (a) Tetrahedral sp^3 orbitals. (b) Predicted shape, showing unshared pairs: H nuclei located for maximum overlap. (c) Shape and size.

of a tetrahedron. The other two corners of the tetrahedron are occupied by unshared pairs of electrons (Figure 1.8).

As actually measured, the H—O—H angle is 105°, smaller than the calculated tetrahedral angle, and even smaller than the angle in ammonia. Here there are two bulky unshared pairs of electrons compressing the bond angles. The oxygen–hydrogen bond length is 0.96 A; it takes 118 kcal/mole to break one of the bonds of water.

Because of the unshared pairs of electrons on oxygen, water is basic, although less strongly so than ammonia (Sec. 1.17).

1.10   Polarity of bonds

Besides the properties already described, certain covalent bonds have another property: **polarity.** Two atoms joined by a covalent bond share electrons; their nuclei are held by the same electron cloud. But in most cases the two nuclei do not share the electrons equally; the electron cloud is denser about one atom than the other. One end of the bond is thus relatively negative and the other end is relatively positive, that is, there is a *negative pole* and a *positive pole*. Such a bond is said to be a **polar bond,** or to *possess polarity*.

We can indicate polarity by using the symbols δ_+ and δ_-, which indicate *partial* + and − charges. For example:

$$\overset{\delta_+\ \ \delta_-}{\text{H—F}} \qquad \overset{\overset{\textstyle \delta_-}{\text{O}}}{\underset{\text{H}\qquad\text{H}}{\delta_+\diagup\ \diagdown\delta_+}} \qquad \overset{\overset{\textstyle \delta_-}{\text{N}}}{\underset{\underset{\delta_+}{\text{H}\ \ \text{H}\ \ \text{H}}}{\delta_+\diagup\,|\,\diagdown\delta_+}}$$

Polar bonds

We can expect a covalent bond to be polar if it joins atoms that differ in their tendency to attract electrons, that is, atoms that differ in *electronegativity*. Furthermore, the greater the difference in electronegativity, the more polar the bond will be.

The most electronegative elements are those located in the upper right-hand corner of the Periodic Table. Of the elements we are likely to encounter in organic chemistry, fluorine has the highest electronegativity, then oxygen, then nitrogen and chlorine, then bromine, and finally carbon. Hydrogen does not differ very much from carbon in electronegativity; it is not certain whether it is more or less electronegative.

Electronegativity $F > O > Cl, N > Br > C, H$

Bond polarities are intimately concerned with both chemical and physical properties. The polarity of a bond determines the kind of reaction that can take place at that bond, and even affects reactivity at nearby bonds. The polarity of bonds can lead to polarity of molecules, and thus profoundly affect melting point, boiling point, and solubility.

1.11   Polarity of molecules

A molecule is polar if the center of negative charge does not coincide

with the center of positive charge. Such a molecule constitutes a *dipole:*
two equal and opposite charges separated in space. A dipole is often
symbolized by $\longmapsto$ where the arrow points from positive to negative.
The molecule possesses a dipole moment, μ, which is equal to the magnitude
of the charge, e, multiplied by the distance, d, between the centers of
charge:

$$\mu \;=\; e \times d$$

in   in   in

Debye   e.s.u.   Angstroms

units, D

In a way that cannot be gone into here, it is possible to measure the
dipole moments of molecules; some of the values obtained are listed in
Table 1.2. We shall be interested in the values of dipole moments as
indications of the relative polarities of different molecules.

TABLE 1.2

DIPOLE MOMENTS, D

H_2	0	HF	1.75	CH_4	0
O_2	0	H_2O	1.84	CH_3Cl	1.86
N_2	0	NH_3	1.46	CCl_4	0
Cl_2	0	NF_3	0.24	CO_2	0
Br_2	0	BF_3	0		

It is the *fact* that some molecules are polar that has given rise to the
speculation that some bonds are polar. We have taken up bond polarity
first simply because it is convenient to consider that the polarity of a
molecule is a composite of the polarities of the individual bonds.

Molecules like H_2, O_2, N_2, Cl_2, and Br_2 have zero dipole moments, that is,
are non-polar. The two identical atoms of each of these molecules have,
of course, the same electronegativity and share electrons equally; e is
zero and hence μ is zero, too.

A molecule like hydrogen fluoride has the large dipole moment of 1.75 D.
Although hydrogen fluoride is a small molecule, the very highly electronegative fluorine pulls the electrons strongly; although d is small, e is
large, and hence μ is large, too.

Water has a dipole moment of 1.84 D. This is a net dipole moment
(a *vector sum*) resulting from the two individual bond moments, and is
in the direction shown in Figure 1.9. In a similar way ammonia has a
net dipole moment of 1.46 D.

Methane and carbon tetrachloride, CCl_4, have zero dipole moments.
We certainly would expect the individual bonds — of carbon tetrachloride
at least — to be polar; because of the very symmetrical tetrahedral arrangement, however, they exactly cancel each other out (Figure 1.9).
In methyl chloride, CH_3Cl, the polarity of the carbon–chlorine bond is
not cancelled, however, and methyl chloride has a dipole moment of 1.86 D.
Thus the polarity of a molecule depends not only upon the polarity of its
individual bonds but also upon the way the bonds are directed, that is,
upon the shape of the molecule.

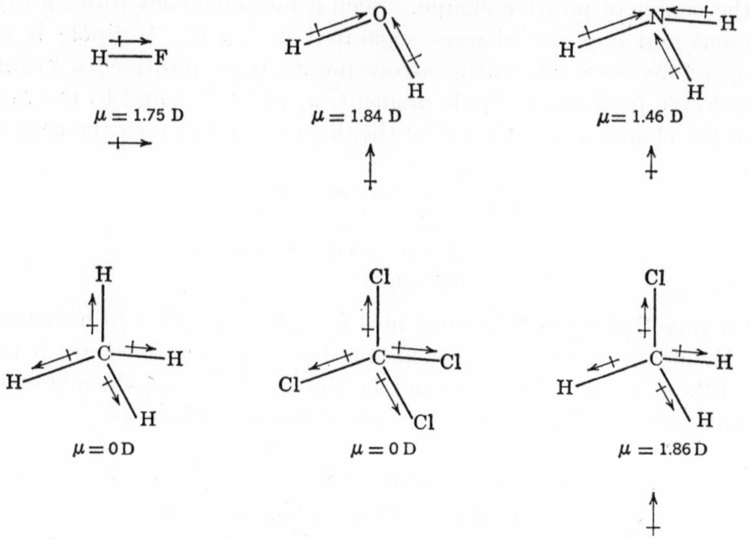

FIGURE 1.9. Dipole moments of some molecules. Polarity of bonds and of molecules.

Dipole moments can give valuable information about the structure of molecules. For example, any structure for carbon tetrachloride that would result in a polar molecule can be ruled out on the basis of dipole moment alone. The evidence of dipole moment thus supports the tetrahedral structure for carbon tetrachloride. (However, it does not prove this structure, since there are other conceivable structures that would also result in a non-polar molecule.)

Problem 1.3 Which of the following conceivable structures of CCl_4 would also have a zero dipole moment? (a) Carbon at the center of a square with a chlorine at each corner. (b) Carbon at the apex of a pyramid with a chlorine at each corner of a square base.

Problem 1.4 Although we would certainly expect a carbon–oxygen bond or a boron–fluorine bond to be polar, the compounds CO_2 and BF_3 have zero dipole moments. Suggest an arrangement of atoms for each compound that would account for the lack of polarity.

Problem 1.5 It is likely that much of the polarity of compounds like ammonia and water is due to the unshared electrons on the central atom.

(a) Indicate the direction of the dipole due to the unshared pair(s) on the nitrogen of ammonia; on the oxygen of water.

(b) Show how this idea is supported by the following fact: the dipole moment of NF_3 ($\mu = 0.24$ D) is much *smaller* than that of NH_3 ($\mu = 1.46$ D) even though the N—F bond is almost certainly much more polar than the N—H bond.

The dipole moments of most compounds have never been measured. For these substances, we must predict polarity from structure. From our knowledge of electronegativity, we can estimate the polarity of bonds; from our knowledge of bond angles, we can then estimate the polarity of molecules.

1.12　Structure and physical properties

We have just discussed one physical property of compounds: dipole moment. Other physical properties — like melting point, boiling point, or solubility in a particular solvent — are also of concern to us. The physical properties of a new compound give valuable clues about its structure. Conversely, the structure of a compound often tells us what physical properties to expect of it.

In attempting to synthesize a new compound, for example, we must plan a series of reactions to convert a compound that we have into the compound that we want. In addition, we must work out a method of separating our product from all the other compounds making up the reaction mixture: unconsumed reactants, solvent, catalyst, by-products. Usually the *isolation* and *purification* of a product take much more time and effort than the actual making of it. The feasibility of isolating the product by distillation depends upon its boiling point and the boiling points of the contaminants; isolation by recrystallization depends upon its solubility in various solvents and the solubility of the contaminants. Success in the laboratory often depends upon making a good prediction of physical properties from structure.

We have seen that there are two extreme kinds of chemical bonds: ionic bonds, formed by the transfer of electrons; and covalent bonds, formed by the sharing of electrons. The physical properties of a compound depend largely upon which kind of bonds hold its atoms together in the molecule.

1.13　Melting point

In a crystalline solid the particles acting as structural units — ions or molecules — are arranged in some very regular, symmetrical way; there is a geometric pattern repeated over and over within a crystal.

Melting is the change from the highly ordered arrangement of particles in the crystalline lattice to the more random arrangement that characterizes a liquid (see Figures 1.10 and 1.11). Melting occurs when a temperature is reached at which the thermal energy of the particles is great enough to overcome the intracrystalline forces that hold them in position.

An **ionic compound** forms crystals in which the structural units are *ions*. Solid sodium chloride, for example, is made up of positive sodium ions and negative chloride ions alternating in a very regular way. Surrounding each positive ion and equidistant from it are six negative ions: one on each side of it, one above and one below, one in front and one in back. Each negative ion is surrounded in a similar way by six positive ions. There is nothing that we can properly call a *molecule* of sodium chloride. A particular sodium ion does not "belong" to any one chloride ion; it is equally attracted to six chloride ions. The crystal is an extremely strong, rigid structure, since the electrostatic forces holding each ion in position are powerful. These powerful *interionic* forces are overcome only at a very high temperature; sodium chloride has a melting point of 801°.

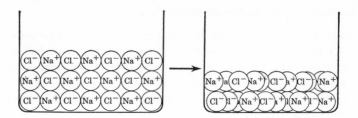

FIGURE 1.10. Melting of an ionic crystal. Units are ions.

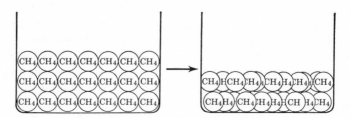

FIGURE 1.11. Melting of a non-ionic crystal. Units are molecules.

Crystals of other ionic compounds resemble crystals of sodium chloride in having an ionic lattice, although the exact geometric arrangement may be different. As a result, these other ionic compounds, too, have high melting points. Many molecules contain both ionic and covalent bonds. Potassium nitrate, KNO_3, for example, is made up of K^+ ions and NO_3^- ions; the oxygen and nitrogen atoms of the NO_3^- ion are held to each other by covalent bonds. The physical properties of compounds like these are largely determined by the ionic bonds; potassium nitrate has very much the same sort of physical properties as sodium chloride.

A **non-ionic compound,** one whose atoms are held to each other entirely by covalent bonds, forms crystals in which the structural units are *molecules*. It is the forces holding these molecules to each other that must be overcome for melting to occur. In general, these *intermolecular* forces are very weak compared with the forces holding ions to each other. To melt sodium chloride we must supply enough energy to break ionic bonds between Na^+ and Cl^-. To melt methane, CH_4, we do not need to supply enough energy to break covalent bonds between carbon and hydrogen; we need only supply enough energy to break CH_4 molecules away from each other. In contrast to sodium chloride, methane melts at $-183°$.

1.14 Intermolecular forces

What kind of forces hold molecules to each other? Like interionic forces these forces seem to be electrostatic in nature, involving attraction of positive charge for negative charge. There are two kinds of intermolecular forces: *dipole-dipole interactions*, and *van der Waals forces*.

Dipole-dipole interaction is the attraction of the positive end of one polar molecule for the negative end of another polar molecule. In hydrogen chloride, for example, the relatively positive hydrogen of one molecule is attracted to the relatively negative chlorine of another:

As a result of dipole-dipole interaction, polar molecules are generally held to each other more strongly than are non-polar molecules of comparable molecular weight; this difference in strength of intermolecular forces is reflected in the physical properties of the compounds concerned.

There must be forces between the molecules of a non-polar compound, since even such compounds can solidify. Such attractions are called **van der Waals forces.** The existence of these forces is accounted for by quantum mechanics. We can roughly visualize them arising in the following way. The average distribution of charge about, say, a methane molecule is symmetrical, so that there is no net dipole moment. However, the electrons move about, so that at any instant of time the distribution will probably be distorted, and a small dipole will exist. This momentary dipole will affect the electron distribution in a second methane molecule nearby. The negative end of the dipole tends to repel electrons, and the positive end tends to attract electrons; the dipole thus *induces* an oppositely oriented dipole in the neighboring molecule:

Although the momentary dipoles and induced dipoles are constantly changing, the net result is attraction between the two molecules. These van der Waals forces have a very short range; they act only between the portions of different molecules that are in close contact, that is, between the surfaces of molecules. As we shall see, the relationship between the strength of van der Waals forces and the surface areas of molecules (Sec. 3.12) will help us to understand the effect of molecular size and shape on physical properties.

1.15 Boiling point

Although the particles in a liquid are arranged less regularly and are freer to move about than in a crystal, each particle is attracted by a number of other particles. Boiling involves the breaking away from the liquid of individual molecules or pairs of oppositely charged ions (see Figures 1.12 and 1.13). This occurs when a temperature is reached at which the thermal energy of the particles is great enough to overcome the cohesive forces that hold them in the liquid.

In the liquid state the unit of an ionic compound is again the ion. Each ion is still held strongly by a number of oppositely charged ions. Again there is nothing we could properly call a molecule. A great deal of energy is required for a pair of oppositely charged ions to break away from the liquid; boiling occurs only at a very high temperature. The boiling point of sodium chloride, for example, is 1413°. In the gaseous state we have an *ion-pair*, which can be considered a sodium chloride molecule.

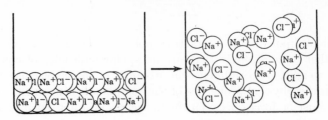

FIGURE 1.12. Boiling of an ionic liquid. Units are ions and ion-pairs.

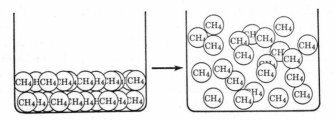

FIGURE 1.13. Boiling of a non-ionic liquid. Units are molecules.

In the liquid state the unit of a non-ionic compound is again the molecule. The weak intermolecular forces here — dipole-dipole interactions and van der Waals forces — are more readily overcome than the strong interionic forces of ionic compounds, and boiling occurs at a very much lower temperature. Non-polar methane boils at −161.5°, and polar ammonia at −33°; even very polar water has the relatively low boiling point of +100°.

1.16 Solubility

When a solid or liquid dissolves, the structural units — ions or molecules — become separated from each other and the spaces in between become occupied by solvent molecules. In dissolution, as in melting and boiling, energy must be supplied to overcome the interionic or intermolecular forces. Where does the necessary energy come from? The energy required to break the bonds between solute particles is supplied by the formation of bonds between the solute particles and the solvent molecules: the old attractive forces are replaced by new ones.

A great deal of energy is necessary to overcome the powerful electrostatic forces holding together an ionic lattice. In general, only water or a few other highly polar solvents are able to dissolve ionic compounds appreciably. What kind of bonds are formed between ions and a solvent like water? We have seen that a water molecule is extremely polar; it has a positive end and a negative end. Consequently there is electrostatic

attraction between a positive ion and the negative end of a water molecule'
and between a negative ion and the positive end of a water molecule·
These attractions are called **ion-dipole bonds.** Each ion-dipole bond is
relatively weak, but in the aggregate they supply enough energy to overcome the interionic forces in the crystal. In solution each ion is surrounded
by a cluster of solvent molecules, and is said to be **solvated;** if the solvent
happens to be water, the ion is said to be **hydrated.** In solution, as in the
solid and liquid states, the unit of a substance like sodium chloride is the
ion, although in this case it is a solvated ion (see Figure 1.14).

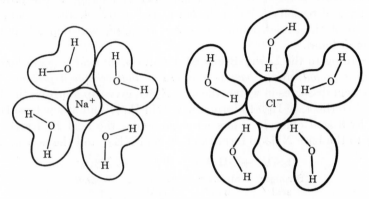

FIGURE 1.14. Ion-dipole interactions: hydrated Na^+ and Cl^- ions.

Water owes its great superiority as a solvent for ionic substances partly
to its polarity, which permits it to solvate ions strongly. In addition,
water has high insulating properties (it is said to have a high *dielectric
constant*) which lower the attractions between oppositely charged ions
once they are solvated. Finally, water contains the hydroxyl group, $-OH$.
Liquids containing hydrogen attached to oxygen or to nitrogen have unusually high solvating powers; the special role of hydrogen is discussed
later (Sec. 11.5).

The solubility characteristics of non-ionic compounds are determined
chiefly by their polarity. Non-polar or weakly polar compounds dissolve
in non-polar or weakly polar solvents; highly polar compounds dissolve in
highly polar solvents. "Like dissolves like" is an extremely useful rule of
thumb. Methane dissolves in carbon tetrachloride because the forces
holding methane molecules to each other and carbon tetrachloride molecules to each other are replaced by very similar forces holding methane
molecules to carbon tetrachloride molecules.

Neither methane nor carbon tetrachloride is readily soluble in water.
The highly polar water molecules are held to each other by very strong
dipole-dipole interactions; there could be only very weak attractive forces
between water molecules on the one hand and the non-polar methane or
carbon tetrachloride molecules on the other.

In contrast the highly polar organic compound methanol, CH_3OH, is
quite soluble in water. Dipole-dipole interactions between water and

methanol molecules can readily replace the very similar attractions between different methanol molecules and different water molecules.

1.17 Acids and bases

Turning from physical to chemical properties, let us review briefly one familiar topic that is fundamental to the understanding of organic chemistry: acidity and basicity.

The terms *acid* and *base* have been defined in a number of ways, each definition corresponding to a particular way of looking at the properties of acidity and basicity. We shall find it useful to look at acids and bases from two of these viewpoints; the one we select will depend upon the problem at hand.

According to the **Lowry-Brønsted** definition, *an acid is a substance that gives up a proton*, and *a base is a substance that accepts a proton*. When sulfuric acid dissolves in water, the acid H_2SO_4 gives up a proton (hydrogen nucleus) to the base H_2O to form a new acid H_3O^+ and a new base HSO_4^-. When hydrogen chloride reacts with ammonia, the acid HCl gives up a proton to the base NH_3 to form the new acid NH_4^+ and the new base Cl^-.

$$H_2SO_4 \ + \ H_2O \ \leftrightarrows \ H_3O^+ \ + \ HSO_4^-$$

Stronger acid	Stronger base	Weaker acid	Weaker base

$$HCl \ + \ NH_3 \ \leftrightarrows \ NH_4^+ \ + \ Cl^-$$

Stronger acid	Stronger base	Weaker acid	Weaker base

According to the Lowry-Brønsted definition, the strength of an acid depends upon its tendency to give up a proton, and the strength of a base depends upon its tendency to accept a proton. Sulfuric acid and hydrogen chloride are strong acids since they tend to give up a proton very readily; conversely, bisulfate ion, HSO_4^-, and chloride ion must necessarily be weak bases since they have little tendency to hold on to protons. In each of the reactions just described, the equilibrium favors the formation of the weaker acid and the weaker base.

If aqueous H_2SO_4 is mixed with aqueous NaOH, the acid H_3O^+ (hydronium ion) gives up a proton to the base OH^- to form the new acid H_2O and the new base H_2O.

$$H_3O^+ \ + \ OH^- \ \leftrightarrows \ H_2O \ + \ H_2O$$

Stronger acid	Stronger base	Weaker acid	Weaker base

$$NH_4^+ \ + \ OH^- \ \leftrightarrows \ H_2O \ + \ NH_3$$

Stronger acid	Stronger base	Weaker acid	Weaker base

When aqueous NH_4Cl is mixed with aqueous NaOH, the acid NH_4^+ (ammonium ion) gives up a proton to the base OH^- to form the new acid H_2O and the new base NH_3. In each case the strong base, hydroxide ion, has accepted a proton to form the weak acid H_2O. If we arrange these acids in the order shown, we must necessarily arrange the corresponding (conjugate) bases in the opposite order.

Acid strength
$$\begin{matrix} H_2SO_4 \\ HCl \end{matrix} > H_3O^+ > NH_4^+ > H_2O$$

Base strength
$$\begin{matrix} HSO_4^- \\ Cl^- \end{matrix} < H_2O < NH_3 < OH^-$$

Like water, many organic compounds that contain oxygen can act as bases and accept protons; ethyl alcohol and ethyl ether, for example, form the *oxonium ions* I and II.

$$C_2H_5\overset{..}{\underset{..}{O}}H + H_2SO_4 \leftrightarrows C_2H_5\overset{\overset{+}{..}}{\underset{..}{O}}H + HSO_4^-$$
$$|$$
$$H$$
$$\text{I}$$

Ethyl alcohol   An oxonium ion
                  Protonated ethyl alcohol

$$(C_2H_5)_2\overset{..}{O}: + HCl \leftrightarrows (C_2H_5)_2\overset{\overset{+}{..}}{O}:H + Cl^-$$
$$\text{II}$$

Ethyl ether   An oxonium ion
                 Protonated ethyl ether

For convenience we shall often refer to a structure like I as a *protonated alcohol* and a structure like II as a *protonated ether*.

According to the **Lewis** definition, *a base is a substance that can furnish an electron pair to form a covalent bond*, and *an acid is a substance that can take up an electron pair to form a covalent bond*. Thus **an acid is an electron-pair acceptor** and **a base is an electron-pair donor**. This is the most fundamental of the acid-base concepts, and the most general; it includes all the other concepts.

A proton is an acid because it is deficient in electrons, and needs an electron pair to complete its valence shell. Hydroxide ion, ammonia, and water are bases because they contain electron pairs available for sharing. In boron trifluoride, BF_3, boron has only six electrons in its outer shell and hence tends to accept another pair to complete its octet. Boron trifluoride is an acid and combines with such bases as ammonia or ethyl ether.

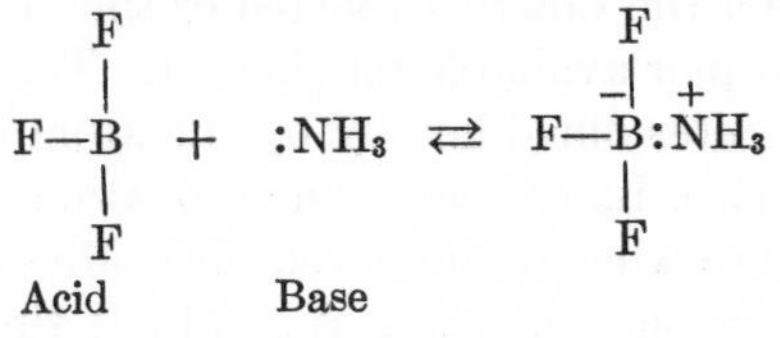

$$\begin{matrix} & F & & & & F \\ & | & & & & -| \; + \\ F&-B & + & :NH_3 & \rightleftarrows & F-B:NH_3 \\ & | & & & & | \\ & F & & & & F \end{matrix}$$
$$\;\;\text{Acid} \qquad\;\; \text{Base}$$

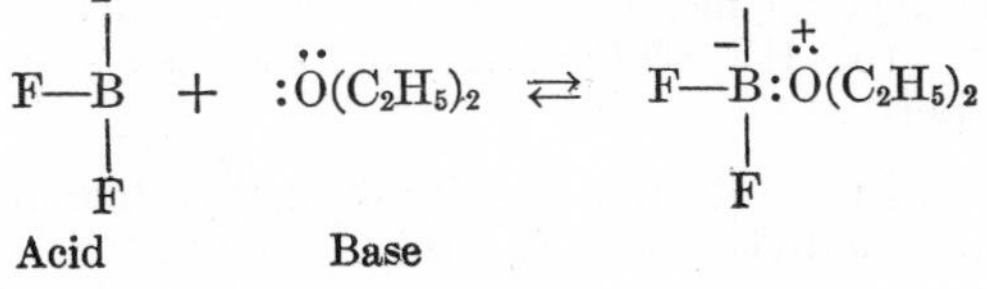

$$\begin{matrix} & F & & & & F \\ & | & & & & -| \; \overset{+}{..} \\ F&-B & + & :\overset{..}{O}(C_2H_5)_2 & \rightleftarrows & F-B:O(C_2H_5)_2 \\ & | & & & & | \\ & F & & & & F \end{matrix}$$
$$\;\;\text{Acid} \qquad\qquad \text{Base}$$

Aluminum chloride, $AlCl_3$, is an acid, and for the same reason. In stannic chloride, $SnCl_4$, tin has a complete octet but can accept additional pairs of electrons (e.g., in $SnCl_6{}^{--}$) and hence it is an acid, too.

We shall find the Lewis concept of acidity and basicity fundamental to our understanding of organic chemistry. To make it clear that we are talking about this kind of acid or base, we shall often use the expression *Lewis acid* (or base), or sometimes *acid* (or base) *in the Lewis sense*.

Chemical properties, like physical properties, depend upon molecular structure. Just what features in a molecule's structure tell us what to expect about its acidity or basicity? We can try to answer this question in a general way now, although we shall return to it many times later.

To be acidic in the Lowry-Brønsted sense, a molecule must, of course, contain hydrogen. The degree of acidity is determined largely by the kind of atom that holds the hydrogen and, in particular, by that atom's ability to accommodate the electron pair left behind by the departing hydrogen ion. This ability to accommodate the electron pair seems to depend upon several factors, including (a) the atom's *electronegativity*, and (b) its *size*. Thus, within a given row of the Periodic Table, acidity increases as electronegativity increases:

Acidity
$$H-CH_3 \; < \; H-NH_2 \; < \; H-OH \; < \; H-F$$
$$H-SH \; < \; H-Cl$$

And within a given family, acidity increases as the size increases:

Acidity
$$H-F \; < \; H-Cl \; < \; H-Br \; < \; H-I$$
$$H-OH \; < \; H-SH \; < \; H-SeH$$

Among organic compounds, we can expect appreciable Lowry-Brønsted acidity from those containing O—H, N—H, and S—H groups.

To be acidic in the Lewis sense, a molecule must be electron-deficient; in particular, we would look for an atom bearing only a sextet of electrons.

Problem 1.6 Predict the relative acidity: (a) of methyl alcohol (CH_3OH) and methylamine (CH_3NH_2); (b) of methyl alcohol (CH_3OH) and methanethiol (CH_3SH); (c) of H_3O^+ and NH_4^+.

Problem 1.7 Which is the stronger acid of each pair: (a) H_3O^+ or H_2O; (b) NH_4^+ or NH_3; (c) H_2S or HS^-; (d) H_2O or OH^-? (e) What relationship is there between *charge* and acidity?

To be basic in either the Lowry-Brønsted or the Lewis sense, a molecule must have an electron pair available for sharing. The availability of these unshared electrons is determined largely by the atom that holds them: its electronegativity, its size, its charge. The operation of these factors here is necessarily opposite to what we observed for acidity; the better an atom accommodates the electron pair, the less available the pair is for sharing.

Problem 1.8 Arrange the members of each group in order of basicity: (a) F^-, OH^-, NH_2^-, CH_3^-; (b) HF, H_2O, NH_3; (c) Cl^-, SH^-; (d) F^-, Cl^-, Br^-, I^-; (e) OH^-, SH^-, SeH^-.

Problem 1.9 Predict the relative basicity of methyl fluoride (CH_3F), methyl alcohol (CH_3OH), and methylamine (CH_3NH_2).

Problem 1.10 Arrange the members of each group in order of basicity: (a) H_3O^+, H_2O, OH^-; (b) NH_3, NH_2^-; (c) H_2S, HS^-, S^{--}. (d) What relationship is there between charge and basicity?

Like acidity and basicity, other chemical properties, too, depend upon molecular structure. Indeed, most of this book will be concerned with finding out what this relationship is.

1.18   Isomerism

Before we start our systematic study of the different kinds of organic compounds, let us look at one further concept which illustrates especially well the fundamental importance of molecular structure: the concept of **isomerism.**

The compound *ethyl alcohol* is a liquid boiling at 78°. Analysis (by the methods described later, Sec. 2.26) shows that it contains carbon, hydrogen, and oxygen in the proportions 2C : 6H :1O. Measurement of the density of its vapor shows that it has a molecular weight of 46. The molecular formula of ethyl alcohol must therefore be C_2H_6O. Ethyl alcohol is a quite reactive compound. For example, if a piece of sodium metal is dropped into a test tube containing ethyl alcohol, there is a vigorous bubbling and the sodium metal is consumed; hydrogen gas is evolved and there is left behind a compound of formula C_2H_5ONa. Ethyl alcohol reacts with hydriodic acid to form water and a compound of formula C_2H_5I.

The compound *methyl ether* is a gas with a boiling point of $-24°$. It is clearly a different substance from ethyl alcohol, differing not only in its physical properties but also in its chemical properties. It does not react at all with sodium metal. Like ethyl alcohol it reacts with hydriodic acid, but it yields a compound of formula CH_3I. Analysis of methyl ether shows that it contains carbon, hydrogen, and oxygen in the same proportions as ethyl alcohol, 2C : 6H : 1O. It has the same molecular weight as ethyl alcohol, 46. We conclude that it has the same molecular formula, C_2H_6O.

Here we have two substances, ethyl alcohol and methyl ether, which have the same molecular formula, C_2H_6O, and yet quite clearly are different compounds. How can we account for the existence of these two compounds? The answer is: *they differ in molecular structure.* Ethyl alcohol has the structure represented by I, and methyl ether the structure represented by II. As we shall see, the differences in physical and chemical properties of these two compounds can readily be accounted for on the basis of the difference in structure.

I
Ethyl alcohol

II
Methyl ether

Different compounds that have the same molecular formula are called **isomers** (Gr., *isos*, equal; *meros*, part). They contain the same numbers of the same kinds of atoms, but the atoms are attached to one another in different ways. Isomers are different compounds because they have different molecular structures.

This difference in molecular structure gives rise to a difference in properties; it is the difference in properties which tells us that we are dealing with different compounds. In some cases, the difference in structure — and hence the difference in properties — is so marked that the isomers are assigned to different chemical families, as, for example, ethyl *alcohol* and methyl *ether*. In other cases the difference in structure is so subtle that it can be described only in terms of three-dimensional models. Other kinds of isomerism fall between these two extremes.

PROBLEMS

1. Which of the following would you expect to be ionic, and which non-ionic? Give a simple electronic structure (Sec. 1.3) for each, showing only valence shell electrons.

(a) KBr	(d) $MgCl_2$	(g) PH_3	(j) NF_3
(b) H_2S	(e) CH_2Cl_2	(h) $SiCl_4$	(k) $CaSO_4$
(c) ICl	(f) NaOCl	(i) NH_4Cl	(l) CH_3OH

2. (a) Why do we write the formulas of both Li^+ and NH_4^+ ions with positive charges? Of both F^- and BF_4^- ions with negative charges? (b) Why do we write the formula of $^-F_3B:NH_3^+$ with positive and negative charges (so-called *formal charges*)?

3. Give a likely simple electronic structure (Sec. 1.3) for each of the following, assuming them to be completely covalent. Assume that every atom (except hydrogen, of course) has a complete octet, and that two atoms may share more than one pair of electrons.

(a) H_2O_2	(e) CO_2	(i) HONO	(m) C_2H_6
(b) N_2	(f) H_2CO_3	(j) HCN	(n) C_2H_4
(c) H_2SO_4	(g) $HONO_2$	(k) ethyl alcohol (Sec. 1.18)	(o) C_2H_2
(d) SO_4^{--}	(h) NO_3^-	(l) methyl ether (Sec. 1.18)	(p) CH_2O

4. (a) How do you account for the fact that the hydrogen molecule, H_2, is much "smaller" than a single hydrogen atom, $H\cdot$? (b) How do you account for the shrinkage of the back lobes of the overlapping p orbitals in the formation of F_2 (Sec. 1.7)? (c) Why might you expect an unshared pair of electrons in an sp^3 orbital to take up more room than a hydrogen atom with a pair of bonding electrons (Sec. 1.9)?

5. What shape would you expect each of the following to have?

(a) H_3O^+	(d) H_2S
(b) the methide ion, CH_3^-	(e) methyl ether
(c) the amide ion, NH_2^-	(f) $(CH_3)_3N$

6. In forming certain compounds, carbon is pictured as utilizing *three* equivalent sp^2 hybrid orbitals, and in others *two* equivalent sp hybrid orbitals. On the basis of maximum separation of orbitals, what geometry would you expect in each case? (Check your answers in Secs. 4.2 and 6.2.)

7. (a) According to one approach, H_2O is considered to result from overlapping of the s orbitals of the hydrogen atoms with two of the three p orbitals of oxygen. What H—O—H bond angle would be expected? How does this compare with the measured value? (b) If the same approach is applied to NH_3, what shape of molecule would be expected? What bond angles? How do these compare with the measured values? (c) What orbital would the unshared pair of NH_3 occupy? (d) If basicity depends upon availability of unshared electrons, which approach — this one or the one involving sp^3 hybrid orbitals (Sec. 1.9) — accounts better for the basicity of NH_3? (*Hint:* contrast the shapes and positions of the orbitals involved.)

8. Although HCl (1.27 A) is a longer molecule than HF (0.92 A), it has a *smaller* dipole moment (1.03 D compared to 1.75 D). How do you account for this fact?

9. Indicate the direction of the dipole moment, *if any*, that you would expect for each of the following:

(a) HBr	(d) CH_2Cl_2	(g) methyl ether
(b) ICl	(e) $CHCl_3$	(h) $(CH_3)_3N$
(c) I_2	(f) CH_3OH	(i) CF_2Cl_2

10. What do the differences in properties between lithium acetylacetonate (m.p. very high, insoluble in chloroform) and beryllium acetylacetonate (m.p. 108°, b.p. 270°, soluble in chloroform) suggest about their structures?

11. Rewrite the following equations to show the Lowry-Brønsted acids and bases actually involved. Label each as stronger or weaker, as in Sec. 1.17.

(a) $HCl(aq) + NaHCO_3(aq) \rightleftharpoons H_2CO_3 + NaCl$
(b) $NaOH(aq) + NaHCO_3(aq) \rightleftharpoons Na_2CO_3 + H_2O$
(c) $NH_3(aq) + HNO_3(aq) \rightleftharpoons NH_4NO_3(aq)$
(d) $NaCN(aq) \rightleftharpoons HCN(aq) + NaOH(aq)$

12. What is the Lowry-Brønsted acid in (a) HCl dissolved in water; (b) HCl (unionized) dissolved in benzene? (c) Which solution is the more strongly acidic?

13. Account for the fact that nearly every organic compound containing oxygen dissolves in cold concentrated sulfuric acid to yield a solution from which the compound can be recovered by dilution with water.

About Working Problems

Working problems is a necessary part of your work for two reasons: it will guide your study in the right direction, and, after you have studied a particular chapter, it will show whether or not you have reached your destination.

You should work all the problems that you can; you should get help with the ones you cannot work yourself. The first problems in each set are easy, but provide the drill in drawing formulas, naming compounds, and using reactions that even the best student needs. The later problems in each set are the kind encountered by practicing chemists, and test your ability to *use* what you have learned.

You can check your answers to many of the problems in the answer section in the back of the book, and by use of the index.

Chapter two_____

METHANE

2.1 Hydrocarbons

Certain organic compounds contain only two elements, hydrogen and carbon, and hence are known as **hydrocarbons.** On the basis of structure, hydrocarbons are divided into two main classes, **aliphatic** and **aromatic.** Aliphatic hydrocarbons are further divided into families: alkanes, alkenes, alkynes, and their cyclic analogs (cycloalkanes, etc.). We shall take up these families in the order given.

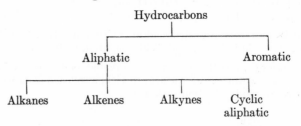

The simplest member of the alkane family and, indeed, the simplest of all organic compounds is **methane, CH₄.** We shall study this single compound at some length, since most of what we learn about it can be carried over with minor modifications to any alkane.

2.2 Structure of methane

As we discussed in the previous chapter (Sec. 1.8), each of the four hydrogen atoms is bonded to the carbon atom by a covalent bond, that is, by the sharing of a pair of electrons. According to quantum mechanics, when carbon is bonded to four other atoms its bonding orbitals (sp^3 orbitals, formed by the mixing of one s and three p orbitals) are directed to the corners of a tetrahedron (Figure 2.1a). This tetrahedral arrangement is the one that permits the orbitals to be as far apart as possible. For each of these orbitals to overlap most effectively the spherical s orbital of a hydrogen atom, and thus to form the strongest bond, each hydrogen nucleus must be located at a corner of this tetrahedron (Figure 2.1b).

The tetrahedral structure of methane has been verified by electron diffraction (Figure 2.1c), which shows beyond question the arrangement of atoms in such simple molecules. Later on, we shall examine some of the evidence that led chemists to accept this tetrahedral structure long before quantum mechanics or electron diffraction was known.

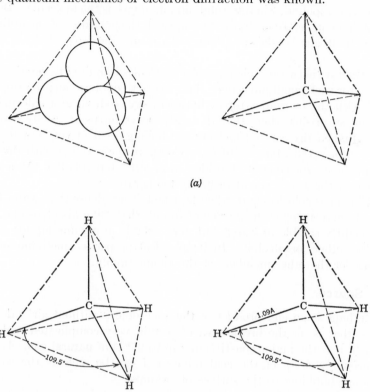

(a)

(b)   (c)

FIGURE 2.1. Methane molecule. (a) Tetrahedral sp^3 orbitals. (b) Predicted shape: H nuclei located for maximum overlap. (c) Shape and size.

We shall ordinarily write methane with a dash to represent each pair of electrons shared by carbon and hydrogen (I). To focus our attention on individual electrons, we may sometimes indicate a pair of electrons by a pair of dots (II). Finally, when we wish to consider the actual shape of the molecule, we shall use a simple three-dimensional picture (III).

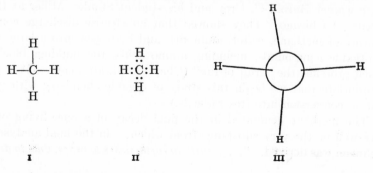

I   II   III

2.3 Physical properties

As we discussed in the previous chapter (Sec. 1.13), the unit of such a non-ionic compound, whether solid, liquid, or gas, is the molecule. Because the methane molecule is highly symmetrical, the polarities of the individual carbon–hydrogen bonds cancel out; as a result, the molecule itself is non-polar.

Attraction between such non-polar molecules is limited to van der Waals forces; for such small molecules, these attractive forces must be tiny compared with the enormous forces between, say, sodium and chloride ions. It is not surprising, then, that these attractive forces are easily overcome by thermal energy, so that melting and boiling occur at very low temperatures: m.p. $-183°$, b.p. $-161.5°$. (Compare these values with the corresponding ones for sodium chloride: m.p. $801°$, b.p. $1413°$.) As a consequence, methane is a gas at ordinary temperatures.

Methane is colorless and, when liquefied, is less dense than water (sp.gr. 0.4). In agreement with the rule of thumb that "like dissolves like," it is only slightly soluble in water, but very soluble in organic liquids such as gasoline, ether, or alcohol. In its physical properties methane sets the pattern for the other members of the alkane family.

2.4 Source

Methane is an end product of the anaerobic ("without air") decay of plants, that is, of the breakdown of certain very complicated molecules. As such, it is the major constituent (up to 97%) of **natural gas.** It is the dangerous *firedamp* of the coal mine, and can be seen as the so-called *marsh gas* bubbling to the surface of swamps.

If methane is desired in very pure form, it can be separated from the other constituents of natural gas (mostly other alkanes) by fractional distillation. Most of it, of course, is consumed as fuel without purification.

According to one theory, the origins of life go back to a primitive earth surrounded by an atmosphere of methane, water, ammonia, and hydrogen. Energy — radiation from the sun, lightning discharges — broke these simple molecules into reactive fragments (free radicals, Sec. 2.12); these combined to form larger molecules which eventually yielded the enormously complicated organic compounds that make up living organisms.

Evidence that this *could* have happened was found in 1953 by the Nobel Prize winner Harold C. Urey and his student Stanley Miller at the University of Chicago. They showed that an electric discharge converts a mixture of methane, water, ammonia, and hydrogen into a large number of organic compounds, including amino acids, the building blocks from which proteins, the "stuff of life" (Chapter 33), are made. (It is perhaps appropriate that we begin this study of organic chemistry with methane and its conversion into free radicals.)

The methane generated in the final decay of a once-living organism may well be the very substance from which — in the final analysis — the organism was derived. *". . . earth to earth, ashes to ashes, dust to dust . . ."*

2.5   Reactions

The alkanes are sometimes referred to by the old-fashioned name of *paraffins*. This name (from the Latin, *parum affinis*, not enough affinity) was given to describe the limited reactivity of these hydrocarbons. So far as most reagents are concerned, this description certainly fits methane. It is inert to acids like hydrochloric acid or sulfuric acid, bases like sodium hydroxide or potassium hydroxide, oxidizing agents like potassium permanganate or sodium dichromate, and reducing agents like stannous chloride or sodium metal. Methane undergoes only two reactions of any importance, and both of these take place only under very vigorous conditions.

REACTIONS OF METHANE

1. Combustion

$$CH_4 + 2O_2 \xrightarrow{\text{flame}} CO_2 + 2H_2O + \text{heat (213 kcal/mole)}$$

2. Halogenation

$$CH_4 \xrightarrow{X_2} \underset{+\ HX}{CH_3X} \xrightarrow{X_2} \underset{+\ HX}{CH_2X_2} \xrightarrow{X_2} \underset{+\ HX}{CHX_3} \xrightarrow{X_2} \underset{+\ HX}{CX_4} \qquad \begin{array}{c} Heat\ or\ light \\ required \end{array}$$

Reactivity of X_2 F_2 $>$ Cl_2 $>$ Br_2 $(> I_2)$

                 Extremely   *Unreactive*

                 reactive

2.6   Combustion.   Heat of combustion

Combustion to carbon dioxide and water is characteristic of organic compounds; under special conditions it is used to determine their content of carbon and hydrogen (Sec. 2.26).

Combustion of methane is the principal reaction taking place during the burning of natural gas. It is hardly necessary to emphasize its importance in the areas where natural gas is available; the important product is not carbon dioxide or water but *heat*.

Burning of hydrocarbons takes place only at high temperatures, as provided, for example, by a flame or a spark. Once started, however, the reaction gives off heat which is often sufficient to maintain the high temperature and to permit burning to continue. *The quantity of heat evolved when one mole of a hydrocarbon is burned to carbon dioxide and water is called the* **heat of combustion;** for methane its value is 213 kcal.

2.7   Chlorination: a substitution reaction

Under the influence of ultraviolet light or at a temperature of 250–400° a mixture of the two gases, methane and chlorine, reacts vigorously to yield hydrogen chloride and a compound of formula CH_3Cl. We say that methane has undergone **chlorination,** and we call the product, CH_3Cl, *chloromethane* or *methyl chloride* ($CH_3 =$ **methyl**).

Chlorination is a typical example of a broad class of organic reactions known as **substitution**. A chlorine atom has been substituted for a hydrogen atom of methane, and the hydrogen atom thus replaced is found combined with a second atom of chlorine.

$$\underset{\text{Methane}}{H-\overset{\displaystyle H}{\underset{\displaystyle H}{C}}-H} + \underset{\text{Chlorine}}{Cl-Cl} \xrightarrow{\text{light or heat}} \underset{\substack{\text{Methyl chloride}\\ \text{(Chloromethane)}}}{H-\overset{\displaystyle H}{\underset{\displaystyle H}{C}}-Cl} + \underset{\text{Hydrogen chloride}}{H-Cl}$$

The methyl chloride can itself undergo further substitution to form more hydrogen chloride and CH_2Cl_2, *dichloromethane* or *methylene chloride* (CH_2 = **methylene**).

$$H-\overset{\displaystyle H}{\underset{\displaystyle H}{C}}-Cl + Cl-Cl \xrightarrow{\text{light or heat}} \underset{\substack{\text{Methylene chloride}\\ \text{(Dichloromethane)}}}{H-\overset{\displaystyle H}{\underset{\displaystyle Cl}{C}}-Cl} + H-Cl$$

In a similar way, chlorination may continue, to yield $CHCl_3$, *trichloromethane* or *chloroform*, and CCl_4, *tetrachloromethane* or *carbon tetrachloride*. These last two compounds are already familiar to us, chloroform as an anesthetic, and carbon tetrachloride as a non-flammable cleaning agent and the fluid in certain fire extinguishers.

$$CH_4 \xrightarrow{Cl_2} CH_3Cl \xrightarrow{Cl_2} CH_2Cl_2 \xrightarrow{Cl_2} CHCl_3 \xrightarrow{Cl_2} CCl_4$$

with HCl produced at each stage. *Heat or light required*

Methane, Methyl chloride, Methylene chloride, Chloroform, Carbon tetrachloride

2.8 Control of chlorination

Chlorination of methane may yield any one of four organic products, depending upon the stage to which the reaction is carried. Can we control this reaction so that methyl chloride is the principal organic product? That is, can we limit the reaction to the first stage, *mono*chlorination?

We might at first expect — naïvely, as it turns out — to accomplish this by providing only one mole of chlorine for each mole of methane. But let us see what happens if we do so. At the beginning of the reaction there is only methane for the chlorine to react with, and consequently only the first stage of chlorination takes place. This reaction, however, yields methyl chloride, so that as the reaction proceeds methane disappears and methyl chloride takes its place.

As the proportion of methyl chloride grows, it competes with the methane for the available chlorine. By the time the concentration of methyl chloride exceeds that of methane, chlorine is more likely to attack methyl chloride than methane, and the second stage of chlorination be-comes more important than the first. A large amount of methylene chloride is formed, which in a similar way is chlorinated to chloroform and this, in turn, is chlorinated to carbon tetrachloride. When we finally work up the reaction product, we find that it is a mixture of all four chlori-nated methanes together with some unreacted methane.

The reaction may, however, be limited almost entirely to monochlorina-tion if we use a large excess of methane. In this case, even at the very end of the reaction unreacted methane greatly exceeds methyl chloride. Chlo-rine is more likely to attack methane than methyl chloride, and thus the first stage of chlorination is the principal reaction.

Because of the great d.fference in their boiling points, it is easy to separate the excess methane (b.p. $-161.5°$) from the methyl chloride (b.p. $-24°$) so that the methane can be mixed with more chlorine and put through the process again. While there is a low **conversion** of methane to methyl chloride in each cycle, the **yield** of methyl chloride based on the chlorine consumed is quite high.

The use of a large excess of one reactant is a common device of the organic chemist when he wishes to limit reaction to only one of a number of reactive sites in the molecule of that reactant.

2.9   Reaction with other halogens: halogenation

Methane reacts with bromine, again at high temperatures or under the influence of ultraviolet light, to yield the corresponding bromomethanes: methyl bromide, methylene bromide, bromoform, and carbon tetrabromide.

$$CH_4 \xrightarrow{Br_2} CH_3Br \xrightarrow{Br_2} CH_2Br_2 \xrightarrow{Br_2} CHBr_3 \xrightarrow{Br_2} CBr_4$$

with $+HBr$ formed at each step. *Heat or light required*

| Methane | Methyl bromide | Methylene bromide | Bromoform | Carbon tetrabromide |

Bromination takes place somewhat less readily than chlorination.

Methane does not react with iodine at all. With fluorine it reacts so vigorously that, even in the dark, the reaction is controlled with difficulty; only the completely fluorinated compound, carbon tetrafluoride, is ob-tained.

We can, therefore, arrange the halogens in order of reactivity.

Reactivity of halogens $F_2 > Cl_2 > Br_2(> I_2)$

This same order of reactivity holds for the reaction of the halogens with other alkanes and, indeed, with most other organic compounds. The spread of reactivities is so great that only chlorination and bromination proceed at such rates as to be useful.

2.10   Relative reactivity

Throughout our study of organic chemistry, we shall constantly be interested in *relative reactivities*. We shall compare the reactivities of various reagents toward the same organic compound, the reactivities of different organic compounds toward the same reagent, and even the reactivities of different sites in an organic molecule toward the same reagent.

It should be understood that when we compare reactivities we compare rates of reaction. When we say that chlorine is *more reactive* than bromine toward methane, we mean that under the same conditions (same concentration, same temperature, etc.) chlorine reacts with methane *faster* than does bromine. From another point of view, we mean that the bromine reaction must be carried out under more vigorous conditions (higher concentration or higher temperature) if it is to take place as fast as the chlorine reaction. When we say that methane and iodine do not react at all, we mean that the reaction is too slow to be significant.

We shall want to know not only what these relative reactivities are, but also, whenever possible, how to account for them. To see what factors cause one reaction to be faster than another, we shall take up in more detail this matter of the different reactivities of the halogens toward methane. Before we can do this, however, we must understand a little more about the reaction itself.

2.11   Reaction mechanisms

It is important for us to know not only *what* happens in a chemical reaction but also *how* it happens, that is, to know not only the *facts* but also the *theory*.

For example, we know that methane and chlorine under the influence of heat or light form methyl chloride and hydrogen chloride. Just how is a molecule of methane converted into a molecule of methyl chloride? Does this transformation involve more than one step, and, if so, what are these steps? Just what is the function of heat or light?

The answer to questions like these, that is, *the detailed, step-by-step description of a chemical reaction, is called a* **mechanism.** It is only a hypothesis; it is advanced to account for the facts. As more facts are discovered, the mechanism must also account for them, or else be modified so that it does account for them; it may even be necessary to discard a mechanism and to propose a new one.

It would be difficult to say that a mechanism had ever been *proved.* If, however, a mechanism accounts satisfactorily for a wide variety of facts; if we make predictions based upon this mechanism and find these predictions borne out; if the mechanism is consistent with mechanisms for other, related reactions; then the mechanism is said to be *well established,* and it becomes part of the theory of organic chemistry.

Why are we interested in the mechanisms of reactions? As an important part of the theory of organic chemistry, they help make up the framework on which we hang the facts we learn. An understanding of mechanisms will help us to see a pattern in the complicated and confusing multitude of organic reactions. We shall find that many apparently unrelated reactions proceed by the same or similar mechanisms, so that most of what we have already learned about one reaction may be applied directly to many new ones.

By knowing how a reaction takes place, we can make changes in the experimental conditions — not by trial and error, but logically — that will improve the yield of the product we want, or that will even alter the course of the reaction completely and give us an entirely different product. As our understanding of reactions grows, so does our power to control them.

2.12 Mechanism of chlorination. Free radicals

It will be worthwhile to examine the mechanism of chlorination of methane in some detail. The same mechanism holds for bromination as well as chlorination, and for other alkanes as well as methane; it even holds for many compounds which, while not alkanes, contain alkane-like portions in their molecules. Closely related mechanisms are involved in oxidation (combustion) and other reactions of alkanes. More important, this mechanism illustrates certain general principles that can be carried over to a wide range of chemical reactions. Finally, by studying the evidence that supports the mechanism, we can learn something of how a chemist finds out what goes on during a chemical reaction.

Among the facts that must be accounted for are these: (a) Methane and chlorine do not react in the dark at room temperature. (b) Reaction takes place readily, however, in the dark at temperatures over 250°, or (c) under the influence of ultraviolet light at room temperature. (d) When the reaction is induced by light, many (several thousand) molecules of methyl chloride are obtained for each photon of light that is absorbed by the system. (e) The presence of a small amount of oxygen slows down the reaction for a period of time, after which the reaction proceeds normally; the length of this period depends upon how much oxygen is present.

The mechanism that accounts for these facts most satisfactorily, and hence is generally accepted, is shown in the following equations:

(1) $$Cl_2 \xrightarrow{\text{heat or light}} 2Cl\cdot$$

(2) $$Cl\cdot + CH_4 \longrightarrow HCl + CH_3\cdot$$

(3) $$CH_3\cdot + Cl_2 \longrightarrow CH_3Cl + Cl\cdot$$

then (2), (3), (2), (3), *etc.*

The first step is the breaking of a chlorine molecule into two chlorine atoms; like the breaking of any bond, this requires energy (58 kcal/mole, in this case). The energy is supplied as either heat or light.

$$\text{energy} + \overset{..}{\underset{..}{:}}\overset{..}{Cl}\!:\!\overset{..}{\underset{..}{Cl}}\!: \longrightarrow :\overset{..}{\underset{..}{Cl}}\cdot + \cdot\overset{..}{\underset{..}{Cl}}:$$

The cleavage of the chlorine–chlorine bond takes place in a symmetrical way, so that each atom retains one electron of the pair that formed the covalent bond. This **odd electron** is not *paired* as are all the other electrons of the chlorine atom, that is, it does not have a partner of opposite spin (Sec. 1.6). *An atom or group of atoms possessing an odd (unpaired) electron* *is called a* **free radical.**   In writing the symbol for a free radical, we generally include a dot to represent the odd electron just as we include a plus or minus sign in the symbol of an ion.

Once formed, what is a chlorine atom most likely to do?   Like most free radicals, it is extremely reactive because of its tendency to gain an additional electron and thus have a complete octet; from another point of view, energy was supplied to each chlorine atom during the cleavage of the chlorine molecule, and this energy-rich particle tends strongly to lose energy by the formation of a new chemical bond.

To form a new chemical bond, that is, to react, the chlorine atom must collide with some other molecule or atom.   What is it most likely to collide with?   Obviously, it is most likely to collide with the particles that are present in the highest concentration: chlorine molecules and methane molecules.   Collision with another chlorine atom is quite unlikely simply because there are very few of these reactive, short-lived particles around at any time.   Of the likely collisions, that with a chlorine molecule causes no net change; reaction may occur, but it can result only in the exchange of one chlorine atom for another:

$$:\ddot{\underset{..}{Cl}}\cdot \; + \; :\ddot{\underset{..}{Cl}}:\ddot{\underset{..}{Cl}}: \; \longrightarrow \; :\ddot{\underset{..}{Cl}}:\ddot{\underset{..}{Cl}}: \; + \; :\ddot{\underset{..}{Cl}}\cdot \quad \textit{Probable but not productive}$$

Collision of a chlorine atom with a methane molecule is both *probable* and *productive*.   The chlorine atom abstracts a hydrogen atom, with one electron, to form a molecule of hydrogen chloride:

$$\underset{\substack{H \\ \text{Methane}}}{\overset{H}{H:\ddot{C}:H}} + \cdot \ddot{\underset{..}{Cl}}: \longrightarrow H:\ddot{\underset{..}{Cl}}: + \underset{\substack{H \\ \text{Methyl radical}}}{\overset{H}{H:\dot{C}}} \quad \textit{Probable and productive}$$

Now the methyl group is left with an odd, unpaired electron; the carbon atom has only seven electrons in its valence shell.   One free radical, the chlorine atom, has been consumed, and a new one, the methyl radical, $CH_3\cdot$, has been formed in its place.   This is step (2) in the mechanism.

Now, what is this methyl radical most likely to do?   Like the chlorine atom, it is extremely reactive, and for the same reason: the tendency to complete its octet, to lose energy by forming a new bond.   Again, collisions with chlorine molecules or methane molecules are the probable ones, not collisions with the relatively scarce chlorine atoms or methyl radicals. But collision with a methane molecule can result only in the exchange of one methyl radical for another:

$$\underset{\ddot{H}}{\overset{H}{H:\ddot{C}:H}} + \cdot \underset{\ddot{H}}{\overset{H}{C}:H} \longrightarrow H:\underset{\ddot{H}}{\overset{H}{\ddot{C}}}\cdot + \underset{\ddot{H}}{\overset{H}{H:\ddot{C}:H}} \quad \textit{Probable but not productive}$$

The collision of a methyl radical with a chlorine molecule is, then, the important one.   The methyl radical abstracts a chlorine atom, with one of the bonding electrons, to form a molecule of methyl chloride:

$$
\begin{array}{c}
H \\
H:\overset{\cdot}{\underset{H}{C}}\cdot
\end{array}
+ :\overset{..}{\underset{..}{Cl}}:\overset{..}{\underset{..}{Cl}}: \longrightarrow
\begin{array}{c}
H \\
H:\overset{\cdot}{\underset{H}{C}}:\overset{..}{\underset{..}{Cl}}:
\end{array}
+ :\overset{..}{\underset{..}{Cl}}\cdot
\qquad \textit{Probable and productive}
$$

Methyl   Methyl chloride
radical

The other product is a chlorine atom. This is step (3) in the mechanism.

Here again the consumption of one reactive particle has been accompanied by the formation of another. The new chlorine atom attacks methane to form a methyl radical, which attacks a chlorine molecule to form a chlorine atom, and so the sequence is repeated over and over. Each step produces not only a new reactive particle but also a molecule of product: methyl chloride or hydrogen chloride.

This process cannot, however, go on forever. As we saw earlier, union of two short-lived, relatively scarce particles is not likely; but every so often it does happen, and when it does, this particular sequence of reactions stops. Reactive particles are consumed but not generated.

$$:\overset{..}{\underset{..}{Cl}}\cdot \ + \ \cdot\overset{..}{\underset{..}{Cl}}: \ \longrightarrow \ :\overset{..}{\underset{..}{Cl}}:\overset{..}{\underset{..}{Cl}}:$$

$$CH_3\cdot \ + \ \cdot CH_3 \longrightarrow CH_3:CH_3$$

$$CH_3\cdot \ + \ \cdot\overset{..}{\underset{..}{Cl}}: \ \longrightarrow CH_3:\overset{..}{\underset{..}{Cl}}:$$

It is clear, then, how the mechanism accounts for facts (a), (b), (c), and (d) above: either light or heat is required to cleave the chlorine molecule and form the initial chlorine atoms; once formed, each atom may eventually bring about the formation of many molecules of methyl chloride.

2.13 Chain reactions

The chlorination of methane is an example of a **chain reaction,** *a reaction that involves a series of steps, each of which generates a reactive substance that brings about the next step.* While chain reactions may vary widely in their details, they all have certain fundamental characteristics in common.

(1)	$Cl_2 \xrightarrow{\text{heat or light}} 2Cl\cdot$	**Chain-initiating step**
(2)	$Cl\cdot + CH_4 \longrightarrow HCl + CH_3\cdot$ ⎫	
(3)	$CH_3\cdot + Cl_2 \longrightarrow CH_3Cl + Cl\cdot$ ⎬	**Chain-propagating steps**

then (2), (3), (2), (3), *etc., until finally:*

(4)	$Cl\cdot + \cdot Cl \longrightarrow Cl_2$ ⎫	
or		
(5)	$CH_3\cdot + \cdot CH_3 \longrightarrow CH_3CH_3$ ⎬	**Chain-terminating steps**
or		
(6)	$CH_3\cdot + \cdot Cl \longrightarrow CH_3Cl$ ⎭	

First in the chain of reactions is a **chain-initiating step,** in which energy is absorbed and a reactive particle generated; in the present reaction it is the cleavage of chlorine into atoms (step 1).

There are one or more **chain-propagating steps,** each of which consumes a reactive particle and generates another; here they are the reaction of chlorine atoms with methane (step 2), and of methyl radicals with chlorine (step 3).

Finally, there are **chain-terminating steps,** in which reactive particles are consumed but not generated; in the chlorination of methane these would involve the union of two of the reactive particles, or the capture of one of them by the walls of the reaction vessel.

Under one set of conditions, about 10,000 molecules of methyl chloride are formed for every quantum (photon) of light absorbed. Each photon cleaves one chlorine molecule to form two chlorine atoms, each of which starts a chain. On the average, each chain consists of 5,000 repetitions of the chain-propagating cycle before it is finally stopped.

2.14   Inhibitors

How does the mechanism of chlorination account for fact (e), that a small amount of oxygen slows down the reaction for a period of time, which depends upon the amount of oxygen, after which the reaction proceeds normally?

Oxygen is believed to react with a methyl radical to form a new free radical:

$$CH_3\cdot + O_2 \longrightarrow CH_3\!-\!O\!-\!O\cdot$$

The $CH_3OO\cdot$ radical is much less reactive than the $CH_3\cdot$ radical, and can do little to continue the chain. By combining with a methyl radical, one oxygen molecule breaks a chain, and thus prevents the formation of thousands of molecules of methyl chloride; this, of course, slows down the reaction tremendously. After all the oxygen molecules present have combined with methyl radicals, the reaction is free to proceed at its normal rate.

A substance that slows down or stops a reaction even though present in small amount is called an **inhibitor.** *The period of time during which inhibition lasts, and after which the reaction proceeds normally, is called the inhibition period.* Inhibition by a relatively small amount of an added material is quite characteristic of chain reactions of any type, and is often one of the clues that first leads us to suspect that we are dealing with a chain reaction. It is hard to see how else a few molecules could prevent the reaction of so many.

2.15   A test of the chlorination mechanism

How could this mechanism for the chlorination of methane be tested? The essence of the proposed mechanism is the formation and reactivity of chlorine atoms. Any method of generating chlorine atoms, then, should bring about the reaction.

It is known from other evidence that tetraethyllead, $(C_2H_5)_4Pb$ (the familiar "ethyl" of ethyl gasoline), breaks apart at only 140° to form metallic lead and ethyl free radicals:

$$(C_2H_5)_4Pb \xrightarrow{140°} Pb + 4C_2H_5\cdot$$

We have postulated that methyl radicals attack chlorine molecules to form methyl chloride and chlorine atoms. It is reasonable to expect ethyl radicals to react similarly, to form *ethyl* chloride and chlorine atoms:

$$C_2H_5\cdot + :\overset{..}{\underset{..}{Cl}}:\overset{..}{\underset{..}{Cl}}: \longrightarrow C_2H_5:\overset{..}{\underset{..}{Cl}}: + \cdot\overset{..}{\underset{..}{Cl}}:$$

Ethyl chloride

Once formed, these chlorine atoms — and there need be only a few of them — are available to start chains.

We would predict, therefore, that a mixture of methane and chlorine containing a little tetraethyllead should undergo reaction at a temperature of only 140°, instead of the usual minimum of 250°. This prediction has been shown to be correct, as little as 0.02% of tetraethyllead being effective.

$$CH_4 + Cl_2 \xrightarrow[140°]{.02\% \ (C_2H_5)_4Pb} CH_3Cl + HCl$$

In addition to strengthening the mechanism, this finding is obviously of practical importance, since it permits the chlorination to be carried out under much milder conditions than otherwise needed.

2.16 Bond strength

In our consideration of the chlorination of methane, we have so far been concerned chiefly with the particles involved — molecules and atoms — and the changes that they undergo. As with any reaction, however, it is important to consider also the energy changes involved, since these changes determine to a large extent how fast the reaction will go, and, in fact, whether it will take place at all.

TABLE 2.1

BOND STRENGTHS (Bond Dissociation Energies), Kcal/mole

$$A : B \longrightarrow A\cdot + \cdot B \qquad \Delta H = \text{Bond Strength}$$

H–H	103			CH₃–H	101		
H–F	135	F–F	38	CH₃–F	107		
H–Cl	103	Cl–Cl	58	CH₃–Cl	80		
H–Br	87	Br–Br	46	CH₃–Br	67		
H–I	71	I–I	36	CH₃–I	55		

CH₃–H	101	CH₃–CH₃	83	CH₃–Cl	80	CH₃–Br	67
C₂H₅–H	98	C₂H₅–CH₃	82	C₂H₅–Cl	80	C₂H₅–Br	65
n-C₃H₇–H	95	n-C₃H₇–CH₃	79	n-C₃H₇–Cl	77		
i-C₃H₇–H	89	i-C₃H₇–CH₃	75	i-C₃H₇–Cl	73	i-C₃H₇–Br	59
t-C₄H₉–H	85	t-C₄H₉–CH₃	74	t-C₄H₉–Cl	75		
H₂C=CH–H	104-122	H₂C=CH–CH₃	109	H₂C=CH–Cl	104		
H₂C=CHCH₂–H	77	H₂C=CHCH₂–CH₃	60	H₂C=CHCH₂–Cl	58	H₂C=CHCH₂–Br	48
C₆H₅–H	102	C₆H₅–CH₃	89	C₆H₅–Cl	86	C₆H₅–Br	71
C₆H₅CH₂–H	78	C₆H₅CH₂–CH₃	63	C₆H₅CH₂–Cl	68	C₆H₅CH₂–Br	51

We have seen that energy must be supplied as heat or light to break chlorine molecules into atoms. An equivalent amount of energy is liberated when chlorine atoms recombine to form molecules. *The amount of energy consumed or liberated when a bond is broken or formed is known as the* **bond strength,** or **bond dissociation energy.** It is characteristic of the particular bond. For the Cl—Cl bond the value is 58 kcal/mole. Table 2.1 lists bond strengths that have been measured for a number of other bonds. As can be seen, they vary widely, from weak bonds like I—I (36 kcal/mole) to very strong bonds like H—F (135 kcal/mole). Although values may change as experimental methods improve, certain trends are clear.

2.17 Heat of reaction

By using these bond strengths, we can calculate the energy changes that take place in a great number of reactions. In the conversion of methane into methyl chloride, two bonds are broken, CH_3—H and Cl—Cl, consuming $101 + 58$, or a total of 159 kcal/mole. At the same time two new bonds are formed, CH_3—Cl and H—Cl, liberating $80 + 103$, or a total of 183 kcal/mole.

$$CH_3\text{—}H + Cl\text{—}Cl \longrightarrow CH_3\text{—}Cl + H\text{—}Cl$$

$\underline{101}$	58	80	103	
	159		183	$\Delta H = -24$ kcal

The result is the liberation of 24 kcal of heat for every mole of methane that is converted into methyl chloride; this is, then, an **exothermic reaction.**

When heat is liberated, the heat content, H, of the molecules themselves must decrease; the change in heat content, ΔH, is therefore given a negative sign. (In the case of an endothermic reaction, where heat is absorbed, the increase in heat content of the molecules is indicated by a positive ΔH.)

Problem 2.1 Calculate ΔH for the corresponding reaction of methane with: (a) bromine; (b) iodine; (c) fluorine.

The value of -24 kcal that we have just calculated is the *net* ΔH for the over-all reaction. A more useful picture of the reaction is given by the ΔH's of the individual steps. These are calculated below:

(1) $\qquad\qquad Cl\text{—}Cl \longrightarrow 2Cl\cdot \qquad\qquad \Delta H = +58$ kcal
$\qquad\qquad\qquad$ (58)

(2) $\qquad Cl\cdot + CH_3\text{—}H \longrightarrow CH_3\cdot + H\text{—}Cl \quad \Delta H = -2$
$\qquad\qquad\qquad$ (101) $\qquad\qquad\qquad$ (103)

(3) $\qquad CH_3\cdot + Cl\text{—}Cl \longrightarrow CH_3\text{—}Cl + Cl\cdot \quad \Delta H = -22$
$\qquad\qquad\qquad$ (58) $\qquad\qquad$ (80)

It is clear why this reaction, even though exothermic, occurs only at a high temperature (in the absence of light). The chain-initiating step, without which reaction cannot occur, is highly *endothermic*, and takes place (at a significant rate) only at a high temperature. Once the chlorine atoms are formed, the two exothermic chain-propagating steps occur readily many times before the chain is broken. The difficult cleavage of chlorine is the barrier that must be surmounted before the subsequent easy steps can be taken.

Problem 2.2 Calculate ΔH for the corresponding steps in the reaction of methane with: (a) bromine; (b) iodine; (c) fluorine.

We have assumed so far that exothermic reactions proceed readily, that is, are reasonably fast at ordinary temperatures, whereas endothermic reactions proceed with difficulty, that is, are slow except at very high temperatures. This assumed relationship between ΔH and rate of reaction is a useful rule of thumb when other information is not available; it is *not*, however, a *necessary* relationship, and there are many exceptions to the rule. We shall go on, then, to a discussion of another energy quantity, the *energy of activation*, which is related in a more exact way to rate of reaction.

2.18 Energy of activation

To see what actually happens during a chemical reaction, let us look more closely at a specific example, the attack of chlorine atoms on methane:

$$\text{Cl}\cdot + \text{CH}_3\text{---H} \longrightarrow \text{H---Cl} + \text{CH}_3\cdot \qquad \Delta H = -2 \text{ kcal,}$$
$$\text{(101)} \qquad\qquad\qquad \text{(103)} \qquad\qquad E_{act} = 4 \text{ kcal}$$

This reaction is comparatively simple: it occurs in the gas phase, and is thus not complicated by the presence of a solvent; it involves the interaction of a single atom and the simplest of organic molecules. Yet from it we can learn certain principles that apply to any reaction.

Just what must happen if this reaction is to occur? First of all, a chlorine atom and a methane molecule must **collide**. Since chemical forces are of extremely short range, a hydrogen–chlorine bond can form only when the atoms are in close contact.

Next, to be *effective*, the collision must provide a certain *minimum amount of energy*. We might have expected that the 103 kcal/mole liberated by the formation of the H—Cl bond would suffice to break the weaker (101 kcal) CH₃—H bond; however, this is not so. Bond breaking and bond making evidently are not perfectly synchronized, and the energy liberated by the one process is not completely available for the other. Experiment has shown that if reaction is to occur, an additional 4 kcal/mole of energy must be supplied.

The minimum amount of energy that must be provided by a collision for reaction to occur is called the **energy of activation,** E_{act}. Its source is the kinetic energy of the moving particles. Most collisions provide less than this minimum quantity and are fruitless, the original particles simply bouncing apart. Only solid collisions between particles one or both of which are moving unusually fast are energetic enough to bring about reaction. In the present example, at 275°, only about one collision in 40 is sufficiently energetic.

Finally, in addition to being sufficiently energetic, the collisions must occur when the particles are properly **oriented.** At the instant of collision, the methane molecule must be turned in such a way as to present a hydrogen atom to the full force of the impact. In the present example, only one collision in eight is properly oriented.

In general, then, *a chemical reaction requires collisions of sufficient energy* (E_{act}) *and of proper orientation.* There is an energy of activation for nearly every reaction where bonds are broken, even for an exothermic reaction like this one, in which bond making liberates more energy than is consumed by bond breaking.

In contrast to the chlorine reaction, the attack of bromine atoms on methane is endothermic, with a ΔH of $+14$ kcal.

$$\text{Br} \cdot + \text{CH}_3\text{---H} \longrightarrow \text{H---Br} + \text{CH}_3 \cdot \qquad \Delta H = +14 \text{ kcal,}$$
$$(101) \qquad\qquad (87) \qquad\qquad E_{act} = 18 \text{ kcal}$$

Breaking the CH_3---H bond, as before, requires 101 kcal/mole, of which only 87 kcal is provided by formation of the H---Br bond. It is evident that, even if this 87 kcal were completely available for bond breaking, at least an additional 14 kcal/mole would have to be supplied by the collision. In other words, the E_{act} of an endothermic reaction must be at least as large as the ΔH. As is generally true, the E_{act} of the present reaction (18 kcal) is actually somewhat larger than the ΔH.

2.19 Progress of reaction: energy changes

These energy relationships can be seen more clearly in diagrams like Figures 2.2 and 2.3. Progress of reaction is represented by horizontal movement from reactants on the left to products on the right. Potential energy (i.e., all energy except kinetic) at any stage of reaction is indicated by the height of the curve.

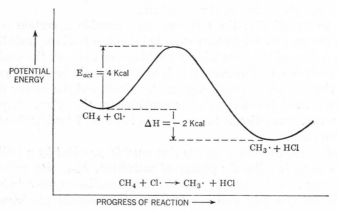

FIGURE 2.2. Potential energy changes during progress of reaction: an exothermic reaction.

Let us follow the course of reaction in Figure 2.2. We start in a potential energy valley with a methane molecule and a chlorine atom. These particles are moving, and hence possess kinetic energy in addition to the potential energy shown. The exact amount of kinetic energy varies with the particular pair of particles, since some move faster than others. They collide, and kinetic energy is converted into potential energy. With this increase in potential energy, reaction begins, and we move up the energy hill. If enough kinetic energy is converted, we reach the top of the hill and start down the far side.

During the descent, potential energy is converted back into kinetic energy, until we reach the level of the products. The products contain less potential energy than did the reactants, and we find ourselves in a lower valley than the one we left. With this net decrease in potential energy there must be a corresponding increase in kinetic energy. The new particles break apart, and since they are moving faster than the particles from which they were formed, we observe a rise in temperature. Heat will be *given off* to the surroundings.

The bromine reaction, shown in Figure 2.3, follows much the same course. In this case, however, the products contain more potential energy than did the reactants, so that we climb to a higher valley than the one we left. Since this time the new particles contain less kinetic energy than the particles from which they were formed, and hence move more slowly, we observe a fall in temperature. Heat will be *taken up* from the surroundings.

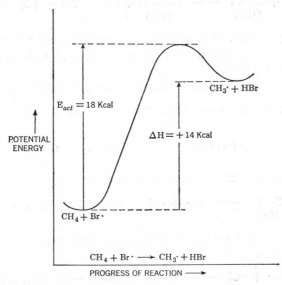

FIGURE 2.3. Potential energy changes during progress of reaction: an endothermic reaction.

In either of these reactions there are many collisions that provide too little energy for us to reach the top of the hill. These collisions are fruitless, and we slide back to our original valley. Many collisions provide sufficient energy, but take place when the molecules are improperly oriented.

We then climb an energy hill, but we are off the road; we may climb very high without finding the pass that leads over into the next valley.

The difference in level between the two valleys is, of course, the ΔH; the difference in level between the reactant valley and the top of the hill is the E_{act}. We are concerned only with these differences, and not with the absolute height at any stage of the reaction. We are not even concerned with the relative levels of the reactant valleys in the chlorine and bromine reactions. We need only to know that in the chlorine reaction we climb a hill 4 kcal high and end up in a valley 2 kcal lower than our starting point; and that in the bromine reaction we climb a hill 18 kcal high and end up in a valley 14 kcal higher than our starting point.

As we shall see, it is the height of the hill, the E_{act}, that determines the rate of reaction, and not the difference in level of the two valleys, ΔH. In going to a lower valley, the hill might be very high, but *could* be very low — or even nonexistent. In climbing to a higher valley, however, the hill can be no lower than the valley to which we are going; that is to say, *in an endothermic reaction the E_{act} must be at least as large as the ΔH.*

An energy diagram of the sort of Figures 2.2 and 2.3 is particularly useful because it tells us not only about the reaction we are considering, but also about the reverse reaction. Let us move from right to left in Figure 2.2, for example. We see that the reaction

$$CH_3\cdot + H—Cl \longrightarrow CH_3—H + Cl\cdot \qquad \Delta H = +2, \quad E_{act} = 6$$
$$(103) \qquad\qquad (101)$$

has an energy of activation of 6 kcal, since we must in this case climb the hill from the lower valley. This is, of course, an endothermic reaction with a ΔH of +2 kcal.

In the same way we can see from Figure 2.3 that the reaction

$$CH_3\cdot + H—Br \longrightarrow CH_3—H + Br\cdot \qquad \Delta H = -14, \quad E_{act} = 4$$
$$(87) \qquad\qquad (101)$$

has an energy of activation of 4 kcal, and is exothermic with a ΔH of −14 kcal.

In reactions like the cleavage of chlorine into atoms,

$$Cl—Cl \longrightarrow Cl\cdot + \cdot Cl \qquad \Delta H = +58, \quad E_{act} = 58$$
$$(58)$$

a bond is broken but no bonds are formed. The reverse of this reaction, the union of chlorine atoms,

$$Cl\cdot + \cdot Cl \longrightarrow Cl—Cl \qquad \Delta H = -58, \quad E_{act} = 0$$
$$(58)$$

involves no bond breaking and hence would be expected to take place very easily, in fact, with no energy of activation at all. This is generally considered to be true for reactions involving the union of two free radicals.

If there is no hill to climb in going from chlorine atoms to a chlorine molecule, but simply a slope to descend, the cleavage of a chlorine molecule must involve simply the ascent of a slope as shown in Figure 2.4.

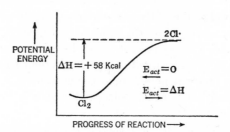

FIGURE 2.4. Potential energy changes during progress of reaction: simple dissociation.

The E_{act} for the cleavage of a chlorine molecule, then, must equal the ΔH, that is, 58 kcal. This equality of E_{act} and ΔH is generally believed to hold for reactions in which molecules dissociate into radicals.

2.20 Rate of reaction

A chemical reaction is the result of collisions of sufficient energy and proper orientation. The rate of reaction, therefore, must be the rate at which these effective collisions occur, the number of effective collisions, let us say, that occur during each second within each cc of reaction space. We can then express the rate as the product of three factors. (The number expressing the probability that a collision will have the proper orientation is commonly called the **probability factor.**) Anything that affects any one of these factors affects the rate of reaction.

number of effective collisions per cc per sec	=	total number of collisions per cc per sec	×	fraction of collisions that have sufficient energy	×	fraction of collisions that have proper orientation
rate	=	collision frequency	×	energy factor	×	probability factor (orientation factor)

The **collision frequency** depends upon (a) how closely the particles are crowded together, i.e., concentration or pressure; (b) how large they are; and (c) how fast they are moving, which in turn depends upon their weight and the temperature.

We can change the concentration and temperature, and thus change the rate. We are familiar with the fact that an increase in concentration causes an increase in rate; it does so, of course, by increasing the collision frequency. A rise in temperature increases the collision frequency; as we shall see, it also increases the energy factor, and this latter effect is so great that the effect of temperature on collision frequency is by comparison unimportant.

The size and weight of the particles are characteristic of each reaction and cannot be changed. Although they vary widely from reaction to reaction, this variation does not affect the collision frequency greatly.

A heavier weight makes the particle move more slowly at a given temperature, and hence tends to decrease the collision frequency. A heavier particle is, however, generally a larger particle, and the larger size tends to increase the collision frequency. These two factors thus tend to cancel out.

The **probability factor** depends upon the geometry of the particles and the kind of reaction that is taking place. For closely related reactions it does not vary widely.

Kinetic energy of the moving molecules is not the only source of the energy needed for reaction; energy can also be provided, for example, from vibrations among the various atoms within the molecule. Thus the probability factor has to do not only with what atoms in the molecule suffer the collision, but also with the alignment of the other atoms in the molecule at the time of collision.

By far the most important factor determining rate is the **energy factor**: the fraction of collisions that are sufficiently energetic. This factor depends upon the temperature, which we can control, and upon the energy of activation, which is characteristic of each reaction.

At a given temperature the molecules of a particular compound have an average velocity and hence an average kinetic energy that is characteristic of this system; in fact, the temperature is a measure of this average kinetic energy. But the individual molecules do not all travel with the same velocity, some moving faster than the average and some slower. The distribution of velocities is shown in Figure 2.5 by the familiar bell-shaped curve that describes the distribution among individuals of so many qualities, for example, height, intelligence, income, or even life expectancy.

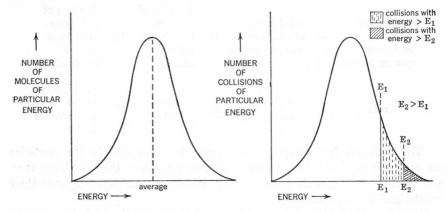

FIGURE 2.5. Distribution of kinetic energy among molecules.

FIGURE 2.6. Distribution of kinetic energy among collisions.

The number of molecules with a particular velocity is greatest for a velocity near the average and decreases as the velocity becomes larger or smaller than the average.

The distribution of collision energies, as we might expect, is described by a similar curve, Figure 2.6. Let us indicate collisions of a particular energy, E_{act}, by a vertical line. The number of collisions with energy equal to or greater than E_{act} is indicated by the shaded area under the curve to the right of the vertical line. The fraction of the total number of collisions that have this minimum energy, E_{act}, is then the fraction of the total area that is shaded. It is evident that *the greater the value of E_{act}, the smaller is the fraction of collisions that possess that energy.*

The exact relationship between energy of activation and fraction of collisions with that energy is:

$$e^{-E_{act}/RT} = \text{fraction of collisions with energy greater than } E_{act}$$

where: e = 2.718 (base of natural logarithms)
$\quad\quad R$ = 1.986 (gas constant)
$\quad\quad T$ = absolute temperature

This exponential relationship is important to us in that it indicates that a small difference in E_{act} has a large effect on the fraction of sufficiently energetic collisions, and hence on the rate of reaction. For example, at 275°, out of every million collisions, 10,000 provide sufficient energy if E_{act} = 5 kcal, 100 provide sufficient energy if E_{act} = 10 kcal, and only one provides sufficient energy if E_{act} = 15 kcal. This means that (all other things being equal) a reaction with E_{act} = 5 kcal will go 100 times as fast as one with E_{act} = 10 kcal, and 10,000 times as fast as one with E_{act} = 15 kcal.

We have so far considered a system held at a given temperature. A rise in temperature, of course, increases the average kinetic energy and average velocities, and hence shifts the entire curve to the right as shown by the dotted line in Figure 2.7. For a given energy of activation, then, a rise in temperature increases the fraction of sufficiently energetic collisions, and hence increases the rate, as we already know.

Here again the exponential relationship leads to a very large change in rate for a small change in temperature. For example, a rise from 250°

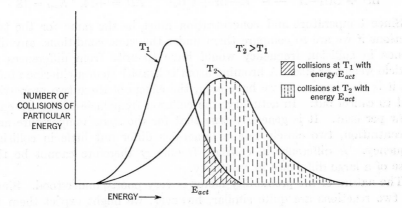

FIGURE 2.7. Change in collision energies with change in temperature.

to 300°, which is only a 10% increase in absolute temperature, increases the rate by 50% if E_{act} = 5 kcal, doubles the rate if E_{act} = 10 kcal, and trebles the rate if E_{act} = 15 kcal. As this example shows, the greater the E_{act}, the greater the effect of a given change in temperature; this follows from the $e^{-E_{act}/RT}$ relationship. Indeed, it is from the relationship between rate and temperature that the E_{act} of a reaction is determined: the rate is measured at different temperatures, and from the results, E_{act} is calculated.

We have examined the factors that determine rate of reaction. What we have learned may be used in many ways. To speed up a particular reaction, for example, we know that we might raise the temperature, or increase the concentration of reactants, or even (in ways that we shall take up later) lower the E_{act}.

Of immediate interest, however, is the matter of relative reactivities. Let us see, therefore, how our knowledge of reaction rates can help us to account for the fact that one reaction proceeds faster than another, even though conditions for the two reactions are identical.

2.21   Relative rates of reaction

We have seen that the rate of a reaction can be expressed as a product of three factors:

rate = collision frequency × energy factor × probability factor

Two reactions could proceed at different rates because of differences in any or all these factors. To account for a difference in rate, we must first see in which of these factors the difference lies.

As an example, let us compare the reactivities of chlorine and bromine atoms toward methane; that is, let us compare the rates, under the same conditions, of the two reactions:

$$Cl\cdot + CH_3-H \longrightarrow H-Cl + CH_3\cdot \qquad \Delta H = -2, \quad E_{act} = 4$$

$$Br\cdot + CH_3-H \longrightarrow H-Br + CH_3\cdot \qquad \Delta H = +14, \quad E_{act} = 18$$

Since temperature and concentration must be the same for the two reactions if we are to compare them under the same conditions, any difference in **collision frequency** would have to arise from differences in particle weight or size. A bromine atom is heavier than a chlorine atom, and it is also larger; as we have seen, the effects of these two properties tend to cancel out. In actuality, the collision frequencies differ by only a few per cent. It is generally true that for the same temperature and concentration, two closely related reactions differ but little in collision frequency. A difference in collision frequency therefore cannot be the cause of a large difference in reactivity.

The nature of the **probability factor** is very poorly understood. Since our two reactions are quite similar, however, we might expect them to have similar probability factors. Experiment has shown this to be true: whether chlorine or bromine atoms are involved, about one in every eight collisions with methane has the proper orientation for reaction. In general, where closely related reactions are concerned, we may assume that a difference in probability factor is *not likely* to be the cause of a large difference in reactivity.

We are left with a consideration of the **energy factor.** At a given temperature, the fraction of collisions that possess the amount of energy required for reaction depends upon how large that amount is, that is, depends upon the E_{act}. In our example, E_{act} is 4 kcal for the chlorine reaction, 18 kcal for the bromine reaction. As we have seen, a difference of this size in the E_{act} causes an enormous difference in the energy factor, and hence in the rate. At 275°, of every 10 million collisions, 250,000 are sufficiently energetic when chlorine atoms are involved, and only *one* when bromine atoms are involved. Because of the difference in E_{act} alone, then, chlorine atoms are 250,000 times as reactive as bromine atoms toward methane.

As we encounter, again and again, differences in reactivity, we shall in general attribute them to differences in E_{act}; in many cases we shall be able to account for these differences in E_{act} on the basis of differences in molecular structure. *It must be understood that we are justified in doing this only when the reactions being compared are so closely related that differences in collision frequency and in probability factor are comparatively insignificant.*

2.22   Relative reactivities of halogens toward methane

With this background, let us return to the reaction between methane and the various halogens, and see if we can account for the order of reactivity given before, $F_2 > Cl_2 > Br_2 > I_2$, and in particular for the fact that iodine does not react at all.

From the table of bond strengths (Table 2.1, page 39) we can calculate for each of the four halogens the ΔH for each of the three steps of halogenation. Since E_{act} has been measured for only a few of these reac-

		X =	F	Cl	Br	I
(1)	$X_2 \longrightarrow 2X\cdot$	$\Delta H =$	+38	+58	+46	+36
(2)	$X\cdot + CH_4 \longrightarrow HX + CH_3\cdot$		−34	−2	+14	+30
(3)	$CH_3\cdot + X_2 \longrightarrow CH_3X + X\cdot$		−69	−22	−21	−19

tions, let us see what tentative conclusions we can reach using only ΔH.

Since step (1) involves simply dissociation of molecules into atoms, we may quite confidently assume (Sec. 2.19 and Fig. 2.4) that ΔH in this case is equal to E_{act}. Chlorine has the largest E_{act}, and should dissociate most slowly; iodine has the smallest E_{act}, and should dissociate most rapidly. Yet this does not agree with the observed order of reactivity. Thus, except possibly for fluorine, dissociation of the halogen into atoms cannot be the step that determines the observed reactivities.

Step (3), attack of methyl radicals on halogen, is exothermic for all four halogens, and for chlorine, bromine, and iodine has very nearly the same ΔH. Although we could not be sure, we would think it likely that none of these reactions has a very great E_{act}, and that even for iodine the reaction proceeds fairly readily. Independent work has shown this to be so: methyl radicals generated in another way (e.g., by the heating of tetramethyllead) react quite readily with iodine molecules to yield methyl iodide. The third step, then, cannot be the cause of the observed relative reactivities.

This leaves step (2), abstraction of hydrogen from methane by a halogen atom. Here we see a wide spread of ΔH's, from the highly exothermic reaction with the fluorine atom to the highly endothermic reaction with the iodine atom. The endothermic bromine atom reaction must have an E_{act} of at least 14 kcal; as we have seen, it is actually 18 kcal. The exothermic chlorine atom reaction could have a very small E_{act}; it is actually 4 kcal. At a given temperature, then, the fraction of collisions of sufficient energy is much larger for methane and chlorine atoms than for methane and bromine atoms. To be specific, at 275° the fraction is about 1 in 40 for chlorine and 1 in 10 million for bromine.

A bromine atom, on the average, collides with many methane molecules before it succeeds in abstracting hydrogen; a chlorine atom collides with relatively few. During its longer search for the proper methane molecule, a bromine atom is more likely to encounter another scarce particle — a second halogen atom or a methyl radical — or be captured by the vessel wall; the chains should therefore be much shorter than in chlorination. Experiment has shown this to be so: where the average chain length is several thousand for chlorination, it is less than 100 for bromination. Even though bromine atoms are formed more rapidly than chlorine atoms at a given temperature because of the lower E_{act} of step (1), over-all bromination is slower than chlorination because of the shorter chain length.

For the endothermic reaction of an iodine atom with methane, E_{act} can be no less than 30 kcal, and is probably somewhat larger. Even for this minimum value of 30 kcal, an iodine atom must collide with an enormous number of methane molecules (10^{12} or a million million at 275°) before reaction is likely to occur. Virtually no iodine atoms last this long, but instead recombine to form iodine molecules; the reaction therefore proceeds at a negligible rate. Iodine atoms are easy to form; it is their inability to abstract hydrogen from methane that prevents iodination from occurring.

We cannot predict the E_{act} for the highly exothermic attack of fluorine atoms on methane, but we would certainly not expect it to be any larger than for the attack of chlorine atoms on methane. It appears actually to be smaller, thus permitting even longer chains. Because of the surprising weakness of the fluorine–fluorine bond, fluorine atoms should be formed faster than chlorine atoms; thus there should be not only longer chains in fluorination but also *more* chains. The over-all reaction is extremely exothermic, with a ΔH of -103 kcal, and the difficulty of removing this heat is one cause of the difficulty of control of fluorination. An additional factor, which we could not have predicted, but which may very well be important, is that the presence of a fluorine atom in the methane molecule greatly activates the molecule toward further fluorination; the formation of carbon tetrafluoride is thus favored.

Problem 2.3 Because of the small size of the fluorine atom, the fluorine–fluorine bond (1.42 A) is much shorter than the chlorine–chlorine bond (1.98 A). (a) Show the electronic configuration of the F_2 molecule, including the unshared pairs. (b) Keeping in mind the Pauli exclusion principle, can you suggest a possible reason why F_2 tends to break apart more easily than Cl_2?

The differences in reactivity toward methane shown by halogens other than fluorine arise chiefly from differences in E_{act} of step (2), that is, from differences in ability to abstract a hydrogen atom from methane. These E_{act}'s, in turn, are related to differences in ΔH. Since the same bond, CH_3—H, is being broken in every case, the differences in ΔH are due to differences in bond strength among the various hydrogen–halogen bonds. We may say, then, that the reactivity of a halogen toward methane depends primarily upon the strength of the bond which that halogen forms with hydrogen.

One further point requires clarification. We have said that an E_{act} of 30 kcal is too great for the reaction between iodine atoms and methane to proceed at a significant rate; yet the initial step in each of these halogenations requires an even greater E_{act}. The difference is this: since halogenation is a chain reaction, dissociation of each molecule of halogen gives rise ultimately to many molecules of methyl halide; hence, even though dissociation is very slow, the over-all reaction can be fast. The attack of iodine atoms on methane, however, is a chain-carrying step and if it is slow the entire reaction must be slow; under these circumstances chain-terminating steps (e.g., union of two iodine atoms) become so important that effectively there is *no* chain.

2.23 Isomer number and tetrahedral carbon

Now that we have learned something about methane and its substitution reactions, let us return to the matter of the *shape* of the methane molecule.

The evidence of electron diffraction, x-ray diffraction, and spectroscopy shows that when carbon is bonded to four other atoms its bonds are directed toward the corners of a tetrahedron. But as early as 1874, years before the direct determination of molecular structure was possible, the tetrahedral carbon atom was proposed by J. H. van't Hoff, while he was still a student at the University of Utrecht. His proposal was based upon the evidence of **isomer number.**

For any group Y, *only one substance of formula* CH_3Y *has ever been found.* Chlorination of methane yields only one compound of formula CH_3Cl; bromination yields only one compound of formula CH_3Br. Similarly, only one CH_3F is known, only one CH_3I, only one CH_3OH, only one CH_3COOH.

What does this tell us about the arrangement of atoms in methane? It tells us that every hydrogen atom in methane is equivalent to every other hydrogen atom, so that replacement of any one of them gives rise to the same product. If the hydrogen atoms of methane were not equivalent, then replacement of one would yield a different compound than replacement of another, and isomeric substitution products would be obtained.

In what ways can the atoms of methane be arranged so that the four hydrogen atoms are equivalent? There are three such arrangements: (a) a *planar* arrangement (I) in which carbon is at the center of a rectangle (or square) and a hydrogen atom is at each corner; (b) a *pyramidal* ar-

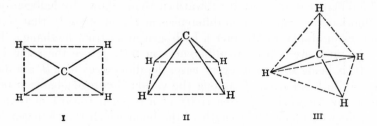

rangement (II) in which carbon is at the apex of a pyramid and a hydrogen atom is at each corner of a square base; (c) a *tetrahedral* arrangement (III) in which carbon is at the center of a tetrahedron and a hydrogen atom is at each corner. (Gumdrops and toothpicks can be used to make structures like I and II, for which the bond angles of ordinary molecular models are not suited.)

So far as compounds of the formula CH_3Y are concerned, the evidence of isomer number limits the structure of methane to one of these three possibilities.

Problem 2.4 How many isomers of formula CH_3Y would be possible if methane were a pyramid with a *rectangular base?* What are they? (*Hint:* if you have trouble with this question now, try it again after you have studied Chapter 11.)

For any group Y and for any group Z, only one substance of formula CH_2YZ has ever been found. Halogenation of methane, for example, yields only one compound of formula CH_2Cl_2, only one compound of formula CH_2Br_2, and only one compound of formula CH_2ClBr.

Of the three possible structures of methane, only the tetrahedral one is consistent with this evidence.

Problem 2.5 How many isomers of formula CH_2YZ would be expected from each of the following structures for methane: (a) structure I with carbon at the center of a rectangle; (b) structure I with carbon at the center of a square; (c) structure II; (d) structure III.

Thus, only the tetrahedral structure for methane agrees with the evidence of isomer number. It is true that this is negative evidence; one might argue that isomers exist which have never been isolated or detected simply because the experimental techniques are not good enough. But any compound, no matter how complicated, that contains carbon bonded to four other atoms can be considered to be a derivative of methane; in the preparation of hundreds of thousands of compounds of this sort, the number of isomers obtained has always been consistent with the concept of the tetrahedral carbon atom.

There is additional, positive evidence for the tetrahedral carbon atom: the existence of isomerism of a particular kind for compounds of the formula

CWXYZ. It was this isomerism (discussed in Sec. 11.19) that convinced van't Hoff that the carbon atom was tetrahedral.

2.24 Molecular formula: its fundamental importance

In this chapter we have been concerned with the structure of methane: the way in which atoms are put together to form a molecule of methane. But first we had to know what kinds of atoms these are and how many of them make up the molecule; we had to know that methane is CH_4. Before we can assign a structural formula to a compound, we must first know its molecular formula.

Much of the chapter was spent in discussing the substitution of chlorine for the hydrogen of methane. But first we had to know that there *is* substitution, that each step of the reaction yields a product that contains one less hydrogen atom and one more chlorine atom than the reactant; we had to know that CH_4 is converted successively into CH_3Cl, CH_2Cl_2, $CHCl_3$, and CCl_4. Before we can discuss the reactions of an organic compound, we must first know the molecular formulas of the products.

Let us review a little of what we know about the assigning of a molecular formula to a compound. We must carry out:

(a) a *qualitative elemental analysis*, to find out what kinds of atoms are present in the molecule;

(b) a *quantitative elemental analysis*, to find out the relative numbers of the different kinds of atoms, that is, to determine the *empirical formula;*

(c) a *molecular weight determination,* which (combined with the empirical formula) shows the actual numbers of the different kinds of atoms, that is, gives us the *molecular formula.*

Most of this should be familiar to the student from previous courses in chemistry. What we shall concentrate on here will be the application of these principles to organic analysis.

2.25 Qualitative elemental analysis: carbon, hydrogen, and halogen

The presence of carbon or hydrogen in a compound is detected by **combustion:** heating with copper oxide, which converts carbon into carbon dioxide and hydrogen into water. (*Problem:* how could each of these products be identified?)

$$(C,H) + CuO \xrightarrow{\text{heat}} Cu + CO_2 + H_2O$$

Detection of halogen in an organic compound usually involves a **sodium fusion:** treatment with hot molten sodium metal, which converts covalently bonded halogen into sodium halide. (*Problem:* how could halide ion be identified?)

$$(C,H,X) + Na \xrightarrow{\text{heat}} Na^+ X^-$$

Sodium fusion is used to convert a number of other covalently bonded elements into inorganic ions: N into CN^- and S into S^{--}, in particular, as discussed in Sec. 8.25. (A simpler method of detecting halogen in *some* organic compounds is discussed in Sec. 13.18.)

By these methods, we could show, for example, that methane contains carbon and hydrogen, or that methyl chloride contains carbon, hydrogen, and chlorine.

Further tests would show the absence of any other element in these compounds, except possibly oxygen, for which there is no simple chemical test; presence or absence of oxygen would be shown by a quantitative analysis.

Problem 2.6   Only carbon and hydrogen were detected by a qualitative elemental analysis of the compound ethyl alcohol; quantitative analysis gave 52.1% carbon and 13.1% hydrogen.   (a) Why would it be assumed that ethyl alcohol contains oxygen?   (b) What percentage of oxygen would be assumed?

2.26   Quantitative elemental analysis: carbon, hydrogen, and halogen

Knowing what elements make up a compound, we must next determine the proportions in which they are present. To do this, we carry out very much the same analysis as before, only this time on a quantitative basis. To find out the relative amounts of carbon and hydrogen in methane, for example, we would completely oxidize a measured amount of methane and weigh the carbon dioxide and water formed.

In a quantitative combustion, a weighed sample of the organic compound is passed through a *combustion train:* a tube packed with copper oxide heated to 600–800°, followed by a tube containing a drying agent (usually Dehydrite, magnesium perchlorate) and a tube containing a strong base (usually Ascarite, sodium hydroxide on asbestos).   The water formed is absorbed by the drying agent, and the carbon dioxide is absorbed by the base; the increase in weight of each tube gives the weight of product formed.

For example, we might find that a sample of methane weighing 9.67 mg produced 26.53 mg of CO_2 and 21.56 mg of H_2O.   Now, only the fraction $C/CO_2 = 12.01/44.01$ of the carbon dioxide is carbon, and only the fraction $2H/H_2O = 2.016/18.02$ of the water is hydrogen.   Therefore

wt.C = 26.53 × 12.01/44.01   wt.H = 21.56 × 2.016/18.02
wt.C (in sample) = 7.24 mg   wt.H (in sample) = 2.41 mg

and the percentage composition is

%C = 7.24/9.67 × 100   %H = 2.41/9.67 × 100
%C (in sample) = 74.9   %H (in sample) = 24.9

Since the total of carbon and hydrogen is 100%, within the limits of error of the analysis, oxygen (or any other element) must be absent.

In quantitative, as in qualitative, analysis, covalently bonded halogen must be converted into halide ion.   The organic compound is heated either (a) in a bomb with sodium peroxide or (b) in a sealed tube with nitric acid (*Carius method*).   The halide ion thus formed is converted into silver halide, which can be weighed.

Problem 2.7   When 7.36 mg of methyl chloride was heated in a bomb with sodium peroxide, the chloride ion liberated yielded 20.68 mg of silver chloride.

(a) What percentage of chlorine is indicated by this analysis?   (b) What percentage of chlorine would be expected from a compound of formula CH_3Cl? (c) What weight of silver chloride would you expect from 7.36 mg of methylene chloride?   (d) Of chloroform?   (e) Of carbon tetrachloride?

(We shall take up other quantitative analytical methods when we need them: nitrogen and sulfur analysis, Sec. 8.26; methoxyl determination, Sec. 15.20; neutralization equivalent, Sec. 16.22; saponification equivalent, Sec. 17.28.)

2.27 Empirical formula

Knowing the percentage composition of a compound, we can now calculate the **empirical formula**: *the simplest formula that shows the relative numbers of the different kinds of atoms in a molecule.* In 100 g (taken for convenience) of methane, for example, there are 74.9 g of carbon and 24.9 g of hydrogen, according to our quantitative analysis. Dividing each quantity by the proper atomic weight gives the number of gram–atoms of each element.

$$\text{C:} \frac{74.9}{12.01} = 6.24 \text{ gram–atoms} \qquad \text{H:} \frac{24.9}{1.008} = 24.7 \text{ gram–atoms}$$

Since a gram–atom of one element contains the same number of atoms as a gram–atom of any other element, we now know the relative number of carbon and hydrogen atoms in methane: $C_{6.24}H_{24.7}$. Conversion to smallest whole numbers gives the empirical formula CH_4 for methane.

C: 6.24/6.24 = 1   H: 24.7/6.24 = 3.96, approximately 4

Problem 2.8   Calculate the percentage composition and then the empirical formula for each of the following compounds:

(a) Combustion of a 3.02-mg sample of a compound gave 8.86 mg of carbon dioxide and 5.43 mg of water.

(b) Combustion of an 8.23-mg sample of a compound gave 9.62 mg of carbon dioxide and 3.94 mg of water. Analysis of a 5.32-mg sample of the same compound by the Carius method gave 13.49 mg of silver chloride.

2.28 Molecular weight determination: vapor density method. Molecular formula

At this stage we know what kinds of atoms make up the molecule we are studying, and in what ratio they are present. This knowledge is summarized in the empirical formula.

But this is not enough. On the basis of just the empirical formula, a molecule of methane, for example, might contain one carbon and four hydrogens, or two carbons and eight hydrogens, or *any* multiple of CH_4. We still have to find the **molecular formula**: *the formula that shows the actual number of each kind of atom in a molecule.*

To find the molecular formula, we must determine the molecular weight. From our study of general chemistry, we are already familiar with several methods for doing this. Since the compounds we are concerned with at this point are gases or volatile liquids, we would probably use a **vapor density method** (the *Dumas method* or the *Victor Meyer method*). The volume occupied by a known weight of gas at a known temperature and pressure is measured. From this, the weight of gas that would occupy 22.4 liters under standard conditions (0° and 760 mm) is calculated; this weight is, of course, the molecular weight.

For example, we might find that 0.309 g of methane occupied 488 cc at 23° and 737 mm pressure. At standard conditions, 0.309 g would occupy

$$\frac{273}{273 + 23} \times \frac{737}{760} \times 488 = 436 \text{ cc}$$

and the weight of methane required to fill 22400 cc would be

$$\frac{22400}{436} \times 0.309 = 15.9 \text{ g}$$

The determination thus shows that the molecular weight of methane is about 15.9. Of the possible molecular formulas, CH_4 (molecular weight 16.04) is clearly closer than C_2H_8 (molecular weight 32.08) or any higher multiple. In this case, the empirical formula and the molecular formula happen to be the same.

Let us look at another example: *ethane*, with an empirical formula of CH_3. Measurement of vapor density indicates a molecular weight of about 30. Of the possible molecular formulas, C_2H_6 (molecular weight 30.07) must be the correct one.

(Molecular weight determination by *cryoscopic* methods is discussed in Sec. 8.27.)

Problem 2.9 Quantitative elemental analysis shows that the empirical formula of a compound is CH. A 0.265-g sample of this compound is found to occupy 105 cc at 99° and 733 mm pressure. What is the (a) measured molecular weight; (b) molecular formula; and (c) correct molecular weight?

Problem 2.10 Combustion of a 5.17-mg sample of a compound gives 10.32 mg of carbon dioxide and 4.23 mg of water. A 0.156-g sample of this compound is found to occupy 53 cc at 100° and 760 mm pressure. What is the molecular formula of the compound?

PROBLEMS

1. Calculate the percentage composition of A, B, and C from the following analytical data:

	wt. sample	wt. CO_2	wt. H_2O	wt. AgCl
A	4.37 mg	15.02 mg	2.48 mg	—
B	5.95 mg	13.97 mg	2.39 mg	7.55 mg
C	4.02 mg	9.14 mg	3.71 mg	—

2. What is the percentage composition of:

(a) C_3H_7Cl (c) $C_4H_8O_2$ (e) CH_4ON_2
(b) C_2H_6O (d) $C_6H_8O_2N_2S$ (f) C_6H_8NCl

3. What is the empirical formula of an organic compound whose percentage composition is:

(a) 85.6% C, 14.4% H   (d) 29.8% C, 6.3% H, 44.0% Cl
(b) 92.2% C, 7.8% H   (e) 48.7% C, 13.6% H, 37.8% N
(c) 40.0% C, 6.7% H   (f) 25.2% C, 2.8% H, 49.6% Cl

(*Note:* remember that oxygen is not determined directly.)

4. A qualitative analysis of *papaverine*, one of the alkaloids in opium, showed carbon, hydrogen, and nitrogen. A quantitative analysis gave 70.8% carbon, 6.2% hydrogen, and 4.1% nitrogen. Calculate the empirical formula of papaverine.

5. *Methyl orange*, an acid-base indicator, is the sodium salt of an acid that contains carbon, hydrogen, nitrogen, sulfur, and oxygen. Quantitative analysis gave 51.4% carbon, 4.3% hydrogen, 12.8% nitrogen, 9.8% sulfur, and 7.0% sodium. What is the empirical formula of methyl orange?

6. Combustion of 6.51 mg of a compound gave 20.47 mg of carbon dioxide and 8.36 mg of water. At 100° and 760 mm pressure, 0.284 g of the compound occupied 100 cc. Calculate (a) percentage composition; (b) empirical formula; and (c) molecular formula of the compound.

7. Analysis of a liquid compound gave 40.0% carbon and 6.7% hydrogen. At 200° and 760 mm pressure, 10.0 mg of the compound occupied 6.47 cc. What is the molecular formula of the compound?

8. A compound of the same empirical formula as the one in Problem 7 is a gas at room temperature; 10.0 mg of it occupied 8.15 cc at 25° and 760 mm. What is its molecular formula?

9. *Indigo*, an important dyestuff, gave an analysis of 73.3% carbon, 3.8% hydrogen, and 10.7% nitrogen. Molecular weight determinations gave values in the range of 250–275. What is the molecular formula of indigo?

10. Analysis of a gas gave 82.7% carbon and 17.3% hydrogen. A glass bulb filled with the gas at 22° and 739 mm weighed 195.10 g. Evacuated, the bulb weighed 194.52 g; filled with water, it weighed 444.50 g. Calculate the molecular formula of the compound.

11. The hormone *insulin* contains 3.4% sulfur. (a) What is the minimum molecular weight of insulin? (b) The actual molecular weight is 5734; how many sulfur atoms are probably present per molecule?

12. Calculate ΔH for:

(a)–(d) $H_2 + X_2 \longrightarrow 2HX$, where X = F, Cl, Br, I
(e) $C_2H_6 + Br_2 \longrightarrow C_2H_5Br + HBr$
(f) $C_6H_5CH_3 + Br_2 \longrightarrow C_6H_5CH_2Br + HBr$
(g) $H_2C=CHCH_3 + Br_2 \longrightarrow H_2C=CHCH_2Br + HBr$
(h) Reactions (e), (f), and (g) proceed by the same free radical mechanism as halogenation of methane. Calculate ΔH for each step in these three reactions.

13. A conceivable mechanism for the chlorination of methane involves the following steps:

(1) $\qquad\qquad Cl_2 \longrightarrow 2Cl\cdot$
(2) $\qquad Cl\cdot + CH_4 \longrightarrow CH_3Cl + H\cdot$
(3) $\qquad H\cdot + Cl_2 \longrightarrow HCl + Cl\cdot$

then (2), (3), (2), (3), etc.

(a) Calculate ΔH for each of these steps. (b) Why does this mechanism seem less likely than the accepted one given in Sec. 2.12? (There is additional, conclusive evidence against this alternative mechanism.)

14. Free methyl radicals react with methane as follows:

$$CH_3\cdot + CH_4 \longrightarrow CH_4 + CH_3\cdot$$

On the basis of the bond strengths involved, show why the above reaction takes place rather than the following:

$$CH_3\cdot + CH_4 \longrightarrow CH_3-CH_3 + H\cdot$$

15. Bromination of methane is slowed down by addition of fairly large amounts of HBr. (a) Suggest a possible explanation for this. (*Hint:* see Sec. 2.19.) (b) Account for the fact that HCl does not have a similar effect upon chlorination. (c) Any reaction tends to slow down as reactants are used up and their concentrations decrease. How do you account for the fact that bromination of methane slows down to an unusually great extent, more than, say, chlorination of methane?

16. A mixture of H_2 and Cl_2 does not react in the dark at room temperature. At high temperatures or under the influence of light (of a wavelength absorbed by chlorine) a violent reaction occurs and HCl is formed. The photochemical reaction yields as many as a million molecules of HCl for each photon absorbed. The presence of a small amount of oxygen slows down the reaction markedly. (a) Outline a possible mechanism to account for these facts. (b) Account for the fact that a mixture of H_2 and I_2 does not behave in the same way. (Hydrogen iodide is actually formed, but by an entirely different mechanism.)

17. A stream of tetramethyllead vapor, $(CH_3)_4Pb$, was passed through a quartz tube which was heated at one spot; a mirror of metallic lead was deposited at the hot point, and the gas escaping from the tube was found to be chiefly ethane. The tube was next heated upstream of the lead mirror while more tetramethyllead was passed through; a new mirror appeared at the hot point, the old mirror disappeared, and the gas escaping from the tube was now found to be chiefly tetramethyllead. Experiments like this, done by Fritz Paneth at the University of Berlin, were considered the first good evidence for the existence of short-lived free radicals like methyl. (a) Show how these experimental results can be accounted for in terms of intermediate free radicals. (b) The farther upstream the tube was heated, the more slowly the old mirror disappeared. Account for this.

ALKANES

3.1   Classification by structure: the family

The basis of organic chemistry, we have said, is the structural theory. We separate all organic compounds into a number of families on the basis of structure. Having done this, we find that we have at the same time classified the compounds as to their physical and chemical properties. A particular set of properties is thus characteristic of a particular kind of structure.

Within a family there are variations in properties. All members of the family may, for example, react with a particular reagent, but some may react more readily than others. Within a single compound there may be variations in properties, one part of a molecule being more reactive than another part. These variations in properties correspond to variations in structure.

As we take up each family of organic compounds, we shall first see what structure and properties are characteristic of the family. Next we shall see how structure and properties vary within the family. We shall not simply memorize these facts, but, whenever possible, shall try to understand properties in terms of structure, and to understand variations in properties in terms of variations in structure.

Having studied methane in some detail, let us now look at the more complicated members of the alkane family. These hydrocarbons have been assigned to the same family as methane on the basis of their structure, and on the whole their properties follow the pattern laid down by methane. However, certain new points will arise simply because of the greater size and complexity of these compounds.

3.2   Structure of ethane

Next in size after methane is **ethane**, C_2H_6. If we connect the atoms of this molecule by covalent bonds, following the rule of one bond (one pair of electrons) for each hydrogen and four bonds (four pairs of electrons) for each carbon, we arrive at the structure

$$\begin{array}{cc} \text{H H} \\ \overset{..}{\text{H}}:\overset{..}{\text{C}}:\overset{..}{\text{C}}:\text{H} \\ \text{H H} \end{array} \qquad \begin{array}{c} \text{H H} \\ \text{H—C—C—H} \\ \text{H H} \end{array}$$

Ethane

Each carbon is bonded to three hydrogens and to the other carbon.

Since each carbon atom is bonded to four other atoms, its bonding orbitals (sp^3 orbitals) are directed toward the corners of a tetrahedron. As in the case of methane, the carbon–hydrogen bonds result from overlapping of these sp^3 orbitals with the s orbitals of the hydrogens. The carbon–carbon bond arises from overlapping of two sp^3 orbitals.

The carbon–hydrogen and carbon–carbon bonds have the same general electron distribution, being cylindrically symmetrical about a line joining the atomic nuclei (see Figure 3.1); because of this similarity in shape, the bonds are given the same name, σ *bonds* (*sigma bonds*).

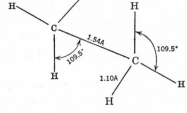

FIGURE 3.1. Ethane molecule. Carbon–carbon single bond: σ bond.

FIGURE 3.2. Ethane molecule: Shape and size.

In ethane, then, the bond angles and carbon–hydrogen bond lengths should be very much the same as in methane, that is, about 109.5° and about 1.09 A, respectively. Electron diffraction and spectroscopic studies have verified this structure in all respects, giving (Figure 3.2) the following measurements for the molecule: bond angles, 109.5°; C—H length, 1.10 A; C—C length, 1.54 A. Similar studies have shown that, with only slight variations, these values are quite characteristic of carbon–hydrogen and carbon–carbon bonds and of carbon bond angles in alkanes.

3.3 Free rotation about the carbon–carbon single bond. Conformations. Non-bonded interaction

This particular set of bond angles and bond lengths still does not limit us to a single arrangement of atoms, since the relationship between the hydrogens of one carbon and the hydrogens of the other carbon is not specified. We could have an arrangement like I in which the hydrogens exactly oppose each other, an arrangement like II in which the hydrogens are completely staggered, or an infinity of intermediate arrangements. Which of these is the actual structure of ethane? The answer is: *all of them.*

Ethane:
eclipsed
conformation

I

Ethane:
staggered
conformation

II

We have seen that the σ bond joining the carbon atoms is cylindrically symmetrical about a line joining the two carbon nuclei; overlapping and hence bond strength should be the same for all these possible arrangements. If the various arrangements do not differ in energy, then the molecule is not restricted to any one of them, but can change freely from one to another. Since the change from one to another involves rotation about the carbon–carbon bond, we describe this freedom to change by saying that *there is free rotation about the carbon–carbon single bond.*

Different arrangements of atoms that can be converted into one another without the breaking of bonds are called **conformations.** I is called the *eclipsed conformation;* II is called the *staggered conformation.*

The picture is not yet quite complete. Certain physical properties indicate that in the eclipsed conformation (I) the hydrogen atoms — or more accurately, perhaps, the electron pairs holding the hydrogen atoms — are *crowded* together. Now, when atoms that are not bonded to each other are brought together, up to a point they attract each other; we call this attraction van der Waals forces (Sec. 1.14). If forced still closer together, however, these atoms tend to repel each other strongly; this repulsion, called **non-bonded interaction,** raises the energy of the system, that is, makes the system less stable.

In the case of ethane, it has been calculated that non-bonded interaction between the crowded hydrogen atoms raises the energy of the eclipsed system by about 3 kcal/mole (Figure 3.3). Most ethane mole·

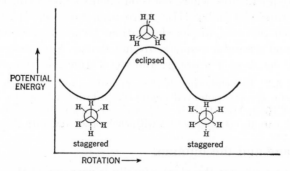

POTENTIAL
ENERGY

eclipsed

staggered

staggered

ROTATION ⟶

FIGURE 3.3 Potential energy changes during rotation about carbon-carbon single bond of ethane.

cules should exist, then, in the more stable, staggered conformation. How free are they to rotate from one staggered arrangement to another? The 3-kcal barrier is not a very high one; even at room temperature the fraction of collisions with sufficient energy is large enough that a rapid transformation between staggered arrangements occurs. We may still consider that, for practical purposes, the carbon–carbon single bond permits free rotation.

Let us examine just one piece of evidence supporting this concept of free rotation: the evidence of isomer number. To do this, we must consider not ethane but the closely related 1,2-dichloroethane (III). We find that

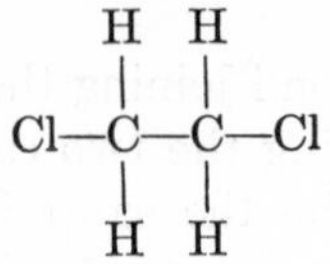

$$
\begin{array}{ccc}
& H & H \\
& | & | \\
Cl- & C- & C-Cl \\
& | & | \\
& H & H
\end{array}
$$

1,2-Dichloroethane

III

the various staggered arrangements (IV and V) of this compound are different from each other.

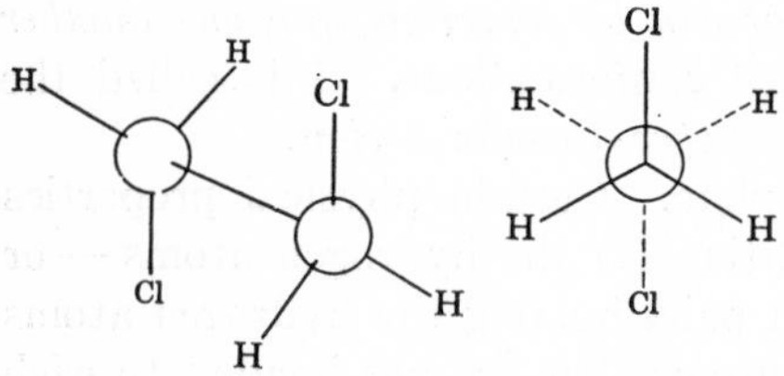

IV 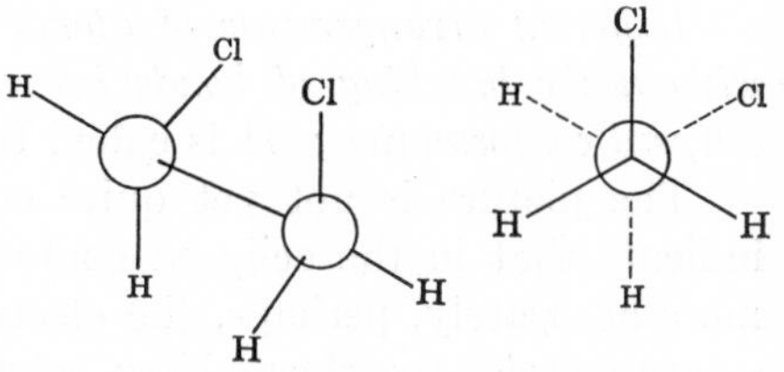   V

We notice, for example, that the chlorine atoms are farther apart in IV than in V. If there were an appreciable barrier to rotation, then some molecules could be "frozen" in conformation IV and others in conformation V. Because of their different properties, the two kinds of molecules could be separated; two isomeric 1,2-dichloroethanes could thus be isolated. But only one 1,2-dichloroethane has been isolated, indicating that the interconversion of IV and V is so rapid that the two cannot be separated.

At low temperatures where collision energies are small, two isomers of the badly crowded $CHBr_2CHBr_2$ have been isolated. Thus the distinctions between free and hindered rotation, between interconvertible conformations and separable isomers, are not sharp. Most cases, however, fall clearly into one class or another, and the distinctions remain useful ones.

Problem 3.1 Remembering that a chlorine atom is much larger than a hydrogen atom, draw a potential energy *vs.* rotation curve like Figure 3.3 for: (a) CH_2Cl-CH_2Cl; (b) $CHCl_2-CHCl_2$; (c) CCl_3-CCl_3. (d) Compare the heights of the various energy barriers with each other and with those in Figure 3.3.

3.4 Propane and the butanes

The next member of the alkane family is **propane**, C_3H_8. Again following the rule of one bond per hydrogen and four bonds per carbon, and

considering free rotation to exist about the carbon–carbon bonds, we arrive
at structure I.

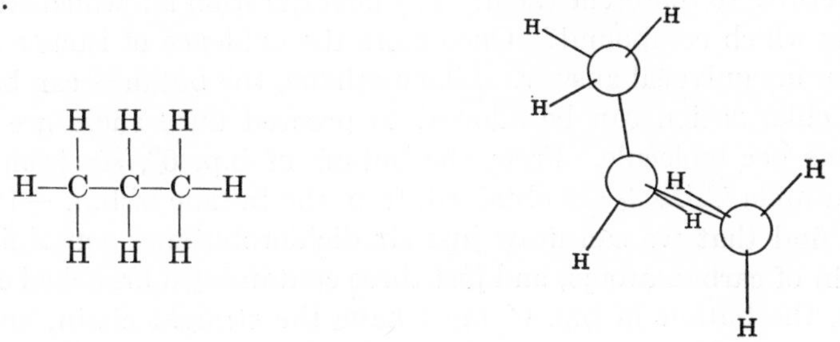

H H H
 | | |
H—C—C—C—H
 | | |
H H H

Propane

I

When we consider **butane**, C_4H_{10}, we find that there are two possible
structures, II and III.

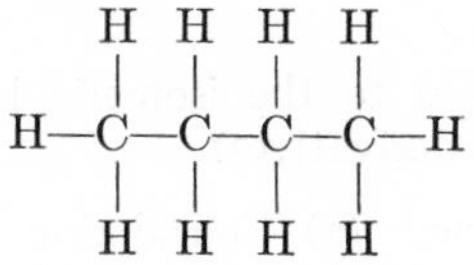

H H H H
 | | | |
H—C—C—C—C—H
 | | | |
H H H H

H   H   H
 | | |
H—C———C———C—H
 | | |
H | H
    H—C—H
       |
       H

n-Butane

II

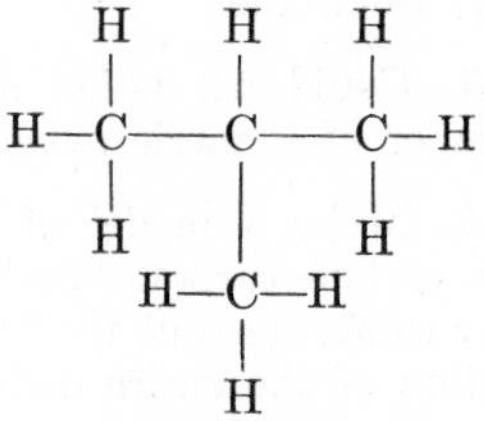

Isobutane

III

II has a four-carbon chain and III has a three-carbon chain with a one-
carbon branch. There can be no doubt that these represent different
structures, since no amount of moving, twisting, or rotating about carbon–
carbon bonds will cause these structures to coincide. We can see that in
the *straight-chain* structure (II) each carbon possesses at least two hydrogens, whereas in the *branched-chain* structure (III) one carbon possesses
only a single hydrogen; or we may notice that in the branched-chain structure (III) one carbon is bonded to three other carbons, whereas in the
straight-chain structure (II) no carbon is bonded to more than two other
carbons.

In agreement with this prediction we find that there actually exist two
compounds that have the same formula, C_4H_{10}. There can be no doubt
that these two substances are different compounds, since they show definite
differences in their physical and chemical properties (see Table 3.1); for
example, one boils at 0° and the other at −12°.

TABLE 3.1

PHYSICAL CONSTANTS OF THE ISOMERIC BUTANES

	n-Butane	Isobutane
b.p.	0°	−12°
m.p.	−138°	−159°
sp. gr. at −20°	0.622	0.604
solub. in		
100 ml alcohol	1813 ml	1320 ml

Two compounds of formula C_4H_{10} are known and we have drawn two structures to represent them. The next question is: which structure represents which compound? Once more the evidence of isomer number gives us an unequivocal answer. Like methane, the butanes can be chlorinated; the chlorination can be allowed to proceed until there are two chlorine atoms per molecule. From the butane of b.p. 0°, *six* isomeric products of formula $C_4H_8Cl_2$ are obtained, from the butane of b.p. $-12°$, only *three*. We find that we can draw just six dichlorobutanes containing a straight chain of carbon atoms, and just three containing a branched chain. Therefore, the butane of b.p. 0° must have the straight chain, and the butane of b.p. $-12°$ must have the branched chain. To distinguish between these two isomers, the straight-chain structure is called **n-butane** (spoken "normal" butane) and the branched-chain structure is called **isobutane.**

Problem 3.2 Draw the structures of all possible dichloro derivatives of (a) *n*-butane, (b) isobutane.

Problem 3.3 Could we assign structures to the isomeric butanes on the basis of the number of isomeric *mono*chloro derivatives?

Problem 3.4 Make a model of propane. (a) Considering rotation about only *one* of the carbon–carbon bonds, what is the most stable conformation? (b) Now consider rotation about the *other* carbon–carbon bond. What is the most stable conformation of the entire molecule?

Problem 3.5 Make a model of *n*-butane. (a) What is the most stable conformation? (*Hint:* concentrate first on the middle carbon–carbon bond.) (b) Are all other conformations of equal stability?

Problem 3.6 Follow the instructions of Problem 3.5 for isobutane.

3.5 Higher alkanes. The homologous series

If we examine the molecular formulas of the alkanes we have so far considered, we see that butane contains one carbon and two hydrogens more than propane, which in turn contains one carbon and two hydrogens more than ethane, etc. *A series of compounds in which each member differs from the next member by a constant amount is called a* **homologous series,** *and the members of the series are called* **homologs.** The family of alkanes forms such a homologous series, the constant difference between successive members being CH_2. We also notice that in each of these alkanes the number of hydrogen atoms equals two more than twice the number of carbon atoms, so that we may write as a *general formula* for members of this series, C_nH_{2n+2}. As we shall see later, other homologous series have their own characteristic general formulas.

In agreement with this general formula, we find that the next alkane, *pentane*, has the formula C_5H_{12}, followed by *hexane*, C_6H_{14}, *heptane*, C_7H_{16}, and so on. We would expect that, as the number of atoms increases, so does the number of possible arrangements of those atoms. As we go up the series of alkanes, we find that this is true: the number of isomers of successive homologs increases at a surprising rate. There are 3 isomeric pentanes, 5 hexanes, 9 heptanes, and 75 decanes (C_{10}); for the twenty-carbon eicosane, there are 366,319 possible isomeric structures! The carbon skeletons of the isomeric pentanes and hexanes are shown below.

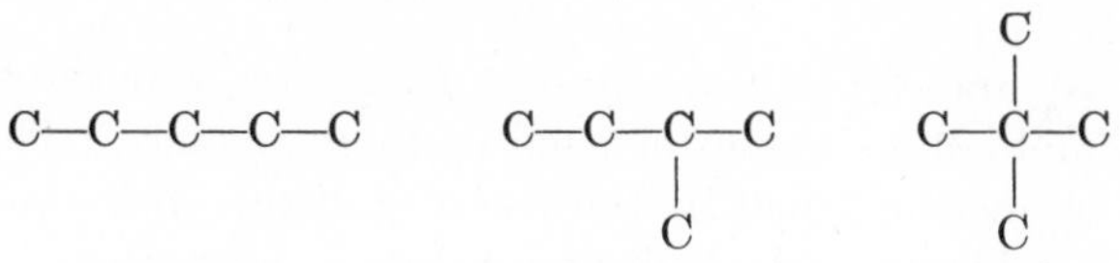

C—C—C—C—C   C—C—C—C

$$\text{C—C—C—C—C} \qquad \text{C—C—C—C} \qquad \text{C—C—C}$$

Pentanes

n-Pentane   Isopentane   Neopentane
b.p. 36°   b.p. 28°   b.p. 9.5°

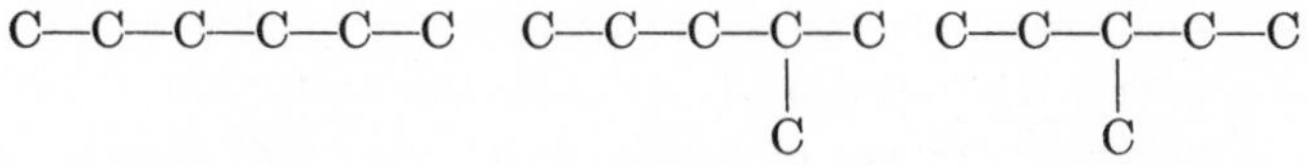

C—C—C—C—C—C   C—C—C—C—C   C—C—C—C—C

b.p. 69°   b.p. 60°   b.p. 63°

Hexanes

C—C—C—C   C—C—C—C

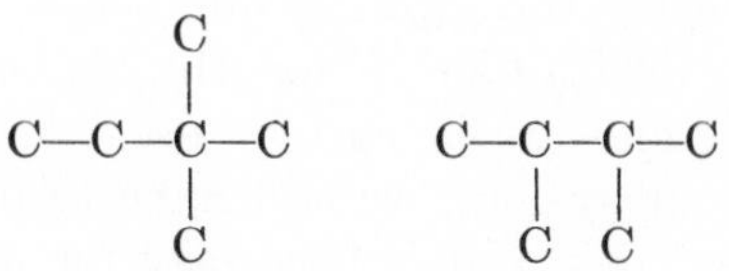

b.p. 50°   b.p. 58°

It is important to practice drawing the possible isomeric structures that correspond to a single molecular formula. In doing this, a set of molecular models is especially helpful since it will show that many structures which appear to be different when drawn on paper are actually identical.

Problem 3.7 Draw the structures of: (a) the nine isomeric heptanes (C_7H_{16}); (b) the eight chloropentanes ($C_5H_{11}Cl$); (c) the nine dibromobutanes ($C_4H_8Br_2$).

3.6 Nomenclature

We have seen that the names *methane, ethane, propane, butane,* and *pentane* are used for alkanes containing respectively one, two, three, four, and five carbon atoms. Table 3.2 gives the names of many larger alkanes.

TABLE 3.2

NAMES OF ALKANES

CH_4	methane	C_9H_{20}	nonane
C_2H_6	ethane	$C_{10}H_{22}$	decane
C_3H_8	propane	$C_{11}H_{24}$	undecane
C_4H_{10}	butane	$C_{12}H_{26}$	dodecane
C_5H_{12}	pentane	$C_{14}H_{30}$	tetradecane
C_6H_{14}	hexane	$C_{16}H_{34}$	hexadecane
C_7H_{16}	heptane	$C_{18}H_{38}$	octadecane
C_8H_{18}	octane	$C_{20}H_{42}$	eicosane

Except for the first four members of the family, the name is simply derived from the Greek prefix for the particular number of carbons in the alkane; thus **pent**ane for five, **hex**ane for six, **hept**ane for seven, **oct**ane for eight, and so on.

The student should certainly memorize the names of at least the first ten alkanes. Having done this, he has at the same time essentially learned the names of the first ten alkenes, alkynes, alcohols, etc., since the names of many families of compounds are closely related. Compare, for example, the names *propane, propene,* and *propyne* for the three-carbon alkane, alkene, and alkyne.

But nearly every alkane can have a number of isomeric structures, and there must be an unambiguous name for each of these isomers. The butanes and pentanes are distinguished by the use of prefixes: **n**-butane and **iso**butane; **n**-pentane, **iso**pentane, and **neo**pentane. But there are 5 hexanes, 9 heptanes, and 75 decanes; it would be difficult to devise, and even more difficult to remember, a different prefix for each of these isomers. It is obvious that some systematic method of naming is needed.

As organic chemistry has developed, several different methods have been devised to name the members of nearly every class of organic compounds; each method was devised when the previously used system had been found inadequate for the growing number of increasingly complex organic compounds. Unfortunately for the student, perhaps, several systems have survived and are in current use. Even if we are content ourselves to use only one system, we still have to understand the names used by other chemists; hence it is necessary for us to learn more than one system of nomenclature. But before we can do this, we must first learn the names of certain organic groups.

3.7 Alkyl groups

In our study of inorganic chemistry, we found it useful to have names for certain groups of atoms that compose only part of a molecule and yet appear many times as a unit. For example, NH_4^+ is called *ammonium;* NO_3^-, *nitrate;* SO_3^{--}, *sulfite;* etc.

In a similar way names are given to certain groups that constantly appear as structural units of organic molecules. We have seen that chloromethane, CH_3Cl, is also known as *methyl chloride.* The CH_3 group is called **methyl** wherever it appears, CH_3Br being *methyl* bromide, CH_3I, *methyl* iodide, and CH_3OH, *methyl* alcohol. In an analogous way, the C_2H_5 group is **ethyl;** C_3H_7, **propyl;** C_4H_9, **butyl;** and so on.

These groups are named simply by dropping *-ane* from the name of the corresponding alkane and replacing it by *-yl.* They are known collectively as **alkyl groups.** The general formula for an alkyl group is C_nH_{2n+1}, since it contains one less hydrogen than the parent alkane, C_nH_{2n+2}.

Among the alkyl groups we again encounter the problem of isomerism. There is only one methyl chloride or ethyl chloride, and correspondingly only one methyl group or ethyl group. We can see, however, that there are two propyl chlorides, I and II, and hence that there must be two propyl groups.

n-Propyl chloride
I

Isopropyl chloride
II

These groups both contain the propane chain, but differ in the point of attachment of the chlorine; they are called **n-propyl** and **isopropyl**.

$$CH_3CH_2CH_2— \qquad\qquad CH_3CHCH_3$$
$$|$$

n-Propyl   Isopropyl

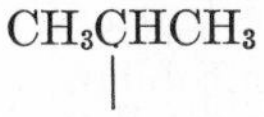

We can distinguish the two chlorides by the names, *n-propyl chloride* and *isopropyl chloride;* we distinguish the two propyl bromides, iodides, alcohols, etc., in the same way.

We find that there are four butyl groups, two derived from the straight-chain *n*-butane, and two derived from the branched-chain isobutane. These are given the designations **n-** (*normal*), **sec-** (*secondary*), **iso-,** and **tert-** (*tertiary*), as shown below. Again the difference between *n*-butyl and *sec*-butyl and between isobutyl and *tert*-butyl lies in the point of attachment of the alkyl group to the rest of the molecule.

$$CH_3CH_2CH_2CH_2— \qquad\qquad CH_3CH_2CHCH_3$$
$$|$$

n-Butyl   sec-Butyl

$$CH_3 \qquad\qquad\qquad\qquad CH_3$$
$$\diagdown \qquad\qquad\qquad\qquad\quad |$$
$$CHCH_2— \qquad CH_3—C—$$
$$\diagup \qquad\qquad\qquad\qquad\quad |$$
$$CH_3 \qquad\qquad\qquad\qquad CH_3$$

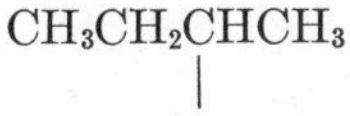

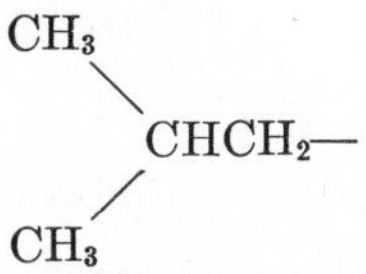

Isobutyl 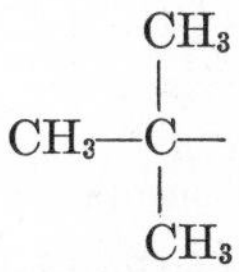   *tert*-Butyl

Beyond butyl the number of isomeric groups derived from each alkane becomes so great that it is impracticable to designate them all by various prefixes. Even though limited, this system is so useful for the small groups just described that it is widely used; a student must therefore memorize these names and learn to recognize these groups at a glance in whatever way they happen to be represented.

However large the group concerned, one of its many possible arrangements can still be designated by this simple system. The prefix *n-* is used to designate any alkyl group in which all carbons form a single continuous chain and in which the point of attachment is the very end carbon. For example:

$$CH_3CH_2CH_2CH_2CH_2Cl \qquad\qquad CH_3(CH_2)_4CH_2Cl$$

n-Pentyl chloride   n-Hexyl chloride

The prefix *iso-* is used to designate any alkyl group (of six carbons or less) that has a single one-carbon branch on the next-to-last carbon of a chain and has the point of attachment at the opposite end of the chain. For example:

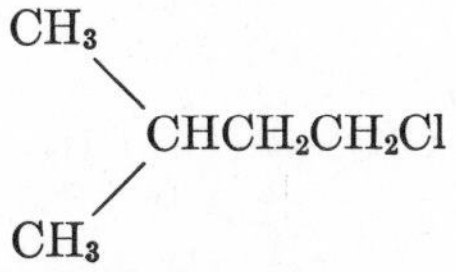

$$CH_3 \qquad\qquad\qquad\qquad\qquad CH_3$$
$$\diagdown \qquad\qquad\qquad\qquad\qquad\quad \diagdown$$
$$CHCH_2CH_2Cl \qquad\qquad CH(CH_2)_2CH_2Cl$$
$$\diagup \qquad\qquad\qquad\qquad\qquad\quad \diagup$$
$$CH_3 \qquad\qquad\qquad\qquad\qquad CH_3$$

Isopentyl chloride 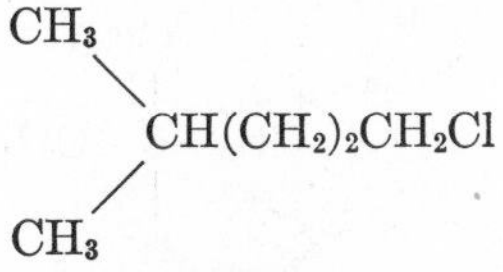   Isohexyl chloride

If the branching occurs at any other position, or the point of attachment is at any other position, this name does not apply.

Now that we have learned the names of certain alkyl groups, let us return to the original problem: the naming of alkanes.

3.8   Common names of alkanes

As we have seen, the prefixes *n-*, *iso-*, and *neo-* are adequate to differentiate the various butanes and pentanes, but beyond this point an impracticable number of prefixes would be required. However, the prefix *n-* has been retained for any alkane, no matter how large, in which all carbons form a continuous chain with no branching:

$$CH_3CH_2CH_2CH_2CH_3 \qquad CH_3(CH_2)_4CH_3$$
n-Pentane   *n*-Hexane

An *isoalkane* is a compound of six carbons or less in which all carbons except one form a continuous chain and that one carbon is attached to the next-to-end carbon:

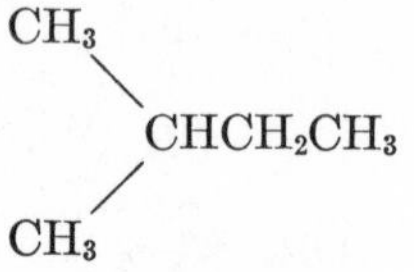

CH₃\CHCH₂CH₃/CH₃   CH₃\CH(CH₂)₂CH₃/CH₃

Isopentane 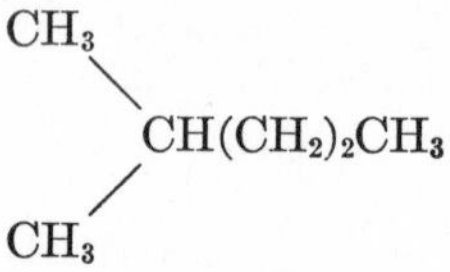   Isohexane

In naming any other of the higher alkanes we must make use of one or the other of the two systems outlined in the following sections.

3.9   Derived names of alkanes

The compounds CH_3Cl, CH_2Cl_2, $CHCl_3$, and CCl_4 have been designated *chloromethane, dichloromethane, trichloromethane,* and *tetrachloromethane;* that is, we have considered these compounds as being derived from methane by the replacement of one or more of its hydrogens, and have retained *-methane* as part of the name.

In a similar way it is possible to consider various alkanes as being derived from methane by the replacement of one or more of its hydrogens by various alkyl groups. We could use *methylmethane* for ethane, *dimethylmethane* for propane, *trimethylmethane* for isobutane, and *methylethylmethane* for *n*-butane.

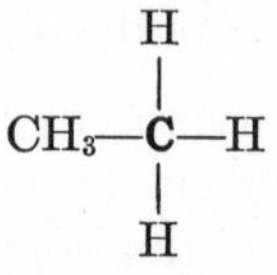

Methylmethane 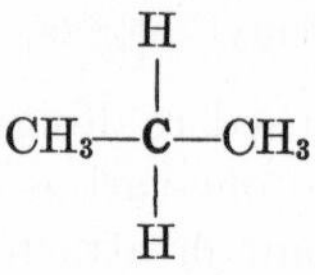   Dimethylmethane

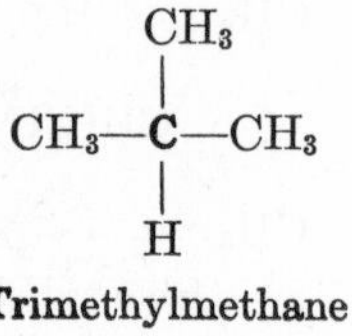

Trimethylmethane 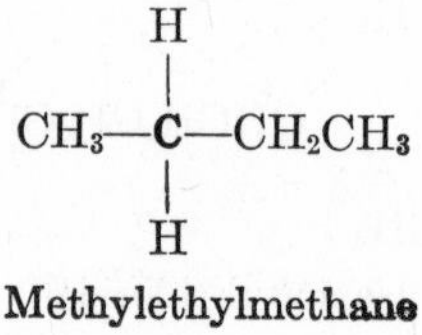   Methylethylmethane

In practice, this *derived* system would probably never be used in naming such simple compounds as those just discussed; for more complicated compounds, however, this system is very useful. In order that the groups attached to methane be as small as possible, we select as the parent carbon atom one situated near the center of the molecule, and generally the one with the largest number of branches. We then simply name the various alkyl groups attached to this carbon, usually in order of increasing size, and finish the name with the ending -*methane* to include the parent carbon atom. For example:

$$
\begin{array}{c}
CH_3 \\
| \\
CH_3-C-CH_2CH_3 \\
| \\
CH_3
\end{array}
\qquad\qquad
\begin{array}{c}
CH_3 \\
| \\
CH_3CH_2-C-CH_2CH_3 \\
| \\
H
\end{array}
$$

Trimethylethylmethane   Methyldiethylmethane

$$
\begin{array}{c}
CH_3 \qquad\quad H \\
\diagdown \qquad | \\
CH-C-CH_2CH_2CH_3 \\
\diagup \qquad | \\
CH_3 \qquad CH_3
\end{array}
\qquad\quad
\begin{array}{c}
CH_3 \\
| \\
CH_3\; CH_2 \qquad\quad CH_3 \\
|\quad\; | \qquad\qquad \diagup \\
CH_3-C-C-CH_2CH \\
|\quad\; | \qquad\qquad \diagdown \\
CH_3\; CH_3 \qquad\quad CH_3
\end{array}
$$

Methyl-*n*-propylisopropylmethane Methylethylisobutyl-*tert*-butylmethane

This derived system is satisfactory for a great many alkanes that are too complicated to have common names. However, when we consider molecules like

$$
\begin{array}{c}
CH_3 \qquad\quad CH_3 \\
\diagdown \qquad\quad | \\
CH-C-CH-CH-CH_3 \\
\diagup \qquad | \quad\; | \quad\; | \\
CH_3 \qquad CH_3\; CH_3 \quad CH_3
\end{array}
$$

we find that the alkyl groups attached to whatever parent carbon atom we may select are themselves too complicated to be named. In this structure there are attached to the most highly branched carbon two methyl groups, an isopropyl group, and a pentyl group that has no simple name. For molecules as complex as this we must resort to the most widely applicable of all the systems, the IUPAC system.

3.10 IUPAC names of alkanes

To devise a system of nomenclature that could be used for even the most complicated compounds, various committees and commissions representing the chemists of the world have met periodically since 1892. In its present modification, the system so devised is known as the **IUPAC system** (International Union of Pure and Applied Chemistry). Since this system follows much the same pattern for all families of organic compounds, we shall consider it in some detail as applied to the alkanes.

Essentially the rules of the IUPAC system are:

1. Select as the parent structure the longest continuous chain, and then consider the compound to have been derived from this structure by the replacement of hydrogen by various alkyl groups.

$$CH_3CHCH_3 \qquad CH_3CH_2CH_2CHCH_3 \qquad CH_3CH_2CHCH_2CH_3$$
$$\quad | \qquad\qquad\qquad\qquad\quad | \qquad\qquad\qquad\qquad\quad |$$
$$\quad CH_3 \qquad\qquad\qquad\qquad CH_3 \qquad\qquad\qquad\qquad CH_3$$

   Methylpropane   2-Methylpentane   3-Methylpentane
    (Isobutane)

      I   II   III

$$\qquad\qquad\qquad\qquad\qquad\qquad\qquad\qquad\qquad\qquad\qquad CH_3$$
$$\qquad\qquad\qquad\qquad\qquad\qquad\qquad\qquad\qquad\qquad\qquad |$$
$$\qquad\qquad\qquad\qquad CH_3 \qquad\qquad\qquad\qquad\qquad\qquad\quad CH_2$$
$$\qquad\qquad\qquad\qquad\ |\qquad\qquad\qquad\qquad\qquad\qquad\qquad |$$
$$CH_3CHCH_2CCH_3 \qquad CH_3CH_2CH_2CH—CH—C—CH_2CH_3$$
$$\qquad |\qquad\quad\ |\qquad\qquad\qquad\qquad\qquad\ |\quad\ |\quad\ |$$
$$\qquad CH_3\quad CH_3 \qquad\qquad\qquad\qquad CH\ \ CH_3\ CH_2$$
$$\qquad\qquad\qquad\qquad\qquad\qquad\qquad\qquad\ \diagup\ \diagdown\qquad\quad |$$
$$\qquad\qquad\qquad\qquad\qquad\qquad\qquad CH_3\quad\ CH_3\quad CH_3$$

  2,2,4-Trimethylpentane   4-Methyl-3,3-diethyl-5-isopropyloctane
          IV   V

Isobutane (I) can be considered to arise from propane by the replacement of a hydrogen atom by a methyl group, and thus may be named *methylpropane*.

2. Where necessary, as in the isomeric methylpentanes (II and III), indicate by a number the carbon to which the alkyl group is attached.

3. In numbering the parent carbon chain, start at whichever end results in the use of the lowest numbers; thus II is called *2-methylpentane* rather than 4-methylpentane.

4. If the same alkyl group occurs more than once as a side chain, indicate this by the prefix *di-*, *tri-*, *tetra-*, etc., to show how many of these alkyl groups there are, and indicate by various numbers the positions of *each* group, as in *2,2,4-trimethylpentane* (IV).

5. If there are several different alkyl groups attached to the parent chain, name them in order of increasing size or in alphabetical order; as in *4-methyl-3,3-diethyl-5-isopropyloctane* (V).

There are additional rules and conventions used in naming very complicated alkanes, but the five fundamental rules mentioned here will suffice for the compounds we are likely to encounter.

Problem 3.8 Give the IUPAC and derived names for: (a) the isomeric hexanes shown on page 65; (b) the nine isomeric heptanes (see Problem 3.7, page 65).

Problem 3.9 The IUPAC names for *n*-propyl and isopropyl chlorides are *1-chloropropane* and *2-chloropropane*. On this basis name: (a) the eight isomeric chloropentanes; (b) the nine isomeric dibromobutanes (see Problem 3.7, page 65).

3.11   Classes of carbon atoms and hydrogen atoms

It has been found extremely useful to classify each carbon atom of an alkane with respect to the number of other carbon atoms to which it is attached. A **primary** (*1°*) *carbon atom is attached to only one other carbon atom; a* **secondary** (*2°*) *is attached to two others; and a* **tertiary** (*3°*) *to three others.* For example:

```
  1°  2°  2°  1°            1°      3°      1°            1°      3°      2°      1°

  H   H   H   H             H       H       H             H       H       H       H
  |   |   |   |             |       |       |             |       |       |       |
H—C—C—C—C—H               H—C——————C——————C—H          H—C——————C——————C——————C—H
  |   |   |   |             |       |       |             |       |       |       |
  H   H   H   H             H       |       H             H       |       H       H
                                  H—C—H                         H—C—H
                                    |                             |
                                    H                             H
                                    1°                            1°
```

Each hydrogen atom is similarly classified, being given the same designation of *primary, secondary,* or *tertiary* as the carbon atom to which it is attached.

We shall make constant use of these designations in our consideration of the relative reactivities of various parts of an alkane molecule.

3.12   Physical properties

The physical properties of the alkanes follow the pattern laid down by methane, and are consistent with the alkane structure. An alkane molecule is held together entirely by covalent bonds. These bonds either join two atoms of the same kind and hence are non-polar, or join two atoms that differ very little in electronegativity and hence are only slightly polar. Furthermore, these bonds are directed in a very symmetrical way, so that the slight bond polarities cancel out. As a result an alkane molecule is non-polar.

As we have seen (Sec. 1.14), the forces holding non-polar molecules together (van der Waals forces) are weak and of very short range; they act only between the portions of different molecules that are in close contact, that is, between the surfaces of molecules. Within a family, therefore, we would expect that the larger the molecule — and hence the larger its surface area — the stronger the intermolecular forces.

Table 3.3 lists certain physical constants for a number of the *n*-alkanes. As we can see, the boiling points and melting points rise as the number of carbons increases. The processes of boiling and melting require overcoming the intermolecular forces of a liquid and a solid; the boiling points and melting points rise because these intermolecular forces increase as the molecules get larger.

TABLE 3.3

ALKANES

Name	Formula	M.p., °C	B.p., °C	Density (at 20°)
Methane	CH_4	−183	−162	
Ethane	CH_3CH_3	−172	− 88.5	
Propane	$CH_3CH_2CH_3$	−187	− 42	
n-Butane	$CH_3(CH_2)_2CH_3$	−138	0	
n-Pentane	$CH_3(CH_2)_3CH_3$	−130	36	0.626
n-Hexane	$CH_3(CH_2)_4CH_3$	− 95	69	.659
n-Heptane	$CH_3(CH_2)_5CH_3$	− 90.5	98	.684
n-Octane	$CH_3(CH_2)_6CH_3$	− 57	126	.703
n-Nonane	$CH_3(CH_2)_7CH_3$	− 54	151	.718
n-Decane	$CH_3(CH_2)_8CH_3$	− 30	174	.730
n-Undecane	$CH_3(CH_2)_9CH_3$	− 26	196	.740
n-Dodecane	$CH_3(CH_2)_{10}CH_3$	− 10	216	.749
n-Tridecane	$CH_3(CH_2)_{11}CH_3$	− 6	234	.757
n-Tetradecane	$CH_3(CH_2)_{12}CH_3$	5.5	252	.764
n-Pentadecane	$CH_3(CH_2)_{13}CH_3$	10	266	.769
n-Hexadecane	$CH_3(CH_2)_{14}CH_3$	18	280	.775
n-Heptadecane	$CH_3(CH_2)_{15}CH_3$	22	292	
n-Octadecane	$CH_3(CH_2)_{16}CH_3$	28	308	
n-Nonadecane	$CH_3(CH_2)_{17}CH_3$	32	320	
n-Eicosane	$CH_3(CH_2)_{18}CH_3$	36		
Isobutane	$(CH_3)_2CHCH_3$	−159	− 12	
Isopentane	$(CH_3)_2CHCH_2CH_3$	−160	28	.620
Neopentane	$(CH_3)_4C$	− 17	9.5	
Isohexane	$(CH_3)_2CH(CH_2)_2CH_3$	−154	60	.654
3-Methylpentane	$CH_3CH_2CH(CH_3)CH_2CH_3$	−118	63	.676
2,2-Dimethylbutane	$(CH_3)_3CCH_2CH_3$	− 98	50	.649
2,3-Dimethylbutane	$(CH_3)_2CHCH(CH_3)_2$	−129	58	.668

Except for the very small alkanes, *the boiling point rises 20 to 30 degrees for each carbon that is added to the chain;* we shall find that this increment of 20–30° per carbon holds not only for the alkanes but also for each of the homologous series that we shall study.

The increase in melting point is not quite so regular, since the intermolecular forces in a crystal depend not only upon the size of the molecules but also upon how well they fit into a crystal lattice.

The first four *n*-alkanes are gases, but, as a result of the rise in boiling point and melting point with increasing chain length, the next 13 (C_5–C_{17}) are liquids, and those containing 18 carbons or more are solids.

Problem 3.10 Using the data of Table 3.3, make a graph (a) of b.p. *vs.* carbon number for the *n*-alkanes; (b) of m.p. *vs.* carbon number; (c) of density *vs.* carbon number.

There are somewhat smaller differences among the boiling points of alkanes that have the same carbon number but different structures. On pages 63 and 65 the boiling points of the isomeric butanes, pentanes, and hexanes are given. We see that in every case *a branched-chain isomer has a lower boiling point than a straight-chain isomer,* and further, that the more numerous the branches, the lower the boiling point. Thus n-butane has a boiling point of 0° and isobutane $-12°$. n-Pentane has a boiling point of 36°, isopentane with a single branch 28°, and neopentane with two branches 9.5°. This effect of branching on boiling point is observed within all families of organic compounds. That branching should lower the boiling point is reasonable: with branching the shape of the molecule tends to approach that of a sphere; and as this happens the surface area decreases, with the result that the intermolecular forces become weaker and are overcome at a lower temperature.

In agreement with the rule of thumb, "like dissolves like," the alkanes are soluble in non-polar solvents such as benzene, ether, and chloroform, and are insoluble in water and other highly polar solvents. Considered themselves as solvents, the liquid alkanes dissolve compounds of low polarity and do not dissolve compounds of high polarity.

The density increases with size of the alkanes, but tends to level off at about 0.8; thus all alkanes are less dense than water. It is not surprising that nearly all organic compounds are less dense than water since, like the alkanes, they consist chiefly of carbon and hydrogen. In general, to be denser than water a compound must contain a heavy atom like bromine or iodine, or several atoms like chlorine.

3.13　Industrial source

The principal source of alkanes is **petroleum,** together with the accompanying **natural gas.** Decay and millions of years of geological stresses have transformed the complicated organic compounds that once made up living plants or animals into a mixture of alkanes ranging in size from one carbon to 30 or 40 carbons. Formed along with the alkanes, and particularly abundant in California petroleum, are *cycloalkanes* (Chapter 7), known to the petroleum industry as *naphthenes.*

Natural gas contains, of course, only the more volatile alkanes, that is, those of low molecular weight; it consists chiefly of methane and progressively smaller amounts of ethane, propane, and higher alkanes. For example, a sample taken from a pipe line supplied by a large number of Pennsylvania wells contained methane, ethane, and propane in the ratio of 12 : 2 : 1, with higher alkanes making up only 3% of the total. The propane-butane fraction is separated from the more volatile components by liquefaction, compressed into cylinders, and sold as *bottled gas* in areas not served by a gas utility.

Petroleum is separated by distillation into the various fractions listed in Table 3.4; because of the relationship between boiling point and molecular weight, this amounts to a rough separation according to carbon number. Each fraction is still a very complicated mixture, however, since it contains alkanes of a range of carbon numbers, and since each carbon number is represented by numerous isomers. The use that each fraction is put to depends chiefly upon its volatility or viscosity, and it matters very little whether it is a complicated mixture or a single pure compound.

TABLE 3.4

PETROLEUM CONSTITUENTS

Fraction	Distillation Temperature, °C	Carbon Number
Gas	Below 20°	C_1–C_4
Petroleum ether	20–60°	C_5–C_6
Ligroin (light naphtha)	60–100°	C_6–C_7
Natural gasoline	40–205°	C_5–C_{10}, and cycloalkanes
Kerosene	175–325°	C_{12}–C_{18}, and aromatics
Gas oil	Above 275°	C_{12} and higher
Lubricating oil	Non-volatile liquids	Probably long chains attached to cyclic structures
Asphalt or petroleum coke	Non-volatile solids	Polycyclic structures

The chief use of all but the non-volatile fractions is as fuel. The gas fraction, like natural gas, is used chiefly for heating. Gasoline is used in those internal combustion engines that require a fairly volatile fuel, kerosene is used in tractor and jet engines, and gas oil is used in Diesel engines. Kerosene and gas oil are also used for heating purposes, the latter being the familiar "furnace oil."

The lubricating oil fraction, especially that from Pennsylvania crude oil (*paraffin-base petroleum*), often contains large amounts of long-chain alkanes (C_{20}–C_{34}) that have fairly high melting points. If these remained in the oil, they might crystallize to waxy solids in an oil line in cold weather. To prevent this, the oil is chilled and the wax is removed by filtration. After purification, this is sold as solid *paraffin wax* (m.p. 50–55°), or used in *petrolatum jelly* (Vaseline). Asphalt is used in roofing and road building. The coke that is obtained from paraffin-base crude oil consists of complex hydrocarbons having a high carbon-to-hydrogen ratio; it is used as a fuel or in the manufacture of carbon electrodes for the electrochemical industries.

Petroleum ether and ligroin are useful solvents for many organic materials of low polarity. In addition to being used directly as just described, certain petroleum fractions are converted into other kinds of chemical compounds. The **cracking** process (page 93) converts higher alkanes into smaller alkanes and alkenes, and thus increases the gasoline yield. In addition, the alkenes thus formed are perhaps the most important raw materials for the large-scale synthesis of aliphatic compounds. The process of **hydroforming** (page 252) converts alkanes and cycloalkanes into aromatic hydrocarbons and thus helps provide the raw material for the large-scale synthesis of another broad class of compounds.

3.14 Industrial source *vs.* laboratory preparation

We shall generally divide the methods of obtaining a particular kind of organic compound into two categories: *industrial source* and *laboratory preparation*. We may contrast the two in the following way, although it must be realized that there are many exceptions to these generalizations.

An industrial source must provide large amounts of the desired material at the lowest possible cost. A laboratory preparation may be required to produce only a few hundred grams or even a few grams; cost is usually of less importance than the time of the investigator.

For many industrial purposes a mixture may be just as suitable as a pure compound; even when a single compound is required it may be economically feasible to separate it from a mixture, particularly when the other components may also be marketed. In the laboratory a chemist nearly always wants a single pure compound. Separation of a single compound from a mixture of related substances is very time-consuming and frequently does not yield material of the required purity. Furthermore, the raw material for a particular preparation may well be the hard-won product of a previous preparation or even series of preparations, and hence he wishes to convert it as completely as possible into his desired compound. On an industrial scale, if a compound cannot be isolated from naturally occurring material it may be synthesized along with a number of related compounds by some inexpensive reaction. In the laboratory, whenever possible, a reaction is selected that forms a single compound in high yield.

In industry, it is frequently worth while to work out a procedure and design apparatus that may be used in the synthesis of only one member of a chemical family. In the laboratory, a chemist is seldom interested in preparing the same compound over and over again, and hence he makes use of methods that are applicable to many or all members of a particular family.

In our study of organic chemistry, we shall concentrate our attention on versatile laboratory preparations rather than on limited industrial methods. In learning these we may, for the sake of simplicity, use as examples the preparation of compounds that may actually never be made by the method shown. We may discuss the synthesis of ethane by the hydrogenation of ethylene, even though we can buy all the ethane we need from the petroleum industry. However, if we know how to convert ethylene into ethane, then when the need arises we also know how to convert 2-methyl-1-hexene into 2-methylhexane, or cholesterol into cholestanol, or for that matter cottonseed oil into oleomargarine.

3.15 Preparation

Each of the smaller alkanes, from methane through n-pentane and isopentane, can be obtained in pure form by fractional distillation of petroleum and natural gas; neopentane does not occur naturally. Above the pentanes the number of isomers of each homolog becomes so large and the boiling point differences so small that it is no longer feasible to isolate individual, pure compounds; these alkanes must be synthesized by one of the methods outlined below.

In some of these equations, the symbol **R** is used to represent **any alkyl group**. This convenient device helps to summarize reactions that are typical of an entire family, and emphasizes the essential similarity of the various members.

In writing these generalized equations, however, we must not lose sight of one important point. An equation involving RCl, to take a specific example, has meaning only in terms of a reaction that we can carry out in the laboratory using a real compound, like methyl chloride or *tert*-butyl chloride. Although *typical* of alkyl halides, a reaction may differ widely in rate or yield depending upon the particular alkyl group actually concerned. We may use quite different experimental conditions for methyl chloride than for *tert*-butyl chloride; in an extreme case, a reaction that goes well for methyl chloride might go so slowly or give so many side products as to be completely useless for *tert*-butyl chloride.

PREPARATION OF ALKANES

1. Hydrogenation of alkenes. Discussed in Sec. 5.3.

$$C_nH_{2n} + H_2 \xrightarrow{\text{Pt, Pd, or Ni}} C_nH_{2n+2}$$
Alkene   Alkane

2. Reduction of alkyl halides

(a) Hydrolysis of Grignard reagent

$$RX + Mg \longrightarrow RMgX \xrightarrow{H_2O} RH$$
Grignard
reagent

Example:

CH$_3$CH$_2$CHCH$_3$ $\xrightarrow{Mg}$ CH$_3$CH$_2$CHCH$_3$ $\xrightarrow{H_2O}$ CH$_3$CH$_2$CHCH$_3$
      | | |
      Br   MgBr   H
sec-Butyl bromide   *sec*-Butylmagnesium   *n*-Butane
                                 bromide

(b) Reduction by metal and acid

$$RX + Zn + H^+ \longrightarrow RH + Zn^{++} + X^-$$
Example:

CH$_3$CH$_2$CHCH$_3$ $\xrightarrow{Zn, H^+}$ CH$_3$CH$_2$CHCH$_3$
      | |
      Br   H
sec-Butyl bromide   *n*-Butane

3. Wurtz reaction

$$2RX + 2Na \longrightarrow R-R + 2NaX \quad \textit{Symmetrical alkanes only}$$
Examples:

2CH$_3$CH$_2$CH$_2$—Cl $\xrightarrow{Na}$ CH$_3$CH$_2$CH$_2$—CH$_2$CH$_2$CH$_3$
n-Propyl chloride   *n*-Hexane

               CH$_3$ CH$_3$ CH$_3$
                | | |
2CH$_3$CH—Cl $\xrightarrow{Na}$ CH$_3$CH—CHCH$_3$
Isopropyl chloride   2,3-Dimethylbutane

By far the most important of these methods is the hydrogenation of alkenes. When shaken under a slight pressure of hydrogen gas in the presence of a small amount of catalyst, alkenes are converted smoothly and quantitatively into alkanes of the same carbon skeleton. The method is limited only by the availability of the proper alkene. This is not a very serious limitation; as we shall see (Sec. 4.12), alkenes are readily prepared, chiefly from alcohols, which in turn can be readily synthesized (Sec. 11.10) in a wide variety of sizes and shapes.

Reduction of an alkyl halide, either via the Grignard reagent or directly with metal and acid, involves simply the replacement of a halogen atom by a hydrogen atom; the carbon skeleton remains intact. This method has about the same applicability as the previous method, since, like alkenes, alkyl halides are generally prepared from alcohols. Where either method could be used, the hydrogenation of alkenes would probably be preferred because of its simplicity and higher yield.

The Wurtz reaction is the only method that generates a new carbon skeleton. As we shall see, this method is limited to the synthesis of *symmetrical* alkanes, R—R.

3.16   The Grignard reagent

When a solution of an alkyl halide in ethyl ether is allowed to stand over turnings of metallic magnesium, a vigorous reaction takes place: the solution turns cloudy, begins to boil, and the magnesium metal gradually disappears. The resulting solution is known as a **Grignard reagent,** after Victor Grignard (of the University of Lyons) who received the Nobel prize in 1912 for its discovery. It is one of the most useful and versatile reagents known to the organic chemist.

The Grignard reagent has the general formula RMgX, and the general name **alkylmagnesium halide.**

$$CH_3I + Mg \xrightarrow{\quad ether \quad} CH_3MgI$$
Methyl   Methylmagnesium iodide
iodide

$$CH_3CH_2Br + Mg \xrightarrow{\quad ether \quad} CH_3CH_2MgBr$$
Ethyl bromide   Ethylmagnesium bromide

The carbon–magnesium bond is considered to be covalent but highly polar; the magnesium–halogen bond is essentially ionic.

$$R{:}Mg^+ \; {:}\overset{\cdot\cdot}{\underset{\cdot\cdot}{X}}{:}^-$$

The structure of the Grignard reagent is actually much more complicated than shown here; indeed, it seems certain that there are *no* RMgX molecules, although this formula is used for convenience by organic chemists.

Since magnesium becomes bonded to the same carbon that previously held halogen, the alkyl group remains intact during the preparation of the reagent. Thus *n*-propyl chloride yields *n*-propylmagnesium chloride, and isopropyl chloride yields isopropylmagnesium chloride.

$$CH_3CH_2CH_2Cl + Mg \xrightarrow{\quad ether \quad} CH_3CH_2CH_2MgCl$$
n-Propyl chloride   *n*-Propylmagnesium chloride

$$CH_3CHClCH_3 + Mg \xrightarrow{\quad ether \quad} CH_3CHMgClCH_3$$
Isopropyl chloride   Isopropylmagnesium chloride

The usefulness of the Grignard reagent is due to its high reactivity. It reacts with numerous inorganic compounds including water, carbon dioxide, and oxygen, and with most kinds of organic compounds; in many of these cases the reaction provides the best way to make a particular class of organic compound.

The reaction with water to form an alkane is typical of the behavior of the Grignard reagent toward acids. As we have said, the carbon-magnesium bond is certainly a very polar one, or, in other language, has considerable ionic character. We may consider the Grignard reagent, therefore, to be the magnesium salt, RMgX, of the extremely weak acid, R—H. The reaction

$$\text{RMgX} + \text{HOH} \longrightarrow \text{R—H} + \text{Mg(OH)X}$$
$$\underset{\text{acid}}{\text{Stronger}} \qquad\qquad \underset{\text{acid}}{\text{Weaker}}$$

is simply the displacement of the weaker acid, R—H, from its salt by the stronger acid, HOH.

An alkane is such a weak acid that it is displaced from the Grignard reagent by compounds that we might ordinarily consider to be very weak acids themselves, or possibly not acids at all. Any compound containing hydrogen attached to oxygen or nitrogen is tremendously more acidic than an alkane, and therefore can decompose the Grignard reagent: for example, ammonia or methyl alcohol.

$$\text{RMgX} + \text{NH}_3 \longrightarrow \text{R—H} + \text{Mg(NH}_2)\text{X}$$
$$\underset{\text{acid}}{\text{Stronger}} \qquad\qquad \underset{\text{acid}}{\text{Weaker}}$$

$$\text{RMgX} + \text{CH}_3\text{OH} \longrightarrow \text{R—H} + \text{Mg(OCH}_3)\text{X}$$
$$\underset{\text{acid}}{\text{Stronger}} \qquad\qquad \underset{\text{acid}}{\text{Weaker}}$$

For the preparation of an alkane, one acid is as good as another, so we naturally choose water as the most available and convenient.

Problem 3.11 Reaction of an aldehyde with a Grignard reagent is an important way of making alcohols. Why must one scrupulously dry the aldehyde before adding it to the Grignard reagent?

Problem 3.12 Why would one not prepare a Grignard reagent from BrCH$_2$—CH$_2$OH?

3.17 The Wurtz reaction

The Wurtz reaction owes its *limited* importance to the fact that it brings about the union of two alkyl groups and thus yields an alkane of higher carbon number than the reactant. In this way we can prepare ethane from methyl bromide, n-butane from ethyl bromide, or 2,3-di-methylbutane from isopropyl bromide.

$$\underset{\text{Methyl bromide}}{2\text{CH}_3\text{Br}} \xrightarrow{\text{Na}} \underset{\text{Ethane}}{\text{CH}_3\text{—CH}_3}$$

$$2CH_3CH_2Br \xrightarrow{\text{Na}} CH_3CH_2-CH_2CH_3$$

Ethyl bromide　　　　　　　　　　　n-Butane

$$\underset{\substack{| \\ H}}{\overset{\substack{CH_3 \\ |}}{2CH_3C}}-Br \xrightarrow{\text{Na}} \underset{\substack{| \quad | \\ H \quad H}}{\overset{\substack{CH_3 \ CH_3 \\ | \quad |}}{CH_3C}}-CCH_3$$

Isopropyl bromide　　　　　2,3-Dimethylbutane

The Wurtz reaction is limited in scope, however, since it is suited *only* to the preparation of *symmetrical* alkanes, R—R. For instance, we cannot prepare propane in good yield by this method. If we should allow sodium to react with a mixture of methyl bromide and ethyl bromide, we would indeed obtain propane; but it would make up only a fraction (about a half) of the total product and would be mixed with ethane formed by the union of two methyl groups, and n-butane formed by the union of two ethyl groups. We would have wasted much of our reagents in forming compounds that we did not want and also would be faced with a difficult purification problem. The Wurtz reaction, then, is *not* suited to the synthesis of *unsymmetrical* alkanes, R—R' (R' different from R).

Although many reactions of simple alkyl halides can be extended to more complicated halogen-containing compounds, this is not so for the Wurtz reaction. Sodium metal is an extremely reactive substance, and it will react not only with the halogen but with almost any other group that might be present in this more complicated compound. For example, a Wurtz reaction could not be carried out with a halogen compound containing an −OH group since sodium metal would react with the hydroxyl group even more rapidly than with the halogen (Sec. 12.6).

The mechanism of the Wurtz reaction is complicated and not yet fully understood, but this much seems clear: in part, at least, the reaction involves first the formation of an organosodium compound, analogous to the organomagnesium compound discussed above,

$$RX + 2Na \longrightarrow RNa + NaX$$

which then reacts with a second molecule of alkyl halide.

$$RNa + RX \longrightarrow R-R + NaX$$

(Grignard reagents are less reactive than organosodium compounds and are able to react with only a few unusually reactive organic halides.)

3.18 Reactions

The inertness that methane shows toward most reagents is characteristic of the alkane structure in general. Like methane, the higher alkanes undergo comparatively few reactions; these reactions take place only under vigorous conditions and usually yield mixtures of products. They are usually free radical chain reactions.

We can account, in a general way, for these characteristics of alkane reactions. Only an extremely reactive particle — typically an atom or free radical — can attack an alkane molecule. It is the generation of this reactive particle that requires the vigorous conditions: the dissociation of a halogen molecule into atoms, for example, or even (as in pyrolysis) dissociation of the alkane molecule itself.

In its attack, the reactive particle abstracts hydrogen from the alkane; the alkane itself is thus converted into a reactive particle which continues the reaction sequence, that is, carries on the chain. But an alkane molecule contains many hydrogen atoms and the particular product eventually obtained depends upon *which* of these hydrogen atoms is abstracted. Although an attacking particle may show a certain selectivity, it can abstract a hydrogen from any part of the molecule, and thus bring about the formation of many isomeric products.

REACTIONS OF ALKANES

1. Halogenation

$$-\overset{\displaystyle |}{\underset{\displaystyle |}{C}}-H + X_2 \xrightarrow{\text{250–400°, or light}} -\overset{\displaystyle |}{\underset{\displaystyle |}{C}}-X + HX$$

Usually a mixture

Reactivity X_2 : $Cl_2 > Br_2$

                H : $3° > 2° > 1° > CH_3-H$

Example:

$$\underset{\text{Isobutane}}{CH_3-\overset{\displaystyle \overset{CH_3}{|}}{CH}-CH_3} \xrightarrow[\text{250–400°}]{Cl_2} \underset{\text{Isobutyl chloride}}{CH_3-\overset{\displaystyle \overset{CH_3}{|}}{CH}-CH_2Cl} \text{ and } \underset{\text{\textit{tert}-Butyl chloride}}{CH_3-\overset{\displaystyle \overset{CH_3}{|}}{\underset{\displaystyle \underset{Cl}{|}}{C}}-CH_3}$$

2. Combustion

$$C_nH_{2n+2} + \text{excess } O_2 \xrightarrow{\text{flame}} nCO_2 + (n+1)H_2O \qquad \Delta H = \text{heat of combustion}$$

Example:

$$n\text{-}C_5H_{12} + 8\,O_2 \xrightarrow{\text{flame}} 5CO_2 + 6H_2O \qquad \Delta H = -845 \text{ kcal}$$

3. Pyrolysis (cracking)

$$\text{alkane} \xrightarrow[\text{without catalysts}]{\text{400–600°; with or}} H_2 + \text{smaller alkanes} + \text{alkenes}$$

3.19   Halogenation

As we might expect, halogenation of the higher alkanes is essentially the same as the halogenation of methane. It is complicated, however, by the formation of mixtures of isomers.

At 250–400° or under the influence of ultraviolet light, chlorine or bromine converts alkanes into chloroalkanes (alkyl chlorides) or bromoalkanes (alkyl bromides); an equivalent amount of hydrogen chloride or hydrogen bromide is formed at the same time. As with methane, fluorination is too vigorous to be controlled readily, and iodination does not take place at all.

Depending upon which hydrogen atom is replaced, any of a number of isomeric products can be formed from a single alkane.

Ethane can yield only one chloroethane:

$$CH_3CH_3 \xrightarrow{\ Cl_2\ } CH_3CH_2\!-\!Cl$$

Ethane   b.p. 13°
Chloroethane
Ethyl chloride

Propane, n-butane, and isobutane can yield two isomers each:

$$CH_3CH_2CH_3 \xrightarrow{\ Cl_2\ } CH_3CH_2CH_2\!-\!Cl \ \text{ and } \ \underset{\overset{|}{Cl}}{CH_3CHCH_3}$$

Propane   b.p. 47°   b.p. 36°
1-Chloropropane   2-Chloropropane
n-Propyl chloride   Isopropyl chloride
(48%)   (52%)

$$CH_3CH_2CH_2CH_3 \xrightarrow{\ Cl_2\ } CH_3CH_2CH_2CH_2\!-\!Cl \ \text{ and } \ \underset{\overset{|}{Cl}}{CH_3CH_2CHCH_3}$$

n-Butane   b.p. 78.5°   b.p. 68°
1-Chlorobutane   2-Chlorobutane
n-Butyl chloride   sec-Butyl chloride
(32%)   (68%)

$$\underset{\text{Isobutane}}{\overset{\overset{\textstyle CH_3}{|}}{CH_3CHCH_3}} \xrightarrow{\ Cl_2\ } \overset{\overset{\textstyle CH_3}{|}}{CH_3CHCH_2}\!-\!Cl \ \text{ and } \ \underset{\overset{|}{Cl}}{\overset{\overset{\textstyle CH_3}{|}}{CH_3CCH_3}}$$

Isobutane   b.p. 69°   b.p. 51°
1-Chloro-2-   2-Chloro-2-
methylpropane   methylpropane
Isobutyl chloride   tert-Butyl chloride
(67%)   (33%)

n-Pentane can yield three isomers:

$$CH_3CH_2CH_2CH_2CH_3 \xrightarrow{\ Cl_2\ } CH_3CH_2CH_2CH_2CH_2\!-\!Cl \ \text{ and } \ \underset{\overset{|}{Cl}}{CH_3CH_2CH_2CHCH_3}$$

n-Pentane   b.p. 108°   b.p. 97°
1-Chloropentane   2-Chloropentane
n-Pentyl chloride
(24%)   (49%)

$$\text{and } \ \underset{\overset{|}{Cl}}{CH_3CH_2CHCH_2CH_3}$$

b.p. 97°
3-Chloropentane
(27%)

Isopentane can yield four isomers:

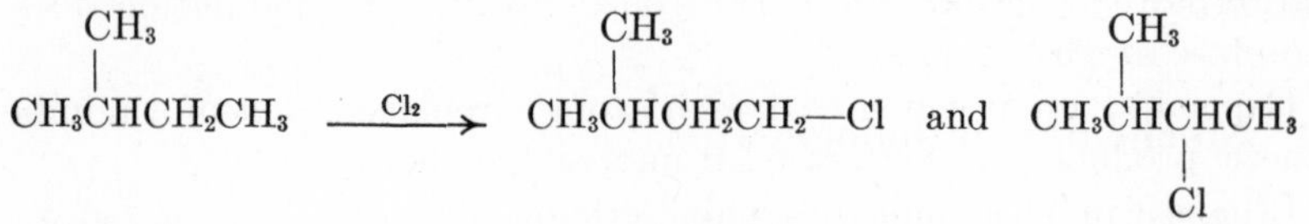

$$\text{CH}_3\text{CHCH}_2\text{CH}_3 \xrightarrow{\text{Cl}_2} \text{CH}_3\text{CHCH}_2\text{CH}_2\text{—Cl} \quad \text{and} \quad \text{CH}_3\text{CHCHCH}_3$$

with CH_3 substituents and Cl.

Isopentane	b.p. 99°	b.p. 93°
2-Methylbutane	1-Chloro-3-	3-Chloro-2-
	methylbutane	methylbutane
	Isopentyl chloride	
	(16.5%)	*(28%)*

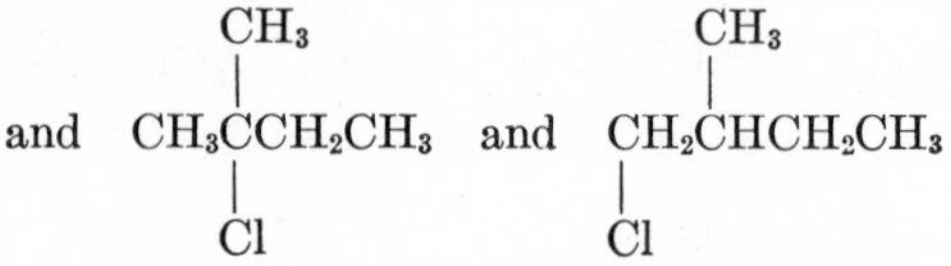

and $\text{CH}_3\text{CCH}_2\text{CH}_3$ and $\text{CH}_2\text{CHCH}_2\text{CH}_3$

with CH_3 and Cl substituents.

b.p. 86°	b.p. 100°
2-Chloro-2-	1-Chloro-2-
methylbutane	methylbutane
tert-Pentyl chloride	
(22%)	*(33.5%)*

Experiment has shown that on halogenation an alkane generally yields a mixture of all possible isomers, indicating that all hydrogen atoms are susceptible to replacement. The results obtained at 300° are summarized in the preceding equations.

Halogenation of an alkane is not generally suitable for the laboratory preparation of an alkyl halide, since the reaction nearly always yields a mixture of products. Any one of these products is necessarily formed in low yield and is difficult to separate from its isomers. Consider, for example, the feasibility of preparing 3-chloro-2-methylbutane by the chlorination of isopentane; as we can see above, it makes up only 28% of the product, and must be separated from isomers whose boiling points are as close as six degrees to its boiling point.

On the other hand, there are a few exceptional cases where direct halogenation is feasible. Neopentane, for example, because of its high symmetry, can yield only one chloride or bromide. Direct halogenation is one feasible way to prepare neopentyl chloride or bromide.

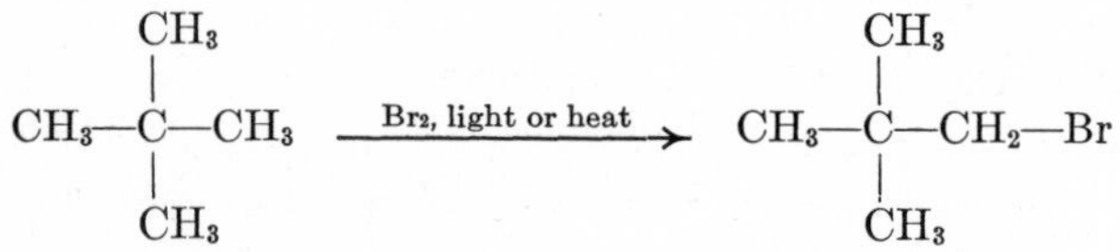

$$\text{CH}_3\text{—C—CH}_3 \xrightarrow{\text{Br}_2,\text{ light or heat}} \text{CH}_3\text{—C—CH}_2\text{—Br}$$

with CH_3 substituents.

Neopentane	Neopentyl bromide
2,2-Dimethylpropane	1-Bromo-2,2-dimethylpropane

On an industrial scale, chlorination of alkanes is important. For many purposes, e.g., use as a solvent, a mixture of isomers is just as suitable as, and much cheaper than, a pure compound. It may even be worth while, when necessary, to separate a mixture of isomers if each isomer can then be marketed.

3.20 Mechanism of halogenation

Halogenation of alkanes proceeds by the same mechanism as halogenation of methane:

(1) $X_2 \xrightarrow[\substack{\text{or} \\ \text{ultraviolet} \\ \text{light}}]{250-400°} 2X\cdot$ **Chain-initiating step**

(2) $X\cdot + RH \longrightarrow HX + R\cdot$ $\left.\begin{array}{c} \\ \\ \end{array}\right\}$ **Chain-propagating steps**
(3) $R\cdot + X_2 \longrightarrow RX + X\cdot$

then (2), (3), (2), (3), etc., until finally a chain is terminated (Sec. 2.13)

A halogen atom abstracts hydrogen from the alkane (RH) to form an alkyl radical (R·). The radical in turn abstracts a halogen atom from a halogen molecule to yield the alkyl halide (RX).

Which alkyl halide is obtained depends upon which alkyl radical is formed. This in turn depends upon the alkane and which hydrogen atom is abstracted from it.

$$CH_4 \xrightarrow{X\cdot} CH_3\cdot \xrightarrow{X_2} CH_3X$$
Methane   Methyl   Methyl
                 radical   halide

$$CH_3CH_3 \xrightarrow{X\cdot} CH_3CH_2\cdot \xrightarrow{X_2} CH_3CH_2X$$
Ethane   Ethyl   Ethyl
                radical   halide

$$CH_3CH_2CH_3 \xrightarrow{X\cdot} \begin{cases} \xrightarrow[\text{of 1° H}]{\text{abstraction}} CH_3CH_2CH_2\cdot \xrightarrow{X_2} CH_3CH_2CH_2X \\ \\ \xrightarrow[\text{of 2° H}]{\text{abstraction}} CH_3\overset{.}{C}HCH_3 \xrightarrow{X_2} CH_3\overset{|}{C}HCH_3 \end{cases}$$

Propane

n-Propyl radical — *n*-Propyl halide

Isopropyl radical — Isopropyl halide (with X below)

For example, *n*-propyl halide is obtained from a *n*-propyl radical, formed from propane by abstraction of a primary hydrogen; isopropyl halide is obtained from an isopropyl radical, formed by abstraction of a secondary hydrogen.

How fast an alkyl halide is formed depends upon how fast the alkyl radical is formed. Of the two chain-propagating steps, we have seen that step (2) is more difficult than step (3), and hence controls the rate of overall reaction. Formation of the alkyl radical is difficult, but once formed the radical is readily converted into the alkyl halide (see Figure 3.4).

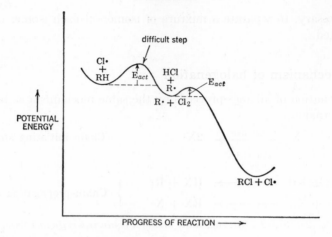

FIGURE 3.4. Potential energy changes during progress of reaction: chlorination of an alkane. Formation of radical is rate-controlling step.

3.21 Orientation of halogenation

With this background let us turn to the problem of **orientation**; that is, let us examine the factors that determine *where* in a molecule reaction is most likely to occur. It is a problem that we shall encounter again and again, whenever we study a compound that offers more than one reactive site to attack by a reagent. It is an important problem, because orientation determines what product we obtain.

As an example let us take chlorination of propane. The relative amounts of *n*-propyl chloride and isopropyl chloride obtained depend upon the relative rates at which *n*-propyl radicals and isopropyl radicals are formed. If, say, isopropyl radicals are formed faster, then isopropyl chloride will be formed faster, and will make up a larger fraction of the product.

As we can see, *n*-propyl radicals are formed by abstraction of primary hydrogens, and isopropyl radicals by abstraction of secondary hydrogens.

Thus *orientation is determined by the relative rates of competing reactions.* In this case we are comparing the rate of abstraction of primary hydrogens with the rate of abstraction of secondary hydrogens. What are the factors that determine the rates of these two reactions, and in which of these factors may the two reactions differ?

First of all, there is the collision frequency. This must be the same for the two reactions, since both involve collisions of the same particles: a propane molecule and a chlorine atom.

Next, there is the probability factor. If a primary hydrogen is to be abstracted, the propane molecule must be so oriented at the time of collision that the chlorine atom strikes a primary hydrogen; if a secondary hydrogen is to be abstracted, the propane must be so oriented that the chlorine collides with a secondary hydrogen. Since there are six primary hydrogens and only two secondary hydrogens in each molecule, we might estimate that the probability factor favors abstraction of primary hydrogens by the ratio of 6 : 2, or 3 : 1.

Considering only collision frequency and probability factor, then, we predict that chlorination of propane would yield *n*-propyl chloride and isopropyl chloride in the ratio of 3 : 1. As shown on page 81, however, the two chlorides are formed (at 300°) in almost equal amounts, that is, in a ratio of 1 : 1 or 3 : 3. The proportion of isopropyl chloride is three times as great as predicted. If our assumption about the probability factor is correct, these results can only mean that three times as many collisions with secondary hydrogens are successful as collisions with primary hydrogens. This, in turn, means that E_{act} is less for abstraction of a secondary hydrogen than for abstraction of a primary hydrogen.

Chlorination of isobutane presents a similar problem.

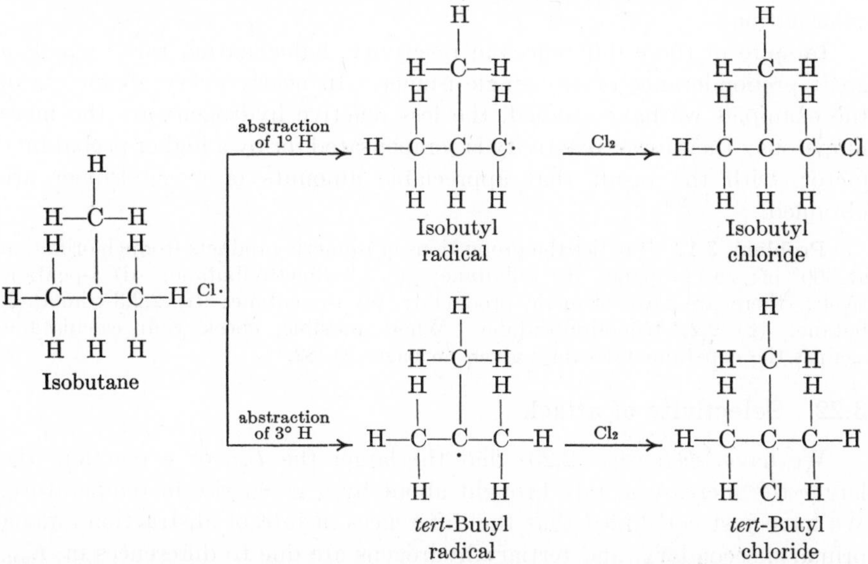

In this case, abstraction of one of the nine primary hydrogens leads to the formation of isobutyl chloride, whereas abstraction of the single tertiary hydrogen leads to the formation of *tert*-butyl chloride. We would estimate, then, that the probability factor favors formation of isobutyl chloride by the ratio of 9 : 1. The experimental results given on page 81 show that the ratio is nearly 2 : 1, or 9 : 4.5. We conclude that 4.5 times as many collisions with the tertiary hydrogen are successful as collisions with the primary hydrogens. This means that E_{act} is less for abstraction of a tertiary hydrogen than for abstraction of a primary hydrogen, and, in fact, even less than for abstraction of a secondary hydrogen.

Study of the chlorination of a great many alkanes has shown that these are typical results. After allowance is made for differences in the probability factor, the rate of abstraction of hydrogen atoms is always found to follow the sequence $3° > 2° > 1°$. At $300°$, for example, the relative rates *per hydrogen atom* are $4.43 : 3.25 : 1.00$. Using these values we can predict quite well the ratio of isomeric chlorination products from a given alkane. For example:

$$CH_3CH_2CH_2CH_3 \xrightarrow[300°]{Cl_2} CH_3CH_2CH_2CH_2Cl \text{ and } CH_3CH_2CHClCH_3$$
$$\text{\textit{n}-Butane} \qquad\qquad \text{\textit{n}-Butyl chloride} \qquad \text{\textit{sec}-Butyl chloride}$$

$$\frac{\textit{n}\text{-butyl chloride}}{\textit{sec}\text{-butyl chloride}} = \frac{\text{no. of } 1° \text{ H}}{\text{no. of } 2° \text{ H}} \times \frac{\text{reactivity of } 1° \text{ H}}{\text{reactivity of } 2° \text{ H}}$$

$$= \frac{6}{4} \times \frac{1.00}{3.25}$$

$$= \frac{6}{13} \quad \text{\textit{equivalent to}} \quad \frac{32\%}{68\%}$$

The same sequence of reactivity, $3° > 2° > 1°$, is found in bromination, although the actual reactivity ratios are different from those observed in chlorination.

In spite of these differences in reactivity, halogenation rarely yields a great preponderance of any single isomer. In nearly every alkane, as in the examples we have studied, the less reactive hydrogens are the more numerous; their lower reactivity is compensated for by a higher probability factor, with the result that appreciable amounts of every isomer are obtained.

Problem 3.13 Predict the proportions of isomeric products from chlorination at $300°$ of: (a) propane; (b) isobutane; (c) 2,3-dimethylbutane; (d) *n*-pentane (*Note:* there are *three* isomeric products); (e) isopentane; (f) 2,2,3-trimethylbutane; (g) 2,2,4-trimethylpentane. Where possible, check your calculations against the experimental values given on pages 81–82.

3.22 Selectivity of attack

We have seen (Sec. 2.20) that the larger the E_{act} of a reaction, the larger the increase in rate brought about by a given rise in temperature. We have just concluded that the differences in rate of abstraction among primary, secondary, and tertiary hydrogens are due to differences in E_{act}. If this conclusion is correct, a rise in temperature should speed up abstraction of primary hydrogens (with the largest E_{act}) most, and abstraction of tertiary hydrogens (with the smallest E_{act}) least; the three classes of hydrogen should then display more nearly the same reactivity.

This leveling-out effect has indeed been observed: as the temperature is raised, the relative rates per hydrogen atom change from 4.43 : 3.25 : 1.00 toward 1 : 1 : 1. At very high temperatures virtually every collision has enough energy for abstraction of even primary hydrogens. It is generally true that as the temperature is raised a given reagent becomes less selective in the position of its attack; conversely, as the temperature is lowered it becomes more selective.

It is also generally true, and for basically the same reason, that the more reactive the reagent, the less the selectivity shown in its attack. The less reactive bromine atom, for example, is more selective in its attack on alkanes than is the chlorine atom.

Just how important the two factors, temperature and reactivity, can be is shown by the following extreme example. When brominated at 80° under the influence of ultraviolet light, 2,2,3-trimethylbutane yields exclusively the 3-bromo product. In spite of a probability factor that favors formation of primary halides by 15 : 1, the combination of low temperature and low reactivity of reagent results in exclusive attack at the tertiary hydrogen.

This case is, of course, an exception to our generalization that halogenation yields mixtures of isomers; it is an exception, however, that is perfectly reasonable in light of the principles we have learned.

Problem 3.14 Using Figures 2.6 and 2.7, pages 46 and 47, show why high temperature and high reactivity of reagent have the same effect on selectivity.

3.23 Relative reactivities of alkanes toward halogenation

To compare the reactivities of *different* alkanes toward halogenation is difficult, and much work remains to be done. The existing data are, however, consistent with this simple generalization: *the reactivity of a hydrogen depends chiefly upon its class, and not upon the alkane to which it is attached.* Each primary hydrogen of propane, for example, is about as easily abstracted as each primary hydrogen of n-butane or isobutane; each secondary hydrogen of propane, about as easily as each secondary hydrogen of n-butane or n-pentane; and so on.

It is still a complicated process to predict the relative reactivities of two alkanes, since the over-all reactivity of each alkane is a composite value that depends upon the relative number of each class of hydrogen in that compound.

Problem 3.15 Which alkane of each pair would you expect to be more reactive toward chlorination? (a) neopentane or *n*-pentane; (b) 2,3-dimethylbutane or 2,2-dimethylbutane; (c) *n*-hexane or 2,2-dimethylbutane.

The hydrogen atoms of methane, which fall into a special class, have been found to be even less reactive than primary hydrogens. By measuring rates of reaction at various temperatures, it has been found that:

$$Cl\cdot \; \begin{cases} \xrightarrow{\;CH_4\;} HCl + CH_3\cdot & E_{act} = 4 \text{ kcal} \\ \xrightarrow{\;C_2H_6\;} HCl + C_2H_5\cdot & E_{act} = 1 \end{cases}$$

$$Br\cdot \; \begin{cases} \xrightarrow{\;CH_4\;} HBr + CH_3\cdot & E_{act} = 18 \\ \xrightarrow{\;C_2H_6\;} HBr + C_2H_5\cdot & E_{act} = 13 \end{cases}$$

3.24 Ease of abstraction of hydrogen atoms

At this stage we can summarize the effect of structure on halogenation of alkanes in the following way. The controlling step in halogenation is abstraction of hydrogen by a halogen atom:

$$R-H + X\cdot \longrightarrow H-X + R\cdot$$

The relative ease with which the different classes of hydrogen atoms are abstracted is:

Ease of abstraction of hydrogen atoms $\qquad 3° > 2° > 1° > CH_4$

This sequence applies (a) to the various hydrogens within a single alkane and hence governs **orientation** of reaction, and (b) to the hydrogens of different alkanes and hence governs **relative reactivities.**

There is, however, a more fundamental relationship between structure and the problems of orientation and reactivity. To see what this is, let us shift our focus from the hydrogen atom being abstracted to the radical being formed.

3.25 Stability of free radicals

In Table 2.1 (page 39) we find the strengths (bond dissociation energies) of the bonds that hold hydrogen atoms to a number of groups. These values are the ΔH's of the following reactions:

$$CH_3-H \longrightarrow CH_2\cdot + H\cdot \qquad\qquad \Delta H = 101 \text{ kcal}$$

$$CH_3CH_2-H \longrightarrow \underset{\text{A 1° radical}}{CH_3CH_2\cdot} + H\cdot \qquad\qquad \Delta H = 98$$

$$CH_3CH_2CH_2-H \longrightarrow \underset{\text{A 1° radical}}{CH_3CH_2CH_2\cdot} + H\cdot \qquad\qquad \Delta H = 95$$

$$\underset{\overset{|}{H}}{CH_3CHCH_3} \longrightarrow \underset{\text{A 2° radical}}{CH_3\overset{\cdot}{C}HCH_3} + H\cdot \qquad\qquad \Delta H = 89$$

$$\underset{\substack{|\\ \text{H}}}{\overset{\substack{\text{CH}_3\\|}}{\text{CH}_3\text{CCH}_3}} \longrightarrow \underset{\text{A 3° radical}}{\overset{\substack{\text{CH}_3\\|}}{\text{CH}_3\overset{\bullet}{\text{C}}\text{CH}_3}} + \text{H}\cdot \qquad \Delta H = 85$$

By definition, bond strength is the amount of energy that must be supplied to convert a mole of alkane into radicals and hydrogen atoms.

$$\text{R}\text{---}\text{H} \longrightarrow \text{R}\cdot + \text{H}\cdot \qquad \Delta H = \text{bond strength}$$

As we can see, the amount of energy needed to form the various classes of radicals decreases in the order: $\text{CH}_3\cdot > 1° > 2° > 3°$.

If less energy is needed to form one radical than another, it can only mean that, *relative to the alkane from which it is formed*, the one radical contains less energy than the other, that is to say, is *more stable* (see Figure 3.5).

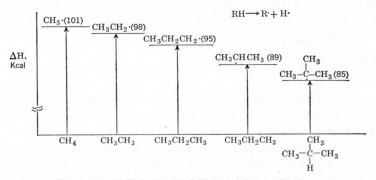

FIGURE 3.5. Relative stabilities of free radicals.

We are not attempting to compare the absolute energy contents of, say, methyl and ethyl radicals; we are simply saying that the difference in energy between methane and methyl radicals is greater than the difference between ethane and ethyl radicals. *When we compare stabilities of free radicals, it must be understood that our standard for each radical is the alkane from which it is formed.* As we shall see, this is precisely the kind of stability that we are interested in.

Relative to the alkane from which each is formed, then, the order of stability of free radicals is:

Stability of free radicals $3° > 2° > 1° > \text{CH}_3\cdot$

3.26 Ease of formation of free radicals

Let us return to the halogenation of alkanes. Orientation and reactivity, we have seen (Sec. 3.24), are governed by the relative ease with which the different classes of hydrogen atoms are abstracted. But by definition, the hydrogen being abstracted and the radical being formed belong to the same class. Abstraction of a primary hydrogen yields a primary radical, abstraction of a secondary hydrogen yields a secondary radical, and so on. For example:

$$CH_3CH_2CH_2\text{—}H + Cl\cdot \longrightarrow H\text{—}Cl + CH_3CH_2CH_2\cdot$$
A 1° hydrogen   A 1° radical

$$CH_3CHCH_3 + Cl\cdot \longrightarrow H\text{—}Cl + CH_3\overset{\cdot}{C}HCH_3$$
|
H   A 2° radical

A 2° hydrogen

$$\underset{\underset{H}{|}}{\overset{\overset{CH_3}{|}}{CH_3CCH_3}} + Cl\cdot \longrightarrow H\text{—}Cl + \underset{}{\overset{\overset{CH_3}{|}}{CH_3\overset{\cdot}{C}CH_3}}$$
A 3° radical

A 3° hydrogen

If the ease of abstraction of hydrogen atoms follows the sequence $3° > 2° > 1° > CH_4$, then the ease of formation of free radicals must follow the same sequence:

Ease of formation of free radicals $3° > 2° > 1° > CH_3\cdot$

In listing free radicals in order of their ease of formation, we find that we have at the same time listed them in order of their stability. **The more stable the free radical, the more easily it is formed.**

This is an extremely useful generalization. *Radical stability seems to govern orientation and reactivity in most reactions where radicals are formed.* The addition of bromine atoms to alkenes (Sec. 5.14), for example, is a quite different sort of reaction from the one we have just studied; yet, there too, orientation and reactivity are governed by radical stability. (Even in those cases where other factors — steric hindrance, polar effects — are significant or even dominant, it is convenient to use radical stability as a point of departure.)

3.27 Transition state

Is it reasonable that the more stable radical should be formed more easily? We have already seen that the differences in reactivity toward halogen atoms are due chiefly to differences in E_{act}: the more stable the radical, then, the lower the E_{act} for its formation.

A chemical reaction is presumably a continuous process involving a gradual transition from reactants to products. It has been found extremely useful, however, to consider the arrangement of atoms at an intermediate stage of reaction as though it were an actual molecule. This intermediate structure is called the **transition state**; its energy content corresponds to the top of the hill in our energy diagrams (see Figure 3.6). The reaction sequence is now:

reactants $\longrightarrow$ transition state $\longrightarrow$ products

The difference in energy content between reactants and products is ΔH; the difference in energy content between reactants and transition state is E_{act}.

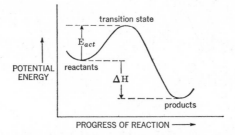

FIGURE 3.6. Potential energy changes during progress of reaction: transition state at top of energy hump.

The transition state concept is useful for this reason: we can analyze the structure of the transition state very much as though it were a molecule, and attempt to estimate its stability. Any factor that stabilizes the transition state relative to the reactants tends to lower the energy of activation; that is to say, any factor that lowers the top of the energy hill more than it lowers the reactant valley reduces the net height we must climb during reaction.

Let us consider the transition state for abstraction of a hydrogen from an alkane by a chlorine atom. Since the transition state is purely hypothetical, any discussion of its structure must necessarily be highly speculative. In the present case, however, the following description would seem to be justified: the carbon–hydrogen bond is stretched but not completely broken; the hydrogen–chlorine bond has started to form but is not yet complete. This condition could be represented as

$$-\overset{|}{\underset{|}{C}}-H + \cdot Cl \longrightarrow \left[-\overset{|}{\underset{|}{C}} \cdots H \cdots Cl \right] \longrightarrow -\overset{|}{\underset{|}{C}} \cdot + H-Cl$$

Reactants   Transition state   Products

where the dotted lines indicate partly broken or partly formed bonds.

Since this is an intermediate stage, we might expect it to possess both the character of the reactants and the character of the products. To the extent that the carbon–hydrogen bond is broken, the alkyl group possesses the character of the free radical that it will become; factors that tend to stabilize the radical should tend to stabilize the transition state.

We have seen that the stabilities of free radicals follow the sequence $3° > 2° > 1° > CH_3 \cdot$. A certain factor (to be discussed later, Sec. 9.19) causes the energy difference between isobutane and the *tert*-butyl radical, for example, to be smaller than between propane and the isopropyl radical. It is not unreasonable that this same factor should cause the energy difference between isobutane and the *incipient tert*-butyl radical in the transition state to be smaller than between propane and the *incipient* isopropyl radical in its transition state (Figure 3.7).

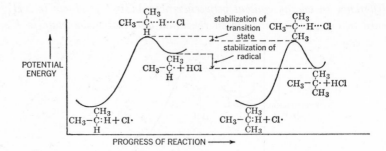

FIGURE 3.7. Molecular structure and rate of reaction. Stability of transition state parallels stability of radical: more stable radical formed faster.

3.28 Orientation and reactivity

Throughout our study of organic chemistry, we shall approach the problems of orientation and reactivity in the following way.

Both problems involve comparing the rates of closely related reactions: in the case of orientation, reactions at different sites in the same compound; in the case of reactivity, reactions with different compounds. For such closely related reactions, variations in rate are due mostly to differences in E_{act}; by definition, E_{act} is the difference in energy content between reactants and transition state.

We shall examine the most likely structure for the transition state, then, to see what structural features affect its stability without at the same time affecting by an equal amount the stability of the reactants; that is, we shall look for factors that tend to increase or decrease the energy difference between reactants and transition state. Having decided what structural features affect the E_{act}, we shall compare the transition states for the reactions whose rates we wish to compare: the more stable the transition state, the faster the reaction.

In most reactions where a free radical is formed, as in the present case, the transition state differs from the reactants chiefly in being like the product. It is reasonable that the factor most affecting the E_{act} should be the *radical character* of the transition state. Hence we find that the more stable the radical, the more stable the transition state leading to its formation, and the faster the radical is formed.

3.29 Combustion

The reaction of alkanes with oxygen to form carbon dioxide, water, and — most important of all — *heat,* is the chief reaction occurring in the internal combustion engine; its tremendous practical importance is obvious.

The mechanism of this reaction is extremely complicated and is not yet fully understood. There seems to be no doubt, however, that it is a free radical chain reaction. The reaction is extremely exothermic and yet requires a very high temperature, that of a flame, for its initiation. As in the case of chlorination, a great deal of energy is required for the bond breaking that generates the initial reactive particles; once this energy barrier is surmounted, the subsequent chain-carrying steps proceed readily and with the evolution of energy.

A higher compression ratio has made the modern gasoline engine more efficient than earlier ones, but has at the same time created a new problem. Under certain conditions the smooth explosion of the fuel-air mixture in the cylinder is replaced by a sharp detonation; this detonation, called **knocking,** greatly reduces the power of the engine.

The problem of knocking has been successfully met in two general ways: (a) proper selection of the hydrocarbons to be used as fuel, and (b) addition of tetraethyllead.

Experiments with pure compounds have shown that hydrocarbons of differing structures differ widely in knocking tendency. The relative antiknock tendency of a fuel is generally indicated by its **octane number.** An arbitrary scale has been set up, with *n*-heptane which knocks very badly being given an octane number of zero, and 2,2,4-trimethylpentane ("iso-octane") being given the octane number of 100. There are available today fuels with better antiknock qualities than "iso-octane."

Alkenes, cycloalkanes, and aromatic hydrocarbons generally have excellent antiknock qualities; branched-chain alkanes are better than straight-chain alkanes. The gasoline fraction obtained by direct distillation of petroleum (*straight-run gasoline*) is improved by addition of compounds of higher octane number; it is sometimes entirely replaced by these better fuels. Alkenes are obtained from alkanes by cracking (Sec. 3.30); highly branched alkanes are synthesized from alkenes and alkanes (Sec. 5.18).

Addition of a small amount of tetraethyllead, $(C_2H_5)_4Pb$, to a given fuel greatly increases its octane number; gasoline so treated is called *ethyl* gasoline. The antiknock properties of tetraethyllead were discovered in 1922 by T. C. Midgley, Jr., and T. A. Boyd, of the General Motors Research Laboratory. Despite decades of intensive research it is still not known how tetraethyllead exerts this effect; it is not even clear whether the effect is due to the lead or to the ethyl radicals.

$$(C_2H_5)_4Pb \xrightarrow{\text{heat}} Pb + 4C_2H_5\cdot$$

3.30 Pyrolysis: cracking

Decomposition of a compound by the action of heat alone is known as **pyrolysis.** This word is taken from the Greek *pyr*, fire + *lysis*, a loosing, and hence to chemists means "cleavage by heat"; compare *hydro-lysis*, "cleavage by water."

The pyrolysis of alkanes, particularly when petroleum is concerned, is known as **cracking.** Alkanes are simply passed through a chamber heated to 400–600°; generally a catalyst consisting of various metallic oxides is used. The products are alkanes smaller than the starting alkanes, various alkenes, and some hydrogen. Propane and *n*-butane, for example, yield the mixtures shown below, where ethylene, propylene, and butylene are alkenes.

$$CH_3CH_2CH_3 \xrightarrow{\text{400–600°}} \begin{cases} H_2 + C_3H_6 \\ \quad \text{Propylene} \\ CH_4 + C_2H_4 \\ \quad \text{Ethylene} \end{cases}$$

$$CH_3CH_2CH_2CH_3 \xrightarrow{\text{400–600°}} \begin{cases} H_2 + C_4H_8 \\ \quad \text{Butylene} \\ CH_4 + C_3H_6 \\ \quad \text{Propylene} \\ CH_3CH_3 + C_2H_4 \\ \quad \text{Ethylene} \end{cases}$$

A larger alkane yields even more products.

In the petroleum industry cracking usually involves the kerosene and gas oil fractions. Breaking these large molecules into smaller ones increases the yield of gasoline from petroleum. Since alkenes, which make up a large part of the cracking product, have good antiknock qualities, cracking improves the gasoline. Through the process of alkylation (Sec. 5.18) certain of the smaller alkanes and alkenes are converted to high-octane synthetic fuels.

The more volatile alkenes, containing up to four or five carbons, can be separated and purified; these reactive compounds are perhaps the most important raw materials for the large-scale synthesis of aliphatic compounds.

3.31   Determination of structure

One of the commonest and most important jobs in organic chemistry is to determine the structural formula of a compound just synthesized or isolated from a natural source.

The compound will fall into one of two groups, although at first we probably shall not know *which* group. It will be either (a) a previously reported compound, which we must identify, or (b) a new compound, whose structure we must prove.

If the compound has previously been encountered by some other chemist who determined its structure, then a description of its properties will be found somewhere in the chemical literature, together with the evidence on which its structure was assigned. In that case, we need only to show that our compound is identical with the one previously described.

If, on the other hand, our compound is a new one that has never before been reported, then we must carry out a much more elaborate proof of structure.

Let us see — in a general way now, and in more detail later — just how we would go about this job. We are confronted by a flask filled with gas, or a few milliliters of liquid, or a tiny heap of crystals. We must find the answer to the question: *what is it?*

First, we purify the compound and determine its physical properties: melting point, boiling point, density, refractive index, and solubility in various solvents. In the laboratory today, we would almost certainly measure the spectrum of the compound, particularly in the infrared region (Sec. 3.32). We would carry out a qualitative elemental analysis to see what elements are present (Sec. 2.25). We might follow this with a quantitative analysis and molecular weight determination, from which we could calculate a molecular formula (Sec. 2.28); we would certainly do this if the compound is suspected of being a new one.

Next, we study systematically the behavior of the compound toward certain reagents. This behavior, taken with the elemental analysis, solubility properties, and spectrum, generally permits us to *characterize* the compound, that is, to decide what family the unknown belongs to. We might find, for example, that the compound is an alkane, or that it is an alkene, or an aldehyde, or an ester.

Now the question is: *which* alkane is it? Or which alkene, or which aldehyde, or which ester? To find the answer, we first go to the chemical literature and look up compounds of the particular family to which our unknown belongs.

If we find one described whose physical properties are identical with those of our unknown, then the chances are good that the two compounds are identical. For confirmation, we generally convert the unknown by a chemical reaction into a new compound called a **derivative,** and show that this derivative is identical with the product derived in the same way from the previously reported compound.

If, on the other hand, we do not find a compound described whose physical properties are identical with those of our unknown, then we have a difficult job on our hands: we have a new compound, and must prove its structure. We may carry out a *degradation:* break the molecule apart, identify the fragments, and deduce what the structure must have been. To clinch any proof of structure, we attempt to *synthesize* the unknown by a method that leaves no doubt about its structure.

Problem 3.16 The final step in proof of structure of an unknown alkane was its synthesis by the Wurtz reaction from isopentyl chloride. What was the alkane?

3.32 Infrared spectra

Of all the properties of an organic compound, the one that, by itself, gives the most information about the compound's structure is its **infrared spectrum.**

When a beam of light — visible or invisible — is passed through a substance, the light can be either absorbed or transmitted, depending upon its frequency and the structure of the molecules it encounters. Light is energy, and hence when a molecule absorbs light, it gains energy. Just how much energy is gained depends upon the frequency of the light: the higher the frequency (the shorter the wavelength), the greater the gain in energy.

PER CENT TRANSMITTANCE

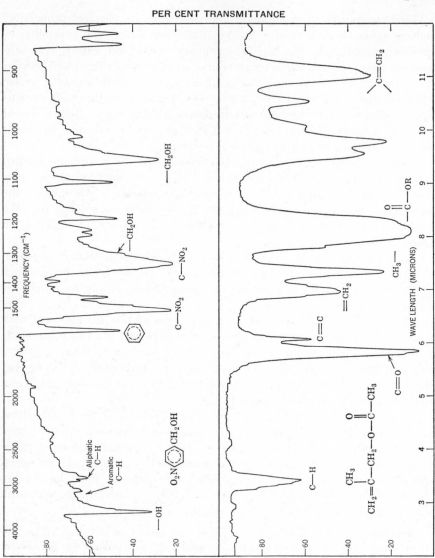

FIGURE 3.8. Infrared spectra of *p*-nitrobenzyl alcohol (upper) and methallyl acetate (lower).

The energy gained by the molecule in this way may bring about increased rotations or vibrations of the atoms, or may raise electrons to higher energy levels. The particular frequency of light that a given molecule can absorb depends upon the changes in rotations or vibrations or electronic states that are permitted to a molecule of that structure. The spectrum of a compound is a continuous plot that shows how much light is absorbed (or transmitted) at each frequency (see, for example, Figure 3.8). It is highly characteristic of the compound's structure.

Changes in rotations and vibrations of atoms are caused by absorption of infrared light: light lying beyond (lower frequency, longer wavelength, less energy) the red end of the visible spectrum. In most cases, it is the infrared region of the spectrum that is most useful in the determination of molecular structure.

The infrared spectrum of an organic compound can be used in two general ways: (a) to prove the identity of two compounds, and (b) to show the presence of certain groups of atoms in a molecule.

Two compounds are shown to be identical by the fact that they have identical physical properties: melting point, boiling point, density, refractive index, etc. The greater the number of physical properties that are measured, the stronger the evidence. Now a single infrared spectrum amounts to thousands of physical properties, since it shows the absorption of light at thousands of different frequencies. If we measure the infrared spectrum of an unknown compound and find it to be identical with the spectrum of a previously reported compound of known structure, then we can conclude — almost beyond a shadow of doubt — that the two compounds are identical. (One region of the infrared spectrum is called, appropriately enough, the *fingerprint* region.) Notice in Figure 3.8, for example, how different the spectra of two different compounds can be.

A particular group of atoms gives rise to *characteristic absorption bands* in the infrared spectrum; that is to say, a particular group absorbs light of certain frequencies that are much the same from compound to compound. For example, the –OH group absorbs strongly at 3100–3600 cm^{-1}, the C=O group at 1710 cm^{-1}, the –C≡N group at 2250 cm^{-1}, –CH$_3$ at 1450 and 1375 cm^{-1}, –CH$_2$– at 1465 cm^{-1}. See, too, the labeling of absorption bands in Figure 3.8. Clearly, the infrared spectrum can tell us much about what groups are present in — or absent from — an unknown compound.

Interpretation of a spectrum is not always a simple matter. In certain cases, for example, interaction between two groups may *shift* the absorption bands of each group so that one band may be mistaken for the band of an entirely different group. But when interpreted by an experienced person with a broad understanding of organic structure, an infrared spectrum, which takes only minutes to measure, can give an enormous amount of information.

3.33 Analysis of alkanes

An unknown compound is characterized as an alkane on the basis of negative evidence.

Upon qualitative elemental analysis, an alkane gives negative tests for all elements except carbon and hydrogen. A quantitative combustion, if one is carried out, shows the absence of oxygen; taken with a molecular weight determination, the combustion gives the molecular formula, C_nH_{2n+2}, which is that of an alkane.

An alkane is insoluble not only in water but also in dilute acid and base and in concentrated sulfuric acid. (As we shall see, most kinds of organic compounds dissolve in one or more of these solvents.)

An alkane is unreactive toward most chemical reagents. Its infrared spectrum lacks the absorption bands characteristic of groups of atoms present in other families of organic compounds (like OH, C=O, C=C, etc.).

Once the unknown has been characterized as an alkane, there remains the second half of the problem: finding out *which* alkane.

On the basis of its physical properties — boiling point, melting point, density, refractive index, and, most reliable of all, infrared spectrum —it may be identified as a previously studied alkane of known structure.

If it turns out to be a new alkane, then proof of structure can be a difficult job. Combustion and molecular weight determination give its molecular formula. Clues about the arrangement of atoms are given by its infrared spectrum. (For compounds like alkanes, it may be necessary to resort to such physical tools as x-ray diffraction and mass spectrometry.)

Final proof lies in synthesis of the unknown by a method that can lead only to the particular structure assigned.

PROBLEMS

1. Give the structural formula and IUPAC name for:

(a) isohexane
(b) dimethyldiethylmethane
(c) methyltriethylmethane
(d) trimethylisobutylmethane
(e) methylethyl-*n*-propyl-*n*-butylmethane

(f) methylisopropyl-*sec*-butylmethane
(g) di-*tert*-butylmethane
(h) isopropyl-*tert*-butylmethane
(i) diethyl-*n*-propylisopropylmethane
(j) diethylisopentylmethane

2. Give the structural formula and derived name for:

(a) 2,2,3,3-tetramethylpentane
(b) 2,3-dimethylbutane
(c) 3,4,4,5-tetramethylheptane
(d) 3,4-dimethyl-4-ethylheptane

(e) 2,4-dimethyl-4-ethylheptane
(f) 2,5-dimethylhexane
(g) 2-methyl-3-ethylpentane
(h) 2,2,4-trimethylpentane

3. Pick out a compound in Problem 1 or 2 that has: (a) no tertiary hydrogen; (b) one tertiary hydrogen; (c) two tertiary hydrogens; (d) no secondary hydrogen; (e) two secondary hydrogens; (f) the same number of secondary hydrogens as primary hydrogens.

4. What alkane or alkanes of molecular weight 86 have: (a) two monobromo derivatives? (b) three? (c) four? (d) five? (e) How many dibromo derivatives does the alkane in (a) have?

5. How many mono-, di-, and trichloro derivatives are possible for cyclopentane? (Structure given in Sec. 7.6.)

6. Without referring to tables, list the following hydrocarbons in order of decreasing boiling points (i.e., highest boiling at top, lowest at bottom).

(a) 3,3-dimethylpentane
(b) *n*-heptane

(c) 2-methylheptane
(d) *n*-pentane

(e) 2-methylhexane

7. Write balanced equations, naming all organic products, for the following reactions:

(a) *n*-butyl bromide + Na; (b) *sec*-butyl bromide + Na;
(c) isobutyl bromide + Mg/ether; (d) *tert*-butyl bromide + Mg/ether;
(e) product of (c) + H_2O; (f) product of (d) + H_2O.

8. Write equations for the preparation of *n*-butane from:

(a) *n*-butyl bromide
(b) *sec*-butyl bromide

(c) ethyl chloride
(d) 1-butene, $CH_3CH_2CH=CH_2$

(e) 2-butene, $CH_3CH=CHCH_3$

9. (a) Which of the isomeric hexanes could be made in reasonable yield and in relatively pure form by the Wurtz method? Why is the method not feasible for the other isomers? (b) Which of the isomeric octanes?

10. (a) What alkanes would be expected from the reaction of sodium with a 50:50 mixture of n-butyl chloride and isobutyl chloride? (b) Assuming that the two halides react equally rapidly with sodium, and equally rapidly with either alkyl-sodium, in what proportions would these alkanes be formed?

11. Draw structures of all products expected from monochlorination at 300° of:

(a) n-hexane (c) 3-methylpentane
(b) isohexane (d) 2,2-dimethylbutane

12. Predict the proportions of products in the previous problem.

13. On the basis of bond strengths in Table 2.1, page 39, add the following free radicals to the stability sequence of Sec. 3.25:

(a) *vinyl*, $H_2C=CH\cdot$
(b) *allyl*, $H_2C=CHCH_2\cdot$
(c) *benzyl*, $C_6H_5CH_2\cdot$

Check your answer on page 267.

14. On the basis of your answer to Problem 13, predict how the following would fit into the sequence (Sec. 3.24) that shows ease of abstraction of hydrogen atoms:

(a) *vinylic* hydrogen, $H_2C=CH$—H
(b) *allylic* hydrogen, $H_2C=CHCH_2$—H
(c) *benzylic* hydrogen, $C_6H_5CH_2$—H

Check your answer against the facts on page 266.

15. (a) If a rocket were fueled with kerosene and liquid oxygen, what weight of oxygen would be required for every liter of kerosene? (Assume kerosene to have the average composition of n-$C_{14}H_{30}$.) (b) How much heat would be evolved in the combustion of one liter of kerosene? (Assume 157 kcal/mole for each $-CH_2-$ group and 186 kcal/mole for each $-CH_3$ group.) (c) If it were to become feasible to fuel a rocket with free hydrogen atoms, what weight of fuel would be required to provide the same heat as a liter of kerosene and the necessary oxygen? (Assume H_2 as the sole product.)

16. By what two quantitative methods could you show that a product isolated from the chlorination of propane was a monochloro or a dichloro derivative of propane? Tell exactly what results you would expect from each of the methods.

17. An alkyl bromide, A, forms a Grignard reagent which on treatment with water yields n-hexane. When A is treated with sodium, 4,5-diethyloctane is formed. What is the structure and name of A? Show your line of reasoning, including all equations.

18. An inflammable gas from an unlabeled cylinder is found to be insoluble in concentrated sulfuric acid. When bubbled into aqueous permanganate or a solution of Br_2 in CCl_4 there is no visible color change. A 142-cc sample collected at 20° and 760 mm weighs 0.337 g. What is the gas likely to be? If there are several possibilities, what simple experiment(s) could you carry out to differentiate between them?

19. On the basis of certain evidence, including its infrared spectrum, an unknown compound of formula $C_{10}H_{22}$ is suspected of being 2,7-dimethyloctane. How could you confirm or disprove this tentatively assigned structure?

Chapter four

ALKENES I. STRUCTURE AND PREPARATION

4.1 Unsaturated hydrocarbons

In our discussion of the alkanes we mentioned briefly another family of hydrocarbons, the **alkenes,** which contain less hydrogen, carbon for carbon, than the alkanes, and which can be converted into alkanes by addition of hydrogen. The alkenes were further described as being obtained from alkanes by loss of hydrogen in the cracking process.

Since alkenes evidently contain less than the maximum quantity of hydrogen, they are referred to as **unsaturated hydrocarbons.** This unsaturation can be satisfied by reagents other than hydrogen and gives rise to the characteristic chemical properties of alkenes.

4.2 Structure of ethylene. The carbon–carbon double bond

The simplest member of the alkene family is **ethylene,** C_2H_4. In view of the ready conversion of ethylene into ethane, we can reasonably expect certain structural similarities between the two compounds.

To start, then, we connect the carbon atoms by a covalent bond, and then attach two hydrogen atoms to each carbon atom. At this stage we find that each carbon atom possesses only six electrons in its valence shell, instead of the required eight, and that the entire molecule needs an additional pair of electrons if it is to be neutral. We can solve both these problems by assuming that the carbon atoms can share two pairs of electrons. To describe this sharing of two pairs of electrons, we say that the carbon atoms are joined by a *double bond.* *The* **carbon–carbon double bond** *is the distinguishing feature of the alkene structure.*

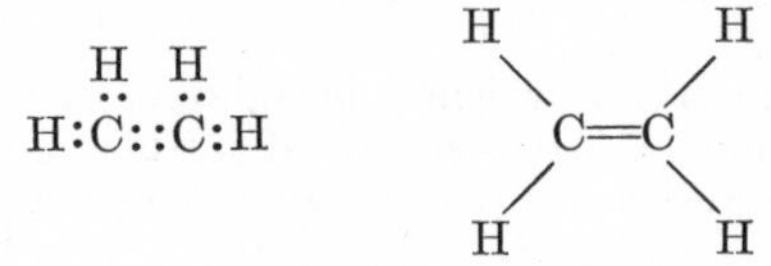

Ethylene

Quantum mechanics gives a more detailed picture of ethylene and the carbon–carbon double bond. To form bonds with three other atoms, carbon makes use of three equivalent hybrid orbitals: sp^2 orbitals, formed by the mixing of *one s* and *two p* orbitals. They lie in one plane, that of the carbon nucleus, and are directed toward the corners of an equilateral triangle; the angle between any pair of orbitals is thus 120°. This **trigonal** arrangement (Figure 4.1) permits the hybrid orbitals to be as far apart as possible. Just as mutual repulsion among orbitals gives four tetrahedral bonds, so it gives three trigonal bonds.

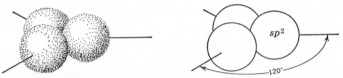

FIGURE 4.1. Atomic orbitals: hybrid sp^2 orbitals. Axes directed toward corners of equilateral triangle.

If we arrange the two carbons and four hydrogens of ethylene to permit maximum overlapping of orbitals, we obtain the structure shown in Figure 4.2. Each carbon atom lies at the center of a triangle, at whose corners are located the two hydrogen atoms and the other carbon atom. Every bond angle is 120°. Although distributed differently about the carbon nucleus, these bonds individually are very similar to the bonds in ethane, being cylindrically symmetrical about a line joining the nuclei, and are given the same designation: σ *bond* (σ = *sigma*).

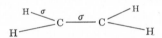

FIGURE 4.2. Ethylene molecule: only σ bonds shown.

The molecule is not yet complete, however. In forming the sp^2 orbitals, each carbon atom has used only two of its three p orbitals. The remaining p orbital consists of two equal lobes, one lying above and the other lying below the plane of the three sp^2 orbitals (Figure 4.3); it is occupied by a single electron. If the p orbital of one carbon atom overlaps the p orbital of the other carbon atom, the electrons pair up and an additional bond is formed.

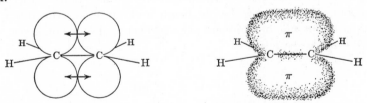

FIGURE 4.3. Ethylene molecule: carbon–carbon double bond. Overlap of p orbitals gives π bond; π cloud above and below plane.

Because it is formed by the overlapping of p orbitals, and to distinguish it from the differently shaped σ bonds, this bond is called a π *bond* (π = *pi*). It consists of two parts, one electron cloud that lies above the plane of the atoms, and another electron cloud that lies below. Because of less over-lapping, the π bond is weaker than the carbon–carbon σ bond. As we can see from Figure 4.3, this overlapping can occur only when all six atoms lie in the same plane. Ethylene, then, is a *flat molecule.*

The carbon–carbon "double bond" is thus made up of a strong σ bond (about 60 kcal) and a weak π bond (about 40 kcal). The total bond strength of 100 kcal is greater than that of the carbon–carbon single bond of ethane (83 kcal). Since the carbon atoms are held more tightly together, the C—C distance in ethylene is less than the C—C distance in ethane; that is to say, the carbon–carbon double bond is shorter than the carbon–carbon single bond.

This quantum mechanical structure of ethylene is verified by direct evidence. Electron diffraction and spectroscopic studies show ethylene (Figure 4.4) to be a flat molecule, with bond angles very close to 120°. The C—C distance is 1.34 A as compared with the C—C distance of 1.54 A in ethane.

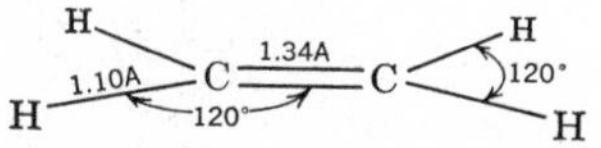

FIGURE 4.4. Ethylene molecule: shape and size.

In addition to these direct measurements, we shall soon see that two important aspects of alkene chemistry are consistent with the quantum mechanical picture of the double bond, and are most readily understood in terms of that picture. These are (a) the concept of *hindered rotation* and the accompanying phenomenon of *geometric isomerism* (Sec. 4.5), and (b) the kind of reactivity characteristic of the carbon–carbon double bond (Sec. 5.2).

Problem 4.1 Compare the electronic configurations of BF_3, which is a flat, triangular molecule (check your answer to Problem 1.4, page 16), and NF_3, which is pyramidal.

4.3 Propylene

The next member of the alkene family is **propylene,** C_3H_6. In view of its great similarity to ethylene, it seems reasonable to assume that this compound, too, contains a carbon–carbon double bond. Starting with two carbons joined by a double bond, and attaching the other atoms according to our rule of one bond per hydrogen and four bonds per carbon, we arrive at the structure

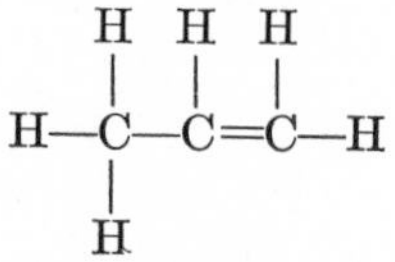

Propylene

4.4 The butylenes

Going on to the **butylenes,** C_4H_8, we find that there are a number of possible arrangements. First of all, we may have a straight-chain skeleton as in *n*-butane, or a branched-chain structure as in isobutane. Next, even when we restrict ourselves to the straight-chain skeleton, we find that there are two possible arrangements that differ in position of the double bond in the chain. So far, then, we have a total of three structures; as indicated, these are given the names *1-butene*, *2-butene*, and *isobutylene*.

| 1-Butene | 2-Butene | Isobutylene |

How do the facts agree with the prediction of three isomeric butylenes? Experiment has shown that not three but *four* alkenes of the formula C_4H_8 exist; they have the physical properties shown in Table 4.1.

TABLE 4.1

PHYSICAL PROPERTIES OF THE BUTYLENES

Name	b.p., °C	m.p., °C	Density ($-20°$)	Refractive index ($-12.7°$)
Isobutylene	-7	-141	0.640	1.3727
1-Butene	-6	< -195	.641	1.3711
trans-2-Butene	$+1$	-106	.649	1.3778
cis-2-Butene	$+4$	-139	.667	1.3868

On hydrogenation, the isomer of b.p. $-7°$ yields isobutane; this butylene evidently contains a branched chain, and has therefore the structure we have designated isobutylene.

On hydrogenation, the other three isomers all yield the same compound, *n*-butane; they evidently have a straight-chain skeleton. In ways that we shall study later (Sec. 5.22), it is possible to break an alkene molecule apart at the double bond, and from the fragments obtained deduce the position of the double bond in the molecule. When this procedure is carried out, the isomer of b.p. $-6°$ yields products indicating clearly that the double bond is at the end of the chain; this butylene has therefore the structure we have designated 1-butene. When the same procedure is carried out on the two remaining isomers, both yield the same mixture of products; these products show that the double bond is in the middle of the chain.

Judging from the products of hydrogenation and the products of cleavage, we would conclude that the butylenes of b.p. $+1°$ and $+4°$ *both* have the structure we have designated 2-butene. Yet the differences in b.p.'s, m.p.'s, and other physical properties show clearly that they are not the same compound, that is, that they are isomers. In what way can their structures differ?

To understand the kind of isomerism that gives rise to two 2-butenes, we must examine more closely the structure of alkenes and the nature of the carbon–carbon double bond. Ethylene is a flat molecule. We have seen that this flatness is a result of the geometric arrangement of the bonding orbitals, and in particular the overlapping that gives rise to the π orbital. For the same reasons, a portion of any alkene molecule must also be flat, the two doubly-bonded carbons and the four atoms attached to them lying in the same plane.

If we examine the structure of 2-butene more closely, and particularly if we use molecular models, we find that there are two quite different ways, I and II, in which the atoms can be arranged (aside from the infinite number of possibilities arising from rotation about the single bonds). In one of the structures the methyl groups lie on the same side of the molecule (I), and in the other structure they lie on opposite sides of the molecule (II).

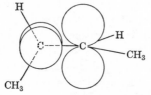

    cis-2-Butene   *trans*-2-Butene

      I   II

Now the question arises, can we expect to isolate two isomeric 2-butenes corresponding to these two different structures, or are they, too, readily interconverted like the conformations of 1,2-dichloroethane (Sec. 3.3)?

Conversion of I into II involves rotation about the carbon–carbon double bond. The possibility of isolating isomers depends upon the energy required for this rotation. We have seen that the formation of the π bond involves overlapping of the p orbitals that lie above and below the plane of the σ orbitals. To pass from one of these 2-butenes to the other, the molecule must be twisted so that the p orbitals no longer overlap; that is, the π bond must be broken (see Figure 4.5). Breaking the π bond requires about 40 kcal of energy; at room temperature an insignificant proportion of collisions possess this necessary energy, and hence the rate of this interconversion is extremely small.

FIGURE 4.5. Hindered rotation about carbon–carbon double bond. Rotation would prevent overlap of p orbitals and would break π bond.

Because of this 40-kcal energy barrier, then, *there is* **hindered rotation** *about the carbon–carbon double bond*. As a result of this hindered rotation, two isomeric 2-butenes can be isolated. These are, of course, the butylenes of b.p. $+1°$ and b.p. $+4°$.

4.5   Geometric isomerism

The isomeric 2-butenes are called **geometric isomers**. The two isomeric structures are called *configurations;* they are differentiated in their names by the prefixes **cis-** (Latin, on this side) and **trans-** (Latin, across), which indicate that the methyl groups are on the same side or on opposite sides of the molecule. In a way that we are not prepared to take up at this time, it has been established that the isomer of b.p. +1° has the *trans* configuration and the isomer of b.p. +4° the *cis* configuration.

<table>
<tr><td>
CH₃   H
\ /
C
‖
C
/ \
H   CH₃
trans-2-Butene
b.p. +1°
</td>
<td>
CH₃   H
\ /
C
‖
C
/ \
CH₃   H
cis-2-Butene
b.p. +4°
</td>
<td>
**Geometric
isomers**
</td>
</tr>
</table>

Isomers that differ from one another *only* in the way the atoms are oriented in space (but are like one another with respect to which atoms are joined to which) are called **stereoisomers** (Gr., *stereos*, solid). The arrangement of atoms that characterizes a particular stereoisomer is called its **configuration**; in general, bonds must be broken to convert one configuration to another.

Geometric isomerism is one kind of stereoisomerism. There are two configurations of 2-butene, the *cis* and the *trans*, corresponding to the two stereoisomers. Each stereoisomer can, of course, exist in an infinite number of conformations resulting from rotation about single bonds.

The aspect of chemistry that deals with the structure and properties of stereoisomers is called **stereochemistry**; an understanding of stereochemistry is one of the most powerful tools that a chemist can use to find out what goes on in a chemical reaction.

There is hindered rotation about *any* carbon–carbon double bond, but it gives rise to geometric isomerism only if there is a certain relationship among the groups attached to the doubly-bonded carbons. We can look for this isomerism by drawing the possible structures (or better yet, by constructing them from molecular models), and then seeing if these are indeed isomeric, or actually identical. On this basis we find that propylene, 1-butene, and isobutylene should not show isomerism;

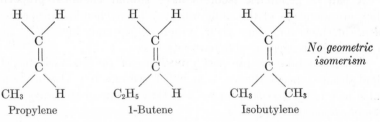

<table>
<tr><td>Propylene</td><td>1-Butene</td><td>Isobutylene</td><td>*No geometric
isomerism*</td></tr>
</table>

this conclusion agrees with the facts. Many higher alkenes may, of course, show geometric isomerism.

If we consider compounds other than hydrocarbons, we find that 1,1-dichloro- and 1,1-dibromoethene should not show isomerism, whereas the 1,2-dichloro- and 1,2-dibromoethenes should. In every case, these predictions have been found correct. Isomers of the following physical properties have been isolated.

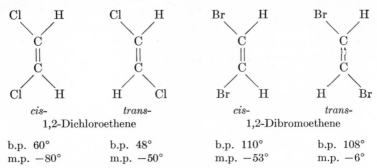

cis-	trans-	cis-	trans-
1,2-Dichloroethene		1,2-Dibromoethene	
b.p. 60°	b.p. 48°	b.p. 110°	b.p. 108°
m.p. −80°	m.p. −50°	m.p. −53°	m.p. −6°

As we soon conclude from our examination of these structures, geometric isomerism cannot exist if either carbon carries two identical groups. Some possible combinations are shown below.

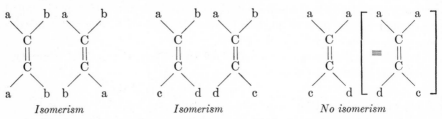

| Isomerism | Isomerism | No isomerism |

The phenomenon of geometric isomerism is a general one and can be encountered in any class of compounds that contain carbon–carbon double bonds (or even double bonds of other kinds).

A pair of geometric isomers differ from one another in their physical properties, having different melting points, boiling points, refractive indices, solubilities, densities, etc. As a result of their differences in boiling point and in solubility, they can, in principle at least, be separated from each other either by fractional distillation or fractional crystallization; as a result of differences in molecular shape and polarity, they differ in adsorption, and can be separated by chromatography.

A pair of geometric isomers have similar chemical properties since they are members of the same family. Their chemical properties are *not identical*, however, since their structures are not identical; they react with a given reagent at different rates.

When we take up physical properties of the alkenes (Sec. 4.10), we shall discuss one of the ways in which we can tell whether a particular substance is the *cis-* or *trans-*isomer, that is, one of the ways in which we *assign configuration*.

4.6 Higher alkenes

As we can see, the butylenes contain one carbon and two hydrogens more than propylene, which in turn contains one carbon and two hydrogens more than ethylene. The alkenes, therefore, form another homologous series, the increment being the same as for the alkanes: CH_2. The general formula for this family is C_nH_{2n}.

As we ascend the series of alkenes, the number of isomeric structures for each member increases even more rapidly than in the case of the alkane series; in addition to variations in the carbon skeletons, there are variations in the position of the double bond for a given skeleton, and the possibility of geometric isomerism.

Problem 4.2 Draw structures of (a) the six isomeric pentylenes (C_5H_{10}); (b) the four chloropropylenes (C_3H_5Cl); (c) the eleven chlorobutylenes (C_4H_7Cl).

4.7   Common names

As in the case of the alkanes, there are three different systems for naming the alkenes. For the simpler alkenes the common names, *ethylene*, *propylene*, and *butylene* are frequently used. The butylenes are differentiated by the arbitrary prefixes, α-, β-, and *iso*. As in all the systems, geometric isomers are differentiated by the prefixes *cis*- and *trans*-. The large number of prefixes that would be required makes this system impracticable for the higher alkenes. The various alkenes of a given carbon number are, however, sometimes referred to collectively as the *pentylenes* (*amylenes*), *hexylenes*, *heptylenes*, etc.

4.8   Derived names

One method of naming the alkanes considered them to be derived from methane by the replacement of one or more hydrogen atoms by alkyl groups. In a similar way we may consider the alkenes to be derived from the parent compound, ethylene, by the substitution of various alkyl groups. The carbon atoms joined by the double bond are considered to be those of the parent ethylene; we then simply name the various alkyl groups attached to these carbon atoms. For example:

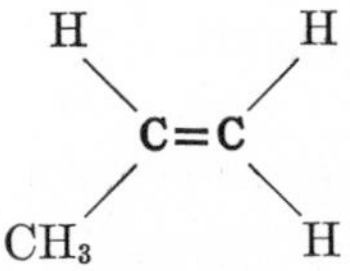

Propylene
Methylethylene

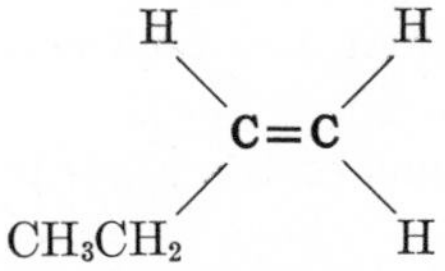

α-Butylene
Ethylethylene

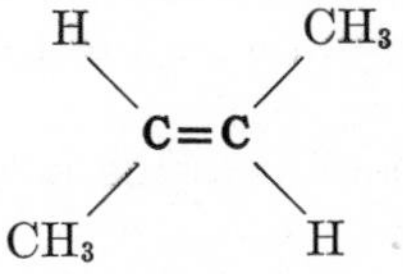

trans-
β-Butylene
sym-Dimethylethylene

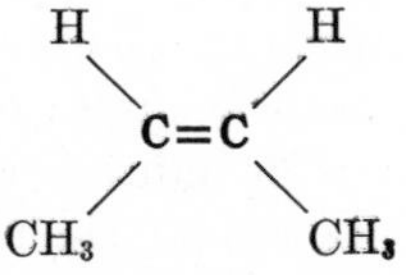

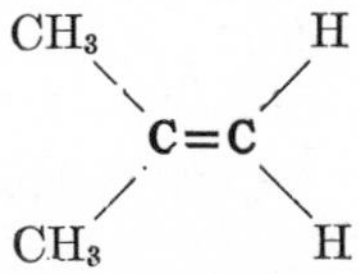

cis-

Isobutylene
unsym-Dimethylethylene

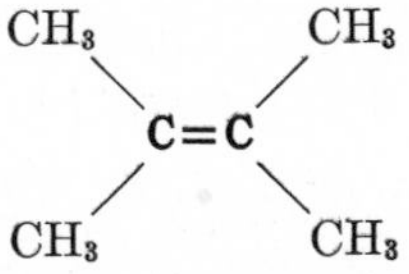

Tetramethylethylene

We can see that there are two dimethylethylenes, one in which the two methyl groups are attached to different carbon atoms, and one in which the two methyl groups are attached to the same carbon atom. These can be easily differentiated by the prefixes *sym-* (symmetrical) and *unsym-* (unsymmetrical).

As with the methane system of naming alkanes, the ethylene system breaks down when the groups attached to the parent ethylene are too complicated to be named readily. For these more complicated molecules, then, we must make use of the IUPAC system.

4.9 IUPAC names

The rules of the IUPAC system are:

1. Select as the parent structure the longest continuous chain *that contains the carbon–carbon double bond;* then consider the compound to have been derived from this structure by replacement of hydrogen by various alkyl groups. The parent structure is known as *ethene, propene, butene, pentene,* etc., depending upon the number of carbon atoms; each name is derived by changing the ending *-ane* of the corresponding alkane name to **-ene.**

$H_2C=CH_2$ $CH_3-CH=CH_2$ $CH_3CH_2CH=CH_2$ $CH_3CH=CHCH_3$

   Ethene   Propene   1-Butene   2-Butene
                                                                        (*cis-* or *trans-*)

$$CH_3-\overset{\overset{\displaystyle CH_3}{|}}{C}=CH_2 \qquad CH_3-\overset{\overset{\displaystyle CH_3}{|}}{\underset{\underset{\displaystyle CH_3}{|}}{C}}-CH=CH_2 \qquad CH_3-\overset{\overset{\displaystyle CH_3}{|}}{\underset{\underset{\displaystyle H}{|}}{C}}-CH=CH-CH_3$$

    2-Methylpropene   3,3-Dimethyl-   4-Methyl-2-pentene
                           1-butene   (*cis-* or *trans-*)

2. Indicate by a number the position of the double bond in the parent chain. Although the double bond involves two carbon atoms, designate its position by the number of the *first* doubly-bonded carbon encountered when numbering from the end of the chain nearest the double bond; thus *1-butene* and *2-butene.*

3. Indicate by numbers the positions of the alkyl groups attached to the parent chain.

4.10 Physical properties

As a class, the alkenes possess physical properties that are essentially the same as those of the alkanes. They are insoluble in water, but quite soluble in non-polar solvents like benzene, ether, chloroform, or ligroin. They are less dense than water. As we can see from Table 4.2, the boiling point rises with increasing carbon content; as with the alkanes, the boiling point rise is 20–30° for each added carbon, except for the very small homologs. As before, branching lowers the boiling point. A comparison of Table 4.2 with Table 3.3 (page 72) shows that the boiling point of an alkene is very nearly the same as that of the alkane with the corresponding carbon skeleton.

The alkanes are completely non-polar. Certain alkenes, on the other hand, because of the particular geometry of the double bond, are weakly polar. Propylene and 1-butene, for example, have the small dipole moments shown below. (Compare these moments with, say, the moment of 1.83 for methyl chloride.)

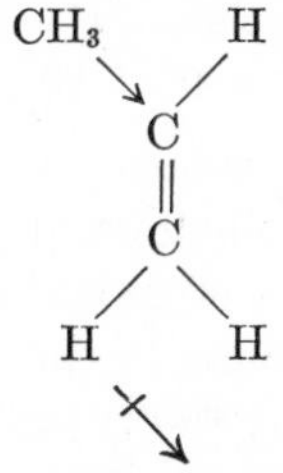

$$
\begin{array}{cc}
CH_3 \quad H & C_2H_5 \quad H \\
\diagdown \diagup & \diagdown \diagup \\
C & C \\
\| & \| \\
C & C \\
\diagup \diagdown & \diagup \diagdown \\
H \quad H & H \quad H \\
\mu = 0.35 & \mu = 0.37
\end{array}
$$

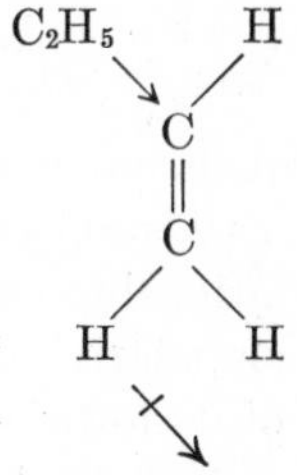

The bond joining the alkyl group to the doubly-bonded carbon has a small polarity, which is believed to be in the direction shown, that is, with the alkyl group releasing electrons to the doubly-bonded carbon. Since this polarity is not canceled by a corresponding polarity in the opposite direction, it gives a net dipole moment to the molecule.

TABLE 4.2

ALKENES

Name	Formula	M.p., °C	B.p., °C	Density (at 20°C)
Ethylene	CH_2=CH_2	−169	−102	
Propylene	CH_2=$CHCH_3$	−185	− 48	
1-Butene	CH_2=$CHCH_2CH_3$		− 6.5	
1-Pentene	CH_2=$CH(CH_2)_2CH_3$		30	0.643
1-Hexene	CH_2=$CH(CH_2)_3CH_3$	−138	63.5	.675
1-Heptene	CH_2=$CH(CH_2)_4CH_3$	−119	93	.698
1-Octene	CH_2=$CH(CH_2)_5CH_3$	−104	122.5	.716
1-Nonene	CH_2=$CH(CH_2)_6CH_3$		146	.731
1-Decene	CH_2=$CH(CH_2)_7CH_3$	− 87	171	.743
cis-2-Butene	cis-CH_3CH=$CHCH_3$	−139	4	
trans-2-Butene	trans-CH_3CH=$CHCH_3$	−106	1	
Isobutylene	CH_2=$C(CH_3)_2$	−141	− 7	
cis-2-Pentene	cis-CH_3CH=$CHCH_2CH_3$	−151	37	.655
trans-2-Pentene	trans-CH_3CH=$CHCH_2CH_3$		36	.647
3-Methyl-1-butene	CH_2=$CHCH(CH_3)_2$	−135	25	.648
2-Methyl-2-butene	CH_3CH=$C(CH_3)_2$	−123	39	.660
2,3-Dimethyl-2-butene	$(CH_3)_2C$=$C(CH_3)_2$	− 74	73	.705

cis-2-Butene, with two methyl groups on one side of the molecule and two hydrogens on the other, should have a small dipole moment. In trans-2-butene, on the other hand, with one methyl and one hydrogen on each side of the molecule, the bond moments should cancel out.

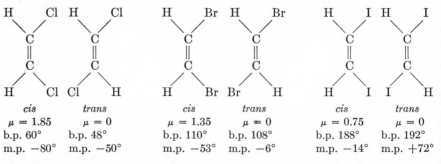

cis-2-Butene
expect small +—→
b.p. +4°
m.p. −139°

trans-2-Butene
expect μ = 0
b.p. +1°
m.p. −106°

Although the dipole moments have not been measured directly, a small difference in polarity is reflected in the higher boiling point of the *cis*-isomer.

This same relationship exists for many pairs of geometric isomers. Because of its higher polarity the *cis*-isomer is generally the higher boiling cf a pair; because of its lower symmetry it fits into a crystalline lattice more poorly, and thus generally has the lower melting point.

The differences in polarity, and hence the differences in melting point and boiling point, are greater for alkenes that contain elements whose electronegativities differ widely from that of carbon. For example:

cis	trans	cis	trans	cis	trans
μ = 1.85	μ = 0	μ = 1.35	μ = 0	μ = 0.75	μ = 0
b.p. 60°	b.p. 48°	b.p. 110°	b.p. 108°	b.p. 188°	b.p. 192°
m.p. −80°	m.p. −50°	m.p. −53°	m.p. −6°	m.p. −14°	m.p. +72°

The relationship between configuration and boiling point or melting point is only a rule of thumb, to which there are many exceptions (for example, the boiling points of the diiodoethenes). Measurement of dipole moment, on the other hand, frequently enables us positively to designate a particular isomer as *cis* or *trans*.

Problem 4.3 (a) Indicate the direction of the net dipole moment for each of the dihaloethenes. (b) Would *cis*-2,3-dichloro-2-butene have a larger or smaller dipole moment than *cis*-1,2-dichloroethene? (c) Indicate the direction of the net dipole moment of *cis*-1,2-dibromo-1,2-dichloroethene. Will it be larger or smaller than the dipole moment of *cis*-1,2-dichloroethene? Why?

4.11 Industrial source

Alkenes are obtained in industrial quantities chiefly by the cracking of petroleum (Sec. 3.30). The smaller alkenes can be obtained in pure form by fractional distillation and are thus available for conversion into a large number of important aliphatic compounds. Higher alkenes, which cannot be separated from the complicated cracking mixture, remain as valuable components of gasoline.

4.12 Preparation

Alkenes containing up to five carbon atoms can be obtained in pure form from the petroleum industry. Pure samples of more complicated alkenes must be prepared by one of the methods outlined below.

The introduction of a carbon–carbon double bond into a molecule containing only single bonds must necessarily involve the **elimination** of atoms or groups from two adjacent carbons.

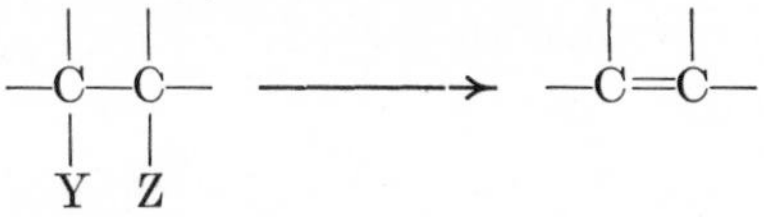

$$-\overset{|}{\underset{\underset{Y}{|}}{C}}-\overset{|}{\underset{\underset{Z}{|}}{C}}- \longrightarrow -\overset{|}{C}=\overset{|}{C}- \qquad \textbf{Elimination}$$

In the cracking process already discussed, for example, the atoms eliminated are both hydrogen atoms.

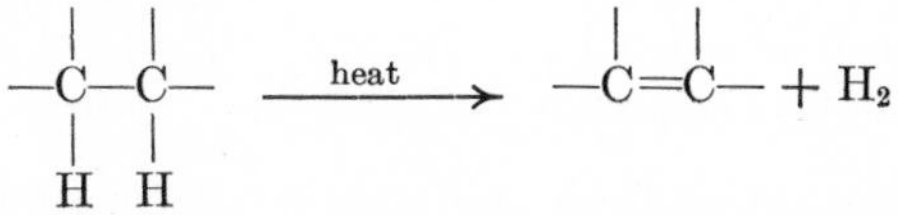

$$-\overset{|}{\underset{\underset{H}{|}}{C}}-\overset{|}{\underset{\underset{H}{|}}{C}}- \xrightarrow{\text{heat}} -\overset{|}{C}=\overset{|}{C}- + H_2$$

The elimination reactions described below not only can be used to make simple alkenes, but also — and this is much more important — provide the best general ways to introduce carbon–carbon double bonds into molecules of all kinds.

PREPARATION OF ALKENES

1. Dehydrohalogenation of alkyl halides

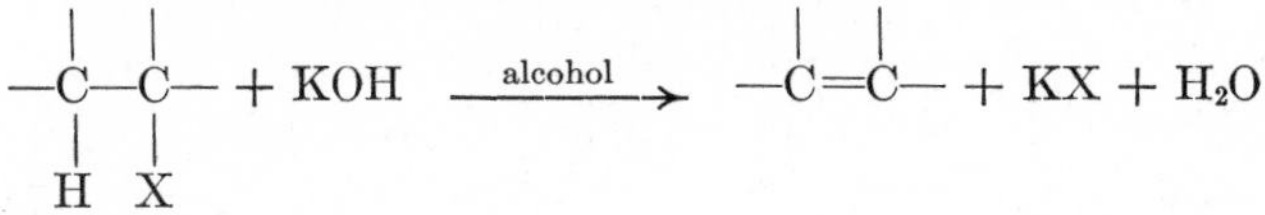

$$-\overset{|}{\underset{\underset{H}{|}}{C}}-\overset{|}{\underset{\underset{X}{|}}{C}}- + KOH \xrightarrow{\text{alcohol}} -\overset{|}{C}=\overset{|}{C}- + KX + H_2O$$

Examples:

$$CH_3CH_2CH_2CH_2Cl \xrightarrow{\text{KOH(alc)}} CH_3CH_2CH=CH_2$$
   n-Butyl chloride   1-Butene

$$CH_3CH_2CHClCH_3 \xrightarrow{\text{KOH(alc)}} CH_3CH=CHCH_3 + CH_3CH_2CH=CH_2$$
   sec-Butyl chloride   2-Butene   1-Butene
   　　　　　　　　　　　　　　　　　　　(*80%*)　　　　　　　(*20%*)

2. Dehydration of alcohols

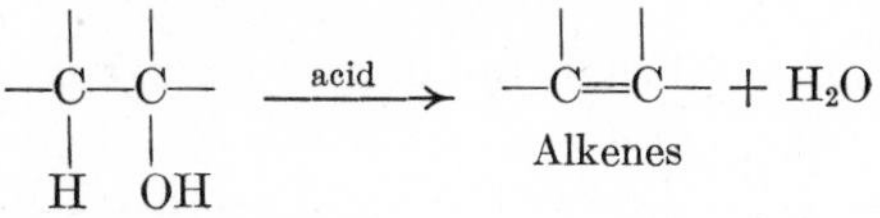

$$-\overset{|}{\underset{\underset{H}{|}}{C}}-\overset{|}{\underset{\underset{OH}{|}}{C}}- \xrightarrow{\text{acid}} -\overset{|}{C}=\overset{|}{C}- + H_2O$$
   Alcohols   Alkenes

Ease of dehydration of alcohols
$$3° > 2° > 1°$$

Examples:

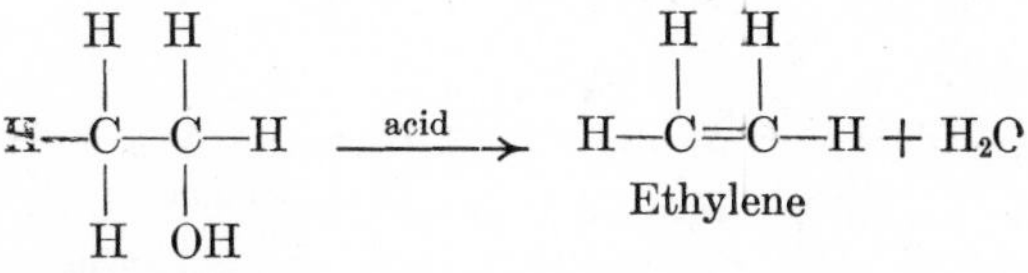

$$H-\overset{\overset{\displaystyle H}{|}}{\underset{\underset{\displaystyle H}{|}}{C}}-\overset{\overset{\displaystyle H}{|}}{\underset{\underset{\displaystyle OH}{|}}{C}}-H \xrightarrow{\text{acid}} H-\overset{\overset{\displaystyle H}{|}}{C}=\overset{\overset{\displaystyle H}{|}}{C}-H + H_2O$$
   Ethyl alcohol   Ethylene

$$CH_3CH_2CH_2CH_2OH \xrightarrow{\text{acid}} CH_3CH_2CH=CH_2 + CH_3CH=CHCH_3$$

n-Butyl alcohol   1-Butene   2-Butene
chief product

$$CH_3CH_2-\underset{\underset{OH}{|}}{CH}-CH_3 \xrightarrow{\text{acid}} CH_3CH=CHCH_3 + CH_3CH_2CH=CH_2$$

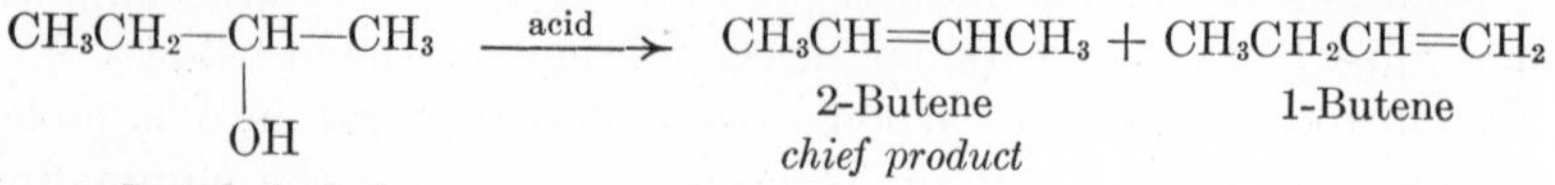

sec-Butyl alcohol   2-Butene   1-Butene
chief product

3. Dehalogenation of vicinal dihalides

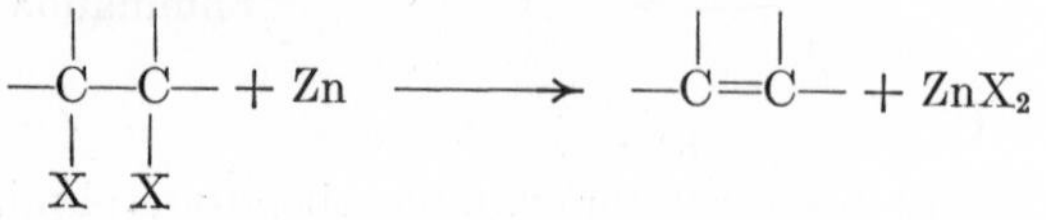

$$-\underset{\underset{X}{|}}{C}-\underset{\underset{X}{|}}{C}- + Zn \longrightarrow -\overset{|}{C}=\overset{|}{C}- + ZnX_2$$

Example:

$$CH_3CHBrCHBrCH_3 \xrightarrow{Zn} CH_3CH=CHCH_3$$

2,3-Dibromobutane   2-Butene

The most important of these methods of preparation are the **dehydrohalogenation of alkyl halides** and the **dehydration of alcohols**. Both methods suffer from the disadvantage that, where the structure permits, hydrogen can be eliminated from the carbon on either side of the carbon bearing the —X or —OH; this frequently produces isomers. Since the isomerism usually involves only the position of the double bond, it is not important in the cases where we plan to convert the alkene into an alkane.

As we shall see later, alkyl halides are generally prepared from the corresponding alcohols, and hence both these methods ultimately involve preparation from alcohols; however, dehydrohalogenation generally leads to fewer complications and is often the preferred method despite the extra step in the sequence.

Dehalogenation of vicinal (Latin, *vicinalis*, neighboring) dihalides is severely limited by the fact that these dihalides are themselves generally prepared from the alkenes. However, it is sometimes useful to convert an alkene to a dihalide while we perform some operation on another part of the molecule, and then to regenerate the alkene by treatment with zinc; this procedure is referred to as *protecting the double bond*.

4.13 Dehydrohalogenation of alkyl halides

Alkyl halides are converted into alkenes by **dehydrohalogenation:** *elimination of the elements of hydrogen halide.* Dehydrohalogenation involves removal of the halogen atom together with a hydrogen atom from a carbon adjacent to the one bearing the halogen.

Dehydrohalogenation: elimination of HX

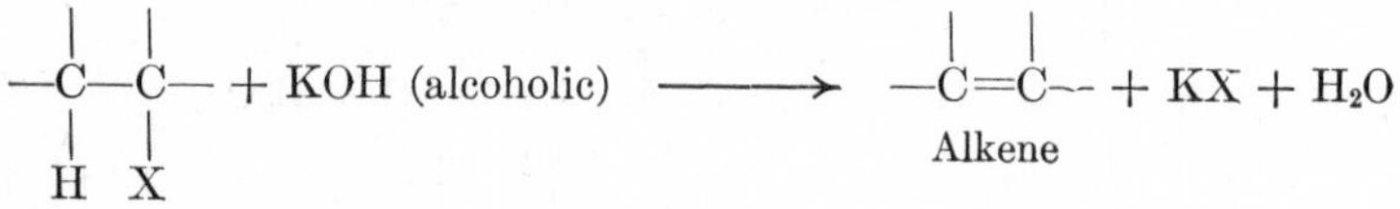

$$-\underset{\underset{H}{|}}{C}-\underset{\underset{X}{|}}{C}- + KOH \text{ (alcoholic)} \longrightarrow -\overset{|}{C}=\overset{|}{C}- + KX + H_2O$$

Alkyl halide   Alkene

It is not surprising that the reagent required for the elimination of what amounts to a molecule of acid is a strong base.

The alkene is prepared by simply heating together the alkyl halide and a solution of potassium hydroxide in alcohol. For example:

$$CH_3CH_2CH_2Cl \xrightarrow{\text{KOH(alc)}} CH_3CH=CH_2 \xleftarrow{\text{KOH(alc)}} CH_3CHCH_3$$
$$\text{n-Propyl chloride} \qquad\qquad \text{Propylene} \qquad\qquad\qquad |$$
$$Cl$$
$$\text{Isopropyl chloride}$$

$$CH_3CH_2CH_2CH_2Cl \xrightarrow{\text{KOH(alc)}} CH_3CH_2CH=CH_2$$
$$\text{n-Butyl chloride} \qquad\qquad\qquad \text{1-Butene}$$

$$CH_3CH_2CHCH_3 \xrightarrow{\text{KOH(alc)}} CH_3CH=CHCH_3 + CH_3CH_2CH=CH_2$$
$$\qquad | \qquad\qquad\qquad\qquad \text{2-Butene} \qquad\qquad \text{1-Butene}$$
$$\qquad Cl \qquad\qquad\qquad\qquad (80\%) \qquad\qquad\quad (20\%)$$
$$\text{sec-Butyl chloride}$$

As we can see, in some cases this reaction yields a single alkene, and in other cases yields a mixture. *n*-Butyl chloride, for example, can eliminate hydrogen only from C-2 and hence yields only 1-butene. *sec*-Butyl chloride, on the other hand, can eliminate hydrogen from either C-1 or C-3 and hence yields both 1-butene and 2-butene. Where the two alkenes can be formed, 2-butene is the chief product; this fact fits into a general pattern for elimination reactions, which is discussed in Sec. 4.19.

Problem 4.4 Give structures of all alkenes expected from dehydrohalogenation of: (a) 1-chloropentane; (b) 2-chloropentane; (c) 3-chloropentane; (d) 2-chloro-2-methylbutane; (e) 3-chloro-2-methylbutane; (f) 2-chloro-2,3-dimethylbutane.

Problem 4.5 What alkyl halide (*if any*) would yield each of the following pure alkenes upon dehydrohalogenation? (a) isobutylene; (b) 1-pentene; (c) 2-pentene; (d) 2-methyl-1-butene; (e) 2-methyl-2-butene; (f) 3-methyl-1-butene.

The function of hydroxide ion is to pull a hydrogen ion away from carbon; simultaneously a halide ion separates and the double bond forms.

We should notice that, in contrast to free radical reactions, the breaking of the C—H and C—X bonds occurs in an unsymmetrical fashion: hydrogen relinquishes *both* electrons to carbon, and halogen retains *both* electrons. The electrons left behind by hydrogen are now available for formation of the second bond (the π bond) between the carbon atoms.

What supplies the energy for the breaking of the carbon–hydrogen and carbon–halogen bonds?

(a) First, there is formation of the bond between the hydrogen ion and the very strong base, hydroxide ion.

(b) Next, there is formation of the π bond which, although weak, does supply about 40 kcal/mole of energy.

(c) Finally, and this is extremely important, there is the energy of solvation of the halide ions. Alcohol, like water, is a polar solvent. A liberated halide ion is surrounded by a cluster of these polar molecules; each solvent molecule is oriented so that the positive end of its dipole is near the negative ion (Figure 4.6). Although each of these *ion-dipole bonds* (Sec. 1.16) is weak, in the aggregate they supply considerable energy. (We should recall that the ion-dipole bonds in hydrated sodium and chloride ions provide the energy for the breaking down of the sodium chloride crystalline lattice, a process which in the absence of water requires a temperature of 801°.) *Just as a hydrogen ion is pulled out of the molecule by a hydroxide ion, so a halide ion is pulled out by solvent molecules.*

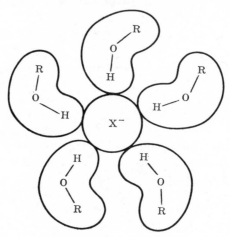

FIGURE 4.6. Ion–dipole interaction: solvated halide ion.

The free radical reactions of the alkanes, which we studied in Chapter 3, are chiefly gas phase reactions. It is significant that ionic reactions (like the one just discussed) occur chiefly in solution.

4.14 Dehydration of alcohols

Alcohols are compounds of the general formula, ROH, where R is any alkyl group; the hydroxyl group, —OH, is characteristic of alcohols, just as the carbon–carbon double bond is characteristic of alkenes. An alcohol is named simply by naming the alkyl group that holds the hydroxyl group and following this by the word *alcohol*. It is classified as *primary* (1°), *secondary* (2°), or *tertiary* (3°) depending upon the nature of the carbon atom holding the hydroxyl group (Sec. 3.11). For example:

$$CH_3CH_2OH \qquad \underset{CH_3}{\overset{CH_3}{\diagdown}}CHCH_2OH \qquad \underset{OH}{CH_3CHCH_3} \qquad CH_3-\underset{OH}{\overset{CH_3}{C}}-CH_3$$

Ethyl alcohol	Isobutyl alcohol	Isopropyl alcohol	*tert*-Butyl alcohol
a primary alcohol	*a primary alcohol*	*a secondary alcohol*	*a tertiary alcohol*

An alcohol is converted into an alkene by **dehydration:** *elimination of a molecule of water.*

$$\underset{\substack{\text{H} \quad \text{OH} \\ \text{Alcohol}}}{-\overset{|}{\underset{|}{\text{C}}}-\overset{|}{\underset{|}{\text{C}}}-} \xrightarrow[\text{heat}]{\text{acid}} \underset{\text{Alkene}}{-\overset{|}{\text{C}}=\overset{|}{\text{C}}-} + \text{H}_2\text{O} \qquad \textbf{Dehydration: elimination of H}_2\textbf{O}$$

Dehydration requires the presence of an acid and the application of heat. It is generally carried out in either of two ways: (a) heating with sulfuric or phosphoric acid to temperatures as high as 200°, or (b) passing the alcohol vapor over alumina, Al_2O_3, at 350–400°, alumina here serving as a Lewis acid (Sec. 1.17).

The various classes of alcohols differ widely in ease of dehydration, the order of reactivity being

Ease of dehydration of alcohols $3° > 2° > 1°$

The following examples show how these differences in reactivity affect the experimental conditions of the dehydration. (Certain tertiary alcohols are so prone to dehydration that they can be distilled only if precautions are taken to protect the system from the acid fumes in the ordinary laboratory.)

$$\underset{\text{Ethyl alcohol}}{\text{CH}_3\text{CH}_2\text{OH}} \xrightarrow[170°]{95\% \text{ H}_2\text{SO}_4} \underset{\text{Ethylene}}{\text{CH}_2{=}\text{CH}_2}$$

$$\underset{n\text{-Butyl alcohol}}{\text{CH}_3\text{CH}_2\text{CH}_2\text{CH}_2\text{OH}} \xrightarrow[140°]{75\% \text{ H}_2\text{SO}_4} \underset{\text{2-Butene (}\textit{chief product}\text{)}}{\text{CH}_3\text{CH}{=}\text{CHCH}_3}$$

$$\underset{sec\text{-Butyl alcohol}}{\text{CH}_3\text{CH}_2\text{CHOHCH}_3} \xrightarrow[100°]{60\% \text{ H}_2\text{SO}_4} \underset{\text{2-Butene (}\textit{chief product}\text{)}}{\text{CH}_3\text{CH}{=}\text{CHCH}_3}$$

$$\underset{\substack{| \\ \text{OH} \\ tert\text{-Butyl alcohol}}}{\text{CH}_3{-}\overset{\overset{\text{CH}_3}{|}}{\text{C}}{-}\text{CH}_3} \xrightarrow[85–90°]{20\% \text{ H}_2\text{SO}_4} \underset{\text{Isobutylene}}{\text{CH}_3{-}\overset{\overset{\text{CH}_3}{|}}{\text{C}}{=}\text{CH}_2}$$

Where isomeric alkenes can be formed, we again find the tendency for one isomer to predominate. Thus, *sec*-butyl alcohol, which might yield both 2-butene and 1-butene, actually yields almost exclusively the 2-isomer (see Sec. 4.19).

The formation of 2-butene from *n*-butyl alcohol illustrates a characteristic of dehydration that is not shared by dehydrohalogenation: the double bond can be formed at a position remote from the carbon originally holding the —OH group. This characteristic is accounted for later (Sec. 12.3). It is chiefly because of the greater certainty as to where the double bond will appear that dehydrohalogenation is often preferred over dehydration as a method of making alkenes.

4.15 The carbonium ion theory

To account for the observed facts a certain mechanism was advanced for the halogenation of alkanes; the heart of this mechanism is the fleeting existence of free radicals, highly reactive neutral particles bearing an odd electron. We have examined in some detail much of the evidence for this mechanism. On the basis of similar kinds of evidence, it is believed that other reactions of alkanes (combustion, cracking) also involve free radicals.

To account for a wide variety of observations that have been made in studying the chemistry of alkenes — as well as alcohols, alkyl halides, and many other kinds of organic compounds — the existence of another kind of reactive particle has been proposed: the **carbonium ion,** *a group of atoms that contains a carbon atom bearing only six electrons.* Carbonium ions are classified as primary, secondary, or tertiary after the carbon bearing the positive charge. For example:

$$
\begin{array}{cccc}
\text{H} & \text{H} & \text{H} & \text{CH}_3 \\
\overset{\cdot\cdot}{\text{H}:\overset{\cdot\cdot}{\text{C}}\oplus} & \text{CH}_3:\overset{\cdot\cdot}{\text{C}}\oplus & \text{CH}_3:\overset{\cdot\cdot}{\text{C}}:\text{CH}_3 & \text{CH}_3:\overset{\cdot\cdot}{\text{C}}:\text{CH}_3 \\
\text{H} & \text{H} & \oplus & \oplus \\
\text{Methyl} & \text{Ethyl} & \text{Isopropyl} & \textit{tert}\text{-Butyl} \\
\text{carbonium ion} & \text{carbonium ion} & \text{carbonium ion} & \text{carbonium ion} \\
 & (\textit{primary, } 1°) & (\textit{secondary, } 2°) & (\textit{tertiary, } 3°)
\end{array}
$$

Like the free radical, the carbonium ion is an exceedingly reactive particle, and for the same reason: the tendency to complete the octet of carbon. Unlike the free radical the carbonium ion carries a positive charge. Neither alkyl free radicals nor alkyl carbonium ions can be isolated and studied directly; we can only infer their momentary existence from the observations we make. The fact that certain more complicated free radicals and carbonium ions are stable and can be studied directly strengthens our belief in the existence of these short-lived particles.

It is not feasible for us to list here the facts on which a particular carbonium ion mechanism is based, and then to show how the mechanism accounts for the facts; to do this would take a large part of several chapters. The carbonium ion theory has a very broad foundation. It is generally accepted because it accounts so well for a great number of observations involving a wide variety of reactions. Taken individually, each observation could perhaps be accounted for in some other way; taken together, these pieces of evidence make the carbonium ion theory one of the most firmly established of organic chemical theories. We shall therefore examine the generally accepted mechanism for the dehydration of alcohols and subsequently, as we encounter various other facts, show how these facts are accounted for by the theory.

4.16 Mechanism of dehydration of alcohols

The generally accepted mechanism for the dehydration of alcohols is summarized in the following equations; for sake of simplicity ethyl alcohol is used as the example.

(1)

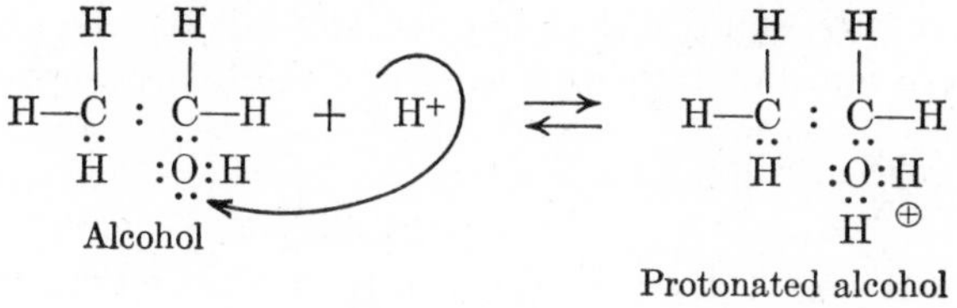

$$
\begin{array}{c}
\underset{\text{Alcohol}}{
\overset{\displaystyle H \quad H}{\underset{\displaystyle H \quad :\overset{..}{\underset{..}{O}}:H}{H-\overset{|}{\underset{|}{C}} : \overset{|}{\underset{|}{C}}-H}}
} + H^+
\end{array}
\rightleftarrows
\underset{\text{Protonated alcohol}}{
\overset{\displaystyle H \quad H}{\underset{\displaystyle H \quad :\overset{..}{O}:H}{\underset{\displaystyle \overset{..}{H} \; \oplus}{H-\overset{|}{\underset{|}{C}} : \overset{|}{\underset{|}{C}}-H}}}
}
$$

(2)

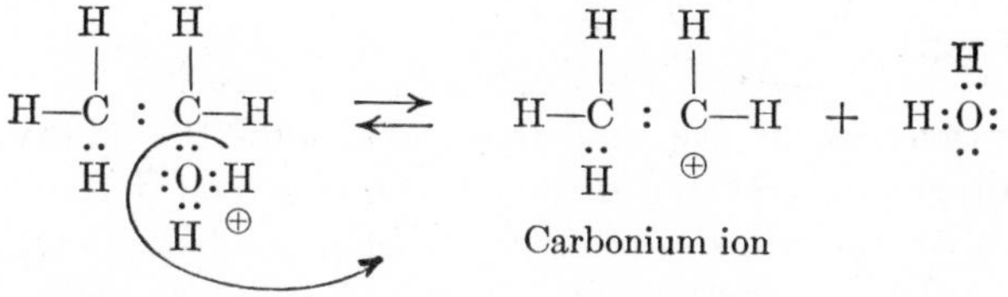

$$
\overset{\displaystyle H \quad H}{\underset{\displaystyle \underset{\displaystyle \overset{..}{H} \; \oplus}{H \quad (:\overset{..}{O}:H}}{H-\overset{|}{\underset{|}{C}} : \overset{|}{\underset{|}{C}}-H}}
\rightleftarrows
\underset{\text{Carbonium ion}}{
\overset{\displaystyle H \quad H}{\underset{\displaystyle \overset{..}{H} \quad \oplus}{H-\overset{|}{\underset{|}{C}} : \overset{|}{\underset{|}{C}}-H}}
} + H:\overset{..}{\underset{..}{O}}:\overset{H}{}
$$

(3)

$$
\overset{\displaystyle H \quad H}{\underset{\displaystyle \underset{\displaystyle H)}{\overset{..}{\underset{..}{C}} \quad \oplus}}{H-\overset{|}{\underset{|}{C}} : \overset{|}{\underset{|}{C}}-H}}
\rightleftarrows
\underset{\text{Alkene}}{
\overset{\displaystyle H \quad H}{H-\overset{|}{\underset{|}{C}} :: \overset{|}{\underset{|}{C}}-H}
} + H^+
$$

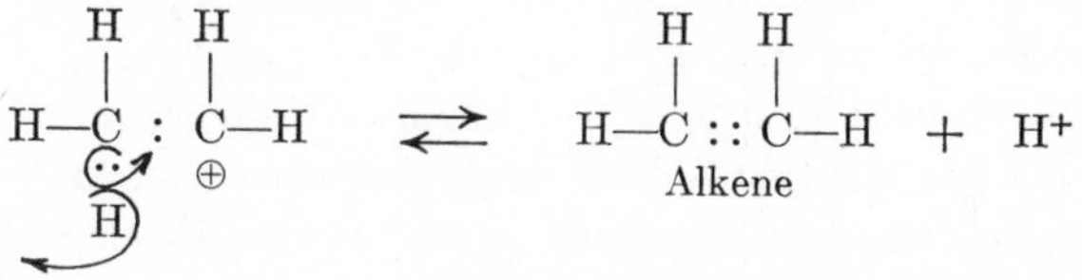

The alcohol unites (step 1) with a hydrogen ion to form the protonated alcohol, which dissociates (step 2) into water and a carbonium ion; the carbonium ion then loses (step 3) a hydrogen ion to form the alkene.

The double bond is thus formed in two stages, —OH being lost (as H_2O) in step (2) and —H being lost in step (3). This is in contrast to dehydrohalogenation (Sec. 4.13), where the halogen and hydrogen are lost simultaneously.

The first step is simply an acid-base equilibrium in the Lowry-Brønsted sense (Sec. 1.17). When sulfuric acid, for example, is dissolved in water, the following reaction occurs.

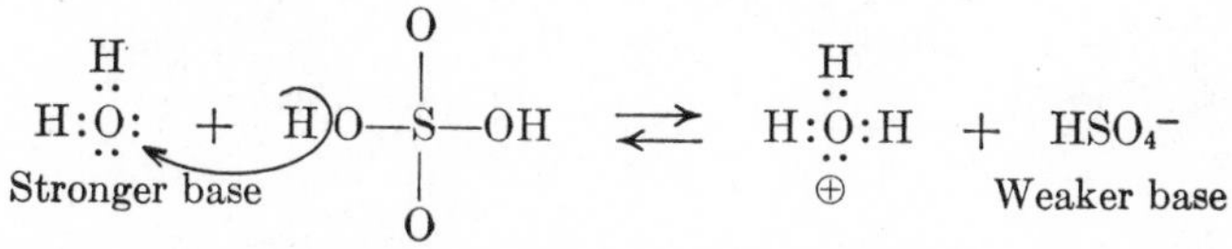

$$
\underset{\text{Stronger base}}{
\overset{\displaystyle H}{H:\overset{..}{\underset{..}{O}}:}
} + \overset{\displaystyle O}{\underset{\displaystyle O}{H)O-\overset{|}{\underset{|}{S}}-OH}}
\rightleftarrows
\underset{\oplus}{
\overset{\displaystyle H}{H:\overset{..}{O}:H}
} + \underset{\text{Weaker base}}{HSO_4^-}
$$

The hydrogen ion is transferred from the very weak base, HSO_4^-, to the stronger base, H_2O, to form the oxonium ion, H_3O^+; the basic properties of each are due, of course, to the unshared electrons which are available for sharing with the hydrogen ion. An alcohol also contains an oxygen atom with unshared electrons and hence displays basicity comparable to that of water. The first step of the mechanism is more properly represented as

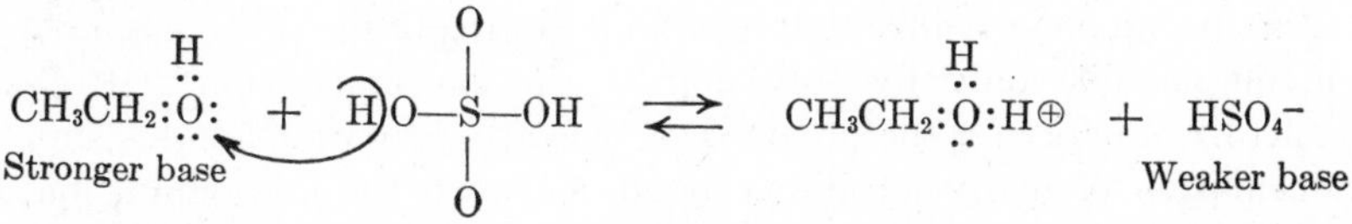

$$
\underset{\text{Stronger base}}{
\overset{\displaystyle H}{CH_3CH_2:\overset{..}{\underset{..}{O}}:}
} + \overset{\displaystyle O}{\underset{\displaystyle O}{H)O-\overset{|}{\underset{|}{S}}-OH}}
\rightleftarrows
\overset{\displaystyle H}{CH_3CH_2:\overset{..}{O}:H\oplus}
+ \underset{\text{Weaker base}}{HSO_4^-}
$$

where the hydrogen ion is transferred from the bisulfate ion to the stronger base, ethyl alcohol, to yield the substituted oxonium ion, $C_2H_5OH_2^+$, the protonated alcohol.

In a similar way, step (3) does not actually involve the expulsion of a naked hydrogen ion, but rather a transfer of the hydrogen ion to a base, say, C_2H_5OH.

$$\underset{\overset{\displaystyle H}{|}}{H-C}:\underset{\overset{\displaystyle H}{|}}{C-H} + C_2H_5OH \rightleftharpoons \underset{\overset{\displaystyle H}{|}}{H-C}::\underset{\overset{\displaystyle H}{|}}{C-H} + C_2H_5OH_2{}^+$$

For convenience we shall frequently show the addition or expulsion of a hydrogen ion, H^+, but it should be understood that in all cases this actually involves the transfer of a proton from one base to another.

All three reactions are shown as equilibria, since each step is readily reversible; as we shall soon see, the exact reverse of this reaction sequence is involved in the formation of alcohols from alkenes (Sec. 5.10). Equilibrium (1) lies very far to the right; sulfuric acid, for example, is known to be nearly completely ionized in alcohol solution. Since there is a very low concentration of carbonium ions present at any time, equilibrium (2) undoubtedly lies very far to the left. Occasionally one of these few carbonium ions undergoes reaction (3) to form the alkene. Under the conditions of dehydration the alkene, being quite volatile, is generally driven from the reaction mixture and thus equilibrium (3) is shifted to the right. As a consequence the entire reaction system is forced toward completion.

The carbonium ion is formed by dissociation of the protonated alcohol; this involves separation of a charged particle, R^+, from a neutral particle, H_2O. It is obvious that this process requires much less energy than would formation of a carbonium ion from the alcohol itself, since the latter process involves separation of a positive particle from a negative particle.

$$ROH_2{}^\oplus \longrightarrow \underset{\text{Weak base}}{R^\oplus + H_2O} \qquad \textit{Easy}$$

$$ROH \longrightarrow \underset{\text{Strong base}}{R^\oplus + OH^-} \qquad \textit{Difficult}$$

Viewed in another way, it is much easier to separate the carbonium ion from the weak base, water, than from the extremely strong base, hydroxide ion. Indeed, the evidence indicates that separation of a hydroxide ion from an alcohol almost never occurs; reactions involving cleavage of the C—O bond of an alcohol seem in nearly every case to require an acidic catalyst, the function of which, as in the present case, is to form the protonated alcohol.

Finally, we must realize that even dissociation of the protonated alcohol is made possible only by solvation of the carbonium ion. (Compare Sec. 4.13.) Energy for the breaking of the carbon–oxygen bond is supplied by formation of many ion-dipole bonds between the carbonium ion and the polar solvent.

As we shall see, a carbonium ion can undergo a number of different reactions; which one occurs depends upon experimental conditions. All reactions of a carbonium ion have a common end: *they provide a pair of electrons to complete the octet of the positively charged carbon.* In the present case, a hydrogen ion is eliminated from the carbon adjacent to the positive, electron-deficient carbon; the pair of electrons formerly shared by this hydrogen are available for formation of a π bond.

$$-\overset{|}{\underset{H}{C}} : \overset{|}{\underset{\oplus}{C}}- \longrightarrow -\overset{|}{C} :: \overset{|}{C}- + H^+$$

We can see how the mechanism accounts for the fact that dehydration is catalyzed by acids. Does the mechanism also account for the fact that the ease with which alcohols undergo dehydration follows the sequence $3° > 2° > 1°$? Before we can answer this question, we must first learn something about the stability of carbonium ions.

4.17 Stability of carbonium ions. Dispersal of charge. Inductive effect

The relative stabilities of free radicals, we have seen (Sec. 3.25), are shown beyond question by the evidence of bond strengths. Our conclusion about relative stabilities of carbonium ions is based on less direct evidence, but is generally believed to be equally valid.

According to the laws of physics, **the stability of a charged system is increased by dispersal of the charge.** Any factor, therefore, that tends to spread out the positive charge of the electron-deficient carbon and distribute it over the rest of the ion must stabilize a carbonium ion.

By definition the distinction among primary, secondary, and tertiary carbonium ions is the number of carbons, and hence the number of alkyl groups, attached to the electron-deficient carbon atom.

| Methyl carbonium ion | Primary carbonium ion | Secondary carbonium ion | Tertiary carbonium ion |

Electron release: *Disperses charge, stabilizes ion*

What is the effect of an alkyl group on the stability of a carbonium ion?

There is much evidence, both physical and chemical, to indicate that, compared with a hydrogen atom, an alkyl group tends to release electrons. An alkyl group attached to the electron-deficient carbon of a carbonium ion tends to release electrons to that carbon and thus to reduce its positive charge; in doing so, the alkyl group itself becomes somewhat positive. This dispersal of the charge stabilizes the carbonium ion.

A tertiary carbonium ion with three alkyl groups is therefore more stable than a secondary with two alkyl groups, which in turn is more stable than a primary with only one; the methyl carbonium ion, with no alkyl groups attached to the electron-deficient carbon, is least stable of all. Among the simple alkyl carbonium ions, the order of stability is:

Stability of carbonium ions $3° > 2° > 1° > CH_3^+$

An effect that is due to the tendency of an atom or a group of atoms to attract or repel electrons is called an **inductive effect.** In the present case we would say that an alkyl group exerts an *electron-releasing inductive effect.*

Other atoms and groups, we shall find, tend to attract electrons, and exert *electron-withdrawing inductive effects.* The presence of an electron-withdrawing atom or group tends to intensify the positive charge on the electron-deficient carbon, and hence makes the carbonium ion less stable.

The **stability of a carbonium ion** *depends chiefly upon the tendency of the attached groups to release or withdraw electrons.*

4.18 Ease of formation of carbonium ions

As we have seen, the ease with which alcohols undergo dehydration follows the sequence $3° > 2° > 1°$. There is evidence that a controlling factor in dehydration is the formation of the carbonium ion, and that one alcohol is dehydrated more easily than another chiefly because it forms a carbonium ion more easily.

Carbonium ions can be formed from compounds other than alcohols, and in reactions other than elimination. In all these cases the evidence indicates that the ease of formation of carbonium ions follows the same sequence:

Ease of formation of carbonium ions $3° > 2° > 1° > CH_3^+$

In listing carbonium ions in order of their ease of formation, we find that we have at the same time listed them in order of their stability. **The more stable the carbonium ion, the more easily it is formed.**

Is it reasonable that the more stable carbonium ion should be formed more easily? To answer this question, we must look at a reaction in which a carbonium ion is formed, and consider the nature of the transition state.

In the dehydration of an alcohol, the carbonium ion is formed by loss of water from the protonated alcohol, ROH_2^+, that is, by breaking of the carbon–oxygen bond. In the reactant the positive charge is mostly on oxygen, and in the product it is on carbon. In the transition state, the C—O bond must be partly broken, oxygen having partly pulled the electron pair away from carbon. The positive charge originally on oxygen is now divided between carbon and oxygen. Carbon has partly gained the positive charge it is to carry in the final carbonium ion.

$$ R{:}OH_2^+ \longrightarrow \left[\overset{\delta_+}{R} {-}{-}{-} \overset{\delta_+}{:}OH_2 \right] \longrightarrow R^+ + {:}OH_2 $$

Reactant	Transition state	Products
Oxygen	*Carbon and oxygen*	*Carbon*
has full	*have partial*	*has full*
positive charge	*positive charges*	*positive charge*

Electron-releasing groups tend to disperse the partial positive charge (δ_+) developing on carbon, and in this way stabilize the transition state.

Stabilization of the transition state lowers E_{act} and permits a faster reaction (see Figure 4.7).

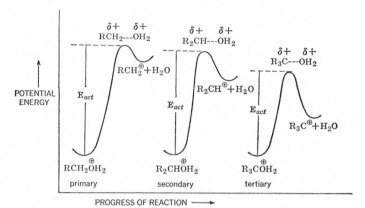

FIGURE 4.7. Molecular structure and rate of reaction. Stability of transition state parallels stability of carbonium ion: more stable carbonium ion formed faster.

Thus the same factor, electron release, that stabilizes the carbonium ion also stabilizes the *incipient* carbonium ion in the transition state. The more stable carbonium ion is formed faster.

We shall return again and again to the relationship between inductive effect and dispersal of charge, and between dispersal of charge and stability. We shall find that these relationships will help us to understand carbonium ion reactions of many kinds, and, in fact, all reactions in which a charge — positive or negative — develops or disappears. These will include reactions as seemingly different from dehydration of alcohols as: addition to alkenes; aromatic and aliphatic substitution; rearrangements; acidity and basicity.

4.19 Orientation of elimination: ease of formation of alkenes

One further aspect of elimination remains to be discussed: *orientation*. In cases where a mixture of isomeric alkenes can be formed, which isomer, if any, will predominate?

Study of many elimination reactions — involving both dehydrohalogenation and dehydration — has shown that one isomer generally does predominate, and that it is usually possible to predict which isomer this will be, on the basis of molecular structure.

The following examples are typical of dehydrohalogenation; dehydration follows a similar pattern, with an even greater predominance of the preferred product.

$$CH_3CH_2CHBrCH_3 \xrightarrow{KOH(alc)} CH_3CH=CHCH_3 \quad \text{and} \quad CH_3CH_2CH=CH_2$$
$$\qquad\qquad\qquad\qquad\qquad\qquad\quad 81\% \qquad\qquad\qquad\qquad 19\%$$

$$CH_3CH_2CH_2CHBrCH_3 \xrightarrow{KOH(alc)} CH_3CH_2CH=CHCH_3 \,\text{and}\, CH_3CH_2CH_2CH=CH_2$$
$$\qquad\qquad\qquad\qquad\qquad\qquad\qquad 71\% \qquad\qquad\qquad\qquad 29\%$$

$$\underset{CH_3CH_2\overset{\overset{\textstyle CH_3}{|}}{C}BrCH_3}{} \xrightarrow{KOH(alc)} \underset{71\%}{CH_3CH=\overset{\overset{\textstyle CH_3}{|}}{C}CH_3} \text{ and } \underset{29\%}{CH_3CH_2\overset{\overset{\textstyle CH_3}{|}}{C}=CH_2}$$

In each case, the preferred product is the alkene that has the greater number of alkyl groups attached to the doubly-bonded carbon atoms.

Ease of formation of alkenes:

$$R_2C=CR_2 > R_2C=CHR > R_2C=CH_2, \ RCH=CHR > RCH=CH_2$$

In Sec. 5.4 we shall find evidence that the stability of alkenes follows exactly the same sequence.

Stability of alkenes:

$$R_2C=CR_2 > R_2C=CHR > R_2C=CH_2, \ RCH=CHR > RCH=CH_2 > CH_2=CH_2$$

In dehydrohalogenation and dehydration, the more stable the alkene the more easily it is formed.

Alkene stability not only determines *orientation* of elimination but also is an important factor in *reactivity* toward elimination (Sec. 6.11). This is true not only for eliminations in which simple alkenes are formed but also for nearly every case where a carbon–carbon double bond is generated in a molecule (Secs. 9.21 and 23.16).

Examination of the transition states involved shows that it is reasonable that the more stable alkene should be formed faster:

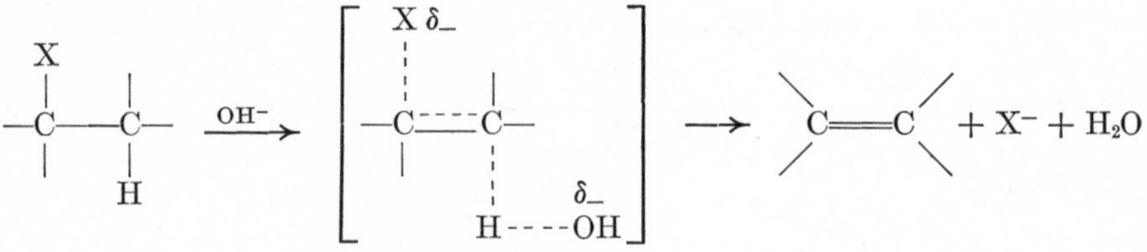

Transition state:
*partly formed
double bond*

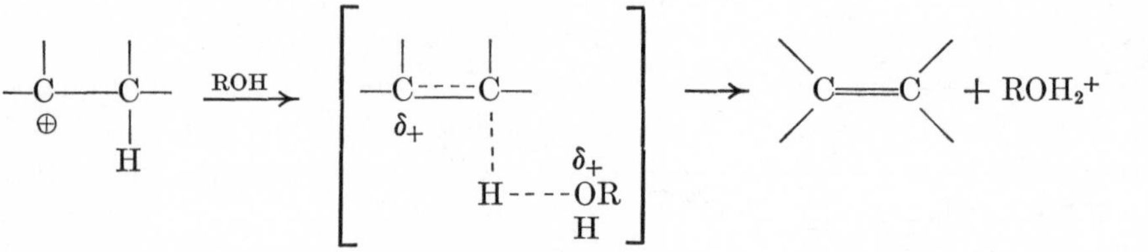

Transition state:
*partly formed
double bond*

Factors that stabilize an alkene also stabilize an *incipient* alkene in the transition state.

Problem 4.6 Predict the *major* product of each dehydrohalogenation in Problem 4.4, page 113.

Problem 4.7   Predict the *major* product of dehydration of each of the following:
(a) $(CH_3)_2C(OH)CH_2CH_3$; (b) $(CH_3)_2CHCHOHCH_3$; (c) $(CH_3)_2C(OH)CH(CH_3)_2$.

PROBLEMS

1. Give the structural formula for:

(a) 2,3-dimethyl-2-butene
(b) 3-chloropropene
(c) *cis*-2-methyl-3-heptene

(d) 3,6-dimethyl-1-octene
(e) 2,4,4-trimethyl-2-pentene
(f) *trans*-3,4-dimethyl-3-hexene

2. Give the structural formula and IUPAC name for:

(a) isobutylene
(b) *cis-sym*-diethylethylene
(c) *tert*-butylethylene

(d) *trans-sym*-diisopropylethylene
(e) *sec*-butylethylene
(f) *unsym*-diethylethylene

3. Indicate which of the following compounds show geometric (*cis-trans*) isomerism, and draw the isomeric structures:

(a) 1-butene
(b) 2-butene
(c) 1,1-dichloroethene
(d) 1,2-dichloroethene
(e) 2-methyl-2-butene
(f) 1-pentene

(g) 2-pentene
(h) 1-chloropropene
(i) 1-chloro-2-methyl-2-butene
(j) 3-methyl-4-ethyl-3-hexene
(k) 2,4-hexadiene $(CH_3CH\!=\!CHCH\!=\!CHCH_3)$

4. There are 13 isomeric hexylenes (C_6H_{12}) disregarding geometric isomerism. (a) Draw the structure and give the IUPAC name for each. (b) Indicate which ones show geometric isomerism, and draw the isomeric structures.

5. In which of the following will *cis*-3-hexene differ from *trans*-3-hexene?

(a) b.p.
(b) m.p.
(c) adsorption on alumina
(d) infrared spectrum
(e) dipole moment

(f) refractive index
(g) rate of hydrogenation
(h) product of hydrogenation
(i) solubility in ethyl alcohol
(j) density

(k) Which *one* of the above would absolutely prove the configuration of each isomer?

6. Write balanced equations for the preparation of propylene from:

(a) $CH_3CH_2CH_2OH$ (*n*-propyl alcohol)
(b) $CH_3CHOHCH_3$ (isopropyl alcohol)
(c) isopropyl chloride
(d) propylene bromide (1,2-dibromopropane)

7. Which alcohol of each pair would you expect to be more easily dehydrated?

(a) $CH_3CH_2CH_2CH_2CH_2OH$ or $CH_3CH_2CH_2CHOHCH_3$
(b) $(CH_3)_2C(OH)CH_2CH_3$ or $(CH_3)_2CHCHOHCH_3$
(c) $(CH_3)_2CHC(OH)(CH_3)_2$ or $(CH_3)_2CHCH(CH_3)CH_2OH$

8. Give structures of the products expected from dehydrohalogenation of:

(a) 1-bromohexane
(b) 2-bromohexane
(c) 1-bromo-2-methylpentane
(d) 2-bromo-2-methylpentane

(e) 3-bromo-2-methylpentane
(f) 4-bromo-2-methylpentane
(g) 1-bromo-4-methylpentane
(h) 3-bromo-2,3-dimethylpentane

9. In those cases in Problem 8 where more than one product can be formed. predict the *major* product.

10. (a) Show all steps in the synthesis of propylene from propane by ordinary laboratory methods (*not* cracking). (b) If the steps in (a) were carried out starting with *n*-butane, would a single product or a mixture be expected?

Chapter five

ALKENES II. REACTIONS OF THE CARBON–CARBON DOUBLE BOND

5.1 The functional group

The characteristic feature of the alkene structure is the carbon–carbon double bond. The characteristic reactions of an alkene are those that take place at the double bond. *The atom or group of atoms that defines the structure of a particular family of organic compounds and, at the same time, determines their properties is called the* **functional group.**

In alkyl halides the functional group is the halogen atom, and in alcohols the —OH group; in alkenes it is the carbon–carbon double bond. We must not forget that an alkyl halide, alcohol, or alkene has alkyl groups attached to these functional groups; under the proper conditions, the alkyl portions of these molecules undergo the reactions typical of alkanes. However, the reactions that are *characteristic* of each of these compounds are those that occur at the halogen atom or the hydroxyl group or the carbon–carbon double bond.

A large part of organic chemistry is therefore the chemistry of the various functional groups. We shall learn to associate a particular set of properties with a particular group wherever we may find it. When we encounter a complicated molecule, which contains a number of different functional groups, we may expect the properties of this molecule to be roughly a composite of the properties of the various functional groups. The properties of a particular group may be modified, of course, by the presence of another group and it is important for us to understand these modifications, but our point of departure is the chemistry of individual functional groups.

5.2 Reactions of the carbon–carbon double bond: addition

Alkene chemistry is the chemistry of the carbon–carbon double bond.

What kind of reaction may we expect of the double bond? The double bond consists of a strong σ bond and a weak π bond; we might expect, therefore, that reaction would involve the breaking of this weaker bond. This expectation is correct: the typical reactions of the double bond are of the sort,

$$-\overset{\displaystyle |}{\underset{\displaystyle |}{C}}=\overset{\displaystyle |}{\underset{\displaystyle |}{C}}-\;+\;YZ\;\longrightarrow\;-\overset{\displaystyle |}{\underset{\displaystyle |}{\underset{\displaystyle Y}{C}}}-\overset{\displaystyle |}{\underset{\displaystyle |}{\underset{\displaystyle Z}{C}}}-\qquad\textbf{Addition}$$

where the π bond is broken and two strong σ bonds are formed in its place.

A reaction in which two molecules combine to yield a single molecule of product is called an **addition reaction.** The reagent is simply *added to* the organic molecule, in contrast to a substitution reaction where part of the reagent is *substituted for* a portion of the organic molecule. Addition reactions are necessarily limited to compounds that contain atoms sharing more than one pair of electrons, that is, to compounds that contain multiply-bonded atoms.

What kind of reagent may we expect to add to the carbon–carbon double bond? In our structure of the bond there is a cloud of π electrons above and below the plane of the atoms (see Figure 5.1).

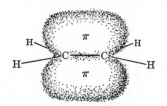

FIGURE 5.1. Carbon–carbon double bond: π bond is source of electrons.

These π electrons are less involved than the σ electrons in holding together the carbon nuclei. As a result, they are themselves held less tightly. These loosely held π electrons are particularly available to a reagent that is seeking electrons. It is not surprising, then, that in most of its reactions the carbon–carbon double bond serves as a **source of electrons:** that is, it acts as a **base.** The compounds with which it chiefly reacts are those that are deficient in electrons, that is, are *acids.* *These acidic, electron-seeking reagents are called* **electrophilic reagents** (from the Greek, electron-loving). *The typical reaction of an alkene is* **electrophilic addition,** or in other words, addition of acidic reagents.

Most alkenes contain not only the carbon–carbon double bond but also alkyl groups, which have essentially the alkane structure. Besides the electrophilic addition characteristic of the carbon–carbon double bond, therefore, alkenes may undergo the free radical substitution characteristic of alkanes. The most important of these addition and substitution reactions are summarized below, and will be discussed in detail in following sections.

The alkyl groups attached to the doubly-bonded carbons modify the reactions of the double bond; the double bond modifies the reactions of the alkyl groups. We shall be concerned with seeing what these modifications are, and where possible how they can be accounted for.

REACTIONS OF ALKENES
Addition Reactions

$$-\overset{|}{C}=\overset{|}{C}- \;+\; YZ \;\longrightarrow\; -\overset{|}{\underset{Y}{C}}-\overset{|}{\underset{Z}{C}}-$$

1. Addition of hydrogen

$$-\overset{|}{C}=\overset{|}{C}- \;+\; H_2 \;\xrightarrow{\text{Pt, Ni, Pd}}\; -\overset{|}{\underset{H}{C}}-\overset{|}{\underset{H}{C}}-$$

Example:

$$CH_3CH=CH_2 \;\xrightarrow{\;H_2,\ Ni\;}\; CH_3CH_2CH_3$$

Propene   Propane
(Propylene)

2. Addition of halogens

$$-\overset{|}{C}=\overset{|}{C}- \;+\; X_2 \;\longrightarrow\; -\overset{|}{\underset{X}{C}}-\overset{|}{\underset{X}{C}}- \qquad X_2 = Cl_2,\ Br_2$$

Example:

$$CH_3CH=CH_2 \;\xrightarrow{\;Br_2\ in\ CCl_4\;}\; CH_3CHBrCH_2Br$$

Propene   1,2-Dibromopropane
(Propylene)   (Propylene bromide)

3. Addition of hydrogen halides

$$-\overset{|}{C}=\overset{|}{C}- \;+\; HX \;\longrightarrow\; -\overset{|}{\underset{H}{C}}-\overset{|}{\underset{X}{C}}- \qquad HX = HCl,\ HBr,\ HI$$

Examples:

$$CH_3CH=CH_2 \;\xrightarrow{\;HI\;}\; CH_3CHICH_3$$

Propene   2-Iodopropane
(Isopropyl iodide)

$$CH_3CH=CH_2 \;\xrightarrow{\;HBr\;}\;$$

Propene

     $\xrightarrow{\text{no peroxides}}$ $CH_3CHBrCH_3$ **Markovnikov addition**
                2-Bromopropane
                (Isopropyl bromide)

     $\xrightarrow{\text{peroxides}}$ $CH_3CH_2CH_2Br$ **Anti-Markovnikov addition**
                1-Bromopropane
                (*n*-Propyl bromide)

4. Addition of sulfuric acid

$$-\overset{|}{C}=\overset{|}{C}- \;+\; H_2SO_4 \;\longrightarrow\; -\overset{|}{\underset{H}{C}}-\overset{|}{\underset{OSO_3H}{C}}-$$

Example:

$$CH_3CH=CH_2 \;\xrightarrow{\;conc.\ H_2SO_4\;}\; CH_3\underset{OSO_3H}{CHCH_3}$$

Propene

Isopropyl hydrogen sulfate

5. Addition of water. Hydration

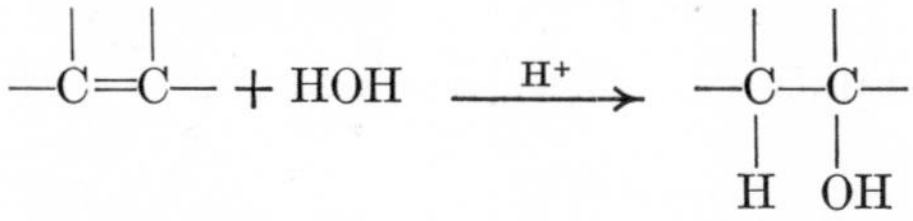

$$-\overset{|}{C}=\overset{|}{C}- + HOH \xrightarrow{H^+} -\overset{|}{\underset{H}{C}}-\overset{|}{\underset{OH}{C}}-$$

Example:

$$CH_3CH=CH_2 \xrightarrow{H_2O,\ H^+} CH_3\underset{OH}{CH}CH_3$$

Propene   Isopropyl alcohol
(2-Propanol)

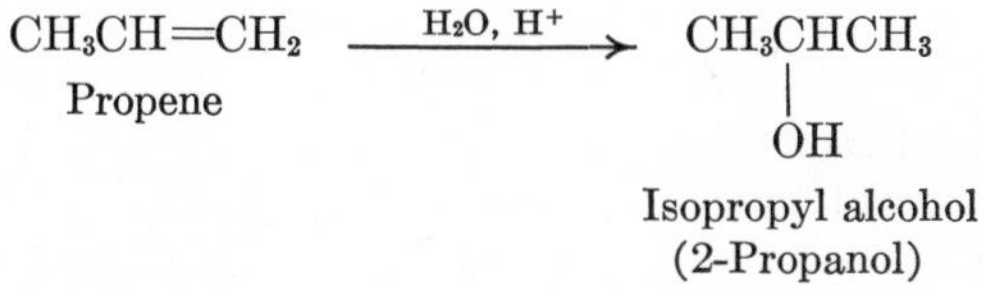

6. Halohydrin formation

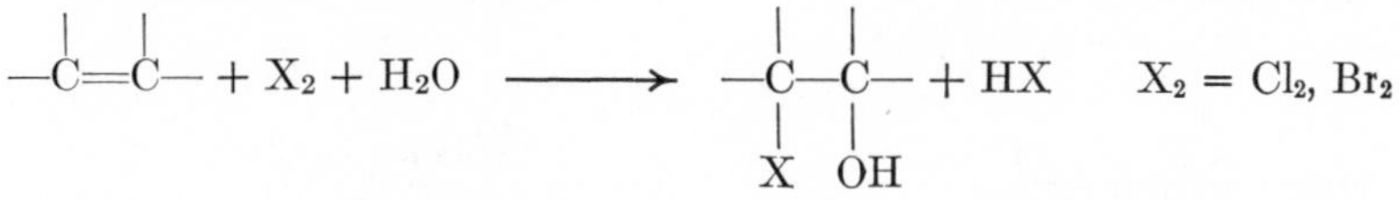

$$-\overset{|}{C}=\overset{|}{C}- + X_2 + H_2O \longrightarrow -\overset{|}{\underset{X}{C}}-\overset{|}{\underset{OH}{C}}- + HX \qquad X_2 = Cl_2,\ Br_2$$

Example:

$$CH_3CH=CH_2 \xrightarrow{Cl_2,\ H_2O} CH_3\underset{OH}{CH}-\underset{Cl}{CH_2}$$

Propylene   Propylene chlorohydrin
(Propene)   (1-Chloro-2-propanol)

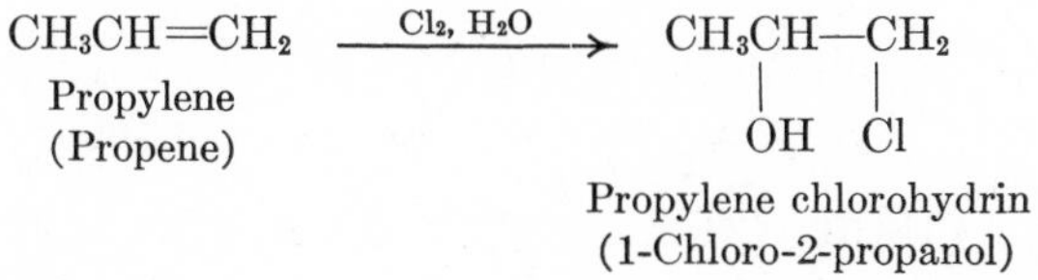

7. Dimerization

Example:

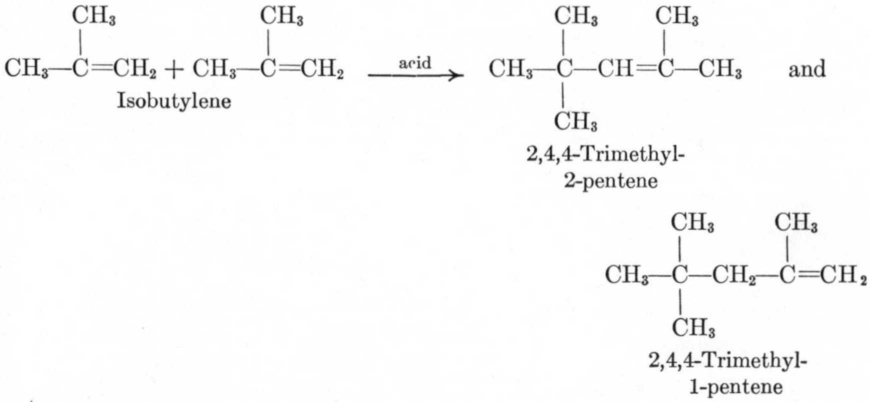

$$CH_3-\overset{\overset{CH_3}{|}}{C}=CH_2 + CH_3-\overset{\overset{CH_3}{|}}{C}=CH_2 \xrightarrow{acid} CH_3-\overset{\overset{CH_3}{|}}{\underset{\underset{CH_3}{|}}{C}}-CH=\overset{\overset{CH_3}{|}}{C}-CH_3 \quad and$$

Isobutylene   2,4,4-Trimethyl-
2-pentene

$$CH_3-\overset{\overset{CH_3}{|}}{\underset{\underset{CH_3}{|}}{C}}-CH_2-\overset{\overset{CH_3}{|}}{C}=CH_2$$

2,4,4-Trimethyl-
1-pentene

8. Alkylation

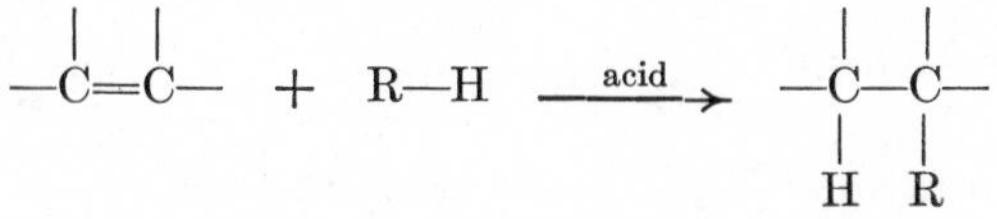

$$-\overset{|}{C}=\overset{|}{C}- + R-H \xrightarrow{acid} -\overset{|}{\underset{H}{C}}-\overset{|}{\underset{R}{C}}-$$

Example:

$$CH_3-\overset{\overset{CH_3}{|}}{C}=CH_2 + CH_3-\overset{\overset{CH_3}{|}}{\underset{\underset{CH_3}{|}}{C}}-H \xrightarrow{H_2SO_4} CH_3-\overset{\overset{CH_3}{|}}{\underset{\underset{H}{|}}{C}}-CH_2-\overset{\overset{CH_3}{|}}{\underset{\underset{CH_3}{|}}{C}}-CH_3$$

Isobutylene   Isobutane   2,2,4-Trimethylpentane

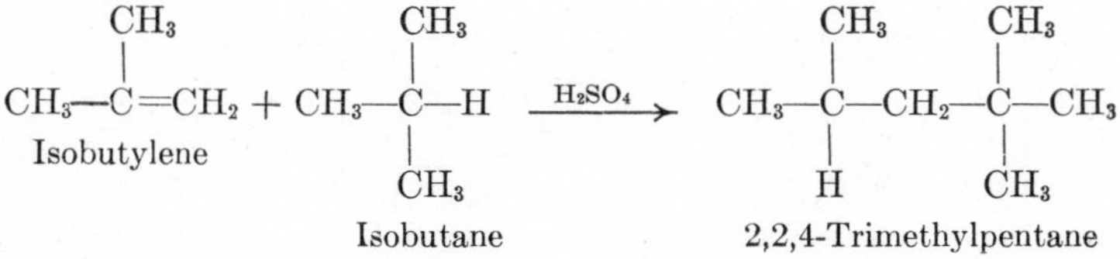

9. Hydroxylation. Glycol formation

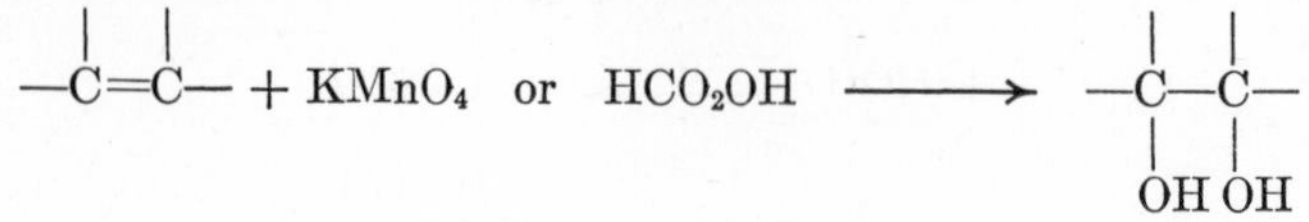

$$-\overset{|}{C}=\overset{|}{C}- + KMnO_4 \quad \text{or} \quad HCO_2OH \longrightarrow -\overset{|}{\underset{OH}{C}}-\overset{|}{\underset{OH}{C}}-$$

Example:

$$CH_3CH=CH_2 \xrightarrow{KMnO_4 \text{ or } HCO_2OH} CH_3-\overset{|}{\underset{OH}{CH}}-\overset{|}{\underset{OH}{CH_2}}$$

Propylene
(Propene)

Propylene glycol
(1,2-Propanediol)

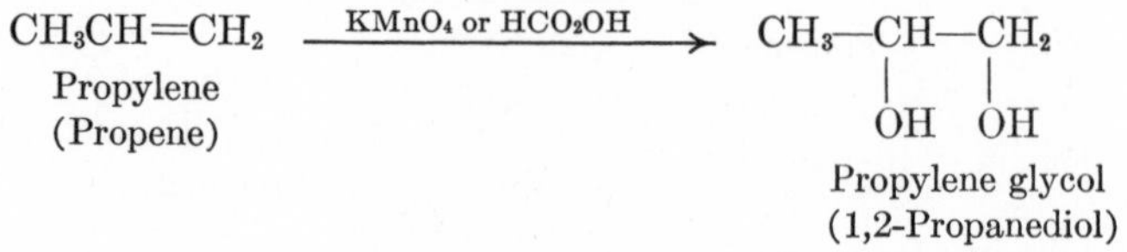

10. Polymerization. Discussed in Secs. 6.20–6.23.

Substitution Reactions

11. Halogenation

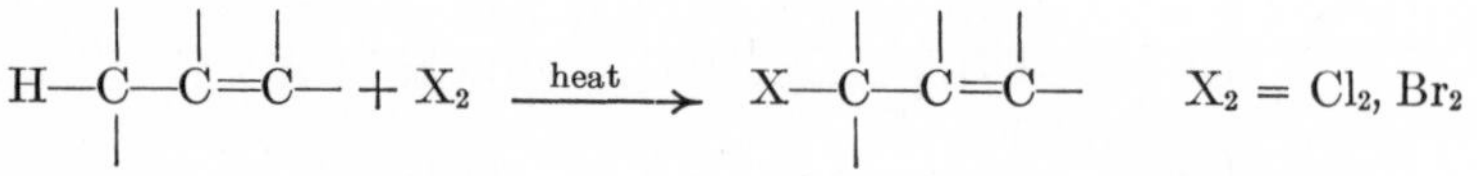

$$H-\overset{|}{C}-\overset{|}{C}=\overset{|}{C}- + X_2 \xrightarrow{heat} X-\overset{|}{C}-\overset{|}{C}=\overset{|}{C}- \quad X_2 = Cl_2, Br_2$$

Example:

$$CH_3CH=CH_2 \xrightarrow{Cl_2,\ 600°} Cl-CH_2CH=CH_2$$

Propylene
(Propene)

Allyl chloride
(3-Chloro-1-propene)

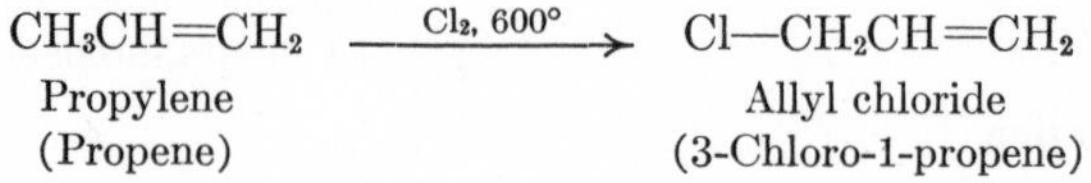

Cleavage Reactions

12. Ozonolysis

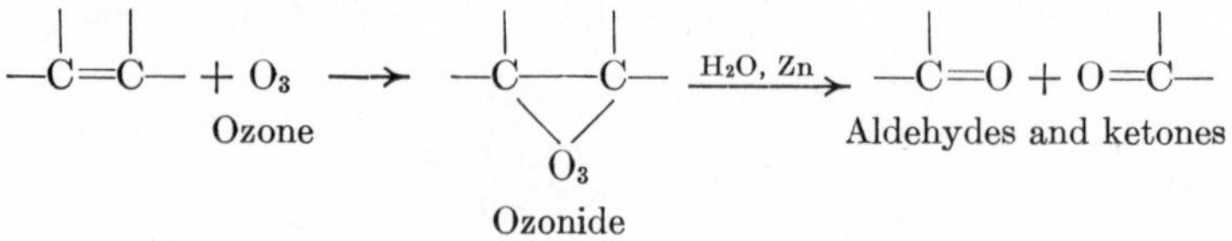

$$-\overset{|}{C}=\overset{|}{C}- + O_3 \longrightarrow -\overset{|}{C}-\overset{|}{\underset{O_3}{C}}- \xrightarrow{H_2O,\ Zn} -\overset{|}{C}=O + O=\overset{|}{C}-$$

Ozone

Ozonide

Aldehydes and ketones

Used to determine structure

Examples:

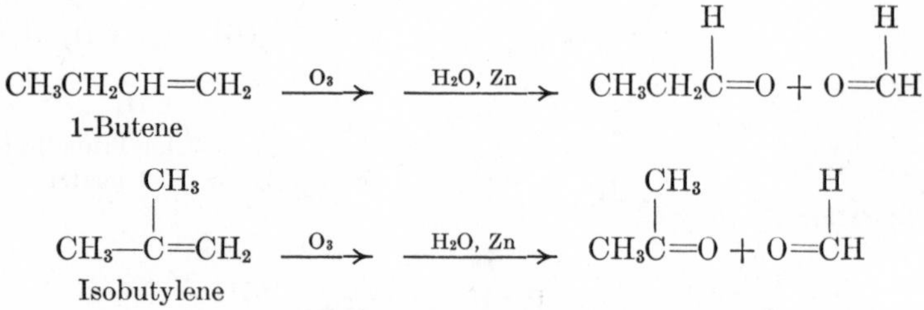

$$CH_3CH_2CH=CH_2 \xrightarrow{O_3} \xrightarrow{H_2O,\ Zn} CH_3CH_2\overset{H}{\underset{}{C}}=O + O=\overset{H}{\underset{}{CH}}$$

1-Butene

$$CH_3-\overset{CH_3}{\underset{}{C}}=CH_2 \xrightarrow{O_3} \xrightarrow{H_2O,\ Zn} CH_3\overset{CH_3}{\underset{}{C}}=O + O=\overset{H}{\underset{}{CH}}$$

Isobutylene

5.3 Hydrogenation. Heat of hydrogenation

We have already encountered this reaction as the most useful method for preparing alkanes (Sec. 3.15). It is not limited to the synthesis of alkanes, but is a general method for the conversion of a carbon–carbon double bond into a carbon–carbon single bond: using the same apparatus, the same catalyst, and very nearly the same conditions, we can convert an alkene into an alkane, an unsaturated alcohol to a saturated alcohol, or an unsaturated ester to a saturated ester. Since the reaction is generally quantitative, and since the volume of hydrogen consumed can be easily measured, hydrogenation is frequently used as an analytical tool; it can, for example, tell us the number of double bonds in a compound.

Hydrogenation involves the breaking of a π bond (about 40 kcal) and a H—H bond (103 kcal), and the formation of two C—H bonds (average value, 87 kcal); the net result is the evolution of about 31 kcal.

$$
\underset{(\pi\ \text{bond}\ =\ 40)}{-\overset{|}{C}=\overset{|}{C}-} + \underset{(103)}{H-H} \longrightarrow \underset{\substack{\\ (2 \times 87)}}{-\overset{|}{\underset{H}{C}}-\overset{|}{\underset{H}{C}}-} \qquad \Delta H = -31\ \text{kcal}
$$

TABLE 5.1

HEATS OF HYDROGENATION OF ALKENES

Alkene	Heat of hydrogenation, kcal/mole
Ethylene	32.8
Propylene	30.1
1-Butene	30.3
1-Pentene	30.1
1-Heptene	30.1
3-Methyl-1-butene	30.3
3,3-Dimethyl-1-butene	30.3
4,4-Dimethyl-1-pentene	29.5
cis-2-Butene	28.6
trans-2-Butene	27.6
Isobutylene	28.4
cis-2-Pentene	28.6
trans-2-Pentene	27.6
2-Methyl-1-butene	28.5
2,3-Dimethyl-1-butene	28.0
2-Methyl-2-butene	26.9
2,3-Dimethyl-2-butene	26.6

The quantity of heat evolved when one mole of an unsaturated compound is hydrogenated is called the **heat of hydrogenation;** *it is simply ΔH of the reaction, but the minus sign is not included.* The heat of hydrogenation of nearly every alkene is fairly close to this approximate value of 31 kcal for each double bond in the compound (see Table 5.1).

Although hydrogenation is an exothermic reaction, it proceeds at a negligible rate in the absence of a catalyst even at elevated temperatures. The uncatalyzed reaction must have, therefore, a very large energy of activation. The function of the catalyst is to lower the energy of activation (E_{act}) so that the reaction can proceed rapidly at room temperature. The catalyst does not, of course, affect the net energy change of the over-all reaction; it simply lowers the energy hill between the reactants and products (see Figure 5.2).

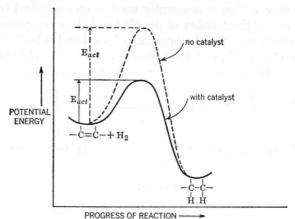

FIGURE 5.2. Potential energy changes during progress of reaction: effect of catalyst.

A catalyst lowers E_{act} by permitting reaction to take place in a different way, that is, by a different mechanism. In this case, the reactants are adsorbed on the enormous surface of the finely divided metal, where reaction actually occurs. Reaction between the adsorbed molecules is very different from the reaction that would have to take place otherwise; it is believed, for example, that the catalytic surface breaks the π bond of the alkene prior to reaction with hydrogen.

Lowering the energy hill, as we can see, decreases the energy of activation of the reverse reaction as well, and thus increases the rate of *de*hydrogenation. We might expect, therefore, that platinum, palladium, and nickel, under the proper conditions, should serve as dehydrogenation catalysts; this is indeed the case. We are familiar with the fact that, while a catalyst speeds up a reaction, it does not shift the position of equilibrium; this is, of course, because it speeds up both the forward and the reverse reactions. (See Sec. 31.7.)

Like hydrogenation, the addition of other reagents to the double bond is generally exothermic. The energy consumed by the breaking of the Y—Z and π bonds is almost always less than that liberated by formation of the C—Y and C—Z bonds.

$$\overset{|\quad\;|}{-C=C-} + Y-Z \longrightarrow \overset{|\quad\;|}{\underset{Y\quad Z}{-C-C-}} + \text{heat}$$

5.4 Heat of hydrogenation and stability of alkenes

Heats of hydrogenation can often give us valuable information about the relative stabilities of unsaturated compounds. For example, of the isomeric 2-butenes, the *cis*-isomer has a heat of hydrogenation of 28.6

kcal, the *trans*-isomer one of 27.6 kcal. Both reactions consume one mole of hydrogen and yield the same product, *n*-butane. Therefore, if the *trans*-isomer *evolves* 1 kcal less energy than the *cis*-isomer, it can only mean that it *contains* 1 kcal less energy; in other words, the *trans*-isomer is *more stable* by 1 kcal than the *cis*-isomer (see Figure 5.3). In a similar way,

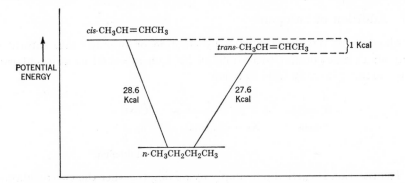

FIGURE 5.3. Heats of hydrogenation and stability: *cis*- and *trans*-2-butene.

trans-2-pentene (heat of hydrogenation = 27.6 kcal) must be more stable by 1.0 kcal than *cis*-2-pentene (heat of hydrogenation = 28.6 kcal).

Of simple disubstituted ethylenes it is usually the *trans*-isomer that is the more stable. The two larger substituents are located farther apart than in the *cis*-isomer; there is less crowding, and less non-bonded interaction (Sec. 3.3).

Heats of hydrogenation show that the stability of an alkene also depends upon the position of the double bond. The following examples are typical:

$CH_3CH_2CH{=}CH_2$ $CH_3CH{=}CHCH_3$ (*cis*- or *trans*-)
30.3 kcal   28.6 or 27.6

$CH_3CH_2CH_2CH{=}CH_2$ $CH_3CH_2CH{=}CHCH_3$ (*cis*- or *trans*-)
30.1 kcal   28.6 or 27.6

$\overset{\displaystyle CH_3}{\underset{\displaystyle}{|}}$
$CH_3CHCH{=}CH_2$ $CH_2{=}CCH_2CH_3$ $CH_3C{=}CHCH_3$
30.3 kcal   28.5   26.9

Each set of isomeric alkenes yields the same alkane. The differences in heat of hydrogenation must therefore be due to differences in stability. In each case, **the greater the number of alkyl groups attached to the doubly-bonded carbon atoms, the more stable the alkene.**

Stability of alkenes

$R_2C{=}CR_2 > R_2C{=}CHR > R_2C{=}CH_2, RCH{=}CHR > RCH{=}CH_2 > CH_2{=}CH_2$

We have seen in Sec. 4.19 that the stability of alkenes determines orientation in dehydrohalogenation and dehydration.

Problem 5.1 (a) Write a balanced equation for combustion of 1-butene. (b) How does this equation compare with the corresponding one for *cis*-2-butene? For *trans*-2-butene? (c) The following heats of combustion have been measured for these three butenes: 648.1, 647.1, 649.8 kcal. Which heat of combustion do you think applies to each butene? (d) Assign the following heats of combustion to 1-pentene, and *cis*- and *trans*-2-pentene: 804.3, 806.9, 805.3.

5.5 Addition of halogens

Alkenes are readily converted by chlorine or bromine into saturated compounds that contain two atoms of halogen attached to adjacent carbons; iodine generally fails to react.

$$\underset{\text{Alkene}}{-\overset{|}{C}=\overset{|}{C}-} + \underset{(X_2 = Cl_2, Br_2)}{X_2} \longrightarrow \underset{\underset{\text{Vicinal dihalide}}{X\ \ X}}{-\overset{|}{\underset{|}{C}}-\overset{|}{\underset{|}{C}}-}$$

The reaction is carried out simply by mixing together the two reactants, usually in an inert solvent like carbon tetrachloride. The addition proceeds rapidly at room temperature or below, and does not require exposure to ultraviolet light; in fact, we deliberately avoid higher temperatures and undue exposure to light, as well as the presence of excess halogen, since under those conditions substitution might become an important side reaction.

This reaction is by far the best method of preparing **vicinal dihalides.** For example:

$$\underset{\substack{\text{Ethene}\\\text{(Ethylene)}}}{CH_2=CH_2} + Br_2 \xrightarrow{CCl_4} \underset{\substack{Br\ \ \ \ Br\\\text{1,2-Dibromoethane}\\\text{(Ethylene bromide)}}}{CH_2-CH_2}$$

$$\underset{\substack{\text{Propene}\\\text{(Propylene)}}}{CH_3CH=CH_2} + Br_2 \xrightarrow{CCl_4} \underset{\substack{Br\ \ \ \ Br\\\text{1,2-Dibromopropane}\\\text{(Propylene bromide)}}}{CH_3-CH-CH_2}$$

$$\underset{\substack{\text{2-Methylpropene}\\\text{(Isobutylene)}}}{\overset{\overset{\displaystyle CH_3}{|}}{CH_3-C=CH_2}} + Br_2 \xrightarrow{CCl_4} \underset{\substack{Br\ \ Br\\\text{1,2-Dibromo-2-methylpropane}\\\text{(Isobutylene bromide)}}}{\overset{\overset{\displaystyle CH_3}{|}}{CH_3-C-CH_2}}$$

Addition of bromine is extremely useful for detection of the carbon–carbon double bond. A solution of bromine in carbon tetrachloride is red; the dihalide, like the alkene, is colorless. Rapid decolorization of a bromine solution is characteristic of compounds containing the carbon–carbon double bond. (However, see Sec. 5.23.)

A common method of naming alkene derivatives is illustrated here. As we see, the product of the reaction between ethylene and bromine has the IUPAC name of 1,2-dibromoethane. It is also frequently called *ethylene bromide*, the word *ethylene* forming part of the name even though the compound is actually saturated. This is an old-fashioned name, and is meant to indicate the product of the reaction between ethylene and bromine, just as, for example, *sodium bromide* would indicate the product of the reaction between sodium and bromine. It should not be confused with the different compound, 1,2-dibromoethene, $BrCH = CHBr$. In a similar way, we have *propylene bromide, isobutylene bromide*, etc.

We shall shortly encounter other saturated compounds that are named in a similar way, e.g., *ethylene bromohydrin, ethylene glycol*, etc. These names have in common the use of two words, the first of which is the name of the alkene; in this way they can be recognized as applying to compounds no longer containing the double bond.

5.6 Addition of hydrogen halides. Markovnikov's rule

An alkene is converted by hydrogen chloride, hydrogen bromide, or hydrogen iodide into the corresponding alkyl halide.

$$-\underset{\text{Alkene}}{C}=C- \quad + \quad \underset{\text{(HX = HCl, HBr, HI)}}{HX} \longrightarrow \quad -\underset{\underset{\text{Alkyl halide}}{H \quad X}}{C}-C-$$

The reaction is frequently carried out by passing the dry gaseous hydrogen halide directly into the alkene. Sometimes the moderately polar solvent, acetic acid, which will dissolve both the polar hydrogen halide and the non-polar alkene, is used. The familiar aqueous solutions of the hydrogen halides are not generally used; in part, this is to avoid the addition of water to the alkene (Sec. 5.9).

Problem 5.2 (a) What is the acid in an aqueous solution of HBr? In dry HBr? (b) Which is the stronger acid? (c) Which can better transfer a hydrogen ion to an alkene?

In this way, ethylene is converted into an ethyl halide, the hydrogen becoming attached to one doubly-bonded carbon and the halogen to the other.

$$\underset{\text{Ethylene}}{CH_2 = CH_2} + HI \longrightarrow \underset{\text{Ethyl iodide}}{CH_3CH_2I}$$

Propylene could yield either of two products, the *n*-propyl halide **or** the isopropyl halide, depending upon the orientation of addition, that is, depending upon which carbon atoms the hydrogen and halogen become attached to. Actually, it is found that the isopropyl halide greatly **pre**dominates.

$$CH_3-CH=CH_2 \quad \xrightarrow{\quad\times\quad} \quad CH_3-CH-CH_2$$

$$\overset{(\quad\quad)}{H-I} \qquad\qquad\qquad \overset{|\quad|}{H\quad I}$$

n-Propyl iodide

$$CH_3-CH=CH_2 \quad \longrightarrow \quad CH_3-CH-CH_2 \qquad \textit{Actual product}$$

$$\overset{(\quad\quad)}{I-H} \qquad\qquad\qquad \overset{|\quad|}{I\quad H}$$

Isopropyl iodide

In the same way, isobutylene could yield either of two products, isobutyl halide or *tert*-butyl halide; here the orientation of addition is such that the *tert*-butyl halide greatly predominates.

$$\overset{\displaystyle CH_3}{\overset{|}{CH_3-C=CH_2}} \quad \xrightarrow{\quad\times\quad} \quad \overset{\displaystyle CH_3}{\overset{|}{CH_3-C-CH_2}}$$

$$\overset{(\quad\quad)}{H-I} \qquad\qquad\qquad \overset{|\quad|}{H\quad I}$$

Isobutyl iodide

$$\overset{\displaystyle CH_3}{\overset{|}{CH_3-C=CH_2}} \quad \longrightarrow \quad \overset{\displaystyle CH_3}{\overset{|}{CH_3-C-CH_2}} \qquad \textit{Actual product}$$

$$\overset{(\quad\quad)}{I-H} \qquad\qquad\qquad \overset{|\quad|}{I\quad H}$$

tert-Butyl iodide

Orientation in alkane substitutions (Sec. 3.21) depends on which hydrogen is replaced; orientation in alkene additions depends on which doubly-bonded carbon accepts Y and which accepts Z of a reagent YZ.

Examination of a large number of such additions showed the Russian chemist Vladimir Markovnikov (of the University of Kazan) that where two isomeric products are possible, one product usually predominates. He pointed out in 1869 that the orientation of addition follows a pattern which we can summarize as: *In the ionic addition of an acid to the carbon–carbon double bond of an alkene, the hydrogen of the acid attaches itself to the carbon atom that already holds the greater number of hydrogens.* This statement is generally known as **Markovnikov's rule.** It is frequently paraphrased by the Biblical quotation: "Unto everyone that hath shall be given," or by the more colloquial expression, "Them as has, gits."

Thus, in the addition to propylene we see that the hydrogen goes to the carbon bearing two hydrogen atoms rather than to the carbon bearing one. In the addition to isobutylene, the hydrogen goes to the carbon bearing two hydrogens rather than to the carbon bearing none.

Using Markovnikov's rule, we can correctly predict the principal product of many reactions. For example:

$$CH_3CH_2CH=CH_2 + HI \longrightarrow CH_3CH_2CHICH_3$$

1-Butene *sec*-Butyl iodide
(2-Iodobutane)

$$\underset{\text{2-Methyl-2-butene}}{CH_3\overset{\overset{\displaystyle CH_3}{|}}{C}=CH-CH_3} + HI \longrightarrow CH_3-\overset{\overset{\displaystyle CH_3}{|}}{\underset{\underset{\displaystyle I}{|}}{C}}-CH_2-CH_3$$

tert-Pentyl iodide
(2-Iodo-2-methylbutane)

$$\underset{\text{2-Butene}}{CH_3CH=CHCH_3} + HI \longrightarrow \underset{\substack{\text{sec-Butyl iodide} \\ \text{(2-Iodobutane)}}}{CH_3CHICH_2CH_3}$$

$$\underset{\substack{\text{Vinyl chloride} \\ \text{(Chloroethene)}}}{CH_2=CHCl} + HI \longrightarrow \underset{\text{1-Chloro-1-iodoethane}}{CH_3CHICl}$$

$$\underset{\text{2-Pentene}}{CH_3CH_2CH=CHCH_3} + HI \longrightarrow \underset{\text{3-Iodopentane}}{CH_3CH_2CHICH_2CH_3} + \underset{\text{2-Iodopentane}}{CH_3CH_2CH_2CHICH_3}$$

In 2-pentene each of the doubly-bonded carbons holds one hydrogen, so that according to the rule we should expect neither product to predominate. Here again the prediction is essentially correct, roughly equal quantities of the two isomers actually being obtained.

While the examples have involved the addition of hydrogen iodide, exactly similar results are obtained in the addition of hydrogen chloride and, except for special conditions indicated in the following section, of hydrogen bromide.

Addition of hydrogen halides to alkenes can be used to make alkyl halides. The fact that addition occurs with a specific orientation, as summarized by Markovnikov's rule, rather than at random, is an advantage since a fairly pure product can generally be obtained. At the same time, the synthesis is, of course, limited to those products that are formed in agreement with Markovnikov's rule; for example, we can make isopropyl iodide in this way, but not n-propyl iodide. (As we shall see later, there are other, more important ways to prepare alkyl halides.)

5.7 Addition of hydrogen bromide. Peroxide effect

Addition of hydrogen chloride and hydrogen iodide to alkenes follows Markovnikov's rule. Until 1933 the situation with respect to hydrogen bromide was exceedingly confused. It had been reported by some workers that addition of hydrogen bromide to a particular alkene yields a product in agreement with Markovnikov's rule; by others, a product in contradiction to Markovnikov's rule; and by still others, a mixture of both products. It had been variously reported that the product obtained depends upon the presence or absence of water, or of light, or of certain metallic halides; it had been reported that the product obtained depends upon the solvent used, or on the nature of the surface of the reaction vessel.

In 1933, M. S. Kharasch and F. W. Mayo at the University of Chicago brought order to this chemical chaos by discovering that the orientation of addition of hydrogen bromide to the carbon–carbon double bond is determined solely by the presence or absence of **peroxides.**

Organic peroxides are compounds containing the —O—O— group; they are formed, generally in only very small amounts, by the action of oxygen on various organic compounds. Kharasch and Mayo found that if one carefully excludes peroxides (and the oxygen that forms them) from the reaction system, or if one adds certain compounds (called **antioxidants**), the addition of HBr to alkenes follows Markovnikov's rule. On the other hand, if one does not exclude peroxides and oxygen, or if one deliberately puts peroxides into the reaction system, HBr adds to alkenes in exactly the reverse direction.

$$CH_3CH{=}CH_2 \xrightarrow{\text{HBr}} \begin{cases} \xrightarrow{\text{no peroxides}} CH_3CHBrCH_3 & \textbf{Markovnikov addition} \\ & \text{Isopropyl bromide} \\ \xrightarrow{\text{peroxides}} CH_3CH_2CH_2Br & \textbf{Anti-Markovnikov addition} \\ & \textit{n}\text{-Propyl bromide} \end{cases}$$

Propylene

$$\begin{matrix} CH_3 \\ | \\ CH_3{-}C{=}CH_2 \end{matrix} \xrightarrow{\text{HBr}}$$

Isobutylene

$$\xrightarrow{\text{no peroxides}} \begin{matrix} CH_3 \\ | \\ CH_3{-}C{-}CH_3 \\ | \\ Br \end{matrix}$$ **Markovnikov addition**

tert-Butyl bromide

$$\xrightarrow{\text{peroxides}} \begin{matrix} CH_3 \\ | \\ CH_3{-}C{-}CH_2Br \\ | \\ H \end{matrix}$$ **Anti-Markovnikov addition**

lsobutyl bromide

This reversal of the orientation of addition caused by the presence of peroxides is known as the **peroxide effect.** Of the reactions we are studying, *only* the addition of hydrogen bromide shows the peroxide effect. The presence or absence of peroxides has no effect on the orientation of addition of hydrogen chloride, hydrogen iodide, sulfuric acid, water, etc. As we shall see (Secs. 5.12 and 5.14), both Markovnikov's rule and the peroxide effect can readily be accounted for in ways that are quite consistent with the chemistry we have learned so far.

5.8 Addition of sulfuric acid

Alkenes react with cold, concentrated sulfuric acid to form compounds of the general formula $ROSO_3H$, known as **alkyl hydrogen sulfates.** These products are formed by addition of hydrogen ion to one side of the double bond and bisulfate ion to the other.

$$\begin{matrix} & & & O \\ & & & \| \\ {-}\overset{|}{C}{=}\overset{|}{C}{-} & + & H{-}O{-}\overset{|}{\underset{\|}{S}}{-}O{-}H & \longrightarrow & {-}\overset{|}{\underset{|}{C}}{-}\overset{|}{\underset{|}{C}}{-}O{-}\overset{\|}{\underset{\|}{S}}{-}O{-}H \\ & & O & & H \quad\quad O \end{matrix}$$

Alkene   Sulfuric acid   Alkyl hydrogen sulfate

It is important to notice that carbon is bonded to oxygen and not to sulfur.

Reaction is carried out simply by bringing the reactants into contact: a gaseous alkene is bubbled through the acid, and a liquid alkene is stirred or shaken with the acid. Since alkyl hydrogen sulfates are soluble in sulfuric acid, a clear solution results. The alkyl hydrogen sulfates are deliquescent solids, and are difficult to isolate. As the examples below show, the concentration of sulfuric acid required for reaction depends upon the particular alkene involved; we shall later account for this in a reasonable way (Sec. 5.11).

If the sulfuric acid solution of the alkyl hydrogen sulfate is diluted with water and heated, there is obtained an alcohol bearing the same alkyl group as the original alkyl hydrogen sulfate. The alkyl hydrogen sulfate has been cleaved by water to form the alcohol and sulfuric acid, and is said to have been *hydrolyzed*. This sequence of reactions affords a route to the alcohols, and it is for this purpose that addition of sulfuric acid to alkenes is generally carried out.

$$CH_2{=}CH_2 \xrightarrow{98\% \ H_2SO_4} CH_3CH_2OSO_3H \xrightarrow{H_2O, \ heat} CH_3CH_2OH + H_2SO_4$$

Ethylene $\qquad\qquad$ Ethyl hydrogen sulfate $\qquad\qquad$ Ethyl alcohol

$$CH_3CH{=}CH_2 \xrightarrow{80\% \ H_2SO_4} \underset{\underset{OSO_3H}{|}}{CH_3CHCH_3} \xrightarrow{H_2O, \ heat} \underset{\underset{OH}{|}}{CH_3CHCH_3}$$

Propylene $\qquad\qquad$ Isopropyl hydrogen sulfate $\qquad$ Isopropyl alcohol

$$\underset{\underset{CH_3}{|}}{CH_3{-}C{=}CH_2} \xrightarrow{63\% \ H_2SO_4} \overset{\overset{CH_3}{|}}{\underset{\underset{OSO_3H}{|}}{CH_3{-}C{-}CH_3}} \xrightarrow{H_2O, \ heat} \overset{\overset{CH_3}{|}}{\underset{\underset{OH}{|}}{CH_3{-}C{-}CH_3}}$$

Isobutylene $\qquad\qquad$ *tert*-Butyl hydrogen sulfate $\qquad$ *tert*-Butyl alcohol

This is an excellent method for the large-scale manufacture of alcohols, since alkenes are readily obtained by the cracking of petroleum. Because the addition of sulfuric acid follows Markovnikov's rule, certain alcohols cannot be obtained by this method. For example, isopropyl alcohol can be made but not *n*-propyl alcohol; *tert*-butyl alcohol, but not isobutyl alcohol.

The fact that alkenes dissolve in cold, concentrated sulfuric acid to form the alkyl hydrogen sulfates is made use of in the purification of certain other kinds of compounds. Alkanes or alkyl halides, for example, which are insoluble in sulfuric acid, can be freed from alkene impurities by washing with sulfuric acid. A gaseous alkane is bubbled through several bottles of sulfuric acid, and a liquid alkane is shaken with sulfuric acid in a separatory funnel.

5.9 Addition of water. Hydration

Water adds to the more reactive alkenes in the presence of acids to yield alcohols. Since this addition, too, follows Markovnikov's rule, the

$$-\overset{|}{\underset{}{C}}=\overset{|}{\underset{}{C}}- + H_2O \xrightarrow{H^+} -\overset{|}{\underset{H}{C}}-\overset{|}{\underset{OH}{C}}-$$

Alkene   Alcohol

alcohols are the same as those obtained by the two-step synthesis just described; this direct hydration is, of course, the simpler and cheaper of the two processes. Hydration of alkenes is the principal industrial source of those lower alcohols whose formation is consistent with Markovnikov's rule.

$$CH_3-\overset{\overset{\displaystyle CH_3}{|}}{C}=CH_2 \xrightarrow{H_2O,\ H^+} CH_3-\overset{\overset{\displaystyle CH_3}{|}}{\underset{\underset{\displaystyle OH}{|}}{C}}-CH_3$$

Isobutylene   *tert*-Butyl alcohol

5.10 Mechanism of addition of acids

Before we consider other reactions of alkenes, it will be helpful to examine the mechanism of some of the reactions we have already discussed. After we have done this, we shall return to our systematic consideration of alkene reactions, prepared to understand them better in terms of these earlier reactions.

We shall take up first the addition of those reagents which contain ionizable hydrogen: the hydrogen halides, sulfuric acid, and water. The generally accepted mechanism will be outlined, and then we shall see how this mechanism accounts for certain facts. Like dehydration of alcohols, addition is pictured as involving carbonium ions. We shall notice certain resemblances between these two kinds of reaction; these resemblances are evidence that a common intermediate is involved.

Addition of the acidic reagent, HZ, is believed to proceed by two steps:

(1) $-\overset{|}{\underset{}{C}}=\overset{|}{\underset{}{C}}- + H:Z \longrightarrow -\overset{|}{\underset{H}{C}}-\overset{|}{\underset{\oplus}{C}}- + :Z$ HZ = HCl, HBr, HI, H_2SO_4, H_3O^+

(2) $-\overset{|}{\underset{H}{C}}-\overset{|}{\underset{\oplus}{C}}- + :Z \longrightarrow -\overset{|}{\underset{H}{C}}-\overset{|}{\underset{Z}{C}}-$:Z = Cl⁻, Br⁻, I⁻, HSO_4^-, H_2O

Step (1) involves transfer of hydrogen ion from :Z to the alkene to form a carbonium ion; this is a transfer of a proton from one base to another.

$$\underset{Z:\textcircled{H}}{\overset{\diagdown}{\underset{\diagup}{C}}\overset{..}{:}\overset{\diagup}{\underset{\diagdown}{C}}} \longrightarrow Z: + -\overset{|}{\underset{H}{C}}\ :\ \overset{|}{\underset{\oplus}{C}}-$$

Step (2) is the union of the carbonium ion with the base :Z. (The mechanism is somewhat simplified here, and will be expanded in Sec. 5.13.) This general mechanism is illustrated below by several specific examples.

(1) $CH_3-CH{=}CH_2 + H{:}\ddot{C}l{:}\ \longrightarrow\ CH_3-\overset{\oplus}{CH}-CH_3 + {:}\ddot{C}l{:}^-$

(2) $CH_3-\underset{\oplus}{CH}-CH_3 + {:}\ddot{C}l{:}^-\ \longrightarrow\ CH_3-\underset{\underset{Cl}{|}}{CH}-CH_3$

(1) $CH_3-CH{=}CH_2 + H{:}OSO_3H\ \longrightarrow\ CH_3-\overset{\oplus}{CH}-CH_3 + {:}OSO_3H^-$

(2) $CH_3-\underset{\oplus}{CH}-CH_3 + {:}OSO_3H^-\ \longrightarrow\ CH_3-\underset{\underset{OSO_3H}{|}}{CH}-CH_3$

(1) $CH_3-CH{=}CH_2 + H{:}OH_2^+\ \rightleftarrows\ CH_?-\overset{\oplus}{CH}-CH_3 + {:}OH_2$

(2a) $CH_3-\underset{\oplus}{CH}-CH_3 + {:}OH_2\ \rightleftarrows\ CH_3-\underset{\underset{\oplus OH_2}{|}}{CH}-CH_3$

(2b) $CH_3-\underset{\underset{\oplus OH_2}{|}}{CH}-CH_3 + {:}OH_2\ \rightleftarrows\ CH_3-\underset{\underset{OH}{|}}{CH}-CH_3 + H{:}OH_2^+$

We notice that the carbonium ion combines with water to form not the alcohol but the protonated alcohol; in a subsequent reaction this protonated alcohol releases a hydrogen ion to another base to form the alcohol. This sequence of reactions, we can see, is just the reverse of that proposed for the dehydration of alcohols (Sec. 4.16). In dehydration, the equilibria are shifted in favor of the alkene chiefly by the removal of the alkene from the reaction mixture by distillation; in hydration, the equilibria are shifted in favor of the alcohol partly by the high concentration of water.

Let us see how this mechanism accounts for some of the facts.

First, the mechanism is consistent with (a) *the acidic nature of the reagents*. According to the mechanism, the first step in all these reactions is the transfer of a hydrogen ion to the alkene. This agrees with the fact that all these reagents except water are strong acids in the classical sense; that is, they can readily supply hydrogen ions. The exception, water, requires the presence of a strong acid for reaction to occur. In the following sections we shall see that the mechanism is also consistent with (b) *the basic nature of alkenes*, (c) *the relative reactivities of alkenes*, and (d) *the orientation of addition*.

5.11 Alkenes as bases. Relative reactivities toward addition

The mechanism of addition is consistent with the structure of the carbon–carbon double bond. Furthermore, it is consistent with the way in which groups attached to the doubly-bonded carbon atoms affect the reactivity of alkenes.

The mechanism pictures the alkene as a base, supplying electrons to an attacking acid. This agrees with the structure of the carbon–carbon double bond: the basicity is due to the loosely held, mobile π electrons.

If this is so, we would expect that the more basic the alkene the more reactive it should be toward acidic reagents. The basicity of an alkene depends upon the availability of its π electrons, which in turn depends upon the inductive effects of the atoms or groups that are attached to the doubly-bonded carbons. An electron-withdrawing substituent should pull the loosely held π electrons to itself and thus make them less available to an attacking acid. An electron-releasing substituent should make the π electrons more available to an attacking acid.

Halogens, like other elements in the upper right-hand corner of the Periodic Table, tend to attract electrons. Alkyl groups, on the other hand, tend to repel electrons. In agreement with the mechanism we find that the presence of a halogen atom in an alkene molecule greatly reduces the reactivity of that alkene toward addition of acids; the presence of alkyl groups greatly increases the reactivity of an alkene.

Alkenes generally show the following order of reactivity toward addition of acids:

Reactivity of alkenes toward acids

$$CH_3 \diagdown$$
$$C=CH_2 > CH_3CH=CHCH_3 > CH_3CH_2CH=CH_2 > CH_3CH=CH_2 >$$
$$CH_3 \diagup$$
$$CH_2=CH_2 > CH_2=CHCl$$

In Sec. 5.8, for example, we saw that the concentration of sulfuric acid needed for reaction with alkenes varies with the structure of the alkene. We can now see that the lowest concentration of acid is needed by the alkene containing the largest number of alkyl substituents, that is, by the most basic alkene.

Toward addition of acids, an electron-withdrawing substituent *deactivates* the double bond of an alkene, and an electron-releasing substituent *activates* the double bond.

$$-\overset{|}{C}=\overset{|}{C}\leftarrow G \qquad\qquad -\overset{|}{C}=\overset{|}{C}\rightarrow G \qquad\qquad \textbf{Electrophilic addition}$$

G *releases electrons:*   G *withdraws electrons:*
activates   *deactivates*

Reactivity of an alkene is determined not only by its basicity but also by another, perhaps more important, factor: stability of the carbonium ion that is formed. But before going into this, let us look at the matter of orientation.

5.12   Orientation of addition

The mechanism is consistent with the orientation of addition of acidic reagents,

Addition of hydrogen chloride to three typical alkenes is outlined below, with the two steps of the mechanism shown. In accord with Markovnikov's rule propylene yields isopropyl chloride, isobutylene yields *tert*-butyl chloride, and 2-methyl-2-butene yields *tert*-pentyl chloride.

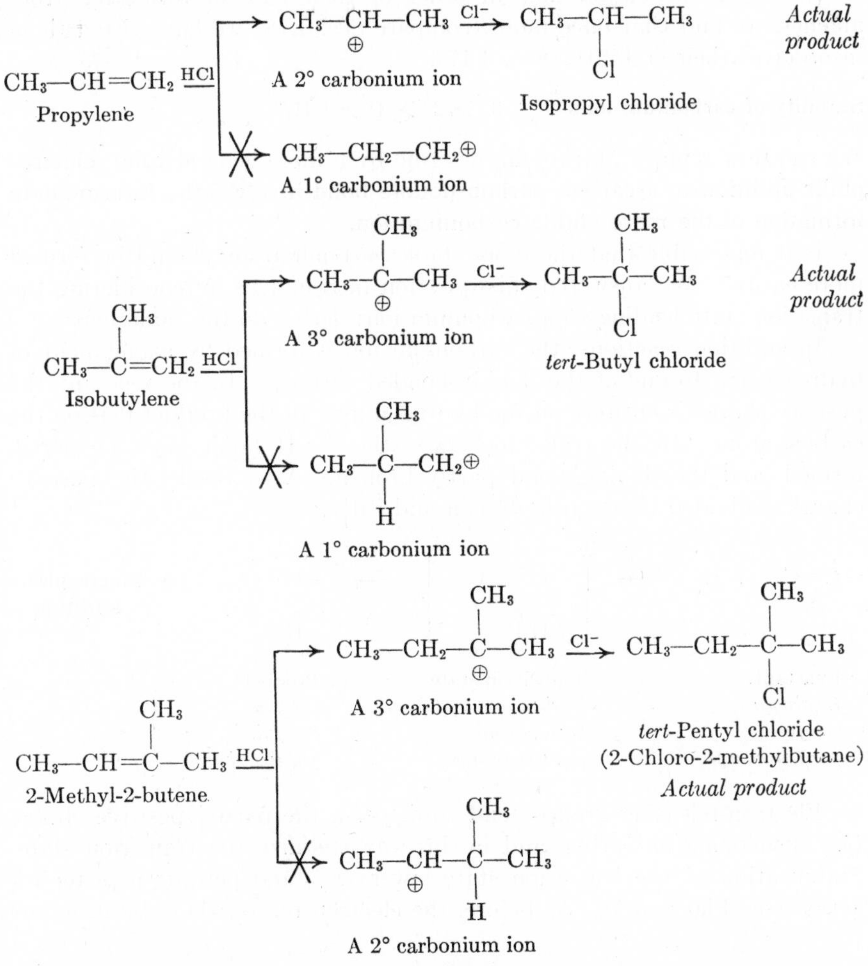

$$CH_3-CH=CH_2 \xrightarrow{HCl}$$
Propylene

$$\rightarrow CH_3-\overset{\oplus}{CH}-CH_3 \xrightarrow{Cl^-} CH_3-\underset{\underset{Cl}{|}}{CH}-CH_3 \quad \textit{Actual product}$$
A 2° carbonium ion
Isopropyl chloride

$$\xrightarrow{} CH_3-CH_2-CH_2\oplus$$
A 1° carbonium ion

$$CH_3-\underset{\underset{CH_3}{|}}{C}=CH_2 \xrightarrow{HCl}$$
Isobutylene

$$\rightarrow CH_3-\underset{\oplus}{\overset{\overset{CH_3}{|}}{C}}-CH_3 \xrightarrow{Cl^-} CH_3-\underset{\underset{Cl}{|}}{\overset{\overset{CH_3}{|}}{C}}-CH_3 \quad \textit{Actual product}$$
A 3° carbonium ion
tert-Butyl chloride

$$\xrightarrow{} CH_3-\underset{\underset{H}{|}}{\overset{\overset{CH_3}{|}}{C}}-CH_2\oplus$$
A 1° carbonium ion

$$CH_3-CH=\underset{\underset{CH_3}{|}}{C}-CH_3 \xrightarrow{HCl}$$
2-Methyl-2-butene

$$\rightarrow CH_3-CH_2-\underset{\oplus}{\overset{\overset{CH_3}{|}}{C}}-CH_3 \xrightarrow{Cl^-} CH_3-CH_2-\underset{\underset{Cl}{|}}{\overset{\overset{CH_3}{|}}{C}}-CH_3$$
A 3° carbonium ion
tert-Pentyl chloride
(2-Chloro-2-methylbutane)
Actual product

$$\xrightarrow{} CH_3-CH-\underset{\underset{H}{|}}{\overset{\overset{CH_3}{|}}{C}}-CH_3$$
A 2° carbonium ion

Which alkyl halide is obtained depends upon which intermediate carbonium ion is formed. This in turn depends upon the alkene and upon which carbon of the double bond hydrogen goes to. Propylene, for example, could yield a *n*-propyl carbonium ion if hydrogen went to C-2 or an isopropyl carbonium ion if hydrogen went to C-1.

Orientation is thus determined by the relative rates of two competing reactions: formation of one carbonium ion or another. The fact that propylene is converted into the isopropyl carbonium ion instead of the *n*-propyl carbonium ion means that the isopropyl carbonium ion is formed *faster* than the *n*-propyl carbonium ion.

In each of the examples given above, the product obtained shows that in the initial step a secondary carbonium ion is formed faster than a primary, or a tertiary faster than a primary, or a tertiary faster than a secondary. Examination of many cases of addition of acids to alkenes shows that this is a general rule: orientation is governed by the ease of formation of carbonium ions, which follows the sequence $3° > 2° > 1°$.

In listing carbonium ions in order of their ease of formation from alkenes, we find that once more (compare Sec. 4.18) we have listed them in order of their stability (Sec. 4.17).

Stability of carbonium ions $3° > 2° > 1° > CH_3^+$

We can now replace Markovnikov's rule by a more general rule: **electrophilic addition to a carbon–carbon double bond involves the intermediate formation of the more stable carbonium ion.**

Is it reasonable that the more stable carbonium ion should be formed more easily? We answered this question in Sec. 4.18 by considering the transition state leading to a carbonium ion; let us do the same here.

In addition reactions, the carbonium ion is formed by attachment of hydrogen ion to one of the doubly-bonded carbons. In the reactant the positive charge is entirely on the hydrogen ion; in the product it is on the carbon atom. In the transition state, the C—H bond must be partly formed, and the double bond partly broken. As a result, the positive charge is divided between hydrogen and carbon.

$$-\overset{|}{C}=\overset{|}{C}- \ + \ H^+ \quad \longrightarrow \quad \left[\ -\overset{|}{C}\text{----}\overset{|}{C}- \atop \underset{H \ \delta+}{\vdots} \ \ {}^{\delta+} \right] \quad \longrightarrow \quad -\overset{|}{\underset{H}{C}}-\overset{|}{\underset{\oplus}{C}}- \qquad \begin{array}{l}\textbf{Electrophilic}\\\textbf{addition}\end{array}$$

Reactants   Transition state   Product
Hydrogen   *Carbon and hydrogen*   *Carbon*
has full   *have partial*   *has full*
positive charge   *positive charges*   *positive charge*

Electron-releasing groups tend to disperse the partial positive charge (δ_+) developing on carbon and in this way stabilize the transition state. Stabilization of the transition state lowers E_{act} and permits a faster reaction (see Figure 5.4). As before, the electron release that stabilizes the

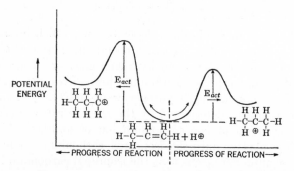

FIGURE 5.4. Molecular structure and orientation of reaction. Stability of transition state parallels stability of carbonium ion: more stable carbonium ion formed faster.

carbonium ion also stabilizes the *incipient* carbonium ion in the transition state. The more stable carbonium ion is formed faster.

If we look back to page 140, we see that the order of reactivity of alkenes is also consistent with this generalization. Isobutylene, which forms a tertiary carbonium ion, reacts faster than 2-butene, which forms a secondary carbonium ion; we could not have predicted this simply from the relative basicities of the alkenes, since each of these alkenes contains two methyl groups attached to the doubly-bonded carbon atoms. 1-Butene, 2-butene, and propylene, which form secondary carbonium ions, react faster than ethylene, which forms a primary carbonium ion.

$$CH_3-\underset{\underset{\text{Isobutylene}}{|}}{\overset{\overset{CH_3}{|}}{C}}=CH_2 + H^+ \rightleftharpoons CH_3-\underset{\oplus}{\overset{\overset{CH_3}{|}}{C}}-CH_3$$
A 3° carbonium ion

$$CH_3CH=CHCH_3 + H^+ \rightleftharpoons CH_3CH_2\underset{\oplus}{CH}CH_3$$
2-Butene
A 2° carbonium ion

$$CH_3CH_2CH=CH_2 + H^+ \rightleftharpoons CH_3CH_2\underset{\oplus}{CH}CH_3$$
1-Butene
A 2° carbonium ion

$$CH_3CH=CH_2 + H^+ \rightleftharpoons CH_3\underset{\oplus}{CH}CH_3$$
Propylene
A 2° carbonium ion

$$CH_2=CH_2 + H^+ \rightleftharpoons CH_3CH_2\oplus$$
Ethylene   A 1° carbonium ion

We see that the rate of addition of a hydrogen ion to a double bond depends upon the stability of the carbonium ion being formed; this factor determines the **orientation of addition** in a single alkene and the **relative reactivities** of different alkenes.

We can begin to see what a powerful weapon we have for attacking the problems that arise in connection with the wide variety of reactions that involve carbonium ions. We know that the more stable the carbonium ion, the faster it is formed; that its stability depends upon dispersal of the charge; and that dispersal of charge is determined by the inductive effects of the attached groups. We have already found that this same approach enables us to deal with such seemingly different facts as (a) the relative ease of dehydration of alcohols; (b) the relative reactivities of alkenes toward addition of acids; and (c) the orientation of addition of acids to alkenes.

5.13 Addition of acids: the π-complex

Certain evidence (of a kind we cannot take up in this book) gives us a more detailed picture of the addition of acids to alkenes, and enables us to expand the mechanism of Sec. 5.10.

When an alkene and an acid H:Z are mixed together, they exist in equilibrium with a **π-complex:** *a compound in which an acid is bound, not to either of the doubly-bonded carbon atoms, but to the π-cloud.* When the acid is a hydrogen ion, the π-complex is often called a *protonated double bond.* In the addition reaction, it is the π-complex that is converted into the carbonium ion which reacts to yield the final product:

| Alkene | Protonated double bond: a π-complex | Carbonium ion | Addition product |

The hydrogen ion can attach itself to — and break away from — a double bond rather easily; the more basic the alkene the larger the proportion of it that is protonated. Every so often a molecule of π-complex gains the energy needed to form the carbonium ion; the more stable the carbonium ion — and the transition state leading to it — the more often this happens. Once formed, the carbonium ion rapidly combines with a base to yield the final addition product.

Formation of the carbonium ion is the *difficult* step (the *rate-determining* step, Sec. 13.12) that must be taken if reaction is to occur; it is the step that determines orientation and much of the reactivity. Reactivity is also affected by the concentration of the π-complex, which in turn is determined by the basicity of the alkene.

Problem 5.3 According to the *principle of microscopic reversibility,* a reaction and its reverse follow exactly the same path but in opposite directions. If dehydration of alcohols is the reverse of hydration of alkenes, how must the mechanism of Sec. 4.16 be modified?

5.14 Mechanism of the peroxide-initiated addition of HBr

In the absence of peroxides, hydrogen bromide adds to alkenes in agreement with Markovnikov's rule; in the presence of peroxides, the direction of addition is exactly reversed (see Sec. 5.7).

To account for this *peroxide effect,* Kharasch and Mayo proposed that addition can take place by two entirely different mechanisms: Markovnikov addition by the ionic mechanism that we have just discussed, and anti-Markovnikov addition by a free radical mechanism. Peroxides initiate the free radical reaction; in their absence (or if an antioxidant, page 136, is added), addition follows the usual ionic path.

The essence of the mechanism is that hydrogen and bromine add to the double bond as *atoms* rather than as ions; the intermediate is a *free radical* rather than a carbonium ion. Like halogenation of alkanes, this

(1)   peroxides $\longrightarrow$ Rad·

(2)   Rad· + H:Br $\longrightarrow$ Rad:H + Br·

$\left.\right\}$ **Chain-initiating steps**

(3)   Br· + —C=C— $\longrightarrow$ —C—C—
                                 Br

$\left.\right\}$ **Chain-propagating steps**

(4)   —C—C— + H:Br $\longrightarrow$ —C—C— + Br·
      Br   Br H

then (3), (4), (3), (4), etc.

is a chain reaction, this time involving addition rather than substitution.

Decomposition of the peroxide (step 1) to yield free radicals is a well known reaction. The free radical thus formed abstracts hydrogen from hydrogen bromide (step 2) to form a bromine atom. The bromine atom adds to the double bond (step 3) and, in doing so, converts the alkene into a free radical.

$$\text{C} \cdot\!\cdot\, \text{C} \longrightarrow -\text{C} : \text{C}- \\ \text{(Br·)} \qquad\qquad \text{Br}$$

This free radical, like the free radical initially generated from the peroxide, abstracts hydrogen from hydrogen bromide (step 4). Addition is now complete, and a new bromine atom has been generated to continue the chain. As in halogenation of alkanes, every so often a reactive particle combines with another one, or is captured by the wall of the reaction vessel, and a chain is terminated.

The mechanism is well supported by the facts. The fact that a very few molecules of peroxide can change the orientation of addition of many molecules of hydrogen bromide strongly indicates a chain reaction. So, too, does the fact that a very few molecules of antioxidant can prevent this change in orientation; this reminds us of the inhibition of chlorination of methane by oxygen. It is not surprising to find that these same anti-oxidants are efficient inhibitors of many other chain reactions. Although their exact mode of action is not understood, it seems clear that they break the chain, presumably by forming unreactive radicals.

The mechanism involves addition of a bromine atom to the double bond. It is supported, therefore, by the fact that anti-Markovnikov addition is caused not only by the presence of peroxides but also by ir-radiation with light of a wavelength known to dissociate hydrogen bromide into hydrogen and bromine atoms.

The mechanism is supported most strongly, perhaps, by the fact that exactly analogous free radical mechanisms account for the addition to the double bond of dozens of other reagents, including the already familiar carbon tetrachloride and chloroform. These additions, too, are initiated by peroxides or light, and show all the characteristics of a chain reaction.

Is it reasonable that free radical addition of hydrogen bromide should occur with orientation opposite to that of ionic addition? Let us compare the two kinds of addition to propylene.

Ionic addition: *Markovnikov orientation*

$$CH_3—CH=CH_2 \xrightarrow{HBr} \begin{cases} \longrightarrow CH_3—\overset{\oplus}{CH}—CH_3 \xrightarrow{Br^-} CH_3—CH—CH_2 \\ \text{A 2° carbonium ion} | \\ Br \\ \text{Isopropyl bromide} \\ \xcancel{\longrightarrow} CH_3—CH_2—CH_2\oplus \\ \text{A 1° carbonium ion} \end{cases}$$

CH₃—CH=CH₂ Propylene

Free radical addition: *anti-Markovnikov orientation*

$$CH_3—CH=CH_2 \xrightarrow{Br·} \begin{cases} \longrightarrow CH_3—\overset{·}{CH}—CH_2Br \xrightarrow{HBr} CH_3—CH_2—CH_2Br \\ \text{A 2° free radical} \text{n-Propyl bromide} \\ \xcancel{\longrightarrow} CH_3—CH—CH_2· \\ | \\ Br \\ \text{A 1° free radical} \end{cases}$$

CH₃—CH=CH₂ Propylene

Ionic addition yields isopropyl bromide because a secondary carbonium ion is formed faster than a primary. Free radical addition yields *n*-propyl bromide because a secondary free radical is formed faster than a primary. Examination of many cases of anti-Markovnikov addition shows that orientation is governed by the ease of formation of free radicals, which follows the sequence 3° > 2° > 1°.

In listing free radicals in order of their ease of formation from alkenes, we find that once more (compare Sec. 3.26) we have listed them in order of their stability (Sec. 3.25).

Stability of free radicals $3° > 2° > 1° > CH_3·$

Free radical addition to a carbon–carbon double bond involves the intermediate formation of the more stable free radical.

Thus we find the chemistry of free radicals and the chemistry of carbonium ions following much the same pattern: the more stable particle is formed more easily, whether by abstraction or dissociation, or by addition to a double bond. Even the order of stability of the two kinds of particle is the same: $3° > 2° > 1° > CH_3$. In this particular case orientation is reversed simply because the hydrogen adds first in the ionic reaction, and bromine adds first in the radical reaction.

Problem 5.4 In the presence of a trace of peroxide or under the influence of ultraviolet light, 1-octene reacts:

(a) with CCl₄ to form 1,1,1,3-tetrachlorononane;
(b) with CHCl₃ to form 1,1,1-trichlorononane;

(c) with $CHBr_3$ to form 1,1,3-tribromononane;

(d) with $CBrCl_3$ to form 1,1,1-trichloro-3-bromononane;

(e) with $H—S—CH_2COOH$ (thioglycolic acid) to yield n-C_8H_{17}—S—CH_2COOH.

Show all steps of a likely mechanism for these reactions. Arrange the atoms H, Cl, Br in order of ease of abstraction from carbon.

Problem 5.5 (a) Write all steps in the free radical addition of HBr to propylene. (b) Write all steps that would be involved in the free radical addition of HCl to propylene. (c) List ΔH for each reaction in (a) and (b). Assume the following bond strengths: π bond, 40 kcal; 1° R—Br, 65 kcal; 1° R—Cl, 77 kcal; 2° R—H, 89 kcal. (d) Suggest a possible reason why the peroxide effect is observed for HBr but not for HCl.

5.15 Mechanism of addition of halogens

Ionic addition of acids to alkenes seems to involve two steps, the first being attachment of hydrogen ion to form the carbonium ion. What is the mechanism of the addition of chlorine and bromine?

From the structure of the double bond we might expect that here again it is an electron source, a base, and hence that the halogen acts as an electrophilic reagent, an acid. This idea is supported by the fact that alkenes usually show the same order of reactivity toward halogens as toward the acids already studied: electron-releasing substituents activate an alkene, and electron-withdrawing substituents deactivate an alkene.

The commonly accepted mechanism for addition of halogens to alkenes has two steps, and is quite analogous to the mechanism for addition of hydrogen-containing acids (protic acids).

(1)

$$-C{=}C- \ + \ :\ddot{X}:\ddot{X}: \ \longrightarrow \ \underset{\underset{\ddot{X}:}{\oplus}}{-C-C-} \ + \ :\ddot{X}:^-$$

(2)

$$\underset{\underset{:\ddot{X}:}{\oplus}}{-C-C-} \ + \ :\ddot{X}:^- \ \longrightarrow \ \underset{:\ddot{X}::\ddot{X}:}{-C-C-}$$

In step (1) halogen adds as a positive halogen ion to the double bond to form a carbonium ion. In step (2) the carbonium ion combines with a negative halide ion. (The mechanism is somewhat simplified for our present purpose; it will be modified later in Sec. 15.19 to account for certain other facts.)

It seems quite reasonable that an alkene should abstract hydrogen ion from a very polar hydrogen halide molecule. Is it reasonable that an alkene should abstract a positive halogen ion from a non-polar halogen molecule? Let us look at this problem more closely.

It is true that a halogen molecule is non-polar, since the two identical atoms share electrons equally. This is certainly not true, however, for a halogen molecule while it is under the influence of the powerful electric field of a nearby carbon–carbon double bond. The dense electron cloud of the double bond tends to repel the similarly charged electron cloud of the halogen molecule; this repulsion makes the halogen atom that is nearer the double bond relatively positive and its partner relatively negative.

$$\underset{\diagdown C \diagup}{\overset{\diagup C \diagdown}{\overset{\|}{C}}} \quad \overset{\delta_+ \quad \delta_-}{Br-Br}$$

Polarization of Br_2 by a double bond

The distortion of the electron distribution in one molecule caused by another molecule is called **polarization.** Here, we would say that the alkene has *polarized* the halogen molecule.

The more positive halogen of this polarized molecule is then abstracted by the alkene to form a carbonium ion, leaving a negative halide ion. This halide ion, or more probably another just like it, finally collides with the carbonium ion to yield the product, a dihalide.

Let us look at some of the evidence for this mechanism. If a carbonium ion is the intermediate, we might expect it to react with almost any negative ion or basic molecule that we care to provide. For example, the carbonium ion formed in the reaction between ethylene and bromine should be able to react not only with bromide ion but also — if these are present — with chloride ion, iodide ion, nitrate ion, or water.

$$CH_2=CH_2 \xrightarrow{Br_2} CH_2Br-CH_2\oplus$$

$$\xrightarrow{Br^-} CH_2Br-CH_2Br$$
1,2-Dibromoethane

$$\xrightarrow{Cl^-} CH_2Br-CH_2Cl$$
2-Bromo-1-chloroethane

$$\xrightarrow{I^-} CH_2Br-CH_2I$$
2-Bromo-1-iodoethane

$$\xrightarrow{NO_3^-} CH_2Br-CH_2ONO_2$$
2-Bromoethyl nitrate

$$\xrightarrow{H_2O} CH_2Br-CH_2\overset{\oplus}{O}H_2 \xrightarrow{-H^+} CH_2Br-CH_2OH$$
2-Bromoethanol

The facts are in complete agreement with this expectation. When ethylene is bubbled into an aqueous solution of bromine and sodium chloride, there is formed not only the dibromo compound but also the bromochloro compound and the bromoalcohol. Aqueous sodium chloride *alone* is completely inert toward ethylene; chloride ion or water can react only after the carbonium ion has been formed by the action of bromine. In a similar way bromine and aqueous sodium iodide or sodium nitrate convert ethylene into the bromoiodo compound or the bromonitrate, as well as into the dibromo compound and the bromoalcohol. Bromine in water with no added ions yields the dibromo compound and the bromoalcohol.

In addition to the elegant work just described, there is powerful stereochemical evidence for a two-step addition of halogen; we shall examine this evidence later (Sec. 15.19).

5.16 Halohydrin formation

As we have just seen, addition of chlorine or bromine in the presence of water can yield compounds containing halogen and hydroxyl groups on adjacent carbon atoms. These compounds are commonly referred to as **halohydrins**. Under proper conditions, they can be made the major products. For example:

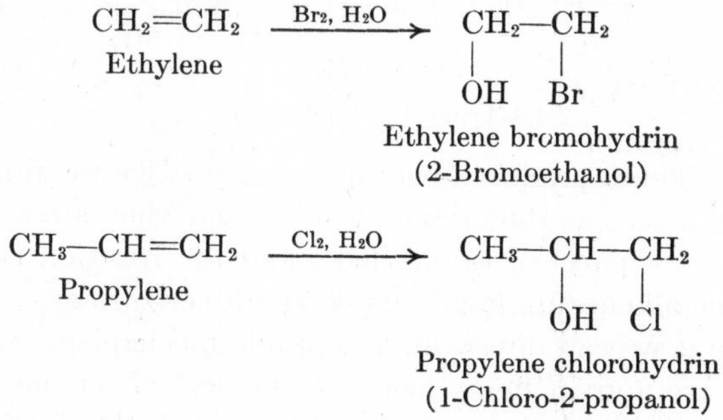

$$CH_2=CH_2 \xrightarrow{Br_2,\ H_2O} CH_2\text{—}CH_2$$
$$\underset{\text{Ethylene}}{} \qquad \underset{OH\quad Br}{\big|\qquad\big|}$$

Ethylene bromohydrin
(2-Bromoethanol)

$$CH_3\text{—}CH=CH_2 \xrightarrow{Cl_2,\ H_2O} CH_3\text{—}CH\text{—}CH_2$$
$$\underset{\text{Propylene}}{} \qquad \underset{OH\quad Cl}{\big|\qquad\big|}$$

Propylene chlorohydrin
(1-Chloro-2-propanol)

There is evidence, of a kind we are not prepared to go into here, that these compounds are formed by reaction of halogen and water (as shown in the last section) rather than by addition of preformed hypohalous acid, HOX. Whatever the mechanism, the result is addition of the elements of hypohalous acid (HO— and —X), and the reaction is often referred to in that way.

We notice that in propylene chlorohydrin chlorine is attached to the terminal carbon. This orientation is, of course, quite reasonable in light of the mechanism, and what we know about formation of carbonium ions.

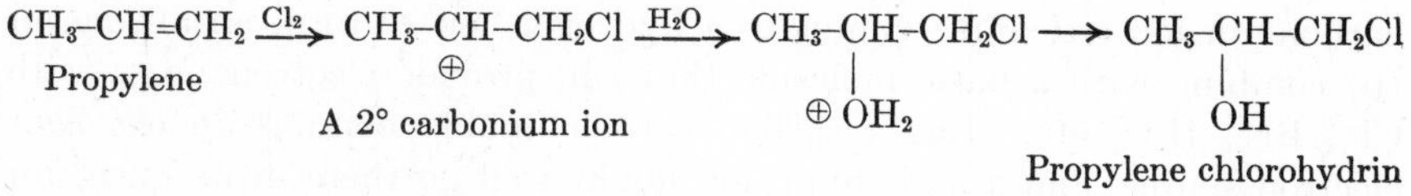

$$CH_3\text{–}CH=CH_2 \xrightarrow{Cl_2} CH_3\text{–}\overset{\oplus}{CH}\text{–}CH_2Cl \xrightarrow{H_2O} CH_3\text{–}CH\text{–}CH_2Cl \longrightarrow CH_3\text{–}CH\text{–}CH_2Cl$$

A 2° carbonium ion $\oplus OH_2$ / OH

Propylene / Propylene chlorohydrin

The initial addition of chlorine occurs in the way that yields the more stable secondary carbonium ion.

5.17 Addition of alkenes. Dimerization

Under the proper conditions, isobutylene is converted by sulfuric or phosphoric acid into a mixture of two alkenes of molecular formula C_8H_{16}. Hydrogenation of either of these alkenes produces the same alkane, 2,2,4-trimethylpentane (Sec. 3.29). The two alkenes are isomers, then, and differ only in position of the double bond. (*Problem:* Could they, instead, be *cis-trans* isomers?) When studied by the methods discussed at the end of this chapter (Sec. 5.22), these two alkenes are found to have the structures shown;

$$CH_3\text{—}C\text{=}CH_2 \xrightarrow[80°]{H_2SO_4}$$

$$\begin{array}{c} \quad\;\; CH_3 \quad\; CH_3 \\ \quad\;\;\; | \qquad | \\ CH_2\text{=}C\text{—}CH_2\text{—}C\text{—}CH_3 \\ \qquad\qquad\qquad | \\ \qquad\qquad\quad CH_3 \\ \text{2,4,4-Trimethyl-1-pentene} \end{array}$$

$$\begin{array}{c} CH_3 \quad\; CH_3 \\ \; | \qquad\quad | \\ CH_3\text{—}C\text{=}CH\text{—}C\text{—}CH_3 \\ \qquad\qquad\quad | \\ \qquad\qquad CH_3 \\ \text{2,4,4-Trimethyl-2-pentene} \end{array}$$

$$\xrightarrow[Ni]{H_2}$$

$$\begin{array}{c} CH_3 \quad\; CH_3 \\ \; | \qquad\quad | \\ CH_3\text{—}C\text{—}CH_2\text{—}C\text{—}CH_3 \\ \; | \qquad\qquad | \\ \; H \qquad\quad CH_3 \\ \text{2,2,4-Trimethylpentane} \\ (\text{"Iso-octane"}) \end{array}$$

Isobutylene: $2CH_3\text{—}C\text{=}CH_2$ with CH_3

Since the alkenes produced contain exactly twice the number of carbon and hydrogen atoms as the original isobutylene, they are known as **dimers** (*di* = two, *mer* = part) of isobutylene, and the reaction is called **dimerization.** Other alkenes undergo analogous dimerizations.

Let us see if we can devise an acceptable mechanism for this dimerization. There are a great many isomeric octenes; if our mechanism should lead us to just the two that are actually formed, this in itself would provide considerable support for the mechanism.

Since the reaction is catalyzed by acid, let us write as step (1) addition of a hydrogen ion to isobutylene to form the carbonium ion; the tertiary carbonium ion would, of course, be the preferred ion.

$$(1) \qquad CH_3\text{—}\underset{\underset{CH_3}{|}}{C}\text{=}CH_2 + H^+ \longrightarrow CH_3\text{—}\underset{\underset{CH_3}{|}}{\overset{\oplus}{C}}\text{—}CH_3$$

A carbonium ion undergoes reactions that provide electrons to complete the octet of the positively charged carbon atom. So far we have seen a carbonium ion either (a) eliminate a hydrogen ion to form an alkene, or (b) combine with a basic molecule that can provide electrons, e.g., with Cl^-, Br^-, H_2O, etc. But a carbon–carbon double bond is an excellent electron source, and a carbonium ion might well go there in its quest for electrons. Let us write as step (2), then, addition of the *tert*-butyl carbonium ion to isobutylene; again, the orientation of addition is such as to yield the more stable tertiary carbonium ion.

$$(2) \quad CH_3\text{—}\underset{\underset{CH_3}{|}}{C}\text{=}CH_2 + {}^{\oplus}\underset{\underset{CH_3}{|}}{C}\text{—}CH_3 \longrightarrow CH_3\text{—}\underset{\oplus}{\underset{}{C}}\text{—}CH_2\text{—}\underset{\underset{CH_3}{|}}{C}\text{—}CH_3$$

with CH_3 groups

Step (2) brings about the union of two isobutylene units, which is, of course, necessary to account for the products.

What is this new carbonium ion likely to do? We might expect that it could add to another molecule of alkene and thus make an even larger molecule; under certain conditions this does indeed happen. Under the present conditions, however, we know that this reaction stops at eight-carbon compounds, and that these compounds are alkenes. Evidently the carbonium ion undergoes a reaction familiar to us: loss of a hydrogen ion (step 3). Since the hydrogen ion can be lost from a carbon on either side of the positively charged carbon, two products should be possible.

$$
\begin{array}{l}
(3)\quad
\underset{\underset{\oplus}{\overset{\displaystyle CH_3}{\overset{|}{C}}}}{CH_3-\overset{}{C}-CH_2-\overset{\overset{\displaystyle CH_3}{|}}{\underset{\underset{\displaystyle CH_3}{|}}{C}}-CH_3}
\end{array}
$$

$$
\longrightarrow H^{+} + CH_2=\overset{\overset{\displaystyle CH_3}{|}}{C}-CH_2-\overset{\overset{\displaystyle CH_3}{|}}{\underset{\underset{\displaystyle CH_3}{|}}{C}}-CH_3
$$

$$
\longrightarrow H^{+} + CH_3-\overset{\overset{\displaystyle CH_3}{|}}{C}=CH-\overset{\overset{\displaystyle CH_3}{|}}{\underset{\underset{\displaystyle CH_3}{|}}{C}}-CH_3
$$

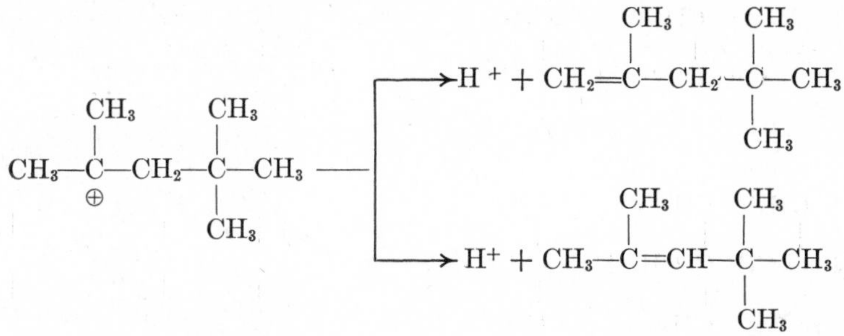

We find that the products expected on the basis of our mechanism are just the ones that are actually obtained. The fact that we can make this prediction simply on the basis of the fundamental properties of carbonium ions as we understand them is, of course, powerful support for the entire carbonium ion theory.

From what we have seen here, we can add one more reaction to those undergone by carbonium ions. **A carbonium ion may:**

(a) eliminate a hydrogen ion to form an alkene;

(b) combine with a negative ion or other basic molecule to form a halide, bisulfate, alcohol, etc.;

(c) add to an alkene to form a larger carbonium ion.

The larger carbonium ion formed in (c) can, of course, then undergo any of these three reactions.

5.18   Addition of alkanes.   Alkylation

The large amounts of 2,2,4-trimethylpentane consumed as aviation fuel are not made today by the dimerization reaction just described, but in another, cheaper way. Isobutylene and isobutane are allowed to react in the presence of an acidic catalyst, to form directly 2,2,4-trimethylpentane, or "iso-octane."

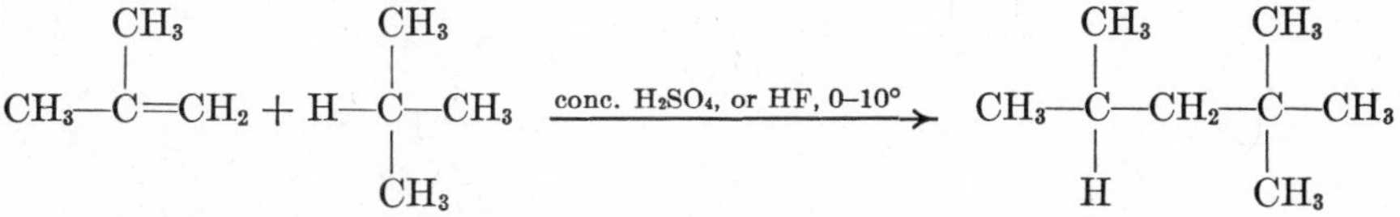

$$
\underset{\text{Isobutylene}}{CH_3-\overset{\overset{\displaystyle CH_3}{|}}{C}=CH_2} + \underset{\text{Isobutane}}{H-\overset{\overset{\displaystyle CH_3}{|}}{\underset{\underset{\displaystyle CH_3}{|}}{C}}-CH_3} \xrightarrow{\text{conc. } H_2SO_4, \text{ or } HF, 0-10^\circ} \underset{\text{2,2,4-Trimethylpentane}}{CH_3-\overset{\overset{\displaystyle CH_3}{|}}{\underset{\underset{\displaystyle H}{|}}{C}}-CH_2-\overset{\overset{\displaystyle CH_3}{|}}{\underset{\underset{\displaystyle CH_3}{|}}{C}}-CH_3}
$$

This reaction is, in effect, addition of an alkane to an alkene.

The commonly accepted mechanism of this **alkylation** is based on the study of many related reactions and involves in step (3) a reaction of carbonium ions that we have not previously encountered.

$$
(1) \qquad \underset{\underset{\displaystyle CH_3}{|}}{CH_3\text{-}C}\text{=}CH_2 + H^+ \longrightarrow CH_3\text{-}\underset{\underset{\displaystyle CH_3}{|}}{\overset{\overset{\displaystyle CH_3}{|}}{C}}\text{-}CH_3
$$

$$
(2) \qquad CH_3\text{-}\overset{\overset{\displaystyle CH_3}{|}}{C}\text{=}CH_2 + \underset{\underset{\displaystyle CH_3}{|}}{\oplus}\overset{\overset{\displaystyle CH_3}{|}}{C}\text{-}CH_3 \longrightarrow CH_3\text{-}\underset{\oplus}{\overset{\overset{\displaystyle CH_3}{|}}{C}}\text{-}CH_2\text{-}\underset{\underset{\displaystyle CH_3}{|}}{\overset{\overset{\displaystyle CH_3}{|}}{C}}\text{-}CH_3
$$

(3) $CH_3\text{-}\underset{\oplus}{C}\text{-}CH_2\text{-}\underset{CH_3}{C}\text{-}CH_3 + H\text{:}\underset{CH_3}{C}\text{-}CH_3 \longrightarrow CH_3\text{-}\underset{H}{C}\text{-}CH_2\text{-}\underset{CH_3}{C}\text{-}CH_3 + \oplus\underset{CH_3}{C}\text{-}CH_4$
(with CH_3 groups above the first, third, and C centers)

then (2), (3), (2), (3), etc.

The first two steps are identical with those of the dimerization reaction. In step (3) a carbonium ion abstracts a hydrogen atom *with its pair of electrons* (a **hydride ion,** essentially) from a molecule of alkane. This abstraction of hydride ion yields an alkane of eight carbons, and a new carbonium ion to continue the chain. As we might expect, abstraction occurs in the way that yields the *tert*-butyl carbonium ion rather than the less stable (1°) isobutyl carbonium ion.

We may now add to our list of reactions of carbonium ions given on page 151. **A carbonium ion may:**

(d) abstract a hydride ion from an alkane.

We are used to considering hydrogen as its positive ion, and hence the concept of a negative hydride ion may seem strange. However, such ions are well known in compounds like sodium hydride (NaH), lithium aluminum hydride (LiAlH₄), etc.

5.19 Hydroxylation. Glycol formation

Certain oxidizing agents convert alkenes into compounds known as **glycols.** Glycols are simply dihydroxy alcohols; their formation amounts to the addition of two hydroxyl groups to the double bond.

$$
-\underset{|}{\overset{|}{C}}\text{=}\overset{|}{\underset{|}{C}}- \xrightarrow[\text{or } HCO_2OH]{\text{dil. neutral } KMnO_4} -\underset{\underset{\displaystyle OH}{|}}{\overset{|}{C}}\text{---}\underset{\underset{\displaystyle OH}{|}}{\overset{|}{C}}-
$$

A glycol

Of the numerous oxidizing agents that cause hydroxylation, two of the most commonly used are (a) cold, dilute, neutral KMnO₄, and (b) peroxyformic acid, HCO_2OH.

Hydroxylation with permanganate is carried out by stirring together the alkene and the dilute aqueous permanganate solution at room temperature. Higher temperatures and the addition of acid or alkali are avoided, since under those more vigorous conditions cleavage of the double bond occurs (Sec. 5.22).

Hydroxylation with peroxyformic acid is carried out by allowing the alkene to stand with a mixture of hydrogen peroxide and formic acid, HCOOH, for a few hours, and then heating the product with water to hydrolyze certain intermediate compounds. (As we shall see in Sec. 7.14, the glycols obtained by these two alternative methods may differ in one important way.)

A glycol is frequently named by adding the word *glycol* to the name of the alkene from which it is formed. For example:

$$3CH_2{=}CH_2 + 2KMnO_4 + 4H_2O \longrightarrow 3CH_2{-}CH_2 + 2MnO_2 + 2KOH$$

Ethylene   OH   OH

                                          Ethylene glycol

$$CH_3{-}CH{=}CH_2 \xrightarrow{HCO_2OH} \xrightarrow{H_2O} CH_3{-}CH{-}CH_2$$

Propylene   OH OH

                                        Propylene glycol

Hydroxylation of alkenes is the most important method for the synthesis of glycols (Chapter 24). Moreover, oxidation by permanganate is the basis of a very useful analytical test known as the **Baeyer test** (Sec. 5.23).

5.20 Substitution by halogen. Allylic hydrogen

So far in our discussion of alkenes, we have concentrated on the carbon–carbon double bond, and on the addition reactions that take place there. Now let us turn to the alkyl groups that are present in most alkene molecules.

Since these alkyl groups have the alkane structure, they should undergo alkane reactions, for example, substitution by halogen. But an alkene molecule presents *two* sites where halogen can attack, the double bond and the alkyl groups. Can we direct the attack to just one of these sites? The answer is: Yes, *by our choice of experimental conditions.*

We know that alkanes undergo substitution by halogen at high temperatures or under the influence of ultraviolet light, and generally in the gas phase: conditions that favor formation of free radicals. We know that alkenes undergo addition of halogen at low temperatures and in the absence of light, and generally in the liquid phase: conditions that favor ionic reactions, or at least do not aid formation of radicals.

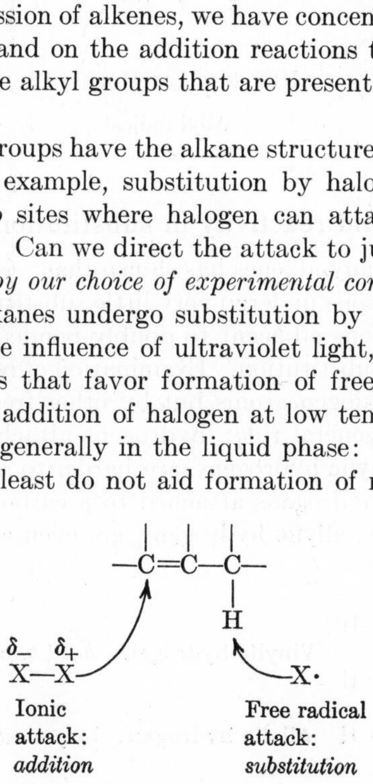

Ionic   Free radical
attack: attack:
addition   *substitution*

If we wish to direct the attack of halogen to the alkyl portion of an alkene molecule, then, we choose conditions that are favorable for the free radical reaction and unfavorable for the ionic reaction. Chemists of the Shell Development Company found that, at a temperature of 500–600°, a mixture of gaseous propylene and chlorine yields chiefly the substitution product, 3-chloro-1-propene, known as *allyl chloride* (CH_2=CH—CH_2— = **allyl**). Bromine behaves similarly.

$$CH_3—CH=CH_2 \xrightarrow{Cl_2} \begin{cases} \xrightarrow[\text{CCl}_4 \text{ soln.}]{\text{low temp.}} & CH_3—CH—CH_2 \\ & \qquad\quad | \quad\ | \\ & \qquad\ Cl \quad Cl \\ & \text{1,2-Dichloropropane} \\ & \text{Propylene chloride} \\ \\ \xrightarrow[\text{gas phase}]{500-600°} & Cl—CH_2—CH=CH_2 + HCl \\ & \text{3-Chloro-1-propene} \\ & \text{Allyl chloride} \end{cases}$$

Propylene

Ionic: *addition*

Free radical: *substitution*

Thus alkenes undergo substitution by halogen in exactly the same way as do alkanes. Furthermore, just as the alkyl groups affect the reactivity of the double bond toward addition, so the double bond affects the reactivity of the alkyl groups toward substitution.

In view of Sec. 5.14, we might wonder why a halogen atom does not add to the double bond, instead of abstracting a hydrogen atom. H. C. Brown (of Purdue University) has suggested that the halogen atom *does* add, but, at these high temperatures, is expelled before the second step of free radical addition can occur:

$$Cl· + CH_3—CH=CH_2 \begin{cases} \nearrow & CH_3—CH—CH_2Cl \\ & \qquad\ \ \cdot \\ \searrow & \end{cases}$$
Propylene

$$HCl + \underset{\cdot}{CH_2}–CH=CH_2 \xrightarrow{Cl_2} ClCH_2–CH=CH_2$$
$$\text{Allyl radical} \qquad\qquad \begin{array}{l} \text{Allyl chloride} \\ \textit{Actual product at} \\ \textit{high temperature} \end{array}$$

5.21 Orientation and reactivity in substitution

Halogenation of many alkenes has shown that: (a) hydrogens attached to doubly-bonded carbons undergo very little substitution; and (b) hydrogens attached to carbons adjacent to doubly-bonded carbons are particularly reactive toward substitution. Examination of reactions which involve attack not only by halogen atoms but by other free radicals as well has shown that this is a general rule: hydrogens attached to doubly-bonded carbons, known as **vinylic** hydrogens, are harder to abstract than ordinary primary hydrogens; hydrogens attached to a carbon atom adjacent to a double bond, known as **allylic** hydrogens, are even easier to abstract than tertiary hydrogens.

$$\left.\begin{array}{l} | \\ C—H \\ || \\ C—H \\ | \end{array}\right\} \textbf{Vinylic hydrogen:} \textit{ hard to abstract}$$

$$\begin{array}{l} | \\ —C—H \quad \textbf{Allylic hydrogen:} \textit{ easy to abstract} \\ | \end{array}$$

We can now expand the reactivity sequence of Sec. 3.24:

Ease of abstraction
of hydrogen atoms   allylic $>$ 3° $>$ 2° $>$ 1° $>$ CH_4 $>$ vinylic

Substitution in alkenes seems to proceed by the same mechanism as substitution in alkanes. For example:

$$CH_2{=}CH{-}H \xrightarrow{\ Cl\cdot\ } CH_2{=}CH\cdot \xrightarrow{\ Cl_2\ } CH_2{=}CH{-}Cl$$
    Ethylene   Vinyl radical   Vinyl chloride

$$CH_2{=}CH{-}CH_2{-}H \xrightarrow{\ Cl\cdot\ } CH_2{=}CH{-}CH_2\cdot \xrightarrow{\ Cl_2\ } CH_2{=}CH{-}CH_2Cl$$
    Propylene   Allyl radical   Allyl chloride

Evidently the vinyl radical is formed very slowly and the allyl radical is formed very rapidly. We can now expand the sequence of Sec. 3.26:

Ease of formation
of free radicals   allyl $>$ 3° $>$ 2° $>$ 1° $>$ $CH_3\cdot$ $>$ vinyl

Are these findings in accord with our rule that *the more stable the radical, the more rapidly it is formed?* Is the slowly formed vinyl radical relatively unstable, and the rapidly formed allyl radical relatively stable?

The bond strengths in Table 2.1 (page 39) show that 104–122 kcal of energy are needed to form vinyl radicals from a mole of ethylene, as compared with 101 kcal for formation of methyl radicals from methane. Relative to the hydrocarbon from which each is formed, then, the vinyl radical contains more energy and is less stable than the methyl radical.

On the other hand, bond strengths show that only 77 kcal are needed for formation of allyl radicals from propylene as compared with 85 kcal for formation of *tert*-butyl radicals. Relative to the hydrocarbon from which each is formed, the allyl radical contains less energy and is more stable than the *tert*-butyl radical.

We can now expand the sequence of Sec. 3 25; relative to the hydrocarbon from which each is formed, the order of stability of free radicals is:

Stability of
free radicals   allyl $>$ 3° $>$ 2° $>$ 1° $>$ $CH_4\cdot$ $>$ vinyl

In some way, then, the double bond affects the stability of certain free radicals; it exerts a similar effect on the incipient radicals of the transition state, and thus affects the rate of their formation. Although the low stability of the vinyl radical is not understood, the high stability of the allyl radical is readily accounted for by the structural theory (Sec. 9.17).

5.22 Ozonolysis. Determination of structure by degradation

Along with addition and substitution we may consider a third general kind of alkene reaction, **cleavage:** a reaction in which the double bond is completely broken and the alkene molecule converted into two smaller molecules.

The classical reagent for cleaving the carbon–carbon double bond is ozone. **Ozonolysis** (cleavage by ozone) is carried out in two stages: first, addition of ozone to the double bond to form an *ozonide;* and second, hydrolysis of the ozonide to yield the cleavage products.

Ozone gas is passed into a solution of the alkene in some inert solvent like carbon tetrachloride; evaporation of the solvent leaves the ozonide as a viscous oil. This unstable, explosive compound is not purified, but is treated directly with water, generally in the presence of a reducing agent.

In the cleavage products a doubly-bonded oxygen is found attached to each of the originally doubly-bonded carbons:

$$-\overset{|}{C}=\overset{|}{C}- \quad \xrightarrow{O_3} \quad -\overset{|}{C}\underset{\diagdown \ \diagup}{}\overset{|}{C}- \quad \xrightarrow[\text{Zn}]{\text{H}_2\text{O}} \quad -\overset{|}{C}=O + O=\overset{|}{C}- \qquad \textbf{Ozonolysis}$$

Alkene $\qquad\qquad\qquad\qquad$ O₃ $\qquad\qquad\qquad$ Cleavage products

$\qquad\qquad\qquad\qquad\qquad$ Ozonide $\qquad\qquad$ (Aldehydes and ketones)

These compounds containing the C=O group are called *aldehydes* and *ketones;* at this point we need only know that they are compounds that can readily be identified (Sec. 23.22). The function of the reducing agent, which is frequently zinc dust, is to prevent formation of hydrogen peroxide, which would otherwise react with the aldehydes and ketones. (Aldehydes, RCHO, are often converted into acids, RCOOH, for ease of isolation.)

Knowing the number and arrangement of carbon atoms in these aldehydes and ketones, we can work back to the structure of the original alkene. For example, for three of the isomeric hexylenes:

$$CH_3CH_2CH_2\overset{\overset{\displaystyle H}{|}}{C}=O + O=\overset{\overset{\displaystyle H}{|}}{C}CH_3 \quad \xleftarrow{\text{H}_2\text{O/Zn}} \quad \xleftarrow{O_3} \quad CH_3CH_2CH_2CH=CHCH_3$$

$\qquad$ Aldehydes $\qquad\qquad\qquad\qquad\qquad\qquad\qquad\qquad$ 2-Hexene

$$CH_3CH_2\overset{\overset{\displaystyle H}{|}}{C}=O + O=\overset{\overset{\displaystyle H}{|}}{C}CH_2CH_3 \quad \xleftarrow{\text{H}_2\text{O/Zn}} \quad \xleftarrow{O_3} \quad CH_3CH_2CH=CHCH_2CH_3$$

$\qquad$ Aldehydes $\qquad\qquad\qquad\qquad\qquad\qquad\qquad\qquad$ 3-Hexene

$$CH_3CH_2\overset{\overset{\displaystyle H}{|}}{C}=O + O=\overset{\overset{\displaystyle CH_3}{|}}{C}-CH_3 \quad \xleftarrow{\text{H}_2\text{O/Zn}} \quad \xleftarrow{O_3} \quad CH_3CH_2CH=\overset{\overset{\displaystyle CH_3}{|}}{C}-CH_3$$

$\qquad$ Aldehyde $\qquad$ Ketone $\qquad\qquad\qquad\qquad\qquad\qquad$ 2-Methyl-2-pentene

One general approach to the determination of the structure of an unknown compound is **degradation,** the breaking down of the unknown compound into a number of smaller, more easily identifiable fragments. Ozonolysis is a typical means of degradation.

Another method of degradation that gives essentially the same information — although somewhat less reliable — is vigorous oxidation by permanganate. Carboxylic acids, RCOOH, are obtained instead of aldehydes, RCHO. Thus 2-methyl-2-pentene yields CH_3CH_2COOH along with the ketone CH_3COCH_3. A terminal $=CH_2$ group is oxidized to CO_2. Reaction is believed to involve formation and cleavage of intermediate glycols (Sec. 5.19).

Problem 5.6 What products would you expect from each of the dimers of isobutylene (Sec. 5.17) upon cleavage by: (a) ozonolysis; (b) $KMnO_4$?

5.23 Analysis of alkenes

The functional group of an alkene is the carbon–carbon double bond. To characterize an unknown compound as an alkene, therefore, we must show that it undergoes the reactions typical of the carbon–carbon double bond. Since there are so many of these reactions, we might at first assume that this is an easy job. But let us look at the problem more closely.

First of all, which of the many reactions of alkenes do we select? Addition of hydrogen bromide, for example? Hydrogenation? Let us imagine ourselves in the laboratory, working with gases and liquids and solids, with flasks and test tubes and bottles.

We could pass dry hydrogen bromide from a tank through a test tube of an unknown liquid. But what would we see? How could we tell whether or not a reaction takes place? A colorless gas bubbles through a colorless liquid; a different colorless liquid may or may not be formed.

We could attempt to hydrogenate the unknown compound. Here, we might say, we could certainly tell whether or not reaction takes place: a drop in the hydrogen pressure would show us that addition had occurred. This is true, and hydrogenation can be a useful analytical tool. But a catalyst must be prepared, and a fairly elaborate piece of apparatus must be used; the whole operation might take hours.

Whenever possible, *we select for a characterization test a reaction that is rapidly and conveniently carried out, and that gives rise to an easily observed change.* We select a test that requires a few minutes and a few test tubes, a test in which a color appears or disappears, or bubbles of gas are evolved, or a precipitate forms or dissolves.

Experience has shown that an alkene is best characterized, then, by its property of decolorizing both a solution of bromine in carbon tetrachloride (Sec. 5.5) and a cold, dilute, neutral permanganate solution (the Baeyer test, Sec. 5.19). Both tests are easily carried out; in one, a red color disappears, and in the other, a purple color disappears and is replaced by brown manganese dioxide.

Granting that we have selected the best tests for the characterization of alkenes, let us go on to another question. We add bromine in carbon tetrachloride to an unknown organic compound, let us say, and the red color disappears. What does this tell us? Only that our unknown is a compound that reacts with bromine. It *may* be an alkene. But it is not enough merely to know that a particular kind of compound reacts with a given reagent; we must also know what *other* kinds of compounds also react with the reagent. In this case, the unknown may equally well be an alkyne. (It may also be any of a number of compounds that undergo rapid *substitution* by bromine; in that case, however, hydrogen bromide would be evolved and could be detected by the cloud it forms when we blow our breath over the test tube.)

In the same way, decolorization of permanganate does not prove that a compound is an alkene, but only that it contains some functional group that can be oxidized by permanganate. The compound *may* be an alkene; but it may equally well be an alkyne, an aldehyde, or a primary or secondary alcohol (but not a tertiary alcohol).

By itself, a single characterization test seldom proves that an unknown is one particular kind of compound. It may limit the number of possibilities, so that a final decision can then be made on the basis of additional tests. Or, conversely, if certain possibilities have already been eliminated, a single test may permit a final choice to be made. Thus, the bromine or permanganate test would be sufficient to differentiate an alkene from an alkane, or an alkene from an alkyl halide.

The tests most used in characterizing alkenes, then, are the following: (a) rapid decolorization of bromine in carbon tetrachloride without evolution of HBr, a test also given by alkynes; (b) decolorization of cold, dilute, neutral, aqueous permanganate solution (the Baeyer test), a test also given by alkynes, aldehydes, and primary and secondary alcohols (but not by tertiary alcohols). Also helpful is the solubility of alkenes in cold concentrated sulfuric acid, a test also given by a great many other compounds, including all those containing oxygen (they form soluble oxonium salts) and compounds that are readily sulfonated (Secs. 9.13 and 15.11). Alkanes or alkyl halides are not soluble in cold concentrated sulfuric acid.

Problem 5.7 Describe simple chemical tests (if any) that would distinguish between: (a) an alkene and an alkane; (b) an alkene and an alkyl halide; (c) an alkene and a secondary alcohol; (d) an alkene, an alkane, an alkyl halide, and a secondary alcohol. Tell exactly what you would *do* and *see*.

Problem 5.8 Assuming the choice to be limited to alkane, alkene, alkyl halide, secondary alcohol, and tertiary alcohol, characterize compounds A, B, C, D, and E on the basis of the following information:

Compound	Qual. elem. anal.	H_2SO_4	Br_2/CCl_4	$KMnO_4$
A	----	Insoluble	Negative	Negative
B	----	Soluble	Negative	Positive
C	Cl	Insoluble	Negative	Negative
D	----	Soluble	Positive	Positive
E	----	Soluble	Negative	Negative

Once characterized as an alkene, an unknown may then be identified as a previously reported alkene on the basis of its physical properties, including its infrared spectrum and molecular weight. Proof of structure of a new compound is best accomplished by degradation: cleavage by ozone or permanganate, followed by identification of the fragments formed (Sec. 5.22).

PROBLEMS

1. Draw a structural formula and give (when you can) an alternative name for:

(a) ethylene bromide
(b) ethyl bromide
(c) bromoethylene
(d) ethylene glycol
(e) propylene glycol
(f) propylene bromohydrin
(g) vinyl bromide
(h) allyl chloride

2. Give structures and names of the products (if any) expected from reaction of isobutylene with:

(a) H_2, Ni
(b) Cl_2
(c) Br_2
(d) I_2
(e) HBr
(f) HBr (peroxides)

(g) HI
(h) HI (peroxides)
(i) H_2SO_4
(j) H_2O, H^+
(k) Br_2, H_2O
(l) Br_2 + NaCl(aq)

(m) H_2SO_4 ($\longrightarrow$ C_8H_{16})
(n) isobutane + HF
(o) cold dil. neut. $KMnO_4$
(p) hot $KMnO_4$
(q) HCO_2OH
(r) O_3; then Zn, H_2O

3. Which alkene of each pair would you expect to be more reactive toward addition of H_2SO_4?

(a) ethylene or propylene
(b) ethylene or vinyl bromide
(c) propylene or 2-butene
(d) 2-butene or isobutylene

(e) vinyl chloride or 1,2-dichloroethene
(f) 1-pentene or 2-methyl-1-butene
(g) ethylene or CH_2=CHCOOH
(h) propylene or 3,3,3-trifluoropropene

4. Give structures and names of the principal products expected from addition of HI to:

(a) 1-pentene
(b) 2-pentene
(c) 2-methyl-1-butene
(d) 2-methyl-2-butene

(e) 3-methyl-1-butene
(f) vinyl bromide
(g) 3-hexene
(h) 2,4,4-trimethyl-2-pentene

5. Arrange the isomers of each set in order of stability on the basis of the indicated heats of combustion:

(a) 1-butene (649.8), isobutylene (646.1)
(b) 2-methyl-2-butene (801.7), *trans*-2-pentene (804.3)
(c) 1-hexene (964.3), 2,3-dimethyl-2-butene (958.3), 2-methyl-2-pentene (959.3)
(d) Could you have predicted these sequences from the structures involved?
(e) Why is it valid to deduce relative stabilities from heats of combustion in these particular cases, but *not* from heats of hydrogenation? (*Hint:* what are the *products* of combustion and of hydrogenation in each of these cases?)

6. Draw the structure of 6-methyl-2-heptene. Label each set of hydrogen atoms to show their relative reactivities toward chlorine atoms, using (1) for the most reactive, (2) for the next, etc.

7. Account for the fact that addition of $CBrCl_3$ in the presence of peroxides takes place faster to 2-ethyl-1-hexene than to 1-octene. (*Hint:* examine the mechanism you proposed in Problem 5.4, page 146.)

8. In methyl alcohol solution (CH_3OH), bromine adds to ethylene to yield not only ethylene bromide but also Br–CH_2CH_2–OCH_3. How can you account for this? Write equations for all steps.

9. Predict the product(s) expected from dimerization of propylene in the presence of H_2SO_4. Show all steps in the most likely mechanism.

10. 2,2-Dimethylbutane (neohexane) is manufactured for use in high-test gasoline by the alkylation of an alkene. What alkane and what alkene would be required? Write equations to show all steps in the most likely mechanism.

11. When kerosene is to be used in the laboratory to study the properties of alkanes, it must first be washed several times with concentrated H_2SO_4. (a) What likely impurities are removed by this treatment? (b) How would you know when to stop washing?

12. Describe simple chemical tests that would distinguish between:

(a) 2-chloropentane and *n*-heptane
(b) 2-hexene and *tert*-butyl bromide
(c) isobutane and isobutylene

(d) allyl bromide and 1-hexene
(e) *sec*-butyl alcohol and *n*-heptane
(f) 1-octene and *n*-pentyl alcohol

(g) *tert*-pentyl alcohol and 2,2-dimethylhexane
(h) *n*-propyl alcohol and allyl alcohol (CH_2=CHCH_2OH)

13. Give the structure of the alkene that yields on ozonolysis:

(a) $CH_3CH_2CH_2CHO$ and $HCHO$

(b) CH_3—CH—CHO and CH_3CHO

       |

      CH_3

(c) Only CH_3—CO—CH_3

(d) CH_3CHO and $HCHO$ and OHC—CH_2—CHO

(e) What would each of these alkenes yield upon cleavage by $KMnO_4$?

14. A hydrocarbon, A, adds one mole of hydrogen in the presence of a platinum catalyst to form *n*-hexane. When A is oxidized vigorously with $KMnO_4$, a single carboxylic acid, containing three carbon atoms, is isolated. Give the structure and name of A. Show your reasoning, including equations for all reactions.

15. When *tert*-butyl chloride is treated in ether with magnesium, the yield of Grignard reagent is seldom higher than 80%. On the basis of the following evidence, what are the products of at least one side reaction? Write a balanced equation for this side reaction.

Evidence: During a preparation of this Grignard reagent, it was observed that a gas was being evolved. When bubbled through a solution of Br_2 in CCl_4, the gas rapidly decolorized the solution; the gas had a similar effect on $KMnO_4$. When a sample of the gas was weighed in a glass bulb, it was found to be about twice as dense as air. When a sample of the gas was shaken with cold concentrated H_2SO_4 in a closed vessel, the gas pressure dropped from 742 mm to 373 mm; the residual gas was again found to be about twice as dense as air.

16. What compound containing a carbon–carbon double bond would react with what reagent to form:

(a) 3-bromo-2-methylbutane

(b) 3-chloro-2-methylpropene

(c) $(CH_3)_2CHC(OH)(CH_3)_2$

(d) CH_3CHCl_2

(e) CH_2BrCH_2Cl

(f) $CH_2BrCHBrCOOH$

(g) $ClCH_2CHOHCH_2Cl$

(h) $ClCH_2CHClCH_2Cl$

17. Outline all steps in a possible laboratory synthesis of each of the following compounds, using only the organic source given, plus any necessary solvents and inorganic reagents.

Each synthesis should be one that gives a reasonably pure product in reasonably good yield.

It is not necessary to complete and balance each equation. Simply draw the structure of the organic compound, and write on the arrow the necessary reagents and any critical conditions. For example:

$$CH_3CH_2OH \xrightarrow{\text{H}^+,\ heat} CH_2\!\!=\!\!CH_2 \xrightarrow{\text{H}_2,\ Ni} CH_3CH_3$$

At this stage you may be asked to make a particular compound by a method that would never actually be used for that compound: for example, the synthesis of ethane just above. But if you can work out a way to make ethane from ethyl alcohol, then, when the need arises, you will also know how to make a complicated alkane from a complicated alcohol, and, in fact, how to replace an –OH group by –H in just about any compound you encounter. Furthermore, you will have gained practice in putting together what you have learned about several different kinds of compounds.

(a) ethylene from ethane

(b) propylene from propane

(c) ethyl iodide from ethane

(d) 2-bromopropane from propane (*Note:* simple monobromination of propane yields, of course, a mixture of 1-bromopropane and 2-bromopropane, and is therefore not satisfactory for this synthesis. The mixture might, however, be used as an *intermediate.*)

(e) 1,2-dibromopropane from propane
(f) 1,2-dibromobutane from 1-bromobutane
(g) 2-iodobutane from 1-chlorobutane
(h) 2,3-dimethylbutane from propylene
(i) 3,4-dimethylhexane from *n*-butyl bromide
(j) 1,2-dibromo-2-methylpropane from isobutane
(k) 2-iodobutane from *n*-butyl alcohol
(l) *n*-propyl bromide from isopropyl bromide
(m) propylene chlorohydrin from *n*-propyl iodide
(n) isohexane from $(CH_3)_2C(OH)CH_2CH_2CH_3$
(o) 2,2-dimethylbutane from 3-chloro-2,2-dimethylbutane

Chapter six_____

ALKYNES. DIENES

6.1 Introduction

Alkanes have the general formula C_nH_{2n+2}; alkenes have the general formula C_nH_{2n}. In this chapter we shall take up two kinds of hydrocarbons that have the same general formula, C_nH_{2n-2}: the **alkynes** and the **dienes**. As the formula indicates, they contain an even smaller proportion of hydrogen than the alkenes, and display an even higher degree of unsaturation. In spite of having the same general formula, alkynes and dienes have different functional groups, and hence different properties.

ALKYNES

6.2 Structure of acetylene. The carbon–carbon triple bond

The simplest member of the alkyne family is **acetylene,** C_2H_2. Using the methods we applied to the structure of ethylene (Sec. 4.2), we arrive at a structure in which the carbon atoms share *three* pairs of electrons, that is, are joined by a *triple bond. The* **carbon–carbon triple bond** *is the distinguishing feature of the alkyne structure.*

H:C:::C:H   H—C≡C—H
Acetylene

Again, quantum mechanics tells us a good deal more about acetylene, and about the carbon–carbon triple bond. To form bonds with two other atoms, carbon makes use of two equivalent hybrid orbitals: *sp* orbitals, formed by the mixing of *one s* and *one p* orbital. They lie along a straight line that passes through the carbon nucleus; the angle between the two orbitals is thus 180°. This **linear** arrangement (Figure 6.1) permits the hybrid orbitals to be as far apart as possible. Just as mutual repulsion among orbitals gives four tetrahedral bonds or three trigonal bonds, so it gives two linear bonds.

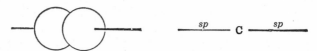

Figure 6.1. Atomic orbitals: hybrid *sp* orbitals. Axes lie along a straight line.

If we arrange the two carbons and the two hydrogens of acetylene to permit maximum overlapping of orbitals, we obtain the structure shown in Figure 6.2.

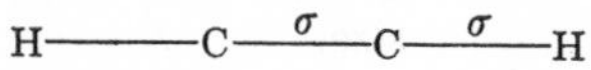

$$H——C \overset{\sigma}{——} C \overset{\sigma}{——} H$$

FIGURE 6.2. Acetylene molecule: only σ bonds shown.

Acetylene is a *linear molecule,* all four atoms lying along a single straight line. Both carbon–hydrogen and carbon–carbon bonds are cylindrically symmetrical about a line joining the nuclei, and are therefore σ bonds.

The molecule is not yet complete, however. In forming the sp orbitals already described, each carbon atom has used only one of its three p orbitals; it has two remaining p orbitals. Each of these consists of two equal lobes, whose axis lies at right angles both to the axis of the other p orbital and to the line of the sp orbitals (Figure 6.3); each p orbital is occupied

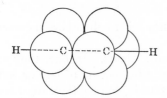

FIGURE 6.3. Acetylene molecule: overlap of p orbitals gives two π bonds.

by a single electron. Each p orbital can overlap a p orbital of the other carbon atom, so that the electrons can pair; in this way, then, two π bonds are formed. If one π cloud is pictured as lying above and below the line joining the nuclei, then the other π cloud lies in front and in back of the line. However, there is overlapping between the π bonds, so that the four lobes of the two bonds merge to form a single cylindrical sheath about the line joining the nuclei (Figure 6.4).

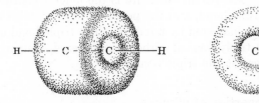

FIGURE 6.4. Acetylene molecule: carbon–carbon triple bond. π cloud forms cylindrical sheath.

The carbon–carbon "triple bond" is thus made up of one strong σ bond and two weaker π bonds; it has a total strength of 123 kcal. It is stronger than the carbon–carbon double bond of ethylene (100 kcal) or the single carbon–carbon bond of ethane (83 kcal), and therefore is shorter than either.

Again, the quantum mechanical structure is verified by direct evidence. Electron diffraction, x-ray diffraction, and spectroscopy show acetylene

(Figure 6.5) to be a linear molecule. The C—C distance is 1.20 A, as compared with 1.34 A in ethylene and 1.54 A in ethane.

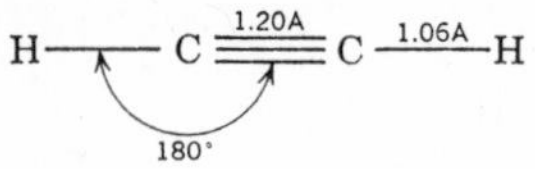

H———C $\xrightarrow{1.20A}$ C $\xrightarrow{1.06A}$ H   FIGURE 6.5. Acetylene molecule: shape and
        180°   size.

As in the case of the double bond, the structure of the triple bond is verified — although this time in a negative way — by the evidence of isomer number. As we can readily see from models, the linearity of the bonding should not permit geometric isomerism; no such isomers have ever been found.

Problem 6.1 Compare the electronic configurations of CO_2, which is a linear molecule (check your answer to Problem 1.4, page 16), and H_2O, which has a bond angle of 105°.

6.3 Higher alkynes. Nomenclature

Like the alkanes and alkenes, the alkynes form a homologous series, the increment again being —CH_2—.

The alkynes are named according to two systems. In one, they are considered to be **derived** from acetylene by replacement of one or both hydrogen atoms by alkyl groups. This system is simpler than the corresponding one for alkenes, since a disubstituted acetylene must necessarily have one group attached to each of the triply-bonded carbon atoms.

H—C≡C—C_2H_5 CH_3—C≡C—CH_3 CH_3—C≡C—$CH(CH_3)_2$
Ethylacetylene   Dimethylacetylene   Methylisopropylacetylene
1-Butyne   2-Butyne   4-Methyl-2-pentyne

For more complicated alkynes the **IUPAC** names are used. The rules are exactly the same as for the naming of alkenes, except that the ending **–yne** replaces *–ene*. The parent structure is the longest continuous chain that contains the triple bond, and the positions both of substituents and of the triple bond are indicated by numbers. The triple bond is given the number of the *first* triply-bonded carbon encountered, starting from the end of the chain nearest the triple bond.

6.4 Physical properties of alkynes

Being compounds of low polarity, the alkynes have physical properties that are essentially the same as those of the alkanes and alkenes. They are insoluble in water but quite soluble in the usual organic solvents of low polarity: ligroin, ether, benzene, carbon tetrachloride. They are less dense than water. Their boiling points (Table 6.1) show the usual increase with increasing carbon number, and the usual effects of chain branching; they are very nearly the same as the boiling points of alkanes or alkenes with the same carbon skeletons.

TABLE 6.1

ALKYNES

Name	Formula	M.p., °C	B.p., °C	Density (at 20°)
Acetylene	$HC\equiv CH$	-82	-75	
Propyne	$HC\equiv CCH_3$	-101.5	-23	
1-Butyne	$HC\equiv CCH_2CH_3$	-122	9	
1-Pentyne	$HC\equiv C(CH_2)_2CH_3$	-98	40	0.695
1-Hexyne	$HC\equiv C(CH_2)_3CH_3$	-124	72	.719
1-Heptyne	$HC\equiv C(CH_2)_4CH_3$	-80	100	.733
1-Octyne	$HC\equiv C(CH_2)_5CH_3$	-70	126	.747
1-Nonyne	$HC\equiv C(CH_2)_6CH_3$	-65	151	.763
1-Decyne	$HC\equiv C(CH_2)_7CH_3$	-36	182	.770
2-Butyne	$CH_3C\equiv CCH_3$	-24	27	.694
2-Pentyne	$CH_3C\equiv CCH_2CH_3$	-101	55	.714
3-Methyl-1-butyne	$HC\equiv CCH(CH_3)_2$		29	.665
2-Hexyne	$CH_3C\equiv C(CH_2)_2CH_3$	-92	84	.730
3-Hexyne	$CH_3CH_2C\equiv CCH_2CH_3$	-51	81	.725
3,3-Dimethyl-1-butyne	$HC\equiv CC(CH_3)_3$	-81	38	.669
4-Octyne	$CH_3(CH_2)_2C\equiv C(CH_2)_2CH_3$		131	.748
5-Decyne	$CH_3(CH_2)_3C\equiv C(CH_2)_3CH_3$		175	.769

6.5   Industrial source of acetylene

The alkyne of chief industrial importance is the simplest member of the family, **acetylene.** It is prepared by the action of water on calcium carbide, CaC_2, which itself is prepared by the reaction between calcium oxide and coke at the very high temperatures of the electric furnace. The calcium oxide and coke are in turn obtained from limestone and coal, respectively. Acetylene is thus obtained by a few steps from three abundant, cheap raw materials: water, coal, limestone.

$$\begin{array}{c} \text{coal} \longrightarrow \text{coke} \\ \text{limestone} \longrightarrow \text{CaO} \end{array} \Big\} \xrightarrow{2000°} CaC_2 \xrightarrow{H_2O} H{-}C\equiv C{-}H$$

Enormous quantities of acetylene are consumed each year. Dissolved under pressure in acetone contained in tanks, it is sold to be used as fuel for the oxyacetylene torch. It is the organic starting material for the large-scale synthesis of important organic compounds, including acetic acid and a number of unsaturated compounds that are used to make plastics and synthetic rubber. Many of the synthetic uses of acetylene have grown out of work done in Germany before and during World War II by W. Reppe (at the I. G. Farbenindustrie). Aimed at replacing petroleum (scarce in Germany) by the more abundant coal as the primary organic source, this work has revolutionized the industrial chemistry of acetylene.

6.6   Preparation of alkynes

A carbon–carbon triple bond is formed in the same way as a double bond: elimination of atoms or groups from two adjacent carbons.

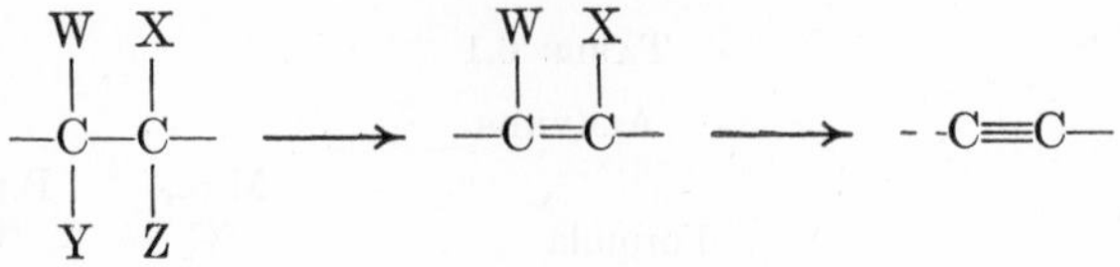

$$\underset{\underset{Y}{|}\;\underset{Z}{|}}{\overset{\overset{W}{|}\;\overset{X}{|}}{-C-C-}} \longrightarrow \underset{}{\overset{\overset{W}{|}\;\overset{X}{|}}{-C=C-}} \longrightarrow -C\equiv C-$$

The groups that are eliminated and the reagents used are essentially the same as in the preparations of alkenes.

PREPARATION OF ALKYNES

1. Dehydrohalogenation of alkyl dihalides

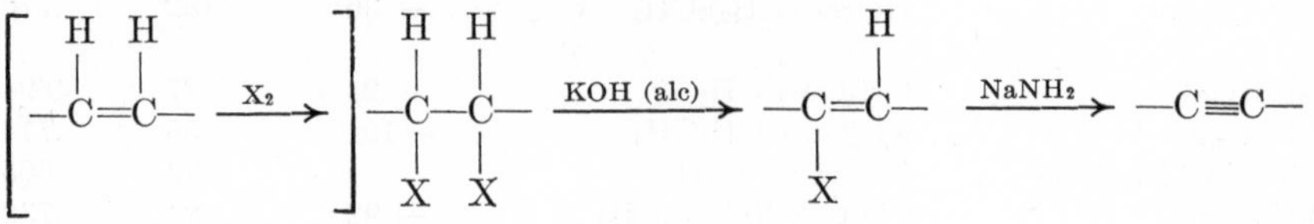

$$\left[\underset{}{\overset{\overset{H}{|}\;\overset{H}{|}}{-C=C-}}\right] \xrightarrow{X_2} \underset{\underset{X}{|}\;\underset{X}{|}}{\overset{\overset{H}{|}\;\overset{H}{|}}{-C-C-}} \xrightarrow{\text{KOH (alc)}} \underset{\underset{X}{|}}{\overset{\overset{H}{|}\;\overset{H}{|}}{-C=C-}} \xrightarrow{\text{NaNH}_2} -C\equiv C-$$

Example:

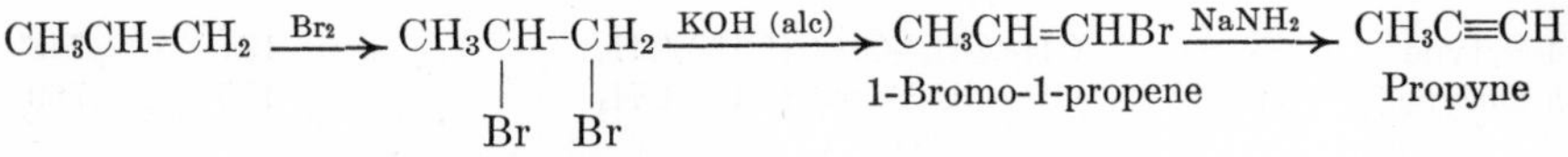

$$CH_3CH=CH_2 \xrightarrow{Br_2} \underset{\underset{Br}{|}\;\underset{Br}{|}}{CH_3CH-CH_2} \xrightarrow{\text{KOH (alc)}} \underset{\text{1-Bromo-1-propene}}{CH_3CH=CHBr} \xrightarrow{\text{NaNH}_2} \underset{\text{Propyne}}{CH_3C\equiv CH}$$

1,2-Dibromopropane
(Propylene bromide)

2. Reaction of sodium acetylides with primary alkyl halides

$$-C\equiv CH \xrightarrow[\substack{\text{or Na} \\ \text{metal}}]{\text{NaNH}_2} -C\equiv C:^-Na^+ + \underset{\substack{R \ must \\ be \ 1°}}{RX} \longrightarrow -C\equiv C-R + NaX$$

Examples:

$$\underset{\text{Sodium acetylide}}{HC\equiv C:^-Na^+} + \underset{\text{n-Butyl bromide}}{CH_3CH_2CH_2CH_2Br} \longrightarrow \underset{\substack{\text{1-Hexyne} \\ \text{(n-Butylacetylene)}}}{HC\equiv CCH_2CH_2CH_2CH_3}$$

$$\underset{\substack{\text{Sodium} \\ \text{methylacetylide}}}{CH_3C\equiv C:^-Na^+} + \underset{\text{Ethyl bromide}}{CH_3CH_2Br} \longrightarrow \underset{\substack{\text{2-Pentyne} \\ \text{(Methylethylacetylene)}}}{CH_3C\equiv CCH_2CH_3}$$

3. Dehalogenation of tetrahalides

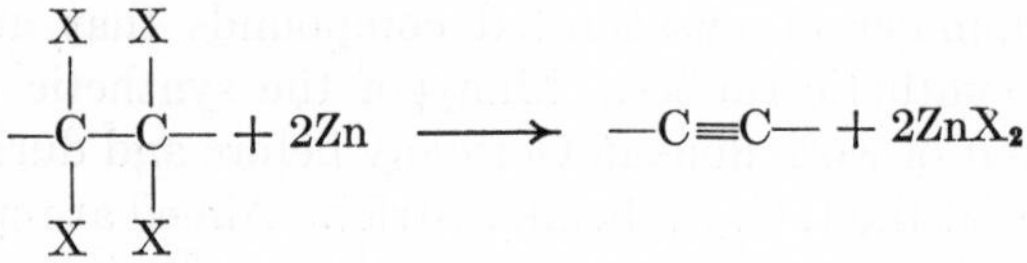

$$\underset{\underset{X}{|}\;\underset{X}{|}}{\overset{\overset{X}{|}\;\overset{X}{|}}{-C-C-}} + 2Zn \longrightarrow -C\equiv C- + 2ZnX_2$$

Example:

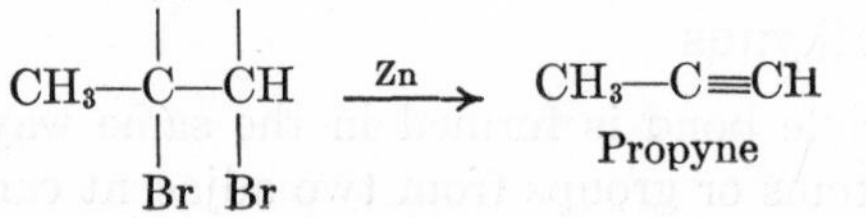

$$\underset{\underset{Br}{|}\;\underset{Br}{|}}{\overset{\overset{Br}{|}\;\overset{Br}{|}}{CH_3-C-CH}} \xrightarrow{Zn} \underset{\text{Propyne}}{CH_3-C\equiv CH}$$

Dehydrohalogenation of vicinal dihalides is particularly useful since the dihalides themselves are readily obtained from the corresponding alkenes by addition of halogen. This amounts to conversion — by several steps — of a double bond into a triple bond.

Dehydrohalogenation can generally be carried out in two stages as shown. Carried through only the first stage, it is a valuable method for

$$
\begin{array}{ccc}
\overset{\displaystyle H}{\underset{\displaystyle X}{-\!\!\overset{|}{\underset{|}{C}}\!\!-}}\overset{\displaystyle H}{\underset{\displaystyle X}{\!\!\overset{|}{\underset{|}{C}}\!\!-}} & \xrightarrow{\text{KOH (alc)}} & \overset{\displaystyle H}{-\!\!\overset{|}{C}\!\!=\!\!\overset{|}{\underset{\displaystyle X}{C}}\!\!-} & \xrightarrow{\text{NaNH}_2} & -\!\!C\!\!\equiv\!\!C\!\!-
\end{array}
$$

A vinyl halide:
Very unreactive

preparing unsaturated halides. The halides thus obtained, with halogen attached directly to doubly-bonded carbon, are called **vinyl halides,** and are very unreactive (Sec. 14.7). Under mild conditions, therefore, dehydrohalogenation stops at the vinyl halide stage; more vigorous conditions — use of a stronger base — are required for alkyne formation.

Reaction of sodium acetylides with alkyl halides permits conversion of smaller alkynes into larger ones. Practically, the reaction is limited to the use of primary halides because of the great tendency for secondary and tertiary halides to undergo a side reaction, elimination; this point will be discussed further (Sec. 6.11) after we have learned something about the nature of acetylides.

Dehalogenation of tetrahalides is severely limited by the fact that these halides are themselves generally prepared from the alkynes. As is the case with the double bond and a dihalide, the triple bond may be protected by conversion into a tetrahalide with subsequent regeneration of the triple bond by treatment with zinc.

6.7 Reactions of alkynes

Just as alkene chemistry is the chemistry of the carbon–carbon double bond, so alkyne chemistry is the chemistry of the carbon–carbon triple bond. Like alkenes, alkynes undergo electrophilic addition, and for the same reason, availability of the loosely held π electrons. For reasons that are not understood, the carbon–carbon triple bond is *less* reactive than the carbon–carbon double bond toward electrophilic reagents.

Reasonably enough, the triple bond is *more* reactive than the double bond toward reagents that are themselves electron-rich. Thus alkynes undergo a set of reactions, *nucleophilic addition*, that are virtually unknown for simple alkenes. Although time does not permit us to go into these particular reactions here, we shall take up nucleophilic addition later in connection with other kinds of compounds (Chapters 23 and 28).

Besides addition, alkynes undergo certain reactions that are due to the acidity of a hydrogen atom held by triply-bonded carbon.

REACTIONS OF ALKYNES

Addition Reactions

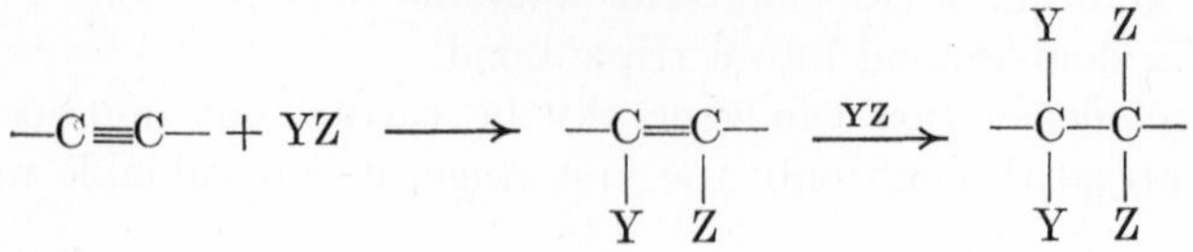

$$-C\equiv C- + YZ \longrightarrow \underset{\underset{Y}{|}\ \ \underset{Z}{|}}{-C=C-} \xrightarrow{YZ} \underset{\underset{Y}{|}\ \ \underset{Z}{|}}{\overset{\overset{Y}{|}\ \ \overset{Z}{|}}{-C-C-}}$$

1. Addition of hydrogen

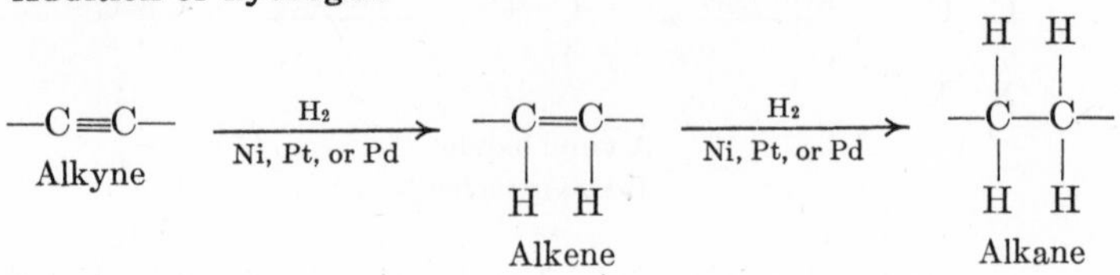

$$\underset{\text{Alkyne}}{-C\equiv C-} \xrightarrow[\text{Ni, Pt, or Pd}]{H_2} \underset{\underset{H}{|}\ \ \underset{H}{|}}{\underset{\text{Alkene}}{-C=C-}} \xrightarrow[\text{Ni, Pt, or Pd}]{H_2} \underset{\underset{H}{|}\ \ \underset{H}{|}}{\overset{\overset{H}{|}\ \ \overset{H}{|}}{\underset{\text{Alkane}}{-C-C-}}}$$

Example:

$$\underset{\text{2-Butyne}}{CH_3-C\equiv C-CH_3} \xrightarrow{H_2,\ Ni} \underset{\text{2-Butene}}{CH_3-CH=CH-CH_3} \xrightarrow{H_2,\ Ni} \underset{n\text{-Butane}}{CH_3CH_2CH_2CH_3}$$

2. Addition of halogens

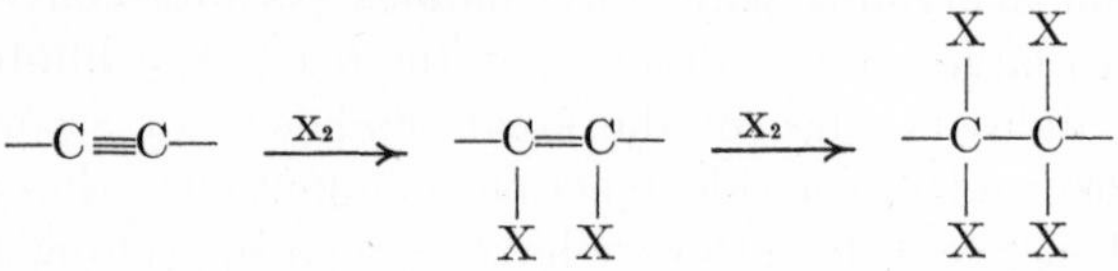

$$-C\equiv C- \xrightarrow{X_2} \underset{\underset{X}{|}\ \ \underset{X}{|}}{-C=C-} \xrightarrow{X_2} \underset{\underset{X}{|}\ \ \underset{X}{|}}{\overset{\overset{X}{|}\ \ \overset{X}{|}}{-C-C-}} \qquad X_2 = Cl_2,\ Br_2$$

Example:

$$CH_3C\equiv CH \xrightarrow{Br_2} \underset{\underset{Br}{|}\ \ \underset{Br}{|}}{CH_3-C=CH} \xrightarrow{Br_2} \underset{\underset{Br}{|}\ \ \underset{Br}{|}}{\overset{\overset{Br}{|}\ \ \overset{Br}{|}}{CH_3-C-CH}}$$

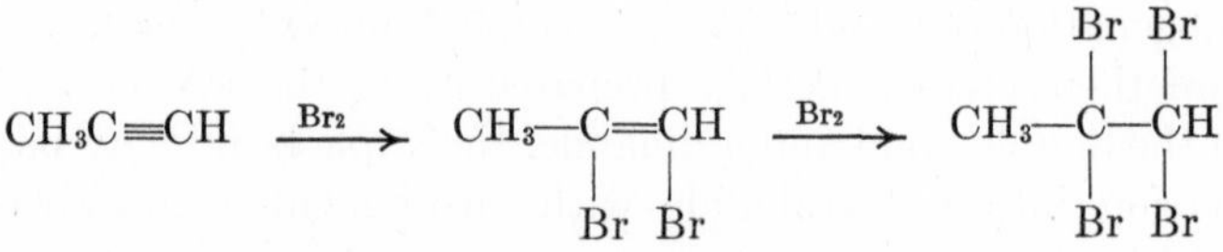

3. Addition of hydrogen halides

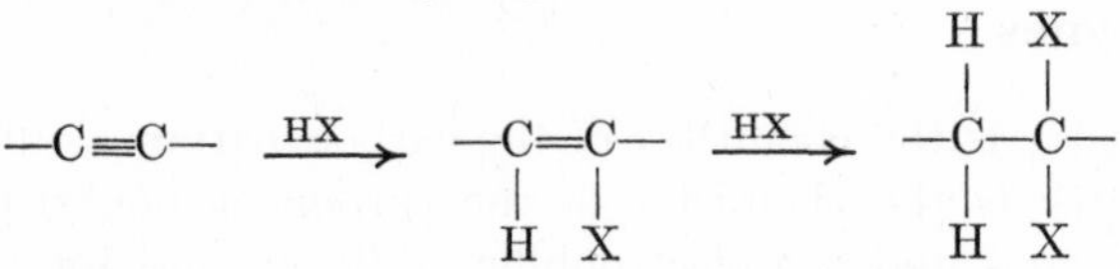

$$-C\equiv C- \xrightarrow{HX} \underset{\underset{H}{|}\ \ \underset{X}{|}}{-C=C-} \xrightarrow{HX} \underset{\underset{H}{|}\ \ \underset{X}{|}}{\overset{\overset{H}{|}\ \ \overset{X}{|}}{-C-C-}} \qquad HX = HCl,\ HBr,\ HI$$

Example:

$$CH_3C\equiv CH \xrightarrow{HCl} \underset{\underset{Cl}{|}}{CH_3C=CH_2} \xrightarrow{HI} \underset{\underset{Cl}{|}}{\overset{\overset{I}{|}}{CH_3-C-CH_3}}$$

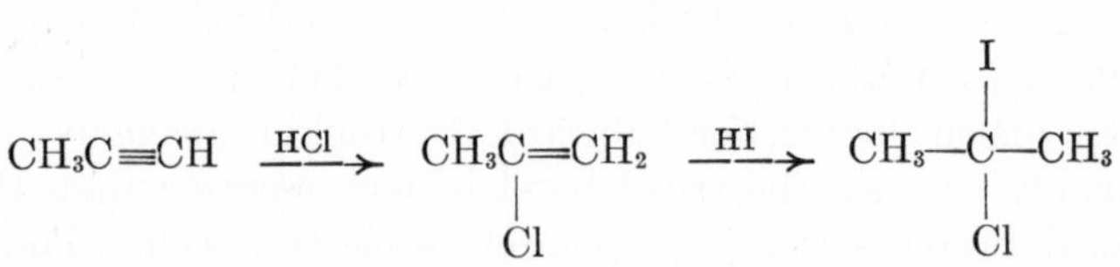

4. Addition of water. Hydration

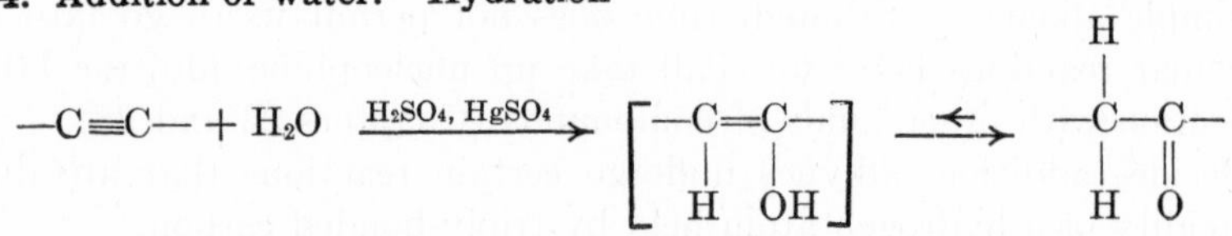

$$-C\equiv C- + H_2O \xrightarrow{H_2SO_4,\ HgSO_4} \left[\underset{\underset{H}{|}\ \ \underset{OH}{|}}{-C=C-}\right] \xleftarrow{\ } \underset{\underset{H}{|}\ \ \underset{O}{\|}}{\overset{\overset{H}{|}}{-C-C-}}$$

Examples:

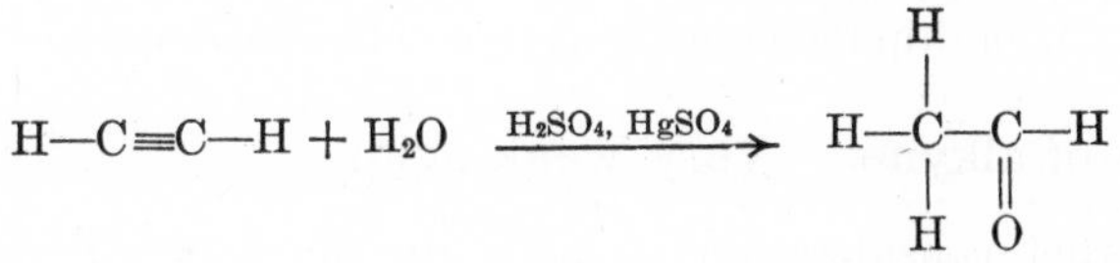

$$H-C{\equiv}C-H + H_2O \xrightarrow{H_2SO_4, HgSO_4} H-\underset{\underset{H}{|}}{\overset{\overset{H}{|}}{C}}-\underset{O}{\overset{\|}{C}}-H$$

Acetaldehyde

$$CH_3-C{\equiv}C-H + H_2O \xrightarrow{H_2SO_4, HgSO_4} H-\underset{\underset{H}{|}}{\overset{\overset{H}{|}}{C}}-\underset{O}{\overset{\|}{C}}-\underset{\underset{H}{|}}{\overset{\overset{H}{|}}{C}}-H$$

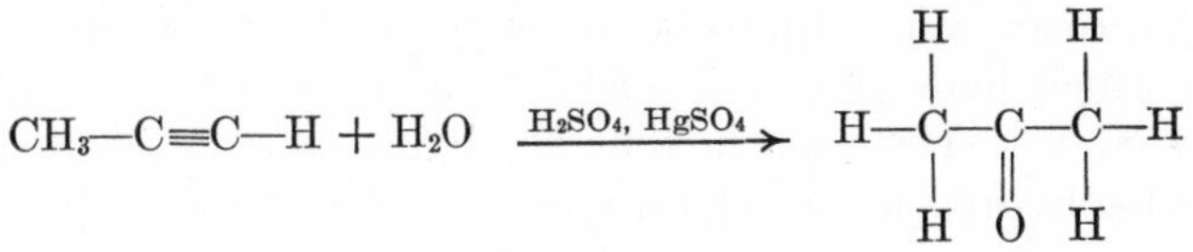

Acetone

Reactions as Acids

$$-C{\equiv}C-H + base \longrightarrow -C{\equiv}C{:}^-$$

5. Formation of heavy metal acetylides

$$-C{\equiv}C-H + M^+ \longrightarrow -C{\equiv}C-M + H^+$$

Examples:

$$H-C{\equiv}C-H + 2Ag^+ \xrightarrow{alcohol} Ag-C{\equiv}C-Ag + 2H^+$$

Silver acetylide

Identification of terminal alkynes

$$CH_3C{\equiv}C-H + Cu(NH_3)_2^+ \longrightarrow CH_3C{\equiv}C-Cu + NH_4^+ + NH_3$$

Cuprous
methylacetylide

6. Formation of alkali metal acetylides

Examples:

$$H-C{\equiv}C-H + Na \xrightarrow{liq. NH_3} H-C{\equiv}C{:}^-Na^+ + \tfrac{1}{2}H_2$$

Sodium acetylide

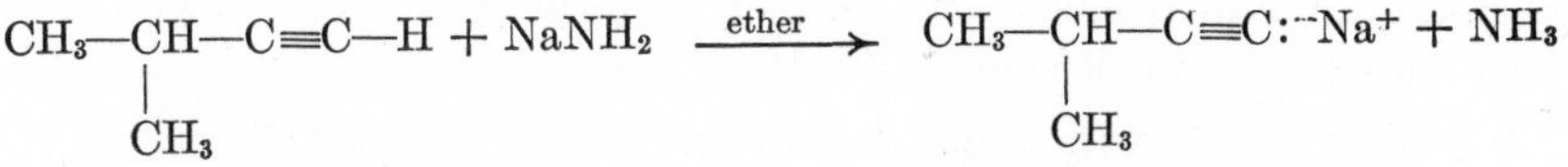

$$CH_3-\underset{\underset{CH_3}{|}}{CH}-C{\equiv}C-H + NaNH_2 \xrightarrow{ether} CH_3-\underset{\underset{CH_3}{|}}{CH}-C{\equiv}C{:}^-Na^+ + NH_3$$

Sodium isopropylacetylide

6.8 Addition reactions of alkynes

Addition of hydrogen, halogens, and hydrogen halides to alkynes is very much like addition to alkenes, except that here *two* molecules of reagent can be consumed for each triple bond. As shown, it is generally possible, by proper selection of conditions, to limit reaction to the first stage of addition, formation of alkenes. In some cases at least, this is made simpler because of the way that the atoms introduced in the first stage affect the second stage.

Problem 6.2 (a) Write the equation for the two-stage addition of bromine to 2-butyne. (b) How will the first two bromine atoms affect the reactivity of the double bond? (c) How will this influence the competition for halogen between 2-butyne and 2,3-dibromo-2-butene? (d) In what proportions would you mix the reagents to help limit reaction to the first stage? (e) Would you bubble 2-butyne into a solution of Br_2 in CCl_4, or drip the bromine solution into a solution of 2-butyne?

6.9 Acidity of alkynes. Very weak acids

In our earlier consideration of acids (in the Lowry-Brønsted sense, Sec. 1.17), we took *acidity* to be a measure of the tendency of a compound to lose a hydrogen ion. Appreciable acidity is generally shown by compounds in which hydrogen is attached to a rather electronegative atom (e.g., N, O, S, X). The bond holding the hydrogen is polar, and the relatively positive hydrogen can separate as the positive ion; considered from another viewpoint, an electronegative element can better accommodate the pair of electrons left behind. In view of the electronegativity series, $Cl > O > N > C$, it is not surprising to find that HCl is a strong acid, H_2O a comparatively weak one, NH_3 still weaker, and CH_4 so weak that we would not ordinarily consider it an acid at all.

In organic chemistry we are frequently concerned with the acidities of compounds that do not turn litmus red or taste sour, yet have a tendency — even though small — to lose a hydrogen ion.

A triply-bonded carbon acts as though it were an entirely different element — a more electronegative one — from a carbon having only single or double bonds. As a result, hydrogen attached to triply-bonded carbon, as in acetylene or any alkyne with the triple bond at the end of the chain ($RC \equiv C—H$), shows appreciable acidity. For example, sodium reacts with acetylene to liberate hydrogen gas and form the compound *sodium acetylide*.

$$HC \equiv C—H + Na \longrightarrow HC \equiv C:^- Na^+ + \tfrac{1}{2}H_2$$
Sodium acetylide

Just how strong an acid is acetylene? Let us compare it with two familiar compounds, ammonia and water.

Sodium metal reacts with ammonia to form sodamide, $NaNH_2$, which is the salt of the weak acid, $H—NH_2$.

$$NH_3 + Na \longrightarrow Na^+ NH_2^- + \tfrac{1}{2}H_2$$
Sodamide

Addition of acetylene to sodamide dissolved in ether yields ammonia and sodium acetylide.

$$HC \equiv C—H + Na^+ NH_2^- \rightleftharpoons H—NH_2 + HC \equiv C^- Na^+$$

| Stronger acid | Stronger base | Weaker acid | Weaker base |

The weaker acid, $H—NH_2$, is displaced from its salt by the stronger acid, $HC \equiv C—H$. In other language, the stronger base, NH_2^-, pulls the hydrogen ion away from the weaker base, $HC \equiv C^-$; if NH_2^- holds the hydrogen ion more tightly than $HC \equiv C^-$, then $H—NH_2$ must necessarily be a weaker acid than $HC \equiv C—H$.

Addition of water to sodium acetylide forms sodium hydroxide and regenerates acetylene.

$$\text{H—OH} + \text{HC} \equiv \text{C—Na}^+ \rightleftharpoons \text{HC} \equiv \text{C—H} + \text{Na}^+ \text{OH}^-$$

Stronger   Stronger   Weaker   Weaker
acid   base   acid   base

The weaker acid, $\text{HC} \equiv \text{C—H}$, is displaced from its salt by the stronger acid, H—OH.

Thus we see that acetylene is a stronger acid than ammonia but a weaker acid than water:

Acidity $\qquad\qquad\qquad$ $\text{H}_2\text{O} > \text{HC} \equiv \text{CH} > \text{NH}_3$

Other alkynes that have a hydrogen attached to triply-bonded carbon show comparable acidity.

The method we have just described for comparing acidities of acetylene, ammonia, and water is a general one, and has been used to determine relative acidities of a number of extremely weak acids. *One compound is shown to be a stronger acid than another by its ability to displace the second compound from salts.*

$$\text{A—H} + \text{B}^-\text{M}^+ \longrightarrow \text{B—H} + \text{A}^-\text{M}^+$$

Stronger   Weaker
acid   acid

How can we account for the fact that hydrogen attached to triply-bonded carbon is especially acidic? How can we account for the fact that acetylene is a stronger acid than, say, ethane? A possible explanation can be found in the electronic configurations of the anions.

If acetylene is a stronger acid than ethane, then the acetylide ion must be a weaker base than the ethide ion, $\text{C}_2\text{H}_5{}^-$.

$$\text{HC} \equiv \text{C:H} \rightleftharpoons \text{H}^+ + \text{HC} \equiv \text{C:}^-$$

Acetylene   Acetylide ion
Stronger   Weaker
acid   base

$$\text{CH}_3\text{CH}_2\text{:H} \longleftarrow \text{H}^+ + \text{CH}_3\text{CH}_2\text{:}^-$$

Ethane   Ethide ion
Weaker   Stronger
acid   base

In the acetylide anion the unshared pair of electrons occupies an sp orbital; in the ethide anion the unshared pair of electrons occupies an sp^3 orbital. The availability of this pair for sharing with acids determines the basicity of the anion. Now, compared with an sp^3 orbital, an sp orbital has less p character and more s character. An electron in an p orbital is at some distance from the nucleus and is held relatively loosely; an electron in an s orbital, on the other hand, is close to the nucleus and is held more tightly. The acetylide ion is the weaker base since its pair of electrons is held more tightly, in an sp orbital.

Problem 6.3 When 1-hexyne was added to a solution of n-propylmagnesium bromide, a gas was evolved. The density of the gas showed that it had a molecular weight of 44. When it was bubbled through aqueous KMnO_4 or Br_2 in CCl_4 there was no visible change. (a) What was the gas? (b) Write an equation to account for its formation. (c) How could you have predicted such a reaction?

6.10 Formation of heavy metal acetylides

The acidic acetylenes react with certain heavy metal ions, chiefly Ag^+ and Cu^+, to form insoluble acetylides. Formation of a precipitate upon addition of an alkyne to a solution of $AgNO_3$ in alcohol, for example, is an indication of hydrogen attached to triply-bonded carbon. This reaction can be used to differentiate *terminal* alkynes (those with the triple bond at the *end* of the chain) from *non-terminal* alkynes.

$$CH_3CH_2C{\equiv}C\text{-}H \xrightarrow{\ Ag^+\ } CH_3CH_2C{\equiv}C\text{-}Ag \left[\ \xrightarrow{\ HNO_3\ } CH_3CH_2C{\equiv}C\text{-}H + Ag^+\right]$$

$\quad$ 1-Butyne $\qquad\qquad\qquad$ Precipitate $\qquad\qquad\qquad\qquad\qquad$ 1-Butyne

A terminal alkyne

$$CH_3\text{---}C{\equiv}C\text{---}CH_3 \xrightarrow{\ Ag^+\ } \text{no reaction}$$

$\quad$ 2-Butyne

A non-terminal alkyne

If allowed to dry these heavy metal acetylides are likely to explode. They should be destroyed while still wet by warming with nitric acid; the strong mineral acid regenerates the weak acid, acetylene.

6.11 Reaction of sodium acetylides with alkyl halides. Substitution vs. elimination

Sodium acetylides are used in the synthesis of higher alkynes. For example:

$$HC{\equiv}C\!:^-Na^+ + C_2H_5\!:\!\ddot{X}\!: \longrightarrow HC{\equiv}C\text{---}C_2H_5 + Na^+\ :\!\ddot{X}\!:^-$$

$\qquad\qquad\qquad\qquad\qquad\qquad\qquad$ 1-Butyne

$$C_2H_5C{\equiv}C\!:^-Na^+ + CH_3\!:\!\ddot{X}\!: \longrightarrow C_2H_5C{\equiv}C\text{---}CH_3 + Na^+\ :\!\ddot{X}\!:^-$$

$\qquad\qquad\qquad\qquad\qquad\qquad\qquad$ 2-Pentyne

This reaction involves substitution of acetylide ion for halide ion. It involves attack of the acetylide ion on carbon.

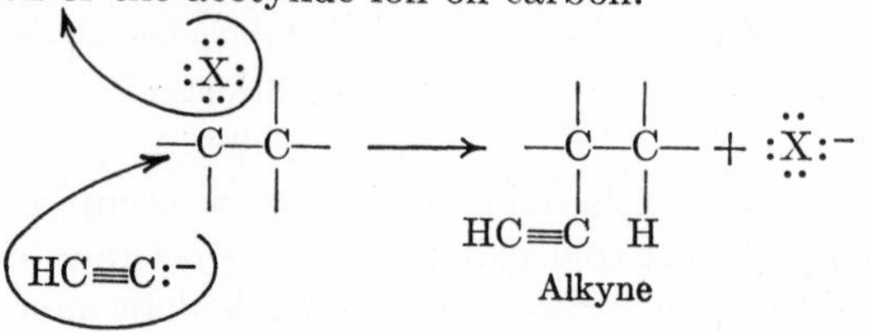

$\qquad\qquad\qquad\qquad\qquad\qquad\qquad\qquad\qquad\qquad$ **Attack on C:** *substitution*

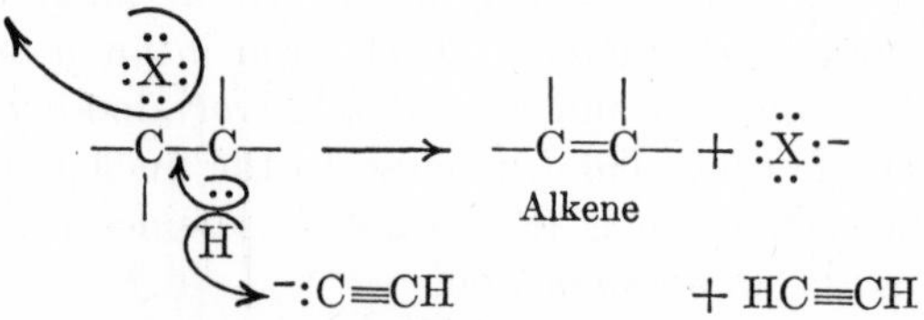

$\qquad\qquad\qquad\qquad\qquad\qquad\qquad\qquad\qquad\qquad$ **Attack on H:** *elimination*

Since sodium acetylide is the salt of the extremely weak acid, acetylene, the acetylide ion is an extremely strong base, stronger in fact than hydroxide ion. In our discussion of the synthesis of alkenes from alkyl halides (Sec. 4.13) we saw that the basic hydroxide ion causes elimination by abstracting a hydrogen ion. It is not surprising that the even more basic acetylide ion can also cause elimination.

The acetylide ion, then, can react with an alkyl halide in two ways: by attack at carbon to give **substitution,** or by attack at hydrogen to give **elimination.** Without going into the factors that determine the relative rates of these two competing reactions (Sec. 13.17), we can at least become acquainted with the facts: *Where substitution and elimination are competing reactions, the proportion of elimination increases as the structure of an alkyl halide is changed from primary to secondary to tertiary.* Many tertiary halides yield exclusively alkenes under these conditions.

Elimination increases

⟶

RX = 1°　　2°　　3°　　**Elimination vs. substitution**

⟵

Substitution increases

When the attacking reagent is a *strong* base like hydroxide or acetylide, that is, when the reagent has a strong affinity for hydrogen ion, elimination is particularly important. Practically speaking, *only primary halides give good yields of the substitution product, the alkyne.* With secondary and tertiary halides, elimination predominates to such an extent that the method is essentially useless. We shall encounter this competition between substitution and elimination again and again in our study of organic chemistry.

Problem 6.4 (a) Draw structural formulas of the alkenes formed by dehydrohalogenation of the following chlorides: ethyl, isopropyl, *tert*-butyl. (b) In Sec. 4.19 we devised a rule relating stability of alkenes to orientation of elimination, that is, relating stability to ease of formation of different alkenes from the same halide. Assuming that the same relationship holds (which it does) for formation of alkenes from *different* halides, arrange the alkenes whose structures you have drawn in order of their ease of formation. (c) What is one factor, then, that tends to increase the proportion of elimination in the reaction of tertiary and secondary halides?

Problem 6.5 (a) Draw the structural formula of the alkene obtained by dehydrohalogenation of *tert*-butyl chloride and of isobutyl chloride. (b) How many different hydrogen atoms are subject to attack by hydroxide ion in dehydrohalogenation of *tert*-butyl chloride? Of isobutyl chloride? (c) What is another factor tending to favor elimination from tertiary and secondary halides? This second factor is less important than the first.

Problem 6.6 Which would be dehydrohalogenated faster: (a) Isopropyl chloride or *sec*-butyl chloride? (b) Isobutyl chloride or isopentyl chloride?

6.12 Hydration of alkynes. Tautomerism

Addition of water to acetylene to form *acetaldehyde*, which can then be oxidized to *acetic acid*, is an extremely important industrial process.

From the structure of acetaldehyde, it at first appears that this reaction follows a different pattern from the others, in which two groups attach themselves to the two triply-bonded carbons. Actually, however, the product can be accounted for in a rather simple way.

$$\underset{\text{Acetylene}}{\text{H—C≡C—H}} \xrightarrow{\text{H}_2\text{O, H}_2\text{SO}_4,\ \text{HgSO}_4} \underset{\text{Vinyl alcohol}}{\underset{\underset{\text{H\ \ OH}}{|\ \ \ |}}{\text{H—C=C—H}}} \ \underset{\text{Acetaldehyde}}{\overset{\overset{\text{H\ \ H}}{|\ \ \ |}}{\underset{\underset{\text{H\ \ O}}{|\ \ \ ||}}{\text{H—C—C}}}}$$

If hydration of acetylene followed the same pattern as hydration of alkenes, we would expect addition of H— and —OH to the triple bond to yield the structure that we would call *vinyl alcohol*. But all attempts to prepare vinyl alcohol result — like hydration of acetylene — in the formation of acetaldehyde.

A structure with —OH attached to doubly-bonded carbon is called an **enol** (*-ene* for the carbon–carbon double bond, *-ol* for *alcohol*). It is almost always true that when we try to make a compound with the enol structure, we obtain instead a compound with the **keto** structure (one that contains a C=O group).

$$\underset{\text{Enol structure}}{\overset{|\ \ \ |}{\text{—C=C—OH}}} \quad\rightleftharpoons\quad \underset{\text{Keto structure}}{\underset{\underset{\text{H}}{|}}{\overset{|\ \ \ |}{\text{—C—C=O}}}} \qquad \textbf{Keto-enol tautomerism}$$

There is an equilibrium between the two structures, but it generally lies very much in favor of the keto form. Thus, vinyl alcohol is formed initially by hydration of acetylene, but it is rapidly converted into an equilibrium mixture that is almost all acetaldehyde.

Rearrangements of this enol-keto kind take place particularly easily because of the polarity of the —O—H bond. A hydrogen ion separates readily from oxygen, but when a hydrogen ion (most likely a *different* one) returns it may attach itself either to oxygen or to carbon. When it returns to oxygen it may readily come off again; but when it attaches itself to carbon it tends to stay there.

$$\underset{\text{Stronger acid}}{\overset{|\ \ \ |}{\text{—C=C—O—H}}} \ \rightleftharpoons\ \left[\overset{|\ \ \ |}{\text{—C=C—O}}\right]^{\ominus} + \text{H}^+ \ \rightleftharpoons\ \underset{\text{Weaker acid}}{\underset{\underset{\text{H}}{|}}{\overset{|\ \ \ |}{\text{—C—C=O}}}} \qquad \begin{array}{l}\textbf{Keto-enol}\\ \textbf{tautomerism}\end{array}$$

We recognize this reaction as another example of the conversion of a stronger acid into a weaker acid (Sec. 6.9).

Compounds whose structures differ markedly in arrangement of atoms, but which exist in equilibrium, are called **tautomers.** The most common kind of **tautomerism** involves structures that differ in the point of attachment of *hydrogen.* In these cases, as in **keto-enol tautomerism,** the tautomeric equilibrium generally favors the structure in which hydrogen is bonded to carbon rather than to a more electronegative atom; that is, equilibrium favors the weaker acid. We shall discuss factors affecting the position of the equilibrium later (Sec. 26.7).

Problem 6.7 Hydration of propyne yields the ketone *acetone*, CH_3COCH_3, rather than the aldehyde CH_3CH_2CHO. What does this suggest about the orientation of the initial addition?

DIENES

6.13 Structure and nomenclature of dienes

Dienes are simply alkenes that contain two carbon–carbon double bonds. They therefore have essentially the same properties as the alkenes we have already studied. For certain of the dienes, these alkene properties are *modified* in important ways; we shall focus our attention on these modifications. Although we shall consider chiefly *di*enes in this section, what we shall say applies equally well to compounds with more than two double bonds.

Dienes are named by the IUPAC system in the same way as alkenes, except that the ending **–diene** is used, with *two* numbers to indicate the positions of the *two* double bonds. This system is easily extended to compounds containing any number of double bonds.

$CH_2=CH-CH=CH_2$ $CH_2=CH-CH_2-CH=CH_2$ $CH_2=CH-CH=CH-CH=CH_2$
1,3-Butadiene   1,4-Pentadiene   1,3,5-Hexatriene

Dienes are divided into two important classes according to the arrangement of the double bonds. Double bonds that alternate with single bonds are said to be **conjugated**. Double bonds that are separated by more than one single bond are said to be **isolated**.

$$-\overset{|}{C}=\overset{|}{C}-\overset{|}{C}=\overset{|}{C}-\qquad\qquad -\overset{|}{C}=\overset{|}{C}-\overset{|}{\underset{|}{C}}-\overset{|}{C}=\overset{|}{C}-$$

Conjugated   Isolated
double bonds   double bonds

A third, less important class of dienes contain *cumulated* double bonds; these compounds are known as **allenes**:

$$-\overset{|}{C}=C=\overset{|}{C}-\qquad\text{cumulated double bonds: allenes}$$

6.14 Preparation and properties of dienes

Dienes are usually prepared by adaptations of the methods used to make simple alkenes. For example, the most important diene, **1,3-butadiene** (used to make synthetic rubber, Sec. 6.21), has been made in this country by a cracking process, and in Germany by dehydration of an alcohol containing two —OH groups:

$$CH_3CH_2CH_2CH_3 \xrightarrow[\text{catalyst}]{\text{heat}} \begin{bmatrix} CH_3CH_2CH=CH_2 \\ \text{1-Butene} \\[1em] CH_3CH=CHCH_3 \\ \text{2-Butene} \end{bmatrix} \xrightarrow[\text{catalyst}]{\text{heat}} CH_2=CH-CH=CH_2 \\ \text{1,3-Butadiene}$$

n-Butane

$$CH_2CH_2CH_2CH_2 \xrightarrow{\text{heat, acid}} CH_2=CH-CH=CH_2$$
$$\quad | \qquad \quad |$$
$$\quad OH \qquad OH \qquad\qquad \text{1,3-Butadiene}$$

The chemical properties of a diene depend upon the arrangement of its double bonds. Isolated double bonds exert little effect on each other, and hence each reacts as though it were the only double bond in the molecule. Except for the consumption of larger amounts of reagents, then, the chemical properties of the non-conjugated dienes are identical with those of the simple alkenes.

Conjugated dienes differ from simple alkenes in three ways: (a) they are *more stable*, (b) they undergo *1,4-addition*, and (c) they are *more reactive*.

6.15 Stability of conjugated dienes

If we look closely at Table 5.1 (page 129) we find that the heats of hydrogenation of alkenes having similar structures are remarkably constant. For monosubstituted alkenes ($RCH=CH_2$) the values are very close to 30 kcal/mole; for disubstituted alkenes ($R_2C=CH_2$ or $RCH=CHR$), 28 kcal/mole; and for trisubstituted alkenes ($R_2C=CHR$), 27 kcal/mole. For a compound containing more than one double bond we might expect a heat of hydrogenation that is the sum of the heats of hydrogenation of the individual double bonds.

For non-conjugated dienes this additive relationship is found to hold. As shown in Table 6.2, 1,4-pentadiene and 1,5-hexadiene, for example, have heats of hydrogenation very close to 2 × 30 kcal, or 60 kcal/mole.

TABLE 6.2

HEATS OF HYDROGENATION OF DIENES

Diene	ΔH of hydrogenation, kcal/mole
1,4-Pentadiene	60.8
1,5-Hexadiene	60.5
1,3-Butadiene	57.1
1,3-Pentadiene	54.1
2-Methyl-1,3-butadiene (Isoprene)	53.4
2,3-Dimethyl-1,3-butadiene	53.9
1,2-Propadiene (Allene)	71.3

For conjugated dienes, however, the measured values are slightly lower than expected. For 1,3-butadiene we might expect 2 × 30, or 60 kcal: the actual value, 57 kcal, is 3 kcal lower. In the same way the values for 1,3-pentadiene and 2,3-dimethyl-1,3-butadiene are also below the expected values by 2-4 kcal.

Heats of Hydrogenation

$$CH_2=CH-CH=CH_2 \qquad\qquad CH_3-CH=CH-CH=CH_2$$

Expected: 30 + 30 = 60 kcal   *Expected:* 28 + 30 = 58 kcal
Observed: 57   *Observed:* 54

$$
\begin{array}{cc}
\text{CH}_3 & \text{CH}_3 \\
| & | \\
\text{CH}_2{=}\text{C}\!\!-\!\!-\!\!\text{C}{=}\text{CH}_2
\end{array}
$$

Expected: $28 + 28 = 56$ kcal
Observed: 54

What do these heats of hydrogenation tell us about the conjugated dienes? Using the approach of Sec. 5.4 let us compare, for example, 1,3-pentadiene (heat of hydrogenation, 54 kcal) and 1,4-pentadiene (heat of hydrogenation, 61 kcal). They both consume two moles of hydrogen and yield the same product, *n*-pentane. If 1,3-pentadiene *evolves* less energy than 1,4-pentadiene, it can only mean that it *contains* less energy; that is to say, the conjugated 1,3-pentadiene is more stable than the non-conjugated 1,4-pentadiene.

Although there are no dienes with isolated double bonds to compare directly with the butadienes, the fact that they evolve less energy than we might have expected, suggests that they, too, are more stable. Unusual stability of conjugated dienes is strongly indicated by the fact that, where possible, they are the preferred diene products of elimination reactions (Sec. 4.19). The origin of this stability will be discussed later (Sec. 8.16).

Problem 6.8 Predict the major product of dehydrohalogenation of 4-bromo-1-hexene.

Problem 6.9 (a) Predict the heat of hydrogenation of *allene*, $\text{CH}_2{=}\text{C}{=}\text{CH}_2$. (b) The actual value is 71 kcal. What can you say about the stability of a *cumulated* diene?

6.16 Electrophilic addition to conjugated dienes. 1,4-Addition

When 1,4-pentadiene is treated with bromine under conditions (what are they?) that favor formation of the *dihalide*, there is obtained the expected product, 4,5-dibromo-1-pentene. Addition of more bromine yields the 1,2,4,5-tetrabromopentane.

$$
\text{CH}_2{=}\text{CH}{-}\text{CH}_2{-}\text{CH}{=}\text{CH}_2 \xrightarrow{\text{Br}_2}
\underset{\substack{| \quad | \\ \text{Br} \; \text{Br}}}{\text{CH}_2{-}\text{CH}{-}\text{CH}_2{-}\text{CH}{=}\text{CH}_2}
\xrightarrow{\text{Br}_2}
\underset{\substack{| \quad | \qquad | \quad | \\ \text{Br} \; \text{Br} \quad\; \text{Br} \; \text{Br}}}{\text{CH}_2{-}\text{CH}{-}\text{CH}_2{-}\text{CH}{-}\text{CH}_2}
$$

This is typical of the behavior of dienes containing isolated double bonds; the double bonds react independently, as though they were in different molecules.

When 1,3-butadiene is treated with bromine under similar conditions, there is obtained not only the expected 3,4-dibromo-1-butene, but also 1,4-dibromo-2-butene. Treatment with HCl yields not only 3-chloro-1-butene, but also 1-chloro-2-butene. Hydrogenation yields not only 1-butene but also 2-butene.

$$\text{CH}_2\text{=CH–CH=CH}_2 \quad
\begin{cases}
\xrightarrow{\text{Br}_2} & \underset{\text{1,2-addition}}{\overset{\displaystyle \text{CH}_2\text{–CH–CH=CH}_2}{\underset{\text{Br}}{|}\;\underset{\text{Br}}{|}}} \quad\text{and}\quad \underset{\text{1,4-addition}}{\overset{\displaystyle \text{CH}_2\text{–CH=CH–CH}_2}{\underset{\text{Br}}{|}\qquad\qquad\underset{\text{Br}}{|}}}\\[2em]
\xrightarrow{\text{HCl}} & \underset{\text{1,2-addition}}{\overset{\displaystyle \text{CH}_2\text{–CH–CH=CH}_2}{\underset{\text{H}}{|}\;\underset{\text{Cl}}{|}}} \quad\text{and}\quad \underset{\text{1,4-addition}}{\overset{\displaystyle \text{CH}_2\text{–CH=CH–CH}_2}{\underset{\text{H}}{|}\qquad\qquad\underset{\text{Cl}}{|}}}\\[2em]
\xrightarrow[\text{cat.}]{\text{H}_2} & \underset{\text{1,2-addition}}{\overset{\displaystyle \text{CH}_2\text{–CH–CH=CH}_2}{\underset{\text{H}}{|}\;\underset{\text{H}}{|}}} \quad\text{and}\quad \underset{\text{1,4-addition}}{\overset{\displaystyle \text{CH}_2\text{–CH=CH–CH}_2}{\underset{\text{H}}{|}\qquad\qquad\underset{\text{H}}{|}}}
\end{cases}$$

CH₂=CH–CH=CH₂ — 1,3-Butadiene

Study of many conjugated dienes and many reagents shows that such behavior is typical: *in* **additions to conjugated dienes,** *a reagent may attach itself not only to a pair of adjacent carbons* (**1,2-addition**), *but also to the carbons at the two ends of the conjugated system* (**1,4-addition**). Very often the 1,4-addition product is the major one.

$$\underset{1\quad2\quad3\quad4}{-\text{C=C–C=C}-} \quad\xrightarrow{\text{YZ}}\quad \underset{\text{1,2-addition}}{-\text{C–C–C=C}-\ \underset{\text{Y}\ \ \text{Z}}{|\ |}} \quad\text{and}\quad \underset{\text{1,4-addition}}{-\text{C–C=C–C}-\ \underset{\text{Y}\qquad\text{Z}}{|\qquad|}}$$

How can we account for the products obtained? We have seen (Secs. 5.10 and 5.12) that electrophilic addition is a two-step process, and that the first step takes place in the way that yields the more stable carbonium ion. Let us apply this principle to the addition, for example, of HCl to 2,4-hexadiene, which yields 4-chloro-2-hexene and 2-chloro-3-hexene:

$$\text{CH}_3\text{–CH=CH–CH=CH–CH}_3 \xrightarrow{\text{HCl}} \underset{\text{4-Chloro-2-hexene}}{\text{CH}_3\text{–CH–CH–CH=CH–CH}_3 \atop \underset{\text{H}}{|}\ \underset{\text{Cl}}{|}}$$

2,4-Hexadiene

$$+\ \underset{\text{2-Chloro-3-hexene}}{\text{CH}_3\text{–CH–CH=CH–CH–CH}_3 \atop \underset{\text{H}}{|}\qquad\qquad\underset{\text{Cl}}{|}}$$

These products show that hydrogen adds to C–2 to yield carbonium ion I, rather than to C–3 to yield carbonium ion II:

$$\text{CH}_3\text{–CH=CH–CH=CH–CH}_3 + \text{H}^+ \begin{cases}
\longrightarrow & \underset{\mathbf{I}}{\text{CH}_3\text{–CH–CH–CH=CH–CH}_3 \atop \underset{\text{H}}{|}\ \overset{\oplus}{}}\\[2em]
\not\longrightarrow & \underset{\mathbf{II}}{\text{CH}_3\text{–CH–CH–CH=CH–CH}_3 \atop \underset{\oplus}{}\ \underset{\text{H}}{|}}
\end{cases}$$

Since both I and II are secondary carbonium ions, how can we account for the preference? I is not simply a secondary carbonium ion, but is an *allyl* carbonium ion as well, since the carbon bearing the positive charge is attached to a doubly-bonded carbon. We have already seen (Sec. 5.21) that allyl radicals are unusually stable; there is considerable evidence that allyl carbonium ions are also unusually stable, and good theoretical reasons (Sec. 9.23) that they *should be*. We can now expand the sequence of Sec. 4.17.

Stability of carbonium ions $\text{allyl} > 3° > 2° > 1° > CH_3^+$

The products obtained from addition to conjugated dienes are always consistent with the formation of an intermediate allyl carbonium ion; this requires the first step to be *addition to one of the ends* of the conjugated system.

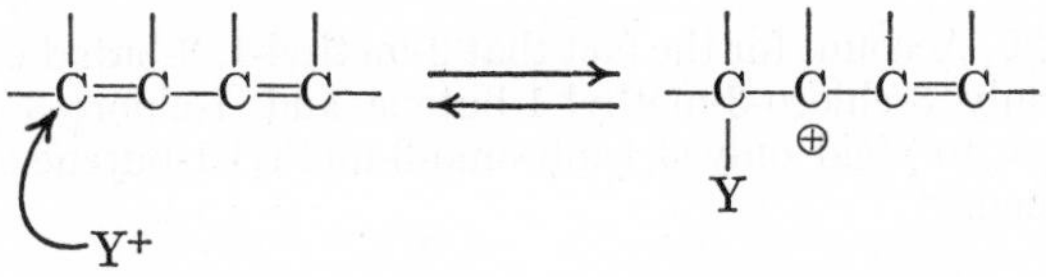

Adds to end of conjugated system   An allyl carbonium ion

How is it that the second step of addition to 2,4-hexadiene yields both 1,2- and 1,4-addition products? If we examine the allyl carbonium ion (I) more closely we see that we could just as well have drawn its structure as in III:

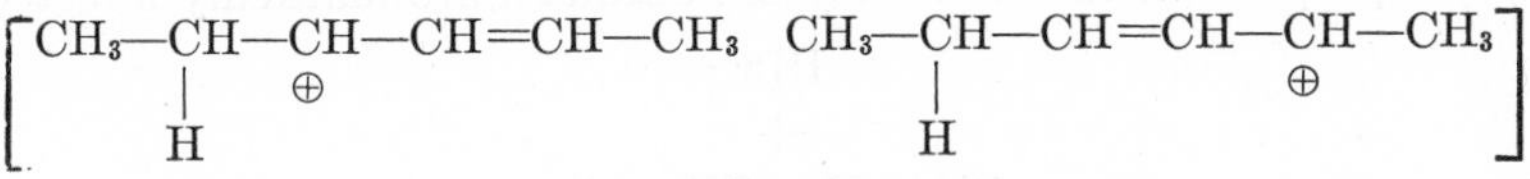

equivalent to

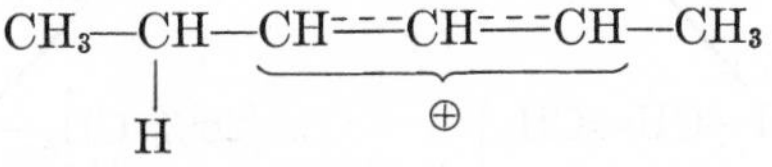

III differs from I in location of the double bond and of the positive charge. Without going into details now, we can simply say that whenever we can draw two structures that differ only in the positions of the electrons — as

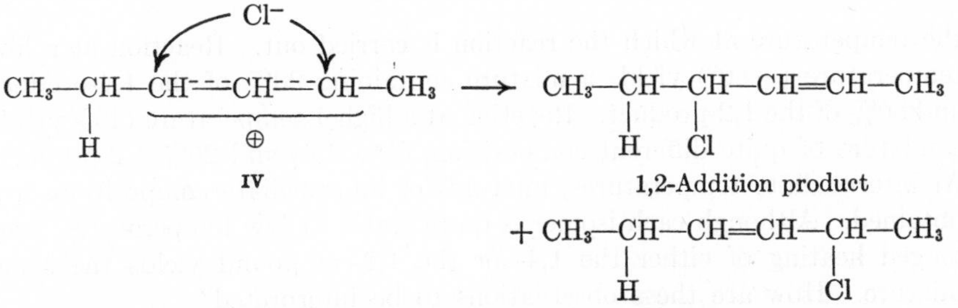

                                        1,2-Addition product

                                        $+$ CH₃—CH—CH=CH—CH—CH₃

                                        1,4-Addition product

these do — neither structure alone adequately represents the molecule concerned (Resonance, Chapter 8). For the present let us accept the fact that the positive charge is not localized on either carbon atom but is spread over both (IV). The negative chloride ion can attach itself to either of these carbons and thus yield the 1,2- or 1,4-product.

We have not shown *why* 1,4-addition occurs; we have simply shown that it is not unreasonable that it *does* happen. In summary,

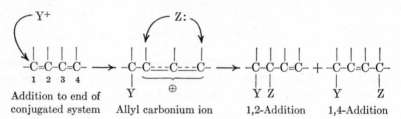

| Addition to end of conjugated system | Allyl carbonium ion | 1,2-Addition | 1,4-Addition |

Problem 6.10 Account for the fact that 2-methyl-1, 3-butadiene reacts (a) with HCl to yield only 3-chloro-3-methyl-1-butene and 1-chloro-3-methyl-2-butene; (b) with bromine to yield only 3,4-dibromo-3-methyl-1-butene and 1,4-dibromo-2-methyl-2-butene.

6.17   1,2- vs. 1,4-Addition.   Rate vs. equilibrium

A very important principle emerges when we look at the relative amounts of 1,2- and 1,4-addition products obtained.

Addition of HBr to 1,3-butadiene yields both the 1,2- and the 1,4-products; the *proportions* in which they are obtained are markedly affected by

$$HBr$$
$$+$$
$$CH_2=CH—CH=CH_2$$

−80° ↙   ↘ 40°

$$\left\{\begin{array}{l} 80\% \ CH_2—CH—CH=CH_2 \\ \qquad \quad | \qquad | \\ \qquad \quad H \quad \ Br \\[4pt] 20\% \ CH_2—CH=CH—CH_2 \\ \qquad \quad | \qquad \qquad \quad | \\ \qquad \quad H \qquad \qquad \ Br \end{array}\right\}$$

$$\xrightarrow{40°}$$

$$\left\{\begin{array}{l} 20\% \ CH_2—CH—CH=CH_2 \\ \qquad \quad | \qquad | \\ \qquad \quad H \quad \ Br \\[4pt] 80\% \ CH_2—CH=CH—CH_2 \\ \qquad \quad | \qquad \qquad \quad | \\ \qquad \quad H \qquad \qquad \ Br \end{array}\right\}$$

the temperature at which the reaction is carried out. Reaction at a low temperature (−80°) yields a mixture containing 20% of the 1,4-product and 80% of the 1,2-product. Reaction at a higher temperature (40°) yields a mixture of quite different composition, 80% 1,4- and 20% 1,2-product. At intermediate temperatures, mixtures of intermediate compositions are obtained. Although each isomer is quite stable at low temperatures, prolonged heating of either the 1,4- or the 1,2-compound yields the same mixture. How are these observations to be interpreted?

The fact that either compound is converted into the same mixture by heating indicates that this mixture is the result of equilibrium between the two compounds. The fact that the 1,4-compound predominates in the equilibrium mixture indicates that it is the more stable of the two.

The fact that more 1,2- than 1,4-product is obtained at $-80°$ indicates that the 1,2-product is formed *faster* than the 1,4-product; since each compound remains unchanged at $-80°$, the proportions in which they are isolated show the proportions in which they were initially formed. As the reaction temperature is raised, the proportions in which the products are initially formed may remain the same, but there is faster conversion of the initially formed products into the equilibrium mixture.

The proportions of products actually isolated from the low-temperature addition is determined by the **rates** of addition, whereas for the high-temperature addition it is determined by the **equilibrium** between the two isomers.

Let us examine the matter of 1,2- and 1,4-addition more closely by drawing a potential energy curve for the reactions involved (Figure 6.6).

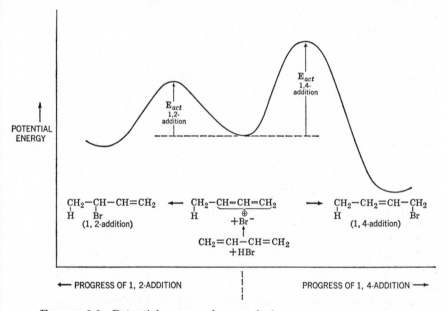

FIGURE 6.6. Potential energy changes during progress of reaction: 1,2- vs. 1,4-addition.

The carbonium ion initially formed reacts faster to yield the 1,2-product than 1,4-product; consequently the energy of activation leading to the 1,2-product must be less than that leading to the 1,4-product. We represent this by the lower hill leading from the ion to the 1,2-product. More collisions have enough energy to climb the low hill than the high hill, so that the 1,2-compound is formed faster than the 1,4-compound. The 1,4-product, however, is more stable than the 1,2-product, and hence we must place its valley at a lower level than that of the 1,2-product.

We shall see later (Sec. 13.12) that alkyl halides, and particularly allyl halides, can undergo ionization. Now ionization of either bromo compound yields the same carbonium ion; the most likely — and simplest — way in which the 1,2- and 1,4-products reach equilibrium is through this ion.

$$\text{CH}_2\text{—CH—CH=CH}_2 \underset{\longrightarrow}{\longleftrightarrow} \text{CH}_2\text{—CH} \overset{\oplus}{=\!=\!=} \text{CH} =\!=\!= \text{CH}_2 \underset{\longleftarrow}{\rightharpoonup} \text{CH}_2\text{—CH=CH—CH}_2$$

$$\begin{array}{cccc} | \quad | & & | & | \quad\quad | \\ \text{H} \quad \text{Br} & & \text{H} & \text{H} \quad\quad \text{Br} \\ \text{1,2-} & + \text{Br}^- & & \text{1,4-} \end{array}$$

$$\uparrow$$

$$\text{CH}_2\text{=CH—CH=CH}_2$$
$$+ \text{HBr}$$

Ionization of the bromides involves climbing the potential hills back toward this carbonium ion. But there is a higher hill separating the ion from the 1,4-product than from the 1,2-product; consequently the 1,4-product will ionize more slowly than the 1,2-product. Equilibrium is reached when the rates of the opposing reactions are equal. The 1,2-product is formed rapidly, but ionizes rapidly. The 1,4-product is formed slowly, but ionizes even more slowly; once formed the 1,4-product tends to persist. At temperatures high enough for equilibrium to be reached, the more stable 1,4-product predominates.

We have not tried to account for the fact that the 1,2-product is formed faster than the 1,4-product, or for the fact that the 1,4-product is more stable than the 1,2-product (although we notice that this is consistent with our generalization that disubstituted alkenes are more stable than mono-substituted alkenes). We have accepted these facts and have simply tried to show what they mean in terms of energy considerations. Similar relationships have been observed for other dienes and reagents.

These facts illustrate two important points. First, we must be cautious when we interpret product composition in terms of rates of reaction; we must be sure that one product is not converted into the other *after* its formation. Second, the more stable product is by no means *always* formed faster. *On the basis of much evidence,* we have concluded that *generally* the more stable a carbonium ion or free radical, the faster it is formed; a consideration of the transition states for the various reactions has shown (Secs. 3.27, 4.18, and 5.12) that this is reasonable. W*e must not, however, extend this principle to other reactions unless the evidence warrants this.*

Problem 6.11   Addition of one mole of bromine to 1,3,5-hexatriene yields only 5,6-dibromo-1,3-hexadiene and 1,6-dibromo-2,4-hexadiene. (a) Are these products consistent with the formation of the most stable intermediate carbonium ion? (b) What other product or products would also be consistent? (c) Actually, which factor appears to be in control, rate or position of equilibrium?

6.18   Free radical addition to conjugated dienes: orientation

Like other alkenes, conjugated dienes undergo addition not only by electrophilic reagents but also by free radicals. In free radical addition, conjugated dienes show two special features: they undergo 1,4-addition as well as 1,2-addition, and they are **much more reactive** than ordinary alkenes. We can account for both features — *orientation* and *reactivity* — by examining the structure of the intermediate free radical.

Let us take as an example addition of $BrCCl_3$ to 1,3-butadiene in the presence of a peroxide. The peroxide decomposes (step 1) to yield a free radical, which abstracts bromine from $BrCCl_3$ (step 2) to generate a $\cdot CCl_3$ radical.

(1) $\qquad\qquad\qquad$ Peroxide $\longrightarrow$ Rad$\cdot$

(2) $\qquad\qquad$ Rad$\cdot$ + BrCCl$_3$ $\longrightarrow$ Rad—Br + $\cdot$CCl$_3$

The $\cdot CCl_3$ radical thus formed adds to the butadiene (step 3). Addition to one of the *ends* of the conjugated system is the preferred reaction, since this yields an *allyl* free radical, which we know to be an extremely stable one (Sec. 5.21). The allyl free radical (like the allyl carbonium ion) can be represented by two structures that differ only in arrangement of electrons; as a result the radical does not correspond to either, but to an intermediate structure in which the odd electron is distributed over two carbons (see Resonance, Chapter 8).

(3) $\underset{1 \quad\;\; 2 \quad\;\; 3 \quad\;\; 4}{CH_2{=}CH{-}CH{=}CH_2}$ $\overset{\cdot CCl_3}{\nearrow}$ $\longrightarrow$ $\begin{bmatrix} Cl_3C{-}CH_2{-}\overset{\cdot}{C}H{-}CH{=}CH_2 \\ Cl_3C{-}CH_2{-}CH{=}CH{-}\overset{\cdot}{C}H_2 \end{bmatrix}$

Addition to end of conjugated system

equivalent to

$$Cl_3C{-}CH_2{-}CH{=\!=\!=}CH{=\!=\!=}CH_2$$

Allyl free radical

The allyl free radical then abstracts bromine from a molecule of $BrCCl_3$ (step 4) to complete the addition, and in doing so forms a new $\cdot CCl_3$ radical which can carry on the chain. In step (4) bromine can become attached to either C–2 or C–4, to yield either the 1,2- or 1,4-product.

(4) $Cl_3C{-}CH_2{-}CH{=\!=\!=}CH{=\!=\!=}CH_2$ $\xrightarrow{\;BrCCl_3\;}$ $Cl_3C{-}CH_2{-}\underset{\underset{Br}{|}}{CH}{-}CH{=}CH_2$

Allyl free radical $\qquad\qquad$ 1,2-Addition product

and $\qquad$ $Cl_3C{-}CH_2{-}CH{=}CH{-}CH_2{-}Br$

1,4-Addition product

Problem 6.12 *N-Bromosuccinimide*, $C_4H_4O_2N$–Br, is a reagent often used to replace selectively allylic hydrogen by bromine; it is believed to do this by a free radical mechanism analogous to the one described in Sec. 2.12. When 1-octene is

$\qquad$ Rad$\cdot$ + C$_4$H$_4$O$_2$N—Br $\longrightarrow$ Rad—Br + C$_4$H$_4$O$_2$N$\cdot$

$\qquad$ C$_4$H$_4$O$_2$N$\cdot$ + RH $\longrightarrow$ C$_4$H$_4$O$_2$N—H + R$\cdot$

$\qquad$ R$\cdot$ + C$_4$H$_4$O$_2$NBr $\longrightarrow$ R—Br + C$_4$H$_4$O$_2$N$\cdot$

allowed to react with this reagent, there is obtained not only 3-bromo-1-octene but also 1-bromo-2-octene. How could you account for this?

6.19   Free radical addition to conjugated dienes: reactivity

If $BrCCl_3$ is allowed to react with a 50:50 mixture of 1,3-butadiene and a simple alkene like 1-octene, addition occurs almost exclusively to the 1,3-butadiene.   Evidently the $\cdot CCl_3$ radical adds much more rapidly to the conjugated diene than to the simple alkene.   Similar results have been observed in a great many radical additions.

How can we account for the unusual reactivity of conjugated dienes? In our discussion of halogenation of the simple alkanes (Sec. 3.26), we found that not only orientation but also relative reactivity was related to the stability of the free radical formed in the first step.   On this basis alone, we might expect addition to a conjugated diene, which yields a stable allyl free radical, to occur faster than addition to a simple alkene.

On the other hand, we have just seen (Sec. 6.15) that conjugated dienes are more stable than simple alkenes.   On this basis alone, we might expect addition to conjugated dienes to occur more slowly than to simple alkenes.

The relative rates of the two reactions depend chiefly upon the E_{act}'s. Stabilization of the incipient allyl free radical lowers the energy level of the transition state; stabilization of the diene lowers the energy of the reactants.   Whether the net E_{act} is larger or smaller than for addition to a simple alkene depends upon *which* is stabilized *more* (see Figure 6.7).

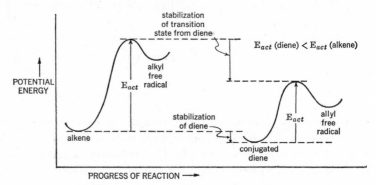

FIGURE 6.7.   Molecular structure and rate of reaction.   Stability of transition state parallels stability of free radical: more stable free radical formed faster.

The fact is that conjugated dienes are more reactive than simple alkenes. In the present case, then — and in most cases involving alkenes and free radicals, or alkenes and carbonium ions — the factors stabilizing the transition state are more important than the factors stabilizing the reactant.   However, this is *not always* true.

POLYMERIZATION

6.20   Free radical polymerization of alkenes

One of the most important reactions of simple alkenes and conjugated dienes is **polymerization**.

When ethylene is heated under pressure with oxygen, there is obtained a compound of high molecular weight (about 20,000), which is essentially an alkane with a very long chain. This compound is made up of many

$$nCH_2\!\!=\!\!CH_2 \quad \xrightarrow{\text{O}_2,\ \text{heat, pressure}} \quad \text{\textasciitilde}CH_2\!-\!CH_2\!-\!CH_2\!-\!CH_2\!-\!CH_2\!-\!CH_2\text{\textasciitilde}$$

$$\text{or} \quad (-CH_2CH_2-)_n$$
Polyethylene

ethylene units and hence is called *polyethylene* (**poly** = many). As Polythene it is familiar to most of us as the plastic material of flexible bottles, children's toys, and packaging films.

The formation of polyethylene is a simple example of the process called **polymerization**: *the joining together of many small molecules to make very large molecules.* The compound composed of these very large molecules is called a **polymer** (from the Greek, *poly + meros*, many parts). The simple compounds from which polymers are made are called **monomers** (*mono* = one).

The particular kind of polymerization undergone by ethylene, in which many molecules of monomer are simply added together, is called *addition polymerization.* (Later on, in Sec. 25.5, we shall encounter *condensation polymerization*, in which monomer molecules combine with the loss of some simple molecules, usually water.) Addition polymerization is one of the most important reactions of alkenes and conjugated dienes alike — and, indeed, of compounds of all kinds that contain carbon–carbon double bonds.

Polymerization of substituted ethylenes yields compounds whose structures contain the long chain of polyethylene, with substituents attached at more or less regular intervals. For example, vinyl chloride

$$nCH_2\!\!=\!\!CH \quad \xrightarrow{\text{peroxides}} \quad \text{\textasciitilde}CH_2\!-\!CH\!-\!CH_2\!-\!CH\!-\!CH_2\!-\!CH\text{\textasciitilde}$$

$$\underset{Cl}{|} \qquad\qquad \underset{Cl}{|} \quad \underset{Cl}{|} \quad \underset{Cl}{|}$$
Vinyl chloride

$$\text{or} \quad (-CH_2\!-\!CH\!-\!)_n$$
$$\underset{Cl}{|}$$
Polyvinyl chloride

yields *polyvinyl chloride*, used in phonograph records, enamels, and as the basis of Koroseal (shower curtains, raincoats, and a substitute for rubber). Many other groups (e.g., $-COOCH_3$, $-CN$, $-C_6H_5$) may be attached to the doubly-bonded carbons. These substituted ethylenes polymerize more or less readily, and yield plastics of widely differing physical properties and uses, but the polymerization process and the structure of the polymer are basically the same as for ethylene or vinyl chloride.

Polymerization requires the presence of a small amount of an **initiator.** Among the commonest of these initiators are peroxides, the same compounds that bring about free radical addition to alkenes (Sec. 5.7). Here, too, a peroxide is believed to function by breaking down to form a free radical. This radical adds to a molecule of alkene, and in doing so generates another free radical. This radical adds to another molecule of alkene to generate a still larger radical, which in turn adds to another molecule of alkene, and so on. Eventually the chain is terminated by steps, such as union of two radicals, that consume but do not generate radicals.

$$\text{Peroxide} \longrightarrow \text{Rad}\cdot$$

$$\left. \begin{array}{l} \text{Rad}\cdot + \text{CH}_2\text{=CH} \longrightarrow \text{RadCH}_2\text{–CH}\cdot \\ \qquad\qquad\quad | \qquad\qquad\qquad\quad | \\ \qquad\qquad\quad R \qquad\qquad\qquad\quad R \end{array} \right\} \quad \text{Chain-initiating steps}$$

$$\text{RadCH}_2\text{–CH}\cdot + \text{CH}_2\text{=CH} \longrightarrow \text{RadCH}_2\text{–CH–CH}_2\text{–CH}\cdot \longrightarrow etc.$$
$$\qquad\quad | \qquad\qquad\quad | \qquad\qquad\qquad\quad | \qquad\quad\; | $$
$$\qquad\quad R \qquad\qquad\quad R \qquad\qquad\qquad\quad R \qquad\quad R$$

Chain-propagating step

Problem 6.13 Give the structure of the monomer from which each of the following polymers would most likely be made:

Orlon (fibers, fabrics): $\sim\!\!\sim\!\text{CH}_2\text{CH(CN)CH}_2\text{CH(CN)}\sim\!\!\sim$

Saran (packaging film, seat covers): $\sim\!\!\sim\!\text{CH}_2\text{CCl}_2\text{CH}_2\text{CCl}_2\sim\!\!\sim$

Teflon (chemically resistant articles): $\sim\!\!\sim\!\text{CF}_2\text{CF}_2\text{CF}_2\text{CF}_2\sim\!\!\sim$

Problem 6.14 Can you suggest a reason why polymerization should take place in a way ("head-to-tail") that yields a polymer with regularly alternating groups?

6.21 Free radical polymerization of dienes. Synthetic rubber

Polymerization of conjugated dienes is of special interest because it leads to synthetic rubbers. Indeed, polymerization of dienes to form substitutes for rubber was the forerunner of the enormous present-day plastics industry. Polymerization of 1,3-butadiene or 2-chloro-1,3-butadiene (*chloroprene*), for example, yields products whose structures indicate that 1,4-addition occurs predominantly:

$$\text{Rad}\cdot + \text{CH}_2\text{=CH–CH=CH}_2 + \text{CH}_2\text{=CH–CH=CH}_2 + \text{CH}_2\text{=CH–CH=CH}_2 + \ldots$$
1,3-Butadiene

$$\text{Rad—CH}_2\text{—CH=CH—CH}_2\text{—CH}_2\text{—CH=CH—CH}_2\text{—CH}_2\text{—CH=CH—CH}_2 \sim\!\!\sim$$

$$\text{Rad}\cdot + \text{CH}_2\text{=CH–C=CH}_2 + \text{CH}_2\text{=CH–C=CH}_2 + \text{CH}_2\text{=CH–C=CH}_2 + \ldots$$
$$\qquad\qquad\qquad\quad | \qquad\qquad\qquad\qquad | \qquad\qquad\qquad\qquad |$$
$$\qquad\qquad\qquad\; \text{Cl} \qquad\qquad\qquad\quad \text{Cl} \qquad\qquad\qquad\quad \text{Cl}$$
Chloroprene

$$\text{Rad—CH}_2\text{—CH=C—CH}_2\text{—CH}_2\text{—CH=C—CH}_2\text{—CH}_2\text{—CH=C—CH}_2\sim\!\!\sim$$
$$\qquad\qquad\qquad\quad | \qquad\qquad\qquad\qquad | \qquad\qquad\qquad\qquad |$$
$$\qquad\qquad\qquad\; \text{Cl} \qquad\qquad\qquad\quad \text{Cl} \qquad\qquad\qquad\quad \text{Cl}$$

These polymers differ in one very important way from the polymers of simple alkenes: each unit still contains one double bond. In this respect they resemble natural rubber, which has a structure we might consider to be a polymer of the conjugated diene 2-methyl-1,3-butadiene, **isoprene.**

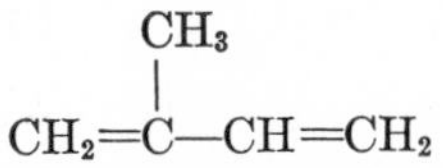

$$\begin{matrix} & CH_3 \\ & | \\ CH_2{=}C{-}CH{=}CH_2 \end{matrix} \qquad \left[\begin{matrix} CH_3 \\ | \\ {-}CH_2{-}C{=}CH{-}CH_2{-} \end{matrix} \right]_n$$

Isoprene 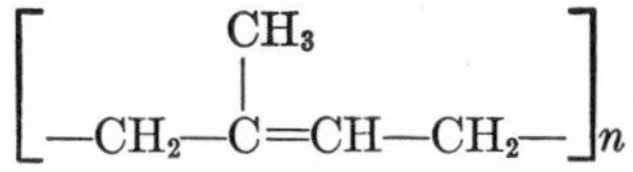   Natural rubber

The double bonds in the rubber molecule are highly important, since they permit *vulcanization*, the formation of sulfur bridges between different chains. These *cross-links* make the rubber harder and stronger, and do away with the tackiness of the untreated rubber.

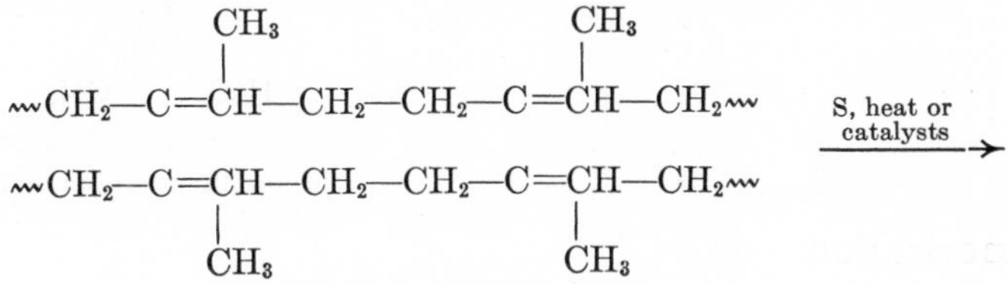

$$\begin{matrix} & CH_3 & & CH_3 \\ & | & & | \\ \text{\small www}CH_2{-}C{=}CH{-}CH_2{-}CH_2{-}C{=}CH{-}CH_2\text{\small www} \\ \\ \text{\small www}CH_2{-}C{=}CH{-}CH_2{-}CH_2{-}C{=}CH{-}CH_2\text{\small www} \\ & | & & | \\ & CH_3 & & CH_3 \end{matrix} \qquad \xrightarrow{\substack{S, \text{ heat or} \\ \text{catalysts}}}$$

Natural rubber

$$\begin{matrix} & CH_3 & & CH_3 \\ & | & & | \\ \text{\small www}CH{-}C{=}CH{-}CH_2{-}CH{-}C{=}CH{-}CH_2\text{\small www} \\ & | & & \\ & S & & S \\ & | & & \\ \text{\small www}CH{-}C{=}CH{-}CH_2{-}CH_2{-}C{=}CH{-}CH\text{\small www} \\ & | & & | \\ & CH_3 & & CH_3 \end{matrix}$$

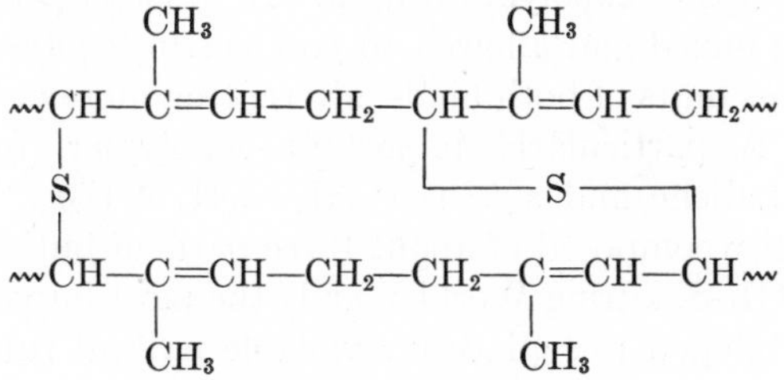

Vulcanized rubber

The properties of a synthetic rubber — like those of other polymers — are determined, in part, by the nature of the substituent groups. For example, *polychloroprene* (Neoprene, Duprene), which was the first commercially successful artificial rubber in the United States, is inferior to natural rubber in some properties but superior in its resistance to oil, gasoline, and other organic solvents.

The isoprene unit seems to be one of nature's favorite building blocks, occurring in a great number of compounds isolated from plant and animal sources. For example, nearly all the **terpenes** (found in the essential oils of many plants) have carbon skeletons made up of isoprene units joined in a regular, head-to-tail way. Recognition of this fact — the so-called **isoprene rule** — has been of great help in working out structures of terpenes.

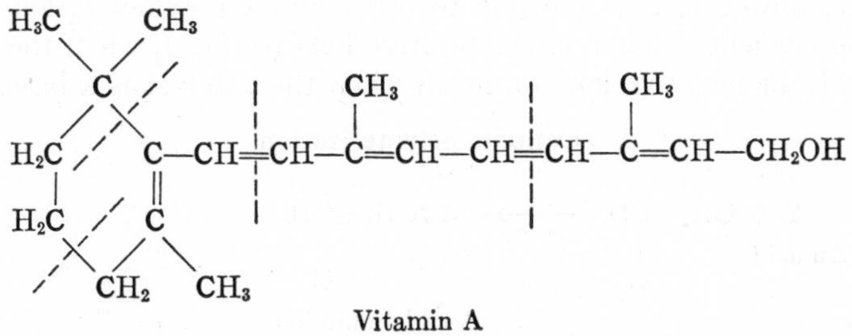

Vitamin A

$$CH_2\!\!=\!\!\underset{\underset{CH_3}{|}}{C}\!\!-\!\!CH_2\!\!-\!\!CH_2\!\!-\!\!CH_2\!\!-\!\!\underset{\underset{CH_3}{|}}{CH}\!\!-\!\!CH_2\!\!-\!\!CH_2OH$$

Citronellol: *a terpene*
(found in oil of geranium)

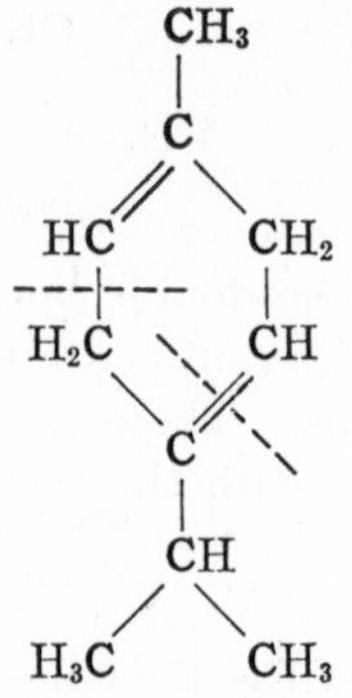

γ-Terpinene: *a terpene*
(found in coriander oil)

6.22 Copolymerization

A further way to modify the properties of a polymer is through the process of **copolymerization.** Here two (or more) unsaturated compounds are mixed and allowed to polymerize together. The polymer formed contains units of both kinds, alternating more or less regularly along the chain.

A particularly important copolymer, for example, is one between butadiene and *styrene* (C_6H_5—CH=CH$_2$). This material, which is generally composed of about three parts of butadiene and one part of styrene, is GR-S, during World War II the most important of the synthetic rubbers developed to replace unavailable natural rubber. Since the war the synthetic rubber industry has continued to expand, largely because of the demands of the automobile industry.

$$CH_2\!\!=\!\!CH\!\!-\!\!CH\!\!=\!\!CH_2 + CH_2\!\!=\!\!CH\!\!-\!\!CH\!\!=\!\!CH_2 + \underset{\underset{C_6H_5}{|}}{CH_2\!\!=\!\!CH} + CH_2\!\!=\!\!CH\!\!-\!\!CH\!\!=\!\!CH_2$$

1,3-Butadiene   Styrene

initiator

$$\sim\!\!CH_2\!\!-\!\!CH\!\!=\!\!CH\!\!-\!\!CH_2\!\!-\!\!CH_2\!\!-\!\!CH\!\!=\!\!CH\!\!-\!\!CH_2\!\!-\!\!CH_2\!\!-\!\!\underset{\underset{C_6H_5}{|}}{CH}\!\!-\!\!CH_2\!\!-\!\!CH\!\!=\!\!CH\!\!-\!\!CH_2\!\!\sim$$

GR-S

6.23 Ionic polymerization

So far, we have discussed only the kind of addition polymerization that takes place by way of free radicals. By use of different initiators or catalysts, however, it is possible to bring about polymerization that involves intermediate ions: either positive ions (*cations*), when the catalyst is an acid; or negative ions (*anions*), when the catalyst is a base.

Cationic polymerization

$$Y + \underset{\underset{G}{|}}{CH_2\!\!=\!\!CH} \longrightarrow Y\!:\!CH_2\!\!-\!\!\overset{\oplus}{\underset{\underset{G}{|}}{CH}}$$

An acid

A carbonium ion

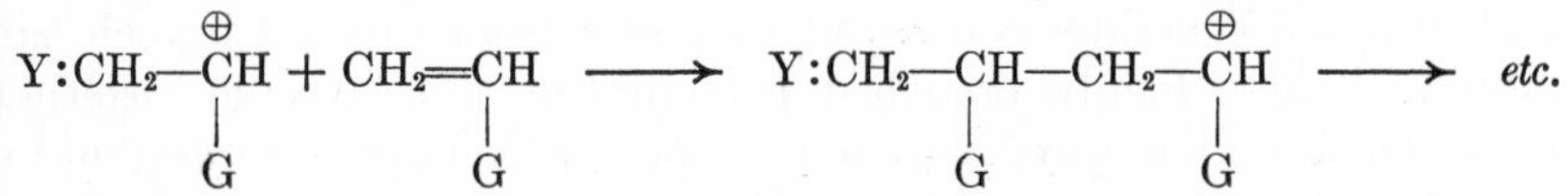

$$Y:CH_2\overset{\oplus}{-}CH + CH_2=CH \longrightarrow Y:CH_2-CH-CH_2\overset{\oplus}{-}CH \longrightarrow etc.$$
$$\qquad\ \ \ \ \ |\qquad\qquad\ \ | \qquad\qquad\qquad\qquad |\qquad\qquad\ \ |$$
$$\qquad\ \ \ \ \ G\qquad\qquad\ \ G \qquad\qquad\qquad\qquad G\qquad\qquad\ \ G$$

Anionic polymerization

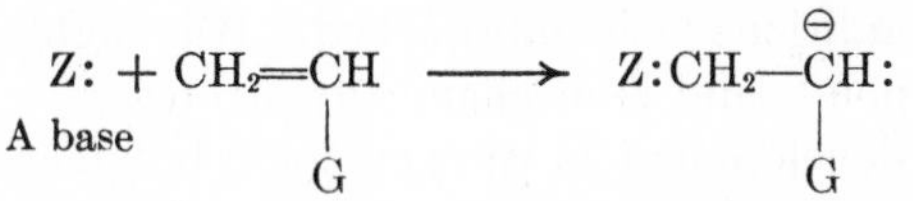

$$Z: + CH_2=CH \longrightarrow Z:CH_2\overset{\ominus}{-}CH:$$
A base
$$\qquad\qquad\qquad |\qquad\qquad\qquad\qquad\ \ |$$
$$\qquad\qquad\qquad G\qquad\qquad\qquad\qquad\ \ G$$

A carbanion

$$Z:CH_2\overset{\ominus}{-}CH: + CH_2=CH \longrightarrow Z:CH_2-CH-CH_2\overset{\ominus}{-}CH: \longrightarrow etc.$$
$$\qquad\ \ |\qquad\qquad\qquad\ \ |\qquad\qquad\qquad\qquad\ \ |\qquad\qquad\ \ |$$
$$\qquad\ \ G\qquad\qquad\qquad\ \ G\qquad\qquad\qquad\qquad\ \ G\qquad\qquad\ \ G$$

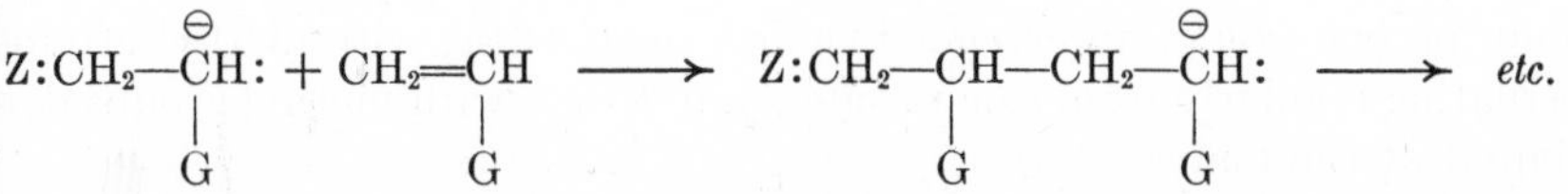

Until 1953, almost all addition polymerizations of commercial importance were of the free radical type. A notable exception was the acid-catalyzed (cationic) polymerization of isobutylene with a little butadiene to yield *butyl rubber*, used to make automobile inner tubes. We recognize this process as an extension of the dimerization we discussed earlier (Sec. 5.17).

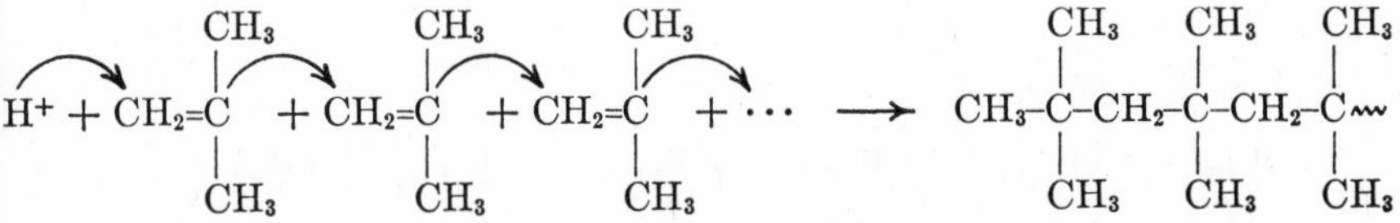

Since 1953, however, ionic polymerization has grown to such an extent that it has revolutionized the field of polymerization. Following discoveries by Karl Ziegler (of the Max Planck Institute for Coal Research) and by Giulio Natta (of the Polytechnic Institute of Milan), catalysts have been developed that permit control of the polymerization process to a degree never before possible. These catalysts include such substances as a triethylaluminum-titanium trichloride complex and finely divided lithium metal. Let us look briefly at just two aspects of these new developments, which illustrate the importance of the basic concepts of structural theory.

First, there is the matter of *chain branching*. Polyethylene made by the free radical process has highly branched chains. At the high temperature required for this particular polymerization, the growing free radicals not only *add* to the double bond of a monomer molecule but also *abstract* hydrogen from a chain already formed.

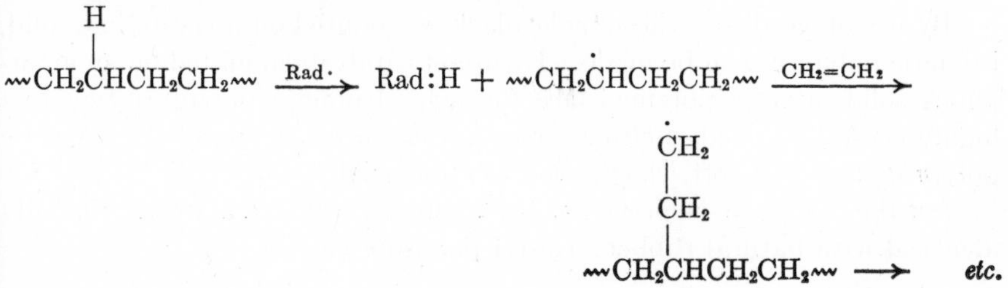

This abstraction generates a free radical center from which a branch can now grow. These highly branched polyethylene molecules fit together poorly and in a random way; the compound is said to have low *crystallinity*. It has a low melting point, and is mechanically weak.

In contrast, the newer polyethylene — made via ions instead of free radicals, and under mild conditions — is unbranched. It is highly crystalline, has a higher melting point, and is mechanically strong.

A second, far-reaching development in the new ionic polymerization is *stereochemical control*. Propylene, for example, could polymerize to any of three different arrangements (Figure 6.8): *isotactic*, with all methyl groups on one side of an extended chain; *syndiotactic*, with methyl groups alternating regularly from side to side; and *atactic*, with methyl groups distributed at random.

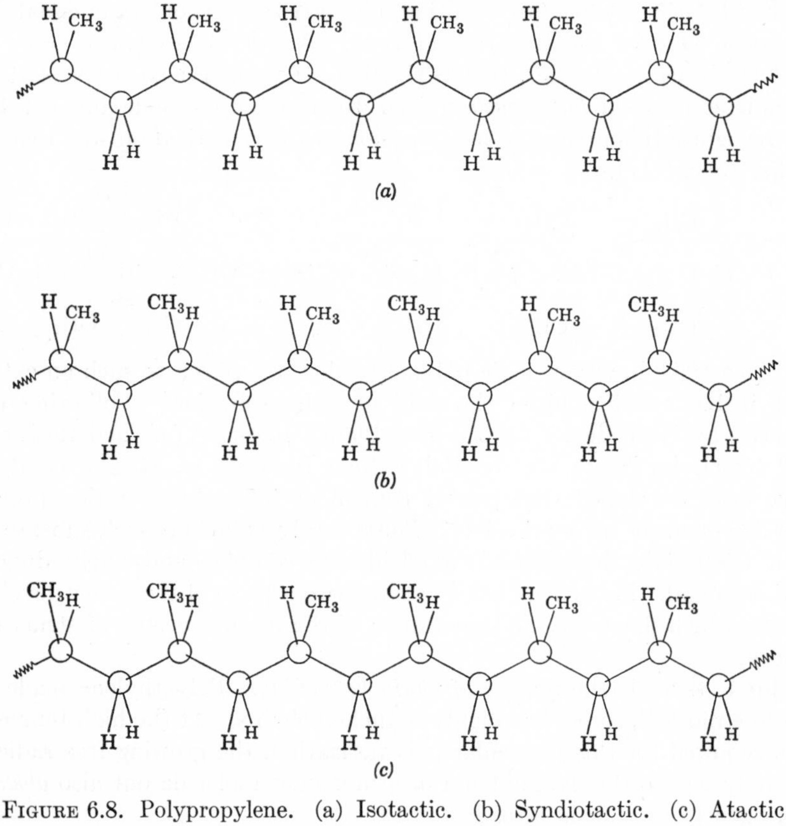

(a)

(b)

(c)

FIGURE 6.8. Polypropylene. (a) Isotactic. (b) Syndiotactic. (c) Atactic.

By use of catalysts whose molecules are mounted on a crystalline solid, isotactic polymers can be made. By use of catalysts mounted on an amorphous solid, atactic polymers are formed. Isotactic polypropylene is a highly crystalline, high-melting material that forms strong fibers. Atactic polypropylene is a soft, elastic, rubbery material.

For the first time, isoprene has been polymerized to a material virtually identical with natural rubber: *cis*-1,4-polyisoprene.

$$
\begin{array}{c}
\text{H} \qquad\qquad \text{CH}_3\ \text{H} \qquad\qquad \text{CH}_3\ \text{H} \qquad\qquad \text{CH}_3 \\
\diagdown \qquad\qquad\ \diagdown\ \diagdown \qquad\qquad\ \diagdown\ \diagdown \qquad\qquad\ \diagdown \\
\quad \text{C}\!=\!\text{C} \qquad\quad \text{C}\!=\!\text{C} \qquad\quad \text{C}\!=\!\text{C} \\
\diagup \qquad\ \diagdown\qquad\ \diagup \qquad\ \diagdown\qquad\ \diagup \qquad\ \diagdown \\
\text{\~CH}_2 \qquad \text{CH}_2\text{CH}_2 \qquad \text{CH}_2\text{CH}_2 \qquad \text{CH}_2\text{\~}
\end{array}
$$

"A chemist setting out to build a giant molecule is in the same position as an architect designing a building. He has a number of building blocks of certain shapes and sizes, and his task is to put them together in a structure to serve a particular purpose. . . . What makes high polymer chemistry still more exciting just now is that almost overnight, within the last few years, there have come discoveries of new ways to put the building blocks together — discoveries which promise a great harvest of materials that have never existed on the earth." (Giulio Natta, *Scientific American*, September 1957, p. 98.)

6.24 Analysis of alkynes and dienes

Alkynes and dienes respond to characterization tests in the same way as alkenes: they decolorize bromine in carbon tetrachloride without evolution of hydrogen bromide, and they decolorize cold, neutral, dilute permanganate. They are, however, more unsaturated than alkenes. This property can be detected by determination of their molecular formulas (C_nH_{2n-2}) and by a quantitative hydrogenation (two moles of hydrogen are taken up per mole of hydrocarbon).

Proof of structure is best accomplished by the same degradative methods that are used in studying alkenes. Upon ozonolysis alkynes yield carboxylic acids, whereas alkenes yield aldehydes and ketones. For example:

$$
\text{CH}_3\text{CH}_2\text{C}\!\equiv\!\text{CCH}_3 \ \xrightarrow{\text{O}_3}\ \xrightarrow{\text{H}_2\text{O}}\ \text{CH}_3\text{CH}_2\text{COOH} + \text{HOOCCH}_3
$$

2-Pentyne   Carboxylic acids

Ozonolysis of dienes yields aldehydes and ketones, including double-ended ones containing two C=O groups per molecule. For example:

$$
\begin{array}{c}
\text{CH}_3 \qquad\qquad\qquad\qquad\qquad \text{H} \qquad \text{CH}_3 \qquad\qquad \text{H} \\
| \qquad\qquad\qquad\qquad\qquad\qquad\ | \qquad\quad | \qquad\qquad\quad | \\
\text{CH}_2\!=\!\text{C}\!-\!\text{CH}\!=\!\text{CH}_2 \ \xrightarrow{\text{O}_3}\ \xrightarrow{\text{H}_2\text{O, Zn}}\ \text{H}\!-\!\text{C}\!=\!\text{O} + \text{O}\!=\!\text{C}\!-\!\text{C}\!=\!\text{O} + \text{O}\!=\!\text{C}\!-\!\text{H} \\
| \\
\text{H}
\end{array}
$$

A terminal alkyne ($RC\!\equiv\!CH$) is characterized, and differentiated from isomers, by its conversion into insoluble silver and cuprous acetylides (Sec. 6.10).

Problem 6.15 Contrast the ozonolysis products of the following isomers: (a) 1-pentyne; (b) 2-pentyne; (c) 3-methyl-1-butyne; (d) 1,3-pentadiene; (e) 1,4-pentadiene; (f) isoprene (2-methyl-1,3-butadiene).

Problem 6.16 Predict the ozonolysis products from polybutadiene, $(C_4H_6)_n$: (a) if 1,2-addition is involved in the polymerization; (b) if 1,4-addition is involved.

Problem 6.17 Ozonolysis of natural rubber yields chiefly (90%) the compound shown on the next page. What does this tell us about the structure of rubber?

$$\begin{array}{ccc} H & & CH_3 \\ | & & | \\ O{=}C{-}CH_2{-}CH_2{-}C{=}O \end{array}$$

PROBLEMS

1. (a) Draw structures of the seven isomeric alkynes of formula C_6H_{10}. (b) Give the IUPAC and derived name of each. (c) Indicate which ones will react with Ag^+ or $Cu(NH_3)_2{}^+$. (d) Draw structures of the ozonolysis products expected from each.

2. (a) Draw structures of all isomeric dienes of formula C_6H_{10}, omitting cumulated dienes. (b) Name each one. (c) Indicate which ones are conjugated. (d) Indicate which ones can show geometric isomerism, and draw the isomeric structures. (e) Draw structures of the ozonolysis products expected from each. (f) Which isomers (other than *cis-trans* pairs) could not be distinguished on the basis of (e)?

3. Write equations for all steps in the manufacture of acetylene starting from limestone and coal.

4. Outline all steps in the synthesis of propyne from each of the following compounds, using any needed organic or inorganic reagents. Follow the other directions given in Problem 17, page 160.

(a) 1,2-dibromopropane
(b) propylene
(c) isopropyl bromide
(d) propane
(e) *n*-propyl alcohol
(f) 1,1-dichloropropane
(g) acetylene
(h) 1,1,2,2-tetrabromopropane

5. Outline all steps in the synthesis from acetylene of each of the following compounds, using any needed organic or inorganic reagents.

(a) ethylene
(b) ethane
(c) ethylidene bromide (1,1-dibromoethane)
(d) vinyl chloride
(e) 1,2-dichloroethane
(f) acetaldehyde
(g) propyne
(h) 1-butyne
(i) 2-butyne
(j) 1-pentyne
(k) 2-pentyne
(l) 3-hexyne
(m) silver acetylide

6. Give structures and names of the organic products expected from the reaction (if any) of 1-butyne with:

(a) 1 mole H_2, Ni
(b) 2 moles H_2, Ni
(c) 1 mole Br_2
(d) 2 moles Br_2
(e) 1 mole HCl
(f) 2 moles HCl
(g) H_2O, H^+, Hg^{++}
(h) Ag^+
(i) product (h) + HNO_3
(j) $NaNH_2$
(k) product (j) + C_2H_5Br
(l) product (j) + *tert*-butyl chloride
(m) C_2H_5MgBr
(n) product (m) + H_2O
(o) O_3, then H_2O
(p) hot $KMnO_4$

7. Answer Problem 6 for 1,3-butadiene instead of 1-butyne.

8. Answer Problem 6 for 1,4-pentadiene instead of 1-butyne.

9. Give structures and names of the products expected from dehydrohalogenation of each of the following halides. Where more than one product is expected, indicate which will be the major product.

(a) 1-chlorobutane; 2-chlorobutane
(b) 1-chlorobutane; 4-chloro-1-butene
(c) 2-bromo-2-methylbutane; 3-bromo-2-methylbutane
(d) 1-bromo-2-methylbutane; 4-bromo-2-methylbutane
(e) 1-chloro-2,3-dimethylbutane; 2-chloro-2,3-dimethylbutane
(f) 4-chloro-1-butene; 5-chloro-1-pentene

10. Which alkyl halide of each pair in Problem 9 would you expect to undergo dehydrohalogenation faster?

11. Give structures of the chief product or products expected from addition of HCl to:

(a) 1,3-butadiene; 1-butene   (c) 1,3-butadiene; 2-methyl-1,3-butadiene
(b) 1,3-butadiene; 1,4-pentadiene   (d) 1,3-butadiene; 1,3-pentadiene

12. Which compound of each pair in Problem 11 would you expect to be more reactive toward addition of HCl?

13. Answer Problems 11 and 12 for the addition of $BrCCl_3$ in the presence of peroxides (Sec. 6.18) instead of addition of HCl.

14. (a) The heat of hydrogenation of acetylene (converted into ethane) is 75.0 кcal/mole. Calculate ΔH for hydrogenation of acetylene to ethylene. (b) How does the stability of an alkyne relative to an alkene compare with the stability of an alkene relative to an alkane? (c) Solely on the basis of your answer to (b), would you expect acetylene to be more or less reactive than ethylene toward addition of a free methyl radical, $CH_3 \cdot$? (d) Draw the structure of the free radical expected from addition of $CH_3 \cdot$ to acetylene: from addition of $CH_3 \cdot$ to ethylene. Judging only from the relative stabilities of the radicals being formed, would you expect $CH_3 \cdot$ to add to acetylene faster or slower than to ethylene? (e) $CH_3 \cdot$ has been found to add more slowly to acetylene than to ethylene. Which factor — reactant stability or radical stability — is more important here?

15. (a) Describe the electronic configuration of allene, $H_2C{=}C{=}CH_2$, a cumulated diene. (*Hint:* how many atoms are attached to the middle carbon? to each of the end carbons?) (b) What shape would you expect the molecule to have? In particular, what is the geometric relationship between the two hydrogens at one end of the molecule and the two hydrogens at the other end? (*Hint:* use models.)

16. A useful method of preparing 1-alkenes involves reaction of Grignard reagents with the unusually reactive halide, allyl bromide:

$$RMgX + BrCH_2CH{=}CH_2 \longrightarrow R{-}CH_2CH{=}CH_2$$

When 1-hexene (b.p. 63.5°) is prepared in this way, it is contaminated with *n*-hexane (b.p. 69°) and 1,5-hexadiene (b.p. 60°); these are difficult to remove because of the closeness of boiling points. The mixture is treated with bromine and the product distilled. There are obtained three fractions: b.p. 68–69°; b.p. 77–78° at 15 mm pressure; and a high-boiling residue.

(a) What does each of these fractions contain? (b) What would you do next to get pure 1-hexene? (c) Show how this procedure could be applied to the separation of *n*-pentane (b.p. 36°) and 1-pentene (b.p. 30°); 1-decene (b.p. 171°) and 5-decyne (b.p. 175°).

17. *Gutta percha* is a non-elastic naturally-occurring polymer used in covering golf balls and underwater cables. It has the same formula, $(C_5H_8)_n$, and yields the same hydrogenation product and the same ozonolysis product (Problem 6.17, page 191) as natural rubber. Using structural formulas, show the most likely structural difference between gutta percha and rubber.

18. Isobutylene does not give the kinds of stereoisomeric polymers (isotactic, etc.) that propylene does. Why not? What can you say about 1-butene?

19. Like other oxygen-containing compounds, alcohols dissolve in cold concentrated H_2SO_4 (Sec. 5.23). In the case of some secondary and tertiary alcohols, dissolution is followed by the gradual separation of an insoluble liquid of high boiling point. How do you account for this behavior?

20. Describe simple chemical tests that would distinguish between:

(a) 2-pentyne and *n*-pentane
(b) 1-pentyne and 1-pentene
(c) 1-pentyne and 2-pentyne
(d) 1,3-pentadiene and *n*-pentane

(e) 1,3-pentadiene and 1-pentyne
(f) 2-hexyne and isopropyl alcohol
(g) allyl bromide and 2,3-dimethyl-1,3-butadiene

Tell exactly what you would *do* and *see*.

21. Describe chemical methods (not necessarily simple tests) that would distinguish between:

(a) 2-pentyne and 2-pentene
(b) 1,4-pentadiene and 2-pentene

(c) 1,4-pentadiene and 2-pentyne
(d) 1,4-pentadiene and 1,3-pentadiene

22. On the basis of physical properties, an unknown compound is believed to be one of the following:

n-pentane (b.p. 36°)
2-pentene (b.p. 36°)
1-chloropropene (b.p. 37°)
trimethylethylene (b.p. 39°)

1-pentyne (b.p. 40°)
methylene chloride (b.p. 40°)
3,3-dimethyl-1-butene (b.p. 41°)
1,3-pentadiene (b.p. 42°)

Describe how you would go about finding out which of the possibilities the unknown actually is. Where possible, use simple chemical tests; where necessary, use more elaborate chemical methods like quantitative hydrogenation and cleavage. Tell exactly what you would *do* and *see*.

23. A hydrocarbon of formula C_6H_{10} absorbs only *one* mole of H_2 upon catalytic hydrogenation. Upon ozonolysis the hydrocarbon yields

$$O=\overset{\overset{H}{|}}{C}-CH_2-CH_2-CH_2-CH_2-\overset{\overset{H}{|}}{C}=O$$

What is the structure of the hydrocarbon? (Check your answer in Sec. 7.15.)

24. A hydrocarbon was found to have a molecular weight of 80–85. A 10.02-mg sample took up 8.40 cc of H_2 gas measured at 0° and 760 mm pressure. Ozonolysis yielded only

$$H-\underset{\underset{O}{\|}}{C}-H \quad \text{and} \quad H-\underset{\underset{O}{\|}}{C}-\underset{\underset{O}{\|}}{C}-H$$

What was the hydrocarbon?

25. *Myrcene*, $C_{10}H_{16}$, a terpene isolated from oil of bay, absorbs three moles of hydrogen to form $C_{10}H_{22}$. Upon ozonolysis myrcene yields:

$$CH_3-\underset{\underset{O}{\|}}{C}-CH_3 \quad H-\underset{\underset{O}{\|}}{C}-H \quad H-\underset{\underset{O}{\|}}{C}-CH_2-CH_2-\underset{\underset{O}{\|}}{C}-\underset{\underset{O}{\|}}{C}-H$$

(a) What structures are consistent with these facts?
(b) On the basis of the isoprene rule (Sec. 6.21), what is the most likely structure for myrcene?

26. *Dihydromyrcene*, $C_{10}H_{18}$, formed from myrcene (Problem 25), absorbs two moles of hydrogen to form $C_{10}H_{22}$. Upon cleavage by $KMnO_4$, dihydromyrcene yields:

$$CH_3-\underset{\underset{O}{\|}}{C}-CH_3 \quad CH_3-\underset{\underset{O}{\|}}{C}-OH \quad CH_3-\underset{\underset{O}{\|}}{C}-CH_2-CH_2-\underset{\underset{O}{\|}}{C}-OH$$

(a) Keeping in mind the isoprene rule, what is the most likely structure for dihydromyrcene? (b) Is it surprising that a compound of this structure is formed by reduction of myrcene?

Chapter seven

CYCLIC ALIPHATIC
HYDROCARBONS

7.1 Open-chain and cyclic compounds

In the compounds that we have studied in previous chapters, the carbon atoms are attached to one another to form *chains;* these are called **open-chain** compounds. In many compounds, however, the carbon atoms are arranged to form *rings;* these are called **cyclic** compounds.

In this chapter we shall take up the *cycloalkanes* and *cycloalkenes.* We already know most of the chemistry of these cyclic aliphatic hydrocarbons, since it is essentially the same as the chemistry of open-chain alkanes and alkenes. There are, however, certain differences in properties that are due to the cyclic nature of these compounds, and it is on these exceptional properties that we shall focus our attention.

7.2 Nomenclature

Cyclic aliphatic hydrocarbons are named by prefixing **cyclo-** to the name of the corresponding open-chain hydrocarbon having the same number of carbon atoms as the ring. For example:

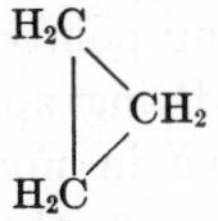

Cyclopropane 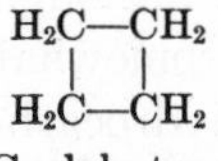   Cyclobutane 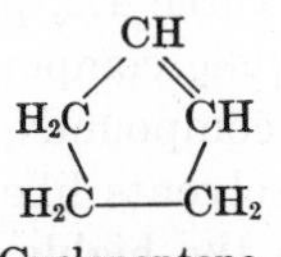   Cyclopentene

Substituents on the ring are named, and their positions are indicated by numbers, the lowest combination of numbers being used. In simple cyclo-alkenes and cycloalkynes the doubly- and triply-bonded carbons are considered to occupy positions 1 and 2. For example:

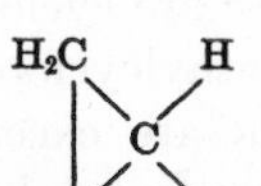

Chlorocyclopropane 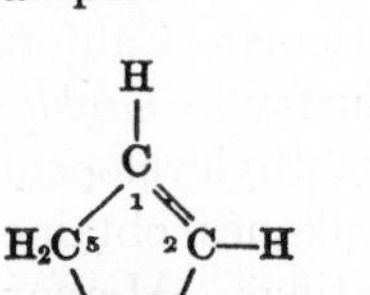   3-Ethylcyclopentene

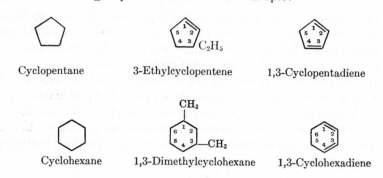

For convenience, aliphatic rings are often represented by simple geometric figures: a triangle for cyclopropane, a square for cyclobutane, a pentagon for cyclopentane, a hexagon for cyclohexane, and so on. It is understood that two hydrogens are located at each corner of the figure unless some other group is indicated. For example:

Cyclopentane   3-Ethylcyclopentene   1,3-Cyclopentadiene

Cyclohexane   1,3-Dimethylcyclohexane   1,3-Cyclohexadiene

7.3 Physical properties

The physical properties of cyclic aliphatic hydrocarbons (Table 7.1) resemble those of the corresponding open-chain hydrocarbons (Table 3.3, page 72, and Table 4.2, page 109), although the boiling points and densities of the cyclic compounds are somewhat higher. Being non-polar or weakly polar compounds, cyclic hydrocarbons dissolve in non-polar or weakly polar solvents like carbon tetrachloride, ligroin, or ether, and do not dissolve in the highly polar solvent water.

7.4 Industrial source

We have already mentioned (Sec. 3.13) that petroleum from certain areas (in particular, California) is rich in cycloalkanes, known to the petroleum industry as *naphthenes*. Among these are cyclohexane, methylcyclohexane, methylcyclopentane, and 1,2-dimethylcyclopentane.

The cycloalkanes obtained from petroleum are excellent fuels with high octane ratings. Moreover, these cycloalkanes can be converted (by *hydroforming*, Sec. 9.4) into aromatic hydrocarbons, and thus they provide one of the major sources of those important compounds.

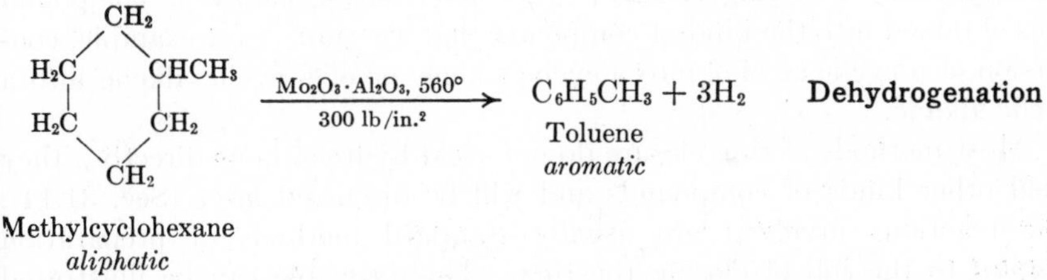

$$\text{Methylcyclohexane} \xrightarrow[\text{300 lb/in.}^2]{\text{Mo}_2\text{O}_3 \cdot \text{Al}_2\text{O}_3,\ 560°} \text{C}_6\text{H}_5\text{CH}_3 + 3\text{H}_2 \qquad \textbf{Dehydrogenation}$$

Methylcyclohexane
aliphatic

Toluene
aromatic

Just as elimination of hydrogen from cyclic aliphatic compounds yields aromatic compounds, so addition of hydrogen to aromatic compounds yields cyclic aliphatic compounds, specifically cyclohexane derivatives. An important example of this is the hydrogenation of phenol (Sec. 22.1) to the cyclic alcohol, *cyclohexanol*.

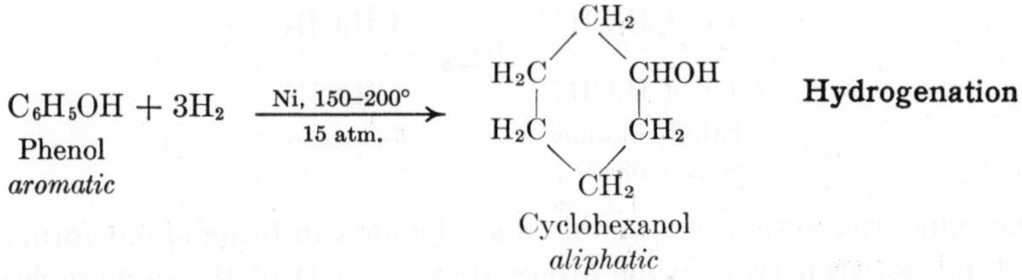

$$\text{C}_6\text{H}_5\text{OH} + 3\text{H}_2 \xrightarrow[\text{15 atm.}]{\text{Ni, 150–200°}} \qquad \textbf{Hydrogenation}$$

Phenol
aromatic

Cyclohexanol
aliphatic

From cyclohexanol many other cyclic compounds containing a six-membered ring can be made.

TABLE 7.1

CYCLIC ALIPHATIC HYDROCARBONS

Name	M.p., °C	B.p., °C	Density at 20°C
Cyclopropane	−127	− 33	
Cyclobutane	− 80	13	
Cyclopentane	− 94	49	0.746
Cyclohexane	6.5	81	.778
Cycloheptane	− 12	118	.810
Cyclooctane	14	149	.830
Methylcyclopentane	−142	72	.749
cis-1,2-Dimethylcyclopentane	− 62	99	.772
trans-1,2-Dimethylcyclopentane	−120	92	.750
Methylcyclohexane	−126	100	.769
Cyclopentene	− 93	46	.774
1,3-Cyclopentadiene	− 85	42	.798
Cyclohexene	−104	83	.810
1,3-Cyclohexadiene	− 98	80.5	.840
1,4-Cyclohexadiene	− 49	87	.847

7.5 Preparation

Preparation of cyclic aliphatic hydrocarbons from other aliphatic compounds generally involves two stages: (a) conversion of some compound that contains an open chain into a compound that contains a ring, a process called *cyclization* or **ring closure;** (b) conversion of the cyclic compound thus obtained into the kind of compound that we want — for example, conversion of a cyclic alcohol into a cyclic alkene, or of a cyclic alkene into a cyclic alkane.

Most methods of ring closure do not yield hydrocarbons directly; they yield other kinds of compounds and will be discussed later (Sec. 31.14). The reactions involved are usually standard methods of preparation *adapted* to the job of closing the ring. This principle can be illustrated by the preparation of cyclopropane, one of the few cyclic aliphatic hydrocarbons that can be prepared in good yield by direct cyclization.

In the Wurtz reaction (Sec. 3.17), action of a metal (usually sodium) on an alkyl halide brings about formation of a bond between carbon atoms of two alkyl groups:

$$\text{Cl—CH}_2\text{CH}_3$$
$$\xrightarrow{\text{Na}}$$
$$\text{Cl—CH}_2\text{CH}_3$$

$$\begin{array}{c} \text{CH}_2\text{CH}_3 \\ | \\ \text{CH}_2\text{CH}_3 \end{array}$$

Ethyl chloride   *n*-Butane
(2 moles)

In the same way action of a metal on a *di*halide can bring about formation of a bond between two carbon atoms that are part of the same molecule:

$$\begin{array}{c} \text{Cl—CH}_2 \\ \diagdown \\ \text{CH}_2 \\ \diagup \\ \text{Cl—CH}_2 \end{array} \xrightarrow{\text{Zn, NaI, aqueous alcohol, 125}^\circ} \begin{array}{c} \text{H}_2\text{C} \\ \diagdown \\ \text{CH}_2 \\ \diagup \\ \text{H}_2\text{C} \end{array}$$

1,3-Dichloropropane   Cyclopropane

In this case zinc does a better job than sodium. Although this method gives good yields only in the preparation of cyclopropane, and hence is not useful for the preparation of most cycloalkanes, the synthesis does illustrate the principle of adapting a standard synthetic method to the special problem of preparing a cyclic compound.

Cyclic aliphatic hydrocarbons are prepared from other cyclic compounds (e.g., halides or alcohols) by exactly the same methods that are used for preparing open-chain hydrocarbons from other open-chain compounds.

Problem 7.1 Cyclohexanol is available from the hydrogenation of phenol, C_6H_5OH. How would you prepare cyclohexene? Cyclohexane?

Problem 7.2 Bromocyclobutane can be obtained from open-chain compounds. How would you prepare cyclobutane?

7.6 Reactions

With a few very important and interesting exceptions, cyclic aliphatic hydrocarbons undergo the same reactions as their open-chain analogs.

Cycloalkanes undergo chiefly free radical substitution (compare Sec. 3.13). For example:

$$
\begin{array}{c}
\text{H}_2\text{C} \\
\diagdown \\
\text{CH}_2 + \text{Cl}_2 \xrightarrow{\text{light}} \\
\diagup \\
\text{H}_2\text{C}
\end{array}
\qquad
\begin{array}{c}
\text{H}_2\text{C} \\
\diagdown \\
\text{CHCl} + \text{HCl} \\
\diagup \\
\text{H}_2\text{C}
\end{array}
$$

Cyclopropane   Chlorocyclopropane

$$
\begin{array}{c}
\text{CH}_2 \\
\diagup\diagdown \\
\text{H}_2\text{C}\text{CH}_2 \\
\diagdown\diagup \\
\text{H}_2\text{C}-\text{CH}_2
\end{array}
+ \text{Br}_2 \xrightarrow{300°}
\begin{array}{c}
\text{CH}_2 \\
\diagup\diagdown \\
\text{H}_2\text{C}\text{CHBr} \\
\diagdown\diagup \\
\text{H}_2\text{C}-\text{CH}_2
\end{array}
+ \text{HBr}
$$

Cyclopentane   Bromocyclopentane

Cycloalkenes undergo chiefly addition reactions, both electrophilic and free radical (compare Sec. 5.2); like other alkenes they can also undergo cleavage and allylic substitution. For example:

$$
\begin{array}{c}
\text{H} \\
|\\
\text{C} \\
\diagup\diagdown \\
\text{H}_2\text{C}\text{C}-\text{H} \\
||\\
\text{H}_2\text{C}\text{CH}_2 \\
\diagdown\diagup \\
\text{CH}_2
\end{array}
+ \text{Br}_2 \longrightarrow
\begin{array}{c}
\text{CHBr} \\
\diagup\diagdown \\
\text{H}_2\text{C}\text{CHBr} \\
||\\
\text{H}_2\text{C}\text{CH}_2 \\
\diagdown\diagup \\
\text{CH}_2
\end{array}
$$

Cyclohexene   1,2-Dibromocyclohexane

$$
\begin{array}{c}
\text{CH}_3 \\
|\\
\text{C} \\
\diagup\diagdown \\
\text{H}_2\text{C}\text{C}-\text{H} \\
||\\
\text{H}_2\text{C}-\text{CH}_2
\end{array}
+ \text{HI} \longrightarrow
\begin{array}{c}
\text{I}\text{CH}_3 \\
\diagdown\diagup \\
\text{C} \\
\diagup\diagdown \\
\text{H}_2\text{C}\text{CH}_2 \\
||\\
\text{H}_2\text{C}-\text{CH}_2
\end{array}
$$

1-Methylcyclopentene   1-Iodo-1-methylcyclopentane

$$
\begin{array}{c}
\text{H} \\
|\\
\text{C} \\
\diagup\diagdown \\
\text{CH}_3-\text{HC}\text{C}-\text{H} \\
||\\
\text{H}_2\text{C}-\text{CHCH}_3
\end{array}
\xrightarrow{\text{O}_3} \xrightarrow{\text{H}_2\text{O}/\text{Zn}}
\begin{array}{c}
\text{H}\text{CH}_3\text{CH}_3\text{H} \\
|||| \\
\text{O}=\text{C}-\text{CH}-\text{CH}_2-\text{CH}-\text{C}=\text{O}
\end{array}
$$

 A dialdehyde

3,5-Dimethylcyclopentene

The two smallest cycloalkanes, cyclopropane and cyclobutane, show certain chemical properties that are entirely different from those of the other members of their family. Although these exceptional properties may at first seem surprising, they can be accounted for in a reasonable way.

7.7 Reactions of small-ring compounds. Cyclopropane and cyclobutane

Besides the free radical substitution reactions that are characteristic of cycloalkanes and of alkanes in general, cyclopropane and cyclobutane undergo certain addition reactions. These addition reactions destroy the cyclopropane and cyclobutane ring systems, and yield open-chain products.

Cyclopropane reacts with hydrogen in the presence of a catalyst to form propane, with bromine to form 1,3-dibromopropane, and with hydriodic acid to form n-propyl iodide.

$$
\begin{array}{c}
H_2C \\
\diagdown \\
\diagup CH_2 \\
H_2C
\end{array}
\quad
\begin{array}{l}
\xrightarrow{\text{Ni, H}_2,\ 80^\circ}
\begin{array}{c}
CH_2CH_2CH_2 \\
|| \\
HH \\
\text{Propane}
\end{array} \\[2ex]
\xrightarrow{\text{Br}_2.\ \text{CCl}_4}
\begin{array}{c}
CH_2CH_2CH_2 \\
|| \\
BrBr \\
\text{1,3-Dibromopropane}
\end{array} \\[2ex]
\xrightarrow{\text{conc. HI}}
\begin{array}{c}
CH_2CH_2CH_2 \\
|| \\
HI \\
n\text{-Propyl iodide}
\end{array}
\end{array}
$$

Cyclopropane

In each of these reactions a carbon–carbon bond is broken, and the two atoms of the reagent appear at the ends of the propane chain.

$$
\begin{array}{c}
\diagup H_2C\diagdown \\
Y| \\
| ----CH_2 \longrightarrow
\begin{array}{c}
CH_2CH_2CH_2 \\
|| \\
YZ
\end{array} \\
Z| \\
\diagdown H_2C\diagup
\end{array}
$$

Cyclopropane does not undergo these addition reactions so readily as propylene, however, and unlike propylene it does not react with aqueous permanganate.

Cyclobutane reacts with hydrogen in the presence of a catalyst to form n-butane, but only at a higher temperature (200°) than that required for hydrogenation of cyclopropane (80°). Cyclobutane does not react with the other reagents that open the cyclopropane ring.

$$
\begin{array}{c}
H_2C{-}CH_2 \\
|| \\
H_2C{-}CH_2
\end{array}
\xrightarrow{\text{Ni, H}_2,\ 200^\circ}
\begin{array}{c}
CH_2CH_2CH_2CH_2 \\
|| \\
HH \\
n\text{-Butane}
\end{array}
$$

Cyclobutane

Thus cyclobutane undergoes addition reactions less readily than cyclopropane, and cyclopropane less readily than an alkene. The remarkable thing is that these cycloalkanes undergo addition at all.

7.8 Baeyer strain theory

In 1885 Adolf von Baeyer (of the University of Munich) proposed a theory to account for certain aspects of the chemistry of cyclic compounds. The part of his theory dealing with the ring-opening tendencies of cyclopropane and cyclobutane is generally accepted today, although it is dressed in more modern language. Other parts of his theory have been shown to be based on false assumptions, and have been discarded.

Baeyer's argument was essentially the following. In general, when carbon is bonded to four other atoms the angle between any pair of bonds is the tetrahedral angle 109.5°. But the ring of cyclopropane is a triangle with three angles of 60°, and the ring of cyclobutane is a square with four angles of 90°. In cyclopropane or cyclobutane, therefore, one pair of bonds to each carbon cannot assume the tetrahedral angle, but must be compressed to 60° or 90° to fit the geometry of the ring.

These deviations of bond angles from the "normal" tetrahedral value cause the molecules to be *strained*, and hence to be unstable compared with molecules in which the bond angles are tetrahedral. Cyclopropane and cyclobutane undergo ring-opening reactions since these relieve the strain and yield the more stable open-chain compounds. Because the deviation of the bond angles in cyclopropane (109.5° − 60° = 49.5°) is greater than in cyclobutane (109.5° − 90° = 19.5°), cyclopropane is more highly strained, more unstable, and more prone to undergo ring-opening reactions than is cyclobutane.

The angles of a regular pentagon (108°) are very close to the tetrahedral angle (109.5°), and hence cyclopentane should be virtually free of angle strain. The angles of a regular hexagon (120°) are somewhat larger than the tetrahedral angle, and hence, Baeyer proposed (incorrectly), there should be a certain amount of strain in cyclohexane. Further, he suggested (incorrectly) that as one proceeded to cycloheptane, cyclooctane, etc., the deviation of the bond angles from 109.5° would become progressively larger, and the molecules would become progressively more strained.

Thus Baeyer considered that rings smaller or larger than cyclopentane or cyclohexane were unstable; it was because of this instability that the three- and four-membered rings underwent ring-opening reactions; it was because of this instability that great difficulty had been encountered in the synthesis of the larger rings. How does Baeyer's strain theory agree with the facts?

7.9 Heats of combustion and relative stabilities of the cyclo-alkanes

We may recall (Sec. 2.6) that the heat of combustion is the quantity of heat evolved when one mole of a compound is burned to carbon dioxide and water. Like heats of hydrogenation (Secs. 5.4 and 6.15), heats of combustion can often furnish valuable information about the relative stabilities of organic compounds. Let us see if the heats of combustion of the various cycloalkanes support Baeyer's proposal that rings smaller or larger than cyclopentane and cyclohexane are unstable.

Examination of the data for a great many compounds has shown that the heat of combustion of an aliphatic hydrocarbon agrees rather closely with that calculated by assuming a certain characteristic contribution from each structural unit. For open-chain alkanes each methylene group, —CH$_2$—, contributes very close to 157.3 kcal/mole to the heat of combustion. Table 7.2 lists the heats of combustion that have been measured for some of the cycloalkanes.

TABLE 7.2

HEATS OF COMBUSTION OF CYCLOALKANES

Ring size	Heat of combustion	Heat of combustion per —CH$_2$—
3	505.5 kcal/mole	168.5 kcal/mole
4	662.5	165.6
5	793.6	158.7
6	944.5	157.4
7	1108.0	158.3
8	1268.8	158.6
15	2356	157.1
17	2673	157.2
30	4665	156
Open-chain		157.3

We notice that for cyclopropane the heat of combustion per —CH$_2$— group is 11 kcal higher than the open-chain value of 157.3; for cyclobutane it is 8 kcal higher than the open-chain value. Whatever the compound in which it occurs, a —CH$_2$— group yields the same products on combustion: carbon dioxide and water. If cyclopropane and cyclobutane evolve more

$$-CH_2- + \tfrac{3}{2} O_2 \longrightarrow CO_2 + H_2O + heat$$

energy per —CH$_2$— group than an open-chain compound, it can mean only that they *contain* more energy per —CH$_2$— group. In agreement with the Baeyer angle strain theory, then, cyclopropane and cyclobutane are less stable than open-chain compounds; it is reasonable to suppose that their tendency to undergo ring-opening reactions is related to this instability.

According to Baeyer, rings larger than cyclopentane and cyclohexane should also be unstable, and hence should also have high heats of combustion. However, we see from Table 7.2 that this is not so. For all rings larger than four carbons, the heat of combustion per —CH$_2$— group does not deviate greatly from the open-chain value of 157.3; indeed, the largest deviation is for Baeyer's "most stable" compound, cyclopentane. Contrary to Baeyer's theory, then, these larger rings are not less stable than open-chain compounds, and hence are not appreciably strained. Furthermore, once they have been synthesized, these large-ring cycloalkanes show little tendency to undergo the ring-opening reactions characteristic of cyclopropane and cyclobutane.

What is wrong with Baeyer's theory that it does not apply to rings larger than four members? Simply this: the angles that Baeyer used for each ring were based on the assumption that the rings were *flat*. For example, the angles of a regular (flat) hexagon are 120°, the angles for a regular decagon are 144°. But the cyclohexane ring is not a regular hexagon, and the cyclodecane ring is not a regular decagon. These rings are

not flat, but are puckered (see Figure 7.1) so that each bond angle of carbon
can be 109.5°.

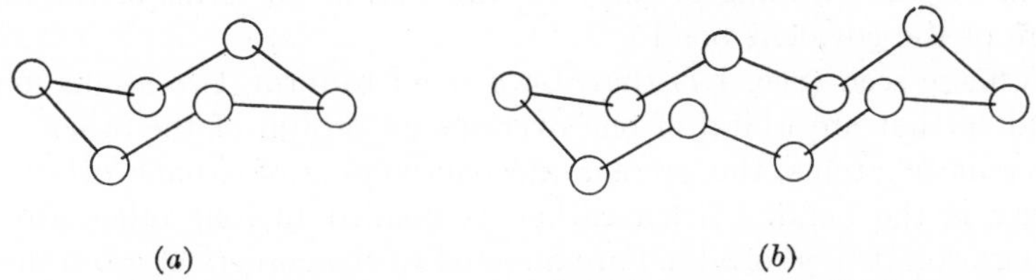

(a)   (b)

FIGURE 7.1. Puckered rings. (a) Cyclohexane. (b) Cyclodecane.

A three-membered ring must be planar, since three points (the three
carbon nuclei) define a plane. A four-membered ring need not be planar,
but puckering here would increase strain. A five-membered ring need
not be planar, but in this case a nearly planar arrangement permits the
bond angles to have the tetrahedral value. Cyclopropane, cyclobutane,
and cyclopentane thus are planar or nearly planar molecules. All rings
larger than this are not planar, but are puckered.

If large rings are stable, why are they difficult to synthesize? Here
we encounter Baeyer's second false assumption. The fact that a compound
is difficult to synthesize does not necessarily mean that it is unstable.
The closing of a ring requires that two ends of a chain be brought close
enough to each other for a bond to form. The larger the ring one wishes
to synthesize, the longer must be the chain from which it is made, and the
less is the likelihood of the two ends of the chain approaching each other.
Under these conditions the end of one chain is more likely to encounter
the end of a *different* chain, and thus yield an entirely different product
(see Figure 7.2).

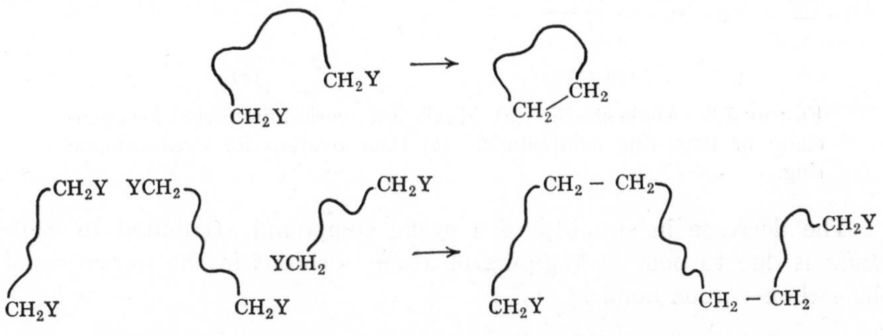

FIGURE 7.2. Ring closure (upper) vs. chain lengthening (lower).

The methods that are used successfully to make large rings take this
fact into consideration. Reactions are carried out in highly dilute solutions
where collisions between two different chains are unlikely; under these
conditions the ring-closing reaction, although slow, is the principal one.
Five- and six-membered rings are the kind most commonly encountered
in organic chemistry because they are large enough to be free of angle
strain, and small enough that ring closure is likely.

7.10   Orbital picture of angle strain

What is the meaning of Baeyer's angle strain in terms of the modern picture of the covalent bond?

We have seen (Sec. 1.7) that, for a bond to form, two atoms must be located so that an orbital of one overlaps an orbital of the other. For a given pair of atoms, the greater the overlapping of atomic orbitals, the stronger is the bond. When carbon is bonded to four other atoms its bonding orbitals (sp^3 orbitals) are directed to the corners of a tetrahedron; the angle between any pair of orbitals is thus 109.5°. Formation of a bond with another carbon atom involves overlapping of one of these sp^3 orbitals with a similar sp^3 orbital of the other carbon atom. This overlapping is most effective, and hence the bond is strongest, when the two atoms are located so that an sp^3 orbital of each atom points toward the other atom. This means that when carbon is bonded to two other carbon atoms the C—C—C bond angle should be 109.5°.

In cyclopropane, however, the C—C—C bond angle cannot be 109.5°, but instead must be 60°. As a result, the carbon atoms cannot be located to permit their sp^3 orbitals to point toward each other (see Figure 7.3). There is less overlapping and the bond is weaker than the usual carbon–carbon bond.

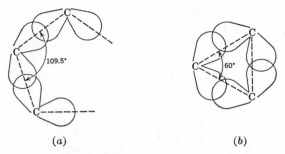

(a)   (b)

FIGURE 7.3. Angle strain. (a) Maximum overlap permitted for open-chain or large-ring compounds. (b) Poor overlap for cyclopropane ring.

The decrease in stability of a cyclic compound attributed to *angle strain* is due to poor overlapping of atomic orbitals in the formation of the carbon–carbon bonds.

7.11   Conformations of cyclohexane

Let us look more closely at the matter of puckered rings, using cyclohexane, the most important of the cycloalkanes, as our example.

If we examine a model of cyclohexane, we find two conformations (see Figure 7.4) that are free of angle strain; these have been given the names **chair conformation** and **boat conformation.** Conversion of one of these conformations into the other involves only rotation about carbon–carbon bonds, but the intermediate conformations through which the molecule

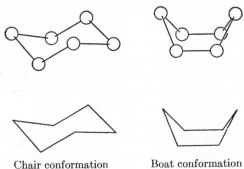

Chair conformation   Boat conformation

FIGURE 7.4. Conformations of cyclohexane that are free of angle strain.

must pass are strained. There is therefore an energy barrier between the chair and boat conformations. This energy barrier is, however, so small that interconversion occurs too readily to permit separation of isomers.

There is a great deal of evidence (including that of electron diffraction and spectroscopy) that the chair conformation is more stable (by about 6 kcal/mole) than the boat conformation and that cyclohexane exists mostly in the chair conformation. The difference in stability between the two conformations cannot be due to angle strain, since both conformations permit bond angles of 109.5°. It is believed that the relative instability of the boat conformation is due to crowding among the hydrogen atoms, and the resulting non-bonded interaction (Sec. 3.3). From a model we can see that in the chair conformation the hydrogens are perfectly staggered about the ring. In the boat conformation, however, five pairs of hydrogen atoms must approach each other rather closely. Repulsion between the hydrogen atoms of each pair — or, perhaps more exactly, repulsion between electrons in different bond orbitals — lowers the stability of the molecule. (That the hydrogen atoms are actually more crowded than in the chair conformation can be seen from scale models, as shown in Figure 7.5a, *frontispiece*).

In addition to angle strain, then, there is a second factor that affects the stability of cyclic compounds: non-bonded interaction among the atoms or groups attached to the ring. This second factor determines not only the relative stabilities of different conformations of a single compound, but also the relative stabilities of different compounds.

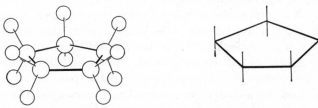

FIGURE 7.6. Cyclopentane: much non-bonded interaction.

The hydrogens in the chair conformation of cyclohexane, as we have seen, are perfectly staggered; hence there is a minimum of non-bonded interaction between them, and the molecule is as stable as an open-chain alkane. If we examine a planar model of cyclopentane (see Figure 7.6), we find almost exactly the opposite situation: the hydrogen atoms are not staggered, but instead are forced into a conformation that gives the worst crowding possible (see Figure 7.5b). In fact, to relieve this non-bonded interaction, cyclopentane takes on a slightly puckered conformation, even at the cost of increased angle strain.

The hydrogens on rings containing seven to twelve carbon atoms are also less perfectly staggered than in cyclohexane and hence these compounds, too, are less stable; notice the crowding of hydrogens inside the ring of cyclodecane (Figure 7.5c). Only quite large ring systems seem to be as stable as cyclohexane.

7.12   Equatorial and axial bonds in cyclohexane

Let us return to the model of the chair conformation of cyclohexane (see Figure 7.7). Although the cyclohexane ring is not flat, we can consider

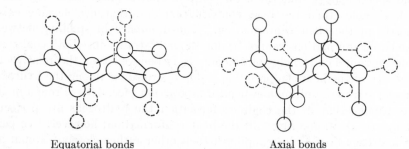

Equatorial bonds   Axial bonds

FIGURE 7.7. Equatorial and axial bonds in cyclohexane.

that the carbon atoms lie roughly in a plane. If we look at the molecule in this way, we see that the hydrogen atoms occupy two kinds of position: six hydrogens lie in the plane, while six hydrogens lie above or below the plane. The bonds holding the hydrogens that are in the plane of the ring lie in a belt about the "equator" of the ring, and are called **equatorial bonds.** The bonds holding the hydrogen atoms that are above and below the plane are pointed along an axis perpendicular to the plane and are called **axial bonds.** In the chair conformation each carbon atom has one equatorial bond and one axial bond.

The chemical properties of a compound depend upon its structure. Since about 1950, it has become increasingly evident that to understand the chemistry of a compound we must understand those subtle differences in structure which we call conformations. The stabilities of the various transition states through which a molecule must pass in the course of various reactions often depend to a surprising degree upon the particular conformations that the atoms must assume. Although we cannot now go into the complicated relationship between conformation and reactivity, we can at least see something of the basis upon which one can estimate the relative stabilties of conformations.

From a scale model of cyclohexane (in the preferred chair conformation, Figure 7.5a) it can be seen that the most severe crowding occurs among groups held by the three axial bonds on the same side of the molecule. Although these groups are attached to alternate carbon atoms, the particular arrangement of the molecule throws them rather closely together; the resulting non-bonded interaction is called **1,3-interaction.** There is much less crowding among groups held by equatorial bonds, even when they are attached to adjacent carbon atoms. *A given atom or group, therefore, has more room in an equatorial position than in an axial position.*

As a simple example of the importance of 1,3-interactions let us consider bromocyclohexane. In estimating relative stabilities of various conformations of this compound, we must focus our attention on bromine, since it is the largest substituent on the ring and hence the one most subject to crowding. There are two possible chair conformations (see Figure 7.8), one with bromine in an equatorial position, the other with bromine in an axial position.

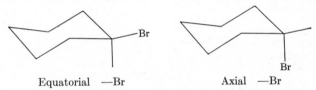

Equatorial —Br	Axial —Br

FIGURE 7.8. Chair conformations of bromocyclohexane.

Scale models show (see Figures 7.5d and 7.9) that two axial hydrogens (on C–3 and C–5) approach the axial —Br (on C–1) more closely than any hydrogens approach the equatorial —Br. We would expect bromocyclohexane to exist mostly in the conformation in which —Br occupies an equatorial position; electron diffraction studies show that this is true.

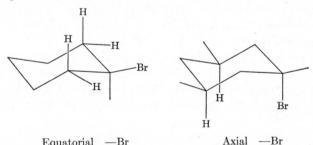

Equatorial —Br	Axial —Br

FIGURE 7.9. 1,3-Interaction in bromocyclohexane. Axial —Br more crowded than equatorial —Br.

In general, then, it has been found that (a) chair conformations are more stable than boat conformations, and (b) the most stable chair conformations are those in which the largest groups are in equatorial positions. There are exceptions to both these generalizations (for example, Problem 8, page 216, Problem 21, page 674, and Problem 30.14, page 795), but the exceptions are reasonable ones.

7.13   Stereoisomerism of cyclic compounds

We have seen (Sec. 5.19) that certain oxidizing agents convert alkenes into glycols.   Two of the commonest of these hydroxylating agents are (a) cold, dilute, neutral potassium permanganate, and (b) peroxyformic acid, HCO_2OH.

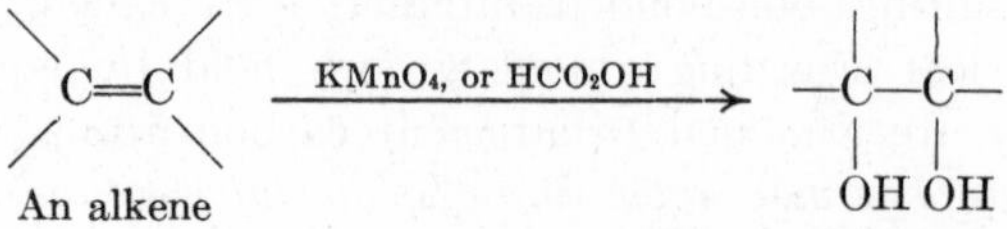

$$\overset{\diagdown}{\underset{\diagup}{C}} = \overset{\diagup}{\underset{\diagdown}{C}} \xrightarrow{\text{KMnO}_4,\ \text{or HCO}_2\text{OH}} -\overset{|}{\underset{|}{C}}-\overset{|}{\underset{|}{C}}-$$

$$\text{An alkene} \qquad\qquad\qquad \underset{\text{A glycol}}{\text{OH OH}}$$

Like open-chain alkenes, cycloalkenes undergo hydroxylation.   Treatment with permanganate converts cyclopentene into a compound of m.p. 30°, b.p. 118° (22 mm), and molecular formula $C_5H_{10}O_2$.   Treatment with peroxyformic acid converts cyclopentene into a compound of m.p. 55°, b.p. 136° (22 mm), and molecular formula $C_5H_{10}O_2$.   The properties of these two products, as well as the methods of synthesis, show clearly that each is a glycol and has the structure we would call 1,2-cyclopentanediol.

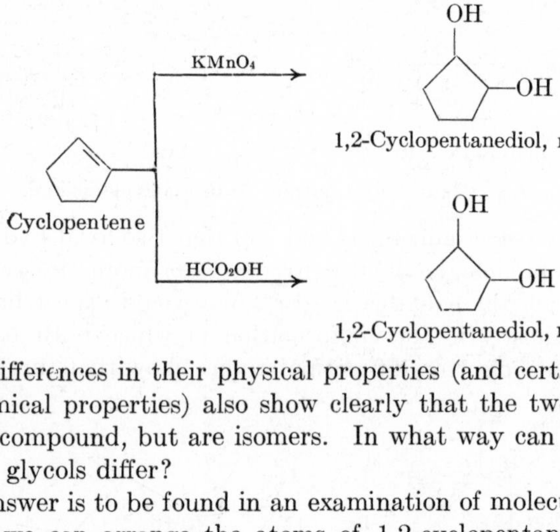

1,2-Cyclopentanediol, m.p. 30°

1,2-Cyclopentanediol, m.p. 55°

Cyclopentene

Yet the differences in their physical properties (and certain differences in their chemical properties) also show clearly that the two glycols are not the same compound, but are isomers.   In what way can the structures of these two glycols differ?

The answer is to be found in an examination of molecular models.   We find that we can arrange the atoms of 1,2-cyclopentanediol as in I, in which both hydroxyls lie below (or above) the plane of the ring, and as in II, in which one hydroxyl lies above and the other lies below the plane of the ring.

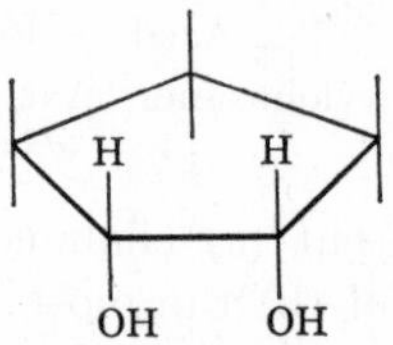

cis-1,2-Cyclopentanediol   *trans*-1,2-Cyclopentanediol

I   II

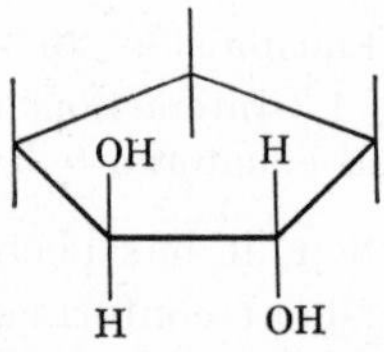

Here I and II are not just conformations of the same compound, since no amount of rotation about bonds can convert one into the other; to convert I and II into each other it is necessary to break bonds. Because of the high energy required for bond breaking, the interconversion of I and II is extremely difficult, and two isomeric compounds can be isolated. Since these isomers differ only in the way the atoms are oriented in space (but are similar with respect to which atoms are attached to which other atoms), they are stereoisomers. Configuration I is designated the *cis*-configuration, and II is designated the *trans*-configuration. (Compare *cis*- and *trans*-alkenes, Sec. 4.5.)

The two 1,2-cyclopentanediols obtained by the action of two different reagents on cyclopentene are stereoisomeric, and have the structures I and II. But now the question arises, which compound has which configuration? Is the glycol of m.p. 30°, say, the *cis*-isomer or the *trans*-isomer?

The answer to this question can be obtained in a number of ways. For example, we can see from the models that the oxygen atoms are closer together in the *cis*-configuration than they are in the *trans*-configuration. Determination of the oxygen–oxygen distance by x-ray diffraction would clearly enable one to assign configuration. Another, very elegant way of assigning configuration to these glycols will be discussed later (Sec. 24.5). Using this latter method, it has been found that the glycol of m.p. 30°, obtained from the permanganate reaction, has the *cis*-configuration, and the glycol of m.p. 55°, obtained from the peroxy acid reaction, has the *trans*-configuration.

Stereoisomerism of this same sort should be possible for compounds other than glycols, and for rings other than cyclopentane. Some examples of isomers that have been isolated are:

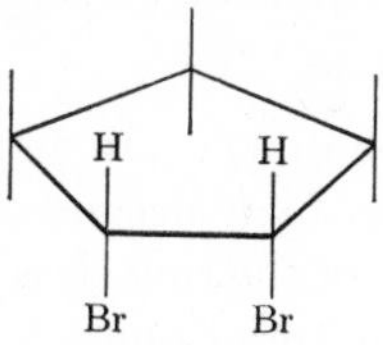

cis-1,2-Dibromocyclopentane 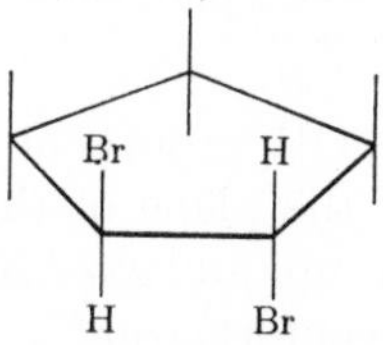   trans-1,2-Dibromocyclopentane

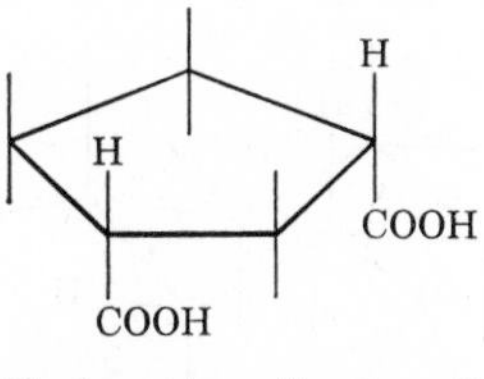

cis-1,3-Cyclopentanedicarboxylic acid 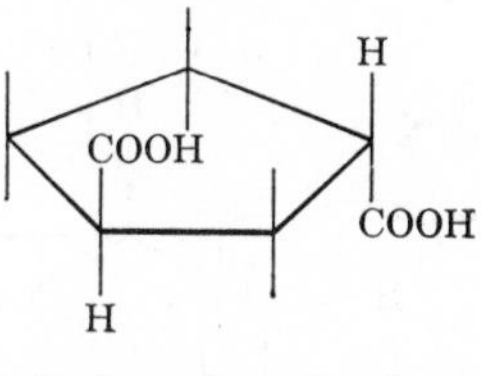   trans-1,3-Cyclopentanedicarboxylic acid

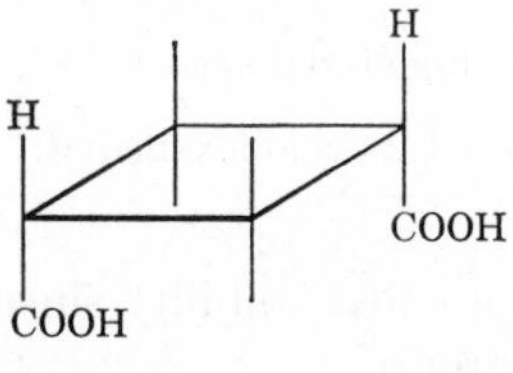

cis-1,3-Cyclobutanedicarboxylic acid 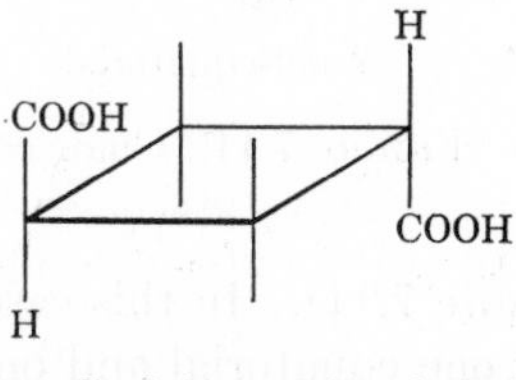   trans-1,3-Cyclobutanedicarboxylic acid cis-1,2-Dimethylcyclopropane   trans-1,2-Dimethylcyclopropane

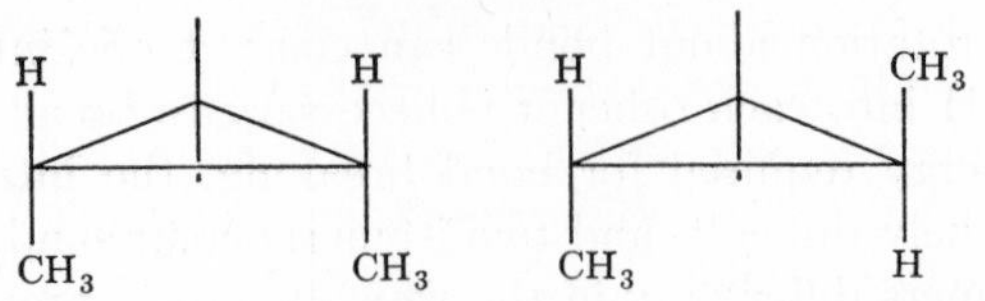

With the smaller, flatter rings, the relative positions of groups in the cis- and trans-isomers are those we have just seen: both groups are below (or above) the plane of the ring, or one group is above and the other is below the plane. With derivatives of cyclohexane, however, which have puckered rings, the situation is more complicated. If we consider only the more stable chair conformations, we find that a particular molecule of trans-1,2-cyclohexanediol, for example, can exist in two conformations (see Figure 7.10). In one, both —OH groups are in equatorial positions, and in the other both —OH groups are in axial positions.

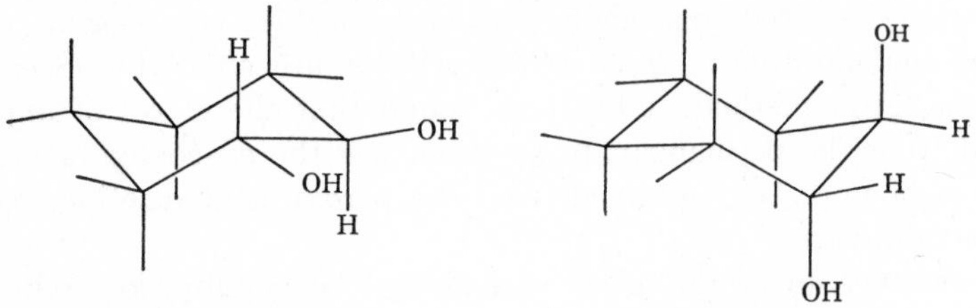

Diequatorial   Diaxial

FIGURE 7.10. Chair conformations of trans-1,2-cyclohexanediol.

Thus the two —OH groups of the trans-isomer are not necessarily on opposite sides of the plane of the ring; in fact, because of less crowding between —OH groups and axial hydrogens of the ring (less 1,3-interaction), the more stable conformation is the diequatorial one.

A molecule of cis-1,2-cyclohexanediol can also exist in two conformations

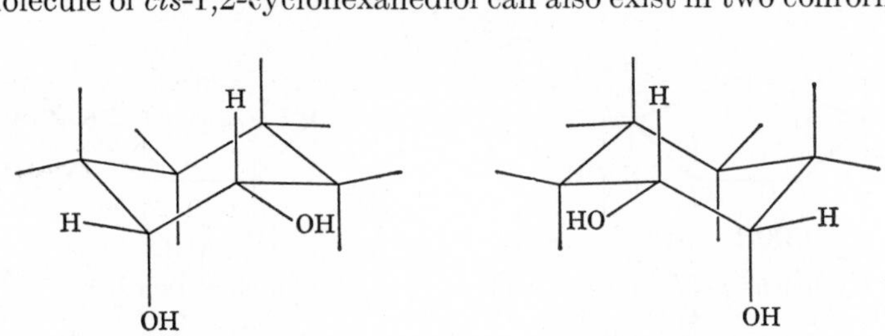

Axial-equatorial   Equatorial-axial

FIGURE 7.11. Chair conformations of cis-1,2-cyclohexanediol.

(see Figure 7.11). In this case, the two are of equal stability since in each there is one equatorial and one axial —OH group.

In the most stable conformation of *trans*-1,2-cyclohexanediol, both —OH groups occupy uncrowded equatorial positions. In either conformation of the *cis*-diol, only one —OH group can occupy an equatorial position. It is not surprising to find that *trans*-1,2-cyclohexanediol is more stable than *cis*-1,2-cyclohexanediol.

It is interesting to note that in the most stable conformation (diequatorial) of the *trans*-isomer, the —OH groups are exactly the same distance apart as they are in either conformation of the *cis*-isomer. Clearly it is not repulsion between the —OH groups that causes the difference in stability between the *trans*- and *cis*-isomers; the cause is 1,3-interaction (Sec. 7.12).

Because of the ready interconversion of chair conformations, one can correctly predict the number of stereoisomers of a cyclohexane derivative by use of simple planar formulas (see Figure 7.12).

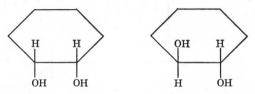

cis-1,2-Cyclohexanediol   trans-1,2-Cyclohexanediol

FIGURE 7.12. Planar formulas for *cis*- and *trans*-1,2-cyclohexanediols.

To understand the true geometry of such molecules, however, and with it the matter of stability, one must use models and formulas like those in Figures 7.10 and 7.11.

Problem 7.3 Compare stabilities of the possible chair conformations of: (a) *cis*-1,2-dimethylcyclohexane; (b) *trans*-1,2-dimethylcyclohexane; (c) *cis*-1,3-dimethylcyclohexane; (d) *trans*-1,3-dimethylcyclohexane; (e) *cis*-1,4-dimethylcyclohexane; (f) *trans*-1,4-dimethylcyclohexane.

Problem 7.4 Predict the relative stabilities of the *cis*- and *trans*-isomers of: (a) 1,2-dimethylcyclohexane; (b) 1,3-dimethylcyclohexane; (c) 1,4-dimethylcyclohexane.

Problem 7.5 It is believed that the energy difference between the two chair conformations of *cis*-1,3-dimethylcyclohexane is much larger than between those of *trans*-1,2-dimethylcyclohexane or of *trans*-1,4-dimethylcyclohexane. Why would you expect this to be so?

7.14 Stereospecific reactions. *cis*- and *trans*-Addition

There are, we have seen, two stereoisomeric 1,2-cyclopentanediols: the *cis* and the *trans*. Yet, of the two, only the *cis*-isomer is obtained when cyclopentene is hydroxylated with permanganate, and only the *trans*-isomer is obtained when cyclopentene is hydroxylated with peroxy acids. There are also two stereoisomeric 1,2-dibromocyclopentanes; yet, it has been found, only the *trans*-isomer is obtained when bromine is added to cyclopentene.

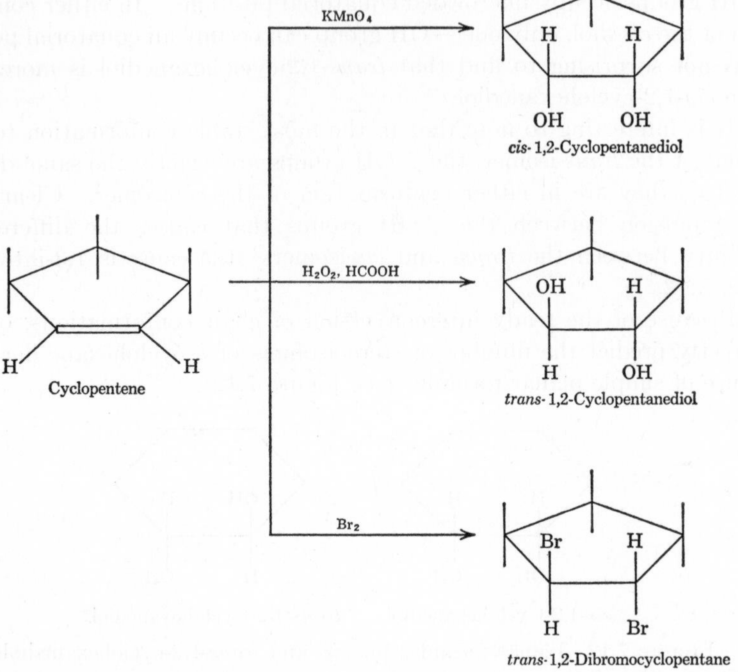

KMnO₄ →

H   H

OH   OH
cis-1,2-Cyclopentanediol

Cyclopentene

H₂O₂, HCOOH →

OH   H

H   OH
trans-1,2-Cyclopentanediol

Br₂ →

Br   H

H   Br
trans-1,2-Dibromocyclopentane

A reaction that yields only certain of the possible stereoisomers is called a **stereospecific reaction.** Hydroxylation, either by permanganate or peroxy acids, is stereospecific; so is addition of halogens. (So, too, is the formation of isotactic polymers, Sec. 6.23.)

The stereospecificity of these addition reactions is not limited to cyclopentene, but can be observed for all alkenes whose structures permit the necessary isomerism. Cyclohexene, for example, is converted into the *cis*-glycol by permanganate and into the *trans*-glycol by peroxy acids; addition of bromine yields the *trans*-dibromide. (Open-chain alkenes show fundamentally the same behavior as cycloalkenes; but it is a more complicated matter to describe, and will be taken up in Sec. 24.7 after we have learned more about stereoisomerism.)

We describe the stereospecificity of these reactions by saying that hydroxylation with peroxy acids and addition of halogen involve ***trans*-addition,** and that hydroxylation with permanganate involves ***cis*-addition.** These terms do not refer to the prefixes, *cis*- and *trans*-, that we may use in certain cases in naming the products; the terms are not names of specific mechanisms. These terms simply indicate the stereochemical facts: that the product obtained is the one to be expected if the two portions of the reagent were to add to opposite faces of the alkene (*trans*) or to the same face (*cis*).

The stereospecificity of a reaction must, of course, be accounted for by a satisfactory mechanism. As we shall see (Sec. 15.18), hydroxylation by peroxy acids and hydroxylation by permanganate give different stereochemical results because they take place by quite different mechanisms, Hydroxylation by peroxy acids and addition of halogen, as it happens, almost certainly take place by basically the same mechanism (Sec. 15.19).

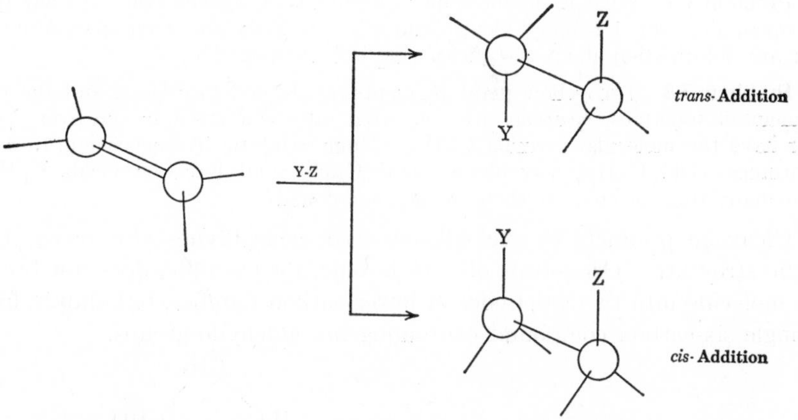

(Many other reactions taken up in this book are also stereospecific, although it is often not possible for us to discuss their stereospecificity. These addition reactions have been selected for detailed discussion simply as examples: they illustrate the concept of stereospecificity, how it is observed experimentally, and how it can be accounted for.)

7.15 Analysis of cyclic aliphatic hydrocarbons

Since — with the exception of cyclopropane and cyclobutane — cyclic aliphatic hydrocarbons have the same kind of properties as their open-chain counterparts, they are characterized in the same way: cycloalkanes by their general inertness, and cycloalkenes and cycloalkynes by their response to tests for unsaturation (bromine in carbon tetrachloride, and aqueous permanganate). That one is dealing with cyclic hydrocarbons is shown by molecular formulas and by degradation products.

The properties of cyclohexane, for example, show clearly that it is an alkane. However, combustion analysis and molecular weight determination show its molecular formula to be C_6H_{12}. Only a cyclic structure (although not necessarily a six-membered ring) is consistent with both sets of data.

Similarly, the absorption of only one mole of hydrogen shows that cyclohexene contains only one carbon–carbon double bond; yet its molecular formula is C_6H_{10}, which in an open-chain compound would correspond to two carbon–carbon double bonds or one triple bond. Again, only a cyclic structure fits the facts.

Problem 7.6 Compare the molecular formulas of: (a) n-hexane and cyclohexane; (b) n-pentane and cyclopentane; (c) 1-hexene and cyclohexene; (d) dodecane, n-hexylcyclohexane, and cyclohexylcyclohexane. (e) In general, how can you deduce the number of rings in a compound from its molecular formula and degree of unsaturation?

Problem 7.7 What is the molecular formula of (a) cyclohexane; (b) methyl-cyclopentane; (c) 1,2-dimethylcyclobutane? (d) Does the molecular formula give any information about the *size* of ring in a compound?

Problem 7.8 The yellow plant pigments α-, β-, and γ-*carotene*, and the red pigment of tomatoes, *lycopene*, are converted into Vitamin A in the liver. All four have the molecular formula $C_{40}H_{56}$. Upon catalytic hydrogenation, α- and β-carotene yield $C_{40}H_{78}$, γ-carotene yields $C_{40}H_{80}$, and lycopene yields $C_{40}H_{82}$. How many rings, if any, are there in each compound?

Cleavage products of cycloalkenes and cycloalkynes also reveal the cyclic structure. Ozonolysis of cyclohexene, for example, does not break the molecule into two aldehydes of lower carbon number, but simply into a single six-carbon compound containing *two* aldehyde groups.

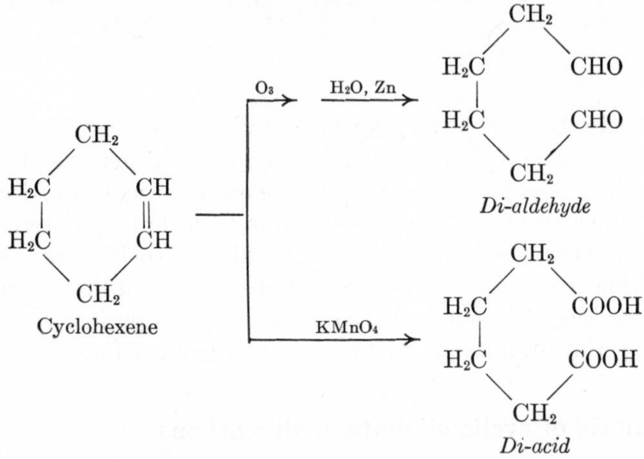

$$
\begin{array}{c}
CH_2 \\
H_2C \qquad CHO \\
H_2C \qquad CHO \\
CH_2 \\
\textit{Di-aldehyde}
\end{array}
$$

$$
\begin{array}{c}
CH_2 \\
H_2C \qquad CH \\
H_2C \qquad CH \\
CH_2 \\
\text{Cyclohexene}
\end{array}
\xrightarrow[]{O_3}\xrightarrow[]{H_2O, Zn}
$$

$$
\xrightarrow[]{KMnO_4}
\begin{array}{c}
CH_2 \\
H_2C \qquad COOH \\
H_2C \qquad COOH \\
CH_2 \\
\textit{Di-acid}
\end{array}
$$

Problem 7.9 Predict the ozonolysis products of: (a) cyclohexene; (b) 1-methylcyclopentene; (c) 3-methylcyclopentene; (d) 1,3-cyclohexadiene; (e) 1,4-cyclohexadiene.

Problem 7.10 Both cyclohexene and 1,7-octadiene yield the di-aldehyde $OHC(CH_2)_4CHO$ upon ozonolysis. What other facts would enable you to distinguish between the two compounds?

PROBLEMS

1. Draw structural formulas of:

(a) methylcyclopentane
(b) 1-methylcyclohexene
(c) 3-methylcyclopentene
(d) *trans*-1,3-dichlorocyclobutane
(e) *cis*-2-bromo-1-methylcyclopentane
(f) cyclohexylcyclohexane
(g) cyclopentylacetylene
(h) 1,1-dimethyl-4-chlorocycloheptane

2. Give structures and names of the principal organic products expected from each of the following reactions:

(a) cyclopropane + Br_2/CCl_4 (room temperature, dark)
(b) cyclopropane + Br_2 (300°)
(c) cyclopentane + Br_2/CCl_4 (room temperature, dark)
(d) cyclopentane + Br_2 (300°)
(e) cyclopentene + Br_2/CCl_4 (room temperature, dark)
(f) cyclopentene + Br_2 (300°)
(g) 1-methylcyclohexene + HCl
(h) 1-methylcyclohexene + HBr (peroxides)

(i)   1-methylcyclohexene + Br$_2$(aq)
(j)   1,3-cyclohexadiene + HCl
(k)   cyclopentanol + H$_2$SO$_4$ (heat)
(l)   bromocyclohexane + KOH(alc)
(m) 1-methylcyclopentene + cold. conc. H$_2$SO$_4$
(n)   3-methylcyclopentene + O$_3$, then H$_2$O/Zn
(o)   cyclopentene + cold, dilute, neutral KMnO$_4$ *cis glycol*
(p)   cyclopentene + HCO$_2$OH *trans glycol*
(q)   cyclopentene + hot KMnO$_4$ *cis glycol carboxyl acid*
(r)   cyclohexene + H$_2$SO$_4$ ⟶ C$_{12}$H$_{20}$
(s)   chlorocyclopentane + Na

3. Outline all steps in the laboratory synthesis of each of the following, using *cyclohexanol* as your only organic source, and any necessary inorganic reagents.

(a) cyclohexene
(b) cyclohexane
(c) *trans*-1,2-dibromocyclohexane
(d) *cis*-1,2-cyclohexanediol
(e) *trans*-1,2-cyclohexanediol
(f) OHC(CH$_2$)$_4$CHO

(g) adipic acid, HOOC(CH$_2$)$_4$COOH
(h) bromocyclohexane
(i) 2-chlorocyclohexanol
(j) 3-bromocyclohexene
(k) 1,3-cyclohexadiene
(l) cyclohexylcyclohexane

4. When 1,2-dibromocyclohexane is treated with base, there is obtained not cyclohexyne but 1,3-cyclohexadiene. Using models, can you see one reason why this might be so?

5. Give structures of all isomers of the following. For cyclohexane derivatives, planar formulas (Figure 7.12) will be sufficient here.

(a) dichlorocyclopropanes
(b) dichlorocyclobutanes
(c) dichlorocyclopentanes

(d) dichlorocyclohexanes
(e) chloro-1,1-dimethylcyclohexanes
(f) 1,3,5-trichlorocyclohexanes

6. Using models and then drawing formulas, show the possible chair conformations of each of the following. Indicate which conformation, if any, would be expected to be the most stable for each compound.

(a) methylcyclohexane
(b) 1,1-dimethylcyclohexane
(c) *trans*-4-*tert*-butyl-1-methylcyclohexane
(d) *cis*-4-*tert*-butyl-1-methylcyclohexane
(e) Which isomer, (c) or (d), should be the more stable?
(f) *trans*-3-*tert*-butyl-1-methylcyclohexane
(g) *cis*-3-*tert*-butyl-1-methylcyclohexane
(h) Which isomer, (f) or (g), should be the more stable?
(i) cyclohexylcyclohexane
(j) each isomer of Problem 5(f)
(k) Which isomer of Problem 5(f) would you expect to be the most stable?
(l) There are a number of stereoisomeric 1,2,3,4,5,6-hexachlorocyclohexanes. Without attempting to draw all of them, give the structure of the most stable isomer.

7. (a) There are two stereoisomeric forms (A and B) of 2,5-dimethyl-1,1-cyclopentanedicarboxylic acid (I). Draw their structures. (b) Upon heating, isomer A yields two 2,5-dimethylcyclopentanecarboxylic acids (II), and isomer B yields only one. Assign configurations to A and B.

HOOC   COOH   H   COOH

H$_3$C—⟨   ⟩—CH$_3$ $\xrightarrow{\text{heat}}$ H$_3$C—⟨   ⟩—CH$_3$

II

8. (a) Using models and then drawing formulas, show the possible chair conformations of *trans*-1,4-dibromocyclohexane; of *trans*-1,2-dibromocyclohexane. (b) Solely on the basis of 1,3-interactions, which conformation of the 1,4-compound would you expect to be more stable? Which conformation of the 1,2-compound?

(c) Actually, it appears that *trans*-1,4-dibromocyclohexane exists largely in the diequatorial conformation, but that *trans*-1,2-dibromocyclohexane exists largely in the diaxial conformation. (The same situation exists for the dichlorocyclohexanes, but not for the dimethylcyclohexanes.) Which of these facts agrees with your prediction in (b)? Can you suggest a factor other than 1,3-interaction that might be at work here? (*Hint:* see Sec. 1.10.)

9. The compound *decalin*, $C_{10}H_{18}$, consists of two fused cyclohexane rings:

Decalin

(a) Using models, show how there can be two isomeric decalins, *cis* and *trans*. (b) How many different conformations free of angle strain are possible for *cis*-decalin? For *trans*-decalin? (c) Which is the most stable conformation of *cis*-decalin? Of *trans*-decalin? (*Hint:* consider each ring in turn. What are the largest substituents on each ring?) (d) Account for the fact that *trans*-decalin is more stable than *cis*-decalin. (e) The difference in stability between *cis*- and *trans*-decalin is about 2 kcal/mole; conversion of one into the other takes place only under very vigorous conditions. The chair and boat forms of cyclohexane, on the other hand, differ in stability by about 6 kcal/mole, yet are readily interconverted at room temperature. How do you account for the contrast? Draw energy curves to illustrate your answer.

10. 1-Bromocyclohexene reacts with HBr in the presence of peroxides to yield *cis*-1,2-dibromocyclohexane. Under similar conditions, 1-methylcyclohexene yields *cis*-2-bromo-1-methylcyclohexane. (a) Judging from this evidence, would you say that the free radical addition of HBr involves *cis*- or *trans*-addition? (*Caution:* use models.) (b) Predict the product of addition of BrCCl₃ (in the presence of peroxides) to cyclohexene.

11. Describe simple chemical tests that would distinguish between:

(a) cyclopropane and propane Br_2/CCl_4
(b) cyclopropane and propylene
(c) 1,2-dimethylcyclopropane and cyclopentane
(d) cyclobutane and 1-butene
(e) cyclopentane and 1-pentene
(f) cyclopentane and cyclopentene
(g) cyclohexanol and *n*-butylcyclohexane $Xm.0_4$
(h) 1,2-dimethylcyclopentene and cyclopentanol
(i) cyclohexane, cyclohexene, cyclohexanol, and bromocyclohexane

12. How many rings does each of the following contain?

(a) *Camphane*, $C_{10}H_{18}$, a terpene related to camphor, takes up no hydrogen. (b) *Cholestane*, $C_{27}H_{48}$, a steroid of the same ring structure as cholesterol, cortisone, and the sex hormones, takes up no hydrogen. (c) *β-Phellandrene*, $C_{10}H_{16}$, a terpene, reacts with bromine to form $C_{10}H_{16}Br_4$. (d) *Vitamin D_2*, $C_{28}H_{44}O$, an alcohol, gives $C_{28}H_{52}O$ upon catalytic hydrogenation. (e) How many double bonds does Vitamin D_2 contain?

13. On the basis of the results of catalytic hydrogenation, how many rings does each of the following aromatic hydrocarbons contain?

(a) *benzene* (C_6H_6) $\longrightarrow$ C_6H_{12}
(b) *naphthalene* ($C_{10}H_8$) $\longrightarrow$ $C_{10}H_{18}$

(c) *toluene* (C_7H_8) $\longrightarrow$ C_7H_{14}
(d) *anthracene* $(C_{14}H_{10})$ $\longrightarrow$ $C_{14}H_{24}$
(e) *phenanthrene* $(C_{14}H_{10})$ $\longrightarrow$ $C_{14}H_{24}$
(f) *3,4-benzpyrene* $(C_{20}H_{12})$ $\longrightarrow$ $C_{20}H_{32}$
(g) *chrysene* $(C_{18}H_{12})$ $\longrightarrow$ $C_{18}H_{30}$
(Check your answers by use of the index.)

14. (a) A hydrocarbon of formula $C_{10}H_{16}$ absorbs only one mole of H_2 upon hydrogenation. How many rings does it contain? (b) Upon ozonolysis it yields 1,6-cyclodecanedione (III). What is the hydrocarbon?

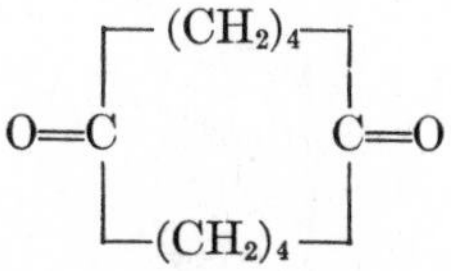

III 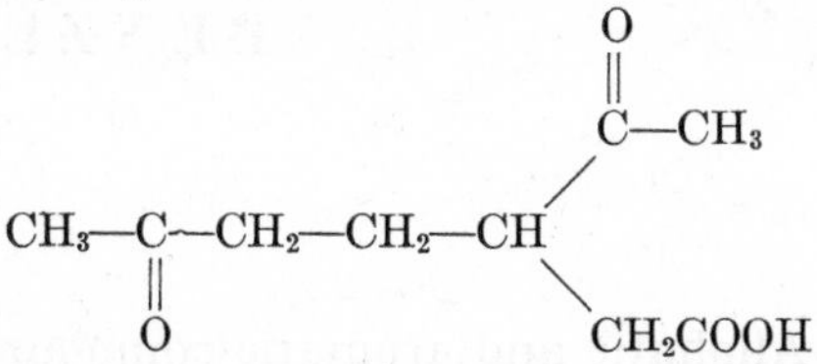   IV

15. *Limonene,* $C_{10}H_{16}$, a terpene found in orange, lemon, and grapefruit peel, absorbs only two moles of hydrogen, forming *p-menthane,* $C_{10}H_{20}$. Oxidation by permanganate converts limonene into IV. (a) How many rings, if any, are there in limonene? (b) What structures are consistent with the oxidation product? (c) On the basis of the isoprene rule (Sec. 6.21), which structure is most likely for limonene? For *p*-menthane? (d) Addition of one mole of H_2O converts limonene into *α-terpineol.* What are the most likely structures for α-terpineol? (e) Addition of two moles of H_2O to limonene yields *terpin hydrate.* What is the most likely structure for terpin hydrate?

16. *α-Terpinene,* $C_{10}H_{16}$, a terpene found in coriander oil, absorbs only two moles of hydrogen, forming *p-menthane,* $C_{10}H_{20}$. Ozonolysis of α-terpinene yields V; permanganate cleavage yields VI.

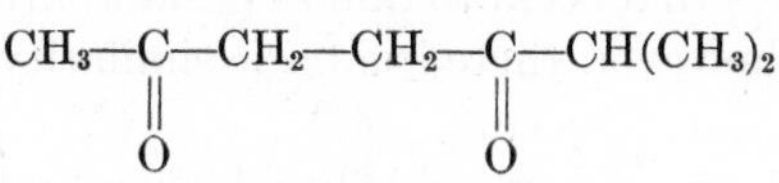

V 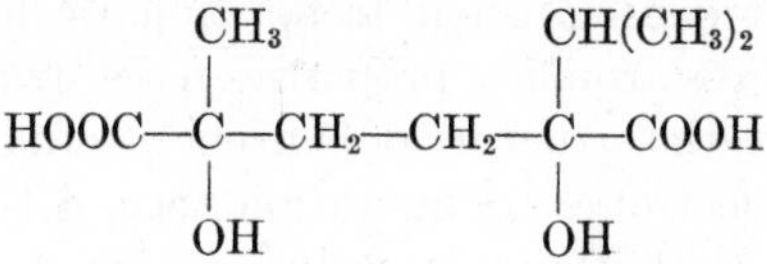   VI

(a) How many rings, if any, are there in α-terpinene? (b) On the basis of the cleavage products, V and VI, and the isoprene rule, what is the most likely structure for α-terpinene? (c) How do you account for the presence of the –OH groups in VI?

17. Using only chemistry that you have already encountered, can you suggest a mechanism for the conversion of *nerol* $(C_{10}H_{18}O)$ into α-terpineol $(C_{10}H_{18}O)$ in the presence of dilute H_2SO_4?

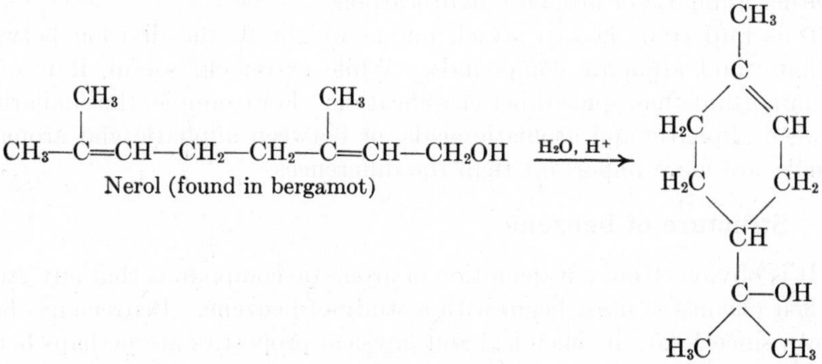

Nerol (found in bergamot)   α-Terpineol

Chapter eight_____

BENZENE. RESONANCE

8.1 Aliphatic and aromatic compounds

Chemists have found it useful to divide all organic compounds into two broad classes: **aliphatic** compounds and **aromatic** compounds. The original meanings of the words "aliphatic" (*fatty*) and "aromatic" (*fragrant*) no longer have any significance.

Aliphatic compounds are open-chain compounds and those cyclic compounds that resemble the open-chain compounds. The families we have studied so far — alkanes, alkenes, alkynes, and their cyclic analogs — are all members of the aliphatic class.

Aromatic compounds *are benzene and compounds that resemble benzene in chemical behavior.* Aromatic properties are those properties of benzene that distinguish it from aliphatic hydrocarbons. Some compounds that possess aromatic properties have structures that seem to differ considerably from the structure of benzene; actually, however, there is a basic similarity in electronic configuration (Sec. 8.13).

Aliphatic hydrocarbons, as we have seen, undergo chiefly addition and free radical substitution; addition occurs at multiple bonds, and free radical substitution occurs at other points along the aliphatic chain. In contrast, we shall find that *aromatic hydrocarbons are characterized by a tendency to undergo ionic substitution.* We shall find this contrast maintained in other families of compounds (i.e., acids, amines, aldehydes, etc.); the hydrocarbon parts of their molecules undergo reactions characteristic of either aliphatic or aromatic hydrocarbons.

It is important not to attach undue weight to the division between aliphatic and aromatic compounds. While extremely useful, it is often less important than some other classification. For example, the similarities between aliphatic and aromatic acids, or between aliphatic and aromatic amines, are more important than the differences.

8.2 Structure of benzene

It is obvious from our definition of aromatic compounds that any study of their chemistry must begin with a study of benzene. Benzene has been known since 1825; its chemical and physical properties are perhaps better known than those of any other single organic compound. In spite of this, no satisfactory structure for benzene had been advanced until about 1931, and it was ten to fifteen years before this structure was generally used by organic chemists.

The difficulty was not the complexity of the benzene molecule, but rather the limitations of the structural theory as it had so far developed. Since an understanding of the structure of benzene is important both in our study of aromatic compounds and in extending our knowledge of the structural theory, we shall examine in some detail the facts upon which this structure of benzene is built. Like any hypothesis, the structure of benzene has been modified to fit the facts as they have become known; as new facts are discovered in the future, the structure will have to be modified further to fit those facts, and, if that is not possible, it will have to be abandoned and a new structure devised.

8.3 Molecular formula. Isomer number. Kekulé structure

(a) *Benzene has the molecular formula* C_6H_6. This was determined from its elemental analysis and molecular weight. Many structures, of course, are consistent with this formula; some of them are shown in structures I–IV, including the one proposed in 1865 by August Kekulé (of the University of Bonn).

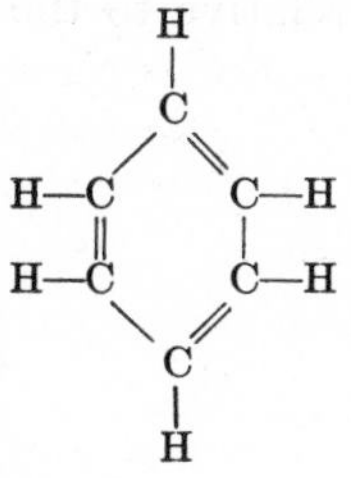

Kekulé formula

It is clear that more information is needed before a choice can be made among these, and the required unique structure can be arrived at.

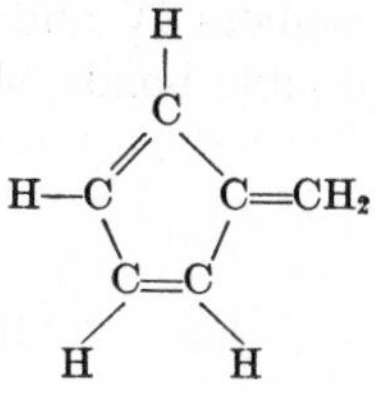

(b) *Benzene yields only one monosubstitution product,* C_6H_5Y. The chief weapon Kekulé used in attacking the problem was one with which we are already familiar: **isomer number** (Secs. 2.23, 3.3, 3.4).

Only one bromobenzene, C_6H_5Br, is obtained when one hydrogen atom is replaced by bromine; similarly, only one chlorobenzene, C_6H_5Cl, or one nitrobenzene, $C_6H_5NO_2$, etc., has ever been made. This fact places a severe limitation on the structure of benzene: each hydrogen must be exactly equivalent to every other hydrogen, since the replacement of any one of them yields the same product.

Structure III, for example, must now be rejected, since it would yield two isomeric monobromo derivatives, the 1-bromo and the 2-bromo compounds; all hydrogens are not equivalent in III. Similar reasoning shows us that IV is likewise unsatisfactory. (How many monosubstitution products would IV yield?)   I and II, among others, are still possibilities, however.

(c) *Benzene yields three isomeric disubstitution products,* $C_6H_4Y_2$ or C_6H_4YZ.   Three and only three isomeric dibromobenzenes, $C_6H_4Br_2$, three chloronitrobenzenes, $C_6H_4ClNO_2$, etc., have ever been made.   This fact further limits our choice of a structure; for example, II must now be rejected.   (How many disubstitution products would II yield?)

At first glance, the Kekulé structure, I, seems to be consistent with this new fact; that is, we can expect three isomeric dibromo derivatives, the 1,2-, the 1,3-, and the 1,4-dibromo compounds shown.

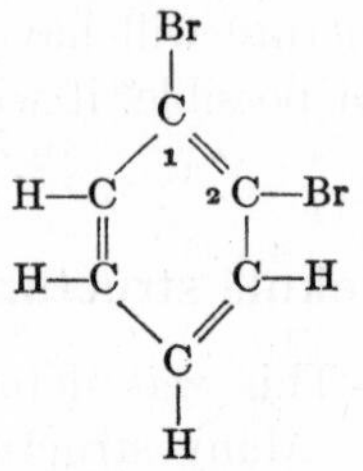

1,2-Dibromobenzene 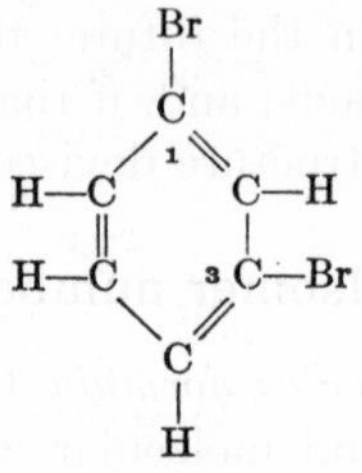   1,3-Dibromobenzene 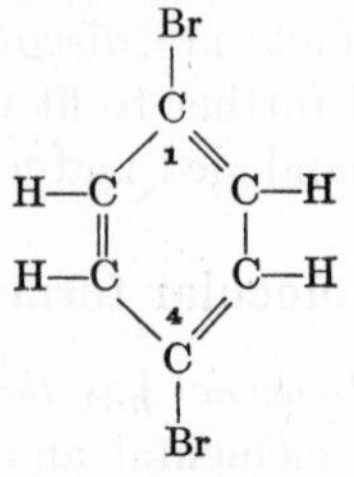   1,4-Dibromobenzene

Closer examination of structure I shows, however, that *two* 1,2-dibromo isomers (V and VI), differing in the positions of bromine relative to the double bonds, should be possible.

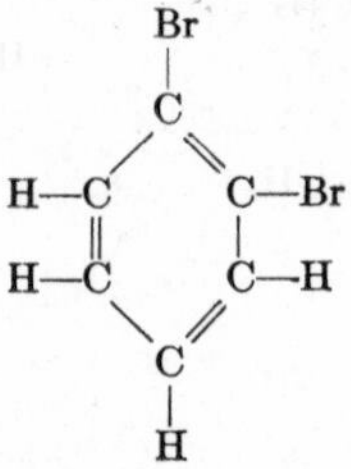

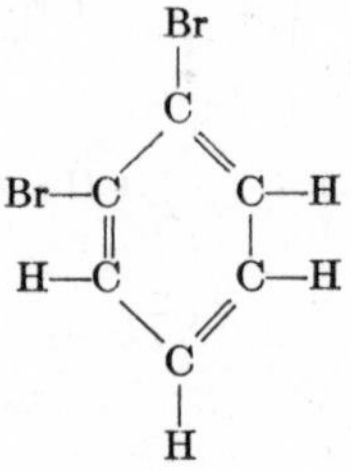

To account for this discrepancy, Kekulé modified his structure by proposing that benzene rapidly alternated between two structures (VII and VIII).   As a consequence, the two 1,2-dibromobenzenes (V and VI)

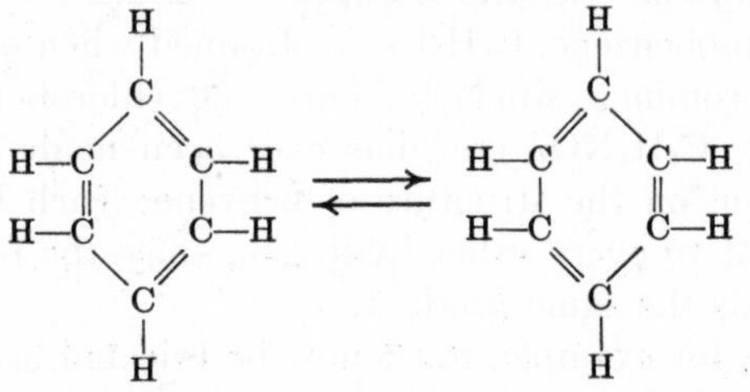

would be in rapid equilibrium and hence could not be separated.   Although the idea of tautomerism had not yet been defined, Kekulé's description of

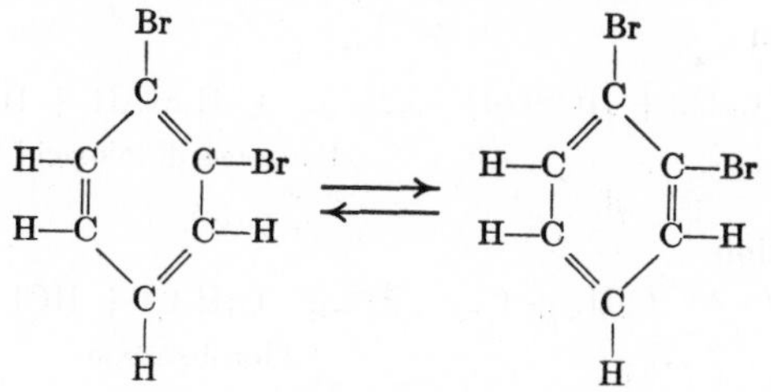

$$V \qquad\qquad VI$$

this "alternation" corresponds rather closely to our present picture of tautomerism (Sec. 6.12).

8.4 Stability of the benzene ring. Reactions of benzene

Kekulé's structure, then, accounts satisfactorily for facts (a), (b), and (c) above, providing this last modification is accepted. But there are a number of facts that are still not accounted for by this structure; most of these unexplained facts seem related to unusual stability of the benzene ring. The most striking evidence of this stability is found in the chemical reactions of benzene.

(d) *Benzene undergoes substitution rather than addition.* Kekulé's structure of benzene is one that we would call "cyclohexatriene." We would expect this cyclohexatriene, like the very similar compounds, cyclohexadiene and cyclohexene, to undergo readily the addition reactions characteristic of the alkene structure. As the examples in Table 8.1 show, this is not the case; under conditions that cause an alkene to undergo rapid addition, benzene reacts either not at all or very slowly.

TABLE 8.1

CYCLOHEXENE VS. BENZENE

Reagent	Cyclohexene gives	Benzene gives
KMnO₄ (cold, dilute, aqueous)	Rapid oxidation	No reaction
Br₂/CCl₄ (in the dark)	Rapid addition	No reaction
HI	Rapid addition	No reaction
H₂ + Ni	Rapid hydrogenation at 25°, 20 lb/in.²	Slow hydrogenation at 100–200°, 1500 lb/in.²

In place of addition reactions, benzene readily undergoes a new set of reactions, all involving **substitution**. The most important are shown below.

REACTIONS OF BENZENE

1. Nitration

$$C_6H_6 + HONO_2 \xrightarrow{\text{H}_2\text{SO}_4} C_6H_5NO_2 + H_2O$$

Nitrobenzene

2. Sulfonation

$$C_6H_6 + HOSO_3H \xrightarrow{SO_3} C_6H_5SO_3H + H_2O$$

Benzenesulfonic acid

3. Halogenation

$$C_6H_6 + Cl_2 \xrightarrow{Fe} C_6H_5Cl + HCl$$

Chlorobenzene

$$C_6H_6 + Br_2 \xrightarrow{Fe} C_6H_5Br + HBr$$

Bromobenzene

4. Friedel-Crafts alkylation

$$C_6H_6 + RCl \xrightarrow{AlCl_3} C_6H_5R + HCl$$

An alkylbenzene

5. Friedel-Crafts acylation. Discussed in Sec. 17.8

$$C_6H_6 + RCOCl \xrightarrow{AlCl_3} C_6H_5COR + HCl$$

An acyl chloride   A ketone

In each of these reactions an atom or group has been substituted for one of the hydrogen atoms of benzene. The product can itself undergo further substitution of the same kind; the fact that it has retained the characteristic properties of benzene indicates that it has retained the characteristic structure of benzene.

It would appear that benzene resists addition, in which the benzene ring system would be destroyed, whereas it readily undergoes substitution, in which the ring system is preserved.

8.5 Stability of the benzene ring. Heats of hydrogenation and combustion

Besides the above qualitative indications that the benzene ring is more stable than we would expect cyclohexatriene to be, there exist quantitative data which show *how much* more stable.

(*e*) *Heats of hydrogenation and combustion of benzene are lower than expected.* We recall (Sec. 5.3) that heat of hydrogenation is the quantity of heat evolved when one mole of an unsaturated compound is hydrogenated. In most cases the value is about 28–30 kcal for each double bond the compound contains. It is not surprising, then, that cyclohexene has a heat of hydrogenation of 28.6 kcal and cyclohexadiene has one about twice that (55.4 kcal).

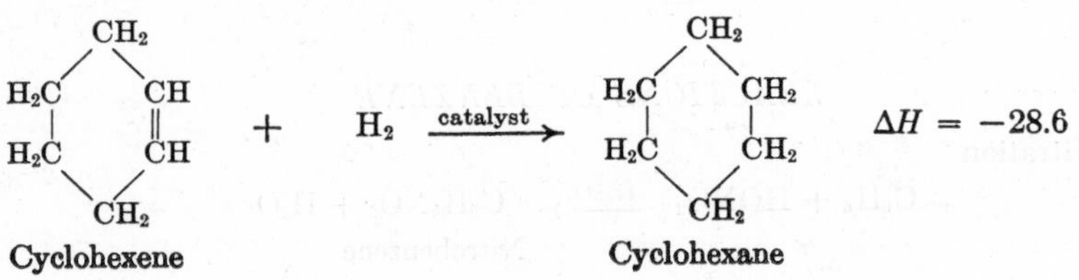

Cyclohexene   + H_2 $\xrightarrow{catalyst}$ Cyclohexane $\Delta H = -28.6$

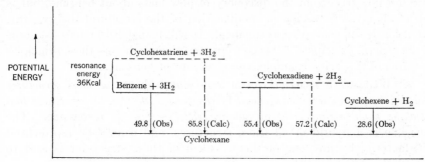

$$\Delta H = -55.4$$
Expected:
$$2 \times (-28.6) = -57.2$$

$$\Delta H = -49.8$$
Expected:
$$3 \times (-28.6) = -85.8$$

We might reasonably expect cyclohexatriene to have a heat of hydrogenation about three times as large as cyclohexene, that is, about 85.8 kcal. Actually, as shown, the value for benzene (49.8 kcal) is *36 kcal less* than this expected amount.

This can be more easily visualized, perhaps, by means of an energy diagram (Figure 8.1), in which the height of a horizontal line represents the potential energy content of a molecule. The broken lines represent the expected values, based upon three equal steps of 28.6 kcal. The final product, cyclohexane, is the same in all three cases.

FIGURE 8.1. Heats of hydrogenation and stability: benzene, cyclohexadiene, and cyclohexene.

The fact that benzene *evolves* 36 kcal less energy than predicted can only mean that benzene *contains* 36 kcal less energy than predicted; in other words, benzene is more stable by 36 kcal than we would have expected cyclohexatriene to be. The heat of combustion of benzene is also lower than that expected, and by about the same amount.

Problem 8.1 From Figure 8.1, determine the ΔH of the following reactions: (a) benzene + $H_2 \longrightarrow$ 1,3-cyclohexadiene; (b) 1,3-cyclohexadiene + $H_2 \longrightarrow$ cyclohexene.

Problem 8.2 For a large number of organic compounds, the heat of combustion actually measured agrees rather closely with that calculated by assuming a certain characteristic contribution from each kind of bond, e.g., 54.0 kcal for each C—H bond, 49.3 kcal for each C—C bond, and 117.4 kcal for each C=C bond (*cis*-1,2-disubstituted). (a) On this basis, what is the calculated heat of combustion for cyclohexatriene?   (b) How does this compare with the measured value of 789.1 kcal for benzene?

8.6   Carbon–carbon bond lengths in benzene

(f) *All carbon–carbon bonds in benzene are equal and are intermediate in length between single and double bonds.*   Each kind of covalent bond has its characteristic length, which is maintained (within a few hundredths of an Angstrom unit) in whatever compound the bond may occur.   The carbon–carbon single bond has been found to have a length very close to 1.54 A, the stronger carbon–carbon double bond, a length of 1.34 A.

If benzene actually possessed three single and three double bonds, as in a Kekulé structure, we would expect to find three bonds of 1.54 A and three of 1.34 A.   Actually, x-ray diffraction studies show that the six carbon–carbon bonds in benzene are equal and have a length of 1.39 A, and are thus intermediate between single and double bonds.

8.7   Resonance theory

The Kekulé structure of benzene, while admittedly unsatisfactory, was generally used by chemists as late as 1945.   The currently accepted structure did not arise from the discovery of new facts about benzene, but is the result of an extension or modification of the structural theory; this extension is the concept of **resonance.**   It will be helpful first to list some of the general principles of this concept, and then to discuss these principles in terms of a specific example, the structure of benzene.

(a) *Whenever a molecule can be represented by two or more structures that differ only in the arrangement of electrons — that is, by structures that have the same arrangement of atomic nuclei — there is* **resonance.**   The molecule is a **hybrid** of all these structures, and cannot be represented satisfactorily by any one of them.   Each of these structures is said to **contribute** to the hybrid.

(b) *When these contributing structures are of about the same stability (that is, have about the same energy content), then* **resonance is important.** The contribution of each structure to the hybrid depends upon the relative stability of that structure: the more stable structures make the larger contribution.

(c) *The resonance hybrid is more stable than any of the contributing structures.*   This increase in stability is called the **resonance energy.**   The more nearly equal in stability the contributing structures, the greater is the resonance energy.

8.8   Resonance structure of benzene

In the language of the resonance theory, then, benzene is a resonance hybrid of the two Kekulé structures, I and II.

This simply means that benzene does not correspond to either I or II, but rather to a structure intermediate between I and II. Further, since I and II are exactly equivalent, and hence have exactly the same stability, the resonance hybrid is equally related to I and to II; that is, I and II are said to make *equal contributions to the hybrid*.

This does *not* mean that benzene consists of molecules half of which correspond to I and half to II, nor does it mean that an individual molecule changes back and forth between I and II (Kekulé's idea). All molecules are the same; each one has a structure intermediate between I and II.

An analogy to biological hybrids that was suggested by Professor G. W. Wheland of the University of Chicago is helpful. When we refer to a mule as a hybrid of a horse and a donkey, we do not mean that some mules are horses and some mules are donkeys; nor do we mean that an individual mule is a horse part of the time and a donkey part of the time. We mean simply that a mule is an animal that is related to both a horse and a donkey, and that can be conveniently defined in terms of those familiar animals.

It must be understood that our drawing of two structures to represent benzene does not imply that either of these structures (or the molecules each would singly represent) has any existence. The two pictures are necessary because of the limitations of our rather crude methods of representing molecules. We draw two pictures because no *single* one would suffice. It is not surprising that certain molecules cannot be represented by one structure of the sort we have employed; on the contrary, the surprising fact is that the crude dot-and-dash representation used by organic chemists has worked out to the extent that it has.

8.9 Bond lengths in benzene

The resonance theory further tells us that benzene does not contain three carbon–carbon single bonds and three carbon–carbon double bonds (as in each Kekulé structure), but rather contains six *identical* bonds, each one intermediate between a single and a double bond. This new type of bond — this **hybrid bond** — has been described as a *one-and-a-half bond* or simply as a *benzene bond*. It is said to possess one-half single bond character and one-half double bond character.

The facts, of course, support this idea of six equivalent bonds: as we have seen, all carbon–carbon bonds of benzene are equal and have a length of 1.39 A, intermediate between the lengths of single and double bonds.

Problem 8.3   The nitro group, —NO₂, is usually represented as

$$-N\overset{\displaystyle O}{\underset{\displaystyle O}{\diagup\diagdown}}$$

Actual measurement shows that the two nitrogen–oxygen bonds of a nitro compound have exactly the same length.   In nitromethane, CH_3NO_2, for example, the two nitrogen–oxygen bond lengths are each 1.21 A, as compared with a usual length of 1.36 A for a nitrogen–oxygen single bond and 1.18 A for a nitrogen–oxygen double bond.   What is a better representation of the —NO₂ group?

8.10   Isomer number

When it is realized that all carbon–carbon bonds in benzene are equivalent, there is no longer any difficulty in accounting for the number of isomeric disubstitution products.   It is clear that there should be just three, in agreement with experiment:

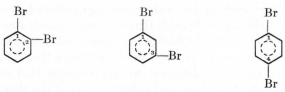

1,2-Dibromobenzene   1,3-Dibromobenzene   1,4-Dibromobenzene

(The representation of the benzene ring used here is discussed in Sec. 8.14.)

8.11   Stability of benzene

A further, most important outcome of the resonance theory is this: *as a resonance hybrid benzene is more stable (i.e., contains less energy) than either of the contributing Kekulé structures.*   This additional stability possessed by benzene is referred to as *resonance energy;* it amounts, as we have seen earlier, to 36 kcal/mole.

As a result of this stabilization, benzene possesses chemical properties that are not intermediate between those expected of the Kekulé structures, but instead are quite different.   It is the 36 kcal of resonance energy that is responsible for the new set of properties we call *aromatic properties.*

Addition reactions convert an alkene into a more stable saturated compound.   Hydrogenation of cyclohexene, for example, is accompanied by the evolution of 28.6 kcal; the product lies 28.6 kcal lower than the reactants on the energy scale (Figure 8.1).

But addition would convert benzene into a *less* stable product by destroying the resonance-stabilized benzene ring system; for example, according to Figure 8.1 the first stage of hydrogenation of benzene requires 5.6 kcal to convert benzene into the less stable cyclohexadiene.   As a consequence, it is easier for reactions of benzene to take an entirely different course, one in which the ring system is retained: *substitution.*

8.12   Orbital picture of benzene

A more detailed picture of the benzene molecule is obtained from a consideration of the bond orbitals in this molecule.

Since each carbon is bonded to three other atoms, its bonding orbitals (sp^2; see Sec. 4.2) lie in the same plane, that of the carbon nucleus, and are directed toward the corners of an equilateral triangle. If we arrange the six carbons and six hydrogens of benzene to permit maximum overlapping of these orbitals, we obtain the structure shown in Figure 8.2*a*.

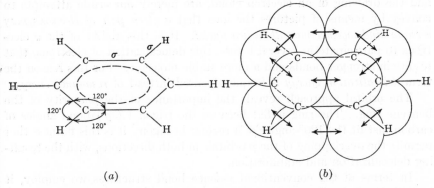

(a)   (b)

FIGURE 8.2.   Benzene molecule.   (*a*) Only σ bonds shown.   (*b*) *p* orbitals overlap to form π bonds.

Benzene is a *flat molecule*, every carbon and every hydrogen lying in the same plane. It is a very *symmetrical molecule*, too, each carbon atom lying at the angle of a regular hexagon; every bond angle is 120°. Each bond orbital is cylindrically symmetrical about the line joining the atomic nuclei and hence, as before, these bonds are designated as σ bonds.

The molecule is not yet complete, however. There are still six electrons to be accounted for. In addition to the three orbitals already described, each carbon atom has a fourth orbital, a *p* orbital. As we have already seen, this *p* orbital consists of two equal lobes, one lying above and the other lying below the plane of the other three orbitals, that is, above and below the plane of the ring; it is occupied by a single electron.

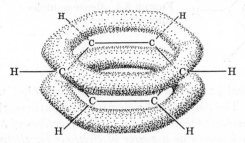

FIGURE 8.3. Benzene molecule. π clouds above and below plane of ring.

As in the case of ethylene, the *p* orbital of one carbon can overlap the *p* orbital of an adjacent carbon atom, permitting the electrons to pair and an additional π bond to be formed (see Figure 8.2*b*). But the overlapping here is not limited to a pair of p orbitals as it was in ethylene; the p orbital of any one carbon atom overlaps equally well the p orbitals of *both* carbon atoms to which it is bonded. The result (see Figure 8.3) is two continuous hexagonal electron clouds, one lying above and the other below the plane of the atoms.

The overlapping of the p orbitals in both directions, and the resulting participation of each electron in several bonds, is equivalent to our earlier description of benzene as a resonance hybrid of two structures. These two methods of representation, the drawing of several resonance structures and the drawing of an electron cloud, are merely our crude attempts to convey by means of pictures the idea that *a given pair of electrons may serve to bind together more than two nuclei.* It is this ability of the π electrons to participate in several bonds, this **delocalization** of electrons, that results in stronger bonds and a more stable molecule. For this reason the term *delocalization energy* is frequently used instead of *resonance energy.*

The orbital approach reveals the importance of the planarity of the benzene ring. The ring is flat because the trigonal (sp^2) bond angles of carbon just fit the 120°-angles of a regular hexagon; it is this flatness that permits the overlapping of the p orbitals in both directions, with the resulting delocalization and stabilization.

In terms of the conventional valence bond structures we employ, it is difficult to visualize a single structure that is intermediate between the two Kekulé structures. The orbital approach, on the other hand, gives us a rather clear picture of the molecule: the carbon–carbon bonds in benzene are represented by six equivalent electron clouds, each intermediate in density between that representing a single bond and that representing a double bond.

The facts are consistent with the orbital picture of the benzene molecule. X-ray and electron diffraction show benzene (Figure 8.4) to be a completely flat, symmetrical molecule with all carbon–carbon bonds equal, and all bond angles 120°.

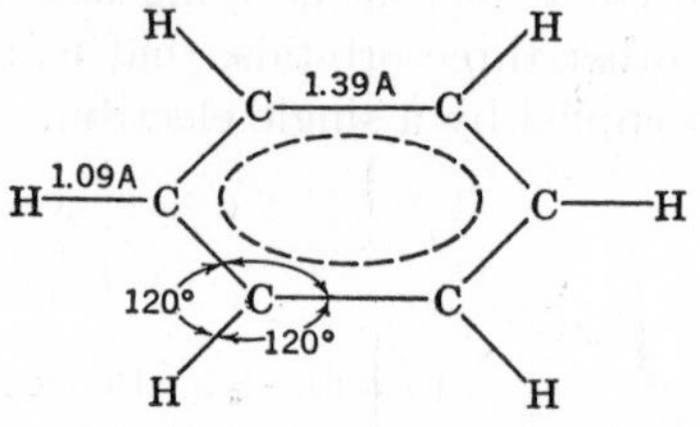

FIGURE 8.4. Benzene molecule: shape and size.

As we shall see, the chemical properties of benzene are just what we would expect of this structure. The loosely held π electrons are particularly available to a reagent that is seeking electrons; *the typical reactions of the benzene ring are those in which it serves as a source of electrons for electrophilic (acidic) reagents.* Because of the resonance stabilization of the benzene ring, *these reactions lead to substitution,* in which the aromatic character of the benzene ring is preserved.

en omit

8.13 Aromatic character. The aromatic sextet

We have defined aromatic compounds as those that resemble benzene. But just which properties of benzene must a compound possess before we speak of it as being aromatic? Besides the compounds that contain benzene rings, there are many other substances that are called aromatic; yet some of these superficially bear no resemblance to benzene.

What properties do all aromatic compounds have in common?

From the experimental standpoint, aromatic compounds are compounds whose molecular formulas would lead us to expect a high degree of unsaturation, and yet which are resistant to the addition reactions generally characteristic of unsaturated compounds. Instead of addition reactions, we find that these aromatic compounds undergo electrophilic substitution reactions like those of benzene. Along with this resistance toward addition — and presumably the cause of it — we find evidence of unusual stability: low heats of hydrogenation and low heats of combustion. Aromatic compounds are cyclic — containing five-, six-, or sometimes even seven-membered rings — and when examined by physical methods are found to have flat (or nearly flat) molecules.

From a theoretical standpoint, aromatic compounds are those whose molecules contain cyclic π clouds above and below the plane of the molecule; the π clouds must contain a **total of six π electrons: the aromatic sextet.** These molecules must be flat (or nearly so) to permit the overlapping of the p orbitals that gives rise to the π clouds. They must contain five-, six-, or seven-membered rings since these numbers of atoms will fit a flat ring without undue distortion of the interatomic bonds. Furthermore, these numbers of atoms can provide the necessary six π electrons.

The requirement that there be just six π electrons is shown by the facts; it has been accounted for on theoretical grounds. Many examples of the application of the "sextet rule" are found in the study of heterocyclic compounds (Chapter 32).

Problem 8.4 The molecules of *pyridine*, C_5H_5N, are flat, with all bond angles about 120°. All carbon–carbon bonds are 1.39 A long and the two carbon–nitrogen bonds are 1.36 A long. The measured heat of combustion is 23 kcal lower than that calculated by the method of Problem 8.2 on page 223. Pyridine undergoes such substitution reactions as nitration and sulfonation (Sec. 8.4). (a) Is pyridine adequately represented by formula I? (b) Account for the properties of pyridine by both valence bond and orbital structures. (Check your answer in Sec. 32.6.)

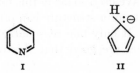

I   II

Problem 8.5 *Ferrocene* (dicyclopentadienyliron), $[(C_5H_5)^-]_2Fe^{++}$, is a "sandwich" of an iron atom between two flat five-membered rings. All carbon–carbon bonds are 1.4 A long. The rings of ferrocene undergo sulfonation and the Friedel-Crafts reaction. (a) Is the cyclopentadienyl ion adequately represented by formula II? (b) Account for the properties of the cyclopentadienyl ion by both valence bond and orbital structures.

Problem 8.6 *1,3,5,7-Cyclooctatetraene*, C_8H_8, has a heat of combustion (compare Problem 8.2, page 223) of 1095 kcal; it rapidly decolorizes cold aqueous $KMnO_4$ and reacts with Br_2/CCl_4 to yield $C_8H_8Br_8$. (a) How should its structure be represented? (b) Upon what theoretical grounds might one have predicted its structure and properties?

8.14   Representation of the benzene ring

For convenience we shall represent the benzene ring by a regular hexagon containing a broken circle (I); it is understood that a hydrogen atom is attached to each angle of the hexagon unless another atom or group is indicated.

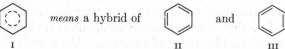

I represents a resonance hybrid of the Kekulé structures II and III. The solid lines stand for the σ bonds joining carbon atoms. The broken circle stands for the cloud of six delocalized π electrons: the aromatic sextet. (From another viewpoint, the solid lines stand for single bonds, and the circle stands for the extra *half bonds*.)

I is a particular useful representation of the benzene ring, since it emphasizes the equivalence of the various carbon–carbon bonds. The presence of the circle distinguishes the benzene ring from the cyclohexane ring, which is often represented today by a plain hexagon. (For speed in writing on paper or the blackboard, some chemists draw the circle as a solid line rather than as a broken line.)

There is no complete agreement among chemists about how to represent the benzene ring. The student should expect to encounter it most often as one of the Kekulé formulas, occasionally as a plain hexagon. The representation adopted in this book has certain advantages, and its use seems to be gaining ground. It is interesting that very much the same representation was advanced as long ago as 1899 by Johannes Thiele (of the University of Munich). He, too, meant the broken line to stand for partial bonds ("partial valences"), although his language was necessarily more vague than that used today.

8.15   Using the resonance theory

The great usefulness, and hence the great value, of the resonance theory lies in the fact that it retains the simple though crude type of structural representation which we have used so far in this book. Particularly helpful is the fact that the stability of a structure can often be roughly estimated from its **reasonableness**. If only one reasonable structure can be drawn for a molecule, the chances are good that this one structure adequately describes the molecule.

The criterion of reasonableness is not so vague as it might appear. The fact that a particular structure seems reasonable to us means that we have previously encountered a compound whose properties are pretty well accounted for by a structure of that type; the structure must, therefore, represent a fairly stable kind of arrangement of atoms and electrons. For example, each of the Kekulé structures for benzene appears quite reasonable because we have encountered compounds, alkenes, that possess essentially this structure.

There are a number of other criteria that we can use to estimate relative stabilities, and hence relative importance, of contributing structures. One of these has to do with (a) *electronegativity and location of charge.*

For example, a convenient way of indicating the polarity (*ionic character*) of the hydrogen–chlorine bond is to represent HCl as a hybrid of structures I and II. We judge that II is appreciably stable and hence

$$\text{H—Cl} \qquad\qquad \text{H}^+\text{Cl}^-$$

$$\text{I} \qquad\qquad\qquad\quad \text{II}$$

makes significant contribution, because in it a negative charge is located on a highly electronegative atom, chlorine.

On the other hand, we consider methane to be represented adequately by the single structure III.

$$
\begin{array}{c}
\text{H} \\
| \\
\text{H—C—H} \\
| \\
\text{H}
\end{array}
$$

$$\text{III}$$

Although it is possible to draw additional, ionic structures like IV and V, we judge these to be unstable since in them a negative charge is located

$$
\begin{array}{cc}
\text{H}^+ & \text{H} \\
\bar{|} & | \\
\text{H—C—H} & \text{H—C}^- \;\; {}^+\text{H} \quad etc. \\
| & | \\
\text{H} & \text{H}
\end{array}
$$

$$\text{IV} \qquad\qquad \text{V}$$

on an atom of low electronegativity, carbon. We expect IV and V to make negligible contribution to the hybrid and hence we ignore them.

In later sections we shall use certain other criteria to help us estimate stabilities of possible contributing structures: (b) *number of bonds* (Sec. 8.16); (c) *dispersal of charge* (Sec. 10.9); (d) *complete vs. incomplete octet* (Sec. 10.10); (e) *separation of charge* (Sec. 10.12).

Finally, we shall find certain cases where the overwhelming weight of evidence — bond lengths, dipole moments, reactivity — indicates that an accurate description of a given molecule requires contribution from structures of a sort that may appear quite unreasonable to us (Sec. 9.19, Sec. 14.8); this simply reminds us that, after all, we know very little about the structure of molecules, and must be prepared to change our ideas of what is reasonable to conform with evidence provided by experimental facts.

8.16 Resonance in conjugated dienes

In our discussion of the hydrogenation of benzene (Sec. 8.5) we saw that the heat of hydrogenation of 1,3-cyclohexadiene is 1.8 kcal lower

than twice that of cyclohexene. Now, in the carbon skeleton of 1,3-cyclo-
hexadiene the double bonds are separated by one single bond, so that this
compound belongs to the class of dienes that we have called *conjugated*.
We may recall from our earlier discussion (Sec. 6.15) that low heats of
hydrogenation are typical of conjugated dienes; non-conjugated dienes,
on the other hand, have the expected heats of hydrogenation. We concluded then that for some reason conjugated dienes are more stable by
2–4 kcal than their non-conjugated isomers. Let us now see if we can
account for this extra stability.

We shall focus our attention on the four key carbon atoms of any conjugated diene system. We ordinarily write the C_1—C_2 and C_3—C_4 bonds
as double, and the C_2—C_3 bond as single:

$$\overset{1}{-}\overset{2}{C}=\overset{3}{C}-\overset{4}{C}=C-$$

This would correspond to an orbital picture of the molecule (see Figure
8.5a) in which π bonds are formed by overlapping of the p orbitals of C_1
and C_2, and overlapping of the p orbitals of C_3 and C_4.

In benzene we saw that resonance resulted from the overlapping of
the p orbital of a carbon atom with p orbitals on *both* sides. We might
expect that, in the same way, there could be a certain amount of overlapping between the p orbitals of C_2 and C_3, as shown in Figure 8.5b.

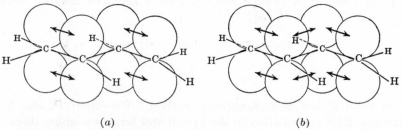

(a)   (b)

FIGURE 8.5. Conjugated diene. (a) Overlap of p orbitals to form two
double bonds. (b) Overlap of p orbitals to form conjugated system:
delocalization of π electrons.

Such delocalization of the π electrons makes the molecule more stable.
Resonance of this sort is sometimes indicated by structures in which
broken lines stand for fractional bonds formed by delocalized π electrons:

$$\overset{1}{-}\overset{2}{C}---\overset{3}{C}---\overset{4}{C}---C-$$

Using the language of conventional valence bond structures, we say
that a conjugated diene is a resonance hybrid of I and II.

$$\overset{1}{-}\overset{2}{C}=\overset{3}{C}-\overset{4}{C}=C- \qquad\qquad -C-C=C-C-$$

$$\text{I} \qquad\qquad\qquad\qquad \text{II}$$

The dotted line in II represents a *formal bond*, and simply means that an electron on C_1 and an electron on C_4 have opposite spins, that is to say, are *paired*.

To the extent that II contributes to the structure, it gives a certain double-bond character to the C_2—C_3 bond and a certain single-bond character to the C_1—C_2 and C_3—C_4 bonds; most important, it makes the molecule more stable than we would expect I (the most stable contributing structure) to be.

Formation of a bond releases energy and stabilizes a system; all other things being equal, the more bonds, the more stable a structure. Consideration of *number of bonds* is one of the criteria (Sec. 8.15) that can be used to estimate relative stability and hence relative importance of a contributing structure. On this basis we would expect II with 10 bonds (the formal bond does not count) to be less stable than I with 11 bonds. The resonance energy for such a hybrid of non-equivalent structures should be less than for a hybrid made up of equivalent structures. The structure of a conjugated diene should resemble I more than II, since the more stable structure I makes the larger contribution to the hybrid.

The expectations are correct. The resonance energy of a conjugated diene is only 2–4 kcal/mole compared with 36 kcal/mole for benzene. The C_2—C_3 bond has indeed double-bond character; in 1,3-butadiene, for example, it is 1.47 A long, as compared with 1.54 A for a pure single bond. The C_1—C_2 and C_3—C_4 bonds have single-bond character; in 1,3-butadiene they are 1.37 A long, as compared with 1.34 A for a pure double bond. However, the C_2—C_3 bond is more single than double, being longer than a benzene bond (1.39 A), and the C_1—C_2 and C_3—C_4 bonds are more double than single, being shorter than a benzene bond.

8.17 Nomenclature of benzene derivatives

In later chapters we shall consider in detail the chemistry of many of the derivatives of benzene. Nevertheless, for our present discussion of the reactions of the benzene ring it will be helpful for us to learn to name some of the more important of these derivatives.

For many of these derivatives we simply prefix the name of the substituent group to the word *–benzene*, as, for example, in *chlorobenzene, bromobenzene, iodobenzene,* or *nitrobenzene*.

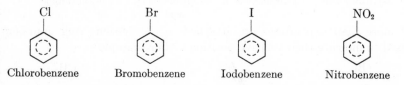

Chlorobenzene   Bromobenzene   Iodobenzene   Nitrobenzene

Other derivatives have special names which may show no resemblance to the name of the attached substituent group. For example, methylbenzene is always known as *toluene*, aminobenzene as *aniline*, hydroxybenzene as *phenol*, and so on. The most important of these special compounds are:

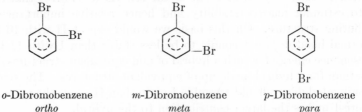

Toluene   Aniline   Phenol   Benzoic acid   Benzenesulfonic
                                                        acid

If several groups are attached to the benzene ring, we must not only tell what they are, but also indicate their relative positions. The three possible isomers of a disubstituted benzene are differentiated by the use of the names, *ortho, meta,* and *para.* For example:

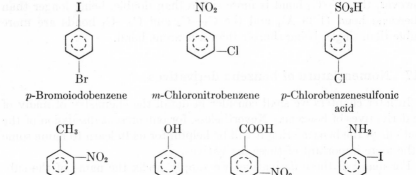

o-Dibromobenzene   m-Dibromobenzene   p-Dibromobenzene
    ortho   meta   para

If the two groups are different, and neither is a group that gives a special name to the molecule, we simply name the two groups successively and end the word with *–benzene;* for example, *chloronitrobenzene, bromoiodobenzene,* etc. If one of the two groups is the kind that gives a special name to the molecule, then the compound is named as a derivative of that special compound; for example, *nitrotoluene, bromophenol,* etc.

p-Bromoiodobenzene   m-Chloronitrobenzene   p-Chlorobenzenesulfonic
                                                        acid

o-Nitrotoluene   p-Bromophenol   m-Nitrobenzoic   o-Iodoaniline
                                        acid

If more than two groups are attached to the benzene ring, numbers are used to indicate their relative positions. For example:

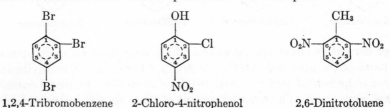

1,2,4-Tribromobenzene   2-Chloro-4-nitrophenol   2,6-Dinitrotoluene

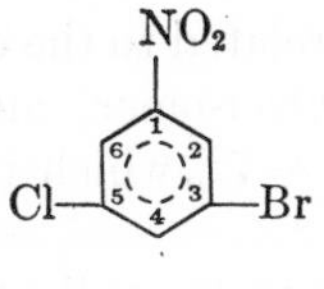

NO₂   NH₂

Cl—⬡—Br   Br—⬡—Br

                                    Br

3-Bromo-5-chloronitrobenzene 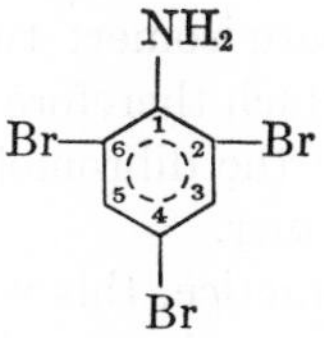   2,4,6-Tribromoaniline

If all the groups are the same, each is given a number, the sequence being the one that gives the lowest combination of numbers; if the groups are different, then the last named group is understood to be in position 1 and the other numbers conform to that, as, for example, in *3-bromo-5-chloro-nitrobenzene*. If one of the groups that gives a special name is present, then the compound is named as having the special group in position 1; thus in *2,6-dinitrotoluene*, the methyl group is considered to be at the 1-position.

8.18   Körner method of absolute orientation

How can the relative positions of groups attached to the benzene ring be determined? We know, for example, that there should be three di-bromobenzenes, *ortho*, *meta*, and *para*. We also know that three dibromo-benzenes have actually been prepared; they have the melting points +87°, +6°, and −7°. But which is which? Is the compound that melts at +87°, say, the *ortho*, the *meta*, or the *para* isomer?

This problem was first solved by Wilhelm Körner (of the University of Milan). His approach was based upon the concept of isomer number. From its structure, *p*-dibromobenzene can have only one mononitro derivative, *o*-dibromobenzene can have two mononitro derivatives, and *m*-dibromobenzene can have three.

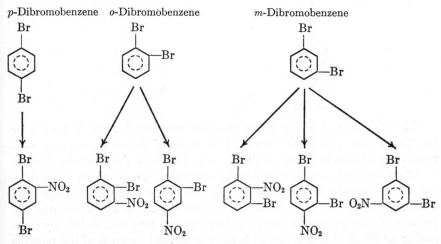

When the six dibromonitrobenzenes were prepared, only one of them was found to be related to the dibromobenzene of m.p. +87°, which therefore

had to be the *para* isomer; two of them were related to the dibromobenzene of m.p. +6°, which therefore had to be the *ortho* isomer; and three of them were related to the dibromobenzene of m.p. −7°, which therefore had to be the *meta* isomer.

In actual practice, this work was much more complicated than merely nitrating the three compounds. As we shall see, not all the possible isomeric products are actually obtained in benzene substitution reactions, and hence some of the nitro compounds outlined above had to be prepared by indirect methods. The principle of the method is, however, as described; this is known as the **Körner method of absolute orientation.**

The Körner method is very time-consuming and has actually been applied to only a relatively few aromatic compounds. The arrangement of groups in most aromatic compounds is determined by indirect methods. For example, we can (Sec. 21.5) replace an amino group (—NH$_2$) by bromine. If we convert one of the three isomeric bromoanilines into a dibromobenzene, and obtain the isomer of m.p. +87°, we conclude that the original bromoaniline was the *para* isomer. If this same bromoaniline is formed when the nitro group (—NO$_2$) of a bromonitrobenzene is converted into —NH$_2$ (Sec. 19.9), then the nitro compound, in turn, must be the *para* isomer, too. The following scheme shows how this method could be extended to still more compounds:

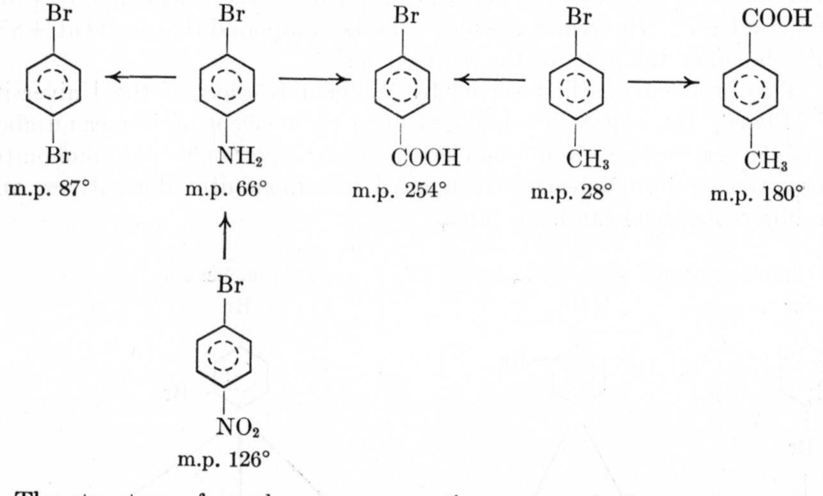

The structure of nearly every aromatic compound, then, is known by its relationship, perhaps through a long chain of reactions, to some compound whose structure was originally determined by the absolute method.

Once the structure of a particular compound has been determined by either the direct or indirect method, and its physical properties have been described in the chemical literature, a chemist can, in a few minutes, determine the structure of a compound he has just prepared simply by comparing its physical properties with those described for each of the possible isomers. In the final analysis, he is comparing his compound with those whose structures were worked out so laboriously by the Körner method.

Problem 8.7 In 1874 Griess reported that he had decarboxylated the six known diaminobenzoic acids, $C_6H_3(NH_2)_2COOH$, to the diaminobenzenes. Three acids gave a diamine of m.p. 63°, two acids gave a diamine of m.p. 104°, and one acid gave a diamine of m.p. 142°. Draw the structural formulas for the three isomeric diaminobenzenes and label each with its melting point.

8.19 Reactions of benzene. Electrophilic aromatic substitution

We have already seen that the characteristic reactions of benzene involve substitution, in which the resonance-stabilized ring system is preserved. What kind of reagents bring about this substitution? What is the mechanism by which these reactions take place?

Above and below the plane of the benzene ring there is a cloud of π electrons. Because of resonance, these π electrons are more involved in holding together carbon nuclei than are the π electrons of a carbon–carbon double bond. Still, in comparison with σ electrons, these π electrons are loosely held and are available to a reagent that is seeking electrons.

It is not surprising that *in its typical reactions the benzene ring serves as a* **source of electrons,** that is, as a **base.** The compounds with which it reacts are deficient in electrons, that is, electrophilic reagents or acids. Just as the typical reactions of the alkenes are electrophilic addition reactions, so *the typical reactions of the benzene ring are* **electrophilic substitution reactions.** These reactions are characteristic not only of benzene itself, but of the benzene ring wherever it is found.

We shall examine the commonly accepted mechanisms for the most important of the substitution reactions. Much of the evidence for these mechanisms is too complicated for us to consider at this time; as we learn more facts about aromatic substitution in subsequent chapters, we shall see that these facts are consistent with the mechanisms outlined below.

8.20 Mechanism of nitration

The commonly accepted mechanism for nitration of benzene and other aromatic compounds involves the following sequence of reactions.

$$(1) \quad HONO_2 + 2H_2SO_4 \rightleftharpoons H_3O^+ + 2HSO_4^- + {}^{\oplus}NO_2$$
$$\text{Nitronium ion}$$

$$(2) \quad {}^{\oplus}NO_2 + C_6H_6 \longrightarrow C_6H_5{\overset{\displaystyle H}{\underset{\displaystyle NO_2}{\big\langle}}}^{\oplus}$$

$$(3) \quad C_6H_5{\overset{\displaystyle H}{\underset{\displaystyle NO_2}{\big\langle}}}^{\oplus} + HSO_4^- \longrightarrow C_6H_5NO_2 + H_2SO_4$$

Step (1) generates the **nitronium ion,** ${}^{\oplus}NO_2$, which is the electrophilic particle that actually attacks the benzene ring. This reaction is simply an acid-base equilibrium in which sulfuric acid serves as the acid and the much weaker nitric acid serves as a base. We may consider that the very strong acid, sulfuric acid, causes nitric acid to ionize in the sense, HO^- $\cdots$ $^+NO_2$, rather than in the usual way, H^+ $\cdots$ $^-ONO_2$. The nitronium ion is well known, existing in salts such as nitronium perchlorate, $NO_2^+ClO_4^-$.

Needing electrons, the nitronium ion finds them particularly available in the π cloud of the benzene ring, and so in step (2) attaches itself to one of the carbon atoms by a covalent bond. This forms the carbonium ion

$$C_6H_5 \overset{\oplus}{\diagdown} \begin{matrix} H \\ \diagup \\ \diagdown \\ NO_2 \end{matrix}$$

Just what is the structure of this carbonium ion? We find that we can represent it by three structures (I, II, and III) that differ from each other only in position of double bonds and positive charge. The actual ion must then be a resonance hybrid of these three structures.

This means, of course, that the positive charge is not localized on one carbon atom, but is distributed over the molecule, being particularly strong on the carbon atoms *ortho* and *para* to the carbon bearing the $—NO_2$ group. (As we shall see later, this *ortho,para* distribution is significant.) The dispersal of the positive charge over the molecule by resonance makes this ion more stable than an ion with a localized positive charge. It is probably because of this stabilization that the carbonium ion forms at all, in view of the stability of the original benzene itself. Sometimes the hybrid carbonium ion is represented as IV, where the broken line stands for the fractional bonds due to the delocalized π electrons.

Thus far the reaction is like addition to alkenes: an electrophilic particle, attracted by the π electrons, attaches itself to the molecule to form a carbonium ion. But the fate of this carbonium ion is different from the fate of the ion formed from an alkene. Attachment of a basic group to the benzene carbonium ion (*phenonium ion*) to yield the addition product would destroy the benzene ring system. Instead, the basic ion, HSO_4^-, abstracts a hydrogen ion (step 3) to yield the substitution product, which retains the resonance-stabilized ring. Loss of a hydrogen ion, as we have seen, is one of the reactions typical of a carbonium ion (Sec. 4.16); it is the *preferred* reaction in this case.

Electrophilic substitution, then, like electrophilic addition, is a stepwise process involving an intermediate carbonium ion. The two reactions differ, however, in the fate of the carbonium ion. While the mechanism of nitration is, perhaps, better established than the mechanisms for other aromatic substitution reactions, it seems clear that all these reactions follow the same course.

8.21　Mechanism of sulfonation

The commonly accepted mechanism for sulfonation of aromatic compounds involves the following steps:

(1) $\qquad 2H_2SO_4 \rightleftarrows H_3O^+ + HSO_4^- + SO_3$

(2) $\qquad SO_3 + C_6H_6 \rightleftarrows C_6H_5{\overset{\displaystyle\overset{H}{\diagup}}{\underset{\diagdown SO_3^-}{}}}$

(3) $\quad C_6H_5{\overset{\displaystyle\overset{H}{\diagup}}{\underset{\diagdown SO_3^-}{}}} + HSO_4^- \rightleftarrows C_6H_5SO_3^- + H_2SO_4$

(4) $\qquad C_6H_5SO_3^- + H_3O^+ \rightleftarrows C_6H_5SO_3H + H_2O$　　*Equilibrium far to the left*

Again the first step, which generates the electrophilic sulfur trioxide, is simply an acid-base equilibrium, this time between two molecules of sulfuric acid. For sulfonation we commonly use sulfuric acid containing an excess of SO_3; even if this is not done it appears that SO_3 formed in step (1) is the attacking reagent.

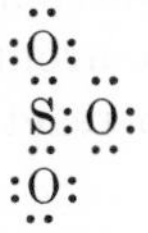

$$\overset{\displaystyle :\overset{..}{O}:}{\underset{\displaystyle :\overset{..}{O}:}{\overset{..}{S}:\overset{..}{O}:}}$$

In step (2), the electrophilic reagent, SO_3, attaches itself to the benzene ring to form the intermediate carbonium ion. Although sulfur trioxide is not positively charged, it is electron-deficient, and hence an acid, nevertheless.

Step (3) is the loss of a hydrogen ion to form the resonance-stabilized substitution product, this time the anion of benzenesulfonic acid which, being a strong acid, is highly ionized (step 4).

8.22　Mechanism of halogenation

The commonly accepted mechanism for aromatic halogenation, illustrated for chlorination, involves the following steps:

(1) $\qquad Cl_2 + FeCl_3 \rightleftarrows FeCl_4^- + {}^+Cl$

(2) $\qquad Cl^+ + C_6H_6 \longrightarrow C_6H_5{\overset{\displaystyle\overset{H}{\diagup}}{\underset{\diagdown Cl}{}}}$

$$(3) \quad \underset{\underset{Cl}{\overset{\oplus}{\diagdown}}}{\overset{\overset{H}{\diagup}}{C_6H_5}} + FeCl_4^- \longrightarrow C_6H_5Cl + HCl + FeCl_3$$

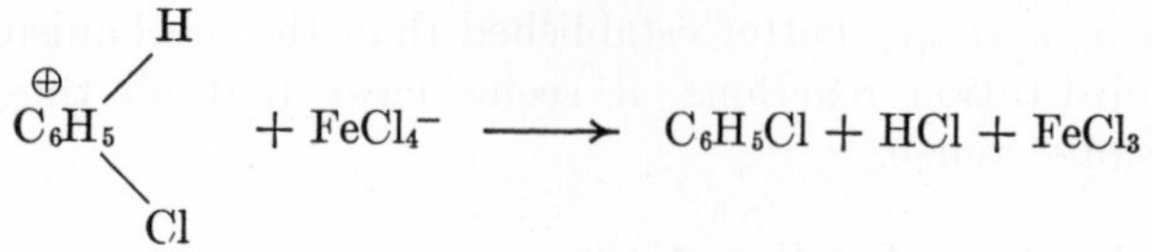

The first step, which generates the attacking electrophilic particle, Cl^+, is an acid-base equilibrium, this time in the Lewis sense (Sec. 1.17). Although metallic iron is commonly used as a catalyst in this reaction, it is undoubtedly converted by chlorine into ferric chloride; preformed ferric chloride or, for that matter, other Lewis acids of comparable strength such as aluminum chloride, serve equally well. Able to accept electrons, the ferric chloride attaches itself to a chlorine molecule to form the $FeCl_4^-$ ion and a positive chlorine ion. This is a simplified picture of step (1). It may well be that no actually *free* Cl^+ ion is formed, but that the ferric chloride serves only to polarize the chlorine molecule;

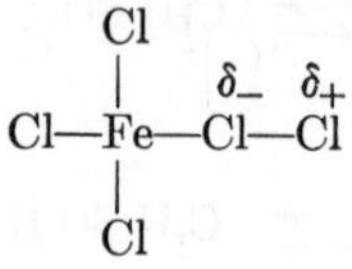

$$\underset{\underset{Cl}{\overset{|}{}}}{\overset{\overset{Cl}{\overset{|}{}}}{Cl-Fe-Cl}}\overset{\delta_- \quad \delta_+}{-Cl}$$

the actual electrophilic reagent would then be the positive end of the polarized chlorine molecule.

In the addition of halogen to an alkene (Sec. 5.15), it was considered that the electrons of the double bond polarized the halogen molecule sufficiently for reaction to occur. It is not surprising that attack on the less reactive benzene molecule requires additional polarization by a Lewis acid. Indeed, more highly reactive aromatic compounds, i.e., those whose π electrons are more available, do react with halogens in the absence of any added Lewis acid.

8.23 Mechanism of Friedel-Crafts alkylation

The commonly accepted mechanism of Friedel-Crafts alkylation is shown in the following equations:

$$(1) \quad RCl + AlCl_3 \; \rightleftharpoons \; AlCl_4^- + R^\oplus$$

$$(2) \quad R^\oplus + C_6H_6 \; \rightleftharpoons \; \underset{\underset{R}{\overset{\oplus}{\diagdown}}}{\overset{\overset{H}{\diagup}}{C_6H_5}}$$

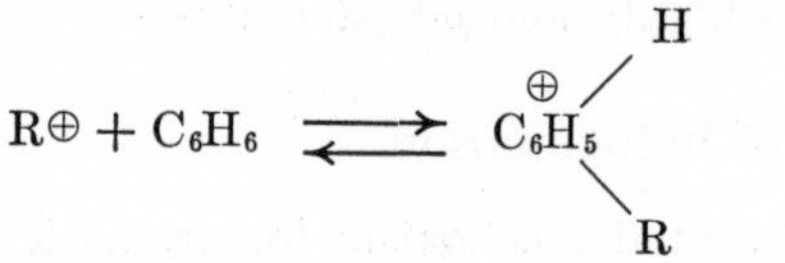

$$(3) \quad \underset{\underset{R}{\overset{\oplus}{\diagdown}}}{\overset{\overset{H}{\diagup}}{C_6H_5}} + AlCl_4^- \; \rightleftharpoons \; C_6H_5R + HCl + AlCl_3$$

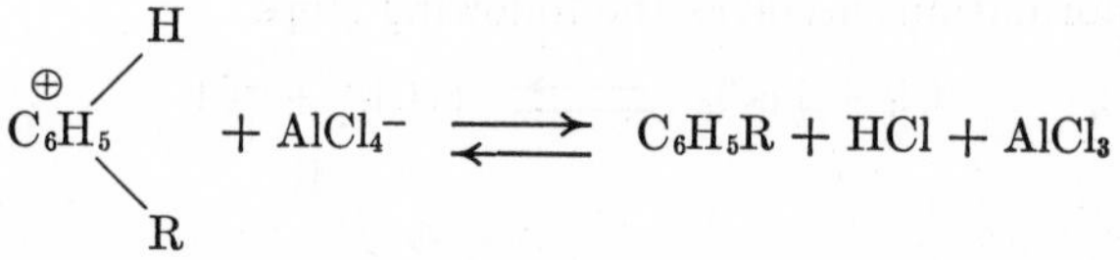

In step (1) the Lewis acid $AlCl_3$ converts the alkyl chloride into an alkyl carbonium ion:

$$R:\overset{\overset{\displaystyle :\ddot{C}l:}{}}{\underset{\underset{\displaystyle :\ddot{C}l:}{}}{\ddot{C}l:}} + \overset{\overset{\displaystyle :\ddot{C}l:}{}}{\underset{\underset{\displaystyle :\ddot{C}l:}{}}{Al}} \rightleftharpoons R\oplus + :\overset{\overset{\displaystyle :\ddot{C}l:}{}}{\underset{\underset{\displaystyle :\ddot{C}l:}{}}{\ddot{C}l:}}:\ddot{Al}:\ddot{C}l:\ominus$$

As we shall see, there is evidence that, in many cases at least, an actually free carbonium ion exists (Sec. 9.8). As we would expect, other Lewis acids than aluminum chloride serve to bring about this reaction; BF_3, $FeCl_3$, $SnCl_4$, and HF are frequently used, some of these having certain practical advantages over the classical aluminum chloride.

8.24 Mechanism of electrophilic aromatic substitution: a summary

Electrophilic aromatic substitution reactions seem, then, to proceed by a single mechanism, whatever the particular reagent involved. This can be summarized for the reagent YZ as follows:

(1) $C_6H_6 + Y^+ \longrightarrow C_6H_5\overset{\oplus}{<}\,^H_Y$

(2) $C_6H_5\overset{\oplus}{<}\,^H_Y + :Z^- \longrightarrow C_6H_5Y + H:Z$

Two essential steps are involved: (1) attack by an electrophilic reagent upon the ring to form a carbonium ion, $C_6H_5\overset{\oplus}{<}\,^H_Y$, and (2) abstraction of a hydrogen ion from this carbonium ion by some base. In each case there is a preliminary acid-base reaction which generates the attacking particle; the actual substitution, however, is contained in these two steps.

The intermediate carbonium ion is a hybrid of structures I, II, and III.

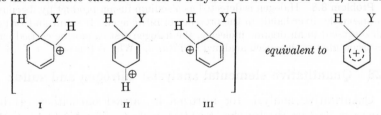

The positive charge is distributed about the ring, being strongest at the positions *ortho* and *para* to the carbon that Y has attacked.

Groups already attached to the benzene ring should affect the stability of this carbonium ion by dispersing or localizing the positive charge, depending upon their electron-withdrawing or electron-releasing nature. *The stabilizing or destabilizing effect of groups located* **ortho** *and* **para** *to the carbon under attack should be especially important.* Further, these groups should stabilize or destabilize the deve oping positive charge of the incipient carbonium ion in the transition state leading to the carbonium ion, and hence should affect the rate of substitution.

As we shall soon see (Chapter 10), groups attached to a benzene ring do affect the reactivity of that ring and determine which positions are preferentially attacked. These effects are completely consistent with the substitution mechanism we have just outlined.

8.25   Qualitative elemental analysis: nitrogen and sulfur

This chapter has dealt with the structure of benzene and with the way in which its reactions take place. It is well to remind ourselves again that all this discussion has meaning only because it is based upon solid facts. As we saw earlier (Sec. 2.24), we can discuss the structure and re-actions of a compound only when we know its molecular formula and the molecular formulas of its products.

To know a molecular formula we must first know what elements are present in the compound. We have seen (Sec. 2.25) how carbon, hydrogen, and halogen can be detected in an organic compound. Now, what can we say about nitrogen and sulfur?

Like halogen, covalently bonded nitrogen and sulfur must be converted into inorganic ions; as with halogen, this conversion is accomplished by a sodium fusion.

$$(C,H,X,N,S) + Na \xrightarrow{\text{heat}} Na^+ X^- + Na^+ CN^- + Na^+ S^{--} Na^+$$

Nitrogen yields cyanide ion, CN^-, which is converted by a series of re-agents into Prussian blue, which can be recognized by its intense blue color. Sulfur yields sulfide ion, S^{--}; this is converted into hydrogen sulfide which is detected by its blackening of lead acetate paper.

$$CN^- \xrightarrow{\text{Fe}^{++}, \text{Fe}^{+++}} \text{Prussian blue}$$

$$S^{--} \xrightarrow{\text{H}^+} H_2S \xrightarrow{\text{Pb}^{++}} \underset{\textit{Black-brown}}{PbS}$$

Problem 8.8   Halogen is detected as a sodium fusion product by its conversion into insoluble silver halide in the presence of nitric acid. If sulfur and/or nitrogen is also present in an organic molecule, the halogen test cannot be carried out until the fusion mixture has been acidified and *boiled*. Why is this so?

8.26   Quantitative elemental analysis: nitrogen and sulfur

Quantitative analysis for nitrogen is carried out either (a) by the *Dumas method* or (b) by the *Kjeldahl method*. The Kjeldahl method is somewhat more convenient, particularly if many analyses must be carried out; however, it cannot be used for all kinds of nitrogen compounds.

In the Dumas method, the organic compound is passed through a tube containing, first, hot copper oxide and, next, hot copper metal gauze. The copper oxide oxidizes the compound (as in the carbon–hydrogen com-bustion, Sec. 2.26), converting combined nitrogen into molecular nitrogen. The copper gauze reduces any nitrogen oxides that may be formed, also to molecular nitrogen. The nitrogen gas is collected, and its volume is measured. For example, an 8.32-mg sample of *aniline* yields 1.11 cc of nitrogen at 21° and 743 mm pressure (corrected for the vapor pressure of water). We calculate the volume at standard temperature and pressure,

$$\text{vol. N}_2 \text{ at S.T.P.} = 1.11 \times \frac{273}{273 + 21} \times \frac{743}{760} = 1.01 \text{ cc}$$

and, from it, the weight of nitrogen,

$$\text{wt. N} = \frac{1.01}{22400} \times (2 \times 14.01) = 0.00126 \text{ g } or \text{ } 1.26 \text{ mg}$$

and, finally, the percentage of nitrogen in the sample

$$\% \text{ N} = \frac{1.26}{8.32} \times 100 = 15.2\%$$

Problem 8.9 Why is the nitrogen in the Dumas analysis collected over 50% aqueous KOH rather than, say, pure water, aqueous NaCl, or mercury?

In the Kjeldahl method, the organic compound is digested with concentrated sulfuric acid, which converts combined nitrogen into ammonium sulfate. The solution is then made alkaline. The ammonia thus liberated is distilled, and its amount is determined by titration with standard acid. For example, the ammonia formed from a 3.51-mg sample of aniline neutralizes 3.69 ml of 0.0103 N acid. For every milliequivalent of acid there is a milliequivalent of ammonia, and a milligram–atom of nitrogen.

milligram–atoms N = milliequivalents NH_3 = milliequivalents acid
$$= 3.69 \times 0.0103 = 0.0380$$

From this, the weight and, finally, the percentage of nitrogen in the compound can be calculated.

$$\text{wt. N} = \text{milligram–atoms N} \times 14.01 = 0.0380 \times 14.01 = 0.53 \text{ mg}$$

$$\% \text{ N} = \frac{0.53}{3.51} \times 100 = 15.1\%$$

Sulfur in an organic compound is converted into sulfate ion by the methods used in halogen analysis (Sec. 2.26): treatment with sodium peroxide or with nitric acid (*Carius method*). This is then converted into barium sulfate, which is weighed.

Problem 8.10 A Dumas nitrogen analysis of a 5.72-mg sample of *p-phenylene-diamine* gave 1.31 cc of nitrogen at 20° and 746 mm. The gas was collected over saturated aqueous KOH solution (the vapor pressure of water, 6 mm). Calculate the percentage of nitrogen in the compound.

Problem 8.11 A Kjeldahl nitrogen analysis of a 3.88-mg sample of *ethanolamine* required 5.73 ml of 0.0110 N hydrochloric acid for titration of the ammonia produced. Calculate the percentage of nitrogen in the compound.

Problem 8.12 A Carius sulfur analysis of a 4.81-mg sample of *p-toluenesulfonic acid* gave 6.48 mg of $BaSO_4$. Calculate the percentage of sulfur in the compound.

Problem 8.13 How does each of the above answers compare with the theoretical value calculated from the formula of the compound? (Each compound is listed in the index.)

8.27 Molecular weight determination: freezing-point lowering. Rast method

For compounds of low volatility, such as the ones we are now beginning to encounter, determination of molecular weights from vapor density (Sec. 2.28) is not feasible. Instead, methods are often used that depend upon freezing-point lowering (*cryoscopic methods*) or boiling-point elevation (*ebullioscopic methods*). Both approaches, of course, are based on the fact that a change in the vapor pressure of a solvent — and, with it, a change in freezing point or boiling point — is proportional to the concentration of dissolved particles.

Organic chemists often use the **Rast method**: a fast, convenient cryoscopic method (carried out in ordinary melting-point capillaries and with ordinary thermometers) that gives results accurate enough for many purposes. This method takes advantage of the unusually large cryoscopic constant of *camphor:* one mole of solute dissolved in 1000 grams of camphor lowers its freezing point by 39.7°.

Consider, for example, a compound of empirical formula $C_3H_2O_2N$. A 0.035-g sample is dissolved in 0.420 g of melted camphor, the mixture is allowed to solidify, and its melting point is compared with that of pure camphor:

$$
\begin{array}{ll}
\text{m.p. pure camphor} & 178.4° \\
\text{m.p. mixture} & \underline{157.8°} \\
\text{m.p. lowering} & 20.6°
\end{array}
$$

Since one mole of solute per 1000 g of camphor lowers the m.p. by 39.7°, the present solution must contain only 20.6/39.7 of a mole per 1000 g of camphor. Now, 0.035 g in 0.420 g of camphor is equivalent to

$$0.035 \times \frac{1000}{0.420} \text{ g in 1000 g of camphor}$$

If

$$\frac{20.6}{39.7} \text{ mole} = 0.035 \times \frac{1000}{0.420} \text{ g}$$

then,

$$1 \text{ mole} = \frac{39.7}{20.6} \times 0.035 \times \frac{1000}{0.420} = 161 \text{ g}$$

Of the possible molecular weights, the value of 168 ($C_6H_4O_4N_2$) is clearly the correct one, rather than 84 ($C_3H_2O_2N$) or 252 ($C_9H_6O_6N_3$).

Problem 8.14 Calculate the molecular weight and select the correct molecular formula for each of the following compounds: (a) 0.052 g of *p-dibromobenzene* (empirical formula C_3H_2Br) dissolved in 0.349 g of camphor lowered the melting point 24.4°. (b) 5.83 mg of *2,6-dimethylnaphthalene* (empirical formula CH) dissolved in 57.3 mg of camphor lowered the melting point 26.4°. (c) 1.02 g of *urea* (empirical formula CH_4N_2O) dissolved in 51.1 g of water lowered the melting point 0.63°. (The cryoscopic constant for water is 1.86°.)

PROBLEMS

1. Draw structures of:

(a) *p*-dinitrobenzene
(b) *m*-bromonitrobenzene
(c) *o*-chlorobenzoic acid
(d) *m*-nitrotoluene
(e) *p*-bromoaniline
(f) *m*-iodophenol

(g) mesitylene (1,3,5-trimethylbenzene)
(h) 3,5-dinitrobenzenesulfonic acid
(i) 4-chloro-2,3-dinitrotoluene
(j) 2-amino-5-bromo-3-nitrobenzoic acid
(k) *p*-hydroxybenzoic acid
(l) 2,4,6-trinitrophenol (picric acid)

2. Give structures and names of all the possible isomeric:

(a) xylenes (dimethylbenzenes)
(b) aminobenzoic acids ($H_2NC_6H_4COOH$)
(c) trimethylbenzenes

(d) dibromonitrobenzenes
(e) bromochlorotoluenes
(f) trinitrotoluenes

3. (a) How many isomeric monosubstitution products are theoretically possible from each of the following structures of formula C_6H_6? (b) How many disubstitution products? (c) Which structures, if any, would be acceptable for benzene on the basis of isomer number?

$$HC\equiv C-CH_2-CH_2-C\equiv CH \qquad HC\equiv C-CH_2-C\equiv C-CH_3 \qquad HC\equiv C-C\equiv C-CH_2-CH_3$$

I   II   III

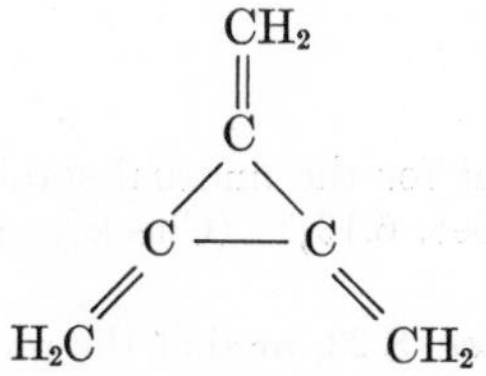

IV 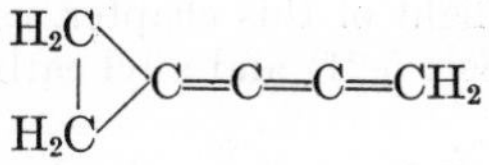   V

4. Give structures and names of all theoretically possible products of the ring mononitration of:

(a) *o*-dichlorobenzene
(b) *m*-dichlorobenzene
(c) *p*-dichlorobenzene
(d) *o*-bromochlorobenzene
(e) *m*-bromochlorobenzene
(f) *p*-bromochlorobenzene

(g) *o*-chloronitrobenzene
(h) *m*-chloronitrobenzene
(i) *p*-chloronitrobenzene
(j) 1,3,5-trimethylbenzene
(k) 4-bromo-1,2-dimethylbenzene
(l) *p*-ethyltoluene

5. Give structures and names of all aromatic hydrocarbons that *theoretically* can have the indicated number of isomeric ring-substituted derivatives.

(a) C_8H_{10}: one monobromo derivative
(b) C_8H_{10}: two monobromo derivatives
(c) C_8H_{10}: three monobromo derivatives
(d) C_9H_{12}: one mononitro derivative
(e) C_9H_{12}: two mononitro derivatives
(f) C_9H_{12}: three mononitro derivatives
(g) C_9H_{12}: four mononitro derivatives

6. There are three known tribromobenzenes of m.p. 44°, 87°, and 120°. Could these isomers be assigned structures by use of the Körner method? Justify your answer.

7. For a time the prism formula VI, proposed in 1869 by Albert Ladenburg of Germany, was considered as a possible structure for benzene, since (disregarding optical isomerism, Sec. 11.19) it would yield one monosubstitution product and three isomeric disubstitution products.

VI

(a) Draw Ladenburg structures of the three possible isomeric dibromobenzenes.
(b) On the basis of the Körner method of absolute orientation, label each Ladenburg structure in (a) as *ortho*, *meta*, or *para*.

8. How do you account for the following facts: formic acid, HCOOH, contains one carbon–oxygen bond of 1.36 A and another of 1.23 A, yet sodium formate, $HCOO^-$ Na^+, contains two equal carbon–oxygen bonds, each of 1.27 A. (Check your answer in Sec. 16.13.)

Formic acid

9. In light of this chapter, can you account for the unusual stability of allyl radicals (Sec. 5.21) and allyl carbonium ions (Sec. 6.16)? (Check your answer in Sec. 9.17.)

10. In light of the mechanism outlined in Sec. 8.23, predict the product of the reaction of benzene with *tert*-butyl alcohol in the presence of H_2SO_4; with isobutylene in the presence of H_2SO_4. (Check your answer in Sec. 9.7.)

11. Nitration by nitric acid alone is believed to proceed by essentially the same mechanism as nitration in the presence of sulfuric acid (Sec. 8.20). Write an equation for the generation of $^+NO_2$ from nitric acid alone.

12. There is evidence that the reaction between HNO_3 and H_2SO_4 to generate $^+NO_2$ (which we have summarized in one equation, Sec. 8.20) actually involves three steps, the second of which is the slowest one and the one that actually produces $^+NO_2$. Can you suggest a reasonable sequence of reactions? (*Hint:* see Sec. 4.16.)

13. From 1,3,5-cycloheptatriene, C_7H_8, there can be prepared a compound, C_7H_7Br, which has the following properties: it is soluble in water, but insoluble in non-polar solvents; it melts above 200°; it gives an immediate precipitate of AgBr when treated with $AgNO_3$; reduction gives cycloheptane, C_7H_{14}.

(a) Suggest a structure for C_7H_7Br using the valence-bond approach; using the orbital approach. (b) How does this orbital structure compare with that of benzene? With that of the anion from cyclopentadiene? (c) Would you expect C_7H_7Br to show aromatic properties?

14. Qualitative analysis of a compound showed carbon, hydrogen, and bromine. Combustion of a 7.91-mg sample gave 9.75 mg of carbon dioxide and 1.71 mg of water. A second sample of 6.20 mg was fused with sodium peroxide; following acidification by nitric acid and addition of silver nitrate, 9.26 mg of silver bromide was collected and weighed. When 7.89 mg of the compound was dissolved in 52.6 mg of camphor (m.p. 176°), the melting point of the mixture was found to be 151.5°.

Calculate (a) percentage composition; (b) empirical formula; and (c) molecular formula. (d) Give structures of all aromatic compounds having this molecular formula.

15. When benzene is treated with chlorine under the influence of ultraviolet light, a solid material is formed. Quantitative analysis gives an empirical formula of CHCl. Freezing-point lowering indicates a molecular weight of about 300. (a) What is the molecular formula of the product? (b) What is a possible structural formula? (c) What kind of reaction has taken place? (d) Is the product aromatic? (e) Actually, the product is a mixture of six isomeric compounds, one of which is used as an insecticide, Gammexane. How do these isomers differ from each other? (f) Are more than six isomers possible?

16. Can you account for the order of acidity:

$$\text{acetylene} > \text{benzene} > \textit{n}\text{-pentane}$$

(*Hint:* see Sec. 6.9.)

Chapter nine_____

ARENES

9.1 Aliphatic-aromatic hydrocarbons

From our study so far, we know what kind of chemical properties to expect of an aliphatic hydrocarbon, that is, of an alkane, alkene, or alkyne. We know what kind of chemical behavior to expect of the parent aromatic hydrocarbon, benzene. Many important compounds are not just aliphatic or just aromatic, however, but contain both aliphatic and aromatic units; hydrocarbons of this kind are known collectively as **arenes.** *Ethylbenzene,* for example, contains a benzene ring and an aliphatic side chain.

Ethylbenzene

What kind of chemical properties might we expect of one of these mixed aliphatic-aromatic hydrocarbons? First, we might expect it to show *two* sets of chemical properties. The ring of ethylbenzene should undergo the electrophilic substitution characteristic of benzene, and the side chain should undergo the free radical substitution characteristic of ethane. Second, the properties of each portion of the molecule should be modified by the presence of the other portion. The ethyl group should modify the aromatic properties of the ring, and the ring should modify the aliphatic properties of the side chain.

These predictions are correct. Treatment of ethylbenzene with nitric acid and sulfuric acid, for instance, introduces a nitro group into the ring; treatment with chlorine in the presence of light introduces a chlorine atom into the side chain. But because of the ethyl group, nitration takes place more readily than with benzene itself, and occurs chiefly at the positions *ortho* and *para* to the ethyl group; and because of the ring, chlorination takes place more readily than with ethane, and occurs chiefly on the carbon nearer the ring.

o-Nitroethylbenzene   p-Nitroethylbenzene
(chief products)

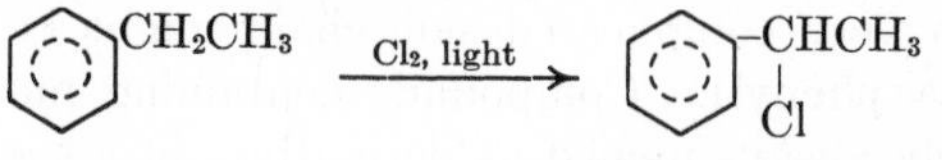

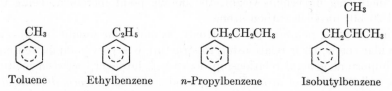

CH₂CH₃ →(Cl₂, light) CHCH₃ | Cl   *More readily than for ethane*

1-Chloro-1-phenylethane
(α-Phenylethyl chloride)
(*chief product*)

Thus *each portion of the molecule affects the* **reactivity** *of the other portion and determines the* **orientation** *of attack.*

In the same way we may have a molecule that is part aromatic and part alkene, or part aromatic and part alkyne. Again each portion of such a molecule shows the properties characteristic of its particular structure, although these properties are modified by the other portion of the molecule.

We shall examine most closely the compounds made up of aromatic and alkane units, the **alkylbenzenes.** We shall look much more briefly at the aromatic-alkene compounds (**alkenylbenzenes**) and aromatic-alkyne compounds (**alkynylbenzenes**).

9.2 Structure and nomenclature

The simplest of the alkylbenzenes, methylbenzene, is given the special name of **toluene.** Compounds containing longer side chains are named by prefixing the name of the alkyl group to the word –*benzene,* as for example, in *ethylbenzene, n-propylbenzene,* and *isobutylbenzene.*

CH₃	C₂H₅	CH₂CH₂CH₃	CH₃ | CH₂CHCH₃
Toluene	Ethylbenzene	*n*-Propylbenzene	Isobutylbenzene

The simplest of the dialkylbenzenes, the dimethylbenzenes, are given the special names of **xylenes;** we have, then, *o-xylene, m-xylene,* and *p-xylene.* Dialkylbenzenes containing one methyl group are named as derivatives of toluene, while others are named by prefixing the names of both alkyl groups to the word –*benzene.*

CH₃
CH₃
o-Xylene

CH₃
CH₃
m-Xylene

CH₃
CH₃
p-Xylene

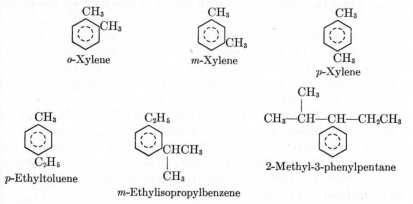

CH₃
C₂H₅
p-Ethyltoluene

C₂H₅
CHCH₃ | CH₃
m-Ethylisopropylbenzene

CH₃ | CH₃—CH—CH—CH₂CH₃
2-Methyl-3-phenylpentane

A compound containing a very complicated side chain might be named as a *phenylalkane* (C_6H_5 = **phenyl**). Compounds containing more than one benzene ring are nearly always named as derivatives of alkanes.

$$\langle○\rangle CH_2 \langle○\rangle \qquad\qquad \langle○\rangle CH_2CH_2 \langle○\rangle$$

Diphenylmethane   1,2-Diphenylethane

The simplest alkenylbenzene has the special name **styrene**. Others are generally named as substituted alkenes, occasionally as substituted benzenes. Alkynylbenzenes are named as substituted alkynes.

$$\langle○\rangle CH=CH_2 \qquad \langle○\rangle CH_2CH=CH_2 \qquad \langle○\rangle \overset{\overset{CH_3}{|}}{C}=CHCH_3 \qquad \langle○\rangle C\equiv CH$$

Styrene   Allylbenzene   2-Phenyl-2-butene   Phenylacetylene
(Vinylbenzene)   (3-Phenylpropene)
(Phenylethylene)

9.3 Physical properties

As compounds of low polarity, the arenes possess physical properties that are essentially the same as those of the hydrocarbons we have already studied. They are insoluble in water, but quite soluble in non-polar solvents like ether, carbon tetrachloride, or ligroin. They are almost always less dense than water. As we can see from Table 9.1, boiling points rise with increasing molecular weight, the boiling point increment being the usual 20–30° for each carbon atom.

Since melting points depend not only on molecular weight but also on molecular shape, their relationship to structure is a very complicated one. One important general relationship does exist, however, between melting point and structure of aromatic compounds: *among isomeric disubstituted benzenes, the para isomer generally melts considerably higher than the other two.* The xylenes, for example, boil within six degrees of one another; yet they differ widely in melting point, the *o*- and *m*-isomers melting at $-25°$ and $-48°$, and the *p*-isomer melting at $+13°$. Since dissolution, like melting, involves overcoming the intermolecular forces of the crystal, it is not surprising to find that *generally the para isomer is also the least soluble in a given solvent.*

The higher melting point and lower solubility of a *para* isomer is only a special example of the general effect of molecular symmetry on intracrystalline forces. The more symmetrical a compound, the better it fits into a crystal lattice and hence the higher the melting point and the lower the solubility. *Para* isomers are simply the most symmetrical of disubstituted benzenes. We can see (Table 9.1) that 1,2,4,5-tetramethylbenzene melts 85° to 100° higher than the less symmetrical 1,2,3,5- and 1,2,3,4-isomers. A particularly striking example of the effect of symmetry on melting point is that of benzene and toluene. The introduction of a single methyl group into the extremely symmetrical benzene molecule lowers the melting point from 5° to $-95°$

TABLE 9.1

ARENES

Name	Formula	M.p., °C	B.p., °C	Density at 20°C
Benzene	C_6H_6	5.5	80	0.879
Toluene	$C_6H_5CH_3$	− 95	111	.866
o-Xylene	$1,2\text{-}C_6H_4(CH_3)_2$	− 25	144	.880
m-Xylene	$1,3\text{-}C_6H_4(CH_3)_2$	− 48	139	.864
p-Xylene	$1,4\text{-}C_6H_4(CH_3)_2$	13	138	.861
Hemimellitene	$1,2,3\text{-}C_6H_3(CH_3)_3$	− 25	176	.895
Pseudocumene	$1,2,4\text{-}C_6H_3(CH_3)_3$	− 44	169	.876
Mesitylene	$1,3,5\text{-}C_6H_3(CH_3)_3$	− 45	165	.864
Prehnitene	$1,2,3,4\text{-}C_6H_2(CH_3)_4$	− 6.5	205	.902
Isodurene	$1,2,3,5\text{-}C_6H_2(CH_3)_4$	− 24	197	
Durene	$1,2,4,5\text{-}C_6H_2(CH_3)_4$	80	195	
Pentamethylbenzene	$C_6H(CH_3)_5$	53	231	
Hexamethylbenzene	$C_6(CH_3)_6$	165	264	
Ethylbenzene	$C_6H_5C_2H_5$	− 95	136	.867
n-Propylbenzene	$C_6H_5CH_2CH_2CH_3$	− 99	159	.862
Cumene	$C_6H_5CH(CH_3)_2$	− 96	152	.862
n-Butylbenzene	$C_6H_5(CH_2)_3CH_3$	− 81	183	.860
Isobutylbenzene	$C_6H_5CH_2CH(CH_3)_2$		171	.867
sec-Butylbenzene	$C_6H_5CH(CH_3)C_2H_5$	− 83	173.5	.864
tert-Butylbenzene	$C_6H_5C(CH_3)_3$	− 58	169	.867
p-Cymene	$1,4\text{-}CH_3C_6H_4CH(CH_3)_2$	− 70	177	.857
Biphenyl	$C_6H_5C_6H_5$	70	255	
Diphenylmethane	$C_6H_5CH_2C_6H_5$	26	263	
Triphenylmethane	$(C_6H_5)_3CH$	93	360	
1,2-Diphenylethane	$C_6H_5CH_2CH_2C_6H_5$	52	284	
Styrene	$C_6H_5CH{=}CH_2$	− 31	145	.907
trans-Stilbene	$trans\text{-}C_6H_5CH{=}CHC_6H_5$	124	307	
unsym-Diphenylethylene	$(C_6H_5)_2C{=}CH_2$	9	277	1.02
Triphenylethylene	$(C_6H_5)_2C{=}CHC_6H_5$	73		
Tetraphenylethylene	$(C_6H_5)_2C{=}C(C_6H_5)_2$	227	425	
Phenylacetylene	$C_6H_5C{\equiv}CH$	− 45	142	0.930
Diphenylacetylene	$C_6H_5C{\equiv}CC_6H_5$	62.5	300	

9.4 Industrial source of alkylbenzenes

It would be hard to exaggerate the importance to the chemical industry and to our entire economy of the large-scale production of benzene and the alkylbenzenes. Just as the alkanes obtained from petroleum are ultimately the source of nearly all our aliphatic compounds, so benzene and the alkylbenzenes are ultimately the source of nearly all our aromatic compounds. When a chemist wishes to make a complicated aromatic compound, whether in the laboratory or in industry, he does not make a benzene ring; he takes a simpler compound already containing a benzene ring and then adds to it, piece by piece, until he has built the structure he wants.

Just where do the enormous quantities of simple aromatic compounds come from? There are two large reservoirs of organic material, **coal and**

petroleum, and aromatic compounds are obtained from both. Aromatic compounds are separated as such from coal tar, and are synthesized from the alkanes of petroleum.

By far the larger portion of coal that is mined today is converted into coke, which is needed for the smelting of iron to steel. When coal is heated in the absence of air, it is partly broken down into simpler, volatile compounds which are driven out; the residue is *coke*. The volatile materials consist of *coal gas* and a liquid known as **coal tar.**

From coal tar by distillation there are obtained a number of aromatic compounds. Upon coking, a ton of soft coal may yield about 120 pounds of coal tar. From this 120 pounds the following aromatic compounds can be separated: benzene, 2 pounds; toluene, 0.5 pound; xylenes, 0.1 pound; phenol, 0.5 pound; cresols, 2 pounds; naphthalene, 5 pounds. Two pounds of benzene from a ton of coal does not represent a very high percentage yield, yet so much coal is coked every year that the annual production of benzene from coal tar is enormous (200 million gallons in 1955).

During World War II, the need for toluene for TNT greatly exceeded the 30–40 million gallons produced each year from coal tar. To meet the demand, methods were adopted to obtain toluene from the aliphatic hydrocarbons of petroleum. These methods involved chiefly the dehydrogenation of the methylcyclohexane that is particularly abundant in California petroleum. This process, known as **hydroforming,** involves passing methylcyclohexane at high temperature and pressure (560° and 300 lb/in²) over

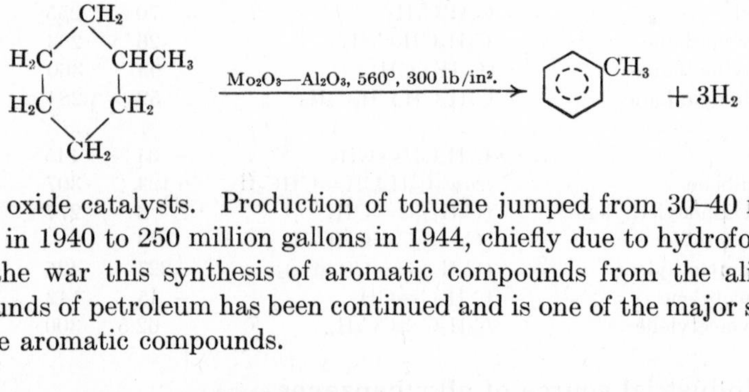

certain oxide catalysts. Production of toluene jumped from 30–40 million gallons in 1940 to 250 million gallons in 1944, chiefly due to hydroforming. Since the war this synthesis of aromatic compounds from the aliphatic compounds of petroleum has been continued and is one of the major sources of these aromatic compounds.

9.5 Preparation of alkylbenzenes

Although a number of the simpler alkylbenzenes are available from industrial sources, the more complicated compounds must be synthesized in one of the ways outlined below.

PREPARATION OF ALKYLBENZENES

1. Attachment of alkyl group: Friedel-Crafts alkylation

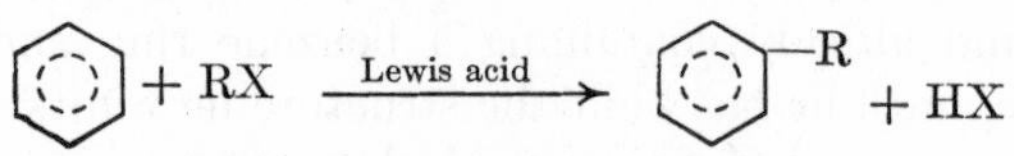

Lewis acid: $AlCl_3$, BF_3, HF, etc.
Ar-X *cannot be used in place of* R-X.

2. **Conversion of side chain**

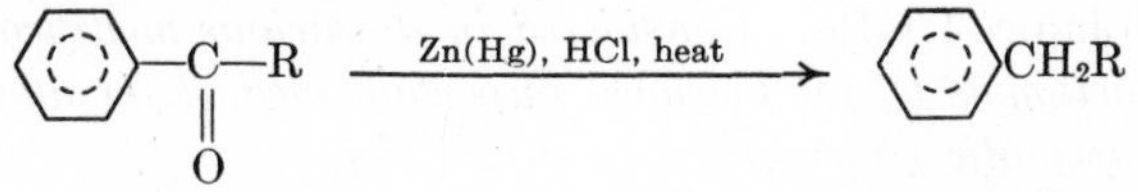

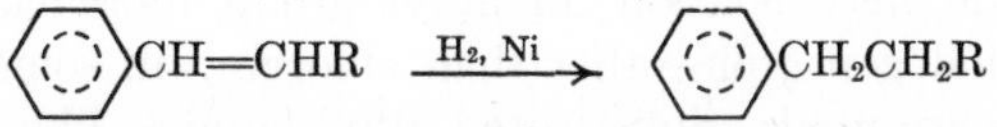

Friedel-Crafts alkylation is extremely useful since it permits the direct attachment of an alkyl group to the aromatic ring. It is limited by the fact that the alkyl group that becomes attached to the ring is not always the same as the alkyl group of the parent halide; this **rearrangement** of the alkyl group is discussed in a following section (Sec. 9.8).

There are frequently available aromatic compounds containing aliphatic side chains that are not simple alkyl groups. An alkylbenzene can be prepared from one of these compounds by converting the side chain into an alkyl group. Although there is an aromatic ring in the molecule, this conversion is essentially the preparation of an alkane from some other aliphatic compound. The methods used are those that we have already learned for the preparation of alkanes: hydrogenation of a carbon–carbon double bond in a side chain, for example. Many problems of the alkylbenzenes are solved by a consideration of simple alkane chemistry.

The most important side-chain conversion involves the **Clemmensen reduction of ketones** by amalgamated zinc and HCl. This method is important because the necessary ketones are readily available through a modification of the Friedel-Crafts reaction that involves acid chlorides (see Sec. 17.8). Unlike alkylation by the Friedel-Crafts reaction, this method does not involve rearrangement. (Alkanes can be prepared from purely aliphatic ketones by the Clemmensen method, but this is of little practical importance since other starting materials are more readily available than the ketones.)

Problem 9.1 How might you prepare ethylbenzene from: (a) benzene and ethyl alcohol; (b) acetophenone, $C_6H_5COCH_3$; (c) styrene, $C_6H_5CH=CH_2$; (d) α-phenylethyl alcohol, $C_6H_5CHOHCH_3$; and (e) β-phenylethyl chloride, $C_6H_5CH_2CH_2Cl$?

Problem 9.2 How might you prepare 2,3-diphenylbutane from α-phenylethyl alcohol, $C_6H_5CHOHCH_3$?

9.6 Friedel-Crafts alkylation

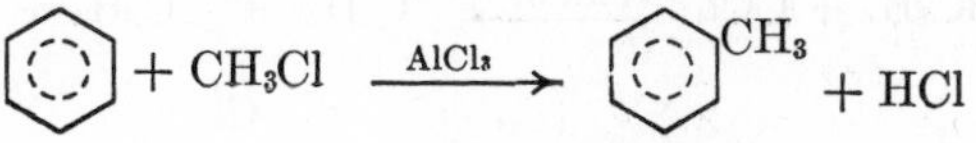

If a small amount of anhydrous aluminum chloride is added to a mixture of benzene and methyl chloride, a vigorous reaction occurs, hydrogen chloride gas is evolved, and toluene can be isolated from the reaction mixture. This is the simplest example of the reaction discovered in 1877

at the University of Paris by the French-American team of chemists, Charles Friedel and James Crafts. *Considered in its various modifications, the Friedel-Crafts reaction is by far the most important method for attaching alkyl side chains to aromatic rings.*

Each of the components of the simple example just given can be varied. The alkyl halide may contain an alkyl group more complicated than methyl, and a halogen atom other than chlorine; in some cases, alcohols or even alkenes are used. Substituted alkyl halides, like benzyl chloride, $C_6H_5CH_2Cl$, also can be used. Because of the low reactivity of halogen attached to an aromatic ring (Sec. 14.7), aryl halides (Ar—X, e.g., bromo- or chlorobenzene) *cannot* be used in place of alkyl halides.

The aromatic ring to which the side chain becomes attached may be that of benzene itself, certain substituted benzenes (chiefly alkylbenzenes and halobenzenes), or more complicated aromatic ring systems like naphthalene and anthracene (Chapter 31).

In place of aluminum chloride, other Lewis acids can be used, in particular BF_3 and HF.

The reaction is carried out by simply mixing together the three components; usually the only problems are those of moderating the reaction by cooling, and trapping the hydrogen halide gas. Since the attachment of an alkyl side chain makes the ring more susceptible to further attack (Sec. 9.13), steps must be taken to limit substitution to *mono*alkylation. As in halogenation of alkanes (Sec. 2.8) this is accomplished by using an *excess* of the hydrocarbon. In this way an alkyl carbonium ion seeking an aromatic ring is more likely to encounter an unsubstituted ring than a substituted one. Frequently the aromatic compound does double duty, serving as solvent as well as reactant.

From polyhalogenated alkanes it is possible to prepare compounds containing more than one aromatic ring:

$$2C_6H_6 + CH_2Cl_2 \xrightarrow{AlCl_3} C_6H_5CH_2C_6H_5 + 2HCl$$
$$\text{Diphenylmethane}$$

$$2C_6H_6 + ClCH_2CH_2Cl \xrightarrow{AlCl_3} C_6H_5CH_2CH_2C_6H_5 + 2HCl$$
$$\text{1,2-Diphenylethane}$$

$$
3C_6H_6 + CHCl_3 \xrightarrow{AlCl_3}
\begin{array}{c}
C_6H_5 \\
| \\
C_6H_5-C-C_6H_5 \\
| \\
H
\end{array}
+ 3HCl
$$
$$\text{Triphenylmethane}$$

$$
3C_6H_6 + CCl_4 \xrightarrow{AlCl_3}
\begin{array}{c}
C_6H_5 \\
| \\
C_6H_5-C-C_6H_5 \\
| \\
Cl
\end{array}
+ 3HCl
$$
$$\textbf{Triphenylchloromethane}$$

We can see that only three of the four chlorine atoms of carbon tetrachloride are replaced; this may be due, in part, to steric hindrance, that is, to the difficulty of crowding four phenyl groups about a single carbon. (However, see also Problem 9.18, page 278.)

9.7 Mechanism of Friedel-Crafts alkylation

As we have already seen (Sec. 8.23), the generally accepted mechanism for Friedel-Crafts alkylation involves the following steps.

(1) $$RCl + AlCl_3 \rightleftharpoons AlCl_4^- + R^\oplus$$

(2) 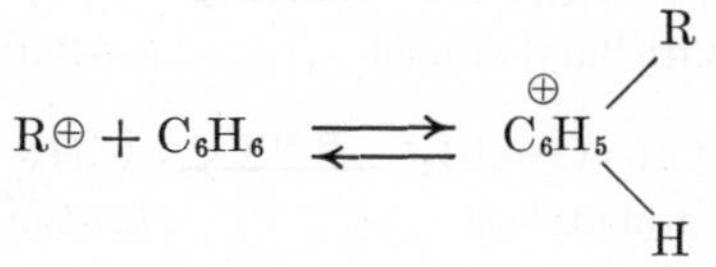 $$R^\oplus + C_6H_6 \rightleftharpoons C_6H_5 \overset{\displaystyle \overset{\oplus}{\diagup}R}{\underset{\diagdown H}{}}$$

(3) $$C_6H_5 \overset{\displaystyle \overset{\oplus}{\diagup}R}{\underset{\diagdown H}{}} + AlCl_4^- \rightleftharpoons C_6H_5R + HCl + AlCl_3$$

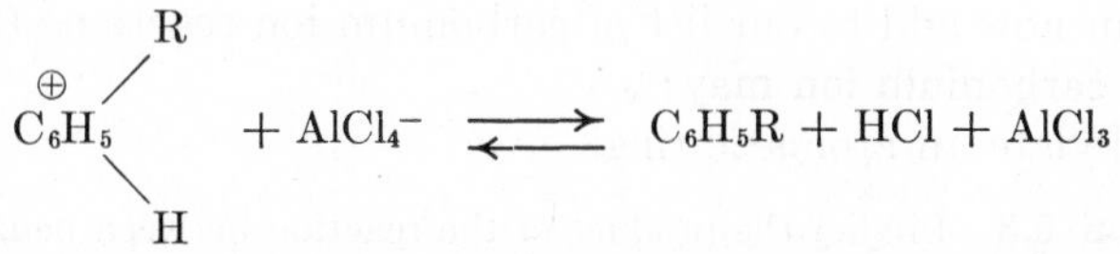

The reaction follows the pattern of electrophilic aromatic substitution, the attacking particle in this case being the alkyl carbonium ion. The function of the aluminum chloride is to generate this carbonium ion by abstracting the halogen from the alkyl halide. It is not surprising that other Lewis acids can function in the same way and thus take the place of aluminum chloride:

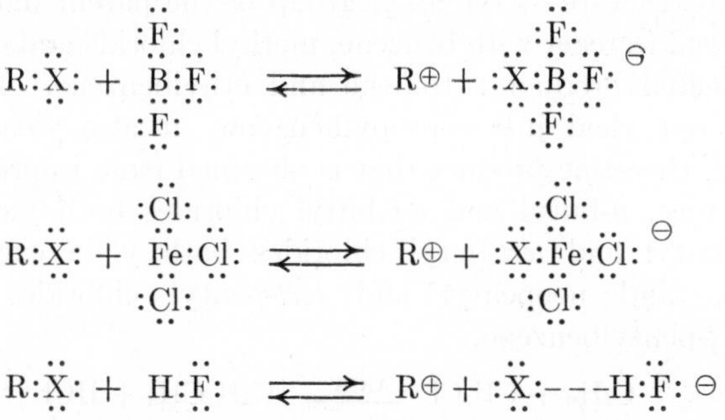

$$R:X: + \ \overset{\displaystyle :F:}{\underset{\displaystyle :F:}{B:F:}} \ \rightleftharpoons R^\oplus + \overset{\displaystyle :F:}{\underset{\displaystyle :F:}{:X:B:F:}}{}^\ominus$$

$$R:X: + \ \overset{\displaystyle :Cl:}{\underset{\displaystyle :Cl:}{Fe:Cl:}} \ \rightleftharpoons R^\oplus + \overset{\displaystyle :Cl:}{\underset{\displaystyle :Cl:}{:X:Fe:Cl:}}{}^\ominus$$

$$R:\ddot{X}: + \ H:\ddot{F}: \ \rightleftharpoons R^\oplus + :\ddot{X}:---H:\ddot{F}: \ominus$$

In certain cases it may be that the Lewis acid does not generate a completely free carbonium ion but simply polarizes the molecule prior to its attack on the benzene ring:

$$\overset{\delta_+}{R}---\overset{\delta_-}{X}---AlCl_3$$

In other cases, however, there is evidence that a free carbonium ion is involved (see the following section).

We earlier considered other ways in which carbonium ions could be generated: by action of acids on alcohols (Sec. 4.16) and on alkenes (Sec. 5.10). Judging from the mechanism just described, we might expect

$$\text{ROH} + \text{H}^+ \rightleftharpoons \text{ROH}_2^{\oplus} \rightleftharpoons \text{R}^{\oplus} + \text{H}_2\text{O}$$

$$-\overset{|}{\text{C}}=\overset{|}{\text{C}}- + \text{H}^+ \rightleftharpoons -\overset{|}{\underset{\text{H}}{\text{C}}}-\overset{|}{\text{C}}^{\oplus}$$

that carbonium ions generated in these other ways should also attack the benzene ring. This expectation is correct: alcohols and alkenes, in the presence of acids, alkylate aromatic rings in what we may consider to be a modification of the Friedel-Crafts reaction.

$$\text{C}_6\text{H}_6 + (\text{CH}_3)_3\text{COH} \xrightarrow{\text{H}_2\text{SO}_4} \text{C}_6\text{H}_5\text{—C}(\text{CH}_3)_3$$
tert-Butyl alcohol $\qquad\qquad$ tert-Butylbenzene

$$\text{C}_6\text{H}_6 + (\text{CH}_3)_2\text{C}=\text{CH}_2 \xrightarrow{\text{H}_2\text{SO}_4} \text{C}_6\text{H}_5\text{—C}(\text{CH}_3)_3$$
Isobutylene $\qquad\qquad$ tert-Butylbenzene

We can now add to our list of carbonium ion reactions (Secs. 5.17 and 5.18). **A carbonium ion may:**

(e) alkylate an aromatic ring.

Problem 9.3 Predict the product of the reaction between benzene and propylene in the presence of HF.

9.8 Rearrangement of carbonium ions

A serious limitation to the use of Friedel-Crafts alkylation is that the alkyl group that becomes attached to the benzene ring does not always have the same structure as the alkyl group of the parent halide.

When allowed to react with benzene, methyl chloride and ethyl chloride yield the expected products: toluene and ethylbenzene. But n-propyl chloride does not yield just n-propylbenzene; it also yields much iso-propylbenzene, the same product that is obtained from isopropyl chloride. In the same way, n-butyl and sec-butyl chlorides both yield sec-butyl-benzene; isobutyl and tert-butyl chlorides both yield exclusively tert-butylbenzene; and neopentyl and tert-pentyl chlorides both yield exclusively tert-pentylbenzene.

$$\text{C}_6\text{H}_6 + \text{CH}_3\text{Cl} \xrightarrow{\text{AlCl}_3} \text{C}_6\text{H}_5\text{CH}_3 + \text{HCl}$$
Toluene

$$\text{C}_6\text{H}_6 + \text{C}_2\text{H}_5\text{Cl} \xrightarrow{\text{AlCl}_3} \text{C}_6\text{H}_5\text{C}_2\text{H}_5 + \text{HCl}$$
Ethylbenzene

$$\text{C}_6\text{H}_6 + \begin{matrix} \text{CH}_3\text{CH}_2\text{CH}_2\text{Cl} \\ or \\ \text{CH}_3\text{CHClCH}_3 \end{matrix} \xrightarrow{\text{AlCl}_3} \text{C}_6\text{H}_5\text{CH}(\text{CH}_3)_2 + \text{HCl}$$
Isopropylbenzene

$$\text{C}_6\text{H}_6 + \begin{matrix} \text{CH}_3\text{CH}_2\text{CH}_2\text{CH}_2\text{Cl} \\ or \\ \text{CH}_3\text{CH}_2\text{CHClCH}_3 \end{matrix} \xrightarrow{\text{AlCl}_3} \text{C}_6\text{H}_5\text{CH}(\text{CH}_3)\text{CH}_2\text{CH}_3 + \text{HCl}$$
sec-Butylbenzene

$$C_6H_6 \; + \; \begin{matrix} (CH_3)_2CCH_2Cl \\ or \\ (CH_3)_3CCl \end{matrix} \; \xrightarrow{AlCl_3} \; C_6H_5C(CH_3)_3 + HCl$$
tert-Butylbenzene

$$C_6H_6 \; + \; \begin{matrix} (CH_3)_3CCH_2Cl \\ or \\ (CH_3)_2CClCH_2CH_3 \end{matrix} \; \xrightarrow{AlCl_3} \; C_6H_5C(CH_3)_2CH_2CH_3 + HCl$$
tert-Pentylbenzene

Until now we have assumed that an alkyl group retains its identity throughout a chemical reaction. For example, when n-propyl chloride reacts with sodium in the Wurtz reaction (Sec. 3.17), two n-propyl groups are joined together to form n-hexane; when isopropyl chloride reacts, two isopropyl groups are joined together to form 2,3-dimethylbutane. Fortunately for the organic chemist, this is *usually* the case in other reactions.

There are, however, certain exceptions: reactions in which **rearrangement** of a portion of the molecule occurs. In some cases rearrangement involves only a shift of hydrogen atoms, in other cases rearrangement of the carbon skeleton itself occurs. There is a certain pattern to rearrangements, so that we can know roughly *when* they are likely to occur, and *in what way* they are likely to occur. As we shall see, reactions that proceed by certain mechanisms are very likely to involve rearrangements, whereas reactions that proceed by certain other mechanisms almost surely will not involve rearrangements. Indeed, occurrence or non-occurrence of rearrangement frequently is taken as evidence for or against a particular mechanism.

Obviously rearrangement occurs in certain of the Friedel-Crafts reactions just described: in formation of isopropylbenzene from n-propyl chloride, for example, or where n-butyl chloride yields *sec*-butylbenzene and isobutyl chloride yields *tert*-butylbenzene. Rearrangement clearly does not occur in certain other cases: in formation of isopropylbenzene from isopropyl chloride, for example. How can we account for the occurrence or non-occurrence of rearrangement, and for the particular way in which rearrangement takes place?

The mechanism for Friedel-Crafts alkylation involves intermediate formation of a carbonium ion. Since most other reactions that seem to proceed by way of a carbonium ion also involve rearrangement, Frank Whitmore (of the Pennsylvania State University) suggested that it is the carbonium ion that undergoes the actual rearrangement. n-Propyl chloride, for example, yields the n-propyl carbonium ion; this ion rearranges to the isopropyl carbonium ion, which attacks the benzene ring. In a

$$CH_3CH_2CH_2Cl + AlCl_3 \longrightarrow CH_3CH_2CH_2^\oplus + AlCl_4^-$$

$$CH_3CH_2CH_2^\oplus \longrightarrow CH_3\underset{\oplus}{C}HCH_3$$

$$C_6H_6 + CH_3\underset{\oplus}{C}HCH_3 \longrightarrow C_6H_5CH(CH_3)_2 + H^+$$

similar way, the *n*-butyl ion rearranges to the *sec*-butyl ion, isobutyl to *tert*-butyl, and neopentyl to *tert*-pentyl. We notice that each case involves rearrangement of a primary carbonium ion to a secondary carbonium ion, or a primary to a tertiary; that is, *rearrangement occurs in the way that yields a more stable carbonium ion.*

Just how does this rearrangement occur? Whitmore has pictured rearrangement as taking place in this way: a hydrogen atom or alkyl group migrates *with a pair of electrons* from an adjacent carbon to the carbon bearing the positive charge. The carbon that loses the migrating group acquires the positive charge. A migration of hydrogen with a pair of electrons is known as a **hydride shift**; a similar migration of an alkyl group is known as an **alkyl shift**. These are just two examples of the most common kind of rearrangement, the **1,2-shifts**: *rearrangements in which the migrating group moves from one atom to the very next atom.*

$$-\underset{\underset{\displaystyle H}{|}}{\overset{|}{C}}-\overset{|}{\underset{|}{C}}- \longrightarrow -\overset{|}{\underset{\oplus}{C}}-\overset{|}{\underset{\displaystyle \overset{..}{H}}{C}}- \qquad \text{A } \textit{hydride} \text{ shift}$$

1,2-Shifts

$$-\underset{\underset{\displaystyle R}{|}}{\overset{|}{C}}-\overset{|}{\underset{|}{C}}- \longrightarrow -\overset{|}{\underset{\oplus}{C}}-\overset{|}{\underset{\displaystyle \overset{..}{R}}{C}}- \qquad \text{An } \textit{alkyl} \text{ shift}$$

We can account for rearrangements in Friedel-Crafts alkylation in the following way. A carbonium ion is formed by loss of halide ion to the Lewis acid. **If a 1,2-shift of hydrogen or alkyl can form a more stable carbonium ion, then such a rearrangement takes place.** The new carbonium ion now attacks the aromatic ring.

In the case of the *n*-propyl carbonium ion a shift of hydrogen yields the more stable isopropyl carbonium ion; migration of a methyl group would simply form a different *n*-propyl carbonium ion. On the other hand, if the isopropyl carbonium ion is formed initially, any rearrangement would have to yield the less stable *n*-propyl carbonium ion; hence no rearrangement occurs. In the same way, *n*-butyl, isobutyl, and neopentyl carbonium ions rearrange, each by the kind of shift that yields a more stable carbonium ion.

$$H-\overset{\overset{\displaystyle H}{|}}{\underset{\underset{\displaystyle H}{|}}{C}}-\overset{\overset{\displaystyle H}{|}}{\underset{\underset{\displaystyle H}{|}}{C}}-\overset{\overset{\displaystyle H}{|}}{C}-H \longrightarrow H-\overset{\overset{\displaystyle H}{|}}{\underset{\underset{\displaystyle H}{|}}{C}}-\overset{\overset{\displaystyle H}{|}}{\underset{\oplus}{C}}-\overset{\overset{\displaystyle H}{|}}{\underset{\displaystyle \overset{..}{H}}{C}}-H$$

n-Propyl   Isopropyl
(1°)   (2°)

$$CH_3-\overset{\overset{\displaystyle CH_3}{|}}{\underset{\underset{\displaystyle H}{|}}{C}}-\overset{\overset{\displaystyle H}{|}}{C}-H \longrightarrow CH_3-\overset{\overset{\displaystyle CH_3}{|}}{\underset{\oplus}{C}}-\overset{\overset{\displaystyle H}{|}}{\underset{\displaystyle \overset{..}{H}}{C}}-H$$

Isobutyl   *tert*-Butyl
(1°)   (3°)

$$
\begin{array}{c}
\underset{\substack{\mid\\\text{CH}_3}}{\text{CH}_3}\ \text{H}\\
\text{CH}_3\!\!-\!\!\overset{\mid}{\underset{\underset{\oplus}{\text{CH}_3}}{\text{C}}}\!\!-\!\!\overset{\mid}{\text{C}}\!\!-\!\!\text{H} \longrightarrow \text{CH}_3\!\!-\!\!\overset{\mid}{\underset{\oplus}{\text{C}}}\!\!-\!\!\overset{\mid}{\underset{\text{CH}_3}{\text{C}}}\!\!-\!\!\text{H}
\end{array}
$$

Neopentyl   *tert*-Pentyl
(1°)   (3°)

We can now make another addition to our list of carbonium ion reactions (Secs. 5.17, 5.18, and 9.7). **A carbonium ion may:**

(a) eliminate a hydrogen ion to form an alkene
(b) combine with a negative ion or other basic molecule
(c) add to an alkene to form a larger carbonium ion
(d) abstract a hydride ion from an alkane
(e) alkylate an aromatic ring
(f) rearrange to a more stable carbonium ion

A carbonium ion formed by (c) or (f) can subsequently undergo any of the reactions.

In rearrangement, as in every other reaction of a carbonium ion, the electron-deficient carbon atom gains a pair of electrons, this time at the expense of a neighboring carbon atom, one that can better accommodate the positive charge.

Problem 9.4 How can you account for the formation: (a) Of 2-butene in the dehydration of *n*-butyl alcohol (Sec. 4.14)? (b) Of 2,3-dimethyl-2-butene and 2,3-dimethyl-1-butene from 3,3-dimethyl-2-butanol, $(CH_3)_3CCHOHCH_3$? (c) Which of the two dimethylbutenes in (b) would you expect to predominate?

Problem 9.5 How can you account for the fact that addition of HCl to 3,3-dimethyl-1-butene yields not only 3,3-dimethyl-2-chlorobutane but also 2,3-dimethyl-2-chlorobutane?

Problem 9.6 Free radicals show much less tendency to rearrange than do carbonium ions. H. C. Brown and Glen Russell of Purdue University photochemically chlorinated deuterium-labeled isobutane (I) and analyzed the products; the

$$
\begin{array}{c}
\text{CH}_3\\
\mid\\
\text{CH}_3\!\!-\!\!\overset{\mid}{\underset{\mid}{\text{C}}}\!\!-\!\!\text{CH}_3\\
\text{D}
\end{array}
$$

I

DCl/HCl ratio was equal (within experimental error) to the *tert*-butyl chloride/isobutyl chloride ratio. Show how these results provide evidence against the rearrangement of simple alkyl free radicals. (*Hint:* what results would be expected if, say, isobutyl radicals were to rearrange to *tert*-butyl radicals?)

Problem 9.7 Deuterium is most readily available as D_2O ("heavy water"). Suggest a way to make I starting from *tert*-butyl alcohol.

9.9 Reactions of alkylbenzenes

The most important reactions of the alkylbenzenes are outlined below, with ethylbenzene as a specific example; essentially the same behavior is shown by compounds bearing other side chains. Except for hydrogenation and oxidation, these reactions involve either **electrophilic substitution in the aromatic ring** or **free radical substitution in the aliphatic side chain.**

In following sections we shall be mostly concerned with (a) how experimental conditions determine which portion of the molecule — aromatic or aliphatic — is attacked, and (b) how each portion of the molecule modifies the reactions of the other portion.

REACTIONS OF ALKYLBENZENES

1. Hydrogenation
Example:

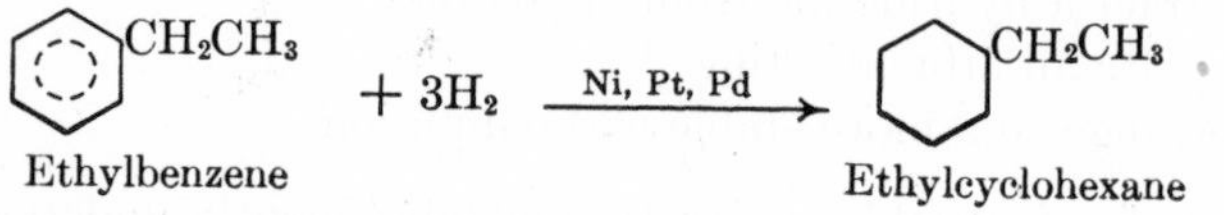

Ethylbenzene $+ 3H_2$ $\xrightarrow{\text{Ni, Pt, Pd}}$ Ethylcyclohexane

2. Oxidation
Example:

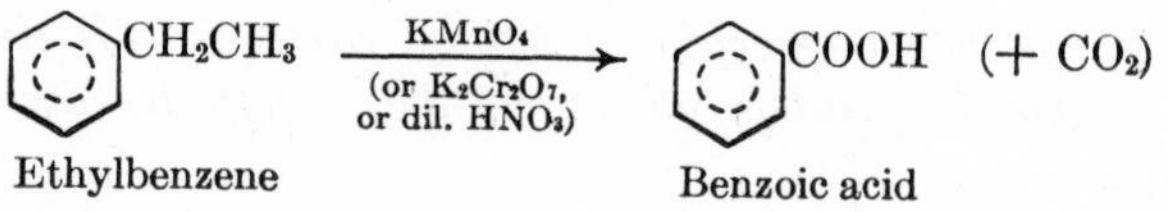

Ethylbenzene $\xrightarrow[\substack{\text{(or } K_2Cr_2O_7, \\ \text{or dil. } HNO_3)}]{KMnO_4}$ Benzoic acid COOH $(+ CO_2)$

3. Nitration
Example:

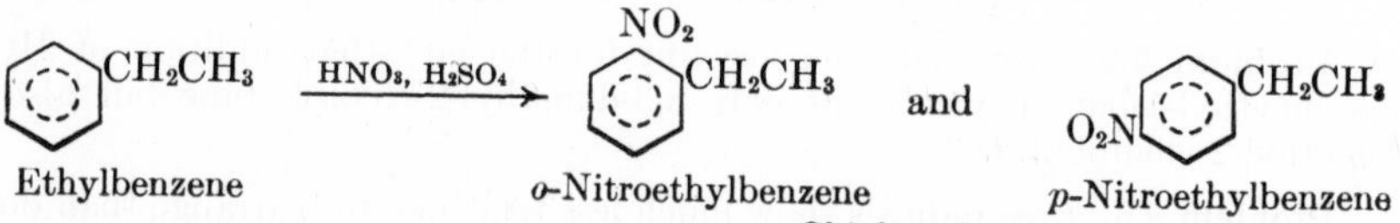

Ethylbenzene $\xrightarrow{HNO_3, H_2SO_4}$ o-Nitroethylbenzene and p-Nitroethylbenzene
Chief products

4. Sulfonation
Example:

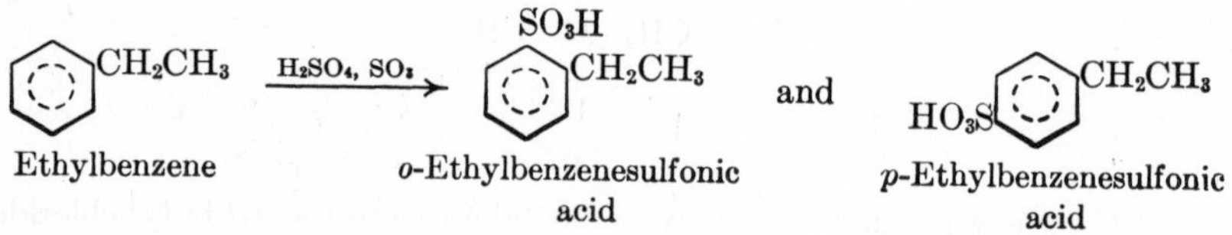

Ethylbenzene $\xrightarrow{H_2SO_4, SO_3}$ o-Ethylbenzenesulfonic acid and p-Ethylbenzenesulfonic acid

5. Friedel-Crafts alkylation
Example:

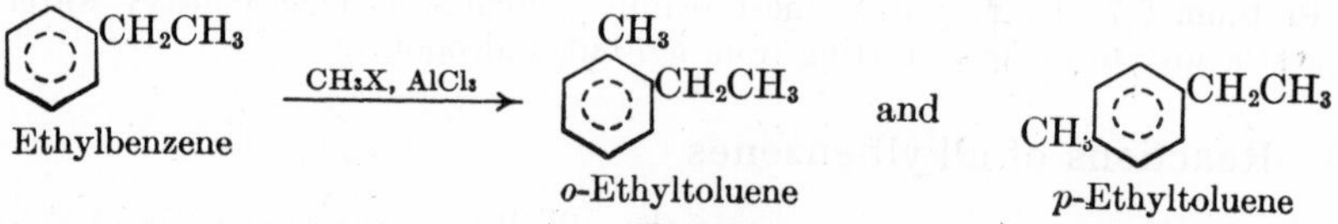

Ethylbenzene $\xrightarrow{CH_3X, AlCl_3}$ o-Ethyltoluene and p-Ethyltoluene
Temperature may affect orientation.

6. Halogenation

Example:

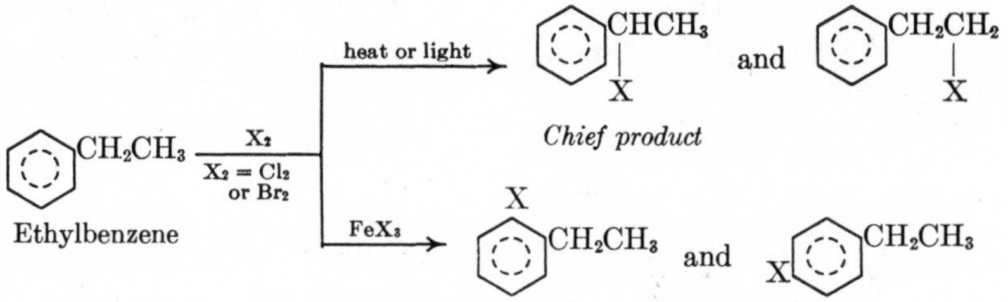

9.10 Hydrogenation of alkylbenzenes

We have seen (Sec. 8.5) that benzene reacts with hydrogen in the presence of a catalyst to yield cyclohexane. In a similar way, *alkyl*benzenes are converted into *alkyl*cyclohexanes; thus, toluene yields methylcyclohexane, and *m*-xylene yields 1,3-dimethylcyclohexane. In many cases the most important source of a pure alkylcyclohexane is hydrogenation of the corresponding alkylbenzene.

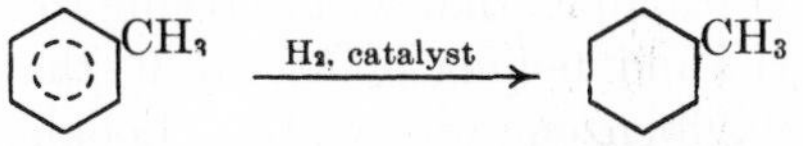

Toluene Methylcyclohexane

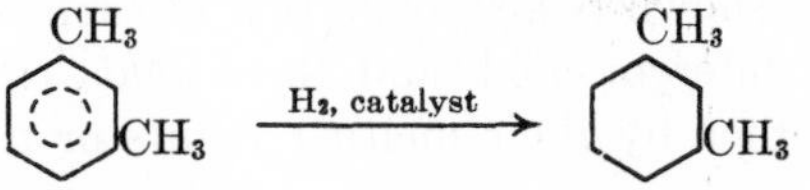

m-Xylene 1,3-Dimethylcyclohexane

9.11 Oxidation of alkylbenzenes

Although benzene and alkanes are quite unreactive toward the usual oxidizing agents ($KMnO_4$, $K_2Cr_2O_7$, etc.) and are oxidized readily only by the process of burning, the benzene ring renders an aliphatic side chain quite susceptible to oxidation. The side chain is oxidized down to the ring, only a carboxyl group (—COOH) remaining to indicate the position of the original side chain. Potassium permanganate is generally used for this purpose, although potassium dichromate or dilute nitric acid also can be used. (Oxidation of a side chain is more difficult, however, than oxidation of an alkene, and requires prolonged treatment with hot $KMnO_4$.)

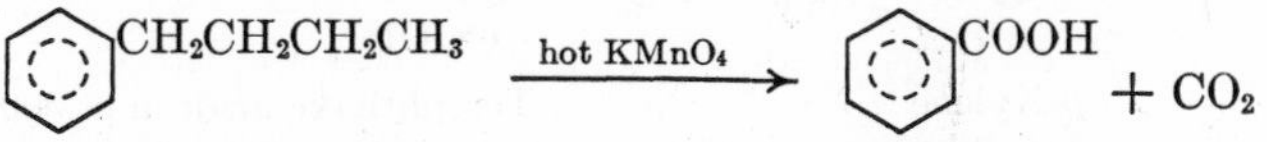

n-Butylbenzene Benzoic acid

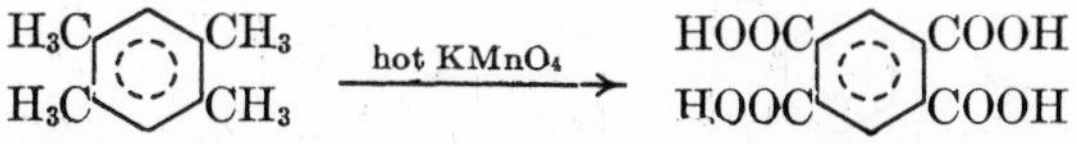

1,2,4,5-Tetramethylbenzene (Durene) 1,2,4,5-Benzenetetracarboxylic acid (Pyromellitic acid)

This reaction is used for two purposes: (a) synthesis of carboxylic acids, and (b) identification of alkylbenzenes.

(a) Synthesis of carboxylic acids. One of the most useful methods of preparing an aromatic carboxylic acid involves oxidation of the proper alkylbenzene. For example:

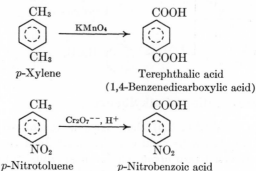

p-Xylene

Terephthalic acid
(1,4-Benzenedicarboxylic acid)

p-Nitrotoluene

p-Nitrobenzoic acid

(b) Identification of alkylbenzenes. The number and relative positions of side chains can frequently be determined by oxidation to the corresponding acids. Suppose, for example, that we are trying to identify an unknown liquid of formula C_8H_{10} and boiling point 137–9° that we have shown in other ways to be an alkylbenzene (Sec. 9.27). Looking in Table 9.1 (page 251) we find that it could be any one of four compounds: o-, m-, or p-xylene, or ethylbenzene. As shown below, oxidation of each of these possible hydrocarbons yields a different acid, and these acids can readily be distinguished from each other by their melting points or the melting points of derivatives.

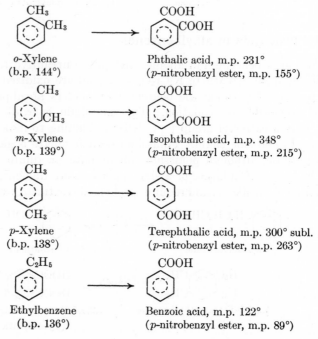

o-Xylene
(b.p. 144°)

Phthalic acid, m.p. 231°
(p-nitrobenzyl ester, m.p. 155°)

m-Xylene
(b.p. 139°)

Isophthalic acid, m.p. 348°
(p-nitrobenzyl ester, m.p. 215°)

p-Xylene
(b.p. 138°)

Terephthalic acid, m.p. 300° subl.
(p-nitrobenzyl ester, m.p. 263°)

Ethylbenzene
(b.p. 136°)

Benzoic acid, m.p. 122°
(p-nitrobenzyl ester, m.p. 89°)

9.12 Nitration of alkylbenzenes

Like benzene, alkylbenzenes are nitrated by a mixture of nitric and sulfuric acids. Although there are three possible products, this reaction actually yields appreciable amounts of only two of them: the o- and p-isomers.

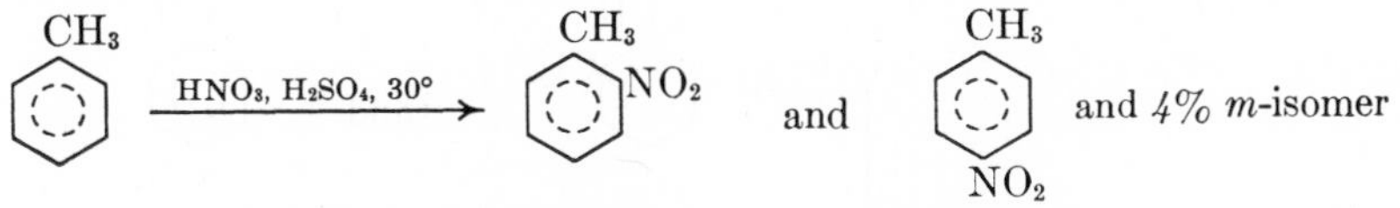

o-Nitrotoluene
(58%)

p-Nitrotoluene
(38%)

In some way, then, the alkyl group is capable of *directing* the attacking reagent to certain positions of the ring, that is, of controlling the **orientation** of substitution.

9.13 Sulfonation of alkylbenzenes

As in nitration, the alkyl substituent tends to direct the entering group in sulfonation to the *ortho* and *para* positions.

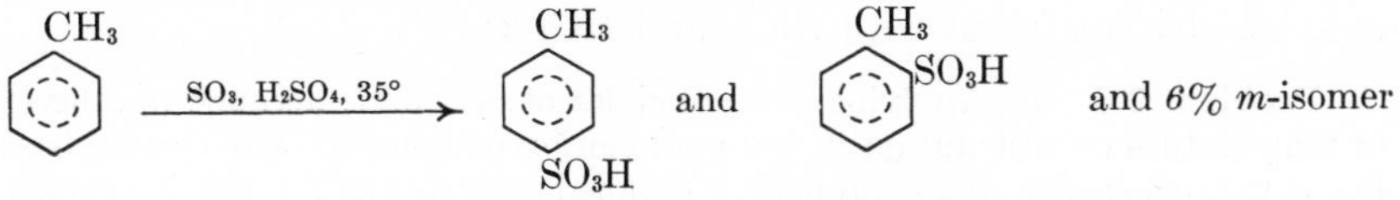

p-Toluenesulfonic
acid
(62%)

o-Toluenesulfonic
acid
(32%)

In addition to the directive effect of the alkyl group, a further effect can be readily observed. An aromatic hydrocarbon is insoluble in sulfuric acid, whereas the sulfonic acid is readily soluble; completion of reaction is indicated simply by the disappearance of the hydrocarbon layer. When shaken with fuming sulfuric acid at room temperature, benzene reacts completely within 20–30 minutes, whereas toluene is found to react within only a minute or two. The presence of the methyl group evidently makes the ring more reactive than unsubstituted benzene. Other alkyl groups show a similar effect. This **activating effect** of the alkyl group can also be demonstrated, but not quite so simply, for the other electrophilic substitution reactions, nitration, Friedel-Crafts alkylation, and halogenation.

Thus an alkyl group attached to a benzene ring has a profound effect on *where* substitution takes place and *how fast*, that is, on both **orientation** and **reactivity**. In Chapter 10 we shall see how effects like these can be accounted for.

9.14 Friedel–Crafts alkylation of alkylbenzenes

Dialkylbenzenes are formed by alkylation of monoalkylbenzenes by the Friedel-Crafts reaction. These dialkylbenzenes in turn can be alkylated further to yield finally benzenes containing as many as six alkyl groups. Each step can be fairly well limited to introduction of just one more group by use of excess hydrocarbon (compare Sec. 2.8).

An interesting point arises here in connection with orientation. Toluene, for example, yields chiefly o- and p-xylene when treated with methyl chloride and $AlCl_3$ at 0°; at higher temperatures, however, the chief product is the *meta* isomer.

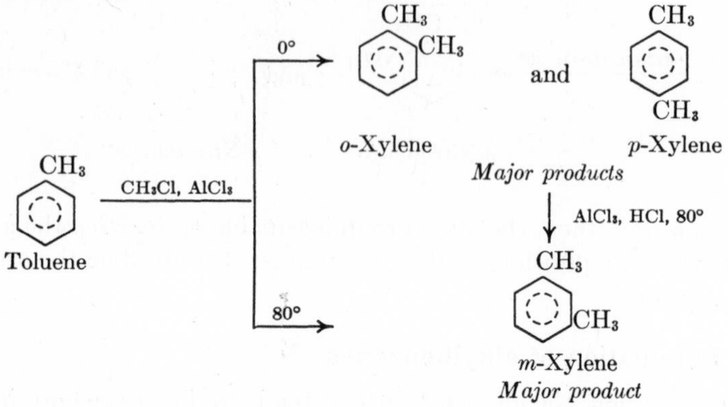

Furthermore, once formed, either o- or p-xylene is readily converted into m-xylene by treatment with $AlCl_3$ and HCl at 80°.

Problem 9.8 (a) Applying the principles of Sec. 6.17, account for the effect of temperature on orientation in the methylation of toluene. (b) On the basis of the equations in Sec. 8.23, propose a detailed mechanism for the conversion of o- or p-xylene into m-xylene.

9.15 Halogenation of alkylbenzenes: ring vs. side chain

Alkylbenzenes clearly offer two main areas to attack by halogens: the ring and the side chain. We can control the position of attack simply by choosing the proper reaction conditions.

Halogenation of alkanes requires conditions under which halogen atoms are formed, that is, high temperature or light. Halogenation of benzene, on the other hand, involves ionization of halogen, which is promoted by acid catalysts like ferric chloride.

$$CH_4 + Cl_2 \xrightarrow{\text{heat or light}} CH_3Cl + HCl$$

$$C_6H_6 + Cl_2 \xrightarrow{\text{FeCl}_3,\ 0°} C_6H_5Cl + HCl$$

We might expect, then, that the position of attack in, say, toluene would be governed by which attacking particle is involved, and therefore by the conditions employed. This is so: if chlorine is bubbled into boiling

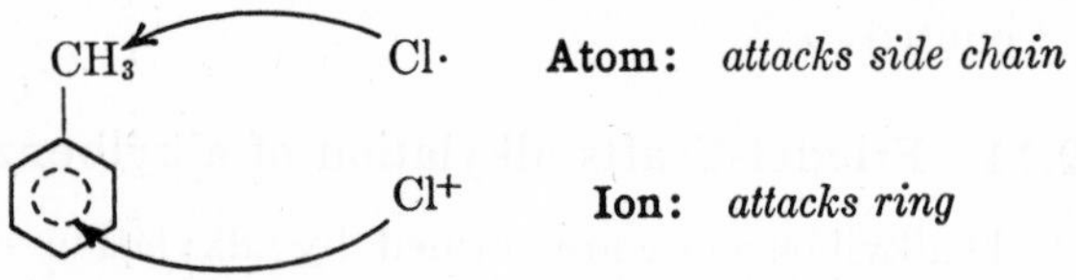

toluene that is exposed to ultraviolet light, substitution occurs almost exclusively in the side chain; in the absence of light and in the presence of ferric chloride, substitution occurs mostly in the ring. (Compare the foregoing with the problem of substitution *vs.* addition in the halogenation of alkenes (Sec. 5.20), where atoms bring about substitution and ions bring about addition.)

Like nitration and sulfonation, ring halogenation yields chiefly the *o*- and *p*-isomers.

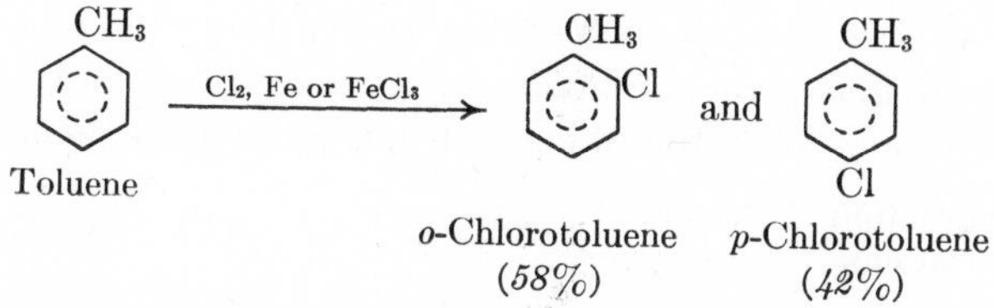

o-Chlorotoluene   p-Chlorotoluene
    (58%)   (42%)

Similar results are obtained with other alkylbenzenes, and with bromine as well as chlorine.

Side-chain halogenation, like halogenation of alkanes, may yield poly-halogenated products; even when reaction is limited to monohalogenation (Sec. 3.19), it may yield a mixture of isomers.

Side-chain chlorination of toluene, for example, can yield successively the mono-, di-, and trichloro compounds. These are known as *benzyl chloride, benzal chloride,* and *benzotrichloride;* such compounds are important intermediates in the synthesis of alcohols, aldehydes, and acids.

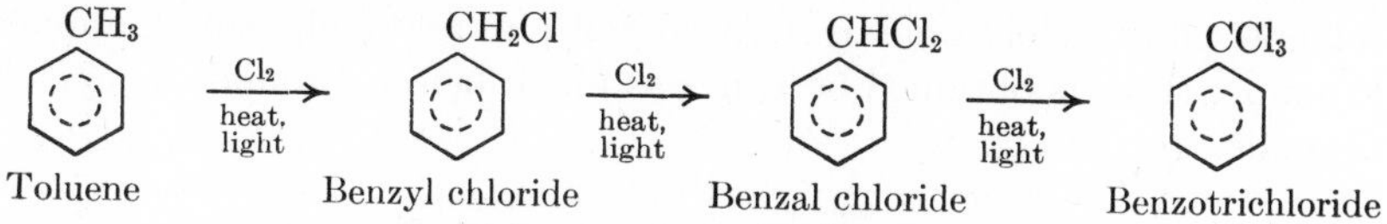

Toluene   Benzyl chloride   Benzal chloride   Benzotrichloride

9.16 Side-chain halogenation of alkylbenzenes: orientation and reactivity

An alkylbenzene with a side chain more complicated than methyl offers more than one position to attack, and generally yields a mixture of isomers. Ethylbenzene, for example, can yield two products: 1-phenyl-1-chloro-ethane and 1-phenyl-2-chloroethane.

Ethylbenzene   1-Phenyl-1-chloroethane   1-Phenyl-2-chloroethane
                   Major product (85%)

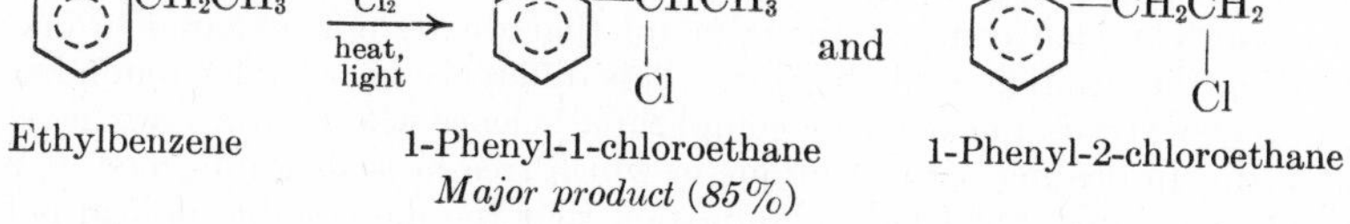

Considering only the collision factors, we might expect 1-phenyl-2-chloroethane to exceed its isomer by a ratio of 3 : 2. It is actually found, however, that 1-phenyl-1-chloroethane is the major product (85%); evidently there is preferential attack on the hydrogens attached to the carbon next to the aromatic ring.

Hydrogen atoms attached to carbon joined directly to an aromatic ring are called **benzylic hydrogens.**

Benzylic hydrogen:
easy to abstract

Examination of reactions that involve attack not only by halogen atoms but by other free radicals as well has shown that this is a general rule: benzylic hydrogens are extremely easy to abstract and thus resemble allylic hydrogens. We can now expand the reactivity sequence of Sec. 5.21:

Ease of abstraction   allylic
of hydrogen atoms   benzylic $> 3° > 2° > 1° > CH_4 >$ vinylic

Problem 9.9 At 25° under the influence of ultraviolet light, chlorine converts isopropylbenzene into a mixture of 74% 2-chloro-2-phenylpropane and 26% 1-chloro-2-phenylpropane; at 80° the proportions are 67% and 33%. (a) Taking the relative reactivity of each primary hydrogen as 1.0, what is the relative reactivity of each benzylic hydrogen at each temperature? (Compare Sec. 3.21.) (b) How can you account for the different relative reactivities at the two temperatures? (c) Under the same conditions bromine yields exclusively the 2-bromo compound; how can you account for this?

The ease with which benzylic hydrogens are abstracted is shown not only by orientation of halogenation but also by comparison of reactivities of two different compounds. If a 50:50 mixture (on a molar basis) of toluene and cyclohexane is treated with a relatively small amount of bromine, there is obtained 60 times as much benzyl bromide as cyclohexyl bromide.

Benzyl bromide   Cyclohexyl bromide
       60   1

In competing for the limited amount of bromine the more reactive benzylic hydrogens of toluene win out over the much less reactive secondary hydrogens of cyclohexane.

Toward most free radicals, as toward bromine atoms, benzylic hydrogens are more reactive than the secondary hydrogens of cyclohexane; toward *chlorine* atoms, on the other hand, benzylic hydrogens are found to be *less* reactive. This difference in behavior can be accounted for; a factor that we are not prepared to take up is at work in the reaction with chlorine. This difference in behavior reminds us that organic chemistry is an extremely complicated science whose surface we have barely scratched. In dealing with reactions in which free radicals are formed, it is most convenient to start with the generalization that the more stable radical is formed faster, and then look for the exceptional cases where other factors are in control.

Side-chain halogenation of alkybenzenes seems to proceed by the same mechanism as halogenation of alkanes. Chlorination of toluene, for example, would include the following steps:

Toluene   Benzyl radical   Benzyl chloride

The fact that benzylic hydrogens are unusually easy to abstract means that benzyl radicals are unusually easy to form.

Ease of formation
of free radicals　allyl, benzyl $> 3° > 2° > 1° > CH_3\cdot > $ vinyl

Again we ask the question: are these findings in accord with our rule that *the more stable the radical, the more rapidly it is formed?* Is the rapidly formed benzyl radical relatively stable?

The bond strengths in Table 2.1 (page 39) show that only 78 kcal are needed for formation of benzyl radicals from a mole of toluene, as compared with 85 kcal for formation of *tert*-butyl radicals and 77 kcal for formation of allyl radicals. Relative to the hydrocarbon from which each is formed, then, a benzyl radical contains less energy and is more stable than a *tert*-butyl radical. It is about as stable as an allyl radical.

We can now expand the sequence of radical stabilities (Sec. 5.21). Relative to the hydrocarbon from which each is formed, the relative stability of free radicals is:

Stability of
free radicals　allyl, benzyl $> 3° > 2° > 1° > CH_3\cdot > $ vinyl

Now that we are familiar with the theory of resonance we are ready to account for this sequence of radical stabilities on a single basis: *delocalization of the odd electron.*

Let us begin with the allyl radical.

9.17　Resonance stabilization of the allyl radical

Dealing with the stability of the allyl radical is basically a matter of comparing two reactions: dissociation of methane to form a methyl radical, and dissociation of propylene to form an allyl radical.

$$CH_4 \longrightarrow CH_3\cdot + H\cdot \qquad \Delta H = +101 \text{ kcal}$$

Methane　　　Methyl radical

$$CH_2{=}CH{-}CH_3 \longrightarrow CH_2{=}CH{-}CH_2\cdot + H\cdot \qquad \Delta H = +77$$

Propylene　　　Allyl radical

How can we account for the fact that the energy difference between propylene and the allyl radical is 24 kcal less (101 − 77) than the energy difference between methane and the methyl radical? Let us examine the structures involved.

Methane, the methyl radical, and propylene are each represented satisfactorily by a single structure.

For the allyl radical, on the other hand, we find two possible structures, I and II, which differ only in the position of the double bond and of the odd electron. These structures are exactly equivalent and hence are of the same stability.

$$\left[CH_2{=}CH{-}CH_2\cdot \qquad \cdot CH_2{-}CH{=}CH_2 \right] \quad equivalent\ to \quad CH_2{\cdots}CH{\cdots}CH_2$$

I　　　　　　　II

The allyl radical is a resonance hybrid of structures I and II. As a hybrid it is more stable — that is, contains less energy — than either contributing structure. We say that the allyl radical is *stabilized by resonance*. We would expect stabilization due to resonance involving structures of equal stability to be large; here, it evidently amounts to 24 kcal/mole.

Drawing these two structures, I and II, is simply our crude way of indicating that each carbon–carbon bond of the allyl radical is neither double nor single but is a hybrid (*half double* and *half single*). The odd electron is not localized on one carbon or the other but is *delocalized*, being equally distributed over both terminal carbon atoms.

What does this resonance mean from the standpoint of orbitals? In either of the contributing structures, I or II, the odd electron would be considered to occupy the p orbital of a trigonally bonded carbon. Overlapping between this p orbital and the π cloud of the double bond results in delocalization of the odd electron and stabilization of the radical.

9.18   Resonance stabilization of the benzyl radical

Next let us consider the stability of the benzyl radical, $C_6H_5CH_2\cdot$. Bond strengths indicate that 23 kcal/mole less energy $(101 - 78)$ is needed to form the benzyl radical from toluene than to form the methyl radical from methane. As before, we shall examine the structures involved.

$$C_6H_5CH_3 \longrightarrow C_6H_5CH_2\cdot + H\cdot \qquad \Delta H = +78 \text{ kcal}$$
Toluene   Benzyl radical

Toluene contains the benzene ring and is therefore a hybrid of the two Kekulé structures, I and II. Similarly the benzyl radical is a hybrid of

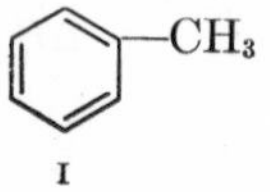

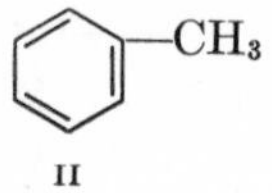

the two Kekulé structures, III and IV.

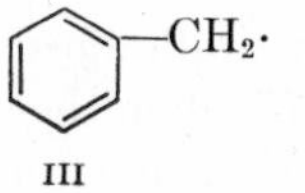

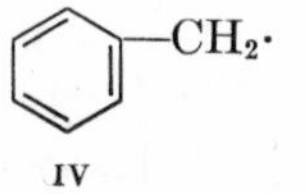

This resonance causes stabilization, that is, lowers the energy content. However, resonance involving Kekulé structures presumably stabilizes both molecule and radical to the same extent, and hence does not affect the *difference* in their energy contents. If there were no other factors involved, then, we might reasonably expect the bond strength of a benzylic hydrogen to be about the same as that of a methane hydrogen (see Figure 9.1).

Considering further, however, we find that we can draw three additional structures for the radical: V, VI, and VII.

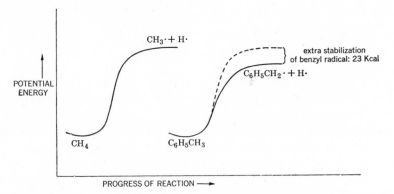

In these structures there is a double bond between the side chain and the ring, and the odd electron is located on the carbon atoms *ortho* and *para* to the side chain. Drawing these pictures is, of course, our way of indicating that the odd electron is not localized on the side chain but is *delocalized*, being distributed about the ring. We cannot draw comparable structures for the toluene molecule.

FIGURE 9.1. Molecular structure and rate of reaction. Resonance-stabilized benzyl radical formed faster than methyl radical.

Contribution from the three structures, V–VII, stabilizes the radical in a way that is not possible for the molecule. Resonance thus lowers the energy content of the benzyl radical more than it lowers the energy content of toluene. This extra stabilization of the radical evidently amounts to 23 kcal/mole (Figure 9.1).

Problem 9.10 Discuss the delocalization of the odd electron of the benzyl radical from the standpoint of orbitals.

We say, then, that the benzyl radical is *stabilized by resonance*. When we use this expression we must always bear in mind that we actually mean that the benzyl radical is stabilized by resonance *to a greater extent than* the hydrocarbon from which it is formed.

9.19 Resonance stabilization of alkyl radicals. Hyperconjugation

To account for the relative stabilities of tertiary, secondary, and primary alkyl radicals we must consider resonance involving structures that may at first appear quite strange. Justification for doing this lies in the fact that in this way we can account for a wide variety of observations that are not understandable on any other basis.

Let us first compare dissociation of ethane to form an ethyl radical with dissociation of methane.

$$CH_4 \longrightarrow CH_3\cdot + \cdot H \qquad \Delta H = +101 \text{ kcal}$$
$$CH_3CH_3 \longrightarrow CH_3CH_2\cdot + \cdot H \qquad \Delta H = +98$$

The difference here is only 3 kcal; although this is a small value, very nearly the same difference is observed for formation of other primary alkyl radicals.

Ethane is presumably represented fairly well by a single structure. The ethyl radical, on the other hand, is considered to be a hybrid of not

only the usual structure, I, but also three additional structures, II, III, and IV, in which a double bond joins the two carbons, and the odd electron is held by a hydrogen atom.

Considered individually, each of these structures is indeed quite strange, since there is no bond joining one hydrogen to carbon. This is, however, our rough way of indicating that the carbon–hydrogen bond is *something less* than a single bond, and that the odd electron is in part accommodated by hydrogen atoms. Resonance involving structures of this kind is usually referred to as **hyperconjugation** (or sometimes *no-bond resonance*). In this case we would say that the ethyl radical is *stabilized by hyperconjugation*.

If we extend this idea to the isopropyl radical we find that instead of three hyperconjugation structures we now have six. (*Draw them.*) The larger number of contributing structures means more extensive delocalization of the odd electron, and hence greater stabilization of the radical. In agreement with this expectation we find that the strength of the isopropyl–hydrogen bond is only 89 kcal, indicating a resonance energy of 12 kcal/mole (101 − 89).

For the *tert*-butyl radical there should be nine such hyperconjugation structures. (*Draw them.*) Here we find a bond strength of 85 kcal, indicating a resonance stabilization of 16 kcal/mole (101 − 85).

In summary, the stability — and hence ease of formation — of benzyl or allyl radicals is due to resonance by which the odd electron is accommodated by carbon atoms of the ring or of the double bond. The relative stabilities of the alkyl radicals, 3° > 2° > 1°, are determined by hyperconjugation: resonance by which the odd electron is accommodated by hydrogen atoms.

Problem 9.11 The strength of the bond holding side-chain hydrogen in *m*-xylene is the same as in toluene; in *o*- and *p*-xylene it is 3–4 kcal lower. How do you account for these differences?

9.20   Triphenylmethyl: a stable free radical

We have said that benzyl and allyl free radicals are stabilized by resonance; but we must realize, of course, that they are stable only in comparison with simple alkyl radicals like methyl or ethyl. Benzyl and allyl free radicals are extremely reactive, unstable particles, whose fleeting existence (a few thousandths of a second) has been proposed simply because it is the best way to account for certain experimental observations. We do not find bottles on the laboratory shelf labeled "benzyl radicals" or "allyl radicals." Is there, then, any direct evidence for the existence of free radicals?

In 1900 a remarkable paper appeared in the *Journal of the American Chemical Society* and in the *Berichte der deutschen chemischen Gesellschaft;* its author was the young Russian-born chemist Moses Gomberg, who was at that time an instructor at the University of Michigan. Gomberg was interested in completely phenylated alkanes. He had prepared tetraphenylmethane (a synthesis a number of eminent chemists had previously attempted, but unsuccessfully), and he had now set himself the task of synthesizing hexaphenylethane. Having available triphenylchloromethane (Sec. 9.6), he went about the job in just the way we would today: he carried out a Wurtz reaction in an attempt to join together two triphenylmethyl groups.

Triphenylchloromethane   Hexaphenylethane
(2 moles)

Since sodium did not work very well, he used instead finely divided silver, mercury, or, best of all, zinc dust. He allowed a benzene solution of triphenylchloromethane to stand over one of these metals, and then filtered the solution free of the metal halide. When the benzene was evaporated there was left behind a white crystalline solid which after recrystallization melted at 185°; this he thought was hexaphenylethane.

As a chemist always does with a new compound, Gomberg analyzed his product for its carbon and hydrogen content. To his surprise the analysis showed 88% carbon and 6% hydrogen, a total of only 94%. Thinking that combustion had not been complete, he carried out the analysis again, this time more carefully and under more vigorous conditions; he obtained the same results as before. Repeated analysis of samples prepared from both triphenylchloromethane and triphenylbromomethane, and purified by recrystallization from a variety of solvents, finally convinced him that he had prepared not a hydrocarbon — not hexaphenylethane — but a compound containing 6% of some other element, probably oxygen.

Oxygen could have come from impure metals; but extremely pure samples of metals, carefully freed of oxygen, gave the same results.

Oxygen could have come from the air, although he could not see how molecular oxygen could react at room temperature with a hydrocarbon. He carried out the reaction again, this time under an atmosphere of carbon dioxide. When he filtered the solution (also under carbon dioxide) and evaporated the solvent, there was left behind not his compound of m.p. 185° but an entirely different substance, much more soluble in benzene than his first product, and having a much lower melting point. This new substance was eventually purified, and on analysis it gave the correct composition for hexaphenylethane: 93.8% carbon, 6.2% hydrogen.

Dissolved in benzene, the new substance gave a yellow solution. When a small amount of air was admitted to the container, the yellow color disappeared, and then after a few minutes reappeared. When more oxygen was admitted the same thing happened: disappearance of the color and slow reappearance. Finally the color disappeared for good; evaporation of the solvent yielded the original compound of m.p. 185°.

Not only oxygen but also halogens were rapidly absorbed by ice-cold solutions of this substance; even solutions of normally unreactive iodine were instantly decolorized.

The compound of m.p. 185° was the peroxide,

$$(C_6H_5)_3C—O—O—C(C_6H_5)_3,$$

as Gomberg showed by preparing it in an entirely different way. The products of the halogen reactions were the triphenylhalomethanes, $(C_6H_5)_3C—X$.

If this new substance he had made was indeed hexaphenylethane, it was behaving very strangely. Cleavage of a carbon–carbon bond by such mild reagents as oxygen and iodine was unknown to organic chemists.

"The experimental evidence presented above forces me to the conclusion that we have to deal here with a free radical, triphenylmethyl, $(C_6H_5)_3C$. On this assumption alone do the results described above become intelligible and receive an adequate explanation." Gomberg was proposing that he had prepared a *stable* free radical.

It was nearly ten years before Gomberg's proposal was generally accepted. It now seems clear that what happens is the following: the metal abstracts a chlorine atom from triphenylchloromethane to form the free radical triphenylmethyl; two of these radicals then combine to form hexaphenylethane. But this carbon–carbon bond is a very weak one, and even at room temperature can break to regenerate the radicals. Thus an equilibrium exists between the free radicals and the hydrocarbon. Although this equilibrium tends to favor the hydrocarbon, any solution of hexaphenylethane contains an appreciable concentration of free triphenylmethyl radicals. The fraction of material existing as free radicals is about 2% in a 1 M solution, 10% in a 0.01 M solution, and nearly 100% in very

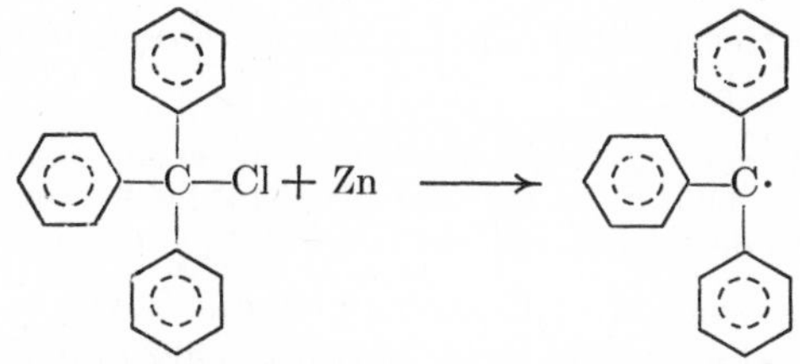

Triphenylchloromethane   Triphenylmethyl

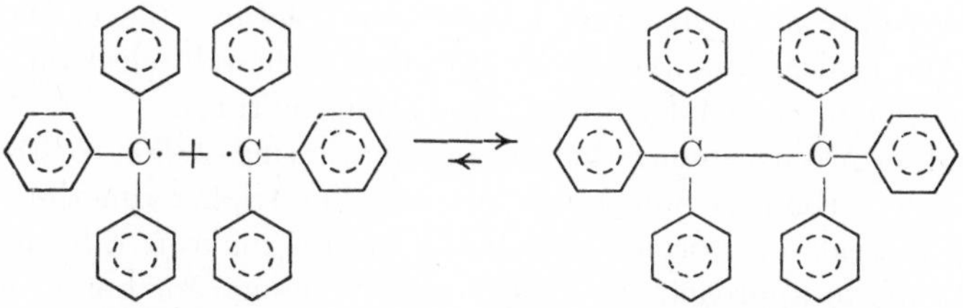

Triphenylmethyl   Hexaphenylethane
Yellow   *Colorless*

dilute solutions. We could quite correctly label a bottle containing a dilute solution of this substance as "triphenylmethyl radicals."

Triphenylmethyl is yellow; both hexaphenylethane and the peroxide are colorless. A solution of hexaphenylethane is yellow because of the triphenylmethyl present in the equilibrium mixture. When oxygen is admitted, the triphenylmethyl rapidly reacts to form the peroxide, and the yellow color disappears. More hexaphenylethane dissociates to restore equilibrium and the yellow color reappears. Only when all the hexaphenylethane-triphenylmethyl mixture is converted into the peroxide does the yellow color fail to reappear. In a similar way it is triphenylmethyl that reacts with iodine.

$$(C_6H_5)_3C—C(C_6H_5)_3 \rightleftarrows 2(C_6H_5)_3C \cdot \begin{cases} \xrightarrow{O_2,\ 0°} (C_6H_5)_3C—O—O—(C_6H_5)_3 \\ \xrightarrow{I_2,\ 0°} 2(C_6H_5)_3C—I \end{cases}$$

Hexaphenylethane   Triphenylmethyl
                          radical

Thus hexaphenylethane undergoes its surprising reactions by first dissociating into triphenylmethyl, which, although unusually stable for a free radical, is nevertheless an exceedingly reactive particle.

Many other hexaarylethanes have been prepared and the existence of free triarylmethyl radicals substantiated in a number of ways; indeed, certain of these compounds seem to exist entirely as the free radical even in the solid state. The most convincing evidence for the free radical nature of these substances is their *paramagnetism*, that is, the fact that (unlike most matter) they are attracted by a magnetic field. Two electrons that occupy the same orbital and thus make up a pair have opposite spins (Sec. 1.6); the magnetic moments corresponding to their spins exactly cancel each other. But, by definition (Sec. 2.12), the odd electron of a free radical is not paired, and hence the effect of its spin is not canceled.

This spin gives to the free radical a net magnetic moment, which is the cause of its paramagnetism.

The *paramagnetic resonance spectrum*, which depends on the orientation of an unpaired electron with or against an external magnetic field, provides a newer and more sensitive way to detect free radicals.

The remarkable dissociation of hexaphenylethane is the result of two factors. First, triphenylmethyl radicals are unusually stable because of resonance of the sort we have proposed for the benzyl radical. Here, of course, there are an even larger number of structures (36 of them) that stabilize the radical but not the hydrocarbon; the odd electron is highly delocalized, being distributed over three aromatic rings.

Second, crowding among the large aromatic rings tends to stretch and weaken the carbon–carbon bond joining the triphenylmethyl groups. Once the radicals are formed, the bulky groups make it difficult for the carbon atoms to approach each other closely enough for bond formation. The remarkable effect of structure on bond strength is shown by the fact that, whereas the carbon–carbon bond of ethane has a strength of 83 kcal and that of 1,2-diphenylethane 47 kcal, the carbon–carbon bond of hexaphenylethane has a strength of only 11 kcal; it is 1.58 A long, as compared with the usual carbon–carbon single bond length of 1.54 A.

It would be hard to overestimate the importance of Gomberg's contribution to the field of free radicals and to organic chemistry as a whole. Although triphenylmethyl was isolable only because it was *not a typical* free radical, its chemical properties showed what kind of behavior to expect of free radicals *in general;* most important of all, it proved that such things as free radicals could exist.

Problem 9.12 The ΔH for dissociation of hexaphenylethane has been measured as 11 kcal/mole, the E_{act} as 19 kcal/mole. (a) Draw the potential energy curve for the reaction. (b) What is the energy of activation for the reverse reaction, combination of triphenylmethyl radicals? (c) How do you account for this unusual fact? (Compare Sec. 2.19.)

Problem 9.13 When 1.5 g of diphenyltetra(*o*-tolyl)ethane is dissolved in 50 g of benzene, the freezing point of the solvent is lowered 0.5° (the cryoscopic constant for benzene is 5°). Interpret these results.

9.21 Preparation of alkenylbenzenes. Conjugation with ring

An arene with a side chain containing a double bond can be prepared by essentially the same methods as simple alkenes (Secs. 4.11 and 4.12). In general, these methods involve elimination of atoms or groups from two adjacent carbons. The presence of the aromatic ring in the molecule may affect the orientation of elimination and the ease with which it takes place.

On an industrial scale, the elimination generally involves *dehydrogenation.* For example, **styrene,** the most important of these compounds — and perhaps the most important synthetic aromatic compound — can be prepared by simply heating ethylbenzene to about 600° in the presence of a catalyst.

$$\text{benzene} + CH_2\!=\!CH_2 \xrightarrow{\text{HF}} \underset{\text{Ethylbenzene}}{\overset{CH_2CH_3}{\bigcirc}} \xrightarrow[\text{90\% yield}]{Cr_2O_3 \cdot Al_2O_3,\ 600°} \underset{\text{Styrene}}{\overset{CH\!=\!CH_2}{\bigcirc}} + H_2$$

The ethylbenzene, in turn, is prepared by a Friedel-Crafts reaction between two simple hydrocarbons, benzene and ethylene.

In the laboratory, however, we are most apt to use dehydrohalogenation or dehydration.

$$\underset{\substack{\text{OH} \\ \text{1-Phenylethanol}}}{\overset{CH\!-\!CH_3}{\bigcirc}} \xrightarrow{\text{ZnCl}_2,\ \text{heat}} \underset{\text{Styrene}}{\overset{CH\!=\!CH_2}{\bigcirc}}$$

$$\underset{\substack{\text{Cl} \\ \text{1-Phenyl-1-chloroethane}}}{\overset{CH\!-\!CH_3}{\bigcirc}} \xrightarrow{\text{KOH (alc), heat}} \underset{\text{Styrene}}{\overset{CH\!=\!CH_2}{\bigcirc}}$$

Dehydrohalogenation of 1-phenyl-2-chloropropane, or dehydration of 1-phenyl-2-propanol, could yield two products: 1-phenylpropene or 3-phenylpropene.

$$\underset{\substack{\text{Cl} \\ \text{1-Phenyl-2-chloropropane}}}{\overset{CH_2\text{-}CH\text{-}CH_3}{\bigcirc}} \xrightarrow[\substack{\text{KOH} \\ \text{(alc)} \\ \text{heat}}]{} \underset{\substack{\text{1-Phenylpropene} \\ \textit{Only product}}}{\overset{CH\!=\!CH\text{-}CH_3}{\bigcirc}} \xleftarrow[\substack{\text{acid} \\ \text{heat}}]{} \underset{\substack{\text{OH} \\ \text{1-Phenyl-2-propanol}}}{\overset{CH_2\text{-}CH\text{-}CH_3}{\bigcirc}}$$

$$\underset{\text{3-Phenylpropene}}{\overset{CH_2CH\!=\!CH_2}{\bigcirc}}$$

Actually only the first of these products is obtained. We saw earlier (Sec. 4.19, page 122), that where isomeric alkenes can be formed by elimination, the preferred product is the more stable alkene. This seems to be the case here, too. That 1-phenylpropene is much more stable than its isomer is shown by the fact that 3-phenylpropene is rapidly converted into 1-phenylpropene by treatment with hot alkali.

$$\underset{\substack{\text{3-Phenylpropene} \\ \text{(Allylbenzene)}}}{\overset{CH_2\!-\!CH\!=\!CH_2}{\bigcirc}} \xrightarrow{\text{KOH, heat}} \underset{\text{1-Phenylpropene}}{\overset{CH\!=\!CH\!-\!CH_3}{\bigcirc}}$$

A double bond that is separated from a benzene ring by one single bond is said to be *conjugated with the ring*. Such conjugation confers unusual stability on a molecule.

$$\overset{|\quad|}{\underset{}{\bigcirc}\!-\!C\!=\!C\!-}$$ **Double bond conjugated with ring:**
unusually stable system

This stability affects not only orientation of elimination, but, as we shall see (Sec. 23.16), affects the ease with which elimination takes place.

Problem 9.14 Stabilization of conjugated dienes was attributed (Sec. 8.16) to overlapping in two directions of p orbitals and the resultant merging of the π clouds of the two double bonds. (a) Show how this idea could be applied to the present case. (b) What structures involving formal bonds would be considered to contribute?

9.22 Reactions of alkenylbenzenes

As we might expect, alkenylbenzenes undergo two sets of reactions: **substitution in the ring,** and **addition to the double bond in the side chain.** Since both ring and double bond are good sources of electrons, there may be competition between the two sites for certain electrophilic reagents; it is not surprising that, in general, the double bond shows higher reactivity than the resonance-stabilized benzene ring. Our main interest in these reactions will be the way in which the aromatic ring affects the reactions of the double bond.

Although both the benzene ring and the carbon–carbon double bond can be hydrogenated catalytically, the conditions required for the double bond are much milder; by proper selection of conditions it is quite easy to hydrogenate the side chain without touching the aromatic ring.

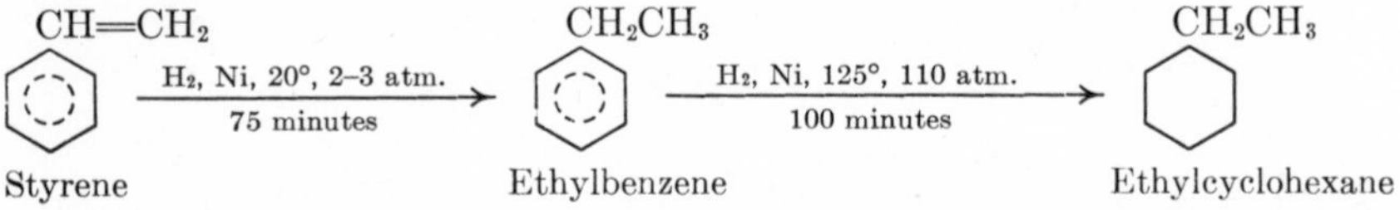

Mild oxidation of the double bond yields a glycol; more vigorous oxidation cleaves the carbon–carbon double bond and generally gives a carboxylic acid in which the —COOH group is attached to the ring.

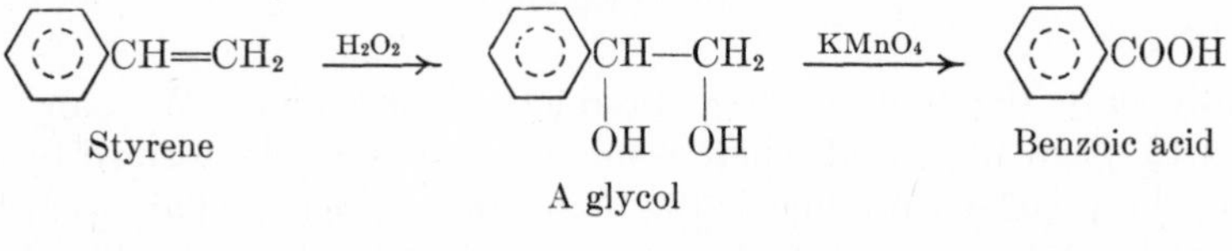

Both double bond and ring react with halogens by ionic mechanisms that have essentially the same first step: attack on the π cloud by positively charged halogen. Halogen is consumed by the double bond first, and only after the side chain is completely saturated does substitution on the ring occur. Ring-halogenated alkenylbenzenes must be prepared, therefore, by generation of the double bond after halogen is already present on the ring. For example:

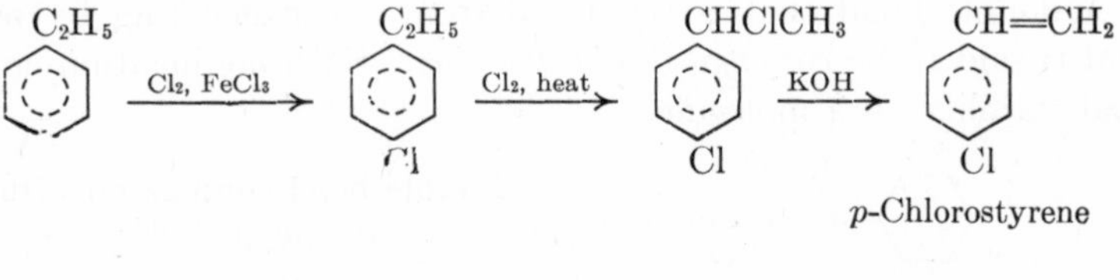

In a similar way, alkenylbenzenes undergo the other addition reactions characteristic of the carbon–carbon double bond. Let us look further at the reactions of *conjugated* alkenylbenzenes, and the way in which the ring affects *orientation* and *reactivity*.

9.23 Addition to conjugated alkenylbenzenes: orientation. Stability of the benzyl carbonium ion

Addition of an unsymmetrical reagent to a double bond may in general yield two different products. In our discussion of alkenes (Secs. 5.12 and 5.14) we found that usually one of the products predominates, and that we can predict which it will be in a fairly simple way: *in either ionic or free radical addition, the first step takes place in the way that yields the more stable particle*, carbonium ion in one kind of reaction, free radical in the other kind. Does this rule apply to reactions of alkenylbenzenes?

The effect of the benzene ring on orientation can be well illustrated by a single example, addition of HBr to 1-phenylpropene. In the absence of peroxides, bromine becomes attached to the carbon adjacent to the ring; in the presence of peroxides, bromine becomes attached to the carbon once removed from the ring. According to the mechanisms proposed for these two reactions, these products are formed as follows:

$$C_6H_5CH{=}CHCH_3 \xrightarrow{\text{HBr}} \underset{\underset{\substack{\text{A benzyl} \\ \text{carbonium ion}}}{\oplus}}{C_6H_5CHCH_2CH_3} \xrightarrow{\text{Br}^-} \underset{\underset{Br}{|}}{C_6H_5CHCH_2CH_3} \quad \textbf{No}$$
$$\textbf{peroxides}$$

$$C_6H_5CH{=}CHCH_3 \xrightarrow{\text{Br}\cdot} \underset{\underset{\substack{Br \\ \text{A benzyl} \\ \text{free radical}}}{|}}{C_6H_5\overset{\cdot}{C}HCHCH_3} \xrightarrow{\text{HBr}} \underset{\underset{Br}{|}}{C_6H_5CH_2CHCH_3} \quad \textbf{Peroxides}$$
$$\textbf{present}$$

The first step of each of these reactions takes place in the way that yields the *benzyl* carbonium ion or the *benzyl* free radical rather than the alternative secondary carbonium ion or secondary free radical. Is this consistent with our rule that the more stable particle is formed faster?

Consideration of bond strengths has already shown us that a benzyl free radical is an extremely stable one. We have accounted for this stability on the basis of resonance involving the benzene ring (Sec. 9.18).

What can we say about a benzyl carbonium ion? As we shall see (Secs. 12.3, 12.4, and 13.14), the ease of formation in other ways of benzyl carbonium ions indicates strongly that they are comparatively stable carbonium ions. The stability of a benzyl carbonium ion — relative to the compounds from which it is made — is also accounted for by resonance involving the benzene ring. Both the carbonium ion and the compound from which it is made are hybrids of Kekulé structures. In addition, the carbonium ion can be represented by three other structures, I, II, and III, in which the positive charge is located on the *ortho* and *para* carbon atoms.

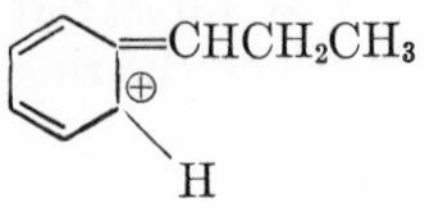

Whether we consider this as resonance stabilization or simply as dispersal
of charge, contribution from these structures stabilizes the carbonium ion.
We can now expand our sequence of Sec. 6.16 to include the benzyl carbonium ion:

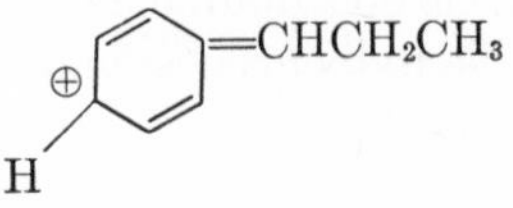

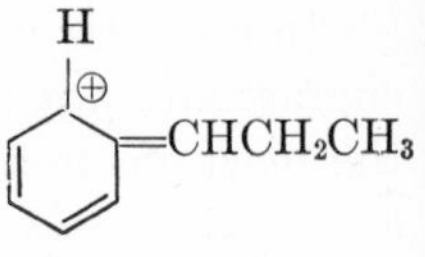

Stability of $\begin{matrix} \text{allyl} \\ \text{benzyl} \end{matrix} > 3° > 2° > 1° > CH_3^+$
carbonium ions

Problem 9.15 In Sec. 6.16 we saw that the allyl carbonium ion is unusually
stable. In light of our discussion in Sec. 9.17 and in the present section, how can
this be accounted for?

Problem 9.16 It is generally considered that the relative stabilities of the
simple alkyl carbonium ions are determined not only by inductive effects but also,
as for the benzyl ion, by resonance stabilization. In light of our discussion in
Sec. 9.19 and in the present section, how might you account for the order of stability
of ions: *tert*-butyl > isopropyl > ethyl > methyl?

Problem 9.17 How do you account for the fact (a) that triphenylchloromethane is completely ionized in certain solvents (e.g., liquid SO_2)? (b) That
triphenylcarbinol, $(C_6H_5)_3COH$, dissolves in concentrated H_2SO_4 to give a solution
that has the same intense yellow color as triphenylchloromethane solutions?
(*Note:* this yellow color is different from that of solutions of hexaphenylethane.)

Problem 9.18 In light of Problem 9.17, can you suggest a possible cause,
besides steric hindrance, why the reaction of CCl_4 with benzene stops at triphenylchloromethane? (See Sec. 9.6.)

9.24 Addition to conjugated alkenylbenzenes: reactivity

On the basis of the stability of the particle being formed, we might expect addition to a conjugated alkenylbenzene, which yields a stable *benzyl*
carbonium ion or free radical, to occur faster than addition to a simple
alkene.

On the other hand, we have seen (Sec. 9.21) that conjugated alkenylbenzenes are more stable than simple alkenes. On this basis alone, we
might expect addition to conjugated alkenylbenzenes to occur more slowly
than to simple alkenes.

The situation is exactly analogous to the one discussed for addition to
conjugated dienes (Sec. 6.19). Both *reactant* and *transition state* are
stabilized by resonance; whether reaction is faster or slower than for
simple alkenes depends upon *which* is stabilized *more* (see Figure 6.7,
page 184).

The fact is that conjugated alkenylbenzenes are much more reactive
than simple alkenes toward both ionic and free radical addition. Here
again — as in *most* cases of this sort — resonance stabilization of the
transition state leading to a carbonium ion or free radical is more im-

portant than resonance stabilization of the reactant. We must realize, however, that this is *not always* true.

Problem 9.19 Draw a potential energy diagram similar to Figure 6.7 (page 184) to summarize what has been said in this section.

Problem 9.20 Suggest one reason why tetraphenylethylene does not react with bromine in carbon tetrachloride.

9.25 Polymerization of styrene

In terms of dollars and cents, by far the most important use of an alkenylbenzene involves free radical addition: the *polymerization of styrene.*

Alone, styrene yields **polystyrene,** an important plastic especially useful as an electric insulator:

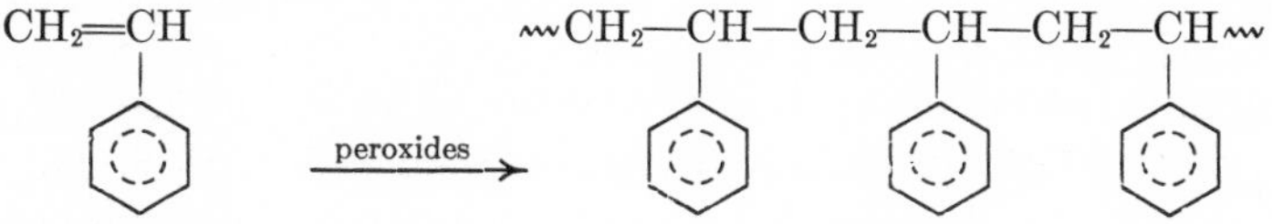

$$CH_2=CH \qquad \qquad \text{\tiny{WW}}CH_2—CH—CH_2—CH—CH_2—CH\text{\tiny{WW}}$$

Styrene $\xrightarrow{\text{peroxides}}$ Polystyrene

Copolymerized with 1,3-butadiene, styrene yields GR–S rubber (Sec. 6.22).

Being a conjugated alkenylbenzene, styrene is unusually reactive toward free radical addition; polymerization just on contact with air is so rapid that styrene can be kept in its monomeric state only if it contains small amounts of certain *stabilizers.*

Problem 9.21 (a) How can relatively few molecules of stabilizer prevent polymerization of so many molecules of styrene? (b) Two of these stabilizers are *hydroquinone* and *diphenylamine*; is it just coincidence that these same compounds serve as antioxidants in the addition of HBr to alkenes (Sec. 5.7)?

9.26 Alkynylbenzenes

The preparations and properties of the alkynylbenzenes are just what we might expect from our knowledge of benzene and the alkynes.

9.27 Analysis of alkylbenzenes

Aromatic hydrocarbons with saturated side chains are distinguished from alkenes by their failure to decolorize bromine in carbon tetrachloride (without evolution of hydrogen bromide) and by their failure to decolorize cold, dilute, neutral permanganate solutions. (Oxidation of the side chains requires more vigorous conditions; see Sec. 9.11.)

They are distinguished from alkanes by the readiness with which they are sulfonated by — and thus dissolve in — cold fuming sulfuric acid (see Sec. 9.13).

Upon treatment with chloroform and aluminum chloride, alkylbenzenes give orange to red colors. These colors are due to triarylmethyl carbonium ions, Ar_3C^+, which are probably produced by a Friedel-Crafts reaction followed by a transfer of hydride ion (Sec. 5.18):

$$ArH \xrightarrow{CHCl_3, AlCl_3} ArCHCl_2 \xrightarrow{ArH, AlCl_3} Ar_2CHCl \xrightarrow{ArH, AlCl_3} Ar_3CH$$

$$Ar_2CHCl \xrightarrow{AlCl_3} Ar_2CH^+ AlCl_4^- \left.\begin{array}{c} \\ \\ Ar_3CH \end{array}\right\} \longrightarrow Ar_2CH_2 + Ar_3C^+ AlCl_4^-$$
Orange to red color

This test is given by any aromatic compound that can undergo the Friedel-Crafts reaction, with the particular color produced being characteristic of the aromatic system involved: orange to red from halobenzenes, blue from *naphthalene*, purple from *phenanthrene*, green from *anthracene* (Chapter 31).

Problem 9.22   Describe simple chemical tests (if any) that would distinguish between: (a) *n*-propylbenzene and *o*-chlorotoluene; (b) benzene and toluene; (c) *m*-chlorotoluene and *m*-dichlorobenzene; (d) bromobenzene and bromocyclohexane; (e) bromobenzene and 3-bromo-1-hexene. Tell exactly what you would *do* and *see*.

The number and orientation of side chains in an alkylbenzene is shown by the carboxylic acid produced on vigorous oxidation (Sec. 9.11).

Problem 9.23   On the basis of characterization tests and physical properties, an unknown compound of b.p. 182° is believed to be either *m*-diethylbenzene or *n*-butylbenzene. How could you distinguish between the two possibilities?

9.28   Analysis of alkenyl- and alkynylbenzenes

Aromatic hydrocarbons with unsaturated side chains undergo the reactions characteristic of aromatic rings and of the carbon–carbon double or triple bond.

Problem 9.24   Predict the response of allylbenzene to the following test reagents: (a) cold concentrated sulfuric acid; (b) Br_2 in CCl_4; (c) cold, dilute, neutral permanganate; (d) $CHCl_3$ and $AlCl_3$.

Problem 9.25   Describe simple chemical tests (if any) that would distinguish between: (a) styrene and ethylbenzene; (b) styrene and phenylacetylene; (c) allylbenzene and 1-nonene. Tell exactly what you would *do* and *see*.

PROBLEMS

1. Draw the structure of:

(a) *m*-xylene
(b) mesitylene
(c) *o*-ethyltoluene
(d) *p*-di-*tert*-butylbenzene
(e) cyclohexylbenzene
(f) 3-phenylpentane

(g) isopropylbenzene (cumene)
(h) *trans*-stilbene
(i) 1,4-diphenyl-1,3-butadiene
(j) *p*-dibenzylbenzene
(k) *m*-bromostyrene
(l) diphenylacetylene (tolan)

2. Outline all steps in the synthesis of ethylbenzene from each of the following compounds, using any needed aliphatic or inorganic reagents.

(a) benzene
(b) styrene
(c) phenylacetylene
(d) α-phenylethyl alcohol ($C_6H_5CHOHCH_3$)
(e) β-phenylethyl alcohol ($C_6H_5CH_2CH_2OH$)

(f) 1-chloro-1-phenylethane
(g) 2-chloro-1-phenylethane
(h) *p*-bromoethylbenzene
(i) acetophenone ($C_6H_5\overset{\text{O}}{\underset{\|}{C}}CH_3$)

PROBLEMS

3. Give structures and names of the principal organic products expected from reaction (if any) of *n*-propylbenzene with each of the following. Where more than one product is to be expected, indicate which will predominate.

(a) H_2, Ni, room temperature, low pressure
(b) H_2, Ni, 200°, 100 atm.
(c) cold dilute $KMnO_4$
(d) hot $KMnO_4$
(e) $K_2Cr_2O_7$, H_2SO_4, heat
(f) boiling NaOH(aq)
(g) boiling HCl(aq)
(h) Na metal
(i) HNO_3, H_2SO_4
(j) H_2SO_4, SO_3

(k) Cl_2, Fe
(l) Br_2, Fe
(m) I_2, Fe
(n) Br_2, heat, light
(o) CH_3Cl, $AlCl_3$, 0°
(p) $C_6H_5CH_2Cl$, $AlCl_3$, 0° (*Note:* a benzyl halide is *not* an aryl halide.)
(q) C_6H_5Cl, $AlCl_3$, 80° *no Reaction*
(r) isobutylene, HF
(s) *tert*-butyl alcohol, H_2SO_4
(t) cyclohexene, HF

4. Give structures and names of the principal organic products expected from reaction (if any) of 1-phenyl-1-propene with:

(a) H_2, Ni, room temperature, low pressure
(b) H_2, Ni, 200°, 100 atm.
(c) Br_2 in CCl_4
(d) excess Br_2, Fe
(e) HCl
(f) HBr
(g) HBr (peroxides)

(h) cold conc. H_2SO_4
(i) Br_2, H_2O
(j) cold dilute $KMnO_4$
(k) hot $KMnO_4$
(l) HCO_2OH *glycol*
(m) O_3, then H_2O/Zn
(n) Br_2, 300°

5. Give structures and names of the principal organic products expected from each of the following reactions:

(a) benzene + cyclohexene + HF
(b) phenylacetylene + alcoholic $AgNO_3$
(c) *m*-nitrobenzyl chloride + $K_2Cr_2O_7$ + H_2SO_4 + heat
(d) allylbenzene + HCl
(e) *p*-chlorotoluene + hot $KMnO_4$
(f) eugenol ($C_{10}H_{12}O_2$, 2-methoxy-4-allylphenol) + hot KOH
$\longrightarrow$ isoeugenol ($C_{10}H_{12}O_2$)
(g) benzyl chloride + Mg + dry ether
(h) product of (g) + H_2O
(i) *p*-xylene + Br_2 + Fe
(j) 1-phenyl-1,3-butadiene + one mole H_2 + Ni, 2 atm., 30°
(k) *trans*-stilbene + O_3, then H_2O/Zn

6. Treatment of benzyl alcohol ($C_6H_5CH_2OH$) with cold concentrated H_2SO_4 yields a high-boiling resinous material. What is a likely structure for this material, and how is it probably formed?

7. Toluene can be oxidized to benzoic acid by 25% nitric acid. What is the objection to using concentrated (70%) nitric acid instead?

8. Label each set of hydrogens in each of the following compounds in order of expected ease of abstraction by bromine atoms. Use (1) for the most reactive, (2) for the next, etc.

(a) 1-phenyl-2-hexene

(b) CH_3⟨◯⟩CH_2⟨◯⟩$CH_2CH_2CH_3$

(c) 1,2,4-trimethylbenzene (*Hint:* see Problem 9.11, page 270.)
(d) What final monobromination product or products would abstraction of each kind of hydrogen in (a) lead to?

9. Give structures and names of the products expected from dehydrohalogenation of each of the following. Where more than one product can be formed, predict the major product.

(a) 1-chloro-1-phenylbutane
(b) 1-chloro-2-phenylbutane
(c) 2-chloro-2-phenylbutane
(d) 2-chloro-1-phenylbutane
(e) 3-chloro-2-phenylbutane

10. Answer Problem 9 for dehydration of the alcohol corresponding to each of the halides given. (*Hint:* do not forget Sec. 9.8.)

11. Arrange in order of ease of dehydration: (a) the alcohols of Problem 10; (b) $C_6H_5CH_2CH_2OH$, $C_6H_5CHOHCH_3$, $(C_6H_5)_2C(OH)CH_3$.

12. (a) Draw structures of all possible products of addition of one mole of Br_2 to 1-phenyl-1,3-butadiene. (b) Which of these possible products are consistent with the intermediate formation of the most stable carbonium ion? (c) Actually, only 1-phenyl-3,4-dibromo-1-butene is obtained. What is the most likely explanation of this fact?

13. (a) The heats of hydrogenation of the stereoisomeric stilbenes (1,2-diphenylethenes) are: *cis-*, 26.3 kcal; *trans-*, 20.6 kcal. Which isomer is the more stable? (b) *cis*-Stilbene is converted into *trans*-stilbene (but not vice versa) either (i) by action of a very small amount of Br_2 in the presence of light, or (ii) by action of a very small amount of HBr (but not HCl) in the presence of peroxides. What is the agent that probably brings about the conversion? Can you suggest a way in which the conversion might take place? (c) Why is *trans*-stilbene not converted into *cis*-stilbene?

14. Treatment of neopentyl alcohol, $(CH_3)_3CCH_2OH$, with hot acid yields an alkene. What alkene would you expect it to be, and how is it formed?

15. One mole of triphenylcarbinol lowers the freezing point of 1000 g of 100% sulfuric acid twice as much as one mole of methanol. How do you account for this?

16. Outline all steps in a possible laboratory synthesis of each of the following compounds from benzene and/or toluene, using any necessary aliphatic or inorganic reagents. Follow instructions of Problem 17, page 160. Assume a pure *para* isomer can be separated from an *ortho,para* mixture.

(a) isopropylbenzene
(b) styrene
(c) 2-phenylpropene
(d) 3-phenylpropene (allylbenzene)
(e) 1-phenylpropene
(f) phenylacetylene
(g) *p-tert*-butyltoluene
(h) *p*-nitrostyrene
(i) *p*-bromobenzal bromide
(j) hexaphenylethane
(k) *p*-nitrobenzyl chloride
(l) *p*-bromobenzoic acid
(m) *p*-chlorodiphenylmethane (p-$ClC_6H_4CH_2C_6H_5$) (*Hint:* see Problem 3(p).)

17. Describe simple chemical tests that would distinguish between:

(a) benzene and cyclohexane
(b) benzene and 1-hexene
(c) toluene and *n*-heptane
(d) cyclohexylbenzene and 1-phenylcyclohexene
(e) benzyl alcohol ($C_6H_5CH_2OH$) and *n*-pentylbenzene
(f) cinnamyl alcohol ($C_6H_5CH=CHCH_2OH$) and 3-phenyl-1-propanol ($C_6H_5CH_2CH_2CH_2OH$)
(g) chlorobenzene and ethylbenzene
(h) nitrobenzene and *m*-dibromobenzene
(i) hexaphenylethane and triphenylmethane

18. Describe chemical methods (not necessarily simple tests) that would enable you to distinguish between the compounds of each of the following sets. (For example, make use of Table 16.1, page 435, and Table 25.1, page 677.)

(a) the three isomeric trimethylbenzenes

(b) 1-phenylpropene, 2-phenylpropene, 3-phenylpropene (allylbenzene)

(c) all alkylbenzenes of formula C_9H_{12}

(d) m-chlorotoluene and benzyl chloride

(e) p-divinylbenzene (p-$C_6H_4(CH{=}CH_2)_2$) and 1-phenyl-1,3-butadiene

(f) $C_6H_5CHClCH_3$, p-$CH_3C_6H_4CH_2Cl$, and p-$ClC_6H_4C_2H_5$

19. An unknown compound is believed to be one of the following. Describe how you would go about finding out which of the possibilities the unknown actually is. Where possible, use simple chemical tests; where necessary, use more elaborate chemical methods like quantitative hydrogenation, cleavage, etc. Where necessary, make use of Table 16.1, page 435, and Table 25.1, page 677.

	b.p.		b.p.
bromobenzene	156°	p-chlorotoluene	162°
3-phenylpropene	157	o-ethyltoluene	162
m-ethyltoluene	158	p-ethyltoluene	163
n-propylbenzene	159	mesitylene	165
o-chlorotoluene	159	2-phenylpropene	165
m-chlorotoluene	162		

20. A liquid, insoluble in water or conc. H_2SO_4, but soluble slowly in fuming sulfuric acid, gave negative tests with dilute $KMnO_4$ and Br_2/CCl_4. It was found upon analysis to contain 90.5% C and 9.5% H. Vigorous treatment with $KMnO_4$ gave a solid which was found upon analysis to contain 68.8% C and 5.0% H. What was the original liquid?

21. A compound of formula $C_{14}H_{12}$ rapidly decolorizes Br_2 in CCl_4, and produces MnO_2 from cold, dilute neutral $KMnO_4$. Only one mole of hydrogen is absorbed readily. Upon vigorous oxidation, the compound gives benzoic acid as the sole carbon-containing product. Give the probable structure or structures. If more than one structure is possible, what further information is needed to make a final decision?

22. A hydrocarbon of formula $C_{15}H_{14}$ takes up readily only one mole of hydrogen or one mole of bromine. Oxidation converts it into benzoic acid and another acid of formula $C_8H_8O_2$. (a) What structures are possible for the hydrocarbon at this point? (b) More vigorous oxidation converts the hydrocarbon into benzoic acid and phthalic acid. What structure(s) in (a) are still possible for the hydrocarbon? Why did you eliminate the other structure(s)?

23. The compound *indene*, C_9H_8, found in coal tar, rapidly decolorizes Br_2/CCl_4 and dilute $KMnO_4$. Only one mole of hydrogen is absorbed readily to form *indane*, C_9H_{10}. More vigorous hydrogenation yields a compound of formula C_9H_{16}. Vigorous oxidation of indene yields phthalic acid. What is the structure of indene? Of indane? (*Hint:* see Problem 7.6, page 213.)

ELECTROPHILIC AROMATIC SUBSTITUTION. REACTIVITY AND ORIENTATION

10.1 Effects of substituent groups

We have seen (Sec. 9.9) that toluene undergoes electrophilic substitution (nitration, halogenation, sulfonation, Friedel-Crafts alkylation) faster than benzene, and that it yields chiefly the *ortho* and *para* isomers. On the other hand, nitrobenzene has been found to undergo substitution more slowly than benzene, and to yield chiefly the *meta* isomer.

Like methyl or nitro, any group attached to a benzene ring affects the **reactivity** of the ring and determines the **orientation** of substitution. When an electrophilic reagent attacks an aromatic ring, it is the group already attached to the ring that determines *how readily* the attack occurs and *where* it occurs.

A group that makes the ring more reactive than benzene is called an **activating group**. A group that makes the ring less reactive than benzene is called a **deactivating group**.

A group that causes attack to occur chiefly at positions **ortho** and **para** to it is called an **ortho,para director**. A group that causes attack to occur chiefly at positions **meta** to it is called a **meta director**.

In this chapter we shall examine the methods that are used to measure these effects on reactivity and orientation, the results of these measurements, and a theory that accounts for these results. It is convenient to take up determination of orientation first.

10.2 Determination of orientation

To determine the effect of a group on orientation is, in principle, quite simple: the compound containing this group attached to benzene is allowed to undergo substitution and the product is analyzed for the proportions of the three isomers. Identification of each isomer as *ortho*, *meta*, or *para* generally involves comparison with an authentic sample of that isomer prepared by some other method from a compound whose structure is known. In the last analysis, of course, all these identifications go back to absolute determinations of the Körner type (Sec. 8.18).

In this way it has been found that every group can be put into one of two classes: *ortho,para* directors or *meta* directors. Table 10.1 summarizes the orientation of nitration in a number of substituted benzenes. Of the five positions open to attack, three (60%) are *ortho* and *para* to the substituent group, and two (40%) are *meta* to the group; if there were no selectivity in the substitution reaction, we would expect the *ortho* and *para* isomers to make up 60% of the product, and the *meta* isomer to make up 40%. We see that seven of the groups direct 96–100% of nitration to the *ortho* and *para* positions; the other six direct 72–100% to the *meta* positions.

TABLE 10.1

ORIENTATION OF NITRATION OF C_6H_5Y

Y	Ortho	Para	Ortho plus Para	Meta
—OH	50–55	45–50	100	trace
—NHCOCH$_3$	19	79	98	2
—CH$_3$	58	38	96	4
—F	12	88	100	trace
—Cl	30	70	100	trace
—Br	38	62	100	trace
—I	41	59	100	trace
—N(CH$_3$)$_3$$^+$	0	0	0	100
—NO$_2$	6.4	0.3	6.7	93.3
—CN	—	—	11.5	88.5
—SO$_3$H	21	7	28	72
—COOH	19	1	20	80
—CHO	—	—	21	79

A given group causes the same general kind of orientation — predominantly *ortho,para* or predominantly *meta* — whatever the electrophilic reagent involved. The actual distribution of isomers may vary, however, from reaction to reaction. In Table 10.2, for example, compare the distribution of isomers obtained from toluene by sulfonation or bromination with that obtained by nitration.

TABLE 10.2

ORIENTATION OF SUBSTITUTION IN TOLUENE

	Ortho	Meta	Para
Nitration	58	4	38
Sulfonation	32	6	62
Bromination	37	–	63

10.3 Determination of relative reactivity

A group is classified as *activating* if the ring it is attached to is more reactive than benzene, and is classified as *deactivating* if the ring it is attached to is less reactive than benzene. The reactivities of benzene and substituted benzene are compared in one of the following ways.

The **time required** for reactions to occur under identical conditions can be measured. Thus toluene is found to react with fuming sulfuric acid in about one-tenth to one-twentieth the time required by benzene (Sec. 9.13). Toluene is more reactive than benzene, and —CH₃ is therefore an activating group.

The **severity of conditions** required for comparable reaction to occur within the same period of time can be observed. For example, benzene is nitrated in less than an hour at 60° by a mixture of concentrated sulfuric acid and concentrated nitric acid; comparable nitration of nitrobenzene requires treatment at 90° with fuming nitric acid and concentrated sulfuric acid. Nitrobenzene is evidently less reactive than benzene, and the nitro group, —NO₂, is a deactivating group.

Competitive reactions can be carried out. This is by far the best method, since it permits an exact and quantitative comparison of reactivities. *Equimolar* amounts of two compounds to be compared are mixed together and allowed to react with a limited amount of a particular reagent. Since there is not enough reagent for both compounds, the two compete with each other. An analysis of the reaction products shows which compound has consumed more of the reagent and hence is more reactive.

For example, if equimolar amounts of benzene and chlorobenzene are mixed with a small amount of nitric and sulfuric acids, about 30 times as much nitrobenzene as nitrochlorobenzene is obtained, showing that benzene is 30 times as reactive as chlorobenzene. On the other hand, a mixture of benzene and toluene yields a product in which the nitrotoluenes exceed nitrobenzene by 25:1, showing that toluene is 25 times as reactive as benzene.

$$NO_2 \quad \xleftarrow{C_6H_6} \quad \overset{HNO_3}{\underset{H_2SO_4}{}} \quad \xrightarrow{C_6H_5Cl} \quad Cl\text{—}\bigcirc\text{—}NO_2 \qquad o\text{-},\ m\text{-},\ \text{and}\ p\text{-}$$

30   1

$$NO_2 \quad \xleftarrow{C_6H_6} \quad \overset{HNO_3}{\underset{H_2SO_4}{}} \quad \xrightarrow{C_6H_5CH_3} \quad CH_3\text{—}\bigcirc\text{—}NO_2 \qquad o\text{-},\ m\text{-},\ \text{and}\ p\text{-}$$

1   25

The chloro group is therefore classified as deactivating, the methyl group as activating. The activation or deactivation caused by some groups is extremely powerful: aniline, $C_6H_5NH_2$, is roughly one million times as reactive as benzene, and nitrobenzene, $C_6H_5NO_2$, is roughly one-millionth as reactive as benzene.

10.4 Classification of substituent groups

The methods described in the last two sections have been used to determine the effects of a great number of groups on electrophilic substitution. As shown in Table 10.3, nearly all groups fall into one of two classes:

activating and *ortho,para*-directing, or deactivating and *meta*-directing.
The halogens are in a class by themselves, being deactivating but *ortho,para*
directors.

TABLE 10.3

EFFECT OF GROUPS ON ELECTROPHILIC AROMATIC SUBSTITUTION

Activating: *Ortho,para* Directors	Deactivating: *Meta* Directors
Strongly activating	—N(CH₃)₃⁺
—NH₂ (—NHR, —NR₂)	—NO₂
—OH	—CN
	—SO₃H
Moderately activating	—COOH (—COOR)
—OCH₃ (—OC₂H₅, etc.)	—CHO, —COR
—NHCOCH₃	
	Deactivating: *Ortho,para* Directors
Weakly activating	—F, —Cl, —Br, —I
—C₆H₅	
—CH₃ (—C₂H₅, etc.)	

Just by knowing the effects summarized in these short lists we can
now predict fairly accurately the course of hundreds of aromatic substitution reactions. We now know, for example, that bromination of
nitrobenzene will yield chiefly the *m*-isomer and that the reaction will
go more slowly than the bromination of benzene itself; indeed, it will
probably require severe conditions to go at all. We now know that nitration of C₆H₅NHCOCH₃ (*acetanilide*) will yield chiefly the *o*- and *p*-
isomers and will take place more rapidly than nitration of benzene.

Although, as we shall see, it is possible to account for these effects in
a reasonable way, it is necessary for the student to memorize the classi-
fications in Table 10.3 so that he may deal rapidly with synthetic problems
involving aromatic compounds.

10.5   Orientation in disubstituted benzenes

The presence of two substituents on a ring makes the problem of orientation more complicated, but even here we can frequently make very
definite predictions. First of all, the two substituents may be located so
that the directive influence of one *reinforces* that of the other; for example,
in I, II, and III the orientation clearly must be that indicated by the
arrows.

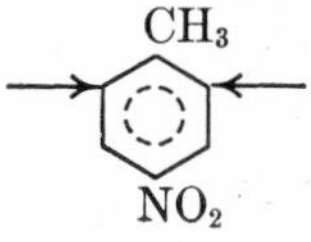

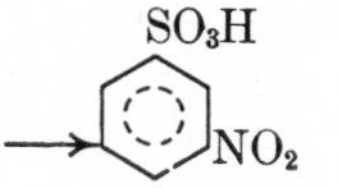

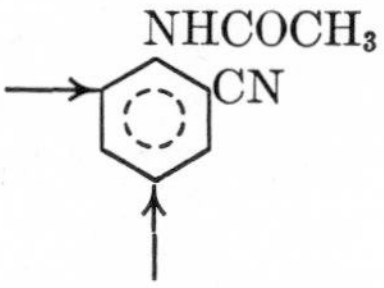

On the other hand, when the directive effect of one group *opposes* that
of the other, it may be difficult to predict the major product; in such cases
complicated mixtures of several products are often obtained.

Even where there are opposing effects, however, it is still possible in certain cases to make predictions in accordance with the following generalizations.

(a) *Strongly activating groups generally win out over deactivating or weakly activating groups.* The differences in directive power in the sequence

$$-NH_2, -OH > -OCH_3, -NHCOCH_3 > -C_6H_5, -CH_3 > meta\ directors$$

are great enough to be used in planning feasible syntheses. For example:

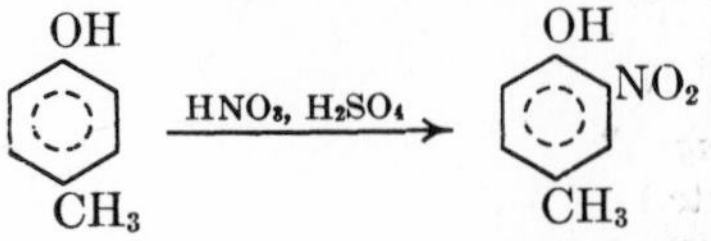

Sole product

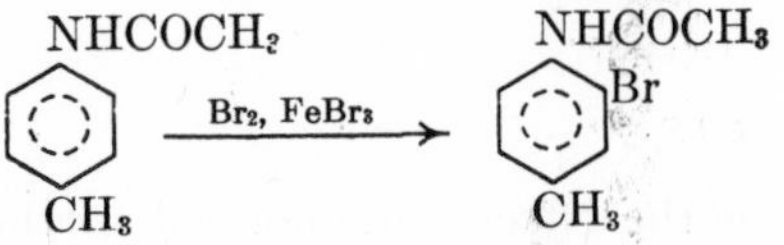

Chief product

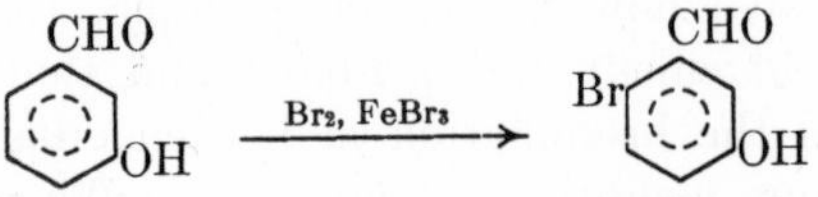

Chief product

There must be, however, a fairly large difference in the effects of the two groups for clean-cut results; otherwise one gets results like these:

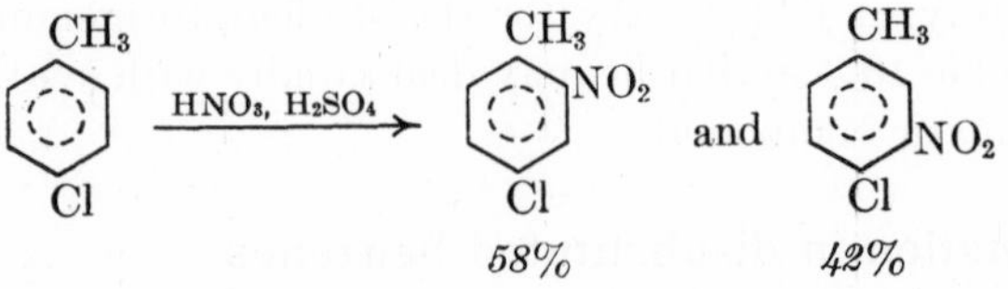

58%　　and　　42%

(b) *There is often little substitution between two groups that are meta to each other.* In many cases it seems as though there just is not enough room between two groups located *meta* to each other for appreciable substitution to occur there, as illustrated by IV and V:

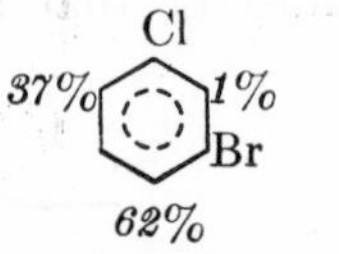

62%　　　　32%

Nitration　　　　Nitration

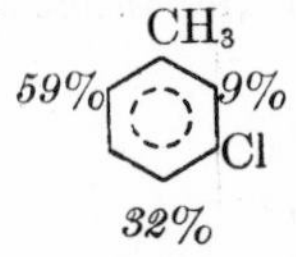

IV　　　　**V**

10.6 Orientation and synthesis

As we discussed earlier (Sec. 3.14), a laboratory synthesis is generally aimed at obtaining a single, pure compound. Whenever possible we should avoid use of a reaction that produces a mixture, since this lowers the yield

of the compound we want and causes difficult problems of purification·
With this in mind, let us see some of the ways in which we can apply our
knowledge of orientation to the synthesis of pure aromatic compounds.

First of all, *we must consider the order in which we introduce these various
substituents into the ring.* In the preparation of the bromonitrobenzenes,
for example, it is obvious that if we nitrate first and then brominate, we
will obtain the *m*-isomer; whereas if we brominate first and then nitrate,
we will obtain a mixture of the *o*- and *p*-isomers. The order in which we
decide to carry out the two steps, then, depends upon which isomer we
want.

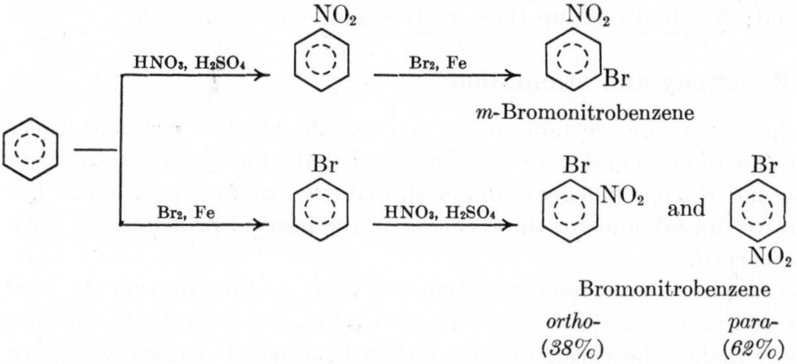

HNO₃, H₂SO₄ → (NO₂) → Br₂, Fe → (NO₂, Br)

m-Bromonitrobenzene

Br₂, Fe → (Br) → HNO₃, H₂SO₄ → (Br, NO₂) and (Br, NO₂)

Bromonitrobenzene

ortho-   *para-*
(38%)   (62%)

Next, if our synthesis involves conversion of one group into another
we must consider the proper time for this conversion. We know, for example,
that oxidation of a methyl group yields a carboxyl group (Sec. 9.11). In
the preparation of nitrobenzoic acids from toluene, the particular product
obtained depends upon whether oxidation or nitration is carried out first:

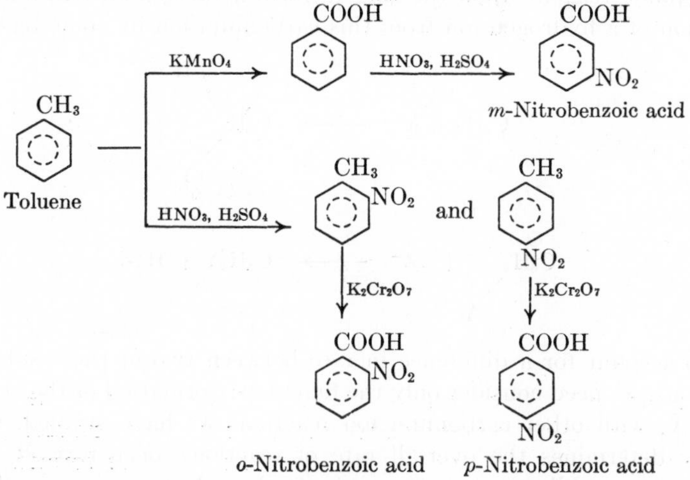

KMnO₄ → (COOH) → HNO₃, H₂SO₄ → (COOH, NO₂)

m-Nitrobenzoic acid

CH₃ / Toluene

HNO₃, H₂SO₄ → (CH₃, NO₂) and (CH₃, NO₂)

K₂Cr₂O₇ ↓   K₂Cr₂O₇ ↓

(COOH, NO₂)   (COOH, NO₂)

o-Nitrobenzoic acid   *p*-Nitrobenzoic acid

Substitution controlled by an activating group yields a mixture of
ortho and *para* isomers; nevertheless, we must often make use of such reactions, as in the examples just shown. It is usually possible to obtain the
pure *para* isomer from the mixture by fractional crystallization. As the

more symmetrical isomer it is the less soluble (Sec. 9.3), and crystallizes while the solvent still retains the soluble *ortho* isomer. Some *para* isomer, of course, remains in solution to contaminate the *ortho* isomer, which is therefore difficult to purify. As we shall see (Chapter 21), special approaches are often used to prepare *ortho* isomers.

In the special case of nitro compounds, the difference in boiling points is often large enough that both *ortho* and *para* isomers can be obtained pure by fractional distillation. As a result, many aromatic compounds are best prepared not by direct substitution but by conversion of one group into another, in the last analysis starting from an original nitro compound; we shall take up these methods of conversion later.

10.7   Reactivity and orientation

We have seen that certain groups activate the benzene ring and direct substitution to *ortho* and *para* positions, and that other groups deactivate the ring and (except halogens) direct substitution to *meta* positions. Let us see if we can account for these effects on the basis of principles we have already learned.

First of all, we must remember that reactivity and orientation are both matters of relative rates of reaction. Methyl is said to activate the ring because it makes the ring react *faster* than benzene; it causes *ortho,para* orientation because it makes the *ortho* and *para* positions react *faster* than the *meta* positions.

In our earlier discussion of electrophilic aromatic substitution (Sec. 8.24) we learned that whatever the specific reagent involved, the same mechanism is followed. There are two essential steps: (1) attack of an electrophilic reagent upon the ring to form a carbonium ion, and (2) abstraction of a hydrogen ion from this carbonium ion by some base.

$$(1) \qquad\qquad C_6H_6 + Y^+ \longrightarrow C_6H_5 \overset{\oplus}{\underset{Y}{\overset{H}{<}}}$$

$$(2) \qquad\qquad \overset{\oplus}{C_6H_5} \overset{H}{\underset{Y}{<}} + :Z^- \longrightarrow C_6H_5Y + H:Z$$

To account for a difference in rate between two of these substitution reactions, we need consider only the first step: formation of the carbonium ion. As with other carbonium ion reactions we have studied, this step largely determines the over-all rate of reaction; once formed, the carbonium ion rapidly reacts to form the final product.

For closely related reactions, a difference in rate of formation of carbonium ions is largely determined by a difference in E_{act}, that is, by a difference in stability of transition states. As with other carbonium ion reactions we have studied, factors that stabilize the ion by dispersing the

positive charge should for the same reason stabilize the incipient carbonium
ion of the transition state. Here again we expect the more stable carbonium ion to be formed more rapidly. We shall therefore concentrate
on the relative stabilities of the carbonium ions.

In electrophilic aromatic substitution the intermediate carbonium ion
is a hybrid of structures I, II, and III, in which the positive charge is
distributed about the ring, being strongest at the positions *ortho* and *para*

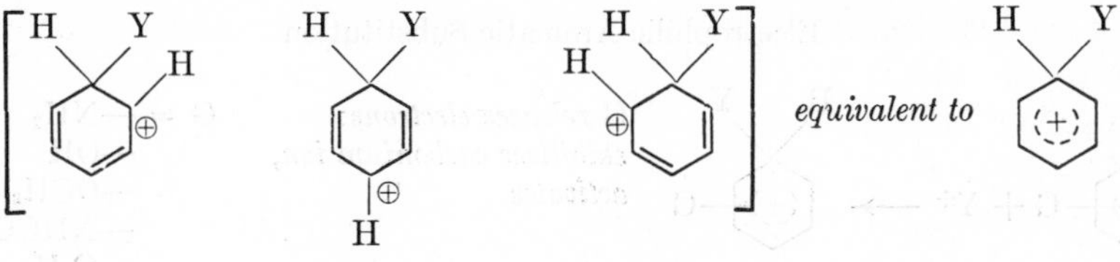

to the carbon atom being attacked. This hybrid is sometimes represented
by the single structure, IV, in which the solid lines represent the single
bonds (σ bonds) and the broken line the partial bonds due to the delocalized
π electrons.

A group already attached to the benzene ring should affect the stability
of the carbonium ion by dispersing or intensifying the positive charge,
depending upon its electron-releasing or electron-withdrawing nature.
It is evident from the structure of the ion (I–III) that this stabilizing or
destabilizing effect should be especially important when the group is
attached *ortho* or *para* to the carbon being attacked.

10.8   Theory of reactivity

To compare rates of substitution in benzene, toluene, and nitrobenzene,
we compare the structures of the carbonium ions formed from the three
compounds:

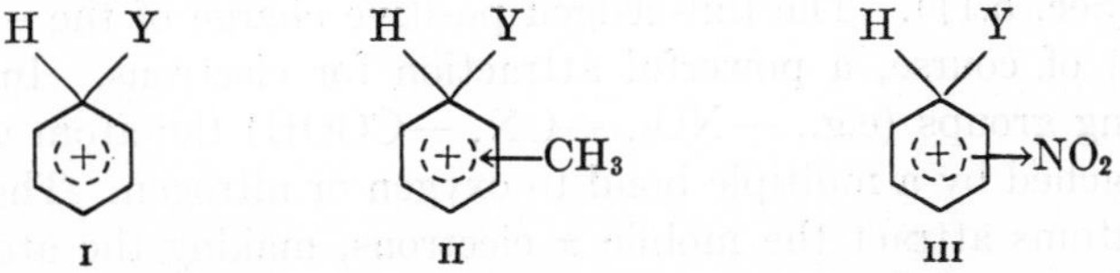

By releasing electrons the methyl group (II) tends to neutralize the
positive charge of the ring and so become more positive itself; this dispersal of the charge stabilizes the carbonium ion. In the same way the
inductive effect stabilizes the developing positive charge in the transition
state and thus leads to a faster reaction.

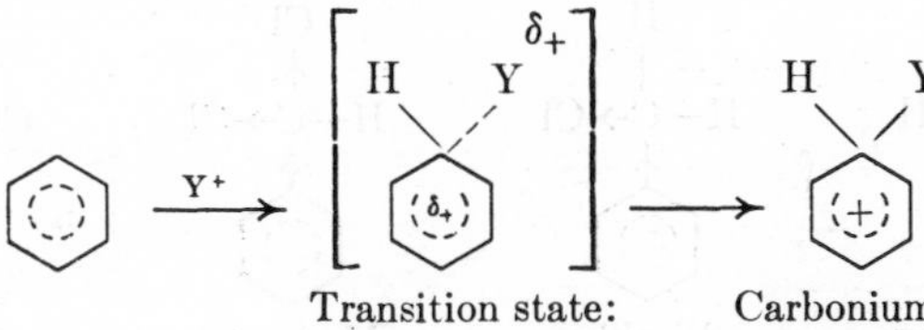

Transition state: Carbonium ion:
developing positive   *full positive*
charge   *charge*

The —NO₂ group, on the other hand, has an electron-withdrawing inductive effect (III); this tends to intensify the positive charge, destabilizes the carbonium ion, and thus causes a slower reaction.

Reactivity in electrophilic aromatic substitution depends, then, upon the tendency of a substituent group to release or withdraw electrons. **A group that releases electrons activates the ring; a group that withdraws electrons deactivates the ring.**

Electrophilic Aromatic Substitution

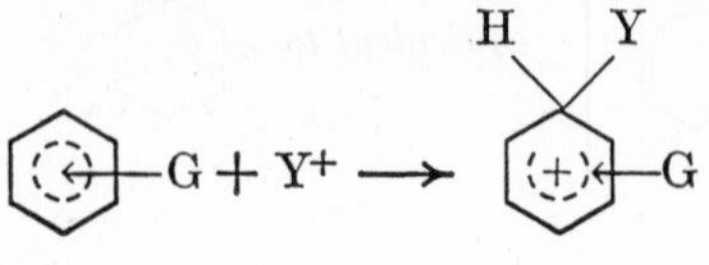

G releases electrons: stabilizes carbonium ion, activates

$$G = —NH_2$$
$$—OH$$
$$—OCH_3$$
$$—NHCOCH_3$$
$$—C_6H_5$$
$$—CH_3$$

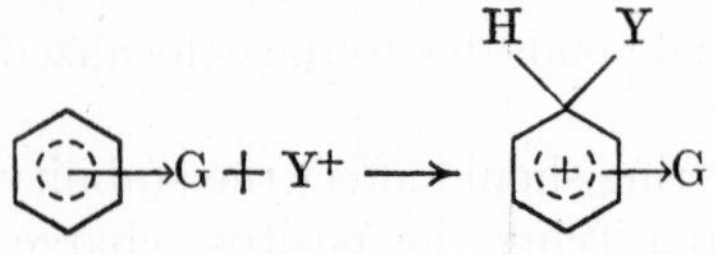

G withdraws electrons: destabilizes carbonium ion, deactivates

$$G = —N(CH_3)_3^+$$
$$—NO_2$$
$$—CN$$
$$—SO_3H$$
$$—COOH$$
$$—CHO$$
$$—COR$$
$$—X$$

Like —CH₃, other alkyl groups release electrons, and like —CH₃ they activate the ring. For example, *tert*-butylbenzene is 16 times as reactive as benzene toward nitration. Electron release by —NH₂ and —OH, and by their derivatives —OCH₃ and —NHCOCH₃, is due not to their inductive effect but to resonance, and is discussed later (Sec. 10.10).

We are already familiar with the electron-withdrawing effect of the halogens (Sec. 5.11). The full-fledged positive charge of the —N(CH₃)₃⁺ group has, of course, a powerful attraction for electrons. In the other deactivating groups (e.g., —NO₂, —CN, —COOH) the atom next to the ring is attached by a multiple bond to oxygen or nitrogen. These electronegative atoms attract the mobile π electrons, making the atom next to the ring electron-deficient; to make up this deficiency the atom next to the ring withdraws electrons from the ring.

We might expect replacement of hydrogen in —CH₃ by halogen to decrease the electron-releasing tendency of the group, and perhaps to convert it into an electron-withdrawing group. This is found to be the

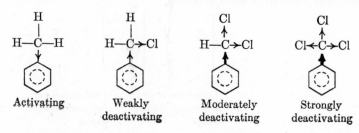

Activating   Weakly deactivating   Moderately deactivating   Strongly deactivating

case. Toward nitration, toluene is 25 times as reactive as benzene; benzyl chloride is only one-third as reactive as benzene. The —CH_2Cl group is thus weakly deactivating. Further replacement of hydrogen by halogen to yield the —$CHCl_2$ and the —CCl_3 groups results in stronger deactivation.

omit

10.9 Theory of orientation

Before we try to account for orientation in electrophilic substitution, let us look more closely at the facts.

An activating group activates all positions of the benzene ring; even the positions *meta* to it are more reactive than any single position in benzene itself. It directs *ortho* and *para* simply because it activates the *ortho* and *para* positions much *more* than it does the *meta*.

A deactivating group deactivates all positions in the ring, even the positions *meta* to it. It directs *meta* simply because it deactivates the *ortho* and *para* positions even *more* than it does the *meta*.

Thus both *ortho,para* orientation and *meta* orientation arise in the same way: **the effect of any group — whether activating or deactivating — is strongest at the ortho and para positions.**

To see if this is reasonable let us compare, for example, the carbonium ions formed by attack at the *para* and *meta* positions of toluene, a compound that contains an activating group. Each of these is a hybrid of three structures, I–III for *para*, IV–VI for *meta*. In one of these six structures, II, the positive charge is located on the carbon atom to which —CH_3

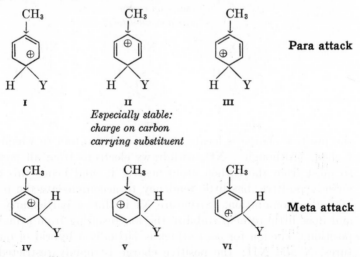

Para attack

I   II   III

Especially stable:
charge on carbon
carrying substituent

Meta attack

IV   V   VI

is attached. Although —CH_3 releases electrons to all positions of the ring, it does so most strongly to the carbon atom nearest it; consequently structure II is a particularly stable one. Because of contribution from structure II, the hybrid carbonium ion resulting from attack at the *para* position is more stable than the carbonium ion resulting from attack at a *meta* position. *Para* substitution, therefore, occurs faster than *meta* substitution.

In the same way, it can be seen that attack at an *ortho* position (VII–

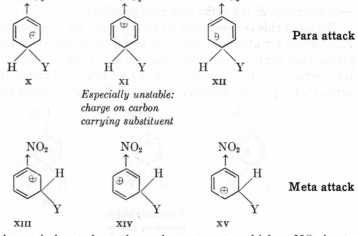

IX) also yields a more stable carbonium ion, through contribution from IX, than attack at a *meta* position.

In toluene, *ortho,para* substitution is thus faster than *meta* substitution because electron release by —CH₃ is more effective during attack at the positions *ortho* and *para* to it.

Next, let us compare the carbonium ions formed by attack at the *para* and *meta* positions of nitrobenzene, a compound that contains a deactivating group. Each of these is a hybrid of three structures, X–XII for *para* attack, XIII–XV for *meta* attack. In one of the six structures, XI, the positive charge is located on the carbon atom to which —NO₂ is attached. Although —NO₂ withdraws electrons from all positions it does so most from the carbon atom nearest it, and hence this carbon atom, already positive, has little tendency to accommodate the positive charge of the carbonium ion. Structure XI is thus a particularly unstable one and does little to help stabilize the ion resulting from attack at the *para* position. The ion for *para* attack is virtually a hybrid of only two structures, X and XII; the positive charge is mainly restricted to only *two* carbon atoms. It is less stable than the ion resulting from attack at a *meta* position, which is a hybrid of three structures, and in which the positive charge is accommodated by *three* carbon atoms. *Para* substitution, therefore, occurs more slowly than *meta* substitution.

In the same way it can be seen that attack at an *ortho* position (XVI–XVIII) yields a less stable carbonium ion, because of the instability of XVIII, than attack at a *meta* position.

Ortho attack

XVI   XVII   XVIII

*Especially unstable:
charge on carbon
carrying substituent*

In nitrobenzene, *ortho,para* substitution is thus slower than *meta* substitution because electron withdrawal by —NO₂ is more effective during attack at the positions *ortho* and *para* to it.

Thus we see that both *ortho,para* orientation by activating groups and *meta* orientation by deactivating groups follow logically from the structure of the intermediate carbonium ion. The charge of the carbonium ion is strongest at the positions *ortho* and *para* to the point of attack, and hence a group attached to one of these positions can exert the strongest effect, whether activating or deactivating.

The unusual behavior of the halogens, which direct *ortho* and *para* although deactivating, results from a combination of two opposing factors, and will be taken up later (Sec. 14.9).

10.10   Electron release via resonance

We have seen that a substituent group affects both reactivity and orientation in electrophilic aromatic substitution by its tendency to release or withdraw electrons. So far, we have considered electron release and electron withdrawal only as inductive effects, that is, as effects due to the electronegativity of the group concerned.

But certain groups (—NH₂ and —OH, and their derivatives) act as powerful activators toward electrophilic aromatic substitution, even though they contain electronegative atoms and can be shown in other ways to have electron-withdrawing inductive effects. If our approach to the problem is correct, these groups must release electrons in some other way than through their inductive effects; they are believed to do this by a resonance effect. But before we discuss this, let us review a little of what we know about nitrogen and oxygen.

Although electronegative, the nitrogen of the —NH₂ group is basic and tends to share its last pair of electrons and acquire a positive charge. Just as ammonia accepts a hydrogen ion to form the ammonium (NH_4^+) ion, so organic compounds related to ammonia accept hydrogen ions to form substituted ammonium ions.

$$\ddot{N}H_3 + H^+ \longrightarrow NH_4^+ \qquad R\ddot{N}H_2 + H^+ \longrightarrow RNH_3^+$$

$$R_2\ddot{N}H + H^+ \longrightarrow R_2NH_2^+ \qquad R_3\ddot{N} + H^+ \longrightarrow R_3NH^+$$

The —OH group shows similar but weaker basicity; we are already familiar with oxonium ions, ROH_2^+.

$$H_2\ddot{O} + H^+ \longrightarrow H_3O^+ \qquad R\ddot{O}H + H^+ \longrightarrow ROH_2^+$$

The effects of —NH₂ and —OH on electrophilic aromatic substitution can be accounted for by assuming that nitrogen and oxygen can share more than a pair of electrons with the ring and can accommodate a positive charge.

The carbonium ion formed by attack *para* to the —NH₂ group of aniline, for example, is considered to be a hybrid not only of structures I, II, and III, with positive charges located on carbons of the ring, but also

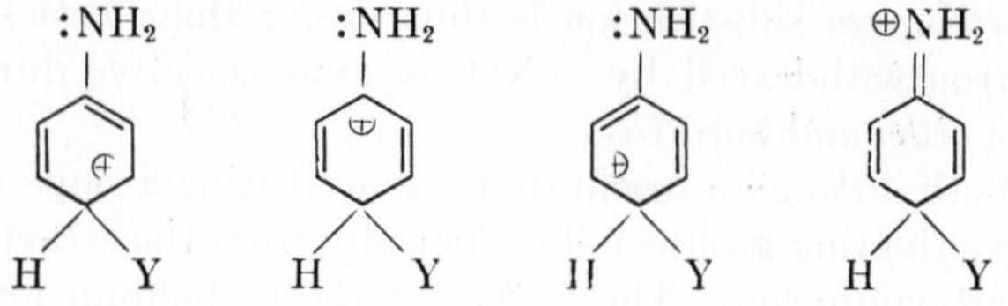

Para attack

I   II   III   IV

Especially stable:
every atom has octet

Meta attack

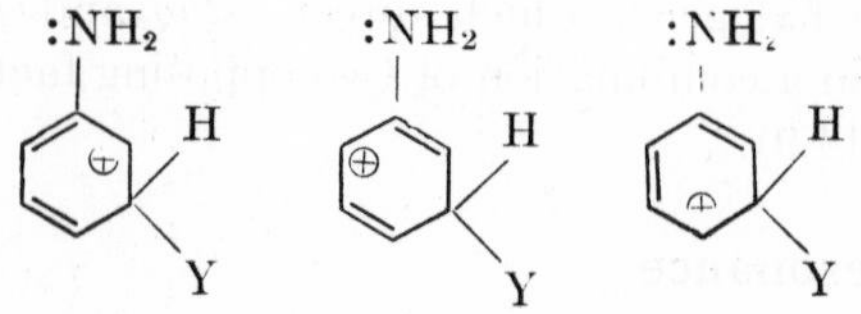

V   VI   VII

of structure IV in which the positive charge is carried by nitrogen. Structure IV is especially stable, since in it *every atom* (except hydrogen, of course) *has a complete octet of electrons.* This carbonium ion is much more stable than the one obtained by attack on benzene itself, or the one obtained (V–VII) from attack *meta* to the —NH₂ group of aniline; in neither of these cases is a structure like IV possible. (Compare, for example, the stabilities of the ions NH_4^+ and CH_3^+. Here it is not a matter of which atom, nitrogen or carbon, can better accommodate a positive charge; it is a matter of which atom has a complete octet of electrons.)

Examination of the corresponding structures (VIII–XI) shows that *ortho* attack is much like *para* attack.

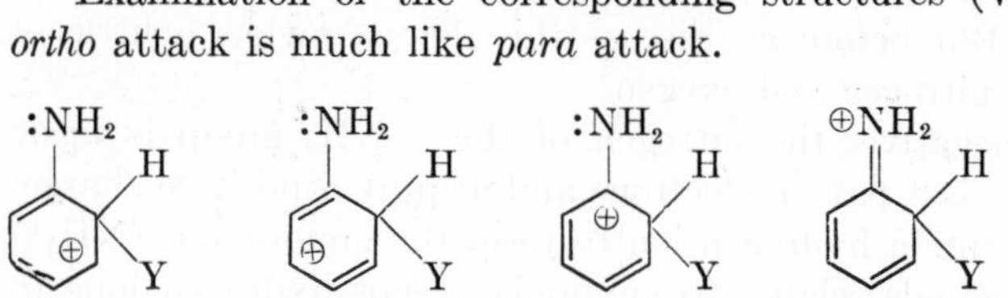

Ortho attack

VIII   IX   X   XI

Especially stable:
every atom has octet

Thus substitution in aniline occurs faster than substitution in benzene, and occurs predominantly at the positions *ortho* and *para* to —NH₂.

In the same way activation and *ortho,para* orientation by the —OH group is accounted for by contribution of structures like XII and XIII, in which every atom has a complete octet of electrons.

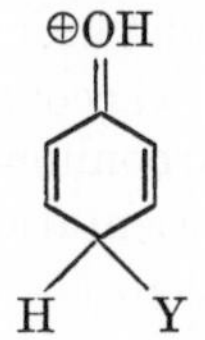

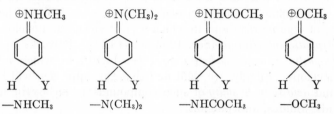

XII	XIII
Para attack	*Ortho* attack

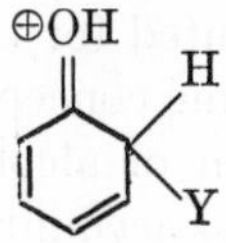

The similar effects of the derivatives of —NH₂ and —OH are accounted for by similar structures (shown only for *para* attack):

The tendency of oxygen and nitrogen in groups like these to share more than a pair of electrons with an aromatic ring is shown in a number of other ways, which will be discussed later (Sec. 20.3 and Sec. 22.8).

Although the effect on reactivity and orientation exerted by such groups as —NO₂ and —CN can be accounted for simply by their inductive effects, it is generally considered that electron withdrawal by resonance is also involved. We shall discuss the kind of structures proposed later (Sec. 14.14).

Problem 10.1 It is generally considered that alkyl groups release electrons during electrophilic aromatic substitution not only by an inductive effect but also by resonance, that is, by hyperconjugation (Sec. 9.19, and Problem 9.17, page 278). Draw the structures that correspond to such an effect for substitution in: (a) toluene; (b) in ethylbenzene; (c) in isopropylbenzene; (d) in *tert*-butylbenzene. (e) In which of these compounds should the hyperconjugation effect be the strongest? (f) The weakest?

10.11 Relation to other carbonium ion reactions

In summary, we can say that both reactivity and orientation in electrophilic aromatic substitution are determined by the stabilities of the intermediate carbonium ions concerned. The stabilities of the carbonium ions, in turn, are determined by the electron-releasing or electron-withdrawing tendencies of the substituent groups.

A group may release or withdraw electrons by an inductive effect, a resonance effect, or both. These effects oppose each other only for the —NH₂ and —OH groups (and their derivatives) and for the halogens, —X. For —NH₂ and —OH the resonance effect is much the more important; for —X the effects are more evenly matched. It is because of this that the halogens occupy the unusual position of being deactivating groups but *ortho,para* directors; we shall consider this point in detail later (Sec. 14.9).

We have accounted for the facts of electrophilic aromatic substitution by means of the same concept that we first used to account for the relative ease of dehydration of alcohols: **stability of carbonium ions.** We have used this concept to account for reactivity and orientation in additions to the carbon–carbon double bonds of alkenes, and to account for the kind of rearrangement that takes place in Friedel-Crafts alkylation.

In all this we have estimated the stability of a carbonium ion on the same basis: **the dispersal or concentration of the charge** due to electron release or electron withdrawal by the substituent groups. As we shall see, the approach that has worked so well for elimination, for addition, and for electrophilic aromatic substitution works for still another important class of organic reactions in which a positive charge develops: *nucleophilic aliphatic substitution* (Sec. 12.5, Sec. 13.14). It works equally well for *nucleophilic aromatic substitution* (Sec. 14.10), in which a negative charge develops. Finally, we shall find that this approach will help us to understand *acidity* or *basicity* of such compounds as carboxylic acids, sulfonic acids, amines, and phenols.

10.12 Limitations of Friedel-Crafts alkylation

The effects of substituent groups on Friedel-Crafts alkylation require further consideration. Deactivation may be so strong that it prevents reaction from occurring at all, and activation may be so strong that special methods are required for controlling the reaction. Let us look at some of the limitations to the use of Friedel-Crafts alkylation.

First of all, an aromatic ring less reactive than that of the halobenzenes does not undergo the Friedel-Crafts reaction. Thus we may alkylate bromobenzene but not nitrobenzene or benzoic acid or other compounds containing only *meta*-directing groups.

An alkyl carbonium ion, R^+, is evidently a less powerful reagent than the nitronium ion, $^+NO_2$, and the other electron-deficient reagents that bring about electrophilic aromatic substitution.

Second, we must take special precautions to prevent *poly*alkylation. Of the electrophilic substitution reactions, only Friedel-Crafts alkylation introduces a group that is activating. Nitration, for example, introduces an $—NO_2$ group into the aromatic ring; the deactivating effect of this $—NO_2$ group tends to prevent further nitration in the same molecule. For the same reason, we are seldom bothered by polysulfonation and

polyhalogenation. Friedel-Crafts alkylation, on the other hand, introduces an alkyl group, which tends to activate the ring toward further
alkylation. It is to prevent polyalkylation that we generally use an excess of the compound undergoing substitution, just as we did to prevent
polyhalogenation of an alkane (Sec. 2.8).

*Less reactive than benzene
toward further substitution*

*More reactive than benzene
toward further substitution*

Next, aromatic rings containing the —NH$_2$, —NHR, or —NR$_2$ group
do not undergo Friedel-Crafts alkylation, partly because the strongly
basic nitrogen ties up the Lewis acid needed for ionization of the alkyl
halide:

$$C_6H_5\overset{\cdot\cdot}{N}H_2 + AlCl_3 \longrightarrow \underset{\oplus}{C_6H_5\overset{\ominus AlCl_3}{\underset{}{\overset{\cdot\cdot}{N}H_2}}}$$

I

Problem 10.2 Tying up of the acidic catalyst by the basic nitrogen is not the
only factor that prevents alkylation, since even when excess catalyst is used, reaction does not occur. Looking at the structure of the complex (I) shown for
aniline, can you suggest another factor? (*Hint:* see Sec. 10.8.)

We have already encountered three other limitations to Friedel-Crafts
alkylation: the possibility that the alkyl group will rearrange (Sec. 9.8);
the fact that aryl halides cannot take the place of alkyl halides (Sec. 9.6);
and the effect of temperature upon orientation in the preparation of poly-
alkylbenzenes (Sec. 9.14).

Finally, as in Grignard syntheses, water must be excluded from the
system; hydration of the aluminum chloride destroys its catalytic activity.

Despite these numerous limitations, the Friedel-Crafts reaction, in its
various modifications (for example, acylation, Sec. 17.8), is an extremely
useful synthetic tool.

PROBLEMS

1. Give structures and names of the principal products expected from the ring
monobromination of each of the following compounds. In each case, tell whether
bromination will occur faster or slower than with benzene itself.

(a) acetanilide (C$_6$H$_5$NHCOCH$_3$)
(b) iodobenzene
(c) *sec*-butylbenzene
(d) N-methylaniline (C$_6$H$_5$NHCH$_3$)
(e) ethyl benzoate (C$_6$H$_5$COOC$_2$H$_5$)
(f) acetophenone (C$_6$H$_5$COCH$_3$)

(g) phenetole (C$_6$H$_5$OC$_2$H$_5$)
(h) diphenylmethane (C$_6$H$_5$CH$_2$C$_6$H$_5$)
(i) benzonitrile (C$_6$H$_5$CN)
(j) benzotrifluoride (C$_6$H$_5$CF$_3$)
(k) biphenyl (C$_6$H$_5$–C$_6$H$_5$)

2. Give structures and names of the principal organic products expected from mononitration of:

(a) o-nitrotoluene

(b) m-dibromobenzene

(c) p-nitroacetanilide
(p-$O_2NC_6H_4NHCOCH_3$)

(d) m-dinitrobenzene

(e) m-cresol (m-$CH_3C_6H_4OH$)

(f) o-cresol

(g) p-cresol

(h) m-nitrotoluene

(i) p-xylene

(j) terephthalic acid (p-$C_6H_4(COOH)_2$)

(k) anilinium hydrogen sulfate
($C_6H_5NH_3^+$ HSO_4^-)

3. Give structures and names of the principal organic products expected from the monosulfonation of:

(a) cyclohexylbenzene

(b) nitrobenzene

(c) anisole ($C_6H_5OCH_3$)

(d) benzenesulfonic acid

(e) salicylaldehyde (o-HOC_6H_4CHO)

(f) m-nitrophenol

(g) o-fluoroanisole

(h) o-nitroacetanilide
(o-$O_2NC_6H_4NHCOCH_3$)

(i) o-xylene

(j) m-xylene

(k) p-xylene

4. Arrange the following in order of reactivity toward ring nitration, listing by structure the most reactive at the top, the least reactive at the bottom.

(a) benzene, mesitylene, toluene, m-xylene, p-xylene

(b) benzene, bromobenzene, nitrobenzene, toluene

(c) acetanilide ($C_6H_5NHCOCH_3$), acetophenone ($C_6H_5COCH_3$), aniline, benzene

(d) terephthalic acid, toluene, p-toluic acid (p-$CH_3C_6H_4COOH$), p-xylene

(e) chlorobenzene, p-chloronitrobenzene, 2,4-dinitrochlorobenzene

(f) 2,4-dinitrochlorobenzene, 2,4-dinitrophenol

(g) m-dinitrobenzene, 2,4-dinitrotoluene

5. Even though 1,3,5-trinitrobenzene (TNB) has more shattering power (more *brisance*) and is no more dangerous to handle, 2,4,6-trinitrotoluene (TNT) is the high explosive in more general use. Can you suggest a reason (connected with manufacture) for the popularity of TNT? (Benzene and toluene are both readily available materials; until recently, benzene has been the cheaper.)

6. For each of the following compounds, indicate which ring you would expect to be attacked in nitration, and give structures of the principal products.

(a)　$O_2N\langle\bigcirc\rangle$—$\langle\bigcirc\rangle$　　(b)　$\langle\bigcirc\rangle$—CH_2—$\langle\bigcirc\rangle$　(c)　$\langle\bigcirc\rangle$—C
　　　　　　　　　　　　　　　　O_2N　　　　　　　　　　　　　　　　　O—$\langle\bigcirc\rangle$

　　p-Nitrobiphenyl　　　　　m-Nitrodiphenylmethane　　　　Phenyl benzoate

7. Arrange the compounds of each set in order of reactivity toward electrophilic substitution. Indicate in each set which would yield the highest percentage of *meta* isomer, and which would yield the lowest.

(a) $C_6H_5N(CH_3)_3^+$, $C_6H_5CH_2N(CH_3)_3^+$, $C_6H_5CH_2CH_2N(CH_3)_3^+$, $C_6H_5CH_2CH_2$-$CH_2N(CH_3)_3^+$

(b) $C_6H_5NO_2$, $C_6H_5CH_2NO_2$, $C_6H_5CH_2CH_2NO_2$

(c) $C_6H_5CH_3$, $C_6H_5CH_2COOC_2H_5$, $C_6H_5CH(COOC_2H_5)_2$, $C_6H_5C(COOC_2H_5)_3$

8. There is evidence that the phenyl group, C_6H_5-, has an electron-withdrawing inductive effect. Yet each ring of biphenyl, C_6H_5-C_6H_5, is more reactive than benzene toward electrophilic substitution, and the chief products are *ortho* and *para* isomers. Show how reactivity and orientation can be accounted for on the basis of resonance.

9. Arrange the compounds of each set in order of reactivity toward the indicated reaction.

(a) addition of HCl: styrene, p-chlorostyrene, p-methylstyrene

(b) dehydration: α-phenylethyl alcohol ($C_6H_5CHOHCH_3$), α-(p-nitrophenyl)ethyl alcohol, α-(p-aminophenyl)ethyl alcohol

10. Outline all steps in the laboratory synthesis of the following compounds from benzene and/or toluene, using any needed aliphatic or inorganic reagents. (Review the general instructions of Problem 17, page 160. Assume that a pure *para* isomer can be separated from an *ortho,para* mixture.)

(a) p-nitrotoluene
(b) p-bromonitrobenzene
(c) p-dichlorobenzene
(d) m-bromobenzenesulfonic acid
(e) p-bromobenzenesulfonic acid
(f) p-bromobenzoic acid
(g) m-bromobenzoic acid
(h) 1,3,5-trinitrobenzene
(i) 2-bromo-4-nitrotoluene

(j) p-bromobenzyl bromide
(k) p-nitroethylbenzene
(l) 2-bromo-4-nitrobenzoic acid
(m) 4-bromo-3-nitrobenzoic acid
(n) 3,5-dinitrobenzoic acid
(o) 4-nitro-1,2-dibromobenzene
(p) 2-nitro-1,4-dichlorobenzene
(q) p-nitrodiphenylmethane
(r) 2,4-dinitrodiphenylmethane

11. Outline all steps in the following laboratory syntheses, using any needed aliphatic or inorganic reagents. (Follow the other instructions in Problem 10.)

(a) 4-nitro-2,6-dibromoanisole from anisole ($C_6H_5OCH_3$)
(b) 4-bromo-2-nitrobenzoic acid from o-nitrotoluene
(c) 2,4,6-tribromoaniline from aniline
(d) 2,4-dinitroacetanilide from acetanilide ($C_6H_5NHCOCH_3$)
(e) 5-nitroisophthalic acid from m-xylene
(f) 4-nitroisophthalic acid from m-xylene
(g) 2-nitroterephthalic acid from p-xylene (two ways)
(h) Which way in (g) is preferable? Why?

Chapter eleven

ALCOHOLS I. PREPARATION
AND PHYSICAL PROPERTIES

11.1 Structure

Alcohols are compounds of the general formula, ROH, where R is any alkyl or substituted alkyl group. The group may be primary, secondary, or tertiary; it may be open-chain or cyclic; it may contain a double bond, a halogen atom, or an aromatic ring. For example:

$$CH_3-\underset{\underset{OH}{|}}{\overset{\overset{CH_3}{|}}{C}}-CH_3$$

tert-Butyl alcohol

$$H_2C=CH-CH_2OH$$

Allyl alcohol

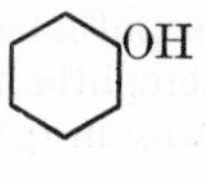

OH

Cyclohexanol

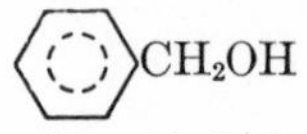

CH₂OH

Benzyl alcohol

$$\underset{\underset{Cl}{|}\;\;\underset{OH}{|}}{CH_2-CH_2}$$

Ethylene chlorohydrin
(β-Chloroethyl alcohol)

$$\underset{\underset{OH}{|}\;\;\underset{OH}{|}\;\;\underset{OH}{|}}{CH_2-CH-CH_2}$$

Glycerol

All alcohols contain the hydroxyl (—OH) group, which, as the functional group, determines the properties characteristic of this family. Variations in structure of the R group may affect the rate at which the alcohol undergoes certain reactions, and even, in a few cases, may affect the kind of reaction.

Compounds in which the hydroxyl group is attached directly to an aromatic ring are not alcohols; they are *phenols*, and differ so markedly from the alcohols that we shall consider them in a separate chapter.

11.2 Classification

We classify a carbon atom as *primary*, *secondary*, or *tertiary* according to the number of other carbon atoms attached to it (Sec. 3.11). An alcohol is classified according to the kind of carbon that bears the —OH group:

$$
\begin{array}{ccc}
\text{H} & \text{R} & \text{R} \\
| & | & | \\
\text{R—C—OH} & \text{R—C—OH} & \text{R—C—OH} \\
| & | & | \\
\text{H} & \text{H} & \text{R} \\
\text{Primary} & \text{Secondary} & \text{Tertiary} \\
(1°) & (2°) & (3°)
\end{array}
$$

One reaction, oxidation, which directly involves the hydrogen atoms attached to the carbon bearing the —OH group, takes an entirely different course for each class of alcohol. Usually, however, alcohols of different classes differ only in *rate* or *mechanism* of reaction, and in a way consistent with their structures. Certain substituents may affect reactivity in such a way as to make an alcohol of one class resemble the members of a different class; benzyl alcohol, for example, although formally a primary alcohol, often acts like a tertiary alcohol. We shall find that these variations, too, are consistent with the structures involved.

11.3 Nomenclature

Alcohols are named by three different systems, which are analogous to the ones used for alkanes and alkenes.

For the simpler alcohols the **common names,** which we have already encountered (Sec. 4.14), are most often used. These consist simply of the name of the alkyl group followed by the word *alcohol.* For example:

$$
\begin{array}{ccc}
& & \text{CH}_3 \\
& & | \\
\text{CH}_3\text{CH}_2\text{OH} & \text{CH}_3\text{CHCH}_3 & \text{CH}_3\text{CHCH}_2\text{OH} \\
& | & \\
& \text{OH} & \\
\text{Ethyl alcohol} & \text{Isopropyl alcohol} & \text{Isobutyl alcohol}
\end{array}
$$

$$
\begin{array}{ccc}
\text{CH}_3 & & \\
| & & \alpha \quad \beta \\
\text{CH}_3\text{CH}_2\text{—C—CH}_3 & \text{O}_2\text{N}\langle \; \rangle\text{CH}_2\text{OH} & \langle \; \rangle\text{CHCH}_3 \\
| & & | \\
\text{OH} & & \text{OH} \\
\textit{tert-}\text{Pentyl alcohol} & \textit{p-}\text{Nitrobenzyl alcohol} & \alpha\text{-Phenylethyl alcohol}
\end{array}
$$

We should notice that similar names do not always mean the same classification; for example, isopropyl alcohol is a secondary alcohol, whereas isobutyl alcohol is a primary alcohol.

As before, compounds too complicated for common names may be given **derived names.** According to this system, alcohols are considered to be derived from *methyl alcohol,* CH_3OH, by the replacement of one or more hydrogen atoms by other groups. We simply name the groups attached to the carbon bearing the —OH and then add the suffix **–carbinol** to include the C—OH portion:

Triphenylcarbinol

$$CH_3CH_2—\overset{\displaystyle CH_3}{\underset{\displaystyle CH_2}{\overset{|}{\underset{|}{C}}}}—OH$$

Triethylcarbinol

$$CH_3CH_2\overset{\displaystyle CH_3}{\underset{|}{CH}}—\overset{\displaystyle H}{\underset{\displaystyle H}{\overset{|}{\underset{|}{C}}}}—OH$$

sec-Butylcarbinol

Finally, there is the most versatile system, the **IUPAC.** The rules are:

(1) Select as the parent structure the longest continuous carbon chain *that contains the —OH group;* then consider the compound to have been derived from this structure by replacement of hydrogen by various groups. The parent structure is known as *ethanol, propanol, butanol,* etc., depending upon the number of carbon atoms; each name is derived by replacing the terminal *–e* of the corresponding alkane name by *–ol.*

(2) Indicate by a number the position of the —OH group in the parent chain, generally using the lowest possible number for this purpose.

(3) Indicate by numbers the positions of other groups attached to the parent chain.

CH_3OH

Methanol

$$CH_3CH_2\overset{\displaystyle CH_3}{\underset{|}{CH}}CH_2OH$$

2-Methyl-1-butanol

CH_2CH_2OH

2-Phenylethanol

$$CH_3CH_2—\overset{\displaystyle CH_3}{\underset{\displaystyle OH}{\overset{|}{\underset{|}{C}}}}—CH_3$$

2-Methyl-2-butanol

$$CH_3\overset{\displaystyle CH_3}{\underset{\displaystyle OH}{\overset{|}{\underset{|}{CH}}}}CHCH_3$$

3-Methyl-2-butanol

$ClCH_2CH_2OH$

2-Chloroethanol

$$CH_3\underset{\displaystyle OH}{\overset{|}{CH}}CH=CH_2$$

3-Buten-2-ol

11.4 Physical properties

The compounds we have studied so far, the various hydrocarbons, have the physical properties that we might expect of such non-polar compounds: the relatively low melting points and boiling points that are characteristic of substances with weak intermolecular forces; solubility in non-polar solvents and insolubility in polar solvents like water. We shall find alcohols to be considerably different from hydrocarbons because of the presence in alcohol molecules of the very polar —OH group, and in particular because this polar group contains hydrogen.

Physical constants of a number of alcohols are listed in Table 11.1.

A striking difference between alcohols and hydrocarbons is the miscibility of the lower alcohols with water. Because of the polar —OH group, alcohols are held together by very much the same sort of intermolecular forces as those holding together water molecules. As a result there can be mixing of the two kinds of molecules, the energy required to break apart two water molecules or two alcohol molecules being supplied by formation of a similar bond between a water molecule and an alcohol molecule.

TABLE 11.1

ALCOHOLS

Name	Formula	M.p., °C	B.p., °C	Density at 20°C	Solub., g/100g H_2O
Methyl	CH_3OH	− 97	64.5	0.793	∞
Ethyl	CH_3CH_2OH	−115	78.3	.789	∞
n-Propyl	$CH_3CH_2CH_2OH$	−126	97	.804	∞
n-Butyl	$CH_3(CH_2)_2CH_2OH$	− 90	118	.810	7.9
n-Pentyl	$CH_3(CH_2)_3CH_2OH$	− 78.5	138	.817	2.3
n-Hexyl	$CH_3(CH_2)_4CH_2OH$	− 52	156.5	.819	0.6
n-Heptyl	$CH_3(CH_2)_5CH_2OH$	− 34	176	.822	0.2
n-Octyl	$CH_3(CH_2)_6CH_2OH$	− 15	195	.825	0.05
n-Decyl	$CH_3(CH_2)_8CH_2OH$	6	228	.829	
n-Dodecyl (Lauryl)	$CH_3(CH_2)_{10}CH_2OH$	24			
n-Tetradecyl (Myristyl)	$CH_3(CH_2)_{12}CH_2OH$	38			
n-Hexadecyl (Cetyl)	$CH_3(CH_2)_{14}CH_2OH$	49			
n-Octadecyl	$CH_3(CH_2)_{16}CH_2OH$	58.5			
Isopropyl	$CH_3CHOHCH_3$	− 86	82.5	.789	∞
Isobutyl	$(CH_3)_2CHCH_2OH$	−108	108	.802	10.0
sec-Butyl	$CH_3CH_2CHOHCH_3$	−114	99.5	.806	12.5
tert-Butyl	$(CH_3)_3COH$	25.5	83	.789	∞
Isopentyl	$(CH_3)_2CHCH_2CH_2OH$	−117	132	.813	2
active-Amyl [(-)-2-Methyl-1-butanol]	$CH_3CH_2CH(CH_3)CH_2OH$		128	.816	3.6
tert-Pentyl	$CH_3CH_2C(OH)(CH_3)_2$	− 12	102	.809	12.5
Cyclopentanol	cyclo-C_5H_9OH		140	.949	
Cyclohexanol	cyclo-$C_6H_{11}OH$	24	161.5	.962	
Allyl	$CH_2=CHCH_2OH$	−129	97	.855	∞
Crotyl	$CH_3CH=CHCH_2OH$		118	.853	16.6
Methylvinyl-carbinol	$CH_2=CHCHOHCH_3$		97		
Benzyl	$C_6H_5CH_2OH$	− 15	205	1.046	4
α-Phenylethyl	$C_6H_5CHOHCH_3$		205	1.013	
β-Phenylethyl	$C_6H_5CH_2CH_2OH$	− 27	221	1.02	1.6
Diphenylcarbinol (Benzhydrol)	$(C_6H_5)_2CHOH$	69	298		0.05
Triphenylcarbinol	$(C_6H_5)_3COH$	162.5			
Cinnamyl	$C_6H_5CH=CHCH_2OH$	33	257.5		

This is true, however, only for the lower alcohols, where the —OH group constitutes a large portion of the molecule. A long aliphatic chain with a small —OH group at one end is mostly alkane, and its physical properties reflect this. The change in solubility with carbon number is a gradual one: the first three primary alcohols are miscible with water; n-butyl alcohol is soluble to the extent of 8 g per 100 g water; n-pentyl, 2 g; n-hexyl, 1 g; and the higher alcohols still less. For practical purposes we consider that the borderline between solubility and insolubility in water occurs at about 4 to 5 carbon atoms for normal primary alcohols.

The boiling points show the usual increase with increasing carbon number, and the usual decrease with branching. The unusual thing about the boiling points of alcohols is that they are so much higher than those of the corresponding hydrocarbons.

11.5 Hydrogen bonding. Association

Among hydrocarbons the factors that determine boiling point seem to be chiefly molecular weight and shape; this is reasonable for molecules that are held together chiefly by van der Waals forces (Sec. 3.12).

In Table 11.2 are compared the boiling points of a number of compounds with about the same molecular weight but with different structures. We see that ethyl ether, which differs from n-pentane by having an oxygen (weight 16) instead of a —CH_2— (weight 14) in the middle of the chain, has practically the same boiling point as n-pentane. The isomeric n-butyl alcohol, on the other hand, has a boiling point more than 80 degrees higher. It is this large difference in boiling point that we must account for.

TABLE 11.2

STRUCTURE AND BOILING POINT

Name	Structure	Mol. Wt.	Dipole Moment, D	B.p., °C
n-Pentane	$CH_3CH_2CH_2CH_2CH_3$	72	0	36
Ethyl ether	CH_3CH_2—O—CH_2CH_3	74	1.18	35
n-Propyl chloride	$CH_3CH_2CH_2Cl$	79	2.10	47
n-Butyraldehyde	$CH_3CH_2CH_2CHO$	72	2.72	76
n-Butyl alcohol	$CH_3CH_2CH_2CH_2OH$	74	1.63	118

Alcohols contain the strongly polar —OH group, and we might first consider that the difference in boiling point is due to the greater polarity of the alcohol molecule. This is undoubtedly a factor. The dipole moment of n-butyl alcohol (1.63) is larger than that of the ether (1.18) and much larger than the zero moment for n-pentane. The stronger intermolecular forces arising from dipole–dipole attractions are overcome, and boiling occurs, only at higher temperatures.

Examination of the other compounds in Table 11.2, however, suggests that some *additional* factor is involved, and that in some way —OH is a special sort of group. Both n-butyraldehyde, which contains the C=O group, and n-propyl chloride have much higher dipole moments than n-butyl alcohol, and yet both have much lower boiling points. The effect of the —OH group seems too large to be accounted for by a simple increase in polarity.

To help us understand this problem, let us turn for a moment to inorganic chemistry and examine the boiling points of a number of hydrogen

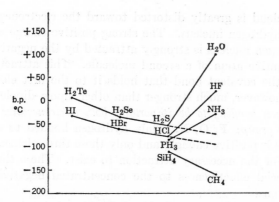

FIGURE 11.1. Boiling points of hydrides vs. molecular weight. Effect of hydrogen bonding on boiling point.

compounds (Figure 11.1). In general, we see that within a family of the Periodic Table a decrease in molecular weight is accompanied by a decrease in boiling point. There are three important exceptions to this rule: HF, H_2O, and NH_3. The boiling point decreases as we proceed from HI to HBr to HCl; at HF (which we might have expected to boil at about $-100°$) it jumps to $+19°$. Although the lightest, HF has by far the highest boiling point. In the next two families there are similar jumps in boiling point at H_2O and NH_3. In the fourth family, however, we find no jump: CH_4 (the lighter compound) boils lower than SiH_4. Just three compounds in Figure 11.1, HF, H_2O, and NH_3, fall out of line and have abnormally high boiling points.

To account for these "abnormalities," and on the basis of evidence of many kinds, **hydrogen bonding** has been proposed: *a hydrogen atom serves as a bridge between two electronegative atoms, holding one by a covalent bond and the other by purely electrostatic forces.* This electrostatic bond has a strength of about 5 kcal/mole (compared with 50–100 kcal/mole for most covalent bonds). Liquids whose molecules are held together by hydrogen bonds are called *associated liquids;* their abnormally high boiling points are due to the greater energy required to break the hydrogen bonds. Hydrogen bonding is generally indicated in formulas by a broken line:

$$H\!-\!F\,-\,-\,H\!-\!F \qquad \underset{\underset{H}{\mid}}{H}\!-\!O\,-\,-\,H\!-\!\underset{\underset{H}{\mid}}{O} \qquad \underset{\underset{H}{\mid}}{\overset{\overset{H}{\mid}}{H}}\!-\!N\,-\,-\,H\!-\!\underset{\underset{H}{\mid}}{\overset{\overset{H}{\mid}}{N}}$$

$$\underset{\underset{H}{\mid}}{\overset{\overset{H}{\mid}}{H}}\!-\!N\,-\,-\,H\!-\!\underset{\underset{H}{\mid}}{O} \qquad \underset{\underset{H}{\mid}}{\overset{\overset{R}{\mid}}{R}}\!-\!O\,-\,-\,H\!-\!\underset{\underset{H}{\mid}}{O} \qquad R\!-\!O\,-\,-\,H\!-\!\underset{\underset{H}{\mid}}{O}$$

Hydrogen bonding is simply an especially strong kind of *dipole–dipole* attraction. When hydrogen is attached to a highly electronegative atom the electron cloud is greatly distorted toward the electronegative atom, exposing the hydrogen nucleus. The strong positive charge of the thinly shielded hydrogen nucleus is strongly attracted by the negative charge of the electronegative atom of a second molecule. This attraction is much weaker than the covalent bond that holds it to the first electronegative atom. It is, however, much stronger than other dipole–dipole attractions.

For hydrogen bonding to be important, both electronegative atoms must come from the group: **F, O, N**. Only hydrogen bonded to one of these three elements is positive enough, and only these three elements are negative enough, for the necessary attraction to exist. These three elements owe their special effectiveness to the concentrated negative charge on their small atoms.

Like water, alcohols are associated liquids, their abnormal boiling points arising from hydrogen bonding. Although ethers and aldehydes contain oxygen, they contain hydrogen that is bonded only to carbon; these hydrogens are not positive enough to bond appreciably with oxygen. The solubility of the lower alcohols in water is due to the hydrogen bond that can exist between a molecule of water and a molecule of alcohol, as well as between two molecules of alcohol or between two molecules of water.

Problem 11.1 It has been suggested that there is weak hydrogen bonding: (a) between chloroform molecules; (b) between HCN molecules. Is this reasonable? (*Hint:* see Sec. 6.9.)

11.6 Industrial source

If an organic chemist were allowed to choose ten aliphatic compounds with which to be stranded on a desert island, he would almost certainly pick alcohols. From them he could make nearly every other kind of aliphatic compound: alkenes, alkyl halides, ethers, aldehydes, ketones, acids, esters, and a host of others. From the alkyl halides he could make Grignard reagents, and from the reaction between these and the aldehydes and ketones obtain more complicated alcohols, and so on. Our stranded chemist would use his alcohols not only as raw materials but frequently as the solvents in which reactions are carried out and from which products are recrystallized.

For alcohols to be such important starting materials in aliphatic chemistry, they must be not only versatile in their reactions but also available in large amounts and at low prices. There are two principal ways to get the simple alcohols that are the backbone of aliphatic organic synthesis: by **hydration of alkenes** obtained from the cracking of petroleum, and by **fermentation of carbohydrates**. In addition to these two chief methods, there are some others that have more limited application.

(a) **Hydration of alkenes.** We have already seen (Sec. 3.30) that alkenes containing up to four or five carbon atoms can be separated from the mixture obtained from the cracking of petroleum. We have also seen (Secs. 5.8 and 5.9) that alkenes are readily converted into alcohols either by direct addition of water, or by addition of sulfuric acid followed by hy-

$$CH_2=CH_2 + H_2SO_4 \longrightarrow CH_3CH_2OSO_3H \xrightarrow{\ H_2O\ } CH_3CH_2OH$$

Ethyl alcohol   (1°)

$$CH_3-CH=CH_2 + H_2SO_4 \longrightarrow CH_3-\underset{\underset{OSO_3H}{|}}{CH}-CH_3 \xrightarrow{\ H_2O\ } CH_3-\underset{\underset{OH}{|}}{CH}-CH_3$$

Isopropyl alcohol (2°)

$$CH_3CH_2CH=CH_2 + H_2SO_4 \longrightarrow CH_3CH_2-\underset{\underset{OSO_3H}{|}}{CH}-CH_3 \xrightarrow{\ H_2O\ } CH_3CH_2-\underset{\underset{OH}{|}}{CH}-CH_3$$

sec-Butyl alcohol (2°)

$$CH_3-\underset{\underset{CH_3}{|}}{\overset{\overset{CH_3}{|}}{C}}=CH_2 + H_2O \xrightarrow{\ H^+\ } CH_3-\underset{\underset{+OH_2}{|}}{\overset{\overset{CH_3}{|}}{C}}-CH_3 \xrightarrow{\ -H^+\ } CH_3-\underset{\underset{OH}{|}}{\overset{\overset{CH_3}{|}}{C}}-CH_3$$

tert-Butyl alcohol (3°)

drolysis. By this process there can be obtained only those alcohols whose formation is consistent with the application of Markovnikov's rule: for example, isopropyl but not n-propyl, sec-butyl but not n-butyl, tert-butyl but not isobutyl. Thus the *only* primary alcohol obtainable in this way is ethyl alcohol.

(b) **Fermentation of carbohydrates.** Fermentation of sugars by yeast, the oldest synthetic chemical process used by man, is still of enormous importance for the preparation of **ethyl alcohol** and certain other alcohols. The sugars come from a variety of sources, mostly molasses from sugar cane or starch obtained from various grains; the name "grain alcohol" has been given to ethyl alcohol for this reason. In addition to ethyl alcohol there is obtained a smaller amount of a substance known as *fusel oil*, a mixture of primary alcohols: mostly isopentyl alcohol with smaller amounts of n-propyl alcohol, isobutyl alcohol, and 2-methyl-1-butanol, known as *active amyl alcohol* (*amyl = pentyl*).

Much newer is the *Weizmann process* for the bacterial fermentation of starch, which yields a mixture consisting of n-butyl alcohol (60%), ethyl alcohol (10%), and acetone (30%), CH_3COCH_3. Discovered at the time of World War I by Chaim Weizmann (then at the University of Manchester, and at his death in 1952 the first President of Israel), this process was first important as a source of acetone, needed in the manufacture of smokeless powder; the butyl alcohol was considered a by-product and was simply stockpiled. After the war, the development of lacquers for the rapidly expanding automobile industry made butyl alcohol the more valuable product, and in a sense acetone became the by-product. Now both are important.

(c) **Hydrolysis of alkyl halides.** A mixture of five isomeric pentyl alcohols (known as Pentasol) is obtained by the chlorination of a mixture of n-pentane and isopentane and hydrolysis of the resulting mixture of isomeric chloropentanes (see Sec. 11.10 and Sec. 13.6). For many purposes, e.g., use as a solvent, a mixture of compounds may be just as suitable as a single pure compound; this mixture of alcohols is frequently used as such. Pure 1-pentanol, the highest boiling isomer, can be separated from the mixture by distillation.

(d) **Synthesis of methanol.** As is very often the case for the smallest member of a family, methanol is prepared quite differently from the others: from simple inorganic compounds. At 350–400°, and in the presence of certain metallic oxides, carbon monoxide and hydrogen react to yield methanol.

$$CO + 2H_2 \xrightarrow{\text{Cr}_2\text{O}_3 + \text{ZnO, 350–400°, 3000 lb/in.}^2} CH_3OH$$
$$\text{Methanol}$$

Methanol is poisonous: drinking it, breathing it for prolonged periods, or allowing it to remain long on the skin can lead to blindness or death.

Problem 11.2 (a) By what familiar process can a mixture of carbon monoxide and hydrogen be obtained? (b) What is ultimately the source of methanol?

(e) **Aldol condensation.** The methods just outlined yield comparatively simple alcohols. More complicated alcohols are prepared on an industrial scale from aldehydes and ketones by what is essentially an aldol condensation; this method, which is also used in the laboratory, is discussed later (Sec. 23.17).

(f) **Oxo process.** Addition of carbon monoxide and hydrogen to alkenes (*hydroformylation*) in the presence of a catalyst yields aldehydes and ketones, which can be reduced to alcohols. This is the *Oxo process*, initially developed in Germany, and of growing importance in the chemical industry. For example:

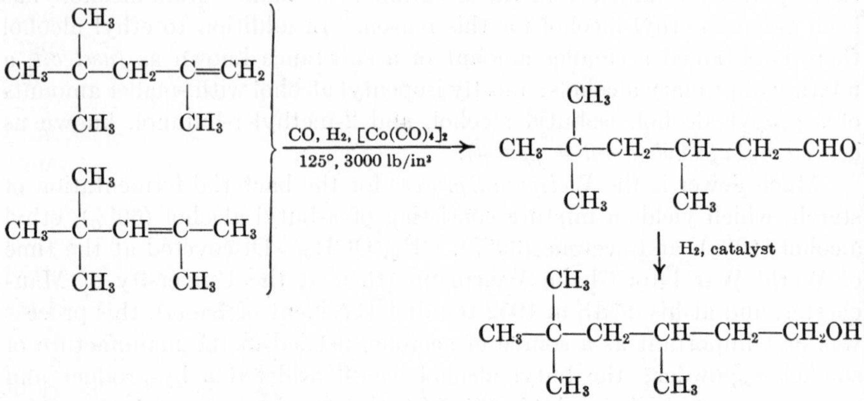

11.7 Ethyl alcohol

Ethyl alcohol is not only the oldest synthetic organic chemical used by man, but also one of the most important.

In industry ethyl alcohol is widely used as a solvent for lacquers, varnishes, perfumes, and flavorings; as a medium for chemical reactions; and in recrystallizations. In addition it is an important raw material for synthesis; after we have learned more about the reactions of alcohols

(Chapter 12) we can better appreciate the role played by the leading member of the family. For these industrial purposes ethyl alcohol is prepared both by hydration of ethylene and by fermentation of sugar from molasses (or sometimes starch); thus its ultimate source is petroleum, sugar cane, and various grains.

Ethyl alcohol is the alcohol of "alcoholic" beverages. For this purpose it is prepared by fermentation of sugar from a truly amazing variety of vegetable sources. The particular beverage obtained depends upon what is fermented (rye or corn, grapes or elderberries, cactus pulp or dandelions), how it is fermented (whether carbon dioxide is allowed to escape or is bottled up, for example), and what is done after fermentation (whether or not it is distilled). The special flavor of a beverage is not due to the ethyl alcohol but to other substances either characteristic of the particular source, or deliberately added.

Medically, ethyl alcohol is classified as an *hypnotic* (sleep producer); it is less toxic than other alcohols.

Because of its unique position as both a highly taxed beverage and an important industrial chemical, ethyl alcohol poses a special problem: it must be made available to the chemical industry in a form that is unfit to drink. This problem is solved by addition of a **denaturant,** a substance that makes it unpalatable or even poisonous. Two of the eighty-odd legal denaturants, for example, are methanol and aviation gasoline. When necessary, pure undenatured ethyl alcohol is available for chemical purposes, but its use is strictly controlled by the federal government.

11.8   95% alcohol: an azeotrope

Except for alcoholic beverages, nearly all the ethyl alcohol used is a mixture of 95% alcohol and 5% water, known simply as **95% alcohol.** Although pure alcohol (known as *absolute alcohol*) is available, it is much more expensive and is used only when definitely required.

What is so special about the concentration of 95%? Whatever the method of preparation, ethyl alcohol is obtained first mixed with water; this mixture is then concentrated by fractional distillation. As in any distillation, the first material to distill is the one of highest volatility, that is, of lowest boiling point. In a mixture of ethyl alcohol and water the lowest boiling component is not water (b.p. 100°) or ethyl alcohol (b.p. 78.3°) but a mixture of 95% alcohol and 5% water (b.p. 78.15°). If an efficient fractionating column is used, there is obtained first 95% alcohol, then a small intermediate fraction of lower concentration, and then water. But no matter how efficient the fractionating column used, 95% alcohol cannot be further concentrated.

As we know, separation of a mixture by distillation occurs because the vapor has a different composition from the liquid from which it distills, the vapor being richer in the more volatile component. We cannot separate 95% alcohol into its components by distillation because here the vapor has exactly the same composition as the liquid; toward distillation, then, 95% alcohol behaves exactly like a pure compound.

A liquid mixture that has the peculiar property of giving a vapor of the same composition is called an **azeotrope** *or a* **constant-boiling mixture.** Since it contains two components 95% alcohol is a *binary* azeotrope.

Most azeotropes, like 95% alcohol, have boiling points lower than those of their components, and are known as *minimum-boiling mixtures;* azeotropes having boiling points higher than those of their components are known as *maximum-boiling mixtures.*

11.9   Absolute alcohol

If 95% alcohol cannot be further concentrated by distillation, where does the commercially available 100% ethyl alcohol known as **absolute alcohol** come from? It is obtained by taking advantage of the existence of another azeotrope, this time a three-component one (*ternary* azeotrope). A mixture of 7.5% water, 18.5% ethyl alcohol, and 74% benzene forms an azeotrope of b.p. 64.9° (a minimum-boiling mixture).

Let us see what happens if we distill a mixture containing, say, 150 g of 95% alcohol (142.5 g of alcohol and 7.5 g H_2O) and 74 g of benzene. The first material to distill is the ternary azeotrope; 100 g of it will distill, carrying over 7.5 g of water, 18.5 g of alcohol, and 74 g of benzene. Thus all the water and all the benzene, but only part of the alcohol, have been removed; 124 g of pure anhydrous alcohol is left behind. In actual practice a slight excess of benzene is added; this is removed, after the distillation of the ternary mixture, as a binary azeotrope with alcohol (b.p. 68.3°).

The case of ethyl alcohol illustrates the fact that, although they are sometimes nuisances, azeotropes can often be turned to practical advantage (see also Sec. 16.16).

For certain special purposes (Sec. 25.9, Sec. 26.4) even the slight trace of water found in commercial absolute alcohol must be removed. This can be accomplished by treatment of the alcohol with metallic magnesium; water is converted into insoluble $Mg(OH)_2$, from which the alcohol is then distilled.

11.10   Preparation of alcohols

Most of the simple alcohols and a few of the complicated ones are available from the industrial sources described in Sec. 11.6. Other alcohols must be prepared by one of the methods outlined below.

PREPARATION OF ALCOHOLS

1. Grignard synthesis

$$-\overset{|}{C}{=}O + RMgX \longrightarrow -\overset{|}{\underset{R}{C}}-OMgX \xrightarrow{\;H_2O\;} -\overset{|}{\underset{R}{C}}-OH + Mg^{++} + X^-$$

$$\underset{\text{Formaldehyde}}{\overset{\displaystyle H}{\underset{}{H-C=O}} + RMgX} \longrightarrow \underset{}{\overset{\displaystyle H}{\underset{R}{H-C-OMgX}}} \xrightarrow{H_2O} \underset{}{\overset{\displaystyle H}{\underset{R}{H-C-OH}}} \quad \text{1° alcohol}$$

$$\underset{\text{Other aldehydes}}{\overset{\displaystyle H}{\underset{}{R'-C=O}} + RMgX} \longrightarrow \underset{}{\overset{\displaystyle H}{\underset{R}{R'-C-OMgX}}} \xrightarrow{H_2O} \underset{}{\overset{\displaystyle H}{\underset{R}{R'-C-OH}}} \quad \text{2° alcohol}$$

$$\underset{\text{Ketones}}{\overset{\displaystyle R''}{\underset{}{R'-C=O}} + RMgX} \longrightarrow \underset{}{\overset{\displaystyle R''}{\underset{R}{R'-C-OMgX}}} \xrightarrow{H_2O} \underset{}{\overset{\displaystyle R''}{\underset{R}{R'-C-OH}}} \quad \text{3° alcohol}$$

2. Hydrolysis of alkyl halides

$$R-X + OH^- \text{ (or } H_2O) \longrightarrow R-OH + X^- \text{ (or } HX)$$

Examples:

$$\underset{\text{n-Propyl bromide}}{CH_3CH_2CH_2Br} \xrightarrow{\text{aqueous NaOH}} \underset{\text{n-Propyl alcohol}}{CH_3CH_2CH_2OH}$$

$$\underset{\text{Benzyl chloride}}{\langle \bigcirc \rangle CH_2Cl} \xrightarrow{\text{aqueous NaOH}} \underset{\text{Benzyl alcohol}}{\langle \bigcirc \rangle CH_2OH}$$

$$\underset{\text{\textit{tert}-Butyl chloride}}{\overset{\displaystyle CH_3}{\underset{Cl}{CH_3-C-CH_3}}} \xrightarrow{H_2O} \underset{\text{\textit{tert}-Butyl alcohol}}{\overset{\displaystyle CH_3}{\underset{OH}{CH_3-C-CH_3}}} \quad (+ \text{ much } \underset{\text{Isobutylene}}{\overset{\displaystyle CH_3}{CH_3-C=CH_2}})$$

3. Aldol condensation. Discussed in Sec. 23.17.

4. Reduction of carbonyl compounds. Discussed in Sec. 23.9.

By far the most important of these methods is the **Grignard synthesis.** In the laboratory a chemist is chiefly concerned with preparing the more complicated alcohols that he cannot buy; these are readily prepared by the Grignard synthesis from rather simple starting materials. The alkyl halides from which the Grignard reagents are made, as well as the aldehydes and ketones themselves, are most conveniently prepared from alcohols; thus the method ultimately involves the synthesis of alcohols from less complicated alcohols.

Hydrolysis of alkyl halides is severely limited as a method of synthesizing alcohols, since alcohols are usually more available than the corresponding halides; indeed, the best general preparation of halides is from alcohols. The synthesis of benzyl alcohol from toluene, however, is an example of a useful application of this method.

CH₃   CH₂Cl   CH₂OH

         $\xrightarrow{\text{Cl}_2, \text{ heat, light}}$ $\xrightarrow{\text{aqueous NaOH}}$

Toluene   Benzyl chloride   Benzyl alcohol

For those halides that can undergo elimination, the formation of alkene must always be considered a possible side reaction. Selection of solvent permits some control, *aqueous* base favoring substitution, and *alcoholic* base favoring elimination. Tertiary alkyl halides, and to a lesser extent secondary alkyl halides, are so prone to dehydrohalogenation, however, that they may yield much — or even mostly — alkene even when aqueous base is used. For these halides simple hydrolysis with water is best, although even here considerable alkene is obtained. This competition between substitution and elimination has already been encountered (Sec. 6.11), and will be discussed in more detail later (Sec. 13.17).

11.11   Grignard synthesis of alcohols

The Grignard reagent, we should recall, has the formula RMgX, and is prepared by the reaction of metallic magnesium with the appropriate organic halide (Sec. 3.16). This halide can be alkyl (1°, 2°, 3°), allylic,

$$RX + Mg \xrightarrow{\text{anhydrous ether}} RMgX$$

A Grignard
reagent

aralkyl (e.g., benzyl), or aryl (phenyl or substituted phenyl). The halogen may be —Cl, —Br, or —I. (Arylmagnesium *chlorides* must be made in the cyclic ether tetrahydrofuran instead of ethyl ether.)

One of the most important uses of the Grignard reagent is its reaction with aldehydes and ketones to yield alcohols. Aldehydes and ketones have the general formulas:

       H   R
       | |
R—C=O   R—C=O

   An aldehyde   A ketone

The functional group of both is the **carbonyl group,** —C=O, and as we shall see later (Chapter 23) aldehydes and ketones resemble each other closely in most of their reactions. Like the carbon–carbon double bond, the carbonyl group is unsaturated, and like the carbon–carbon bond, it undergoes addition. One of its typical reactions is addition of the Grignard reagent.

Since the electrons of the carbonyl double bond hold together atoms of quite different electronegativity, we would not expect the electrons to be equally shared; in particular, the mobile π cloud should be pulled strongly toward the more electronegative atom, oxygen. Whatever the mechanism involved, addition of an unsymmetrical reagent is oriented so that the nucleophilic (basic) portion attaches itself to carbon, and the electrophilic (acidic) portion attaches itself to oxygen.

The carbon–magnesium bond of the Grignard reagent is a highly polar bond, carbon being negative relative to electropositive magnesium. It is not surprising, then, that in the addition to carbonyl compounds, the organic group becomes attached to carbon and magnesium to oxygen. The product is the magnesium salt of the weakly acidic alcohol and is

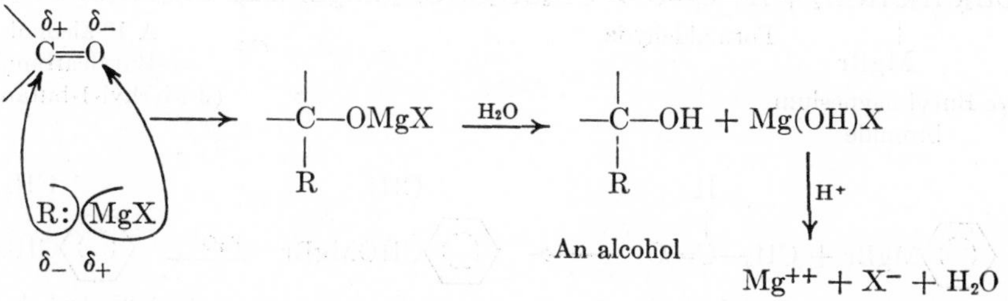

$$
\begin{array}{c}
\overset{\delta_+ \; \delta_-}{C=O} \\
\\
R: MgX \\
\delta_- \; \delta_+
\end{array}
\longrightarrow
\;
\underset{R}{-\overset{|}{\underset{|}{C}}-OMgX}
\;\xrightarrow{\;H_2O\;}\;
\underset{R}{-\overset{|}{\underset{|}{C}}-OH} + Mg(OH)X
$$

An alcohol

$$\downarrow H^+$$

$$Mg^{++} + X^- + H_2O$$

easily converted into the alcohol itself by the addition of the stronger acid, water. Since the $Mg(OH)X$ thus formed is a gelatinous material difficult to handle, dilute mineral acid (HCl, H_2SO_4) is commonly used instead of water, so that water-soluble magnesium salts are formed.

11.12 Products of the Grignard synthesis

The class of alcohol that is obtained from a Grignard synthesis depends upon the type of carbonyl compound used: *formaldehyde, HCHO, yields primary alcohols; other aldehydes, RCHO, yield secondary alcohols;* and *ketones, R_2CO, yield tertiary alcohols.*

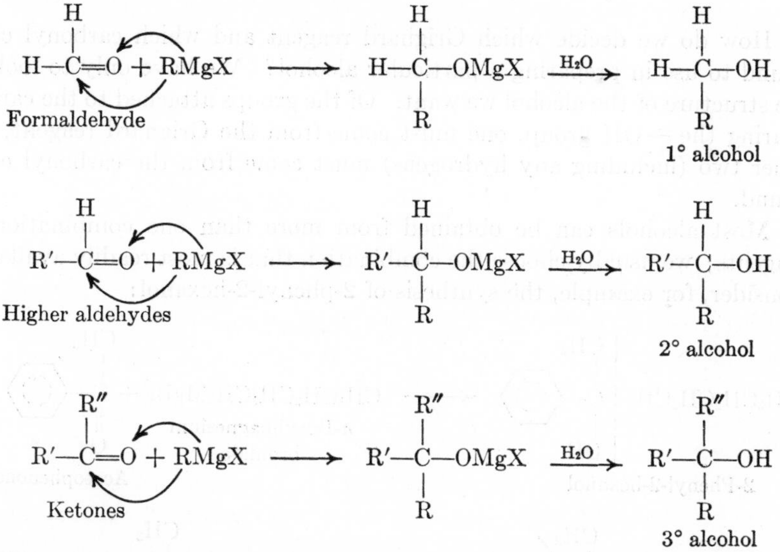

$$
\underset{\text{Formaldehyde}}{H-\overset{H}{\underset{}{C}}=O} + RMgX
\longrightarrow
\underset{R}{H-\overset{H}{\underset{|}{\overset{|}{C}}}-OMgX}
\xrightarrow{\;H_2O\;}
\underset{\substack{R \\ 1^\circ \text{ alcohol}}}{H-\overset{H}{\underset{|}{\overset{|}{C}}}-OH}
$$

$$
\underset{\text{Higher aldehydes}}{R'-\overset{H}{\underset{}{C}}=O} + RMgX
\longrightarrow
\underset{R}{R'-\overset{H}{\underset{|}{\overset{|}{C}}}-OMgX}
\xrightarrow{\;H_2O\;}
\underset{\substack{R \\ 2^\circ \text{ alcohol}}}{R'-\overset{H}{\underset{|}{\overset{|}{C}}}-OH}
$$

$$
\underset{\text{Ketones}}{R'-\overset{R''}{\underset{}{C}}=O} + RMgX
\longrightarrow
\underset{R}{R'-\overset{R''}{\underset{|}{\overset{|}{C}}}-OMgX}
\xrightarrow{\;H_2O\;}
\underset{\substack{R \\ 3^\circ \text{ alcohol}}}{R'-\overset{R''}{\underset{|}{\overset{|}{C}}}-OH}
$$

This relationship arises directly from our definitions of aldehydes and ketones, and our definitions of primary, secondary, and tertiary alcohols. The number of hydrogens attached to the carbonyl carbon defines the carbonyl compound as formaldehyde, higher aldehyde, or ketone. The carbonyl carbon is the one that finally bears the —OH group in the product; here the number of hydrogens defines the alcohol as primary, secondary, or tertiary. For example:

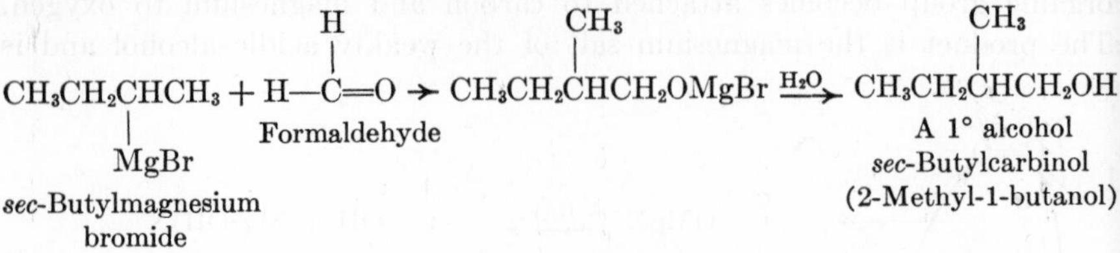

$$CH_3CH_2\overset{\underset{\displaystyle |}{H}}{\underset{\underset{\displaystyle \text{MgBr}}{\displaystyle |}}{C}}HCH_3 + H-\overset{\displaystyle H}{\underset{\displaystyle |}{C}}=O \rightarrow CH_3CH_2\overset{\displaystyle CH_3}{\underset{\displaystyle |}{C}}HCH_2OMgBr \xrightarrow{H_2O} CH_3CH_2\overset{\displaystyle CH_3}{\underset{\displaystyle |}{C}}HCH_2OH$$

sec-Butylmagnesium bromide   Formaldehyde   A 1° alcohol *sec*-Butylcarbinol (2-Methyl-1-butanol)

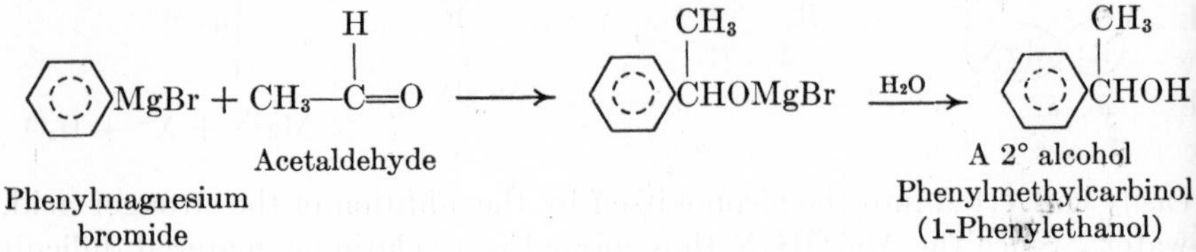

Phenylmagnesium bromide + Acetaldehyde → A 2° alcohol Phenylmethylcarbinol (1-Phenylethanol)

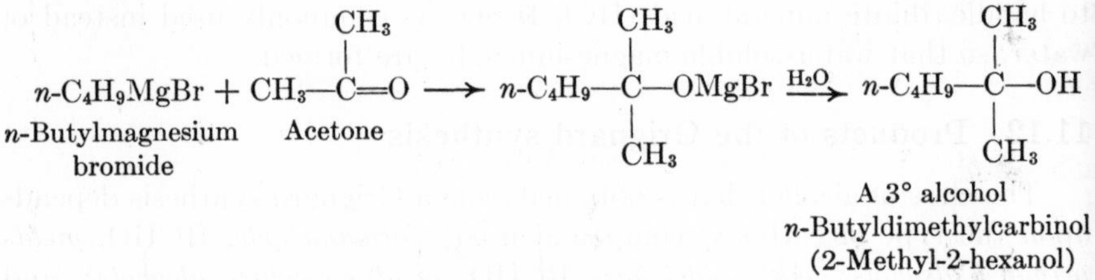

$$n\text{-}C_4H_9MgBr + CH_3-\overset{\displaystyle CH_3}{\underset{\displaystyle \|}{C}}=O \rightarrow n\text{-}C_4H_9-\overset{\overset{\displaystyle CH_3}{\displaystyle |}}{\underset{\underset{\displaystyle CH_3}{\displaystyle |}}{C}}-OMgBr \xrightarrow{H_2O} n\text{-}C_4H_9-\overset{\overset{\displaystyle CH_3}{\displaystyle |}}{\underset{\underset{\displaystyle CH_3}{\displaystyle |}}{C}}-OH$$

n-Butylmagnesium bromide   Acetone   A 3° alcohol *n*-Butyldimethylcarbinol (2-Methyl-2-hexanol)

11.13 Planning a Grignard synthesis

How do we decide which Grignard reagent and which carbonyl compound to use in preparing a particular alcohol? We have only to look at the structure of the alcohol we want. Of the groups attached to the carbon bearing the —OH group, one must come from the Grignard reagent, the other two (including any hydrogens) must come from the carbonyl compound.

Most alcohols can be obtained from more than one combination of reagents; we usually choose the combination that is most readily available. Consider, for example, the synthesis of 2-phenyl-2-hexanol:

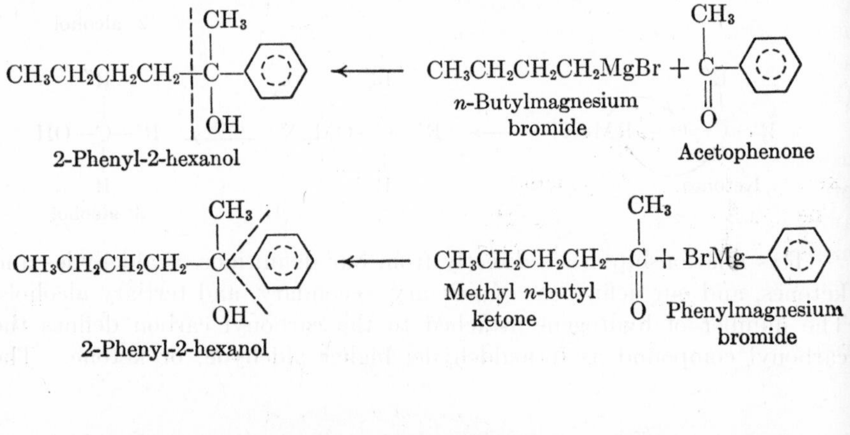

2-Phenyl-2-hexanol ← CH₃CH₂CH₂CH₂MgBr + Acetophenone
     n-Butylmagnesium bromide

2-Phenyl-2-hexanol ← Methyl *n*-butyl ketone + BrMg— Phenylmagnesium bromide

As shown, we could make this either from the four-carbon Grignard reagent and the aromatic ketone, or from the phenyl Grignard reagent and the six-carbon aliphatic ketone. As we shall know when we have studied aldehydes and ketones (Chapter 23), the first route uses the more readily available carbonyl compound and is the one actually used to make this alcohol.

11.14   Limitations of the Grignard synthesis

The very reactivity that makes a Grignard reagent so useful strictly limits how we may use it. We must keep this reactivity in mind when we plan the experimental conditions of the synthesis, when we select the halide that is to become the Grignard reagent, and when we select the compound with which it is to react.

In our first encounter with the Grignard reagent (Sec. 3.16) we allowed it to react with water to form an alkane; the stronger acid, water, displaced the extremely weak acid, the alkane, from its salt. In the same way, *any* compound containing hydrogen attached to an electronegative element — oxygen, nitrogen, sulfur, or even triply-bonded carbon — is acidic enough to decompose a Grignard reagent. A Grignard reagent reacts rapidly with oxygen and carbon dioxide, and with nearly every organic compound containing a carbon–oxygen or carbon–nitrogen multiple bond.

How does all this affect our reaction between a Grignard reagent and, say, an aldehyde? First of all, alkyl halide, aldehyde, and the ether used as solvent must be scrupulously dried and freed of the alcohol from which each was very probably made; a Grignard reagent will not even form in the presence of water. Our apparatus must be completely dry before we start. We must protect the reaction system from the water vapor, oxygen, and carbon dioxide of the air: water vapor can be kept out by use of calcium chloride tubes, and oxygen and carbon dioxide can be swept out of the system with dry nitrogen. Having done all this, we may hope to obtain a good yield of product — providing we have properly chosen the halide and the aldehyde.

We cannot prepare a Grignard reagent from a compound (e.g., $HOCH_2CH_2Br$) that contains, in addition to halogen, some group (e.g., —OH) that will react with a Grignard reagent; if this were tried, as fast as a molecule of Grignard reagent formed it would react with the active group (—OH) in another molecule to yield an undesired product ($HOCH_2CH_2$—H).

We must be particularly watchful in the preparation of an arylmagnesium halide, in view of the wide variety of substituents that might be present on the benzene ring. Carboxyl (—COOH), hydroxyl (—OH), amino (—NH_2), and —SO_3H all contain hydrogen attached to oxygen or nitrogen, and therefore are so acidic that they will decompose a Grignard reagent. We have just learned that a Grignard reagent adds to the carbonyl group (C=O), and we shall learn that it adds similarly to —COOR and —C≡N groups. The nitro (—NO_2) group oxidizes a Grignard rea-

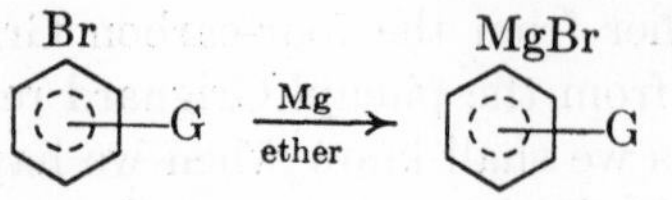

G *may not be:*

—COOH	—C=O
—OH	—COOR
—NH₂	—C≡N
—SO₃H	—NO₂

and many others

G *may be:*

—R	—OR
—Ar (aryl)	—Cl

gent. It turns out that only a comparatively few groups may be present in the halide molecule from which we prepare a Grignard reagent; among these are —R, —Ar, —OR, and —Cl (of an aryl chloride).

By the same token, the aldehyde (or other compound) with which a Grignard reagent is to react may not contain other groups that are reactive toward a Grignard reagent. For example, a Grignard reagent would be decomposed before it could add to the carbonyl group of:

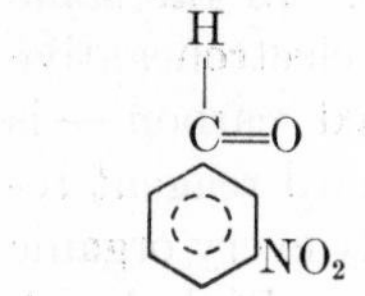

m-Nitrobenzaldehyde 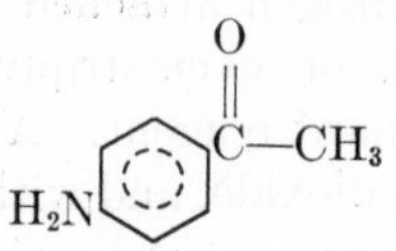   *p*-Aminoacetophenone 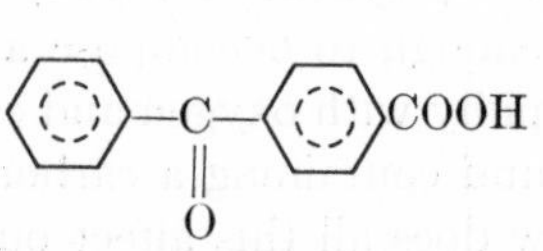   *p*-Benzoylbenzoic acid

These may seem like severe limitations, and they are. Nevertheless, the number of acceptable combinations is so great that the Grignard reagent is one of our most valuable synthetic tools. The kind of precautions described here must be taken in any kind of organic synthesis: we must not restrict our attention to the group we happen to be interested in, but must look for possible interference by other functional groups.

OPTICAL ISOMERISM

11.15 Optical activity.   Plane-polarized light

In our discussion of the fermentation of sugars (Sec. 11.6), we learned that one of the alcohols making up fusel oil is called *active amyl alcohol.* Just what kind of "activity" does 2-methyl-1-butanol possess that it should be given this name? The answer is **optical activity.** But to understand what this means we must first review a little of what we know about the properties of light.

Light possesses certain properties that are best understood by considering it to be a wave phenomenon in which the vibrations occur at right angles to the direction in which the light travels. There are an infinite number of planes passing through the line of propagation, and ordinary light is vibrating in all these planes. If we consider that we are looking directly into the beam of a flashlight, Figure 11.2 shows schematically the sort of vibrations that are taking place, all perpendicular to a

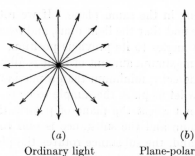

(a)   (b)
Ordinary light   Plane-polarized light

FIGURE 11.2. Schematic representation of (a) ordinary light and (b) plane-polarized light. Light traveling perpendicular to page; vibrations in plane of page.

line between our eye and the paper (flashlight). **Plane-polarized light** *is light whose vibrations take place in only one of these possible planes.* Ordinary light is turned into plane-polarized light by passing it through a lens made of the material known as Polaroid or more traditionally through pieces of calcite (a particular crystalline form of $CaCO_3$) so arranged as to constitute what is called a *Nicol prism*.

An **optically active substance** *is one that rotates the plane of polarized light.* When polarized light, vibrating in a certain plane, is passed through an optically active substance, it emerges vibrating in a different plane.

11.16   The polarimeter

How can this rotation of the plane of polarized light — this optical activity — be detected? It is both detected and measured by an instrument called the **polarimeter,** which is represented schematically in Figure

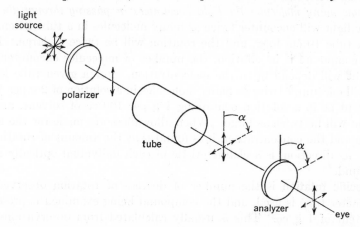

FIGURE 11.3. Schematic representation of a polarimeter. Solid lines: before rotation. Broken lines: after rotation. α is angle of rotation.

11.3. It consists of a light source, two lenses (Polaroid or Nicol), and between the lenses a tube to hold the substance that is being examined for optical activity. These are arranged so that the light passes through one of the lenses (*polarizer*), then the tube, then the second lens (*analyzer*), and finally reaches our eye. When the tube is empty we find that the maximum amount of light reaches our eye when the two lenses are so arranged that they pass light vibrating in the same plane. If we rotate the lens that is nearer our eye, say, we find that the light dims, and reaches a minimum when the lens is at right angles to its previous position.

Let us adjust the lenses so that a maximum amount of light is allowed to pass. (In practice, it is easier to detect a minimum than a maximum; the principle remains the same.) Now let us place the sample to be tested in the tube. If the substance does not affect the plane of polarization, light transmission is still at a maximum and the substance is said to be **optically inactive.** If, on the other hand, the substance rotates the plane of polarization, then the lens nearer our eye must be rotated to conform with this new plane if light transmission is again to be a maximum, and the substance is said to be **optically active.** If the rotation of the plane, and hence our rotation of the lens, is to the right (clockwise), the substance is **dextrorotatory** (Latin, *dexter*, right); if the rotation is to the left (counterclockwise), the substance is **levorotatory** (Latin, *laevus*, left).

We can determine not only that the substance has rotated the plane, and in which direction, but also *by how much.* The amount of rotation is simply the number of degrees that we must rotate the lens to conform with the light. The symbols + and − are used to indicate rotations to the right and to the left, respectively.

11.17 Specific rotation

Since optical rotation of the kind we are interested in is caused by individual molecules of the active compound, *the amount of rotation depends upon how many molecules the light encounters in passing through the tube.*

The light will encounter twice as many molecules in a tube 20 cm long as in a tube 10 cm long, and the rotation will be twice as large. If the active compound is in solution, the number of molecules encountered by the light will depend upon the concentration. For a given tube length, light will encounter twice as many molecules in a solution of 2 g per 100 cc of solvent as in a solution containing 1 g per 100 cc of solvent, and the rotation will be twice as large. When allowances are made for the length of tube and the concentration, it is found that the amount of rotation, as well as its direction, is a characteristic of each individual optically active compound.

Specific rotation is the number of degrees of rotation observed if a 1-decimeter tube is used, and the compound being examined is present to the extent of 1 g/cc. This is usually calculated from observations with tubes of other lengths and at different concentrations by means of the equation

$$[\alpha] = \frac{\alpha}{l \times d}$$

$$\text{specific rotation} = \frac{\text{observed rotation (degrees)}}{\text{length (dm)} \times \text{g/cc}}$$

where d represents density for a pure liquid or concentration for a solution.

The specific rotation is as much a property of a compound as its melting point, boiling point, density, or refractive index. Thus the specific rotation of the 2-methyl-1-butanol obtained from fusel oil, that is, *active amyl alcohol*, is

$$\left[\alpha\right]_D^{20} = -5.756°$$

Here 20 is the temperature and D is the wavelength of the light used in the measurement (*D* line of sodium, 5893 A).

11.18 Structure and optical activity

What kind of compounds rotate the plane of polarized light, that is, are optically active? In so far as chemical families are concerned, the answer is *all kinds:* alcohols, like active amyl, *sec*-butyl, α-phenylethyl; halides, like *sec*-butyl chloride; acids, like lactic acid, $CH_3CHOHCOOH$; even hydrocarbons, like *sec*-butylbenzene and 3-methylhexane.

These compounds differ widely in their chemical properties; what do they have in common that gives rise to optical activity? Just this: a molecule of any of these compounds is not superimposable on its mirror image.

A compound is **optically active** *if its molecules* **are not superimposable** *on their mirror images. A compound is* **optically inactive** *if its molecules* **are superimposable** *on their mirror images.*

When we say that a molecule and its mirror image are superimposable, we mean that if — in our mind's eye — we were to bring the image from behind the mirror where it seems to be, it could be made to coincide in all its parts with the molecule. That is, a molecule and its mirror image are **superimposable** if they (a) are identical or (b) can be *made* identical by rotation about single bonds.

Some molecules are superimposable on their mirror images, and other molecules are not. To predict optical activity or inactivity on this basis, we *must* consider that the mirror image of a molecule possesses the properties of an actual molecule, in particular, free rotation about single bonds.

Molecules that are not superimposable on their mirror images are said by chemists to be **asymmetric.** Defined in this way, an asymmetric compound is optically active and a non-asymmetric compound is optically inactive.

True geometric *asymmetry* (or *dissymmetry*) is not an adequate criterion for predicting optical activity or inactivity, since it is a property of rigid objects. Most molecules are not rigid, but change their shapes as their atoms rotate about bonds. In this book we shall use *asymmetry* to mean *non-superimposability on a mirror image*, with freedom of rotation about single bonds being understood.

We can tell whether a compound is asymmetric or not simply by examining its molecular structure. This is most safely done by use of molecular models, and is the way it should be done by every student when first dealing with the subject. There are also convenient ways of representing three-dimensional structures on paper or on the blackboard, which, used with caution and a full realization of what they stand for, enable us to predict optical activity.

11.19 Structure and optical isomerism

Let us make a model of an optically active compound, say, 2-methyl-1-butanol. To simplify the model we can let a single ball represent a group of atoms, using a different color for each different group. We might use yellow for —H, red for —CH$_2$OH, green for —CH$_3$, and blue for —C$_2$H$_5$, and then attach these four to a black ball which represents C–2 of the chain. Let us then imagine that we are holding this model before a mirror, and construct a second model of what its mirror image would look like. We now have two models which look something like this:

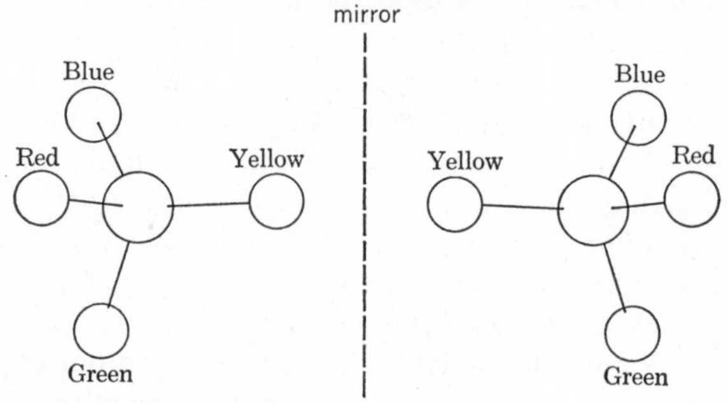

which are understood to stand for this:

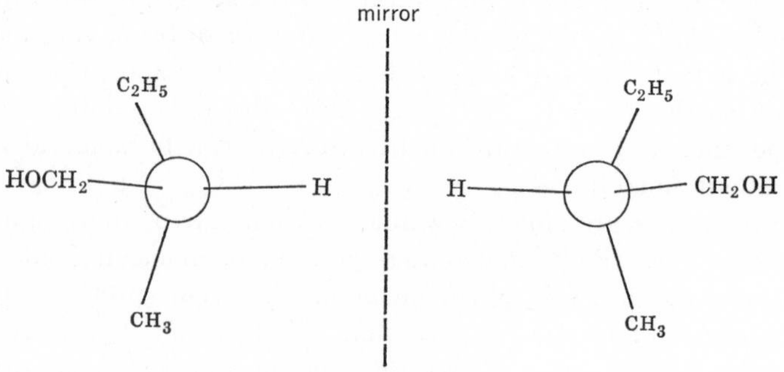

Not superimposable
2-Methyl-1-butanol

We have made a model of a molecule of 2-methyl-1-butanol, and a model of its mirror image; are they superimposable or not? If they are superimposable they can be made to coincide in all their parts by rotations about single bonds. We find that we cannot superimpose these two models. We may twist and turn them as much as we please (so long as no bonds are broken), but although two groups of each may coincide, the other two do not. Each model — and the molecule it represents — is not superimposable on its mirror image: 2-methyl-1-butanol is an asymmetric compound. It is its asymmetry that gives rise to its optical activity.

We have just made two models, each of which represents a molecule in which an —H, —CH$_3$, —CH$_2$OH, and —C$_2$H$_5$ are attached to a carbon atom; that is, each represents a molecule that we would call 2-methyl-

1-butanol. But the models are different, and therefore the molecules they represent must be different. Are there, then, *two* 2-methyl-1-butanols? The answer is *yes*. The asymmetry that gives rise to optical activity must necessarily give rise to **optical isomerism.**

Since optical isomers differ from one another *only* in the way the atoms are oriented in space (but are like one another with respect to which atoms are attached to which other atoms), they belong to the general class we have called *stereoisomers* (Sec. 4.5). *Geometric isomerism* and *optical isomerism* are thus two kinds of stereoisomerism.

11.20   Optical isomers: enantiomers

Isomers that are mirror images of each other are called **enantiomers.** The two different 2-methyl-1-butanols whose models we have made are enantiomers (Gr., *enantio–*, opposite). Each is said to be the enantiomer of the other. How do the properties of enantiomers compare?

Enantiomers have identical chemical properties except toward optically active reagents. The two 2-methyl-1-butanols not only form the same products — alkenes on dehydration, bromides on treatment with HBr, esters on treatment with acetic acid — but also form them at exactly the same rate. This is not surprising, since the atoms undergoing attack in each case are influenced in their reactivity by exactly the same combination of substituents. A reagent approaching either kind of molecule encounters the same environment, except, of course, that one environment is the mirror image of the other. Except for the special case of a reagent that is itself optically active, the influences exerted on the reagent are identical in the two cases.

Enantiomers have identical physical properties, except for the direction of rotation of the plane of polarized light. The two 2-methyl-1-butanols have identical melting points, boiling points, densities, refractive indices, and any other physical constant one might measure, except for this: one rotates plane-polarized light to the right, the other to the left. This again is quite reasonable since the interactions of both kinds of molecule with

	(+)-2-Methyl-1-butanol	(−)-2-Methyl-1-butanol (fermentation product)
Specific rotation	+5.756°	−5.756°
Boiling point	128.9°	128.9°
Density	0.8193	0.8193
Refractive index	1.4107	1.4107

their fellows should be the same. Only the *direction* of rotation is different; the *amount* of rotation is the same, the specific rotation of one being +5.756°, the other −5.756°. It is reasonable that these molecules, being so similar, can rotate light by the same amount.

When enantiomers are mixed together, the rotation caused by a molecule of one isomer is exactly canceled by an equal and opposite rotation caused by a molecule of its enantiomer. *A mixture of equal parts of enantiomers is called a* **racemate.** As we might expect, *a racemate is optically inactive.*

It is useful to compare a racemate with a compound whose molecules are superimposable on their mirror images, that is, with a non-asymmetric compound. They are both optically inactive; consideration shows that they are inactive for exactly the same reason.

The racemate is inactive because it contains equal amounts of enantiomers; because of the random distribution of the large number of molecules, for every molecule that the light encounters, there is another (isomeric) molecule, the mirror image of the first, aligned just right to cancel the effect of the first one.

What is the situation for a non-asymmetric compound? Any molecule of such a compound can serve as the mirror image of any other one; thus, again, for every molecule that the light encounters there is another (identical) molecule, the mirror image of the first, aligned just right to cancel the effect of the first one. The inactivity of a non-asymmetric compound is not a property, then, of the individual molecules, but rather of the random distribution of molecules that can serve as mirror images of each other.

For an optically active substance uncontaminated by its enantiomer, such cancellation of rotation cannot occur since no molecule can serve as the mirror image of another, no matter how random the distribution.

Problem 11.3 To confirm the statements of the three preceding paragraphs, make models of: (a) a pair of enantiomers, e.g., 2-methyl-1-butanol; (b) a pair of identical non-asymmetric molecules, e.g., 2-methylbutane; (c) a pair of identical asymmetric molecules, e.g., 2-methyl-1-butanol. (d) Which pairs are mirror images?

11.21 Prediction of optical activity. The asymmetric carbon atom

Examination of molecular models shows us quite clearly that a molecule of 2-methyl-1-butanol is not superimposable on its mirror image. This method can be used to predict the optical activity or inactivity of any compound whatsoever, so long as we consider the models of the molecule and its mirror image to have the properties of actual molecules with respect to free rotation about single bonds. It is the safest method since properly handled it must give us the right answer. It is the method that the student should use until he has become quite familiar with the ideas involved; even then, it is the method he should use when he encounters a new type of compound.

After considerable practice with models, it is possible to draw simple pictures representing the models, and to determine their asymmetry or non-asymmetry by attempting mentally to superimpose the pictures.

Let us examine the structures of some of the compounds that we have said are optically active:

| 2-Methyl-1-butanol | sec-Butyl alcohol | sec-Butyl chloride | sec-Butylbenzene |

We see that in every molecule there is a carbon (C*) that holds four different groups. *A carbon atom to which four different groups are attached is called an* **asymmetric carbon atom.**

Most — *but not all* — molecules that contain an asymmetric carbon are asymmetric. Most — *but not all* — asymmetric molecules contain an asymmetric carbon. There are compounds that contain asymmetric carbon atoms and yet are non-asymmetric (Sec. 24.5). There are asymmetric compounds that contain no asymmetric carbon atoms (Problem 11.4, page 327).

The presence or absence of an asymmetric carbon is no criterion of optical activity or inactivity. However, most of the asymmetric compounds that we shall take up do contain asymmetric carbon atoms, and it will be useful for us to look for such atoms; if we find an asymmetric carbon atom, then we should consider the *possibility* that the compound is asymmetric, and hence optically active. We shall later (Sec. 24.5) learn to recognize the kind of compound that may be non-asymmetric in spite of the presence of asymmetric carbon atoms; such compounds contain more than one asymmetric carbon atom.

Let us construct a model of *sec*-butyl alcohol, using a black ball for the asymmetric carbon atom, and attaching to it four balls of different colors to stand for each of the four groups, —H, —OH, —CH₃, —CH₂CH₃. We can draw the following picture to represent this model:

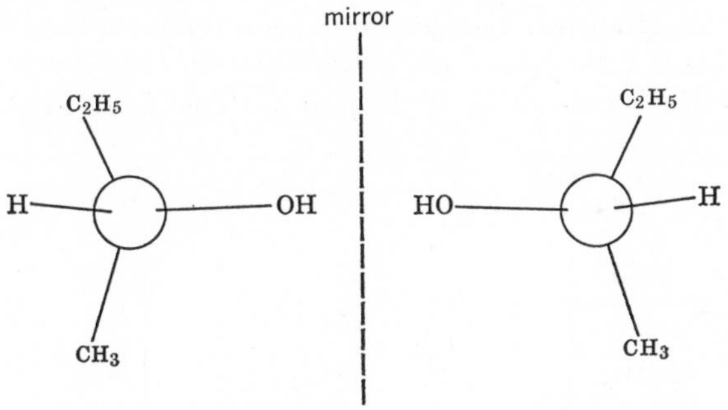

Not superimposable
sec-Butyl alcohol

Let us next construct a model that is the mirror image of this one (or draw the mirror image of our picture), and then see if the two are superimposable. In the same way we may examine *sec*-butyl chloride, where the four groups are —H, —Cl, —CH₃, and —CH₂CH₃, and *sec*-butylbenzene, where the groups are —H, —CH₃, —CH₂CH₃, and —C₆H₅. In each case we find that we cannot superimpose the models nor can we mentally superimpose the pictures of the models. There are two enantiomeric *sec*-butyl alcohols, two *sec*-butyl chlorides, and two *sec*-butylbenzenes, and each of these is optically active.

On the other hand, let us build (or draw) a model of a molecule like isopropyl alcohol and a model of its mirror image. No matter how we

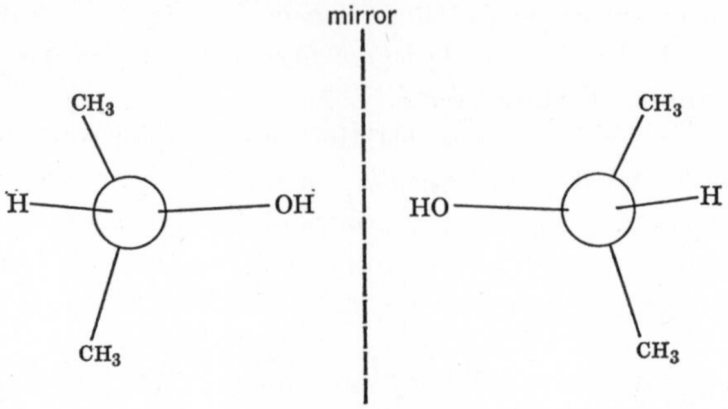

mirror

CH_3 H——OH   HO——H CH_3

CH_3 CH_3

Superimposable
Isopropyl alcohol

represent the structures, we find that simply sliding one over, or perhaps rotating it end for end, permits us to superimpose the two structures. There is only one isopropyl alcohol, and it is optically inactive.

After becoming familiar with the use of models and of pictures of models, the student can make use of even simpler representations, which can be drawn much faster. This is a more dangerous method, however, and must be used properly to give the right answers. We simply draw a cross and attach to the four ends the four groups that are attached to the asymmetric carbon atom. The asymmetric carbon atom is understood to be located where the lines cross. Chemists have agreed that such a diagram stands for a particular structure: *the horizontal lines represent bonds coming toward us out of the plane of the paper, whereas the vertical lines represent bonds going away from us behind the plane of the paper.* That is to say,

C_2H_5

H———OH   HO———H

CH_3 C_2H_5

CH_3

stands for

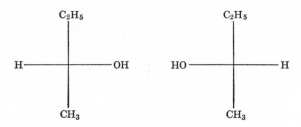

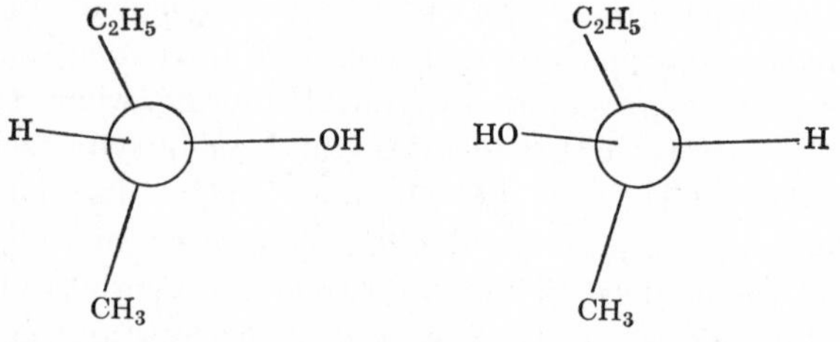

In testing the superimposability of two of these flat, two-dimensional representations of three-dimensional objects, we must obey certain rules. First, these representations should be used only for molecules that contain an asymmetric carbon atom. Second, in our mind's eye we may slide these formulas or rotate them end for end, *but we may not remove them from the plane of the paper.* Used with caution, this method of representation is convenient; it is not foolproof, however, and in doubtful cases models or pictures of models should be used.

Problem 11.4 Optically active isomers of each of the following compounds are known:

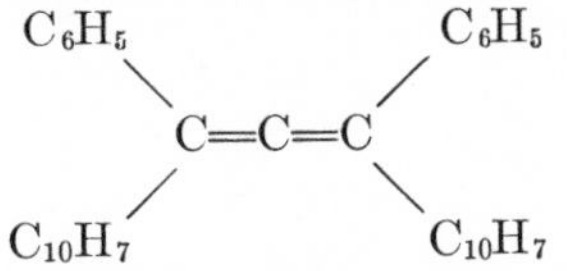

An allene

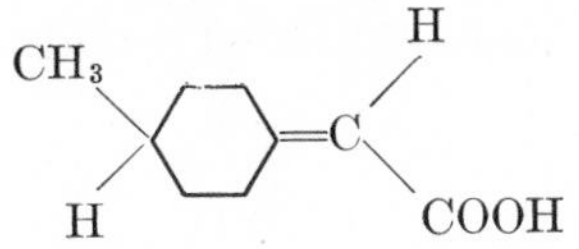

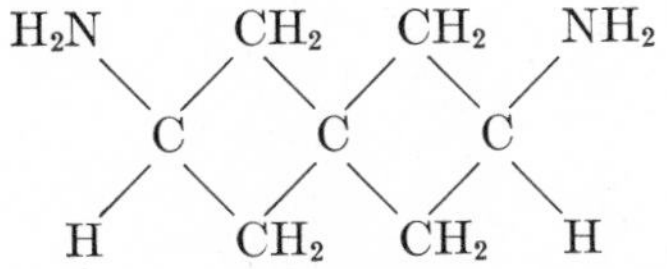

A spirane

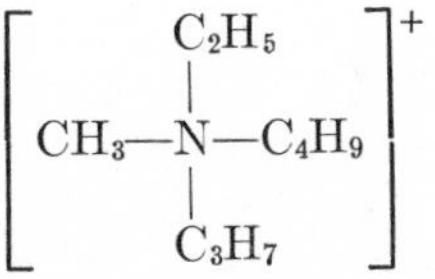

A substituted ammonium ion

(a) Using models, show that a molecule of each is not superimposable on its mirror image. (b) Which (if any) of these molecules contain an asymmetric atom?

Problem 11.5 (a) Make a model of conformation V of 1,2-dichloroethane (page 62), and a model of its mirror image. (b) As made, are these models identical? (c) Are they superimposable? (d) Would you predict optical activity for 1,2-dichloroethane?

Problem 11.6 (a) Make a model of a chair conformation of *cis*-1,2-cyclohexanediol (page 210), and a model of its mirror image. (b) As made, are these models identical? (c) Are they superimposable? (d) Would you predict optical activity for *cis*-1,2-cyclohexanediol? (e) Repeat (a)–(d) for *trans*-1,2-cyclohexanediol. (Check your answers in Sec. 24.5.)

11.22 Configuration: absolute and relative

We recall (Sec. 4.5) that *the arrangement of atoms that characterizes a particular stereoisomer is called its* **configuration.**

We have made two models to represent the two configurations of 2-methyl-1-butanol. We have seen that two isomeric 2-methyl-1-butanols are known; one isomer rotates the plane of polarized light to the right, the other isomer rotates it to the left. Now the question arises, which configuration does each isomer have? Does (−)-2-methyl-1-butanol — the isomer that is found in fusel oil — have configuration I or configuration II on the next page?

Until 1949, this question could not be answered for (−)-2-methyl-1-butanol, or, indeed, for any other optically active compound. But in that year J. M. Bijvoet — most fittingly Director of the van't Hoff Laboratory at the University of Utrecht (Sec. 2.23) — reported that, using x-ray diffraction, he had determined the actual arrangement in space of the atoms of an optically active compound, a salt of (+)-tartaric acid

(Sec. 27.6). Over the years prior to 1949, the relationships between the configuration of (+)-tartaric acid and the configurations of hundreds of optically active compounds had been worked out (by methods that we shall take up later, Secs. 15.8 and 27.5); when the configuration of (+)-tartaric acid became known, these other configurations, too, immediately became known. For example, it became known that (−)-2-methyl-1-butanol has configuration I; the (+)-isomer, therefore, has configuration II. Similarly the 2-methyl-1-chlorobutanes and the 2-methylbutanoic acids have configurations III and IV, and V and VI.

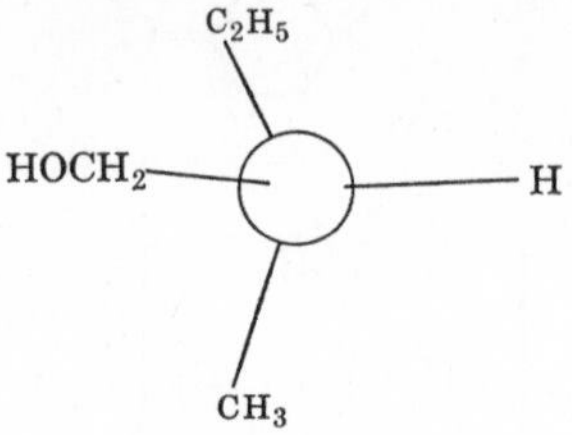

(−)-2-Methyl-1-butanol
I

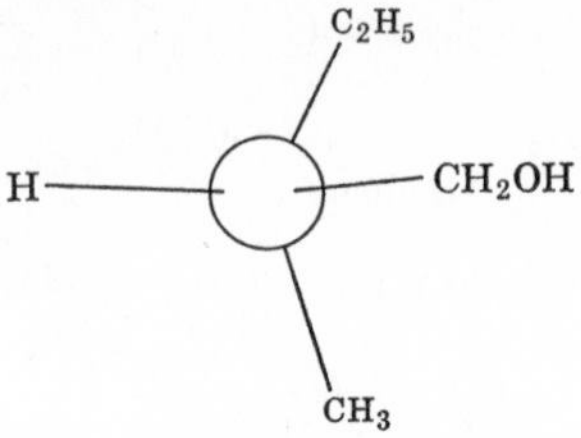

(+)-2-Methyl-1-butanol
II

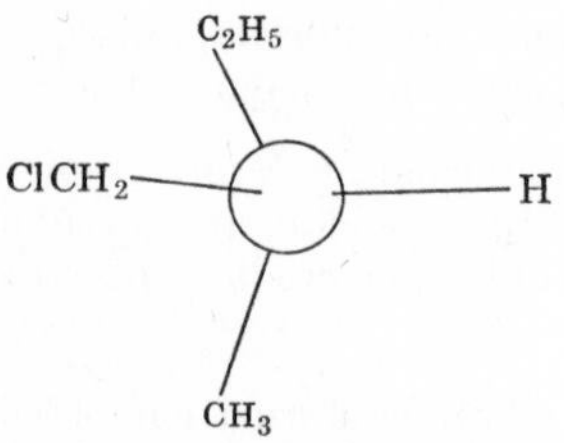

(+)-2-Methyl-1-chlorobutane
III

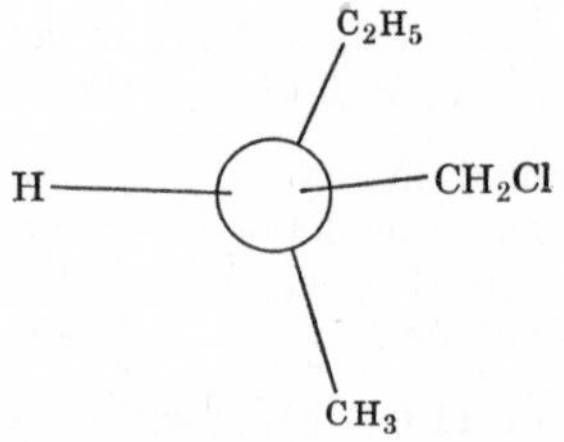

(−)-2-Methyl-1-chlorobutane
IV

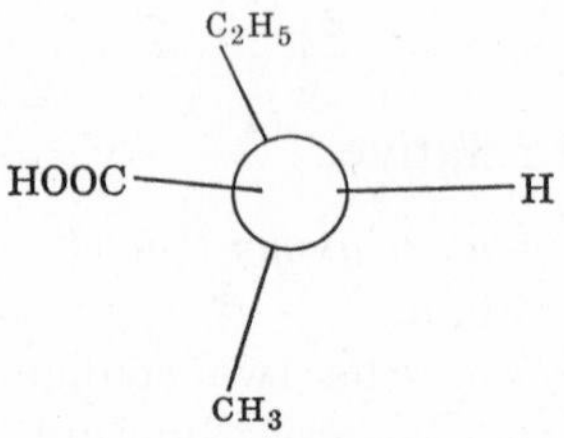

(+)-2-Methylbutanoic acid
V

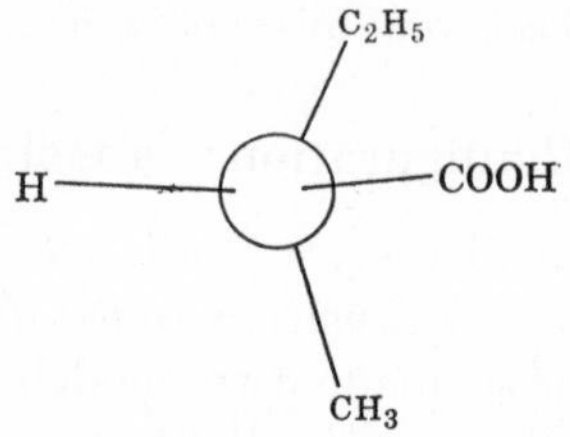

(−)-2-Methylbutanoic acid
VI

If we compare the structures of the alcohols and chlorides, we see that configuration III clearly resembles I more closely than it does II: the —CH_2Cl in the (+)-chloride occupies the same relative position as the —CH_2OH in the (−)-alcohol. We say, then, that (−)-2-methyl-1-butanol and (+)-2-methyl-1-chlorobutane have *similar* (or *same*) configurations; the (+)-chloride and (+)-alcohol have *opposite* configurations. In the same way, we see that the (+)-acid (V) is related configurationally to the (−)-alcohol. The (+)-alcohol, (−)-chloride, and (−)-acid (II, IV, VI) form another set of compounds with similar configurations.

As we shall find, we are more interested in knowing whether two compounds have similar configurations than whether they happen to rotate light in the same direction. The sign of rotation is important as a means of identifying a particular isomer — just as the melting point of a dibromobenzene tells us whether we have the *o*-, *m*-, or *p*-isomer — but the fact that two compounds have the same sign of rotation means little; they may or may not have similar configurations.

As we shall also find, we are more interested in knowing whether two compounds have similar configurations than in knowing what the actual configuration of either compound is. That is to say, we are more interested in *relative* configurations than in *absolute* configurations.

(Similarity of configuration among a set of compounds is often indicated by prefixing to their names the same letter: D for one set, L for the other. We shall discuss the use of these symbols later, Sec. 27.5.)

11.23 Synthesis and optical activity

A number of the compounds that we have just seen to be optically active are ones that we have encountered earlier. *sec*-Butyl chloride, for example, was one of the products of the chlorination of butane. *sec*-Butylbenzene was mentioned in the chapter on arenes (Chapter 9); we might have prepared it by the hydrogenation of 2-phenyl-2-butene. If we were to put the *sec*-butyl chloride or the *sec*-butylbenzene prepared in these ways into a polarimeter, would they rotate the plane of polarized

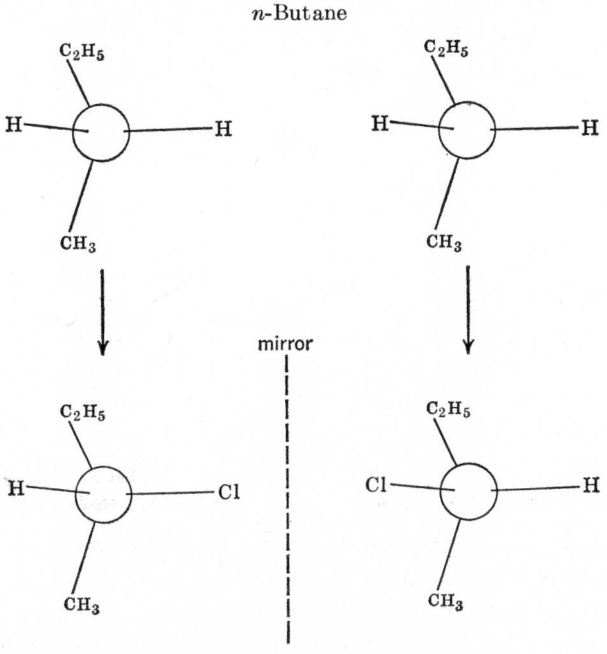

Enantiomers
racemic *sec*-Butyl chloride

light? The answer is *no*, because prepared as described each would consist of the racemate. The next question is, *why is a racemate formed?*

Let us consider first the preparation of *sec*-butyl chloride by the chlorination of *n*-butane. Since this involves the substitution of a chlorine atom for a hydrogen atom on C–2, we shall focus our attention on the attack at this carbon atom. Let us make models of two molecules of *n*-butane, using a black ball to represent C–2, two yellow ones to represent two hydrogens, and two balls of other colors to represent —CH$_3$ and —C$_2$H$_5$. Next, let us replace a different hydrogen atom in each of the models by chlorine. The *sec*-butyl chlorides thus obtained are mirror images that are not superimposable, and therefore are enantiomers. The particular enantiomer obtained depends, then, upon the particular hydrogen replaced by chlorine.

Returning to the original *n*-butane molecule, is there any reason why one of these hydrogens should be replaced more rapidly than the other? The answer is *no*, since the two hydrogens are exactly equivalent. In reaction, therefore, the chances of one or the other being replaced are exactly equal, and as a result the two enantiomers are obtained in exactly equal amounts, that is, the racemate is produced.

As another example, let us consider the preparation of *sec*-butylbenzene, by a different kind of reaction. Let us construct two models of *trans*-2-phenyl-2-butene, and lay the two models similarly oriented side by side on the table.

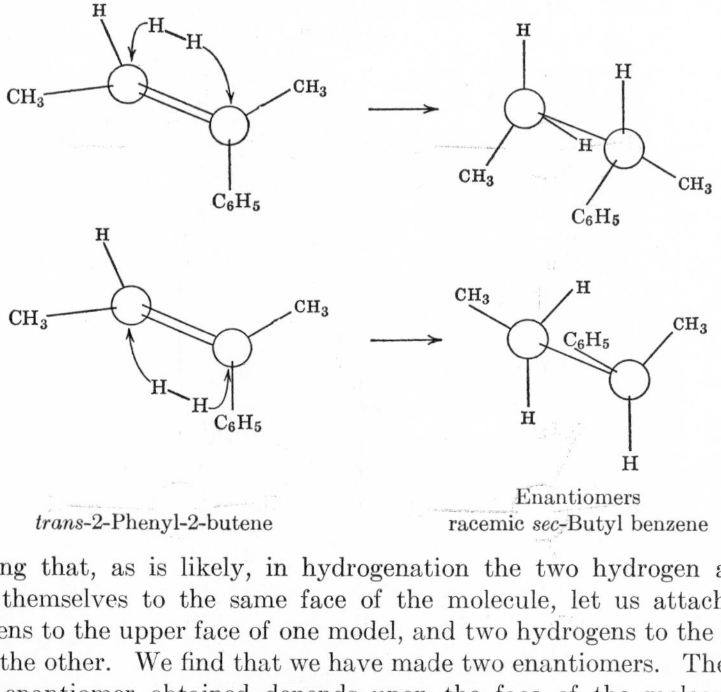

trans-2-Phenyl-2-butene	Enantiomers racemic *sec*-Butyl benzene

Assuming that, as is likely, in hydrogenation the two hydrogen atoms attach themselves to the same face of the molecule, let us attach two hydrogens to the upper face of one model, and two hydrogens to the lower face of the other. We find that we have made two enantiomers. The particular enantiomer obtained depends upon the face of the molecule to which the hydrogens become attached. Since the chances of attachment to one side are exactly the same as for attachment to the other side, the enantiomers are obtained in exactly equal amounts. The hydrogenation product is a racemate.

Problem 11.7 (a) Carry out the steps just described but add the hydrogen atoms to opposite faces. (b) Add hydrogen in both ways to models of *cis*-2-phenyl-2-butene.

If we apply the method just illustrated to the synthesis of any compound whatsoever, we obtain similar results, that is, we obtain an inactive product, so long as neither the starting material nor the reagent is optically active. **Synthesis of asymmetric compounds from non-asymmetric reactants always yields racemates.** This is simply one aspect of the more general rule: **optically inactive reactants yield optically inactive products.**

To purify the *sec*-butyl chloride obtained by chlorination of *n*-butane we would carry out a fractional distillation. But since the enantiomeric *sec*-butyl chlorides have exactly the same boiling point they cannot be separated, and they are collected in the same distillation fraction. If recrystallization is attempted, there can again be no separation since their solubilities in every (optically inactive) solvent are identical. It is easy to see, then, that whenever a racemate is *formed* in a reaction, we will *isolate* a racemate.

If an ordinary chemical synthesis yields a racemate, and if a racemate cannot be separated by our usual methods of distillation, crystallization, etc., how do we know that the product obtained is indeed a racemate? It is optically inactive; how do we know that it is actually made up of a mixture of two optically active substances? The separation of enantiomers (called **resolution**) can be accomplished by special methods; these involve the use of optically active reagents, and will be discussed later (Sec. 20.5).

11.24　Optical isomerism and the tetrahedral carbon atom

We saw earlier (Sec. 2.23) that the evidence of isomer number is consistent with the concept of the tetrahedral carbon atom. At that time, we emphasized the non-existence of isomeric substances of formula CH_3Y and of formula CH_2YZ.

Now we need only point out that our discussion of optical isomerism was based on the tetrahedral carbon atom. Predictions of optical isomerism, and of optical activity and inactivity, based upon the tetrahedral carbon atom have always proved correct. This fact was the strongest evidence for the tetrahedral carbon atom in the days before the techniques of electron diffraction, x-ray diffraction, and spectroscopy were known. It was this fact that led van't Hoff to propose the tetrahedral carbon atom, and that led to its eventual acceptance.

PROBLEMS

1. (a) Draw the structures of the eight isomeric pentyl alcohols, $C_5H_{11}OH$. (b) Name each by the IUPAC system and by the derived system. (c) Label each as primary, secondary, or tertiary. (d) Which one is isopentyl alcohol?

n-Pentyl alcohol? *tert*-Pentyl alcohol? (e) Give the structure of a primary, a secondary, and a tertiary alcohol of the formula $C_6H_{13}OH$. (f) Give the structure of a primary, a secondary, and a tertiary *cyclic* alcohol of the formula C_5H_9OH.

2. Without referring to tables, arrange the following compounds in order of decreasing boiling point: (a) 3-hexanol; (b) *n*-hexane; (c) dimethyl-*n*-propyl-carbinol; (d) *n*-octyl alcohol; (e) *n*-hexyl alcohol.

3. Looking at the beginning of each chapter for the structure involved, tell which families of compounds discussed in this book can: (a) form hydrogen bonds with other molecules of the same kind; (b) form hydrogen bonds with water.

4. Which compound would you expect to have the higher boiling point? (Check your answers in the proper tables.)

(a) *p*-cresol (p-$CH_3C_6H_4OH$) or anisole ($C_6H_5OCH_3$)

(b) methyl acetate ($CH_3C\!\!\underset{OCH_3}{\overset{O}{\diagup\!\!\diagdown}}$) or propionic acid ($CH_3CH_2C\!\!\underset{OH}{\overset{O}{\diagup\!\!\diagdown}}$)

(c) ethylene glycol (CH_2OHCH_2OH) or *n*-propyl alcohol

5. Ethers (ROR) have much lower boiling points than alcohols of comparable molecular weight, yet show about the same solubility in water. How do you account for this? (Check your answer in Sec. 15.2.)

6. Outline briefly the method or methods of industrial production of each of the following alcohols:

(a) methanol   (d) *tert*-butyl alcohol   (g) cyclohexanol
(b) ethyl alcohol   (e) *sec*-butyl alcohol   (h) benzyl alcohol
(c) *n*-butyl alcohol   (f) isopentyl alcohol   (i) β-chloroethyl alcohol ($ClCH_2CH_2OH$)
     (j) Suggest a possible method for allyl alcohol, $CH_2{=}CH{-}CH_2OH$.

7. Write equations to show how isopropyl alcohol might be prepared: (a) from an olefin; (b) from an alkyl halide; (c) by a Grignard reaction. (d) Which method is used industrially? Why?

8. Give structures of the Grignard reagent and the aldehyde or ketone that would react to yield each of the following alcohols. If more than one combination of reactants is possible, show each of the combinations.

(a)–(h) each of the isomeric pentyl alcohols of Problem 1(a)
(i) 1-phenyl-1-propanol   (n) cyclohexylcarbinol
(j) 2-phenyl-2-propanol   (o) 1-cyclohexylethanol
(k) 1-phenyl-2-propanol   (p) 2,4-dimethyl-3-pentanol
(l) 3-phenyl-1-propanol   (q) 1-(*p*-tolyl)ethanol, p-$CH_3C_6H_4CHOHCH_3$
(m) 1-methylcyclohexanol   (r) triphenylcarbinol, $(C_6H_5)_3COH$

9. Define and illustrate:

(a) optical activity   (e) specific rotation   (i) enantiomer
(b) polarimeter   (f) asymmetric molecule   (j) racemate
(c) dextrorotatory   (g) asymmetric carbon   (k) configuration
(d) levorotatory   (h) superimposable   (l) conformation

10. (a) What is the necessary and sufficient condition for optical isomerism? For optical activity? (b) What is often but not always a sufficient condition for optical isomerism? For optical activity? (c) How can you tell from its formula whether a compound will be optically active or inactive? (d) What restrictions, if any, must be applied to the use of planar formulas in (c)? To the use of models in (c)?

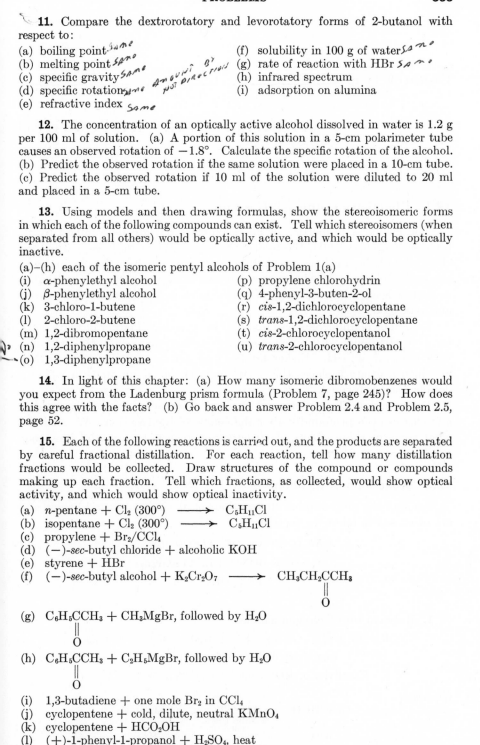

11. Compare the dextrorotatory and levorotatory forms of 2-butanol with respect to:

(a) boiling point *same*
(b) melting point *same*
(c) specific gravity *same*
(d) specific rotation *same — amount same but direction not directional*
(e) refractive index *same*
(f) solubility in 100 g of water *same*
(g) rate of reaction with HBr *same*
(h) infrared spectrum
(i) adsorption on alumina

12. The concentration of an optically active alcohol dissolved in water is 1.2 g per 100 ml of solution. (a) A portion of this solution in a 5-cm polarimeter tube causes an observed rotation of $-1.8°$. Calculate the specific rotation of the alcohol. (b) Predict the observed rotation if the same solution were placed in a 10-cm tube. (c) Predict the observed rotation if 10 ml of the solution were diluted to 20 ml and placed in a 5-cm tube.

13. Using models and then drawing formulas, show the stereoisomeric forms in which each of the following compounds can exist. Tell which stereoisomers (when separated from all others) would be optically active, and which would be optically inactive.

(a)–(h) each of the isomeric pentyl alcohols of Problem 1(a)
(i) α-phenylethyl alcohol
(j) β-phenylethyl alcohol
(k)   3-chloro-1-butene
(l)   2-chloro-2-butene
(m) 1,2-dibromopentane
(n)   1,2-diphenylpropane
(o)   1,3-diphenylpropane
(p)   propylene chlorohydrin
(q)   4-phenyl-3-buten-2-ol
(r)   *cis*-1,2-dichlorocyclopentane
(s)   *trans*-1,2-dichlorocyclopentane
(t)   *cis*-2-chlorocyclopentanol
(u)   *trans*-2-chlorocyclopentanol

14. In light of this chapter: (a) How many isomeric dibromobenzenes would you expect from the Ladenburg prism formula (Problem 7, page 245)? How does this agree with the facts? (b) Go back and answer Problem 2.4 and Problem 2.5, page 52.

15. Each of the following reactions is carried out, and the products are separated by careful fractional distillation. For each reaction, tell how many distillation fractions would be collected. Draw structures of the compound or compounds making up each fraction. Tell which fractions, as collected, would show optical activity, and which would show optical inactivity.

(a) n-pentane + Cl_2 (300°) $\longrightarrow$ $C_5H_{11}Cl$
(b)   isopentane + Cl_2 (300°) $\longrightarrow$ $C_5H_{11}Cl$
(c)   propylene + Br_2/CCl_4
(d) $(-)$-*sec*-butyl chloride + alcoholic KOH
(e)   styrene + HBr
(f) $(-)$-*sec*-butyl alcohol + $K_2Cr_2O_7$ $\longrightarrow$ $CH_3CH_2CCH_3$, with $\overset{\|}{O}$

(g) $C_6H_5CCH_3$ (with $\overset{\|}{O}$) + CH_3MgBr, followed by H_2O

(h) $C_6H_5CCH_3$ (with $\overset{\|}{O}$) + C_2H_5MgBr, followed by H_2O

(i)   1,3-butadiene + one mole Br_2 in CCl_4
(j)   cyclopentene + cold, dilute, neutral $KMnO_4$
(k)   cyclopentene + HCO_2OH
(l) $(+)$-1-phenyl-1-propanol + H_2SO_4, heat
(m) optically active $CH_3CH_2CH(CH_3)CH_2MgBr$ + D_2O

ALCOHOLS II.   REACTIONS

12.1   Chemistry of the —OH group

The chemical properties of an alcohol, ROH, are determined by its functional group, —OH, the hydroxyl group.   When we have learned the chemistry of the alcohols, we shall have learned much of the chemistry of the hydroxyl group in whatever compound it may occur; we shall know, in part at least, what to expect of hydroxyhalides, hydroxyacids, hydroxyaldehydes, etc.

Reactions of an alcohol can involve the breaking of either of two bonds: the C···OH bond, with removal of the —OH group; or the O···H bond, with removal of —H.   Either kind of reaction can involve substitution, in which a group replaces the —OH or —H, or elimination, in which a double bond is formed.

Differences in the structure of R cause differences in reactivity, and in a few cases even profoundly alter the course of the reaction.   We shall see what some of these effects of structure on reactivity are, and how they can be accounted for.

12.2   Reactions of alcohols

Some of the more important reactions of alcohols are listed below, and are discussed in following sections.

REACTIONS OF ALCOHOLS

C···OH BOND CLEAVAGE

$$R—\overset{\vdots}{\underset{\vdots}{|}}—OH$$

1. Reaction with hydrogen halides.

R—OH + HX $\longrightarrow$ RX + H$_2$O   *R may rearrange*

Reactivity of HX: HI > HBr > HCl

Reactivity of ROH: allyl, benzyl > 3° > 2° > 1°

Examples:

$$CH_3CHCH_3 \xrightarrow[\substack{\text{or NaBr, H}_2\text{SO}_4 \\ \text{reflux}}]{\text{conc. HBr}} CH_3CHCH_3$$

$$\quad\ |\qquad\qquad\qquad\qquad\qquad\qquad\ |$$

$$\ \ OH \qquad\qquad\qquad\qquad\qquad\qquad Br$$

Isopropyl alcohol   Isopropyl bromide

$$CH_3CH_2CH_2CH_2CH_2OH \xrightarrow[\text{heat}]{\text{HCl, ZnCl}_2} CH_3CH_2CH_2CH_2CH_2Cl$$

n-Pentyl alcohol   *n*-Pentyl chloride

$$
\begin{array}{c}
CH_3 \\
| \\
CH_3{-}C{-}CH_3 \\
| \\
OH
\end{array}
\xrightarrow[\text{room temp.}]{\text{conc. HCl}}
\begin{array}{c}
CH_3 \\
| \\
CH_3{-}C{-}CH_3 \\
| \\
Cl
\end{array}
$$

tert-Butyl alcohol   *tert*-Butyl chloride

2. Reaction with phosphorus trihalides.

$$R{-}OH + PX_3 \longrightarrow RX + H_3PO_3$$
$$(PX_3 = PBr_3, PI_3)$$

Examples:

$$
\begin{array}{c}
CH_3 \\
| \\
CH_3CH_2CHCH_2OH
\end{array}
\xrightarrow{PBr_3}
\begin{array}{c}
CH_3 \\
| \\
CH_3CH_2CHCH_2Br
\end{array}
$$

2-Methyl-1-butanol   2-Methyl-1-bromobutane

$$
\langle\cdot\cdot\cdot\rangle\!\!
\begin{array}{c}
CHCH_3 \\
| \\
OH
\end{array}
\xrightarrow{PBr_3}
\langle\cdot\cdot\cdot\rangle\!\!
\begin{array}{c}
CHCH_3 \\
| \\
Br
\end{array}
$$

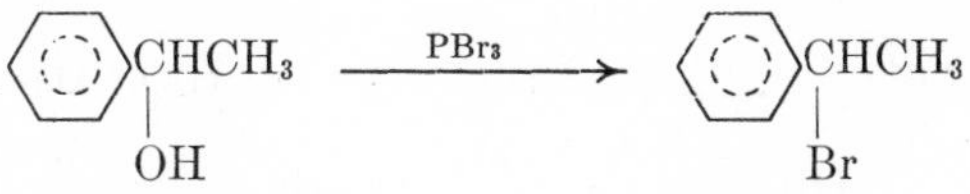

1-Phenylethanol   1-Bromo-1-phenylethane

$$CH_3CH_2OH \xrightarrow{P + I_2} CH_3CH_2I$$

Ethyl alcohol   Ethyl iodide

3. Dehydration

$$
\begin{array}{c}
| \quad | \\
{-}C{-}C{-} \\
| \quad | \\
H \quad OH
\end{array}
\xrightarrow{\text{acid}}
\begin{array}{c}
| \quad | \\
{-}C{=}C{-} \\
\end{array}
+ H_2O
\qquad \textit{Rearrangement may occur.}
$$

Reactivity of ROH: 3° > 2° > 1°

Examples:

$$CH_3CH_2CH_2CH_2OH \xrightarrow{\text{H}_2\text{SO}_4, \text{ heat}} CH_3CH{=}CHCH_3 \text{ and } CH_3CH_2CH{=}CH_2$$

n-Butyl alcohol   2-Butene   1-Butene
                         Major product

$$
\bigcirc\!\!-OH \xrightarrow{\text{Al}_2\text{O}_3, 250°} \bigcirc
$$

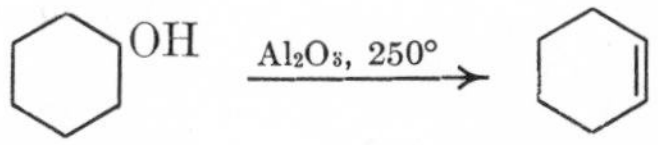

Cyclohexanol   Cyclohexene

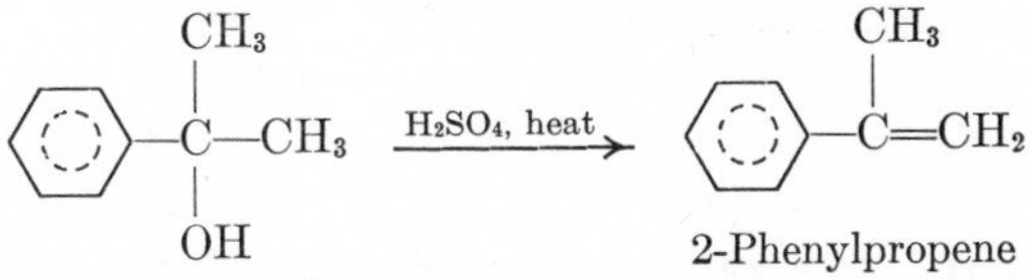

$$
\langle\cdot\cdot\cdot\rangle\!\!
\begin{array}{c}
CH_3 \\
| \\
{-}C{-}CH_3 \\
| \\
OH
\end{array}
\xrightarrow{\text{H}_2\text{SO}_4, \text{ heat}}
\langle\cdot\cdot\cdot\rangle\!\!
\begin{array}{c}
CH_3 \\
| \\
{-}C{=}CH_2
\end{array}
$$

2-Phenyl-2-propanol   2-Phenylpropene

$$\text{O}\cdots\text{H BOND CLEAVAGE}$$
$$\text{RO}\overset{\xi}{-}\text{H}$$

4. Reaction as acids: reaction with active metals

$$RO{-}H + M \longrightarrow RO^-M^+ + \tfrac{1}{2}H_2 \qquad M = Na, Mg, Al, \text{etc.}$$

Reactivity of ROH: $CH_3OH > 1° > 2° > 3°$

Examples:

$$CH_3CH_2OH \xrightarrow{\ Na\ } CH_3CH_2O^- Na^+ + \tfrac{1}{2}H_2$$

Sodium ethoxide

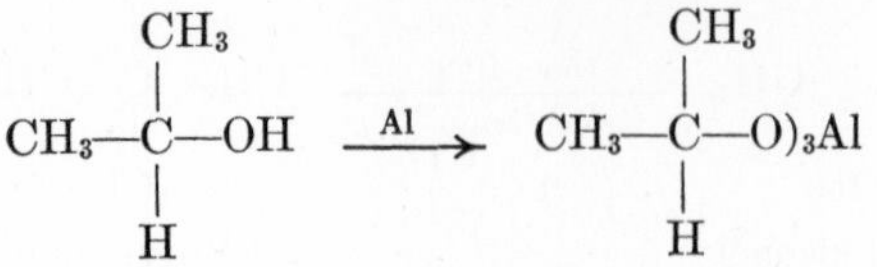

$$\underset{\overset{|}{H}}{\overset{\overset{CH_3}{|}}{CH_3-C-OH}} \xrightarrow{\ Al\ } \underset{\overset{|}{H}}{\overset{\overset{CH_3}{|}}{CH_3-C-O)_3Al}}$$

Aluminum isopropoxide

5. Ester formation

Examples:

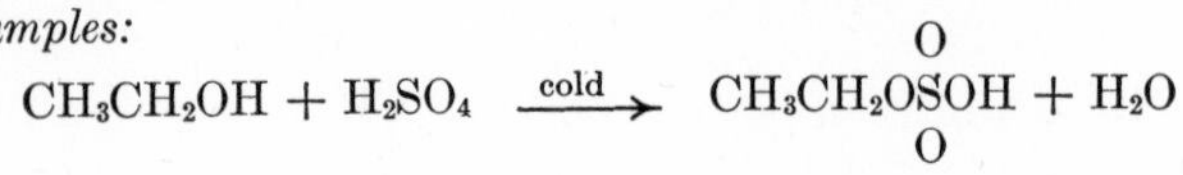

$$CH_3CH_2OH + H_2SO_4 \xrightarrow{\ cold\ } CH_3CH_2O\overset{O}{\underset{O}{S}}OH + H_2O$$

Ethyl hydrogen sulfate

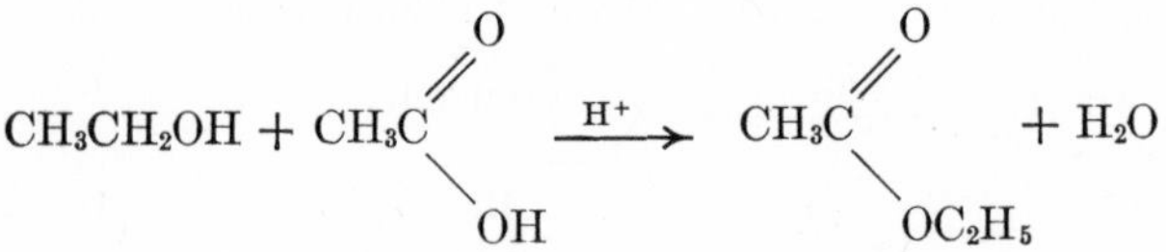

$$CH_3CH_2OH + CH_3C\overset{O}{\diagdown}_{OH} \xrightarrow{\ H^+\ } CH_3C\overset{O}{\diagdown}_{OC_2H_5} + H_2O \quad \text{Discussed in Sec. 16.16.}$$

Acetic acid   Ethyl acetate

6. Oxidation

Primary:

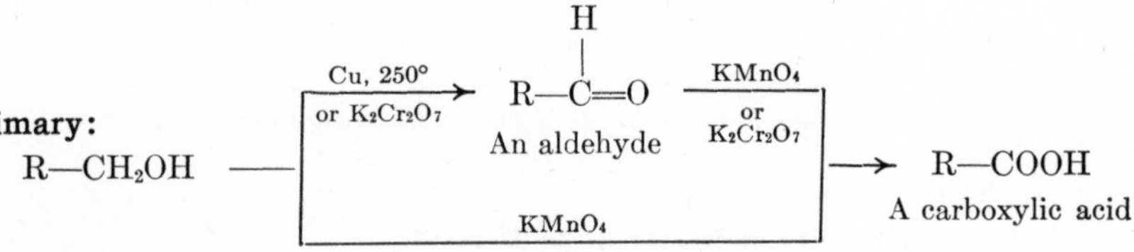

$$R-CH_2OH \longrightarrow \boxed{\xrightarrow[\text{or } K_2Cr_2O_7]{Cu, 250°} \underset{\text{An aldehyde}}{R-\overset{\overset{H}{|}}{C}=O} \xrightarrow[K_2Cr_2O_7]{\overset{KMnO_4}{\text{or}}} \quad KMnO_4} \longrightarrow \underset{\text{A carboxylic acid}}{R-COOH}$$

Secondary:

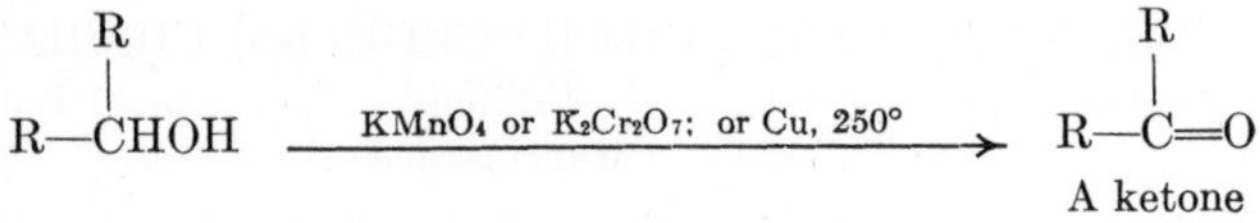

$$R-\overset{\overset{R}{|}}{C}HOH \xrightarrow{KMnO_4 \text{ or } K_2Cr_2O_7; \text{ or } Cu, 250°} \underset{\text{A ketone}}{R-\overset{\overset{R}{|}}{C}=O}$$

Tertiary:

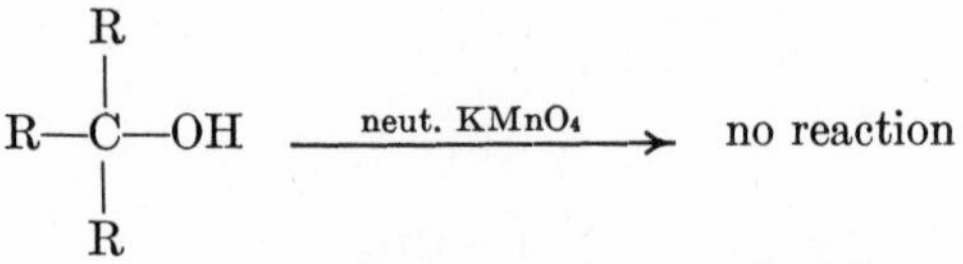

$$R-\underset{\overset{|}{R}}{\overset{\overset{R}{|}}{C}}-OH \xrightarrow{\text{neut. } KMnO_4} \text{no reaction}$$

Examples:

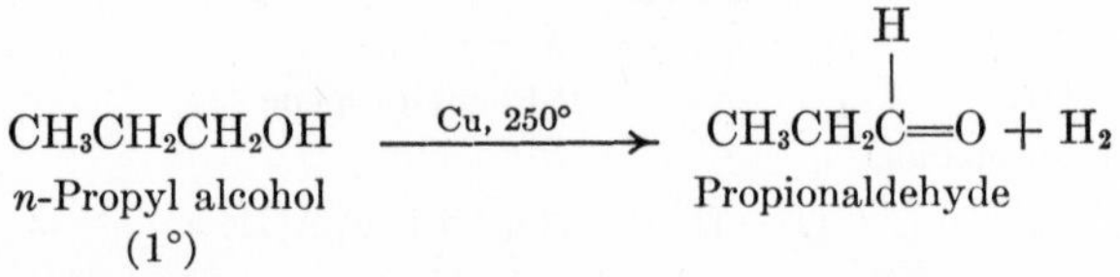

$$\underset{\substack{n\text{-Propyl alcohol}\\(1°)}}{CH_3CH_2CH_2OH} \xrightarrow{Cu, 250°} \underset{\text{Propionaldehyde}}{CH_3CH_2\overset{\overset{H}{|}}{C}=O + H_2}$$

$$\underset{\substack{2\text{-Methyl-1-butanol}\\(1°)}}{\overset{\overset{CH_3}{|}}{CH_3CH_2CHCH_2OH}} \xrightarrow{KMnO_4} \underset{\text{2-Methylbutanoic acid}}{\overset{\overset{CH_3}{|}}{CH_3CH_2CHCOOH}}$$

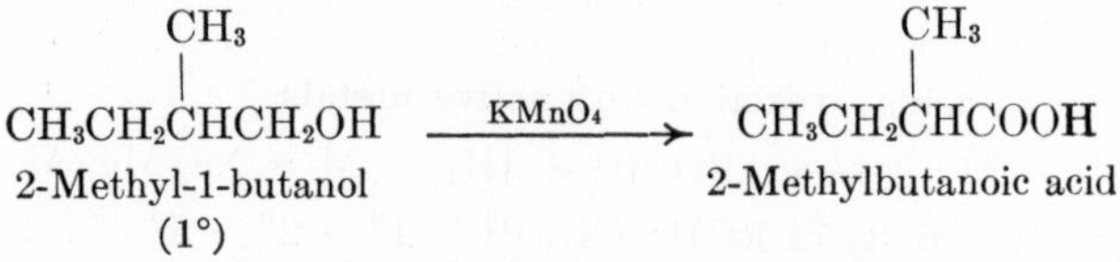

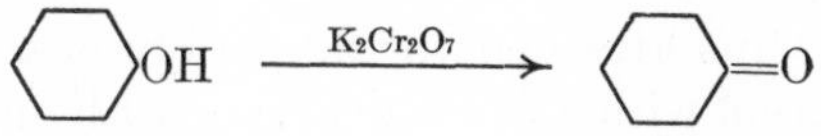

Cyclohexanol → Cyclohexanone
(2°)

We can see that alcohols undergo many kinds of reactions, to yield many kinds of products. Because of the availability of alcohols, each of these reactions is one of the best ways to make the particular kind of product. After we have learned a little more about the reactions themselves, we shall look at some of the ways in which they can be applied to synthetic problems.

12.3 Dehydration of alcohols. Carbonium Ions

We discussed the dehydration of alcohols at some length earlier (Sec. 4.16), and saw that the heart of the reaction is the carbonium ion. Since our first discussion, however, we have learned a good deal more about carbonium ions and about structural theory in general, and so it is worthwhile now to have another look at certain aspects of this reaction.

(a) **Mechanism.** According to the commonly accepted mechanism, we remember, dehydration involves (1) formation of the protonated alcohol, ROH_2^+, (2) its dissociation into a carbonium ion, and (3) expulsion of a hydrogen ion from the carbonium ion to form an alkene.

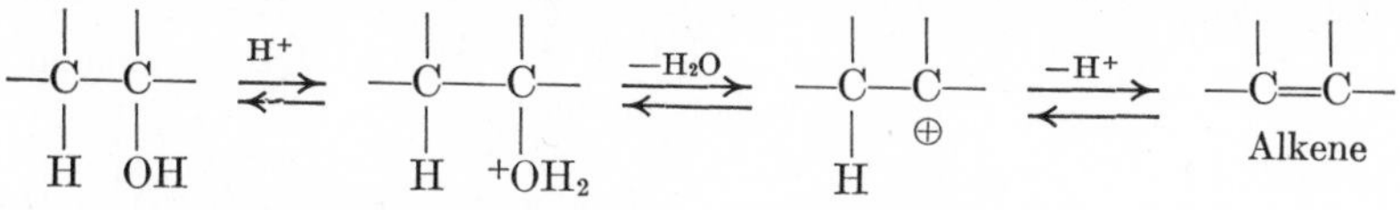

Alcohol   Protonated alcohol   Carbonium ion

Acid is required to convert the alcohol into the protonated alcohol, which dissociates much more easily than the alcohol itself.

(b) **Reactivity.** We know that the rate of elimination depends greatly upon the rate of formation of the carbonium ion, which in turn depends upon its stability.

We know how to estimate the stability of a carbonium ion, on the basis of inductive effects and resonance. Because of the electron-releasing inductive effect of alkyl groups, stability and hence rate of formation of the simple alkyl carbonium ions follows the sequence 3° > 2° > 1°.

We know that because of resonance stabilization (Sec. 9.23) the benzyl carbonium ion should be an extremely stable ion, and so we are not surprised to find that an alcohol such as 1-phenylethanol (like a tertiary alcohol) undergoes dehydration extremely rapidly.

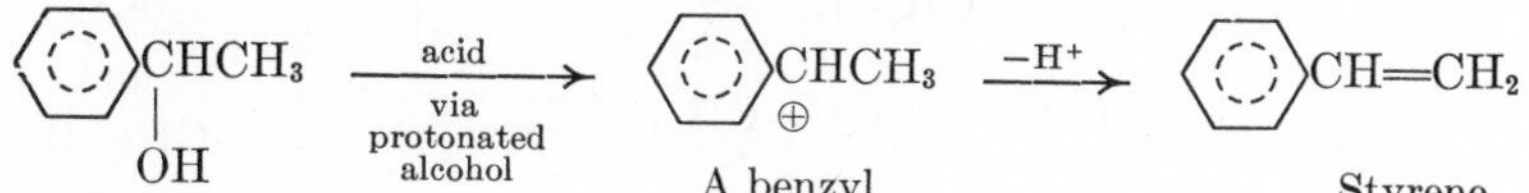

1-Phenylethanol   A benzyl carbonium ion   Styrene

(c) **Orientation.** We know that expulsion of the hydrogen ion takes place in such a way as to favor the formation of the more stable alkene. We can estimate the relative stability of an alkene on the basis of the number of alkyl groups attached to the doubly-bonded carbons, and on the basis of conjugation with a benzene ring or with another carbon–carbon double bond. It is reasonable, then, that *sec*-butyl alcohol yields chiefly 2-butene, and 1-phenyl-2-propanol yields only 1-phenyl-propene.

$$CH_3CH_2CHCH_3 \xrightarrow{\text{acid}} CH_3CH=CHCH_3$$
$$\underset{\text{OH}}{|}$$

2-Butene
Chief product

sec-Butyl alcohol

$$\langle \bigcirc \rangle CH_2CHCH_3 \xrightarrow{\text{acid}} \langle \bigcirc \rangle CH=CHCH_3$$
$$\underset{\text{OH}}{|}$$

1-Phenylpropene
Only product

1-Phenyl-2-propanol

(d) Rearrangement. Finally, we know that a carbonium ion can rearrange, and that this rearrangement seems to occur whenever a 1,2-shift of hydrogen or alkyl group can form a more stable carbonium ion.

2-Butene is obtained from *n*-butyl alcohol because the *n*-butyl carbonium ion initially formed rearranges to the more stable *sec*-butyl carbonium ion, which then yields the more stable alkene, 2-butene:

$$CH_3CH_2CH_2CH_2OH \xrightarrow{\text{acid}} CH_3CH_2-\overset{\overset{H}{|}}{\underset{(H)}{C}}-CH_2\oplus \xrightarrow{\text{rearr.}} CH_3CH_2-\overset{\overset{H}{|}}{\underset{\oplus}{C}}-CH_3$$

n-Butyl alcohol

1° carbonium ion

2° carbonium ion

$$\Big\downarrow -H^+$$

$$CH_3CH=CHCH_3$$

2-Butene
Most highly substituted alkene

3,3-Dimethyl-2-butanol yields only alkenes of rearranged skeleton, because the initially formed secondary carbonium ion rearranges by an alkyl shift to the more stable tertiary carbonium ion. This then yields chiefly the tetrasubstituted ethylene:

$$CH_3-\overset{\overset{CH_3}{|}}{\underset{\underset{CH_3}{|}}{C}}-\overset{\overset{H}{|}}{\underset{\underset{OH}{|}}{C}}-CH_3 \xrightarrow{\text{acid}} CH_3-\overset{\overset{CH_3}{|}}{\underset{\underset{(CH_3)}{}}{C}}-\overset{\overset{H}{|}}{\underset{\oplus}{C}}-CH_3$$

3,3-Dimethyl-2-butanol

2° Carbonium ion

$$CH_3-\overset{\overset{CH_3}{|}}{\underset{\oplus}{C}}-\overset{\overset{H}{|}}{\underset{\underset{CH_3}{|}}{C}}-CH_3 \xrightarrow{-H^+}$$

3° Carbonium ion

$$\left.\begin{array}{c} CH_3-\overset{\overset{CH_3}{|}}{C}=\overset{}{\underset{\underset{CH_3}{|}}{C}}-CH_3 \\ \\ \text{2,3-Dimethyl-2-butene} \\ \textit{Most highly substituted} \\ \textit{alkene} \\ 70\% \\ \text{and} \\ \\ CH_2=\overset{\overset{CH_3}{|}}{C}-\overset{\overset{H}{|}}{\underset{\underset{CH_3}{|}}{C}}-CH_3 \\ \\ \text{2,3-Dimethyl-1-butene} \\ \textit{30\%} \end{array}\right\}$$

In all this we must not lose sight of the fact that the rates of formation of carbonium ions and of alkenes depend chiefly upon the stabilities of the transition states leading to their formation. A more stable carbonium ion is formed faster because the factors — inductive effects and resonance — that disperse the charge of a carbonium ion tend also to disperse the developing positive charge of an incipient carbonium ion in the transition state. In the same way, we might consider that factors that stabilize an alkene tend to stabilize the developing double bond in the transition state.

In the following sections we shall apply to other reactions of alcohols what we have learned about carbonium ions through our study of dehydration, addition (Sec. 5.10), and Friedel-Crafts alkylation (Sec. 9.8).

12.4 Reaction with hydrogen halides: facts

Alcohols react readily with hydrogen halides to yield alkyl halides and water. The reaction is carried out either by passing the dry hydrogen halide gas into the alcohol, or by heating the alcohol with the concentrated aqueous acid. Sometimes hydrogen bromide is generated in the presence of the alcohol by reaction between sulfuric acid and sodium bromide.

The least reactive of the hydrogen halides, HCl, requires the presence of zinc chloride for reaction with primary and secondary alcohols; on the other hand, the very reactive *tert*-butyl alcohol is converted to the chloride by simply being shaken with concentrated hydrochloric acid at room temperature. For example:

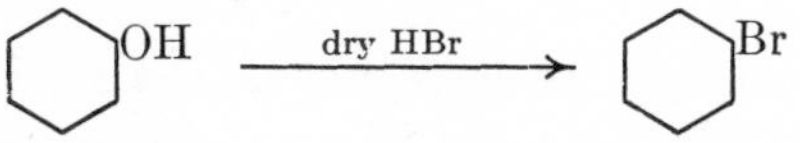

Cyclohexanol   Cyclohexyl bromide

$$CH_3CH_2CH_2CH_2OH \xrightarrow[\text{reflux}]{NaBr, H_2SO_4} CH_3CH_2CH_2CH_2Br$$
n-Butyl alcohol   *n*-Butyl bromide

$$CH_3CH_2CH_2OH \xrightarrow[\text{heat}]{HCl + ZnCl_2} CH_3CH_2CH_2Cl$$
n-Propyl alcohol   *n*-Propyl chloride

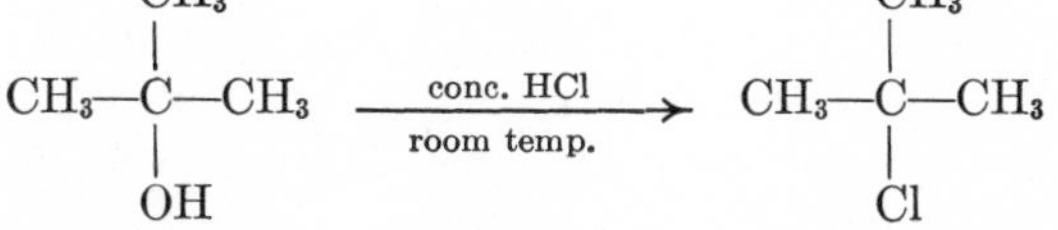

tert-Butyl alcohol   *tert*-Butyl chloride

Let us list some of the facts that are known about the reaction between alcohols and hydrogen halides.

(a) **The reaction is catalyzed by acids.** Even though the aqueous hydrogen halides are themselves strong acids, the presence of additional sulfuric acid speeds up the formation of halides.

Problem 12.1 How do you account for the catalysis by $ZnCl_2$ of the HCl reaction? (*Hint:* $ZnCl_2$ is sometimes used as a (weak) Friedel-Crafts catalyst.)

(b) **The order of reactivity of alcohols toward HX is allyl, benzyl > 3° > 2° > 1°.** This order of reactivity is the basis of the *Lucas test*, which is used to determine the class of an alcohol (Sec. 12.11).

(c) **Rearrangement of the alkyl group may occur.** The alkyl group in the halide does not always have the same structure as the alkyl group of the parent alcohol. For example:

$$
\underset{\substack{\text{3-Methyl-2-butanol}}}{CH_3-\overset{\displaystyle CH_3}{\underset{\displaystyle H}{C}}-\overset{\displaystyle H}{\underset{\displaystyle OH}{C}}-CH_3} \quad\xrightarrow{\;HCl\;}\quad \underset{\substack{\text{2-Chloro-2-methylbutane} \\ (\textit{tert}\text{-Pentyl chloride})}}{CH_3-\overset{\displaystyle CH_3}{\underset{\displaystyle Cl}{C}}-\overset{\displaystyle H}{\underset{\displaystyle H}{C}}-CH_3} \quad (\text{but } no\ CH_3-\overset{\displaystyle CH_3}{\underset{\displaystyle H}{C}}-\overset{\displaystyle H}{\underset{\displaystyle Cl}{C}}-CH_3)
$$

$$
\underset{\substack{\text{Neopentyl alcohol}}}{CH_3-\overset{\displaystyle CH_3}{\underset{\displaystyle CH_3}{C}}-CH_2OH} \quad\xrightarrow{\;HCl\;}\quad \underset{\substack{\textit{tert}\text{-Pentyl chloride}}}{CH_3-\overset{\displaystyle CH_3}{\underset{\displaystyle Cl}{C}}-CH_2-CH_3}
$$

We see that the halogen does not always become attached to the carbon that originally held the hydroxyl (the first example); even the carbon skeleton may be different from that of the starting material (the second example).

12.5 Reaction with hydrogen halides: mechanism

What do the facts that we have just listed suggest to us about the mechanism of reaction between alcohols and hydrogen halides?

Catalysis by acid suggests that here, as in dehydration, the protonated alcohol, ROH_2^+, is involved. The occurrence of the same sort of *rearrangement* that we observed in dehydration, addition to alkenes, and Friedel-Crafts alkylations suggests that all four reactions have something in common: namely, intermediate carbonium ions. The observed *order of reactivity* of alcohols parallels the stability of carbonium ions, and strongly supports the idea that carbonium ions are intermediates.

Reactivity of alcohols toward HX   allyl, benzyl $> 3° > 2° > 1°$

On the basis of this evidence, we may formulate the following mechanism, which is the commonly accepted one.

$$(1) \qquad\qquad ROH + HX \;\rightleftharpoons\; ROH_2^+ + X^-$$

$$(2) \qquad\qquad ROH_2^+ \;\rightleftharpoons\; R^+ + H_2O$$

$$(3) \qquad\qquad R^+ + X^- \;\longrightarrow\; RX$$

The alcohol accepts (step 1) the hydrogen ion to form the protonated alcohol, which dissociates (step 2) into water and a carbonium ion; the carbonium ion then combines (step 3) with a halide ion (not necessarily the one from step 1) to form the alkyl halide.

Reaction (1) is also the first step in dehydration, and in fact appears to be the first step in nearly every reaction involving cleavage of the C—OH bond.

Reaction (2) involves the breaking of the C—O bond and is the most difficult step; its rate determines the rate of the over-all reaction. As in dehydration, this dissociation involves the protonated alcohol rather than the unprotonated alcohol, since it is much easier to separate the positive carbonium ion (an acid) from the neutral, weakly basic water molecule than from the negatively charged, strongly basic hydroxide ion.

The developing positive charge of the incipient carbonium ion in the transition state is dispersed by the same factors that stabilize the carbonium ion itself: inductive effects and resonance. The order of reactivity is thus the familiar one of the stabilities of the carbonium ions. Since primary carbonium ions are the least stable they are the most slowly formed; in fact, in this reaction they are so slowly formed that for some primary alcohols the reaction takes a different course, one that does not involve carbonium ions at all (Sec. 13.16).

Once formed, the carbonium ion may combine (step 3) with halide ion to form the product. If, on the other hand, a 1,2-hydride shift or 1,2-alkyl shift can yield a more stable carbonium ion, this rearrangement takes place, to a greater or lesser extent, and the newly formed carbonium ion may be the one to unite with halide ion. In each of the examples of rearrangement that were shown in Sec. 12.4 the product indicated is consistent with rearrangement from a less stable to a more stable carbonium ion:

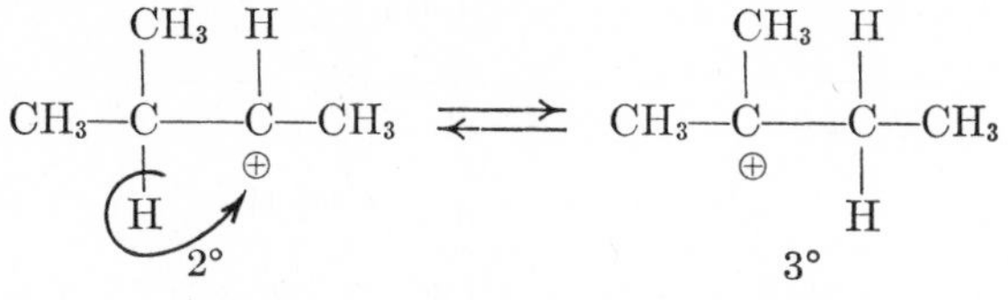

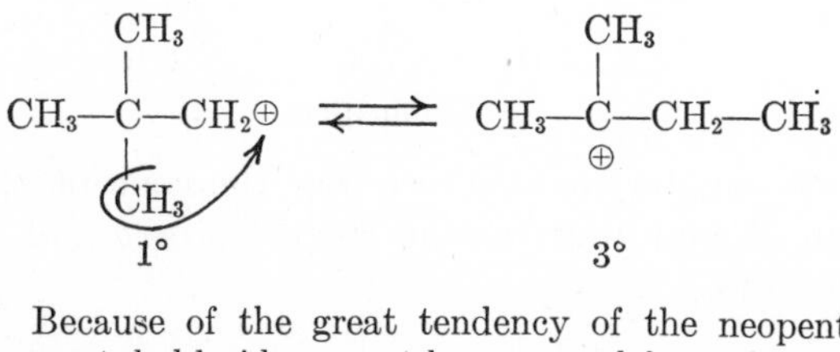

Problem 12.2 Because of the great tendency of the neopentyl carbonium ion to rearrange, neopentyl chloride cannot be prepared from the alcohol. In light of Problem 9.6, page 259, how might neopentyl chloride be prepared?

Problem 12.3 Predict the relative rates at which the following alcohols will react with aqueous HBr:
(a) benzyl alcohol, p-methylbenzyl alcohol, p-nitrobenzyl alcohol
(b) benzyl alcohol, α-phenylethyl alcohol, β-phenylethyl alcohol

Problem 12.4 When allowed to react with aqueous HBr, 3-buten-2-ol ($CH_3CHOHCH=CH_2$) yields not only 3-bromo-1-butene ($CH_3CHBrCH=CH_2$) but also 1-bromo-2-butene ($CH_3CH=CHCH_2Br$). (a) How do you account for these results? (*Hint:* see Sec. 6.16.) (b) Predict the product of the reaction between HBr and 2-buten-1-ol ($CH_3CH=CHCH_2OH$). (c) How does this "rearrangement" differ from those described in the last section?

We can begin to see now how broad are the foundations on which the carbonium ion theory rests. This single concept accounts for both orientation and reactivity in reactions as different as addition, elimination, and substitution. Its application to the understanding of rearrangements as well is strikingly illustrated by the basic similarity of the following three examples of superficially different reactions:

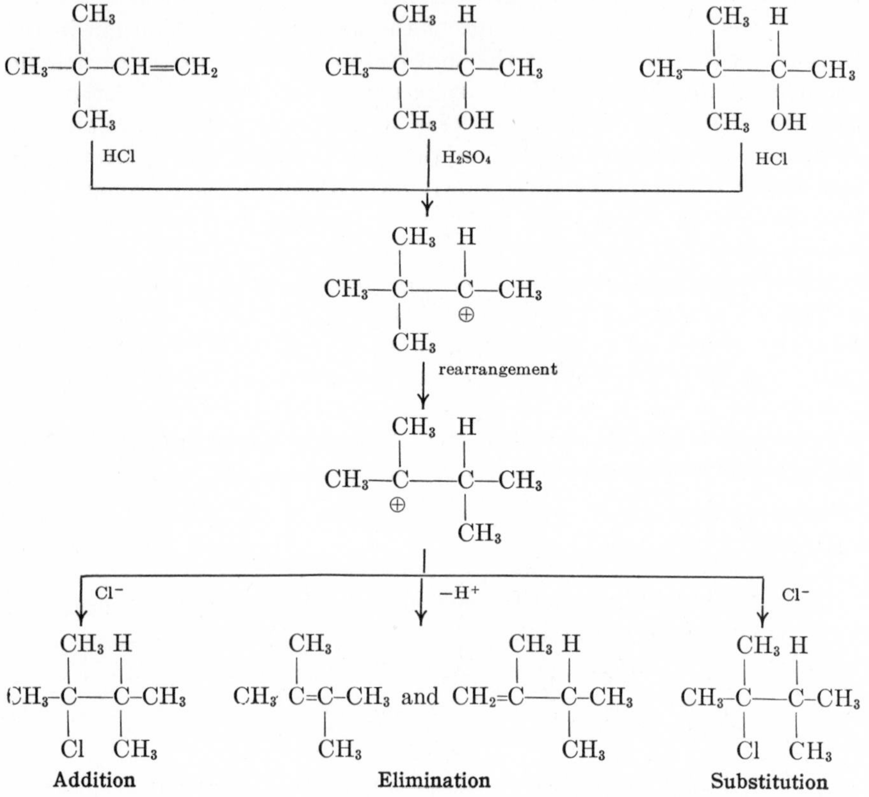

(In the next chapter we shall see how the concept of carbonium ions accounts in an elegant way for the *stereochemistry* and *kinetics* of many important reactions.)

12.6 Alcohols as acids

We have seen that an alcohol, acting as a base, can accept a hydrogen ion to form the protonated alcohol, ROH_2^+. Let us now turn to reactions in which an alcohol, acting as an acid, loses a hydrogen ion to form the alkoxide ion, RO^-.

Since an alcohol contains hydrogen bonded to the very electronegative element oxygen, we would expect it to show appreciable acidity. The polarity of the O—H bond should facilitate the separation of the relatively positive hydrogen as the ion; viewed differently, electronegative oxygen should readily accommodate the negative charge of the electrons left behind.

The acidity of alcohols is shown by their reaction with active metals to form hydrogen gas, and by their ability to displace the weakly acidic hydrocarbons from their salts (e.g., Grignard reagents):

$$\text{ROH} + \text{Na} \longrightarrow \text{RO}^-\text{Na}^+ + \tfrac{1}{2}\text{H}_2$$

Stronger acid		Weaker acid

$$\text{ROH} + \text{R}'\text{MgX} \longrightarrow \text{R}'\text{H} + \text{Mg(OR)X}$$

Stronger acid	Weaker acid

With the possible exception of methanol, they are weaker acids than water, but stronger acids than acetylene or ammonia:

$$\text{RO}^-\text{Na}^+ + \text{H---OH} \longrightarrow \text{Na}^+\text{OH}^- + \text{RO---H}$$

Stronger base	Stronger acid	Weaker base	Weaker acid

$$\text{HC}\equiv\text{C}^-\text{Na}^+ + \text{RO---H} \longrightarrow \text{RO}^-\text{Na}^+ + \text{HC}\equiv\text{C---H}$$

Stronger base	Stronger acid	Weaker base	Weaker acid

As before, these relative acidities are determined by displacement (Sec. 6.9). We may expand our series of acidities and basicities, then, to the following:

Relative acidities: $\quad$ $H_2O > ROH > HC\equiv CH > NH_3 > RH$

Relative basicities: $\quad$ $OH^- < OR^- < HC\equiv C^- < NH_2^- < R^-$

Since an alcohol is a weaker acid than water, an alkoxide cannot be prepared from the reaction of sodium hydroxide with the alcohol, but must be prepared instead by reaction with the active metal itself.

Problem 12.5 Ether to be used as a solvent for the Grignard reagent must be completely free not only of water but also of alcohol. Why is this?

An alcohol differs in structure from water by the presence of an alkyl group. Is it reasonable that the alkyl group should make an alcohol a weaker acid than water? Acidity depends upon how well the anion can accommodate the negative charge (see Sec. 16.14 for fuller discussion). Since an alkyl group tends to release electrons, it should intensify the negative charge — relative to the charge on hydroxide ion — and hence make the anion less stable. The inductive effect of alkyl groups, then should tend to make alcohols weaker acids than water.

$$\text{R} \rightarrow \overset{|}{\underset{|}{\text{C}}}\text{---O---H} \quad \rightleftarrows \quad \text{R} \rightarrow \overset{|}{\underset{|}{\text{C}}}\text{---O}^- + \text{H}^+$$

R *releases electrons:*
intensifies charge,
destabilizes ion,
weakens acid

How does this inductive effect change with changes in structure of the alkyl group? We would expect the inductive effect to be greatest for tertiary alcohols, where three alkyl substituents are releasing electrons to the carbon bearing the —OH, less for secondary, still less for primary, and least of all for methanol. The observed order of acidity agrees with this prediction.

Acidity of alcohols $CH_3OH > 1° > 2° > 3°$

Problem 12.6 Which would you expect to be the stronger acid: (a) β-chloroethyl alcohol or ethyl alcohol? (b) p-Nitrobenzyl alcohol or benzyl alcohol? (c) n-Propyl alcohol or glycerol, $HOCH_2CHOHCH_2OH$?

As we shall see, the alkoxides are extremely useful reagents; they are used as powerful bases (stronger than hydroxide) and to introduce the —OR group into a molecule.

12.7 Oxidation of alcohols

The compound that is formed by oxidation of an alcohol depends upon the number of hydrogens attached to the carbon bearing the —OH group, that is, upon whether the alcohol is primary, secondary, or tertiary. We have already encountered these products — aldehydes, ketones, and carboxylic acids — and should recognize them from their structures, even though we have not yet discussed much of their chemistry. Many oxidizing agents can be used, but we shall consider only the more common ones.

Primary alcohols can be oxidized to carboxylic acids, RCOOH, usually by heating with aqueous $KMnO_4$. The purple color of the permanganate fades and manganese dioxide, MnO_2, separates as a brown precipitate. When reaction is complete the aqueous solution of the soluble potassium salt of the carboxylic acid is filtered from the MnO_2, and the acid is liberated by the addition of a stronger mineral acid.

$$RCH_2OH + KMnO_4 \longrightarrow RCOO^-K^+ + MnO_2 + KOH$$

1° alcohol   *purple*   *sol. in H_2O*   *brown*

$$\downarrow H^+$$

RCOOH
A carboxylic acid
insol. in H_2O

Primary alcohols can be oxidized to aldehydes, RCHO, by contact with copper metal at high temperatures. The carbon–oxygen double bond is formed by elimination of two atoms of hydrogen as a molecule of H_2; hence the process is referred to as **dehydrogenation**. Reaction is carried

$$RCH_2OH \xrightarrow{Cu,\ 200-300°} R-\overset{H}{\underset{}{C}}{=}O + H_2$$

1° alcohol   An aldehyde

out by passing the vapors of the alcohol through a tube packed with copper turnings heated to 200–300°. Aldehyde and any unreacted alcohol can be condensed and then separated by distillation.

Alternatively, primary alcohols are sometimes oxidized to aldehydes by the use of $K_2Cr_2O_7$. Since, as we shall see (Sec. 23.8), aldehydes are themselves oxidized to acids even more readily than alcohols are, the aldehyde must be removed from the reaction mixture by special techniques before it can be oxidized further.

$$RCH_2OH + Cr_2O_7^= \longrightarrow \underset{\text{An aldehyde}}{R-\overset{\overset{\displaystyle H}{|}}{C}=O} + \underset{green}{Cr^{+++}}$$

$$\underset{\text{1° alcohol}}{} \quad \underset{orange\text{-}red}{}$$

$$\downarrow K_2Cr_2O_7$$

$$R-C\overset{\displaystyle O}{\underset{\displaystyle OH}{\diagdown}}$$

A carboxylic acid

Secondary alcohols are oxidized to ketones, R_2CO, either by $KMnO_4$ or $K_2Cr_2O_7$, or by dehydrogenation over copper. Oxidation past the ketone

$$\underset{\text{2° alcohol}}{R-\overset{\overset{\displaystyle R'}{|}}{C}HOH} \xrightarrow{\text{KMnO}_4 \text{ or } K_2Cr_2O_7; \text{ or Cu, 200–300°}} \underset{\text{A ketone}}{R-\overset{\overset{\displaystyle R'}{|}}{C}=O}$$

stage takes place only under quite vigorous conditions, since it involves the breaking of a carbon–carbon bond.

For the same reason, **tertiary alcohols are not oxidized at all under alkaline conditions;** if acid is present, they are rapidly dehydrated to alkenes, which are then readily oxidized.

These oxidations are of great value since they permit the preparation of important compounds from the readily available alcohols. In Secs. 12.9 and 12.10 we shall discuss further the application of these reactions to organic synthesis.

12.8 Balancing oxidation-reduction equations

All the words and pictures, formulas and equations that we use in talking about organic chemistry have significance only to this extent: they describe and interpret operations and observations that we make in the laboratory using real chemical substances. But to carry out a reaction in the laboratory we must mix chemicals together, and we must mix them together in the proper proportions. A **balanced equation** can tell us what those proper proportions are. Most equations can be balanced simply by inspection; this is not generally feasible, however, for oxidation-reduction equations.

When organic substances are involved in oxidation and reduction, two points arise in connection with the balancing of equations. First, the concept of valence number loses much of its significance with these covalent compounds. Second, nearly all these oxidations and reductions involve hydrogen: a substance being oxidized releases H, or a substance being reduced takes up H. *We shall therefore use H as the basis of our balancing procedure.*

The method of balancing oxidation-reduction equations outlined in the next few paragraphs is simple, involving only three short rules. It is by no means the only way to balance these equations, and the student should use whatever method he finds most convenient (though drawing the line, perhaps, at sheer memorization of each one).

Every oxidation is accompanied, of course, by an equivalent reduction; for convenience we shall balance the two separately, as *half reactions,* and then combine them into a single equation.

To balance an equation we must balance both material and ionic charges. In doing this we shall follow three rules:

   I. **Charge is balanced by H^+ in acid solution or OH^- in basic solution.**
   II. **Oxygen is balanced by H_2O.**
   III. **Hydrogen is balanced by H.**

When each half reaction has been balanced in this way, the release and uptake of H are equalized by multiplying the half reactions by the proper numbers. Finally the half reactions are added together, canceling H, to give the balanced equation for the whole reaction.

For the first example let us take the oxidation of ethyl alcohol by acid dichromate. As with the balancing of any equation, we cannot even start unless we know the chemistry involved; in this case our knowledge of organic chemistry tells us that ethyl alcohol forms acetic acid, and our knowledge of inorganic chemistry tells us that dichromate is reduced to chromic ion.

Let us begin with the reduction. First, we write down reactant and product,

$$Cr_2O_7^= \longrightarrow 2Cr^{+++} \qquad (2Cr^{+++} \text{ from each } Cr_2O_7^=)$$

and, following Rule I, balance ionic charges by H^+ (from the acidic medium).

$$8H^+ + Cr_2O_7^= \longrightarrow 2Cr^{+++} \qquad (6+ = 6+)$$

Next, following Rule II, we balance oxygen by H_2O.

$$8H^+ + Cr_2O_7^= \longrightarrow 2Cr^{+++} + 7H_2O \qquad (7\,O = 7\,O)$$

Now, following Rule III, we balance H atoms by seeing how many, besides those furnished by the acid, are required for material balance.

$$6H + 8H^+ + Cr_2O_7^= \longrightarrow 2Cr^{+++} + 7H_2O \qquad (6 + 8 = 14)$$

Let us follow the same steps for the oxidation. First, we write down reactant and product;

$$CH_3CH_2OH \longrightarrow CH_3COOH$$

we see that there are no ionic charges to balance (Rule I). Next (Rule II), we balance oxygen by H_2O.

$$H_2O + CH_3CH_2OH \longrightarrow CH_3COOH \qquad (2\,O = 2\,O)$$

Now (Rule III) we balance H atoms.

$$H_2O + CH_3CH_2OH \longrightarrow CH_3COOH + \mathbf{4H} \qquad (8 = 4 + 4)$$

Having balanced the half reactions separately, we must now put them together. As always, *oxidation must equal reduction;* the release of H in the oxidation must equal the uptake of H in the reduction. In the present case, we multiply the oxidation equation by three:

$$\mathbf{3}H_2O + \mathbf{3}CH_3CH_2OH \longrightarrow \mathbf{3}CH_3COOH + \mathbf{12H}$$

and the reduction equation by two:

$$\mathbf{12H} + \mathbf{16}H^+ + \mathbf{2}Cr_2O_7^= \longrightarrow \mathbf{4}Cr^{+++} + \mathbf{14}H_2O$$

Thus 12H are released, and 12H are taken up.

Finally, we add the two half reactions together; the 12H are canceled out, and we are left with the actual participants in the reaction.

$$3H_2O + 3CH_3CH_2OH \longrightarrow 3CH_3COOH + 12H$$
$$\underline{12H + 16H^+ + 2Cr_2O_7^= \longrightarrow 4Cr^{+++} + 14H_2O}$$
$$3CH_3CH_2OH + 2Cr_2O_7^= + 16H^+ \longrightarrow 3CH_3COOH + 4Cr^{+++} + 11H_2O$$

For our next example let us take the oxidation of toluene by MnO_4^- in alkaline solution. We shall follow the same procedure as before, except that now we shall use OH^- from the basic medium for balancing ionic charges, rather than the H^+ characteristic of acidic media.

As always, we must know the chemistry involved: toluene is oxidized to benzoate, $C_6H_5COO^-$, and MnO_4^- is reduced to MnO_2.

We write down reactant and product;

$$C_6H_5CH_3 \longrightarrow C_6H_5COO^- \qquad MnO_4^- \longrightarrow MnO_2$$

balance ionic charges by OH^- (Rule I);

$$\mathbf{OH^-} + C_6H_5CH_3 \longrightarrow C_6H_5COO^- \qquad (1- = 1-)$$
$$MnO_4^- \longrightarrow MnO_2 + \mathbf{OH^-} \qquad (1- = 1-)$$

balance oxygen by H_2O (Rule II);

$$\mathbf{H_2O} + OH^- + C_6H_5CH_3 \longrightarrow C_6H_5COO^- \qquad (2\ O = 2\ O)$$
$$MnO_4^- \longrightarrow MnO_2 + OH^- + \mathbf{H_2O} \qquad (4\ O = 4\ O)$$

and balance hydrogen by H (Rule III).

$$H_2O + OH^- + C_6H_5CH_3 \longrightarrow C_6H_5COO^- + \mathbf{6H} \qquad (11 = 5 + 6)$$
$$\mathbf{3H} + MnO_4^- \longrightarrow MnO_2 + OH^- + H_2O \qquad (3 = 3)$$

Having balanced the two half reactions, we now equalize the hydrogen release and uptake by multiplying the reduction reaction by two.

$$6H + 2MnO_4^- \longrightarrow 2MnO_2 + 2OH^- + 2H_2O$$

Finally, we add the two half reactions, canceling H.

$$6H + 2MnO_4^- \longrightarrow 2MnO_2 + 2OH^- + 2H_2O$$
$$\underline{H_2O + OH^- + C_6H_5CH_3 \longrightarrow C_6H_5COO^- + 6H}$$
$$C_6H_5CH_3 + 2MnO_4^- \longrightarrow C_6H_5COO^- + 2MnO_2 + OH^- + H_2O$$

We have balanced these equations by using ions, to eliminate wherever possible extraneous substances that undergo neither oxidation nor reduction during the reaction. To calculate the weights of materials required for an actual reaction, we complete these ionic equations by simply inserting the proper cations and anions on both sides of the equation.

$$3CH_3CH_2OH + 2Cr_2O_7^= + 16H^+ \longrightarrow 3CH_3COOH + 4Cr^{+++} + 11H_2O$$
$$+ 4Na^+ \qquad\qquad\qquad\qquad + 4Na^+$$
$$+ 8SO_4^= \qquad\qquad\qquad\qquad\qquad + 8SO_4^=$$

$$3CH_3CH_2OH + 2Na_2Cr_2O_7 + 8H_2SO_4 \longrightarrow$$
$$3CH_3COOH + 2Cr_2(SO_4)_3 + 2Na_2SO_4 + 11H_2O$$

$$C_6H_5CH_3 + 2MnO_4^- \longrightarrow C_6H_5COO^- + 2MnO_2 + OH^- + H_2O$$
$$+ 2K^+ \qquad\qquad\qquad + K^+ \qquad\qquad + K^+$$

$$C_6H_5CH_3 + 2KMnO_4 \longrightarrow C_6H_5COOK + 2MnO_2 + KOH + H_2O$$

In all this we realize, of course, that free H atoms are neither formed nor consumed, and that oxidation and reduction occur separately only on paper. Like all methods of balancing oxidation-reduction equations, this one is artificial. However, *it works:* after a little practice it is possible to balance any equation, no matter how complicated, by this method.

Problem 12.7 Work out balanced equations for the following reactions:

(a) Combustion of *n*-pentane to CO_2 and H_2O.

(b) Hydroxylation of 2-butene to 2,3-butanediol by $KMnO_4$.

(c) Oxidation of *p*-ethyltoluene to $1,4\text{-}C_6H_4(COOH)_2 + CO_2$ by $K_2Cr_2O_7 + H_2SO_4$.

(d) Transformation of isopropyl alcohol by NaOI into $CHI_3 + CH_3COONa$ (iodoform reaction).

(e) Oxidation of styrene to benzoic acid by $KMnO_4 + H_2SO_4$.

(f) $H_2C_2O_4$ (oxalic acid) $+ MnO_4^- + H^+ \longrightarrow CO_2 + Mn^{++}$ (used to standardize $KMnO_4$ in quantitative analysis).

(g) Reduction of $C_6H_5NO_2$ to $C_6H_5NH_2$ by $Fe + H^+$ (the most important reaction of nitro compounds).

(h) *sec*-Butyl alcohol $\xrightarrow{Na_2Cr_2O_7,\ H_2SO_4}$ $CH_3CH_2COCH_3$.

(i) Cyclohexene $+ HNO_3 \longrightarrow HOOC(CH_2)_4COOH + NO$.

(j) $C_6H_5CH{=}CHCH_2OH \xrightarrow{MnO_2,\ H_2SO_4} C_6H_5COOH + CO_2$.

(k) Reduction of CH_3COOH by $LiAlH_4$ to $(CH_3CH_2O)_4AlLi + H_2 + LiAlO_2$. (Remember that $H^+ + H^- \longrightarrow H_2$.)

(l) Oxidation of 2-methyl-2-butene to $CH_3COCH_3 + CH_3COOH$ by $KMnO_4 + H_2SO_4$.

12.9 Synthesis of alcohols

Let us try to get a broader picture of the synthesis of complicated alcohols. We learned (Sec. 11.11) that they are most often prepared by the reaction of Grignard reagents with aldehydes or ketones. In this chapter we have learned that aldehydes and ketones, as well as the alkyl halides from which the Grignard reagents are made, are themselves most often prepared from alcohols. Finally, we know that the simple alcohols are among our most readily available compounds. We have available to us, then, a synthetic route leading from simple alcohols to more complicated ones.

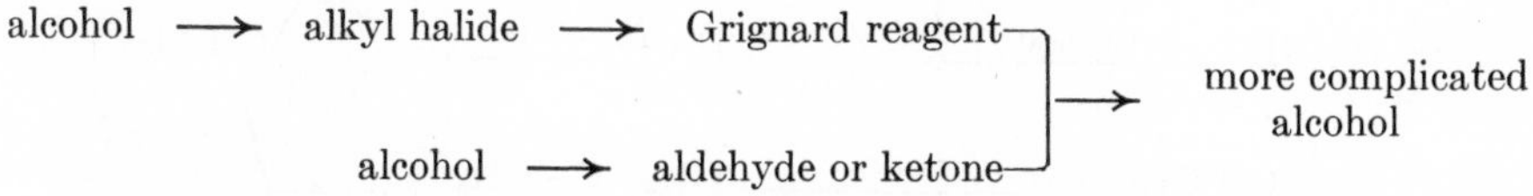

alcohol $\longrightarrow$ alkyl halide $\longrightarrow$ Grignard reagent ⌉
$\longrightarrow$ more complicated alcohol
alcohol $\longrightarrow$ aldehyde or ketone ⌋

As a simple example, consider conversion of the two-carbon ethyl alcohol into the four-carbon *sec*-butyl alcohol:

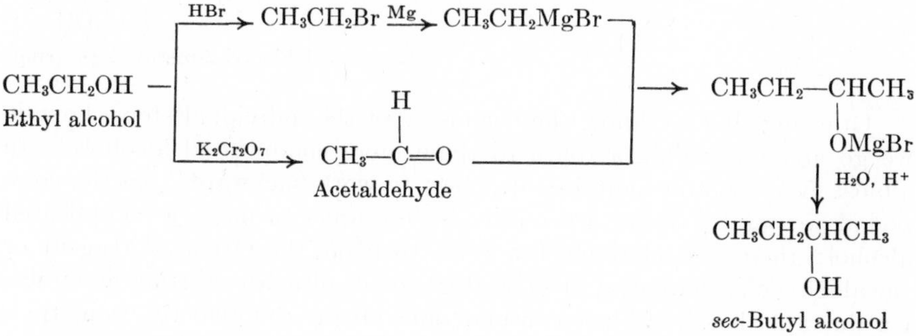

$$CH_3CH_2OH$$
Ethyl alcohol

$\xrightarrow{HBr} CH_3CH_2Br \xrightarrow{Mg} CH_3CH_2MgBr$ ⌉

$\xrightarrow{K_2Cr_2O_7} CH_3\overset{\overset{\displaystyle H}{|}}{C}{=}O$
Acetaldehyde

$\longrightarrow$

$$CH_3CH_2\overset{\overset{\displaystyle }{}}{-}\underset{\underset{\displaystyle OMgBr}{|}}{C}HCH_3$$

$\downarrow$ H$_2$O, H$^+$

$$CH_3CH_2\underset{\underset{\displaystyle OH}{|}}{C}HCH_3$$
sec-Butyl alcohol

Using the *sec*-butyl alcohol thus obtained we could prepare even larger alcohols:

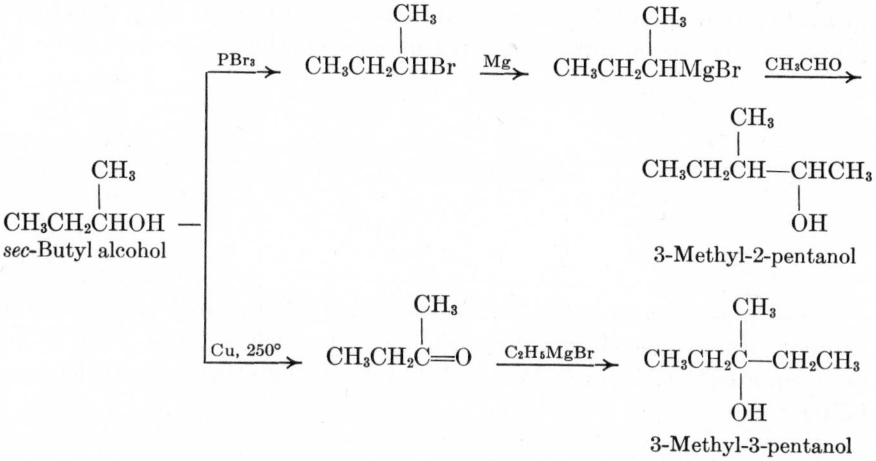

$$CH_3CH_2\underset{\underset{\displaystyle }{}}{\overset{\overset{\displaystyle CH_3}{|}}{C}}HOH$$
sec-Butyl alcohol

$\xrightarrow{PBr_3} CH_3CH_2\overset{\overset{\displaystyle CH_3}{|}}{C}HBr \xrightarrow{Mg} CH_3CH_2\overset{\overset{\displaystyle CH_3}{|}}{C}HMgBr \xrightarrow{CH_3CHO}$

$$CH_3CH_2\overset{\overset{\displaystyle CH_3}{|}}{C}H{-}\underset{\underset{\displaystyle OH}{|}}{C}HCH_3$$
3-Methyl-2-pentanol

$\xrightarrow{Cu, 250°} CH_3CH_2\overset{\overset{\displaystyle CH_3}{|}}{C}{=}O \xrightarrow{C_2H_5MgBr} CH_3CH_2\overset{\overset{\displaystyle CH_3}{|}}{\underset{\underset{\displaystyle OH}{|}}{C}}{-}CH_2CH_3$
3-Methyl-3-pentanol

By combining our knowledge of alcohols with what we know about arenes and aromatic substitution we can extend our syntheses to include aromatic alcohols. For example:

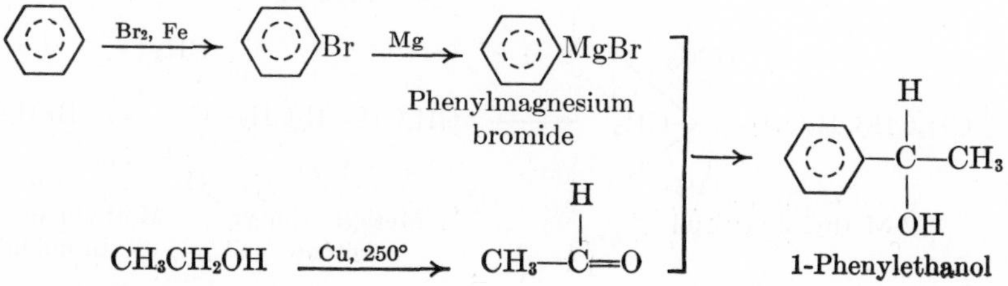

$\bigcirc \xrightarrow{Br_2, Fe} \bigcirc\text{-Br} \xrightarrow{Mg} \bigcirc\text{-MgBr}$
Phenylmagnesium bromide

$CH_3CH_2OH \xrightarrow{Cu, 250°} CH_3\overset{\overset{\displaystyle H}{|}}{C}{=}O$

⌉ $\longrightarrow$ $\bigcirc\text{-}\overset{\overset{\displaystyle H}{|}}{\underset{\underset{\displaystyle OH}{|}}{C}}\text{-CH}_3$
1-Phenylethanol

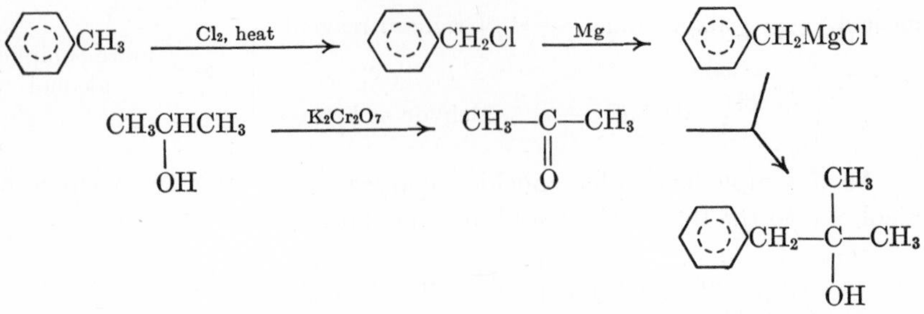

1-Phenyl-2-methyl-2-propanol

Granting that we know the chemistry of the individual steps, how do we go about planning a route to these more complicated alcohols? In almost every organic synthesis it is best to **work backward** from the compound we want. There are relatively few ways to make a complicated alcohol; there are relatively few ways to make the Grignard reagent or the aldehyde or ketone; and so on back to our ultimate starting materials. On the other hand, alcohols can undergo so many different reactions that, if we go at the problem the other way around, we find a bewildering number of paths, few of which take us where we want to go.

Let us suppose (and this is quite reasonable) that we have available all alcohols of four carbons or less, and that we want to make, say, 2-methyl-2-hexanol. Let us set down the structure and see what we need to make it.

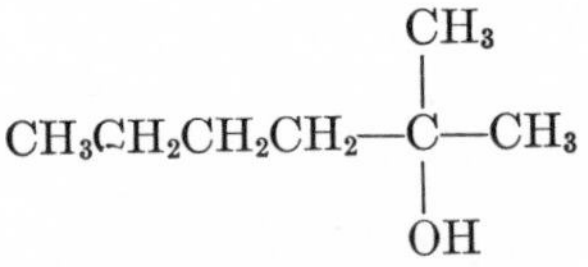

$$CH_3CH_2CH_2CH_2\overset{\overset{\displaystyle CH_3}{|}}{\underset{\underset{\displaystyle OH}{|}}{C}}CH_3$$

2-Methyl-2-hexanol

Since it is a tertiary alcohol, we must use a Grignard reagent and a ketone. But which Grignard reagent? And which ketone? Using the same approach as before (Sec. 11.13), we see that there are two possibilities:

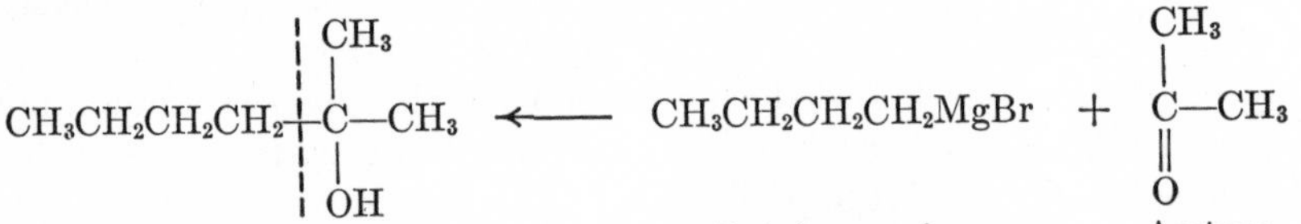

2-Methyl-2-hexanol   n-Butylmagnesium   Acetone
                          bromide

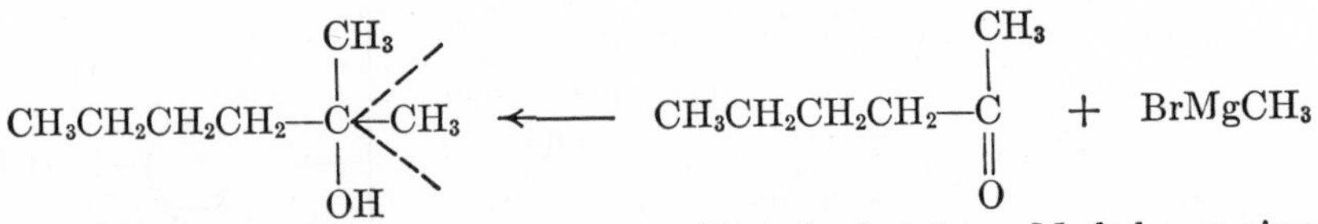

2-Methyl-2-hexanol   Methyl n-butyl   Methylmagnesium
                          ketone   bromide

Of these two possibilities we would select the one involving the four-carbon Grignard reagent and the three-carbon ketone; now how are we to make *them*? The Grignard reagent can be made only from the corresponding alkyl halide, n-butyl bromide, and that in turn most likely from an alcohol, n-butyl alcohol. Acetone requires, of course, isopropyl alcohol. Putting together the entire synthesis, we have the following sequence:

$$CH_3CH_2CH_2CH_2MgBr \xleftarrow{Mg} CH_3CH_2CH_2CH_2Br$$

$$\uparrow HBr$$

$$CH_3CH_2CH_2CH_2OH$$
n-Butyl alcohol

$$
\begin{array}{c}
\text{CH}_3 \\
|\\
\text{CH}_3\text{CH}_2\text{CH}_2\text{CH}_2\!-\!\overset{}{\text{C}}\!-\!\text{CH}_3 \\
|\\
\text{OH}
\end{array}
$$
2-Methyl-2-hexanol

$$
\begin{array}{c}
\text{CH}_3 \\
|\\
\text{C}\!-\!\text{CH}_3 \xleftarrow[\text{heat}]{\text{Cu}} \\
\|\\
\text{O}
\end{array}
\qquad
\begin{array}{c}
\text{CH}_3 \\
|\\
\text{H}\!-\!\text{C}\!-\!\text{CH}_3 \\
|\\
\text{OH}
\end{array}
$$
Isopropyl alcohol

Let us consider that in addition to our alcohols of four carbons or less we have available benzene and toluene, another reasonable assumption, and that we wish to make, say, 1-phenyl-3-methyl-2-butanol. Again we set down the structure of the desired alcohol and work backward to the

$$
\begin{array}{c}
\qquad\quad \text{H}\quad\ \text{H}\quad \text{CH}_3 \\
\qquad\quad |\qquad |\qquad | \\
\langle\bigcirc\rangle\!-\!\text{C}\!-\!\!-\!\text{C}\!-\!\!-\!\text{C}\!-\!\!-\!\text{CH}_3 \\
\qquad\quad |\qquad |\qquad | \\
\qquad\quad \text{H}\quad \text{OH}\quad \text{H}
\end{array}
$$
1-Phenyl-3-methyl-2-butanol

starting materials. For a secondary alcohol, a Grignard reagent and an aldehyde are indicated, and again there are two choices: we may consider the molecule to be put together between (a) C–1 and C–2 or (b) C–2 and C–3. Of the two possibilities we select the first, since this requires

$$
\qquad\qquad\text{(a)}\quad\ \text{(b)}
$$

$$
\begin{array}{c}
\qquad\quad \text{H}\ |\ \text{H}\ |\ \text{CH}_3 \\
\qquad\quad |\quad |\quad |\quad |\quad | \\
\langle\bigcirc\rangle\!-\!\text{C}\!-\!\!|\!-\!\text{C}\!-\!\!|\!-\!\text{C}\!-\!\text{CH}_3 \\
\qquad\quad |\quad |\quad |\quad |\quad | \\
\qquad\quad \text{H}\ |\ \text{OH}\ |\ \text{H}
\end{array}
$$

a compound with only one carbon attached to the benzene ring, which we have available in toluene. We need, then, a four-carbon aldehyde and benzylmagnesium chloride. The aldehyde can readily be made from isobutyl alcohol, but how about benzylmagnesium chloride? This is, of course, made from benzyl chloride, which in turn is made from toluene by free radical chlorination. Our synthesis is complete:

$$\text{(C}_6\text{H}_5)\text{CH}_2\text{MgCl} \xleftarrow{\text{Mg}} \text{(C}_6\text{H}_5)\text{CH}_2\text{Cl}$$

Benzylmagnesium chloride

$$\uparrow \text{Cl}_2, \text{ heat}$$

$$\text{(C}_6\text{H}_5)\text{CH}_2\text{-CH-CH-CH}_3 \text{ (CH}_3\text{)} \leftarrow$$

with CH$_3$ and OH substituents

$$\text{(C}_6\text{H}_5)\text{CH}_3$$

1-Phenyl-3-methyl-2-butanol   Toluene

$$\text{O=C-CH-CH}_3 \text{ (H)(CH}_3\text{)} \xleftarrow{\text{K}_2\text{Cr}_2\text{O}_7} \text{HOCH}_2\text{-CH-CH}_3 \text{ (CH}_3\text{)}$$

Isobutyl alcohol

Now that we know how to make complicated alcohols from simple ones, what can we use them for?

12.10 Syntheses using alcohols

The alcohols that we have learned to make can be converted into other kinds of compounds having the same carbon skeleton; from complicated alcohols we can make complicated aldehydes, ketones, acids, halides, alkenes, alkynes, alkanes, etc.

Alkyl halides are prepared from alcohols by use of hydrogen halides or phosphorus halides. Phosphorus halides are often preferred because they tend less to bring about rearrangement (Sec. 12.4).

Alkenes are prepared from alcohols either by direct dehydration or by dehydrohalogenation of intermediate alkyl halides; to avoid rearrangement we often select dehydrohalogenation of halides even though this route involves an extra step.

alcohol

— $\xrightarrow{\text{acid}}$ dehydration to alkene   *Rearrangements possible*

— $\xrightarrow{\text{PBr}_3 \text{ or PI}_3}$ alkyl halide $\xrightarrow{\text{KOH}}$ alkene $\xrightarrow[\text{cat.}]{\text{H}_2}$ alkane

— $\xrightarrow{\text{HX}}$ alkyl halide   *Rearrangements possible*

Alkanes, we learned (Sec. 3.15), are best prepared from the corresponding alkenes by hydrogenation, so that now we have a route from complicated alcohols to complicated alkanes.

Complicated aldehydes and ketones are made by oxidizing complicated alcohols. By reaction with Grignard reagents these aldehydes and ketones can be converted into even more complicated alcohols, and so on.

Given the time, necessary inorganic reagents, and the single alcohol ethanol, our chemical Crusoe of Sec. 11.6 could synthesize all the aliphatic compounds that have ever been made — and for that matter the aromatic ones, too.

In planning the synthesis of these other kinds of compounds we again follow our system of working backward. We try to limit the synthesis to as few steps as possible, but nevertheless do not sacrifice purity for time. For example, where rearrangement is likely to occur we prepare an alkene in two steps via the halide rather than by the single step of dehydration.

Assuming again that we have available alcohols of four carbons or less, benzene, and toluene, let us take as an example 3-methyl-1-butene.

$$CH_3-\overset{\overset{\displaystyle CH_3}{|}}{CH}-CH=CH_2$$

3-Methyl-1-butene

It could be prepared by dehydrohalogenation of an alkyl halide of the same carbon skeleton, or by dehydration of an alcohol. If the halogen or hydroxyl group were attached to C–2 we would obtain some of the desired product, but much more of its isomer, 2-methyl-2-butene:

$$CH_3-\overset{\overset{\displaystyle CH_3}{|}}{\underset{\underset{\displaystyle H}{|}}{C}}---\overset{\overset{\displaystyle H}{|}}{\underset{\underset{\displaystyle Br}{|}}{C}}-CH_3 \xrightarrow{KOH}$$

$$CH_3-\overset{\overset{\displaystyle CH_3}{|}}{\underset{\underset{\displaystyle H}{|}}{C}}---\overset{\overset{\displaystyle H}{|}}{\underset{\underset{\displaystyle OH}{|}}{C}}-CH_3 \xrightarrow{acid}$$

$$\longrightarrow CH_3-\overset{\overset{\displaystyle CH_3}{|}}{C}=CH-CH_3 + \text{some } CH_3-\overset{\overset{\displaystyle CH_3}{|}}{\underset{\underset{\displaystyle H}{|}}{C}}-CH=CH_2$$

2-Methyl-2-butene   3-Methyl-1-butene
Chief product

We would select, then, the compound with the functional group attached to C–1. Even so, if we were to use the alcohol there would be extensive rearrangement to yield, again, the more stable 2-methyl-2-butene:

$$CH_3-\overset{\overset{\displaystyle CH_3}{|}}{\underset{\underset{\displaystyle H}{|}}{C}}---\overset{\overset{\displaystyle H}{|}}{\underset{\underset{\displaystyle H}{|}}{C}}-\overset{\overset{\displaystyle H}{|}}{\underset{\underset{\displaystyle OH}{|}}{C}}-H \xrightarrow{acid} CH_3-\overset{\overset{\displaystyle CH_3}{|}}{\underset{\underset{\displaystyle H}{|}}{C}}-CH=CH_2 \text{ and mostly } CH_3-\overset{\overset{\displaystyle CH_3}{|}}{C}=CH-CH_3$$

3-Methyl-1-butanol   3-Methyl-1-butene   2-Methyl-2-butene

Only dehydrohalogenation of 1-bromo-3-methylbutane would yield the desired product in pure form:

$$CH_3-\overset{\overset{\displaystyle CH_3}{|}}{\underset{\underset{\displaystyle H}{|}}{C}}---\overset{\overset{\displaystyle H}{|}}{\underset{\underset{\displaystyle H}{|}}{C}}-\overset{\overset{\displaystyle H}{|}}{\underset{\underset{\displaystyle Br}{|}}{C}}-H \xrightarrow{\text{alcoholic KOH}} CH_3-\overset{\overset{\displaystyle CH_3}{|}}{\underset{\underset{\displaystyle H}{|}}{C}}-CH=CH_2$$

1-Bromo-3-methylbutane   3-Methyl-1-butene

How do we prepare the necessary alkyl halide? Certainly not by bromination of an alkane, since even if we could make the proper alkane in some way, halogenation would yield many products. As usual, then, we would prepare the halide from the corresponding alcohol, in this case 3-methyl-1-butanol. Since this is a primary alcohol (without branching near the —OH group), and hence does not form the halide via the carbonium ion, rearrangement is not likely; we might use, then, either hydrogen bromide or PBr$_3$.

$$
\begin{array}{c}
\text{CH}_3 \\
|\\
\text{CH}_3\text{—CH—CH}_2\text{—CH}_2\text{Br}
\end{array}
\quad \xleftarrow{\text{PBr}_3} \quad
\begin{array}{c}
\text{CH}_3 \\
|\\
\text{CH}_3\text{—CH—CH}_2\text{—CH}_2\text{OH} \\
\text{3-Methyl-1-butanol}
\end{array}
$$

Now, how do we make 3-methyl-1-butanol? It is a primary alcohol and contains one carbon more than our largest available alcohol; therefore we would use the reaction of a Grignard reagent with formaldehyde.

$$
\begin{array}{c}
\text{CH}_3 \\
|\\
\text{CH}_3\text{—CH—CH}_2\text{—CH}_2\text{OH} \\
\text{3-Methyl-1-butanol}
\end{array}
\leftarrow
\left[
\begin{array}{c}
\text{H} \\
|\\
\text{H—C}\!\!=\!\!\text{O} \\
\text{Formaldehyde} \\[1em]
\text{CH}_3 \\
|\\
\text{CH}_3\text{—CH—CH}_2\text{MgBr} \\
\text{Isobutylmagnesium bromide}
\end{array}
\right.
$$

The necessary Grignard reagent is isobutylmagnesium bromide, which we could have prepared from isobutyl bromide, and that in turn from isobutyl alcohol. The formaldehyde is made by dehydrogenation of methanol over hot copper. The entire sequence, from which we could expect to obtain quite pure 3-methyl-1-butene, is the following:

$$
\begin{array}{c}
\text{CH}_3 \\
|\\
\text{CH}_3\text{-CH–CH}\!\!=\!\!\text{CH}_2 \\
\text{3-Methyl-1-butene}
\end{array}
\xleftarrow{\text{KOH}}
\begin{array}{c}
\text{CH}_3 \\
|\\
\text{CH}_3\text{-CH–CH}_2\text{–CH}_2\text{Br}
\end{array}
\xleftarrow{\text{PBr}_3}
\begin{array}{c}
\text{CH}_3 \\
|\\
\text{CH}_3\text{-CH–CH}_2\text{–CH}_2\text{OH} \\
\text{3-Methyl-1-butanol}
\end{array}
$$

$$
\begin{array}{c}
\text{CH}_3 \\
|\\
\text{CH}_3\text{–CH—CH}_2\text{—CH}_2\text{OH} \\
\text{3-Methyl-1-butanol}
\end{array}
\leftarrow
\left[
\begin{array}{c}
\text{H} \\
|\\
\text{H—C}\!\!=\!\!\text{O} \xleftarrow{\text{Cu, heat}} \text{CH}_3\text{OH} \\
\hspace{3em}\text{Methanol} \\[1em]
\text{CH}_3 \hspace{6em} \text{CH}_3 \\
|\hspace{8em}|\\
\text{CH}_3\text{—CH—CH}_2\text{MgBr} \xleftarrow{\text{Mg}} \text{CH}_3\text{—CH—CH}_2\text{Br} \\
\hspace{12em}\uparrow \text{PBr}_3 \\
\hspace{11em}\text{CH}_3 \\
\hspace{11em}| \\
\hspace{11em}\text{CH}_3\text{—CH—CH}_2\text{OH} \\
\hspace{11em}\text{Isobutyl alcohol}
\end{array}
\right.
$$

12.11 Analysis of alcohols: characterization. Lucas test. Iodoform test

Alcohols dissolve in cold concentrated sulfuric acid. This property they share with alkenes, amines, practically all compounds containing oxygen, and easily sulfonated compounds. (Alcohols, like other oxygen-containing compounds, form oxonium salts, which dissolve in the highly polar sulfuric acid.)

Primary and secondary alcohols — but not tertiary — are oxidized by cold, dilute, neutral $KMnO_4$ (Sec. 12.7). This property they share with alkenes, alkynes, aldehydes, and certain other easily oxidized compounds.

Alcohols do not decolorize bromine in carbon tetrachloride. This property serves to distinguish them from alkenes and alkynes.

Reaction of alcohols with sodium metal, with the evolution of hydrogen gas, is of some use in characterization; a *wet* compound of any kind, of course, will do the same thing, until the water is used up.

The presence of the —OH group in a molecule is often indicated by the formation of an ester upon treatment with an acid chloride or anhydride (Sec. 17.15). Some esters are sweet-smelling; others are solids with sharp melting points, and can be used as derivatives in identifications. (If the molecular formulas of starting material and product are determined, it is possible to calculate *how many* —OH groups are present.)

Problem 12.8 Make a table to show the response of each kind of compound we have studied so far toward the following reagents: (a) cold concentrated H_2SO_4; (b) cold, dilute, neutral $KMnO_4$; (c) Br_2 in CCl_4; (d) cold fuming sulfuric acid; (e) $CHCl_3$ and $AlCl_3$; (f) sodium metal.

Whether an alcohol is primary, secondary, or tertiary is shown by the **Lucas test,** which is based upon the difference in reactivity of the three classes toward hydrogen halides (Sec. 12.4). Alcohols (of not more than six carbons) are soluble in the *Lucas reagent,* a mixture of concentrated hydrochloric acid and zinc chloride. (Why are they more soluble in this than in water?) The corresponding alkyl chlorides are insoluble. Formation of a chloride from an alcohol is indicated by the cloudiness that appears when the chloride separates from the solution; hence, the time required for cloudiness to appear is a measure of the reactivity of the alcohol.

A tertiary alcohol reacts immediately with the Lucas reagent, and a secondary alcohol reacts within five minutes; a primary alcohol does not react appreciably at room temperature. As we have seen, benzyl alcohol and allyl alcohol react as rapidly as tertiary alcohols with the Lucas reagent; allyl chloride, however, is soluble in the reagent. (Why?)

Whether or not an alcohol contains one particular structural unit is shown by the **iodoform test.** The alcohol is treated with iodine and sodium hydroxide (sodium hypoiodite, NaOI); an alcohol of the structure

$$\begin{array}{c} \text{H} \\ | \\ \text{R} \!-\!\!-\! \text{C} \!-\! \text{CH}_3 \\ | \\ \text{OH} \end{array} \quad \textit{where R is H or an alkyl or aryl group}$$

yields a yellow precipitate of iodoform (CHI_3, m.p. 119°). For example:

Gives positive iodoform test	*Gives negative iodoform test*
$$\begin{array}{c} \text{H} \\ | \\ \text{CH}_3 \!-\! \text{C} \!-\! \text{H} \\ | \\ \text{OH} \end{array}$$	Any other primary alcohol

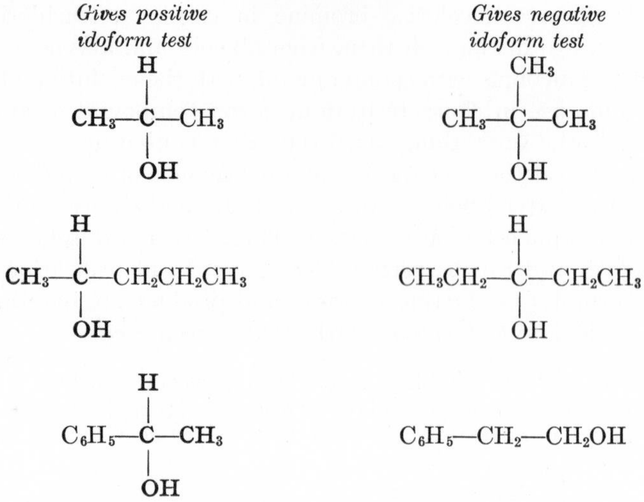

Gives positive idoform test

H
|
CH₃—C—CH₃
|
OH

Gives negative idoform test

CH₃
|
CH₃—C—CH₃
|
OH

H
|
CH₃—C—CH₂CH₂CH₃
|
OH

H
|
CH₃CH₂—C—CH₂CH₃
|
OH

H
|
C₆H₅—C—CH₃
|
OH

C₆H₅—CH₂—CH₂OH

The reaction involves oxidation, halogenation, and cleavage.

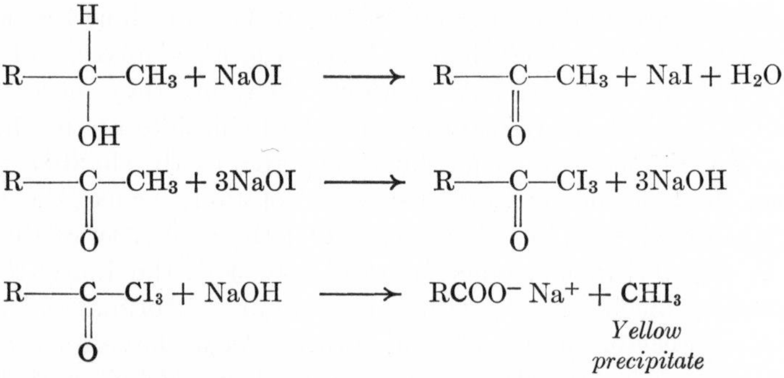

$$R—\underset{\underset{OH}{|}}{\overset{\overset{H}{|}}{C}}—CH_3 + NaOI \longrightarrow R—\underset{\underset{O}{\|}}{C}—CH_3 + NaI + H_2O$$

$$R—\underset{\underset{O}{\|}}{C}—CH_3 + 3NaOI \longrightarrow R—\underset{\underset{O}{\|}}{C}—CI_3 + 3NaOH$$

$$R—\underset{\underset{O}{\|}}{C}—CI_3 + NaOH \longrightarrow RCOO^- Na^+ + CHI_3$$
Yellow precipitate

As would be expected from the equations, a compound of structure

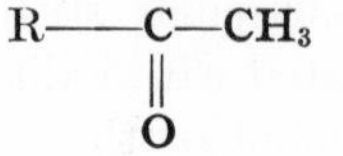

$$R—\underset{\underset{O}{\|}}{C}—CH_3 \quad \textit{where R is H or an alkyl or aryl group}$$

also gives a positive test (Sec. 23.22).

In certain special cases this reaction is used not as a test, but to synthesize the carboxylic acid, RCOOH. Here, hypobromite or the cheaper hypochlorite would probably be used.

PROBLEMS

1. Refer to the isomeric pentyl alcohols of Problem 1(a), page 331. (a) Indicate which (if any) will give a positive iodoform test. (b) Describe how each will respond to the Lucas reagent. (c) Describe how each will respond to dilute, aqueous, neutral KMnO₄. (d) Outline all steps in a possible synthesis of each, starting from alcohols of four carbons or less, and using any necessary inorganic reagents.

2. Give structures and names of the chief products expected from the reaction (if any) of cyclohexanol with:

(a) cold conc. H_2SO_4
(b) H_2SO_4, heat
(c) cold dilute $KMnO_4$
(d) Br_2/CCl_4
(e) conc. aqueous HBr
(f) $P + I_2$
(g) Na
(h) CH_3COOH, H^+
(i) H_2, Ni
(j) CH_3MgBr
(k) Cu, 250°

(l) NaOH(aq)
(m) product (e) + Mg
(n) product (m) + product (k)
(o) product (b) + Br_2/CCl_4
(p) product (b) + C_6H_6, HF
(q) product (b) + H_2, Ni
(r) product (p) + HNO_3/H_2SO_4
(s) product (b) + N-bromosuccinimide (see Problem 6.12, page 183)
(t) product (k) + C_6H_5MgBr

3. Outline all steps in a possible laboratory synthesis of each of the following compounds from *n*-butyl alcohol, using any necessary inorganic reagents. Follow instructions of Problem 17, page 160.

(a) *n*-butyl bromide
(b) 1-butene
(c) *n*-butyl hydrogen sulfate
(d) potassium *n*-butoxide
(e) *n*-butyraldehyde, $CH_3CH_2CH_2CHO$
(f) *n*-butyric acid, $CH_3CH_2CH_2COOH$
(g) *n*-butane
(h) 1,2-dibromobutane
(i) 1-chloro-2-butanol
(j) 1-butyne

(k) 1,2-butanediol, $CH_3CH_2CHOHCH_2OH$
(l) *n*-octane
(m) 3-octyne
(n) 4-octanol
(o) 4-octanone, $CH_3CH_2CH_2CH_2CCH_2CH_2CH_3$ $\overset{\|}{O}$
(p) 5-(*n*-propyl)-5-nonanol
(q) *n*-butyl *n*-butyrate, $CH_3CH_2CH_2C\text{—}OCH_2CH_2CH_2CH_3$ $\overset{\|}{O}$

4. Give structures and (where possible) names of the principal organic products of the following:

(a) benzyl alcohol + Mg
(b) isobutyl alcohol + benzoic acid + H^+
(c) ethylene bromide + excess NaOH(aq)
(d) β-phenylethyl alcohol + Cu, 250°
(e) *n*-butyl alcohol + H_2, Pt
(f) crotyl alcohol ($CH_3CH\text{=}CHCH_2OH$) + Br_2/H_2O
(g) CH_3OH + C_2H_5MgBr
(h) *p*-bromobenzyl bromide + NaOH(aq)
(i) *tert*-butyl alcohol + C_6H_6 + H_2SO_4
(j) $C_6H_5CCH_3$ + NaOI $\overset{\|}{O}$

5. Complete and balance the equations for the following reactions:

(a) cyclohexene + cold dilute $KMnO_4$
(b) cyclohexene + $KMnO_4$ + H_2SO_4 + heat
(c) *p*-nitrotoluene + $K_2Cr_2O_7$ + H_2SO_4
(d) *o*-nitroethylbenzene + $KMnO_4$ + KOH
(e) cyclopentene + peroxyformic acid
(f) 3-methyl-2-butanol + $K_2Cr_2O_7$ + H_2SO_4
(g) 3-methyl-1-butanol + $K_2Cr_2O_7$ + H_2SO_4 $\longrightarrow$ $C_5H_{10}O_2$
(h) 3-methyl-2-butanol + I_2 + NaOH
(i) allylbenzene + HNO_3 $\longrightarrow$ benzoic acid + CO_2 + NO_2

6. Arrange the alcohols of each set in order of reactivity toward aqueous HBr:

(a) the isomeric pentyl alcohols of Problem 1(a), page 331 (*Note:* it may be necessary to list these in groups of about the same reactivity.)

(b) 1-phenyl-1-propanol, 3-phenyl-1-propanol, 1-phenyl-2-propanol

(c) benzyl alcohol, *p*-cyanobenzyl alcohol, *p*-hydroxybenzyl alcohol

(d) 2-buten-1-ol, 3-buten-1-ol

(e) cyclopentylcarbinol, 1-methylcyclopentanol, *trans*-2-methylcyclopentanol

(f) benzyl alcohol, diphenylcarbinol, methanol, triphenylcarbinol

7. Arrange the alcohols of each set in order of acidity:

(a) dimethylethylcarbinol, isopentyl alcohol, 3-methyl-2-butanol

(b) benzyl alcohol, *p*-chlorobenzyl alcohol, *p*-ethylbenzyl alcohol

8. Can you account for the order of acidity: triphenylmethane > diphenylmethane > toluene > *n*-pentane (*Hint:* see Secs. 12.6 and 9.23.)

9. Outline the sequence of steps that best accounts for the following facts.

(a) 3-methyl-1-butene + HCl yields both 3-chloro-2-methylbutane and 2-chloro-2-methylbutane.

(b) Either 2-pentanol or 3-pentanol + HCl yields both 2-chloropentane and 3-chloropentane.

(c) 2,2,4-trimethyl-3-pentanol $\xrightarrow{\text{Al}_2\text{O}_3,\ \text{heat}}$ 2,4,4-trimethyl-2-pentene + 2,4,4-trimethyl-1-pentene + 2,3,4-trimethyl-2-pentene + 2,3,4-trimethyl-1-pentene + 3-methyl-2-isopropyl-1-butene + 3,3,4-trimethyl-1-pentene.

(d) 2,2-dimethylcyclohexanol $\xrightarrow{\text{H}^+}$ 1,2-dimethylcyclohexene + 1-isopropylcyclopentene (*Hint:* use models.)

(e) cyclobutyldiethylcarbinol $\xrightarrow{\text{H}^+}$ 1,2-diethylcyclopentene

(f)

$\xrightarrow{\text{H}^+}$ 1,2-dimethylcyclohexene

10. Outline all steps in a possible laboratory synthesis of each of the following compounds from cyclohexanol and any open-chain alcohols of four carbons or less.

(a) cyclohexanone ($C_6H_{10}O$)
(b) bromocyclohexane
(c) 1-methylcyclohexanol
(d) cyclohexylmethylcarbinol
(e) *trans*-1,2-dibromocyclohexane
(f) cyclohexylcarbinol
(g) 1-cyclohexyl-1-propanol
(h) cyclohexanecarboxylic acid
(i) adipic acid, $HOOC(CH_2)_4COOH$

11. Outline all steps in a possible laboratory synthesis of each of the following compounds from benzene, toluene, and alcohols of four carbons or less.

(a) 2,3-dimethyl-2-butanol
(b) 2-phenyl-2-propanol
(c) 2-phenylpropene
(d) 2-methyl-1-butene
(e) isopentane
(f) 1,2-dibromo-2-methylbutane
(g) 3-hexanol
(h) 3-hexanone (I)
(i) 4-ethyl-4-heptanol
(j) 2-bromo-2-methylhexane

(k) 1-chloro-1-phenylethane (α-phenylethyl chloride)
(l) *sec*-butylbenzene
(m) methyl isopropyl ketone (II)
(n) methylacetylene
(o) 2-methylhexane
(p) benzyl methyl ketone (III)
(q) 2,3-diphenylbutane
(r) 3-heptyne
(s) ethyl propionate (IV)

$$\underset{\underset{\text{I}}{\overset{\|}{\text{O}}}}{CH_3CH_2CH_2\overset{}{C}CH_2CH_3} \qquad \underset{\underset{\text{II}}{\overset{\|}{\text{O}}}}{CH_3\overset{}{C}CH(CH_3)_2} \qquad \underset{\underset{\text{III}}{\overset{\|}{\text{O}}}}{C_6H_5CH_2\overset{}{C}CH_3} \qquad \underset{\underset{\text{IV}}{\overset{\|}{\text{O}}}}{CH_3CH_2\overset{}{C}\text{—}OCH_2CH_3}$$

PROBLEMS

12. Compounds "labeled" at various positions by isotopic atoms are useful in determining reaction mechanisms and in following the fate of compounds in biological systems. Outline a possible synthesis of each of the following labeled compounds using $C^{14}H_3OH$ as the source of C^{14}, and D_2O as the source of deuterium.

(a) 2-methyl-1-propanol-1-C^{14}, $(CH_3)_2CHC^{14}H_2OH$
(b) 2-methyl-1-propanol-2-C^{14}, $(CH_3)_2C^{14}HCH_2OH$
(c) 2-methyl-1-propanol-3-C^{14}, $C^{14}H_3CH(CH_3)CH_2OH$
(d) propene-1-C^{14}, $CH_3CH{=}C^{14}H_2$
(e) propene-2-C^{14}, $CH_3C^{14}H{=}CH_2$
(f) propene-3-C^{14}, $C^{14}H_3CH{=}CH_2$
(g) C_6H_5D
(h) $C_6H_5CH_2D$
(i) $p\text{-}DC_6H_4CH_3$
(j) $CH_3CH_2CHDC^{14}H_3$

13. Assign structures to the compounds A through ZZ.

(a) ethylene + Cl_2(aq) $\longrightarrow$ A (C_2H_5OCl)
    A + $NaHCO_3$(aq) $\longrightarrow$ B ($C_2H_6O_2$)
(b) ethylene + Cl_2(aq) $\longrightarrow$ A (C_2H_5OCl)
    A + HNO_3 $\longrightarrow$ C ($C_2H_3O_2Cl$)
    C + H_2O $\longrightarrow$ D ($C_2H_4O_3$)
(c) propylene + Cl_2 (600°) $\longrightarrow$ E (C_3H_5Cl)
    E + Cl_2(aq) $\longrightarrow$ F ($C_3H_6OCl_2$)
    F + NaOH(aq) $\longrightarrow$ G ($C_3H_8O_3$)
(d) allyl alcohol + Br_2/CCl_4 $\longrightarrow$ H ($C_3H_6OBr_2$)
    H + HNO_3 $\longrightarrow$ I ($C_3H_4O_2Br_2$)
    I + Zn $\longrightarrow$ J ($C_3H_4O_2$)
(e) 1,2,3-tribromopropane + KOH(alc) $\longrightarrow$ K ($C_3H_4Br_2$)
    K + NaOH(aq) $\longrightarrow$ L (C_3H_5OBr)
    L + KOH(alc) $\longrightarrow$ M (C_3H_4O)
(f) 2,2-dichloropropane + NaOH(aq) $\longrightarrow$ [N ($C_3H_8O_2$)] $\longrightarrow$ O (C_3H_6O)
(g) propyne + Cl_2(aq) $\longrightarrow$ [P ($C_3H_6O_2Cl_2$)] $\longrightarrow$ Q ($C_3H_4OCl_2$)
    Q + Cl_2(aq) $\longrightarrow$ R ($C_3H_3OCl_3$)
    R + NaOH(aq) $\longrightarrow$ $CHCl_3$ + S ($C_2H_3O_2Na$)
(h) cyclohexene + $KMnO_4$ $\longrightarrow$ T ($C_6H_{12}O_2$)
(i) T + CH_3COOH, H^+ $\longrightarrow$ U ($C_{10}H_{16}O_4$)
(i) V ($C_3H_8O_3$) + CH_3COOH, H^+ $\longrightarrow$ W ($C_9H_{14}O_6$)
(j) cyclohexanol + $K_2Cr_2O_7$, H^+ $\longrightarrow$ X ($C_6H_{10}O$)
    X + $m\text{-}CH_3C_6H_4MgBr$, followed by H_2O $\longrightarrow$ Y ($C_{13}H_{18}O$)
    Y + heat $\longrightarrow$ Z ($C_{13}H_{16}$)
    Z + Ni (300°) $\longrightarrow$ ZZ ($C_{13}H_{12}$)

14. Describe simple chemical tests that would serve to distinguish between:

(a) n-butyl alcohol and n-octane
(b) n-butyl alcohol and 1-octene
(c) n-butyl alcohol and n-pentyl bromide
(d) n-butyl alcohol and 3-buten-1-ol
(e) 3-buten-1-ol and 2-buten-1-ol
(f) 3-pentanol and 1-pentanol
(g) 3-pentanol and 2-pentanol
(h) 3-phenyl-1-propanol and cinnamyl alcohol (3-phenyl-2-propen-1-ol)
(i) cis-2-methylcyclohexanol, 1-methylcyclohexanol, and cyclohexylcarbinol
(j) n-butyl alcohol and $tert$-pentyl alcohol
(k) p-bromobenzyl alcohol and p-ethylbenzyl alcohol
(l) α-phenylethyl alcohol and β-phenylethyl alcohol

15. By use of Table 12.1 tell which alcohol or alcohols each of the following is likely to be. Tell what further steps you would take to identify it or to confirm your identification. (α-Naphthylurethanes are readily made from most alcohols by reaction with α-naphthyl isocyanate, Sec. 25.14.)

A: b.p. 115–7°; Lucas test, secondary; 3,5-dinitrobenzoate, m.p. 95–6°
B: b.p. 128–30°; negative halogen test; Lucas test, primary
C: b.p. 128–31°; positive iodoform test
D: b.p. 115–8°; 3,5-dinitrobenzoate, m.p. 60–1°
E: b.p. 117–9°; α-naphthylurethane, m.p. 69–71°

TABLE 12.1

DERIVATIVES OF SOME ALCOHOLS

Alcohol	B.p., °C	α-Naphthylurethane M.p., °C	3,5-Dinitrobenzoate M.p., °C
3-Methyl-2-butanol	114	112	76
3-Pentanol	116	71	97
n-Butyl alcohol	118	71	64
2-Pentanol	119	76	61
1-Chloro-2-propanol	127	—	83
2-Methyl-1-butanol	128	97	62
Ethylene chlorohydrin	129	101	92
4-Methyl-2-pentanol	131	88	65
3-Methyl-1-butanol	132	67	62
2-Chloro-1-propanol	132	—	76

16. Although it is a secondary alcohol, 1-chloro-2-propanol behaves like a primary alcohol in the Lucas test. Can you suggest a reason for this behavior?

17. (a) Compound A of formula $C_9H_{12}O$ responded to a series of tests as follows:

(1) Na $\longrightarrow$ slow formation of gas bubbles
(2) acetic anhydride $\longrightarrow$ pleasant smelling product
(3) cold dilute $KMnO_4$ $\longrightarrow$ color discharged
(4) hot $KMnO_4$ $\longrightarrow$ benzoic acid
(5) Br_2/CCl_4 $\longrightarrow$ no decolorization
(6) $I_2 + NaOH$ $\longrightarrow$ yellow solid
(7) rotated plane-polarized light

What was A? Write equations for all the above reactions.

(b) Compound B, an isomer of A, also was found to be optically active. It showed the same behavior as A except for test (6). From the oxidation of B by cold $KMnO_4$ in test (4) there was isolated an acid of formula $C_9H_{10}O_2$. What was B?

18. *Geraniol*, $C_{10}H_{18}O$, a terpene found in rose oil, adds two moles of bromine to form a tetrabromide, $C_{10}H_{18}OBr_4$. It can be oxidized to a ten-carbon aldehyde or to a ten-carbon carboxylic acid. Upon vigorous oxidation, geraniol yields:

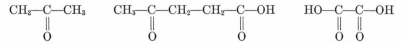

(a) Keeping in mind the isoprene rule (Sec. 6.21), what is the most likely structure for geraniol? (b) Nerol (Problem 17, page 217) can be converted into the same saturated alcohol as geraniol, and yields the same oxidation products as geraniol, yet has different physical properties. What is the most probable structural relationship between geraniol and nerol? (c) Like nerol, geraniol is converted by sulfuric acid into α-terpineol (Problem 17, page 217), but much more slowly than nerol. On this basis, what structures might you assign to nerol and geraniol? (*Hint:* use models.)

19. Upon treatment with HBr, both geraniol (preceding problem) and *linalool* (from oil of lavender, bergamot, coriander) yield the same bromide, of formula $C_{10}H_{17}Br$. How do you account for this fact?

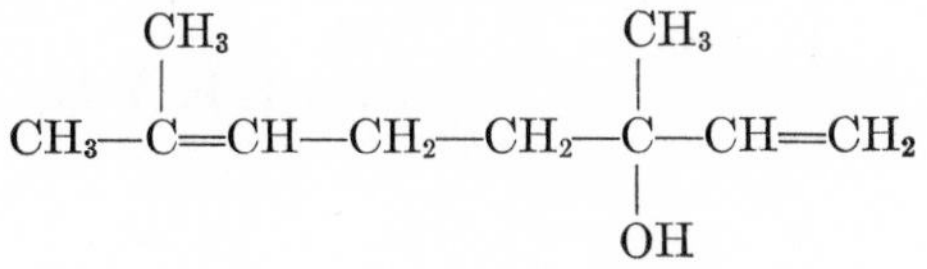

$$CH_3-\underset{\underset{CH_3}{|}}{C}=CH-CH_2-CH_2-\underset{\underset{OH}{|}}{\overset{\overset{CH_3}{|}}{C}}-CH=CH_2$$

Linalool

ALKYL HALIDES

13.1 Structure

We shall consider as alkyl halides all compounds of the general formula R—X, where R is any simple alkyl or substituted alkyl group. For example:

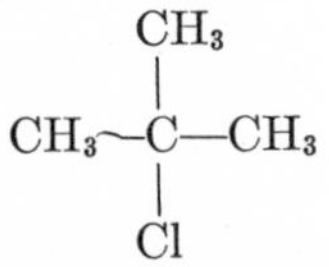

CH$_3$
|
CH$_3$—C—CH$_3$
|
Cl
tert-Butyl chloride
2-Chloro-2-methylpropane

H$_2$C=CH—CH$_2$Br
Allyl bromide
3-Bromo-1-propene

Br
Cyclohexyl bromide

CH$_2$Cl
Benzyl chloride

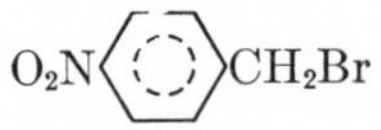

O$_2$N⟨ ⟩CH$_2$Br
p-Nitrobenzyl bromide

CH$_2$=CHCl
Vinyl chloride

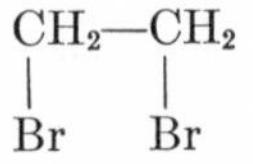

CH$_2$—CH$_2$
| |
Br   Br
Ethylene bromide
1,2-Dibromoethane

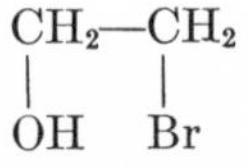

CH$_2$—CH$_2$
| |
OH   Br
Ethylene bromohydrin
2-Bromoethanol

Substituted alkyl halides undergo, of course, the reactions characteristic of their other functional groups — nitration of benzyl chloride, oxidation of ethylene bromohydrin, addition to allyl bromide — but as halides they react very much like ethyl or isopropyl or *tert*-butyl halides.

Compounds in which the halogen atom is attached directly to an aromatic ring (*aryl halides*, e.g., bromobenzene) differ so much from the alkyl halides in their preparations and properties that they will be taken up in a separate chapter (Chapter 14). For the present we need to know that — compared with alkyl halides — *most aryl halides are extremely unreactive.*

13.2 Nomenclature

As we know from our previous acquaintance with these compounds, alkyl halides are given both common names and IUPAC names.

13.3 Physical properties

Because of the polarity of the carbon–halogen bond, haloalkanes have somewhat higher boiling points than alkanes of the same molecular weight. For a given alkyl group, the boiling point increases with increasing atomic weight of the halogen, so that a fluoride is the lowest boiling, an iodide the highest boiling.

In spite of their polarity, alkyl halides are insoluble in water, probably because of their inability to form hydrogen bonds. They are soluble in the typical organic solvents.

Iodo, bromo, and polychloro compounds are more dense than water.

TABLE 13.1

ALKYL HALIDES

	Chloride		Bromide		Iodide	
Name	B.p., °C	Density at 20°C	B.p., °C	Density at 20°C	B.p., °C	Density at 20°C
Methyl	− 24		5		43	2.279
Ethyl	12.5		38	1.440	72	1.933
n-Propyl	47	890	71	1.335	102	1.747
n-Butyl	78.5	.884	102	1.276	130	1 617
n-Pentyl	108	.883	130	1.223	157	1.517
n-Hexyl	134	.882	156	1.173	180	1.441
n-Heptyl	160	.880	180		204	1.401
n-Octyl	185	.879	202		225.5	
Isopropyl	36.5	.859	60	1.310	89.5	1.705
Isobutyl	69	.875	91	1.261	120	1.605
sec-Butyl	68	.871	91	1.258	119	1.595
tert-Butyl	51	.840	73	1.222	100d	
Cyclohexyl	142.5	1.000	165			
Vinyl (Haloethene)	− 14		16		56	
Allyl (3-Halopropene)	45	.938	71	1.398	103	
Crotyl (1 Halo-2-butene)	84				132	
Methylvinylcarbinyl (3-Halo-1-butene)	64					
Propargyl (3-Halopropyne)	65		90	1.520	115	
Benzyl	179	1.102	201		93[10]	
α-Phenylethyl	92[15]		85[10]			
β-Phenylethyl	92[20]		92[11]		127[19]	
Diphenylmethyl	173[19]		184[20]			
Triphenylmethyl	310		230[15]			
Dihalomethane	40	1.336	99	2.49	180d	3.325
Trihalomethane	61	1.489	151	2.89	subl.	4.008
Tetrahalomethane	77	1.595	189.5	3.42	subl.	4.32
1,1-Dihaloethane	57	1.174	110	2.056	179	2.84
1,2-Dihaloethane	84	1.257	132	2.180	d.	2.13
Trihaloethylene	87		164	2.708		
Tetrahaloethylene	121				subl.	
Benzal halide	205		140[20]			
Benzotrihalide	221	1.38				

13.4 Industrial source

On an industrial scale alkyl halides — chiefly the chlorides because of the cheapness of chlorine — are most often prepared by direct halogenation of hydrocarbons at the high temperatures needed for these free radical reactions. For example:

$$\text{C}_6\text{H}_5\text{CH}_3 \xrightarrow[\text{light}]{\text{Cl}_2, 111°} \text{C}_6\text{H}_5\text{CH}_2\text{Cl}$$

Toluene   Benzyl chloride

$$\text{CH}_2\text{=CH—CH}_3 \xrightarrow{\text{Cl}_2, 600°} \text{CH}_2\text{=CH—CH}_2\text{Cl}$$

Propylene   Allyl chloride

$$\text{CH}_4 \xrightarrow[\text{heat}]{\text{Cl}_2} \text{CH}_3\text{Cl} \xrightarrow[\text{heat}]{\text{Cl}_2} \text{CH}_2\text{Cl}_2 \xrightarrow[\text{heat}]{\text{Cl}_2} \text{CHCl}_3 \xrightarrow[\text{heat}]{\text{Cl}_2} \text{CCl}_4$$

Methane

$$\text{CH}_3\text{CH}_2\text{CH}_2\text{CH}_3 \xrightarrow[\text{250–400°}]{\text{Cl}_2} \text{CH}_3\text{CH}_2\text{CH}_2\text{CH}_2\text{Cl} + \text{CH}_3\text{CH}_2\text{CHCH}_3$$

n-Butane   n-Butyl chloride | Cl

sec-Butyl chloride

Even though mixtures containing isomers and compounds of different halogen content are generally obtained, these reactions are useful industrially since often a mixture can be used as such or separated into its components by distillation.

Certain important halides are prepared by the same methods that are used in the laboratory; thus, for vinyl chloride:

$$\text{HC≡CH} \xrightarrow{\text{HCl, HgCl}_2} \text{CH}_2\text{=CHCl}$$

Acetylene   Vinyl chloride

$$\text{CH}_2\text{=CH}_2 \xrightarrow{\text{Cl}_2} \text{CH}_2\text{—CH}_2 \xrightarrow{\text{KOH (alc)}} \text{CH}_2\text{=CHCl}$$

Ethylene | | Vinyl chloride

        Cl   Cl

Many fluorine compounds are not prepared by direct fluorination, but rather by replacement of chlorine, using inorganic fluorides:

$$\text{CH}_3\text{Cl} + \text{Hg}_2\text{F}_2 \longrightarrow \text{CH}_3\text{F} + \text{Hg}_2\text{Cl}_2$$

Methyl fluoride
(b.p. −79°)

$$\text{CCl}_4 + \text{SbF}_3 \longrightarrow \text{CCl}_2\text{F}_2$$

Dichlorodifluoromethane
(Freon-12)
(b.p. −28°)

The increasingly important polyfluorides known as *fluorocarbons* are prepared by replacement of hydrogen using inorganic fluorides:

$$\text{C}_7\text{H}_{16} + 32\text{CoF}_3 \longrightarrow \text{C}_7\text{F}_{16} + 16\text{HF} + 32\text{CoF}_2 \qquad (2\text{CoF}_2 + \text{F}_2 \longrightarrow 2\text{CoF}_3)$$

n-Heptane   Perfluoroheptane
(*per* = fully substituted)
(b.p. 84°)

Cobaltic fluoride, CoF_3, is a convenient fluorinating agent.

13.5   Preparation

In the laboratory alkyl halides are most often prepared by the methods outlined below.

PREPARATION OF ALKYL HALIDES

1. From alcohols

$$R—OH \xrightarrow{\text{HX or PX}_3} R—X$$

Examples:

$$CH_3CH_2CH_2OH \xrightarrow[\substack{\text{or}\\ \text{NaBr, H}_2SO_4,\\ \text{heat}}]{\text{conc. HBr}} CH_3CH_2CH_2Br$$

n-Propyl alcohol   *n*-Propyl bromide

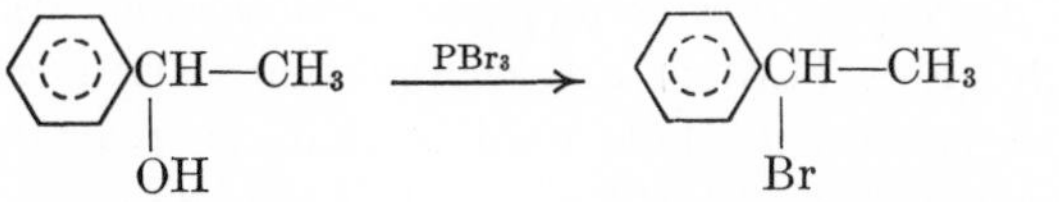

1-Phenylethanol   1-Bromo-1-phenylethane
α-Phenylethyl alcohol   α-Phenylethyl bromide

$$CH_3CH_2OH \xrightarrow{P + I_2} CH_3CH_2I$$

Ethyl alcohol   Ethyl iodide

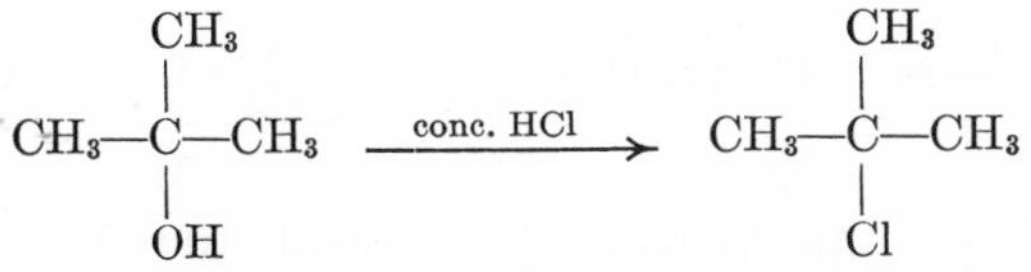

tert-Butyl alcohol   *tert*-Butyl chloride

2. Halogenation of certain hydrocarbons

$$R—H \xrightarrow{X_2} R—X + HX$$

Examples:

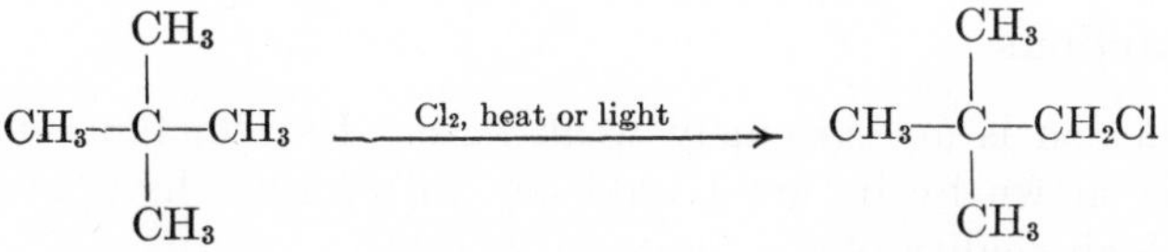

Neopentane   Neopentyl chloride

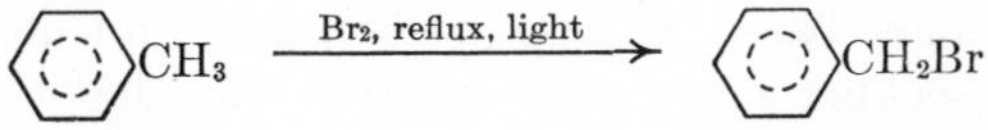

Toluene   Benzyl bromide

3. Addition of hydrogen halides to alkenes

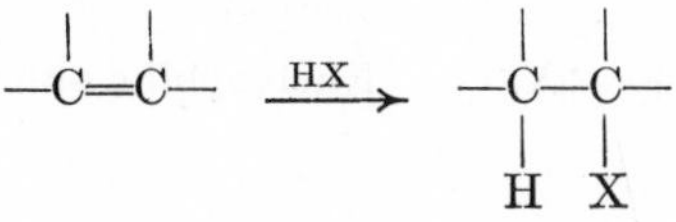

Discussed in Sec. 5.6

4. Addition of halogens to alkenes and alkynes

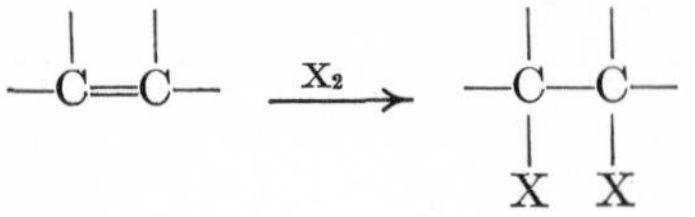

$$-\overset{|}{\underset{|}{C}}=\overset{|}{\underset{|}{C}}- \quad \xrightarrow{\text{X}_2} \quad -\overset{|}{\underset{\underset{X}{|}}{C}}-\overset{|}{\underset{\underset{X}{|}}{C}}- \qquad \text{Discussed in Sec. 5.5}$$

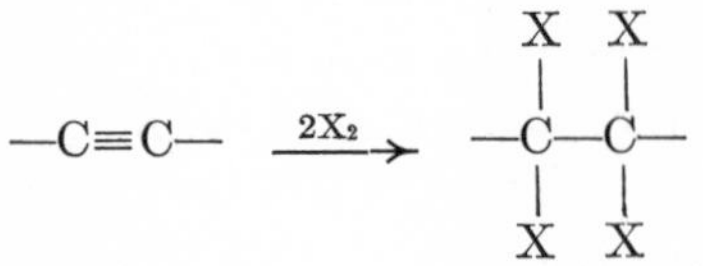

$$-C\equiv C- \quad \xrightarrow{2\text{X}_2} \quad -\overset{\overset{X}{|}}{\underset{\underset{X}{|}}{C}}-\overset{\overset{X}{|}}{\underset{\underset{X}{|}}{C}}- \qquad \text{Discussed in Sec. 6.8}$$

5. Halide exchange

$$R\text{---}X \;+\; I^- \xrightarrow{\text{acetone}} R\text{---}I \;+\; X^-$$

Alkyl halides are nearly always prepared from alcohols, which are available commercially (Sec. 11.6) or are readily synthesized (Secs. 12.9 and 12.10). Although certain alcohols tend to undergo rearrangement (Sec. 12.4) during replacement of —OH by —X, this tendency can be minimized by use of phosphorus halides.

Certain halides are best prepared by direct halogenation. The most important of these preparations involve substitution of —X for the unusually reactive (Why?) allylic or benzylic hydrogens.

Allylic hydrogen   An allyl halide   Benzylic hydrogen   A benzyl halide

An alkyl iodide is often prepared from the corresponding bromide or chloride by treatment with a solution of sodium iodide in acetone; the less soluble sodium bromide or sodium chloride precipitates from solution and can be removed by filtration.

13.6 Reactions

A halide ion is an extremely weak base. Its reluctance to share its electrons is shown by its great tendency to release a hydrogen ion, that is, by the high acidity of the hydrogen halides.

When attached to carbon, halogen can be readily displaced as halide ion by other, stronger bases. These bases possess an unshared pair of electrons and are seeking a relatively positive site, that is, are seeking a nucleus with which to share their electrons.

Basic, electron-rich reagents are called **nucleophilic reagents** (from the Greek, *nucleus-loving*). The typical reaction of alkyl halides is **nucleophilic substitution**:

$$R{:}X \;+\; {:}Z \longrightarrow R{:}Z \;+\; {:}X^- \qquad \textbf{Nucleophilic substitution}$$

A nucleophilic
reagent

(Aryl and vinyl halides undergo these substitution reactions with extreme difficulty, Sec. 14.7.)

Alkyl halides react with a large number of nucleophilic reagents, both inorganic and organic, to yield a wide variety of important organic products. As we shall see, these reagents include not only negative ions like hydroxide, alkoxide, and cyanide, but also neutral bases like ammonia and water; their characteristic feature is an *unshared pair of electrons*.

As a synthetic tool nucleophilic substitution involving alkyl halides is one of the three or four most useful classes of organic reactions. Much of the importance of alcohols is due to their ready conversion into alkyl halides, which have easily replaceable halogen.

A large number of nucleophilic substitutions are listed below to give an idea of the versatility of alkyl halides; many will be left to later chapters for detailed discussion.

We shall look rather closely at the nucleophilic substitution reactions of the alkyl halides, for they provide a particularly good illustration of the effect of structure on reactivity, and of the methods that may be used to determine mechanisms of reactions.

REACTIONS OF ALKYL HALIDES

1. Nucleophilic substitution

$$R{:}X + {:}Z \longrightarrow R{:}Z + {:}X^-$$

$$R{:}X + {:}OH^- \longrightarrow R{:}OH + {\cdot}X^- \qquad \text{Alcohol}$$

$$+ H_2O \longrightarrow R{:}OH \qquad \text{Alcohol}$$

$$+ {:}OR'^- \longrightarrow R{:}OR' \qquad \text{Ether (Williamson synthesis, Sec. 15.7)}$$

$$+ {}^-{:}C{\equiv}CR' \longrightarrow R{:}C{\equiv}CR' \qquad \text{Alkyne (Sec. 6.11)}$$

$$+ Na^+\, {}^-{:}R' \longrightarrow R{:}R' \qquad \text{Alkane (Wurtz synthesis, Sec. 3.17)}$$

$$+ {:}I^- \longrightarrow R{:}I \qquad \text{Alkyl iodide}$$

$$+ {:}CN^- \longrightarrow R{:}CN \qquad \text{Nitrile (Sec. 16.8)}$$

$$+ R'COO{:}^- \longrightarrow R'COO{:}R \qquad \text{Ester}$$

$$+ {:}NH_3 \longrightarrow R{:}NH_2 \qquad \text{Primary amine (Sec. 19.10)}$$

$$+ {:}NH_2R' \longrightarrow R{:}NHR' \qquad \text{Secondary amine (Sec. 19.12)}$$

$$+ {:}NHR'R'' \longrightarrow R{:}NR'R'' \qquad \text{Tertiary amine (Sec. 19.12)}$$

$$+ {:}SH^- \longrightarrow R{:}SH \qquad \text{Thiol (mercaptan)}$$

$$+ {:}SR'^- \longrightarrow R{:}SR' \qquad \text{Thioether (sulfide)}$$

$$+ ArH + AlCl_3 \longrightarrow ArR \qquad \text{Arene (Friedel-Crafts reaction, Sec. 9.6)}$$

$$+ [CH(COOC_2H_5)_2]^- \longrightarrow R{:}CH(COOC_2H_5)_2 \qquad \text{(Malonic ester synthesis, Sec. 25.9)}$$

$$+ [CH_3COCHCOOC_2H_5]^- \longrightarrow CH_3COCHCOOC_2H_5 \qquad \text{(Acetoacetic ester synthesis, Sec. 26.4)}$$
$$\overset{\cdot\cdot}{R}$$

2. Dehydrohalogenation: elimination. Discussed in Sec. 4.13

$$\underset{\underset{H}{|}\;\underset{X}{|}}{-\overset{|}{C}-\overset{|}{C}-} \xrightarrow{\text{base}} -\overset{|}{C}=\overset{|}{C}-$$

3. Preparation of Grignard reagent. Discussed in Secs. 3.16 and 11.11

$$RX + Mg \xrightarrow{\text{dry ether}} RMgX$$

4. Reduction

Catalytic: $RX + H_2 \xrightarrow{\text{Ni}} RH + HX$

Chemical: $RX + M + H^+ \longrightarrow RH + M^+ + X^-$

Example:

$$\underset{\substack{\text{Carbon} \\ \text{tetrachloride}}}{CCl_4} \xrightarrow{\text{Fe, H}_2\text{O}} \underset{\text{Chloroform}}{CHCl_3}$$

As we already know (Sec. 4.13, Sec. 6.11), alkyl halides undergo not only substitution but also **elimination,** a reaction that is important in the synthesis of alkenes. Both elimination and substitution are brought about by basic reagents, and hence there must always be *competition* between the two reactions. We shall be interested to see how this competition is affected by such factors as the structure of the halide or the particular nucleophilic reagent used.

13.7 Rate of reaction: effect of concentration. Kinetics

Before we discuss nucleophilic substitution involving alkyl halides, let us return briefly to the matter of what determines the rate of a reaction.

We have seen (Sec. 2 20) that the rate of a chemical reaction can be expressed as a product of three factors:

$$\text{rate} = \frac{\text{collision}}{\text{frequency}} \times \frac{\text{energy}}{\text{factor}} \times \frac{\text{probability}}{\text{factor}}$$

So far, we have used this relationship to understand problems of orientation and relative reactivity; in doing this we have compared rates of *different* reactions. When the conditions that we can control are kept the same (temperature, concentration), closely related reactions proceed at different rates chiefly because they have different energy factors, that is to say, different E_{act}'s. We have been able to account surprisingly well for many differences in E_{act}'s by using structural theory to estimate stabilities of the transition states.

It is also useful to study an *individual* reaction to see how its rate is affected by deliberate changes in experimental conditions. We can determine E_{act}, for example, if we measure the rate at different temperatures (Sec. 2.20). But perhaps the most valuable information about a reaction is obtained by studying the effect of *changes in concentration* on its rate.

How does a change in concentration of reactants affect the rate of a reaction at a constant temperature? An increase in concentration cannot alter the fraction of collisions that have sufficient energy, or the fraction of collisions that have the proper orientation; it can serve only to increase the total number of collisions. If more molecules are crowded into the same space they will collide more often and the reaction will go faster. Collision frequency, and hence rate, depends in a very exact way upon concentration.

The field of chemistry that deals with rates of reaction, and in particular with dependence of rates on concentration, is called **kinetics.** Let us see what kinetics can tell us about nucleophilic aliphatic substitution.

13.8 Kinetics of nucleophilic aliphatic substitution. Second-order and first-order reactions

Let us take a specific example, the reaction of methyl bromide with sodium hydroxide to yield methanol:

$$CH_3Br + OH^- \longrightarrow CH_3OH + Br^-$$

This reaction would probably be carried out in aqueous ethanol, in which both reactants are soluble.

If the reaction results from collision between a hydroxide ion and a methyl bromide molecule, we would expect the rate to depend upon the concentration of both these reactants. If either OH^- concentration, $[OH^-]$, or CH_3Br concentration, $[CH_3Br]$, is doubled, the collision frequency should be doubled and the reaction rate doubled. If either concentration is cut in half, the collision frequency, and consequently the rate, should be halved.

This is found to be so. We say that the rate of reaction depends upon both $[OH^-]$ and $[CH_3Br]$, and we indicate this by the expression

$$rate = k[CH_3Br][OH^-]$$

If concentrations are expressed in, say, moles per liter, then k is the number which, multiplied by these concentrations, tells us how many moles of methanol are formed in each liter during each second. At a given temperature and for a given solvent, k always has the same value and is characteristic of this particular reaction; k is called the **rate constant.** For example, for the reaction between methyl bromide and hydroxide ion in a mixture of 80% ethanol and 20% water at 55°, the value of k is 0.0214 liters per mole per second.

What we have just seen is, of course, not surprising; we all know that an increase in concentration causes an increase in rate. But now let us look at the corresponding reaction between *tert*-butyl bromide and hydroxide ion:

$$\begin{array}{c} CH_3 \\ | \\ CH_3-C-CH_3 + OH^- \\ | \\ Br \end{array} \longrightarrow \begin{array}{c} CH_3 \\ | \\ CH_3-C-CH_3 + Br^- \\ | \\ OH \end{array}$$

As before, if we double $[RBr]$ the rate doubles; if we cut $[RBr]$ in half the rate is halved. But if we double $[OH^-]$, or if we cut $[OH^-]$ in half, there is no change in the rate. *The rate of reaction is independent of* $[OH^-]$.

The rate of reaction of *tert*-butyl bromide depends only upon [RBr]. This is indicated by the expression

$$\text{rate} = k[\text{RBr}]$$

For the reaction of *tert*-butyl bromide in 80% alcohol at 55° the rate constant is 0.010 per second. This means that of every mole of *tert*-butyl bromide present, 0.010 mole reacts each second, whatever the [OH⁻].

The methyl bromide reaction is said to follow **second-order kinetics,** since its rate is dependent upon the concentrations of *two* substances. The *tert*-butyl bromide reaction is said to follow **first-order kinetics;** its rate depends upon the concentration of only *one* substance.

How are we to account for this difference in kinetic order? How are we to account for the puzzling fact that the rate of the *tert*-butyl bromide reaction is independent of [OH⁻]?

To account for such differences in kinetic order, as well as for many other observations, it has been proposed that *nucleophilic substitution can proceed by two different mechanisms.* In the following sections we shall see what these two mechanisms are, the facts on which they are based, and how they account for the facts.

13.9   The S$_N$2 reaction: mechanism and kinetics

The reaction between methyl bromide and hydroxide ion to yield methanol follows second-order kinetics; that is, the rate depends upon the concentrations of both reactants.

$$CH_3Br + OH^- \longrightarrow CH_3OH + Br^-$$
$$\text{rate} = k[CH_3Br][OH^-]$$

The simplest way to account for the kinetics is to assume that reaction requires a collision between a hydroxide ion and a methyl bromide molecule. On the basis of evidence we shall shortly discuss, it is known that in its attack the hydroxide ion stays as far away as possible from the bromine, that is to say, it attacks the molecule from the rear.

The reaction is believed to take place as shown in Figure 13.1.

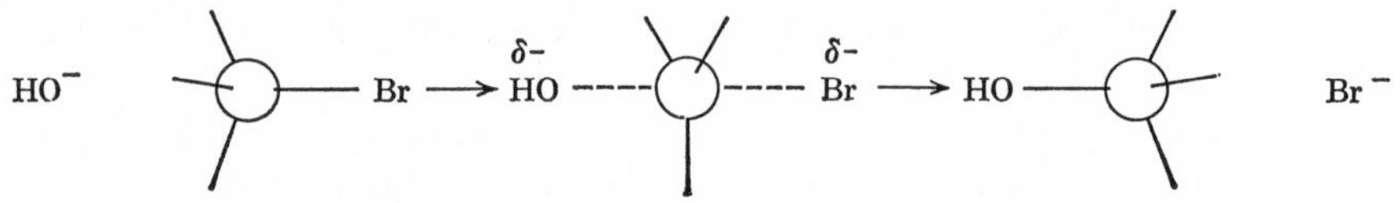

FIGURE 13.1. The S$_N$2 reaction: complete inversion of configuration. Nucleophilic reagent attacks back side.

When hydroxide ion collides with a methyl bromide molecule at the face most remote from the bromine, and when such a collision has sufficient energy, a C—OH bond forms and the C--Br bond breaks, liberating the bromide ion.

The transition state can be pictured as a structure in which carbon is partially bonded to both —OH and —Br; the C—OH bond is not completely formed, the C—Br bond is not yet completely broken. Hydroxide has a diminished negative charge, since it has begun to share its electrons with carbon. Bromine has developed a partial negative charge, since it has partly removed a pair of electrons from carbon. At the same time, of course, ion–dipole bonds between hydroxide ion and solvent are being broken and ion–dipole bonds between bromide ion and solvent are being formed.

The —OH and —Br are located as far apart as possible; the three hydrogens and the carbon lie in a single plane, all bond angles being 120°. The C—H bonds are thus arranged like the spokes of a wheel, with the C—OH and the C—Br bonds lying along the axle.

This is the mechanism that is called **S$_N$2**: *substitution nucleophilic bimolecular*. The term *bimolecular* is used here since the rate-determining step involves collision of *two* particles.

What evidence is there that alkyl halides can react in this manner? First of all, as we have just seen, the mechanism is consistent with the kinetics of a reaction like the one between methyl bromide and hydroxide ion. In general **an S$_N$2 reaction follows second-order kinetics.** Let us look at some of the other evidence.

13.10 The S$_N$2 reaction: stereochemistry

Both 2-bromooctane and 2-octanol are asymmetric compounds, that is, have molecules that are not superimposable on their mirror images. Consequently, these compounds are capable of showing optical activity. By methods to be described later (Sec. 20.5), *optically pure* samples of both compounds have been obtained, that is, samples containing one of the enantiomers uncontaminated by the other.

The specific rotations of these optically pure compounds and their configurations are:

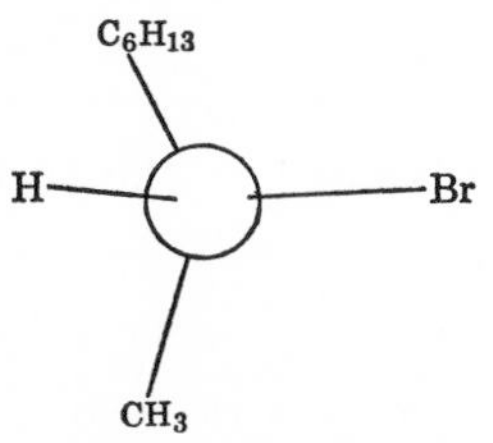

C_6H_{13} · · · H———Br · · · CH_3
(−)-2-Bromooctane
$[\alpha] = -34.6°$

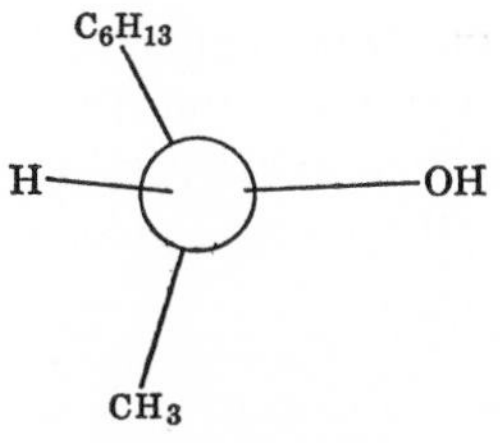

C_6H_{13} · · · H———OH · · · CH_3
(−)-2-Octanol
$[\alpha] = -9.9°$

We notice that the (−)-bromide and the (−)-alcohol have similar configurations; that is, —OH occupies the same relative position in the (−)-alcohol as —Br does in the (−)-bromide. As we know, compounds of similar configuration do not *necessarily* rotate light in the same direction; they just happen to do so in the present case.

When 2-bromooctane of specific rotation −34.6° is allowed to react with sodium hydroxide under conditions where second-order kinetics are followed, there is obtained 2-octanol of specific rotation +9.9°.

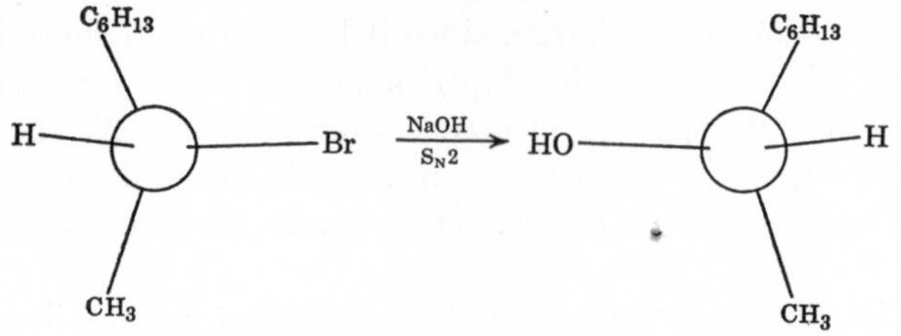

(−)-2-Bromooctane $\xrightarrow[S_N2]{NaOH}$ (+)-2-Octanol

$[\alpha] = -34.6°$ $[\alpha] = +9.9°$
optical purity 100%   optical purity 100%

These results show us two things. First, there has been no loss of
optical activity during the reaction; optically pure bromide yields optically
pure alcohol. Second, the —OH group has not taken the position previously occupied by —Br; the alcohol obtained has the configuration
opposite to that of the bromide.

*A reaction that yields a product whose configuration is opposite to that
of the reactant is said to proceed with* **inversion of configuration.** The fact
that the optical purity of the product is the same as that of the starting
material shows that the configuration of every molecule was inverted; we
say that the reaction proceeds with *complete* inversion.

It is not necessary or even customary to use compounds of 100% optical purity
in studies like this. We can draw exactly the same conclusions from the fact that
2-bromooctane of, say, rotation $-14.9°$ (43% optical purity) yields 2-octanol of
rotation $+4.3°$ (43% optical purity). The specific rotations of the optically pure
bromide and alcohol must be *known*, however, if we are to calculate the purity of
the particular samples we are dealing with.

It was to account for inversion of configuration that back-side attack
was first proposed for substitution of the S_N2 kind. As —OH becomes
attached to carbon, three bonds are forced apart until they reach the
planar "spoke" arrangement of the transition state; then, as bromide is
expelled, they move on to a tetrahedral arrangement *opposite* to the
original one. This process has often been likened to the turning-inside-
out of an umbrella in a gale.

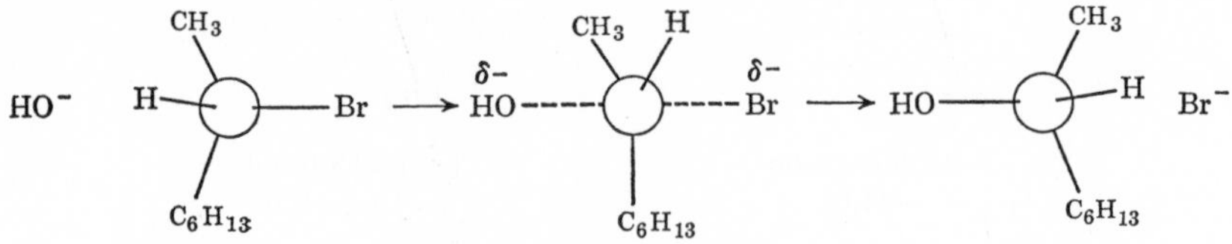

S_N2: *complete inversion*

The stereochemistry of the 2-bromooctane reaction indicates back-side
attack in accordance with the S_N2 mechanism; studies of other optically
active compounds, under conditions where the reactions follow second-
order kinetics, show similar results. It is not possible to study the stereochemistry of most halides, since they are not optically active; however,
there seems no reason to doubt that they, too, undergo back-side attack.

An S_N2 reaction proceeds with complete stereochemical inversion.

The S_N2 mechanism is supported, then, by stereochemical evidence. Indeed, the relationship between mechanism and stereochemistry is so well established that in the absence of other evidence complete inversion is taken to indicate an S_N2 reaction.

Inversion of configuration is the general rule for reactions occurring at asymmetric carbon atoms, being much commoner than retention of configuration. Oddly enough it is the very prevalence of inversion that made its detection difficult. Paul Walden (at the Polytechnicum in Riga, Latvia) discovered the phenomenon of inversion in 1896 when he encountered one of the exceptional reactions in which inversion does *not* take place.

We can begin to see how it is that stereochemistry is one of the most powerful tools we have for finding out what goes on during a reaction.

Problem 13.1 (a) What product would be formed if the reaction of *cis*-4-bromocyclohexanol with OH⁻ proceeded with inversion? (b) Without inversion? (c) Is it always necessary to use optically active compounds to study the stereochemistry of substitution reactions?

13.11 The S_N2 reaction: reactivity

In what way would we expect changes in structure of the alkyl group to affect reactivity in an S_N2 substitution?

First of all, we might consider the matter of electron withdrawal or electron release by the groups attached to the carbon bearing the halogen. Electron withdrawal should make the carbon more positive and hence more easily attacked by the nucleophilic hydroxide ion. But this same electron withdrawal should make it more difficult for the carbon to give up a departing halide ion. Unless one of the two processes, bond making or bond breaking, is much more important than the other, we would expect these two factors very nearly to cancel each other. Therefore we would not expect the electron-withdrawing or electron-releasing ability of substituents to have a large effect on reaction rate.

To understand the factors involved, let us examine the structure of the transition state for the methyl bromide reaction. In contrast to the free radical and carbonium ion reactions we have studied, this time the structure is *not* intermediate between the structures of the reactant and product; this time we cannot simply assume that factors stabilizing the product will also stabilize the transition state. The carbon in reactant and product is tetrahedral, whereas carbon in the transition state is bonded to five atoms. As indicated before, the C—H bonds are arranged like the spokes of a wheel, with the C—OH and C—Br bonds lying along the axle (Figure 13.2).

What would be the effect of replacing the hydrogens successively by methyl groups? That is, how will the transition state differ as we go from methyl bromide through ethyl bromide and isopropyl bromide to *tert*-butyl bromide? As hydrogen atoms are replaced by the larger methyl groups there is increased crowding about the carbon, particularly between the methyls on the one hand and —OH and —Br on the other (Figure

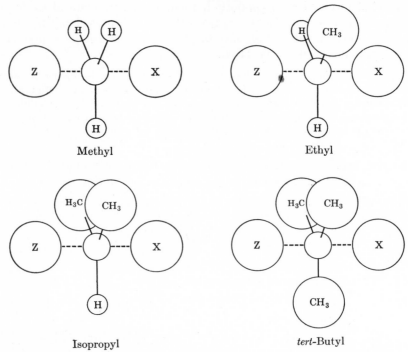

FIGURE 13.2. Steric factor in the S_N2 reaction. Crowding raises energy of transition state and slows down reaction.

13.2). The non-bonded interaction between these crowded groups raises the energy of the transition state and thus slows down the reaction.

In agreement with this prediction, *differences in rate between two S_N2 reactions seem to be due chiefly to* **steric factors,** and not to electronic factors; that is to say, differences in rate are related to the *bulk* of the substituents and not to their ability to withdraw or release electrons. As the number of substituents attached to the carbon bearing the halogen is increased, the reactivity toward S_N2 substitution decreases. These substituents may be aliphatic, or aromatic, or both, as shown in the two sequences:

S_N2 substitution: relative reactivity toward I^-

$$
\underset{\substack{\text{Methyl} \\ 150}}{\overset{\overset{\displaystyle H}{|}}{\underset{\underset{\displaystyle H}{|}}{H-C-Br}}} \; > \;
\underset{\substack{\text{Ethyl} \\ 1}}{\overset{\overset{\displaystyle H}{|}}{\underset{\underset{\displaystyle H}{|}}{CH_3-C-Br}}} \; > \;
\underset{\substack{\text{Isopropyl} \\ .01}}{\overset{\overset{\displaystyle CH_3}{|}}{\underset{\underset{\displaystyle H}{|}}{CH_3-C-Br}}} \; > \;
\underset{\substack{\textit{tert}\text{-Butyl} \\ .001}}{\overset{\overset{\displaystyle CH_3}{|}}{\underset{\underset{\displaystyle CH_3}{|}}{CH_3-C-Br}}}
$$

$$
\underset{\text{Benzyl}}{\overset{\overset{\displaystyle H}{|}}{\underset{\underset{\displaystyle H}{|}}{C_6H_5-C-Br}}} \; > \;
\underset{\alpha\text{-Phenylethyl}}{\overset{\overset{\displaystyle CH_3}{|}}{\underset{\underset{\displaystyle H}{|}}{C_6H_5-C-Br}}} \; > \;
\underset{\beta\text{-Phenylisopropyl}}{\overset{\overset{\displaystyle CH_3}{|}}{\underset{\underset{\displaystyle CH_3}{|}}{C_6H_5-C-Br}}}
$$

(To give an idea of how large these differences may be, the relative rates for a particular S_N2 reaction, substitution by iodide ion, are indicated below the formulas in the first sequence.)

In S_N2 reactions the order of reactivity of RX is $CH_3X > 1° > 2° > 3°$.

In cases where steric factors are kept constant, electronic effects on S_N2 reactions can be observed; however, these effects are found to be comparatively *small*. Some S_N2 reactions are speeded up slightly by electron release, and others are speeded up slightly by electron withdrawal, but it is not usually possible to predict which will be the case simply from the structures involved.

Problem 13.2 (a) Draw the structures of ethyl, *n*-propyl, isobutyl, and neopentyl bromides. These structures can be considered methyl bromide with one of its hydrogens replaced by various alkyl groups (GCH_2Br). What is the group (G) in each case?

(b) The relative rates of reaction (with ethoxide ion) are roughly: methyl bromide, 100; ethyl bromide, 6; *n*-propyl bromide, 2; isobutyl bromide, 0.2; neopentyl bromide, 0.00002. What is the effect of the *size* of the group G attached to carbon bearing the halogen? How does this compare with the effect of changing the *number* of groups?

Thus we see that the S_N2 mechanism is supported by three lines of evidence: kinetics, stereochemistry, and effect of structure on reactivity.

Now let us turn to the other mechanism by which nucleophilic aliphatic substitution can take place.

13.12 The S_N1 reaction: mechanism and kinetics

The reaction between *tert*-butyl bromide and hydroxide ion to yield *tert*-butyl alcohol follows first-order kinetics; that is, the rate depends upon the concentration of only one reactant, *tert*-butyl bromide.

$$CH_3{-}\underset{\underset{Br}{|}}{\overset{\overset{CH_3}{|}}{C}}{-}CH_3 + OH^- \longrightarrow CH_3{-}\underset{\underset{OH}{|}}{\overset{\overset{CH_3}{|}}{C}}{-}CH_3 + Br^-$$

$$\text{rate} = k[RBr]$$

How are we to interpret the fact that the rate is independent of $[OH^-]$? If the rate of reaction does not depend upon $[OH^-]$, it can only mean that the reaction *whose rate we are measuring* does not involve OH^-.

These observations are quite consistent with the following mechanism

(1) $$CH_3{-}\underset{\underset{Br}{|}}{\overset{\overset{CH_3}{|}}{C}}{-}CH_3 \longrightarrow CH_3{-}\overset{\overset{CH_3}{|}}{\underset{\oplus}{C}}{-}CH_3 + Br^-$$ **Slow**

S_N1

(2) $$CH_3{-}\overset{\overset{CH_3}{|}}{\underset{\oplus}{C}}{-}CH_3 + OH^- \longrightarrow CH_3{-}\underset{\underset{OH}{|}}{\overset{\overset{CH_3}{|}}{C}}{-}CH_3$$ **Fast**

tert-Butyl bromide slowly dissociates (step 1) into bromide ions and *tert*-butyl carbonium ions. The carbonium ions then combine rapidly (step 2) with hydroxide ions to yield *tert*-butyl alcohol.

The rate of the over-all reaction is determined by the slow breaking of the C—Br bond to form the carbonium ion; once formed, the carbonium ion reacts rapidly to form the product. *A single step whose rate determines the over-all rate of a stepwise reaction is called a* **rate-determining step.** It is not surprising that the rate-determining step here is the one that involves the *breaking* of a bond, an energy-demanding process. The required energy is supplied by formation of many ion–dipole bonds between the two kinds of ion and the solvent.

This is the mechanism that is called **S$_N$1**: *substitution nucleophilic unimolecular.* The term *uni*molecular is used here since the rate-determining step involves only *one* molecule (disregarding the many necessary solvent molecules).

What evidence is there that alkyl halides can react by this mechanism? As we have just seen, the mechanism is consistent with the first-order kinetics of a reaction like the one between *tert*-butyl bromide and hydroxide ion. In general **an S$_N$1 reaction follows first-order kinetics.** The rate of the entire reaction is determined by how fast the alkyl halide ionizes, and hence depends only upon the concentration of alkyl halide.

In following sections, we shall look at some of the other evidence.

Problem 13.3 When iodine is added to a benzene solution of hexaphenylethane (Sec. 9.20) the color of the iodine gradually fades, at a rate that depends upon [hexaphenylethane] but *is independent of* [I$_2$]. When a benzene solution of hexaphenylethane is shaken under an atmosphere of NO gas the pressure of the gas gradually drops, at a rate that depends upon [hexaphenylethane] but *is independent of* the NO pressure. The rate constants for the two reactions are *identical.* Account for these results.

13.13 The S$_N$1 reaction: stereochemistry

We have proposed that, under the conditions we have described, methyl bromide reacts with hydroxide ion by the S$_N$2 mechanism, and that *tert*-butyl bromide reacts by the S$_N$1 mechanism. Since *sec*-alkyl bromides are intermediate in structure between these two halides, it is not surprising to find that they can react by either or both mechanisms.

An increase in [OH$^-$] speeds up the second-order reaction but has no effect on the first-order reaction. At high [OH$^-$], therefore, the second-order reaction is so much the faster that *sec*-alkyl bromides react almost entirely by the S$_N$2 mechanism. The behavior of optically active 2-bromooctane in an S$_N$2 reaction has been studied (Sec. 13.10) by use of high [OH$^-$].

In the same way, a decrease in [OH$^-$] slows down the second-order reaction, but has no effect on the first-order reaction. The behavior of optically active 2-bromooctane in an S$_N$1 reaction has been studied by use of low [OH$^-$].

Problem 13.4   In 80% ethanol at 55° isopropyl bromide reacts with hydroxide ion according to the following kinetic equation, where the rate is expressed as moles per liter per second:

$$\text{rate} = 4.7 \times 10^{-5}[\text{RX}][\text{OH}^-] + 0.24 \times 10^{-5}[\text{RX}]$$

What percentage of the isopropyl bromide reacts by the S_N2 mechanism when $[\text{OH}^-]$ is: (a) .001 molar?   (b) .01 molar?   (c) 0.1 molar?   (d) 1.0 molar? (e) 5.0 molar?

When 2-bromooctane of specific rotation $-34.6°$ is converted into the alcohol under conditions (low $[\text{OH}^-]$) where first-order kinetics are followed, there is obtained 2-octanol of specific rotation $+3.6°$.

$$(-)\text{-}C_6H_{13}CHBrCH_3 \xrightarrow[\;S_N1\;]{\text{OH}^-,\ H_2O} (+)\text{-}C_6H_{13}CHOHCH_3$$

$$[\alpha] = -34.6° \qquad\qquad\qquad [\alpha] = +3.6°$$

Optical purity 100%   Optical purity $= \dfrac{+3.6}{+9.9} \times 100 = 36\%$

The product has the opposite configuration from the starting material, as in the S_N2 reaction, but this time there has been a loss in optical purity. The starting material contained only one enantiomer, whereas the product clearly must contain both.   The product is thus a mixture of the inverted

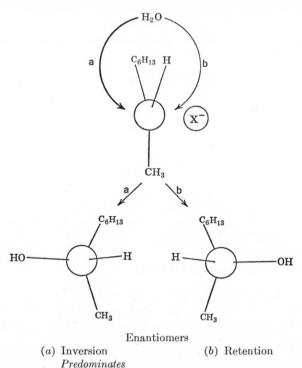

Enantiomers

(a) Inversion   (b) Retention
   Predominates

FIGURE 13.3. The S_N1 reaction: racemization plus inversion. Nucleophilic reagent attacks both (a) back side and (b) front side of carbonium ion. Back-side attack predominates.

compound and the racemate, and we say that the reaction has proceeded with **partial racemization.** How can we account for these stereochemical results?

In the carbonium ion, carbon is bonded to three other atoms, and for this bonding uses sp^2 orbitals (Sec. 4.2); the bonds are therefore trigonal and are directed toward the corners of an equilateral triangle. *The carbonium ion has a flat structure.* Let us see how this affects the stereochemical course of the reaction.

In the first step the optically active 2-bromooctane ionizes to form bromide ion and the flat 2-octyl carbonium ion. The nucleophilic reagent OH^- (or very possibly H_2O) then attaches itself to the carbonium ion. But it may attach itself to either face of this flat ion, and depending upon which face, yields either of two products (see Figure 13.3).

If the attack were purely random we would expect equal amounts of the two isomers, that is to say, we would expect only the racemate. But the product is *not completely* racemized, for the inverted product exceeds its enantiomer. How do we account for this? The simplest explanation is that attack by the nucleophilic reagent occurs before the departing halide ion has completely left the neighborhood of the carbonium ion; to a certain extent the departing ion thus *shields* the front side of the ion from attack. As a result, back-side attack is somewhat preferred.

Racemization in an S_N1 reaction arises, then, from the *loss of configuration* in the intermediate carbonium ion. In some cases racemization may be almost complete; hydrolysis of α-phenylethyl chloride, for example, proceeds with 87% racemization and 13% inversion:

$$C_6H_5CHClCH_3 \xrightarrow[S_N1]{OH^-,\ H_2O} C_6H_5CHOHCH_3$$

$$[\alpha] = -34° \qquad\qquad [\alpha] = +1.7°$$

$$\text{Optical purity} = \frac{-34}{-109} \times 100 = 31\% \qquad \text{Optical purity} = \frac{+1.7}{+42.3} \times 100 = 4\%$$

In contrast to an S_N2 reaction, which proceeds with complete inversion, **an S_N1 reaction proceeds with racemization.**

Problem 13.5 Optically active 2-iodooctane dissolved in acetone undergoes racemization in the presence of sodium iodide at a rate that depends upon both [RI] and [I$^-$]. (a) Account for these results. (b) Does racemization *necessarily* mean an intermediate carbonium ion?

13.14 The S_N1 reaction: reactivity

The rate-determining step of an S_N1 reaction is the formation of a carbonium ion. Judging from our previous experience, therefore, we expect the reactivity of an alkyl halide to depend chiefly upon *how stable a carbonium ion it can form.*

Our expectation is correct: the order of reactivity of alkyl halides in S_N1 reactions is the same as the order of stability of carbonium ions.

In S_N1 reactions the order of reactivity of RX is allyl, benzyl > 3° > 2° > 1° > CH$_3$X.

As the positive charge develops on the carbon atom in the transition state, it is dispersed by the same factors — inductive effect and resonance — that stabilize the full-fledged carbonium ion.

$$RX \longrightarrow \begin{bmatrix} \overset{\delta_+}{R} \text{-}\text{-}\text{-}\text{-} \overset{\delta_-}{X} \end{bmatrix} \longrightarrow R^+ + X^-$$

Transition state	Products
R has partial	*R has full*
positive charge	*positive charge*

The following example gives some idea of how much the rate of an S_N1 reaction can be changed by changes in structure:

$$RBr + H_2O \xrightarrow{\text{formic acid}} ROH + HBr$$

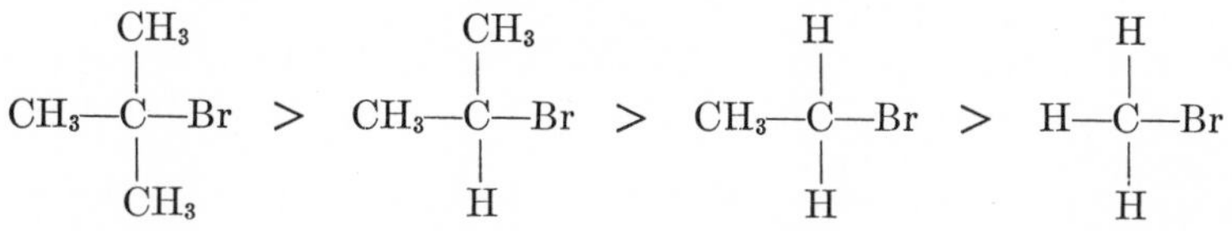

	CH₃		CH₃		H		H
	|		|		|		|
	CH₃—C—Br	>	CH₃—C—Br	>	CH₃—C—Br	>	H—C—Br
	|		|		|		|
	CH₃		H		H		H

Relative	*tert*-Butyl	Isopropyl	Ethyl	Methyl
rate:	100 million	45	1.7	1.0

(Formic acid is used here as an even better ionizing solvent than water.)

The rate of an S_N2 reaction, we saw, is affected largely by steric factors, that is, by the bulk of the substituents. In contrast, the rate of an S_N1 reaction is affected largely by **electronic factors,** that is, by the tendency of substituents to release or withdraw electrons.

Problem 13.6 Neopentyl halides are notoriously slow in nucleophilic substitution, whatever the experimental conditions. How can you account for this?

13.15 The S_N1 reaction: rearrangement

If the S_N1 reaction involves intermediate carbonium ions, we might expect it to show one of the characteristic features of carbonium ion reactions: *rearrangement*. In an S_N2 reaction, on the other hand, the halide ion does not leave until the nucleophilic reagent has become attached;

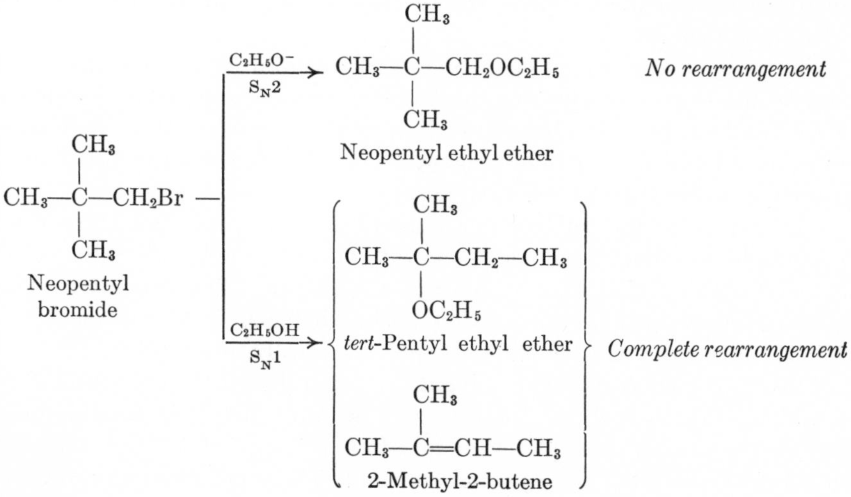

there is no free intermediate particle and hence we would expect no rearrangement. These expectations are correct.

The example on page 379 illustrates this point. We have seen (Sec.
12.5) that the neopentyl carbonium ion is particularly prone to rearrange
to the more stable *tert*-pentyl ion. Neopentyl bromide reacts (slowly) with
ethoxide ion by an S_N2 mechanism to yield neopentyl ethyl ether; it reacts (slowly) with ethyl alcohol by an S_N1 reaction to yield only rearranged
products.

The parallel between rearrangement and formation of carbonium ions is
so strong that in the absence of other information, rearrangement is often
taken as an indication of an S_N1 mechanism (e.g., in the Friedel-Crafts
reaction, Sec. 9.8).

We notice that the S_N1 reaction is accompanied by much elimination;
expulsion of a proton to yield an alkene is of course typical behavior of a
carbonium ion.

13.16 S_N2 vs. S_N1

The strength of the evidence for the two mechanisms, S_N1 and S_N2, lies
in its consistency. Nucleophilic substitutions that follow first-order kinetics
also show racemization and rearrangement, and the reactivity sequence
$3° > 2° > 1°$. Reactions that follow second-order kinetics show complete
stereochemical inversion and no rearrangement, and follow the reactivity
sequence $1° > 2° > 3°$. (The few exceptions to these generalizations are
reasonable exceptions; see Problem 13.10, page 382.)

$$\text{RX} = \overset{\xrightarrow{\text{S_N1 increases}}}{\underset{\xleftarrow{\text{S_N2 increases}}}{1° \quad 2° \quad 3°}} \qquad \text{S_N2 vs. S_N1}$$

As a result of the two reactivity sequences, we may ordinarily expect
primary halides to react by the S_N2 mechanism, tertiary halides by the
S_N1 mechanism, and secondary halides by either or both. However, we
can to a certain extent control the reaction mechanism by our choice of
experimental conditions.

The very way in which changes in experimental conditions affect the
relative importance of the two mechanisms provides additional evidence
for the mechanisms. We have already seen an example of this: high **concentration of the nucleophilic reagent** favors the S_N2 reaction; low concentration favors the S_N1 reaction.

The **nature of the nucleophilic reagent** also plays an important role:
for example, neopentyl bromide reacts with ethoxide ion by the S_N2 mechanism and with ethyl alcohol by the S_N1 mechanism. The strongly nucleophilic (strongly basic) ethoxide ion pushes halogen from the molecule,
whereas the weakly nucleophilic ethanol waits to be invited in.

Finally, the **polarity of the solvent** can often determine the mechanism
by which reaction occurs. Ionization of an alkyl halide is possible only
because the energy needed for dissociation is supplied by formation of
ion–dipole bonds between ions and solvent. The more polar the solvent,

the stronger are the solvation forces and the faster is the ionization. Changing the solvent, say, from 80% ethanol to the much more polar water should speed up ionization and hence the rate of the S$_N$1 reaction. What effect will this have on the S$_N$2 reaction? A more polar solvent will pull the halide ion more strongly away from the molecule, but at the same time will give up a hydroxide ion more reluctantly. The effects tend to cancel each other, and hence for an S$_N$2 reaction we do not expect a large effect in either direction. Other things being equal, the more polar the solvent the more likely it is that an alkyl halide will react by the S$_N$1 mechanism.

These mechanisms give us some idea of the kind of behavior to expect from a halide of a particulars tructure: its reactivity under a given set of conditions, the likelihood of racemization or of rearrangement, the extent of elimination. They tell us how to change the experimental conditions — concentration, solvent, the nucleophilic reagent — to achieve the results we want: to speed up reaction, to avoid racemization or rearrangement, to minimize elimination.

Problem 13.7 Benzyl bromide reacts with H$_2$O in formic acid solution to yield benzyl alcohol; the rate is independent of [H$_2$O]. Under the same conditions p-methylbenzyl bromide reacts 58 times as fast.

Benzyl bromide reacts with ethoxide ion in dry alcohol to yield benzyl ethyl ether (C$_6$H$_5$CH$_2$OC$_2$H$_5$); the rate depends upon both [RBr] and [OC$_2$H$_5$$^-$]. Under the same conditions p-methylbenzyl bromide reacts 1.5 times as fast.

Interpret these results. What do they illustrate concerning the effect of: (a) polarity of solvent, (b) nucleophilic power of the reagent, and (c) electron release by substituents?

Problem 13.8 The rate of reaction of 3-chloro-1-butene with ethoxide ion in ethyl alcohol depends upon both [RCl] and [OC$_2$H$_5$$^-$]; the product is 3-ethoxy-1-butene, CH$_3$CH(OC$_2$H$_5$)CH=CH$_2$. The reaction of 3-chloro-1-butene with ethyl alcohol alone, on the other hand, yields not only 3-ethoxy-1-butene but also 1-ethoxy-2-butene, CH$_3$CH=CHCH$_2$OC$_2$H$_5$. How do you account for these results? (*Hint:* see Sec. 6.16, and Problem 12.4 on page 341.)

So far we have discussed the mechanisms of nucleophilic substitution only in terms of alkyl halides and a relatively few nucleophilic reagents. Although the evidence is not so complete in other instances, it seems clear that the same two mechanisms are involved in the reactions of alkyl halides with many other nucleophilic reagents, and in the reactions of many compounds other than alkyl halides.

For example, we recognize the reaction of alcohols with hydrogen halides as nucleophilic substitution involving the protonated alcohol and the halide ion.

$$\text{ROH}_2^+ \quad \begin{cases} \xrightarrow{} \text{R}^+ \xrightarrow{\text{X}^-} \text{RX} & \text{S}_N1: \textit{ allyl, benzyl, 3°, 2° alcohols;} \\ & \textit{rearrangements frequent} \\ \xrightarrow{\text{X}^-} \text{RX} + \text{H}_2\text{O} & \text{S}_N2: \textit{ most 1° alcohols; no rearrangements} \end{cases}$$

with H$_2$O + shown above the first arrow.

The order of reactivity and the occurrence of rearrangement for most secondary and tertiary alcohols suggest that the reaction is S$_N$1; the stereochemical evidence supports this view. The lack of rearrangement with most primary alcohols suggests that, because of the small tendency for formation of primary carbonium ions, the reaction here changes to an S_N2 mechanism involving direct attack by halide ion.

Problem 13.9 Most primary alcohols seem to react with hydrogen halides by the S_N2 mechanism. However, neopentyl alcohol evidently (since rearrangements occur) reacts by the S_N1 mechanism; how do you account for this? (*Hint:* see Problem 13.2, page 375.)

Problem 13.10 (a) Write the steps in the reaction of an alcohol with HCl by the S_N1 mechanism. (b) What is the rate-determining step? (c) The rate of reaction depends upon the concentration of what substance? (d) The concentration of this substance depends in turn upon the concentrations of what other compounds? (e) Will the rate depend *only* on [ROH]?

13.17   Elimination vs. substitution

Dehydrohalogenation of alkyl halides is already familiar to us as one of the best methods of preparing alkenes (Sec. 4.13). Let us return to this reaction, now focussing our attention on its relationship to substitution.

We encountered competition between substitution and elimination in the reaction between acetylides and alkyl halides (Sec. 6.11). Both reactions result from attack by the same nucleophilic reagent: attack at carbon causes substitution, attack at hydrogen causes elimination.

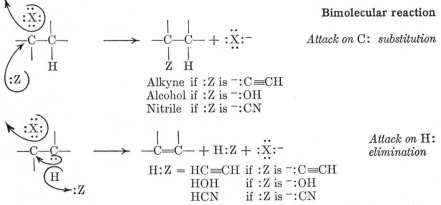

Bimolecular reaction

Attack on C: *substitution*

Alkyne if :Z is $^-$:C≡CH
Alcohol if :Z is $^-$:OH
Nitrile if :Z is $^-$:CN

Attack on H: *elimination*

H:Z = HC≡CH if :Z is $^-$:C≡CH
HOH   if :Z is $^-$:OH
HCN   if :Z is $^-$:CN

We can see more clearly now why reaction with acetylides to form alkynes is limited in practice to *primary* halides. Under the conditions of the reaction — a solvent of low polarity (liquid ammonia or ether) and a powerful nucleophilic reagent (acetylide ion) — we would expect substitution, that is, alkyne formation, to take place by an S_N2 mechanism. Primary halides should therefore form alkynes fastest, tertiary halides the slowest.

On the other hand, the speed with which an alkyl halide undergoes elimination depends chiefly (Sec. 6.11) upon the stability of the alkene formed; tertiary halides, which necessarily yield highly branched (more stable) alkenes, undergo elimination fastest.

Primary halides, then, undergo substitution fastest and elimination slowest; tertiary halides undergo substitution slowest and elimination fastest.   It is not surprising that the yields of alkynes are good for primary halides and very bad for tertiary halides.

Problem 13.11   Which of the two primary halides, *n*-butyl bromide or isobutyl bromide, would you expect to give the higher yield of alkyne upon reaction with sodium acetylide?   Why?

These same considerations apply to the reactions of alkyl halides with hydroxide ion.   The reaction gives good yields of alcohols with primary halides, somewhat poorer yields from secondary halides; it is essentially worthless for the preparation of tertiary alcohols.

Tertiary alcohols are best prepared under conditions that favor the S_N1 reaction: solvent of high polarity, and reagent of low nucleophilic power.   This is accomplished by simply boiling with water, which serves both as solvent and nucleophilic reagent.   Yet even here the yields of alcohol are not high; considerable elimination occurs since the intermediate is a *tertiary* carbonium ion, which can easily expel a hydrogen ion to yield a relatively stable alkene.

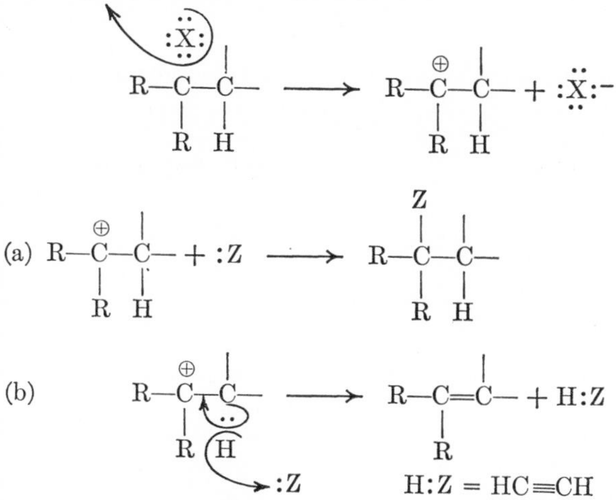

Carbonium ion reaction

Attack on C: *substitution*

Attack on H: *elimination*

$$H:Z = HC{\equiv}CH \quad \text{if :Z is } {}^-{:}C{\equiv}CH$$
$$HOH \quad\quad \text{if :Z is } {}^-{:}OH$$
$$HCN \quad\quad \text{if :Z is } {}^-{:}CN$$

When we want the product of a substitution reaction, elimination is a nuisance to be avoided.   But when we want an alkene from an alkyl halide, elimination is what we are trying to bring about.   To do this we use a solvent of low polarity, and a high concentration of a strong base: concentrated alcoholic potassium hydroxide.

13.18   Analysis of alkyl halides

Simple alkyl halides respond to the common characterization tests in the same manner as alkanes: they are insoluble in cold concentrated sulfuric acid, and they are inert to bromine in carbon tetrachloride and to aqueous permanganate.   They are readily distinguished from alkanes, however, by qualitative elemental analysis (sodium fusion, Sec. 2.25), which shows the presence of halogen.

In many cases, the presence of halogen can be detected without a sodium fusion. An unknown is warmed for a few minutes with alcoholic silver nitrate (the alcohol dissolves both the ionic reagent and the organic compound); halogen is indicated by formation of a precipitate that is insoluble in dilute nitric acid.

As in all reactions of organic halides, reactivity toward alcoholic silver nitrate follows the sequence RI > RBr > RCl. For a given halogen atom, reactivity decreases in the order $3° > 2° > 1°$, the sequence typical of carbonium ion formation; allyl and benzyl halides are highly reactive. Other evidence (stereochemistry, rearrangements) suggests that this reaction is of the S_N1 type.   Silver ion is believed to dispose reaction toward this mechanism (rather than the S_N2) by *pulling* halide away from the alkyl group.

$$R:X + Ag^+ \longrightarrow R^+ + Ag^+ X^-$$

(Vinyl and aryl halides do not react, Sec. 14.7.)

As mentioned earlier (Sec. 13.1), substituted alkyl halides also undergo the reactions characteristic of their other functional groups.

Problem 13.12   Describe simple chemical tests (if any) that would distinguish between: (a) ethylene bromohydrin and ethylene bromide; (b) 4-chloro-1-butene and *n*-butyl chloride; (c) bromocyclohexane and bromobenzene; (d) 1-chloro-2-methyl-2-propanol and 1,2-dichloro-2-methylpropane. Tell exactly what you would *do* and *see*.

PROBLEMS

1. Outline the synthesis of ethyl bromide from: (a) ethane, (b) ethylene, (c) ethanol. Which method would one most probably use in the laboratory?

2. Which methods of Problem 1 would be used to prepare pure samples of:

(a) ethyl chloride
(b) ethyl fluoride
(c) ethyl iodide
(d) *n*-propyl bromide

(e) isopropyl bromide
(f) benzyl chloride
(g) α-phenylethyl chloride
(h) cyclohexyl bromide

3. Outline the synthesis of the following compounds from isopropyl alcohol:

(a) isopropyl bromide
(b) allyl chloride
(c) 1-chloro-2-propanol
(d) 1,2-dibromopropane
(e) 2,2-dibromopropane

(f) 2-bromopropene
(g) 1-bromopropene
(h) chloroform
(i) 1,3-dichloro-2-propanol
(j) 2,3-dibromo-1-propanol

4. Outline all steps in a possible laboratory synthesis of each of the following from cyclohexanol and any necessary aliphatic, aromatic, or inorganic reagents.

(a) bromocyclohexane
(b) iodocyclohexane
(c) *trans*-1,2-dibromocyclohexane
(d) 3-bromocyclohexene
(e) 2-chlorocyclohexanol

(f) 1-methyl-1-bromocyclohexane
(g) cyclohexylcarbinyl bromide,
    cyclo-$C_6H_{11}CH_2Br$
(h) 1-phenyl-1-bromocyclohexane

5. Outline all steps in a possible laboratory synthesis of each of the following, using benzene, toluene, and alcohols of four carbons or less, and any needed inorganic reagents.

(a) 1-bromo-1-phenylpropane
(b) 2-bromo-1-phenylpropane
(c) 2-bromo-2-phenylpropane
(d) 2-bromo-2,3-dimethylbutane
(e) p-bromobenzyl chloride
(f) 3-bromohexane

(g) 1,2-dichloro-2-methylbutane
(h) 2-bromo-2-methylhexane
(i) triphenylchloromethane
(j) allyl iodide
(k) benzal bromide
(l) m-nitrobenzotrichloride

6. Give the structures and names of the chief organic products expected from the reaction (if any) of n-butyl bromide with:

(a) NaOH(aq)
(b) KOH(alc)
(c) cold conc. H_2SO_4 NR
(d) Zn, H^+
(e) Na
(f) Mg, ether
(g) product (f) + CH_3COCH_3, followed by water

(h) H_2, Pt
(i) dilute neutral $KMnO_4$ NR
(j) NaI in acetone
(k) benzene, $AlCl_3$
(l) $CH_3C≡C^-Na^+$
(m) HgF_2
(n) Br_2/CCl_4 NR

7. Referring when necessary to the list on page 367, give structures of the chief organic products expected from the reaction of n-butyl bromide with:

(a) NH_3
(b) $C_6H_5NH_2$
(c) NaCN

(d) $NaOC_2H_5$
(e) CH_3COOAg
(f) $NaSCH_3$

8. Write equations for the most likely side reactions in the following reactions of n-butyl bromide:

(a) conversion into 1-butanol by aqueous NaOH
(b) conversion into methyl n-butyl ether by sodium methoxide
(c) conversion into 1-butene by alcoholic KOH
(d) conversion into 1-hexyne by sodium acetylide

Will each of these side reactions be more or less important if tert-butyl bromide is used instead of n-butyl bromide?

9. Arrange the compounds of each set in order of reactivity toward S_N2 displacement:

(a) 2-bromo-2-methylbutane, 1-bromopentane, 2 bromopentane
(b) 1-bromo-3-methylbutane, 2-bromo-2-methylbutane, 3-bromo-2-methylbutane
(c) 1-bromobutane, 1-bromo-2,2-dimethylpropane, 1-bromo-2-methylbutane, 1-bromo-3-methylbutane

10. Arrange the compounds of each set in order of reactivity toward S_N1 displacement:

(a) the compounds of Problem 9(a)
(b) the compounds of Problem 9(b)
(c) benzyl chloride, p-chlorobenzyl chloride, p-methoxybenzyl chloride, p-methylbenzyl chloride, p-nitrobenzyl chloride
(d) benzyl bromide, α-phenylethyl bromide, β-phenylethyl bromide

11. Arrange the compounds in each set in order of ease of dehydrohalogenation by concentrated alcoholic KOH:

(a) compounds of Problem 9(a)
(b) compounds of Problem 9(b)
(c) 2-bromo-1-phenylpropane and 3-bromo-1-phenylpropane
(d) 5-bromo-1,3-cyclohexadiene, bromocyclohexane, 3-bromocyclohexene

12. Consider, as an example, the reaction between an alkyl halide and NaOH in a mixture of water and ethanol. In a table, with one column for S_N2 and another for S_N1, compare the two mechanisms with regard to:

(a) stereochemistry
(b) kinetic order

(c) occurrence of rearrangements
(d) relative rates of CH_3X, C_2H_5X, iso-C_3H_7X, *tert*-C_4H_9X
(e) relative rates of RCl, RBr, and RI
(f) effect on rate of a rise in temperature
(g) effect on rate of doubling [RX]
(h) effect on rate of doubling [OH⁻]
(i) effect on rate of increasing the water content of the solvent
(j) effect on rate of increasing the alcohol content of the solvent

13. At 55° and in 80% ethanol, alkyl bromides are hydrolyzed by 0.01 N NaOH at the following relative rates:

$$tert\text{-}C_4H_9Br > CH_3Br > C_2H_5Br > iso\text{-}C_3H_7Br$$
$$1010 \qquad 21 \qquad 1.7 \qquad 0.3$$

(a) What is the most likely explanation for this particular order of reactivity?
(b) What kinetics — first-order, second-order, or both — would you expect to find for the reaction of each alkyl bromide?

14. (−)-2-Ethoxyoctane has the configuration and rotation shown on page 415. When 2-bromooctane of rotation −20.8° is treated with sodium ethoxide dissolved in ethanol there is obtained 2-ethoxyoctane of rotation +10.5°.

(a) What is the steric course of this reaction: inversion, racemization, retention, or some combination of these? (Refer to the text for any needed configurations and rotations.) (b) On the basis of your answer to (a) what is the probable mechanism?

15. When 2-bromooctane of rotation +31.1° is treated with AgNO₃ in aqueous ethanol there is obtained 2-octanol of rotation −5.1°. (a) What is the steric course of this reaction? (Refer to the text for any needed configurations and rotations.) (b) On the basis of your answer to (a) what is the probable mechanism? What is the function of the AgNO₃?

16. Optically active *sec*-butyl alcohol retains its activity indefinitely in contact with aqueous base, but is rapidly converted into optically inactive (racemic) *sec*-butyl alcohol by dilute sulfuric acid. How do you account for these facts? Suggest a detailed mechanism or mechanisms for the racemization by dilute acid.

17. When optically active 2-methyl-1-chlorobutane was treated with chlorine under the influence of ultraviolet light, and the products were separated by fractional distillation, the 1,2-dichloro-2-methylbutane obtained was found to be optically *inactive*. (a) How do you account for this? (b) Are the results of this experiment consistent with the mechanism of Sec. 2.12? With the alternative mechanism of Problem 13, page 57? Account for your answers.

18. Describe simple chemical tests that would serve to distinguish between:
(a) allyl chloride and *n*-propyl chloride
(b) allyl chloride and benzyl chloride
(c) ethylene chlorohydrin, ethylene chloride, and ethylene glycol
(d) cyclohexanol, cyclohexyl bromide, and cyclohexene
(e) *tert*-butyl alcohol, *tert*-butyl chloride, and 1-octene
(f) benzyl chloride and *p*-chlorotoluene
Tell exactly what you would *do* and *see*.

19. A liquid of boiling point 39–41° was insoluble in water, dilute acids or bases, or concentrated H_2SO_4. It did not react with Br_2/CCl_4 or dilute $KMnO_4$. It was subjected to sodium fusion, and the resulting solution was filtered, acidified with nitric acid, and boiled. Addition of AgNO₃ gave a precipitate.

(a) On the basis of Table 13.1, what compound or compounds might this have been? (b) Several milliliters of CCl₄ were added to a portion of the acidified solution from the fusion, and the mixture was shaken with chlorine water. A violet color appeared in the CCl₄ layer. Which compound or compounds of (a) are still possible? (c) How would each of the other possibilities have responded in (b)?

20. An unknown compound is believed to be one of the following. Describe how you would go about finding out which of the possibilities the unknown actually is. Where possible, use simple chemical tests; where necessary, use more elaborate chemical methods like quantitative hydrogenation, cleavage, etc. Where necessary, make use of Table 16.1, page 435.

(a)	b.p., °C		b.p., °C
n-decane	174	p-cymene (p-isopropyltoluene)	177
4-methylcyclohexanol	174	limonene (see Problem 15, page 217)	178
1,3-dichloro-2-propanol	176	n-heptyl bromide	180
(b)			
propenylbenzene	177	n-hexyl iodide	180
benzyl chloride	179	cyclohexylcarbinol	182
2-octanol	179		
(c)			
m-diethylbenzene	182	n-octyl chloride	185
n-butylbenzene	183	trans-decalin (see Problem 9, page 216)	186
2-ethyl-1-hexanol	184		

21. Compound A gave a positive test for bromine, and gave negative tests with dilute KMnO₄ and Br₂/CCl₄. When magnesium turnings were added to a solution of A in anhydrous ether, the metal slowly dissolved. The resulting solution was treated with aqueous acid, and the ether layer was separated and dried. Distillation of a portion of the ether solution left no residue. When another portion of the solution was added to concentrated H₂SO₄, an acid-insoluble layer separated; this material boiled at 36° and had a density of 0.63. (a) Draw all possible structures for A. (b) A sample of A was found to be optically active. Now what structures are possible for A?

22. Compound B contains 54.8% carbon, 4.6% hydrogen, and 40.5% chlorine. (a) What is the empirical formula of B? (b) On the basis of what you know about molecular structure, can this empirical formula be the molecular formula of B? (c) What must be the minimum molecular weight of B? What is a possible structure consistent with this molecular weight?

23. Compound C, insoluble in concentrated H₂SO₄, gave qualitative elemental tests for carbon, hydrogen, and bromine, and gave negative tests with dilute KMnO₄ and Br₂/CCl₄. Combustion of a 6.49-mg sample of C gave 5.31 mg of carbon dioxide and 2.16 mg of water. Fusion of a 4.21-mg sample of C with sodium peroxide, followed by treatment with AgNO₃ gave 7.26 mg of AgBr. (a) What is the empirical formula of C? (b) What can you say about the molecular formula of C?

Treatment of C with zinc dust produced a gas, D, free of bromine, that decolorized dilute KMnO₄ and Br₂/CCl₄ solutions. Vigorous oxidation of D yielded CH₃CH₂COOH. (c) What was C? What was D?

24. In the preparation of diphenylmethane by the reaction between benzyl chloride and benzene in the presence of anhydrous AlCl₃, there are obtained high-boiling by-products. Among these are E, C₂₀H₁₈, and F, C₁₄H₁₂. Neither E nor F takes up hydrogen readily, but under vigorous conditions E gives C₂₀H₃₆ and F gives C₁₄H₂₄.

(a) How many rings does each of these compounds contain?
(b) What is the most likely structure of each of them?
(c) How is each of them most probably formed? (d) In carrying out this synthesis, how could you cut down the amounts of E and F formed? (*Hint:* see Sec. 2.8.)

Chapter fourteen_____

ARYL HALIDES

14.1 Structure

Aryl halides are compounds containing halogen attached directly to an aromatic ring. They have the general formula ArX, where Ar is phenyl, substituted phenyl, or one of the other aryl groups that we shall study (e.g., naphthyl, Chapter 31):

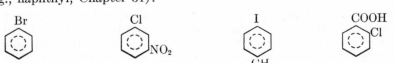

Bromobenzene   *m*-Chloronitrobenzene   *p*-Iodotoluene   *o*-Chlorobenzoic acid

An aryl halide is not just any halogen compound containing an aromatic ring. Benzyl chloride, for example, is not an aryl halide, for halogen is not attached to the aromatic ring; in structure and properties it is simply a substituted alkyl halide and was studied with the compounds it closely resembles (Chapter 13).

We take up the aryl halides in a separate chapter because they differ so much from the alkyl halides in their preparation and properties. In general, aryl halides are quite unreactive toward the nucleophilic substitution reactions so characteristic of the alkyl halides; the presence of certain other groups in the aromatic ring, however, greatly increases the reactivity of aryl halides. One of our main concerns in this chapter will be to account both for the low reactivity and for the effect of substituent groups. We shall take up *nucleophilic aromatic substitution* and compare it with both nucleophilic aliphatic substitution and electrophilic aromatic substitution.

Any other functional groups that are present in the aryl halide molecule undergo, of course, their characteristic reactions. Of these, we shall be particularly interested in the benzene ring itself and its electrophilic substitution reactions. We have already seen (Sec. 10.4) that halogens are unusual in their effect on electrophilic substitution: they are deactivating groups but *ortho,para* directors. The same structural feature that contributes to their low reactivity in nucleophilic aromatic substitution is the cause of this anomalous effect on electrophilic aromatic substitution.

Finally, it will be useful to compare aryl halides with certain other halides that are not aromatic at all: *vinyl halides*, compounds in which

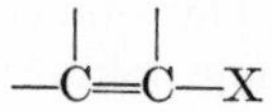

$$-\overset{|}{C}=\overset{|}{C}-X$$

A vinyl halide

halogen is attached directly to a doubly-bonded carbon. Vinyl halides show an interesting parallel to aryl halides: they too are unreactive toward nucleophilic substitution, and they too exert an anomalous effect on reactivity and orientation in the electrophilic reactions of the group to which they are attached, in this case in additions to the carbon–carbon double bond. We shall find that this resemblance between aryl halides and vinyl halides is due to a resemblance in structure.

14.2 Nomenclature

We have already discussed the nomenclature of the aryl halides (Sec. 8.17).

14.3 Physical properties

Unless modified by the presence of some other functional group, the physical properties of the aryl halides are much like those of the corresponding alkyl halides. Chlorobenzene and bromobenzene, for example, have boiling points very nearly the same as those of *n*-hexyl chloride and *n*-hexyl bromide; like the alkyl halides, the aryl halides are insoluble in water and soluble in organic solvents.

TABLE 14.1

ARYL HALIDES

	M.p., °C	B.p., °C	Ortho M.p., °C	Ortho B.p., °C	Meta M.p., °C	Meta B.p., °C	Para M.p., °C	Para B.p., °C
Fluorobenzene	− 45	85						
Chlorobenzene	− 45	132						
Bromobenzene	− 31	156						
Iodobenzene	− 31	189						
Fluorotoluene				115	−111	115		116
Chlorotoluene			−34	159	− 48	162	8	162
Bromotoluene			−26	182	− 40	184	28	185
Iodotoluene				206		211	35	211
Difluorobenzene			−34	92	− 59	83	− 13	89
Dichlorobenzene			−17	180	− 24	173	52	175
Dibromobenzene			6	221	− 7	217	87	219
Diiodobenzene			27	287	35	285	129	285
Nitrochlorobenzene			32	245	48	236	83	239
2,4-Dinitro-chlorobenzene	53	315						
2,4,6-Trinitro-chlorobenzene (picryl chloride)	83							
Vinyl chloride	−160	− 14						
Vinyl bromide	−138	16						

The physical constants listed in Table 14.1 illustrate very well a point previously made (Sec. 9.3) about the boiling points and melting points of *ortho, meta,* and *para* isomers. The isomeric dihalobenzenes, for example, have very nearly the same boiling points: between 173° and 180° for the dichlorobenzenes, 217° to 221° for the dibromobenzenes, and 285° to 287° for the diiodobenzenes. Yet the melting points of these same compounds show a considerable spread; in each case, the *para* isomer has a melting point that is some 70–100 degrees higher than the *ortho* or *meta* isomer. The physical constants of the halotoluenes show a similar relationship.

Here again we see that, having the most symmetrical structure, the *para* isomer fits better into a crystalline lattice and has the highest melting point. We can see how it is that a reaction product containing both *ortho* and *para* isomers frequently deposits crystals of only the *para* isomer upon cooling. Because of the strong intracrystalline forces, the higher melting *para* isomer also is less soluble in a given solvent than the *ortho* isomer, so that purification of the *para* isomer is often possible by recrystallization. The *ortho* isomer that remains in solution is generally heavily contaminated with the *para* isomer, and is difficult to purify.

14.4 Industrial source

On an industrial scale aryl halides are generally prepared by adaptations of the methods used in the laboratory, which are discussed in the following section.

14.5 Preparation

In the laboratory an aryl halide is most often prepared by one of the two methods outlined below.

PREPARATION OF ARYL HALIDES

1. From diazonium salts. Discussed in detail in Chapter 21.

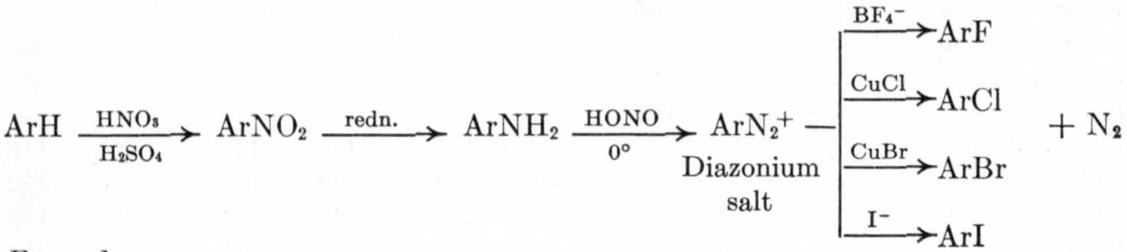

$$ArH \xrightarrow[H_2SO_4]{HNO_3} ArNO_2 \xrightarrow{redn.} ArNH_2 \xrightarrow[0°]{HONO} ArN_2^+ \underset{\substack{Diazonium \\ salt}}{} \begin{cases} \xrightarrow{BF_4^-} ArF \\ \xrightarrow{CuCl} ArCl \\ \xrightarrow{CuBr} ArBr \\ \xrightarrow{I^-} ArI \end{cases} + N_2$$

Example:

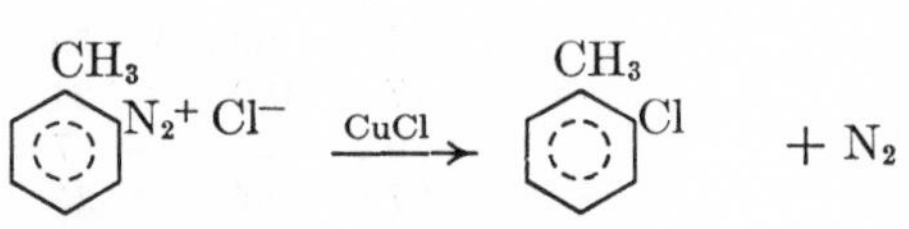

o-Toluenediazonium   o-Chlorotoluene
chloride

2. Halogenation

$$ArH + X_2 \xrightarrow{Lewis\ acid} ArX + HX$$

$$X_2 = Cl_2,\ Br_2$$

Lewis acid = $FeCl_3$, $AlCl_3$, *etc.*

Examples:

$$NO_2 \xrightarrow{\text{Cl}_2,\ \text{AlCl}_3} NO_2,\ Cl$$

Nitrobenzene   *m*-Chloronitrobenzene

$$NHCOCH_3 \xrightarrow{\text{Br}_2} NHCOCH_3,\ Br$$

Acetanilide   *p*-Bromoacetanilide
                               Major product

These methods, we notice, differ considerably from the methods of preparing alkyl halides. (a) Direct halogenation of the aromatic ring is more useful than direct halogenation of alkanes; although mixtures may be obtained (e.g., *ortho* + *para*), attack is not nearly so random as in the free radical halogenation of aliphatic hydrocarbons. (b) Alkyl halides are most often prepared from the corresponding alcohols; aryl halides are not prepared from the phenols. Instead, aryl halides are most commonly prepared by replacement of the nitrogen of a **diazonium salt;** as the sequence above shows, this ultimately comes from a nitro group which was itself introduced directly into the ring. *From the standpoint of synthesis, then, the nitro compounds bear much the same relationship to aryl halides that alcohols do to alkyl halides.* (These reactions of diazonium salts will be discussed in detail in Chapter 21.)

The preparation of aryl halides from diazonium salts is more important than direct halogenation for several reasons. First of all, fluorides and iodides, which can seldom be prepared by direct halogenation, can be obtained from the diazonium salts. Second, where direct halogenation yields a mixture of *ortho* and *para* isomers, the *ortho* isomer, at least, is difficult to obtain pure. On the other hand, the *ortho* and *para* isomers of the corresponding nitro compounds, from which the diazonium salts ultimately come, can often be separated by fractional distillation (Sec. 10.6). For example, the o- and p-bromotoluenes boil only three degrees apart: 182° and 185°. The corresponding o- and p-nitrotoluenes, however, boil sixteen degrees apart: 222° and 238°.

14.6 Reactions

The typical reaction of alkyl halides, we have seen (Sec. 13.6), is nucleophilic substitution. Halogen is displaced as halide ion by such bases as OH⁻, OR⁻, NH₃, CN⁻, etc., to yield alcohols, ethers, amines, nitriles, etc. Even Friedel-Crafts alkylation is, from the standpoint of the alkyl halide, nucleophilic substitution by the basic aromatic ring.

$$R{:}X + {:}Z \longrightarrow R{:}Z + {:}X^-$$

$$Z = OH^-,\ OR^-,\ NH_3,\ CN^-,\ \textit{etc.}$$

It is typical of **aryl halides** *that they undergo nucleophilic substitution only with extreme difficulty.* Except for certain industrial processes where very severe conditions are feasible, one does not ordinarily prepare phenols (ArOH), ethers (ArOR), amines ($ArNH_2$), or nitriles (ArCN) by nucleophilic attack on aryl halides. We cannot use aryl halides as we use alkyl halides in the Friedel-Crafts reaction.

However, aryl halides do undergo nucleophilic substitution readily if the aromatic ring contains, in addition to halogen, certain other properly placed groups: electron-attracting groups like $-NO_2$, —NO, or —CN, located *ortho* or *para* to halogen. For aryl halides having this special kind of structure, nucleophilic substitution proceeds readily and can be used for synthetic purposes.

The aromatic ring to which halogen is attached can, of course, undergo the typical electrophilic aromatic substitution reactions: nitration, sulfonation, halogenation, Friedel-Crafts alkylation. Like any substituent, halogen affects the reactivity and orientation in these reactions. As we have seen (Sec. 10.4), halogen is unusual in being deactivating yet *ortho,para*-directing.

REACTIONS OF ARYL HALIDES

1. Formation of Grignard reagent. Limitations are discussed in Sec. 11.14.

$$ArBr + Mg \xrightarrow{\text{dry ether}} ArMgBr$$

$$ArCl + Mg \xrightarrow{\text{tetrahydrofuran}} ArMgCl$$

2. Substitution in the ring. Electrophilic aromatic substitution

X:
Deactivates, and directs ortho,para in electrophilic substitution

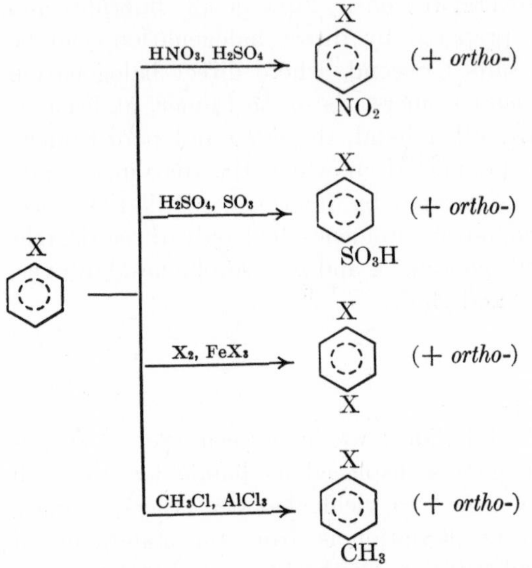

3. Replacement of halogen. Nucleophilic aromatic substitution

$$Ar{:}X + {:}Z \longrightarrow Ar{:}Z + {:}X^-$$

Ar *must contain strongly electron-withdrawing groups ortho and/or para to* —X.

Examples:

2,4-Dinitrochlorobenzene + NaOH (aq) ⟶ (ONa) $\xrightarrow{H^+}$ (OH) 2,4-Dinitrophenol

2,4-Dinitrochlorobenzene + NH₃ ⟶ 2,4-Dinitroaniline

2,4-Dinitrochlorobenzene + NaOC₂H₅ ⟶ 2,4-Dinitrophenyl ethyl ether

14.7 Low reactivity of aryl and vinyl halides

We have seen (Sec. 13.18) that an alkyl halide is conveniently detected by the precipitation of insoluble silver halide when it is warmed with alcoholic silver nitrate. The reaction occurs nearly instantaneously with tertiary, allyl, and benzyl bromides, and within five minutes or so with primary and secondary bromides. Compounds containing halogen joined directly to an aromatic ring or to a doubly-bonded carbon, however, do not yield silver halide under these conditions. Bromobenzene or vinyl bromide can be heated with alcoholic AgNO₃ for days without the slightest trace of AgBr being detected. In a similar way, attempts to convert aryl or vinyl halides into phenols (or alcohols), ethers, amines, or nitriles by treatment with the usual nucleophilic reagents are also unsuccessful; aryl or vinyl halides cannot be used in place of alkyl halides in the Friedel-Crafts reaction.

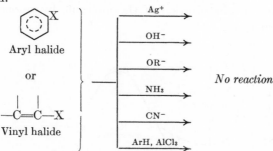

How can the low reactivity of these halides be accounted for? To find at least part of the answer, let us look at their structures.

14.8 Structure of aryl and vinyl halides

Chlorobenzene is considered to be a hybrid of not only the two Kekulé structures, I and II, but also of three structures, III, IV, and V, in which

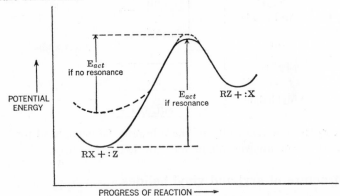

I   II   III   IV   V

.:hlorine is joined to carbon by a double bond; in III, IV, and V chlorine
bears a positive charge and the *ortho* and *para* positions of the ring bear a
negative charge.

In a similar way, vinyl chloride is considered to be a hybrid of structure
VI (the one we usually draw for it) and structure VII, in which chlorine
is joined to carbon by a double bond; in VII chlorine bears a positive
charge and C–2 bears a negative charge.

$$
\begin{array}{cc}
2\ \ 1 & 2\ \ 1 \\
\text{H H} & \text{H H} \\
\text{H:}\overset{..}{\text{C}}\text{::}\overset{..}{\text{C}}\text{:}\overset{..}{\underset{..}{\text{Cl}}}\text{:} & \text{H:}\overset{..}{\text{C}}\text{:}\overset{..}{\text{C}}\text{::}\overset{..}{\underset{..}{\text{Cl}}}\text{:} \\
 & \overset{\ominus}{}\qquad\overset{\oplus}{} \\
\text{VI} & \text{VII}
\end{array}
$$

Other aryl and vinyl halides are considered to have structures exactly
analogous to these.

Contribution from III, IV, and V and from VII stabilizes the chlorobenzene and vinyl chloride molecules, and gives double-bond character
to the carbon–chlorine bond. Carbon and chlorine are thus held together
by something more than a single pair of electrons, and the carbon–chlorine
bond is stronger than if it were a pure single bond. The low reactivity of
these halides toward nucleophilic substitution is due (partly, at least) to
resonance stabilization of the halides (by a factor that in this case does
not stabilize the transition state to the same extent); this stabilization
increases the E_{act} for displacement, and thus slows down reaction (Figure
14.1). For aryl halides, another factor — which may well be the most
important one — is stabilization of the molecule by resonance involving
the Kekulé structures.

POTENTIAL
ENERGY

E_{act}
if no resonance

E_{act}
if resonance

RZ + :X

RX + :Z

PROGRESS OF REACTION ⟶

FIGURE 14.1. Molecular structure and rate of reaction. Resonance-
stabilized aryl and vinyl halides react more slowly than alkyl halides.

What evidence is there for the kind of structure we have described, other than the fact that it helps to account for *the low reactivity of aryl and vinyl halides?*

The carbon–halogen bonds of aryl and vinyl halides are unusually short. A double bond is shorter than a single bond joining the same pair of atoms. For example, the carbon–carbon single bond is 1.54 A long, and the carbon–carbon double bond is 1.34 A long; the carbon–oxygen single bond is 1.43 A long, and the carbon–oxygen double bond is 1.24 A long.

If the carbon–halogen bond in aryl and vinyl halides has double-bond character, it should be shorter than the carbon–halogen bond in alkyl halides. This is found to be so. In chlorobenzene and vinyl chloride the C—Cl bond length is only 1.69 A, as compared with a length of 1.77–1.80 A in a large number of alkyl chlorides (Table 14.2). In bromobenzene and vinyl bromide the C—Br bond length is only 1.86 A, as compared with a length of 1.91–1.92 A in alkyl bromides.

TABLE 14.2

BOND LENGTHS AND DIPOLE MOMENTS OF HALIDES

	Bond lengths, A		Dipole moments, D	
	C—Cl	C—Br	R—Cl	R—Br
CH_3—X	1.77	1.91	—	—
C_2H_5—X	1.77	1.91	2.05	2.02
n-C_3H_7—X	—	—	2.10	2.15
n-C_4H_9—X	—	—	2.09	2.15
$(CH_3)_3C$—X	1.80	1.92	2.13	—
CH_2=CH—X	1.69	1.86	1.44	1.41
C_6H_5—X	1.69	1.86	1.73	1.71

Dipole moments of aryl and vinyl halides are unusually small. Organic halogen compounds are polar molecules; displacement of electrons toward the more electronegative element makes halogen relatively negative and carbon relatively positive. Table 14.2 shows that the dipole moments of a number of alkyl chlorides and bromides range from 2.02 D to 2.15 D. The mobile π electrons of the benzene ring and of the carbon–carbon double bond should be particularly easy to displace; hence we would expect aryl and vinyl halides to have even larger dipole moments than alkyl halides.

However, we see that this is not the case. Chlorobenzene and bromobenzene have dipole moments of only 1.7 D, and vinyl chloride and vinyl bromide have dipole moments of only 1.4 D; halogen is evidently not so negative in these compounds as we expect it to be. This is consistent with the resonance picture of these molecules. In the structures that contain doubly-bonded halogen (III, IV, V, and VII) there is a positive charge on halogen and a negative charge on carbon; to the extent that these structures contribute to the hybrids they tend to oppose the usual displacement of electrons toward halogen. Although there is still a net displacement of electrons toward halogen in aryl halides and in vinyl halides, it is less than in other organic halides.

Finally, contribution from structures in which halogen is doubly bonded and bears a positive charge accounts for *the way halogen affects the reactions of the benzene ring or of the carbon–carbon double bond to which it is joined.* This point is discussed in the following section.

14.9   Effect of halogen on electrophilic aromatic substitution

Halogens are unusual in their effect on electrophilic aromatic substitution: they are deactivating yet *ortho,para*-directing. Deactivation is characteristic of electron withdrawal, whereas *ortho,para* orientation is characteristic of electron release (Sec. 10.9). Can halogen both withdraw and release electrons? This seems to be the case.

We have seen that the effect of substituent groups on both reactivity and orientation in electrophilic aromatic substitution is consistent with this principle: *the more stable the intermediate carbonium ion, the faster it is formed.*

Let us first consider **reactivity.** Electrophilic attack on benzene yields carbonium ion I, attack on chlorobenzene yields carbonium ion II. The

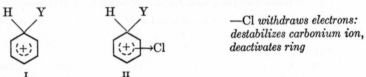

—Cl *withdraws electrons:
destabilizes carbonium ion,
deactivates ring*

electron-withdrawing inductive effect of chlorine intensifies the positive charge in carbonium ion II, makes the ion less stable, and causes a slower reaction.

Next, to understand **orientation,** let us compare the structures of the carbonium ions formed by attack at the *para* and *meta* positions of chlorobenzene.

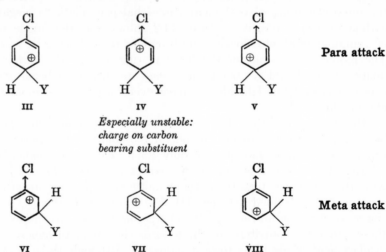

Para attack

*Especially unstable:
charge on carbon
bearing substituent*

Meta attack

Each of these is a hybrid of three structures, III–V for *para*, VI–VIII for *meta.* In one of these six structures, IV, the positive charge is located on the carbon atom to which chlorine is attached. Through its inductive effect chlorine withdraws electrons most from the carbon to which it is joined, and thus makes structure IV especially unstable. As before (Sec. 10.9), we expect IV to make little contribution to the hybrid, which should therefore be less stable than the hybrid ion resulting from attack at the *meta* positions. If only the inductive effect were involved, then, we would expect not only deactivation but also *meta* orientation.

But, to account for difficulty of displacement, bond lengths, and dipole moments, we have considered that halogen can share more than a pair of electrons with a benzene ring and can accommodate a positive charge. If we apply that idea to the present problem, what do we find? The ion resulting from *para* attack is a hybrid not only of structures III–V, but also of structure IX, in which chlorine bears a positive charge and is joined to the ring by a double bond. This structure should be comparatively stable, since in it every atom (except hydrogen, of course) has a *complete octet of electrons.* (Structure IX is exactly analogous to those proposed

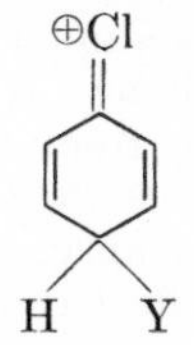

Para attack

IX

Comparatively stable:
every atom has octet

to account for activation and *ortho,para* direction by —NH$_2$ and —OH, Sec. 10.10.) No such structure is possible for the ion resulting from *meta* attack. To the extent that structure IX contributes to the hybrid, it makes the ion resulting from *para* attack more stable than the ion resulting from *meta* attack. Although we could not have predicted the relative importance of the two factors — the instability of IV and the stabilization by IX — the result indicates that the contribution from IX is the more important.

In the same way it can be seen that attack at an *ortho* position also yields an ion (X–XIII) that can be stabilized by accommodation of the positive charge by chlorine.

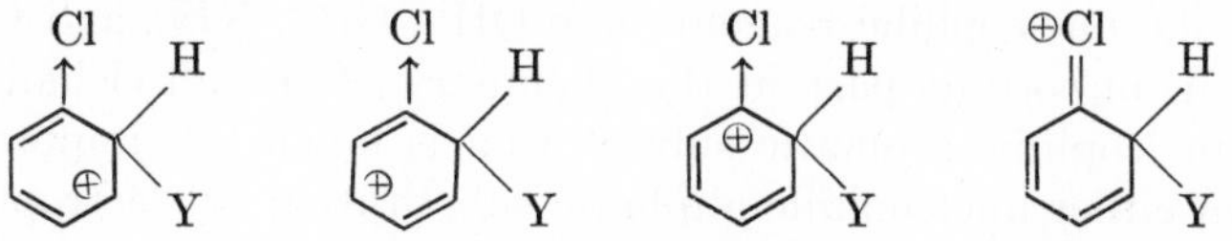

Ortho attack

X   XI   XII   XIII

Especially unstable: *Comparatively stable:*
charge on carbon   *every atom has octet*
bearing substituent

Through its inductive effect halogen tends to withdraw electrons and thus to destabilize the intermediate carbonium ion. This effect is felt at all positions, but particularly at the positions *ortho* and *para* to the halogen

Through its resonance effect halogen tends to release electrons and thus to stabilize the intermediate carbonium ion. This electron release is effective only at the positions *ortho* and *para* to the halogen.

The inductive effect is stronger than the resonance effect and causes net electron withdrawal — and hence deactivation — at all positions. The resonance effect tends to oppose the inductive effect for attack at the *ortho* and *para* positions, and hence makes the deactivation less for *ortho,para* attack than for *meta*.

Reactivity is thus controlled by the stronger inductive effect, and orientation is controlled by the resonance effect, which, although weaker, seems to be more selective.

Problem 14.1 Hydrogen iodide adds to vinyl chloride more slowly than to ethylene, and yields 1-chloro-1-iodoethane. (a) Draw the formula of the carbonium ion formed in the initial step of the addition to vinyl chloride. (b) Of addition to ethylene. (c) Judging from the relative rates of reaction, which would appear to be the more stable carbonium ion? (d) Account for the difference in stability.

(e) Draw the formula for the carbonium ion that would be formed if vinyl chloride were to yield 1-chloro-2-iodoethane. (f) Judging from the actual orientation of addition, which carbonium ion from vinyl chloride is the more stable, (a) or (e)? (g) Account for the difference in stability.

(h) Which effect, inductive or resonance, controls reactivity in electrophilic addition to vinyl halides? (i) Which effect controls orientation?

Thus we find that a single structural concept — partial double bond formation between halogen and carbon — helps to account for unusual physical and chemical properties of such seemingly different compounds as aryl halides and vinyl halides. The structures involving doubly-bonded halogen, which we consider to make important contribution to both molecules and carbonium ions, certainly do not seem to meet our usual standard of reasonableness (Sec. 8.15). The sheer weight of evidence forces us to accept the idea that certain carbon–halogen bonds possess double bond character. If this idea at first appears strange to us, it simply shows how little, after all, we really know about molecular structure.

14.10 Nucleophilic aromatic substitution

We have seen that the aryl halides are characterized by very low reactivity toward the nucleophilic reagents like OH^-, OR^-, NH_3, and CN^- that play such an important part in the chemistry of the alkyl halides. Consequently, nucleophilic aromatic substitution is much less important in synthesis than either nucleophilic aliphatic substitution or electrophilic aromatic substitution.

However, the presence of certain groups at certain positions of the ring markedly activates the halogen of aryl halides toward displacement. We shall have a look at some of these activation effects, and then try to account for them on the basis of the chemical principles we have learned. We shall find a remarkable parallel between the two kinds of aromatic substitution, electrophilic and nucleophilic, with respect both to mechanism and to the ways in which substituent groups affect reactivity and orientation.

Chlorobenzene is converted into phenol by aqueous sodium hydroxide only at temperatures over 300°. The presence of a nitro group *ortho* or *para* to the chlorine greatly increases its reactivity: *o*- or *p*-chloronitrobenzene is converted into the nitrophenol by treatment with aqueous sodium hydroxide at 160°. A nitro group *meta* to the chlorine, on the other hand, has practically no effect on reactivity. As the number of *ortho* and *para* nitro groups on the ring is increased, the reactivity increases: the phenol is obtained from 2,4-dinitrochlorobenzene by treatment with hot aqueous sodium carbonate, and from 2,4,6-trinitrochlorobenzene by simple treatment with water.

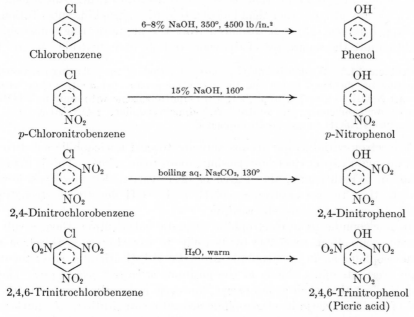

Similar effects are observed when other nucleophilic reagents are used· Ammonia or sodium methoxide, for example, reacts with chloro- or bromobenzene only under very vigorous conditions. For example:

Cl   NH₂

$\xrightarrow{\quad NH_3,\ Cu_2O.\ 200°.\ 900\ lb/in.^2 \quad}$

Chlorobenzene   Aniline

Yet if the ring contains a nitro group — or preferably two or three of them — *ortho* or *para* to the halogen, reaction proceeds quite readily. For example:

Cl NO₂   NH₂ NO₂

$\xrightarrow{\quad NH_3,\ 170° \quad}$

NO₂   NO₂

2,4-Dinitrochlorobenzene   2,4-Dinitroaniline

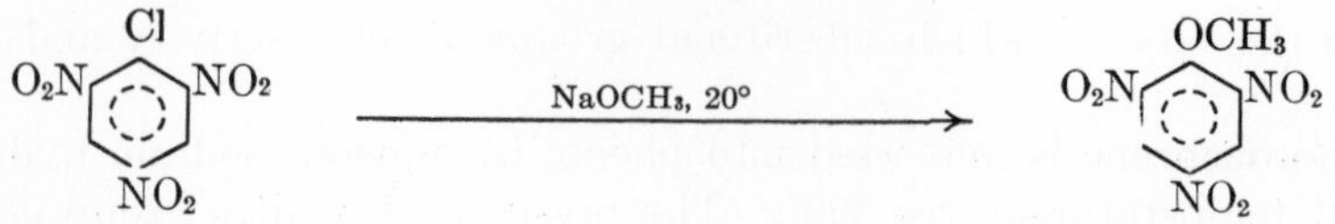

$$O_2N \underset{NO_2}{\overset{Cl}{\bigcirc}} NO_2 \xrightarrow{\quad NaOCH_3,\ 20° \quad} O_2N \underset{NO_2}{\overset{OCH_3}{\bigcirc}} NO_2$$

2,4,6-Trinitrochlorobenzene   2,4,6-Trinitroanisole

Like —NO₂, certain other groups have been found to activate halogen located *ortho* or *para* to them: —N(CH₃)₃⁺, —CN, —SO₃H,—COOH, —CHO,—COR. This is a familiar list. All these are electron-withdrawing groups, which are deactivating and *meta*-directing toward *electrophilic* substitution (see Table 10.3, page 287).

Although our concern here is primarily with displacement of halogen, it is important to know that these electron-withdrawing substituents activate many groups other than halogen toward nucleophilic substitution. (Hydrogen is generally not displaced from the aromatic ring, since this would require the separation of the very strongly basic hydride ion, :H⁻.)

Problem 14.2 Write a balanced equation for each of the following reactions, indicating the displaced group and the activating group: (a) *p*-nitroaniline with aqueous NaOH to give *p*-nitrophenol; (b) *o*-dinitrobenzene with aqueous NaOH to give *o*-nitrophenol; (c) *p*-nitroso-N,N-dimethylaniline, *p*-ONC₆H₄N(CH₃)₂, with aqueous NaOH to give *p*-nitrosophenol.

If electron-withdrawing groups activate toward nucleophilic substitution, we might expect electron-releasing groups to *deactivate*. This is found to be so. Furthermore, the degree of deactivation depends upon how strongly they release electrons: —NH₂ and —OH deactivate strongly; —OR, moderately; and —R, weakly.

In nucleophilic as in electrophilic aromatic substitution, then, a substituent group affects reactivity by its ability to attract or release electrons; in nucleophilic as in electrophilic aromatic substitution, a substituent group exerts its effect chiefly at the positions *ortho* and *para* to it. The kind of effect that each group exerts, however, is exactly opposite to the kind of effect it exerts in electrophilic aromatic substitution. *In* **nucleophilic aromatic substitution** *electron withdrawal causes activation, and electron release causes deactivation.*

To account for these effects we must look at the mechanism of nucleophilic aromatic substitution.

14.11   Mechanism of nucleophilic aromatic substitution

The commonly accepted mechanism for nucleophilic aromatic substitution (shown here for chlorobenzene) is:

$$(1) \qquad C_6H_5Cl + :Z \longrightarrow \underset{\substack{\\ \text{I}}}{\overset{\ominus}{C_6H_5}} \overset{\diagup Cl}{\underset{\diagdown Z}{}}$$

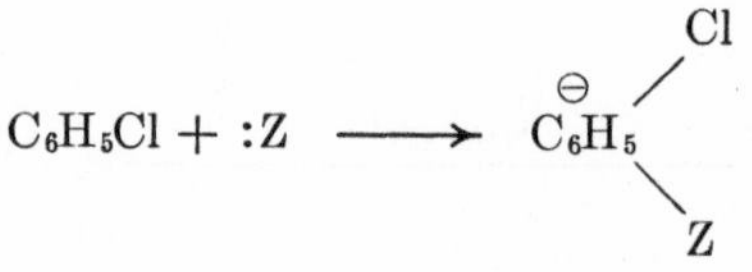

(2)
$$C_6H_5 \overset{\ominus}{\underset{Z}{\overset{Cl}{\Big\backslash}}} \longrightarrow C_6H_5Z + :Cl^-$$

I

There are two essential steps: attack of a nucleophilic reagent upon the ring to form a carbanion (I), and the expulsion of halide ion from this carbanion to yield the product. (*A* **carbanion** *is a negative ion — an anion — in which carbon carries negative charge.*)

The intermediate carbanion (I) is a hybrid of II, III, and IV; this hybrid is sometimes represented by the single structure V.

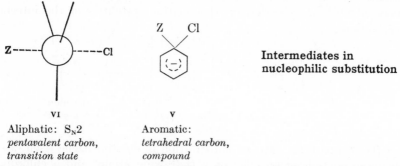

II   III   IV   V

In nucleophilic aliphatic substitution (S_N2) the intermediate in which carbon is bonded to both the attacking group and the displaced group is considered to be a transition state; a structure (VI) containing carbon

VI   V

Aliphatic: S_N2 Aromatic:
pentavalent carbon,   *tetrahedral carbon,*
transition state   *compound*

Intermediates in nucleophilic substitution

bonded to five atoms must be unstable and so corresponds to the top of an energy hill (Figure 14.2). In nucleophilic aromatic substitution, on the other hand, the intermediate is generally considered to be an actual compound; a structure (V) containing tetrahedral carbon and having the negative charge distributed about the ring is comparatively stable, and probably corresponds to an energy valley (Figure 14.3, next page).

14.12   Reactivity in nucleophilic aromatic substitution

For reactions involving an intermediate carbonium ion, we have seen that the over-all rate depends only on the rate of formation of the carbonium ion. In nucleophilic aromatic substitution an analogous situation seems to exist: the first step, formation of the carbanion, largely determines the over-all rate of reaction; once formed, the carbanion rapidly reacts to yield the final product.

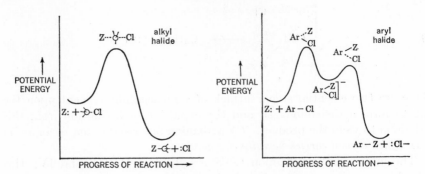

FIGURE 14.2. Energy curve for nucleophilic aliphatic (S_N2) substitution. One-step reaction: intermediate is a transition state.

FIGURE 14.3. Energy curve for nucleophilic aromatic substitution. Two-step reaction: intermediate is a compound.

For closely related reactions, we might expect a difference in rate of formation of carbanions to be largely determined by a difference in E_{act}, that is, by a difference in stability of the transition states. Factors that stabilize the carbanion by dispersing the charge should for the same reason stabilize the incipient carbanion of the transition state. Just as the more stable carbonium ion is formed more rapidly, so, we expect, the more stable carbanion should be formed more rapidly. We shall therefore concentrate our attention on the relative stabilities of the intermediate carbanions.

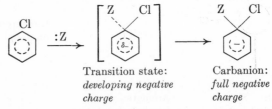

To compare the rates of substitution in chlorobenzene itself, a chlorobenzene containing an electron-withdrawing group, and a chlorobenzene containing an electron-releasing group, we compare the structures of carbanions I, II, and III.

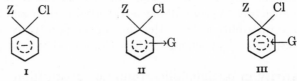

A group that withdraws electrons (II) tends to neutralize the negative charge of the ring and so to become more negative itself; this dispersal of the charge stabilizes the carbanion. In the same way, electron withdrawal stabilizes the transition state with its developing negative charge, and thus speeds up reaction. A group that releases electrons (III) tends to intensify the negative charge, destabilizes the carbanion (and the transition state), and thus slows down reaction.

Nucleophilic Aromatic Substitution

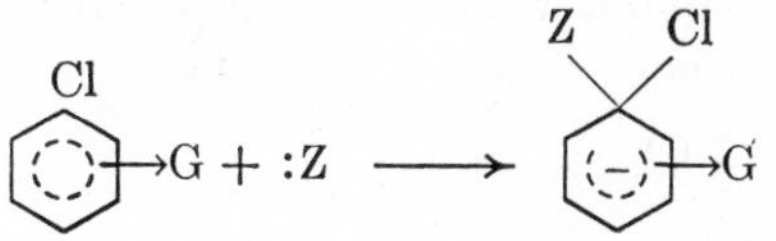

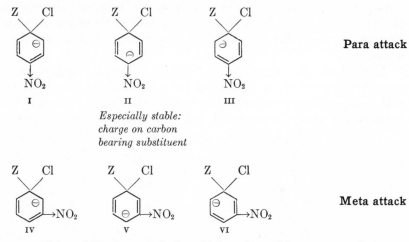

G *withdraws electrons:*
stabilizes carbanion,
activates

$G = -N(CH_3)_3^+$
$-NO_2$
$-CN$
$-SO_3H$
$-COOH$
$-CHO$
$-COR$
$-X$

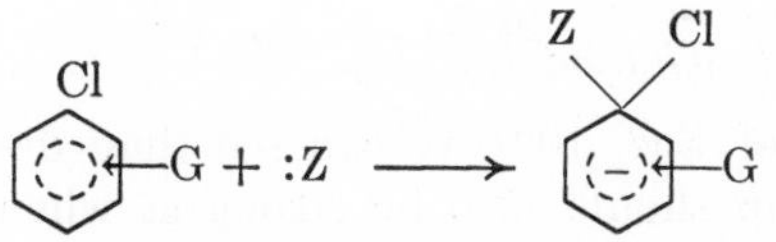

G *releases electrons:*
destabilizes carbanion,
deactivates

$G = -NH_2$
$-OH$
$-OR$
$-R$

It is clear, then, why a given substituent group affects nucleophilic and electrophilic aromatic substitution in opposite ways: it affects the stability of negatively and positively charged ions in opposite ways.

14.13   Orientation in nucleophilic aromatic substitution

To see why it is that a group activates the positions *ortho* and *para* to it most strongly, let us compare, for example, the carbanions formed from *p*-chloronitrobenzene and *m*-chloronitrobenzene. Each of these is a hybrid of three structures, I–III for *para* attack, IV–VI for *meta* attack. In one of these six structures, II, the negative charge is located on the carbon

Para attack

I

II

III

Especially stable:
charge on carbon
bearing substituent

Meta attack

IV   V   VI

atom to which —NO₂ is attached. Although —NO₂ attracts electrons from all positions of the ring, it does so most from the carbon atom nearest it; consequently structure II is a particularly stable one. Because of contribution from structure II, the hybrid carbanion resulting from attack on *p*-chloronitrobenzene is more stable than the carbanion resulting from attack on *m*-chloronitrobenzene. The *para* isomer therefore reacts faster than the *meta* isomer.

In the same way it can be seen that attack on *o*-chloronitrobenzene (VII–IX) also yields a more stable carbanion, because of contribution from IX, than attack on *m*-chloronitrobenzene.

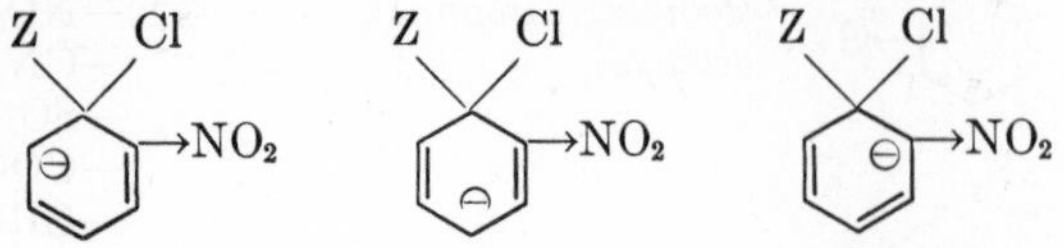

Ortho attack

Especially stable:
charge on carbon
bearing substituent

By considerations similar to those of Sec. 10.9 we can see that de-activation by an electron-releasing group should also be strongest when it is *ortho* or *para* to the halogen.

Nucleophilic and electrophilic aromatic substitution are similar, then, in that a group exerts its strongest influence — whether activating or de-activating — at the positions *ortho* and *para* to it. This similarity is due to a similarity in the intermediate ions: in both cases the charge of the intermediate ion — whether negative or positive — is strongest at the positions *ortho* and *para* to the point of attack, and hence a group attached to one of these positions can exert the strongest influence.

14.14 Electron withdrawal by resonance

The activation by —NO_2 and other electron-attracting groups can be accounted for, as we have seen, simply on the basis of inductive effects. However, it is generally believed that certain of these groups withdraw electrons by resonance as well. Let us see what kind of structures are involved.

The intermediate carbanions formed by nucleophilic attack on *o*- and *p*-chloronitrobenzene are considered to be hybrids not only of structures with negative charges carried by carbons of the ring (as shown in the last section), but also of structures I and II in which the negative charge is

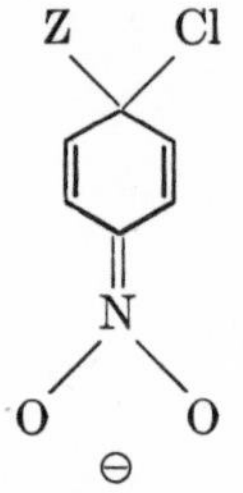

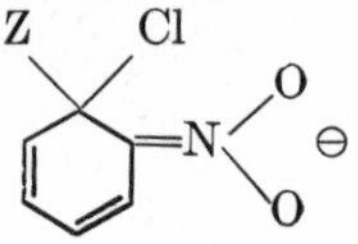

carried by oxygen of the —NO_2 group. Being highly electronegative, oxygen readily accommodates a negative charge, and hence I and II should be especially stable structures. The carbanions to which these structures contribute are therefore much more stable than the ones formed by attack on chlorobenzene itself or on *m*-chloronitrobenzene, for which structures like I and II are not possible. Thus resonance involving the —NO_2 group strengthens the activation toward nucleophilic substitution caused by the inductive effect.

The activating effect of a number of other electron-attracting groups is considered to arise, in part, from the contribution of similar structures (shown only for *para* isomers) to the intermediate carbanions.

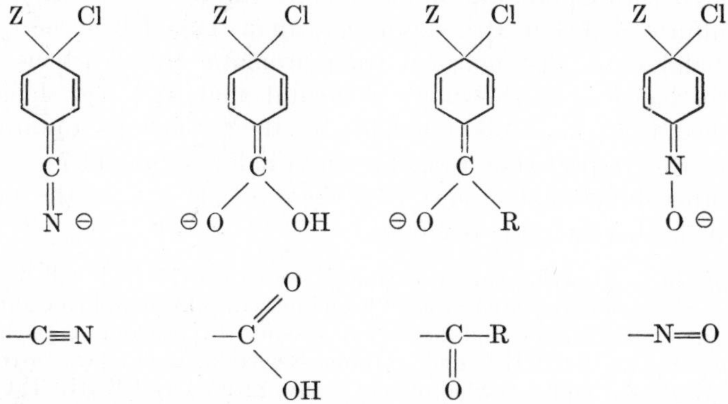

Problem 14.3 There is evidence to suggest that the nitroso group, —$\ddot{N}$=$\ddot{O}$:, activates *ortho* and *para* positions toward *both* nucleophilic and electrophilic aromatic substitution; the group apparently can either withdraw or release electrons upon demand by the attacking reagent. Show how this might be accounted for. (*Hint:* see Sec. 10.10.)

14.15 Nucleophilic substitution: aliphatic and aromatic

We can see a regular progression in the three kinds of nucleophilic substitution that we have studied so far. The departing group leaves the molecule *before* the entering group becomes attached in an S_N1 reaction, *at the same time* in an S_N2 reaction, and *after* in nucleophilic aromatic substitution. A *positive charge* thus develops on carbon during an S_N1 reaction, *no particular charge* during an S_N2 reaction, and a *negative charge* during nucleophilic aromatic substitution. As a result, an S_N1 reaction is favored by *electron release*, an S_N2 reaction is relatively *insensitive to electronic factors*, and nucleophilic aromatic substitution is favored by *electron withdrawal*.

S_N1
Positive charge develops on carbon

S_N2
Little charge develops on carbon

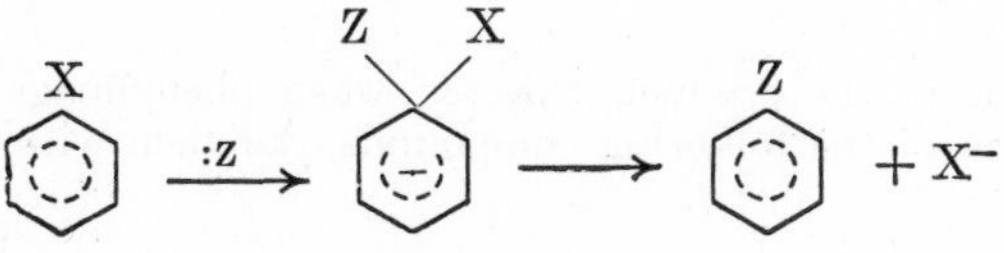

Nucleophilic aromatic
Negative charge develops on carbon

14.16 Analysis of aryl halides

Aryl halides show much the same response to characterization tests as the hydrocarbons from which they are derived: insolubility in cold concentrated sulfuric acid; inertness toward bromine in carbon tetrachloride and toward permanganate solutions; formation of orange to red colors when treated with chloroform and aluminum chloride; dissolution in cold fuming sulfuric acid, but at a slower rate than that of benzene.

Aryl halides are distinguished from aromatic hydrocarbons by the presence of halogen, as shown by elemental analysis. Aryl halides are distinguished from most alkyl halides by their inertness toward silver nitrate; in this respect they resemble vinyl halides (Sec. 14.7).

Any other functional groups that may be present in the molecule undergo their characteristic reactions.

Problem 14.4 Describe simple chemical tests (if any) that will distinguish between: (a) bromobenzene and n-hexyl bromide; (b) p-bromotoluene and benzyl bromide; (c) chlorobenzene and 1-chloro-1-hexene; (d) α-(p-bromophenyl)ethyl alcohol (p-BrC$_6$H$_4$CHOHCH$_3$) and p-bromo-n-hexylbenzene; (e) α-(p-chlorophenyl)ethyl alcohol and β-(p-chlorophenyl)ethyl alcohol (p-ClC$_6$H$_4$CH$_2$CH$_2$OH). Tell exactly what you would *do* and *see*.

Problem 14.5 Outline a procedure for distinguishing by chemical means (not necessarily simple tests) between: (a) p-bromoethylbenzene and 4-bromo-1,3-dimethylbenzene; (b) o-chloropropenylbenzene (o-ClC$_6$H$_4$CH=CHCH$_3$) and o-chloroallylbenzene (o-ClC$_6$H$_4$CH$_2$CH=CH$_2$).

PROBLEMS

1. Give structures and names of the principal organic products of the reaction (if any) of each of the following reagents with bromobenzene:

(a) Mg, ether
(b) boiling 10% aqueous NaOH
(c) boiling alcoholic KOH
(d) sodium acetylide
(e) sodium ethoxide
(f) NH$_3$, 100°
(g) boiling aqueous NaCN
(h) HNO$_3$, H$_2$SO$_4$
(i) fuming sulfuric acid
(j) Cl$_2$, Fe
(k) I$_2$, Fe
(l) C$_6$H$_6$, AlCl$_3$
(m) CH$_3$CH$_2$Cl, AlCl$_3$
(n) cold dilute KMnO$_4$
(o) hot KMnO$_4$

2. Answer Problem 1 for n-butyl bromide.

3. Answer Problem 1, parts (b), (e), (f), and (g) for 2,4-dinitrobromobenzene.

4. Outline a method for the conversion of bromobenzene into each of the following, using any needed aliphatic and inorganic reagents.

(a) benzene
(b) p-bromonitrobenzene
(c) p-bromochlorobenzene
(d) p-bromobenzenesulfonic acid
(e) 1,2,4-tribromobenzene
(f) p-bromotoluene
(g) benzyl alcohol
(h) α-phenylethyl alcohol
(i) 2-phenyl-2-propanol
(j) 2,4-dinitrophenol
(k) allylbenzene (*Hint:* see Problem 16, page 193.)
(l) benzoic acid

5. Give the structure and name of the product expected when phenylmagnesium bromide is treated with each of the following compounds and then with water:

(a) H_2O
(b) HBr (dry)
(c) C_2H_5OH
(d) allyl bromide
(e) HCHO
(f) CH_3CHO
(g) C_6H_5CHO
(h) $p\text{-}CH_3C_6H_4CHO$

(i) CH_3COCH_3
(j) cyclohexanone
(k) 3,3-dimethylcyclohexanone
(l) $C_6H_5COCH_3$
(m) $C_6H_5COC_6H_5$
(n) $(-)\text{-}C_6H_5COCH(CH_3)C_2H_5$
(o) acetylene

Which products (if any) would be single compounds? Which (if any) would be racemates? Which (if any) would be optically active as isolated?

6. Arrange the compounds in each set in order of reactivity toward the indicated reagent. Give the structure and name of the product expected from the compound you select as the most reactive in each set.

(a) NaOH: chlorobenzene, *m*-chloronitrobenzene, *o*-chloronitrobenzene, 2,4-dinitrochlorobenzene, 2,4,6-trinitrochlorobenzene
(b) HNO_3/H_2SO_4: benzene, chlorobenzene, nitrobenzene, toluene
(c) alcoholic $AgNO_3$: 1-bromo-1-butene, 3-bromo-1-butene, 4-bromo-1-butene
(d) fuming sulfuric acid: bromobenzene, *p*-bromotoluene, *p*-dibromobenzene, toluene
(e) KCN: benzyl chloride, chlorobenzene, ethyl chloride
(f) alcoholic $AgNO_3$: 2-bromo-1-phenylethene, α-phenylethyl bromide, β-phenylethyl bromide

7. In the preparation of 2,4-dinitrochlorobenzene from chlorobenzene, the excess nitric acid and sulfuric acid must be washed from the product. Which would you select for this purpose: aqueous sodium hydroxide or aqueous sodium bicarbonate? Why?

8. Give structures and names of the principal organic products expected from each of the following reactions:

(a) 2,3-dibromopropene + NaOH(aq)
(b) *p*-bromobenzyl bromide + NH_3(aq)
(c) *p*-chlorotoluene + hot $KMnO_4$
(d) *m*-bromostyrene + Br_2/CCl_4
(e) 3,4-dichloronitrobenzene + 1 mole $NaOCH_3$
(f) *p*-bromochlorobenzene + Mg, ethyl ether
(g) *p*-bromobenzyl alcohol + cold dilute $KMnO_4$
(h) *p*-bromobenzyl alcohol + conc. HBr
(i) α-(*o*-chlorophenyl)ethyl bromide + KOH(alc)
(j) *p*-bromotoluene + 1 mole Cl_2, heat, light

9. Outline all steps in a possible laboratory synthesis of each of the following compounds from benzene and/or toluene, using any needed aliphatic or inorganic reagents:

(a) *m*-chloronitrobenzene
(b) *p*-chloronitrobenzene
(c) *m*-bromobenzoic acid
(d) *p*-bromobenzoic acid
(e) *m*-chlorobenzotrichloride
(f) 3,4-dibromonitrobenzene
(g) *p*-bromobenzal chloride

(h) 2,4-dinitroaniline
(i) *p*-bromostyrene
(j) 2,4-dibromobenzoic acid
(k) 2,5-dichloronitrobenzene
(l) *p*-bromobenzenesulfonic acid
(m) *p*-chlorobenzyl alcohol
(n) 2-(*p*-tolyl)propane

10. Halogen located at the 2- or 4-position of the aromatic heterocyclic compound *pyridine* (see page 844) is fairly reactive toward nucleophilic displacement. For example:

4-Chloropyridine   4-Aminopyridine

How do you account for the reactivity of these compounds? (Check your answer in Sec. 32.10.)

11. In both S_N1 and S_N2 displacements the reactivity of alkyl halides follows the sequence R—I > R—Br > R—Cl > R—F. The weaker the carbon–halogen bond, the more reactive the alkyl halide. In nucleophilic aromatic substitution, however, this order of reactivity is not generally followed; indeed, aryl fluorides are often the most reactive.

Can you account for the fact that reactivity in S_N1 and S_N2 reactions depends upon carbon–halogen bond strength, whereas reactivity in aromatic substitution does not?

12. An unknown compound is believed to be one of the following. Describe how you would go about finding out which of the possibilities the unknown actually is. Where possible use simple chemical tests; where necessary use more elaborate chemical methods like quantitative hydrogenation, cleavage, etc. Where necessary, make use of Table 16.1, page 435.

(a) $C_6H_5CH=CHBr$ (b.p. 221°), o-$C_6H_4Br_2$ (b.p. 221°), $BrCH_2(CH_2)_3CH_2Br$ (b.p. 224°)

(b) o-$CH_3C_6H_4Br$ (b.p. 182°), m-$CH_3C_6H_4Br$ (b.p. 184°), p-$CH_3C_6H_4Br$ (b.p. 185°)

(c) o-$ClC_6H_4C_2H_5$ (b.p. 178°), $C_6H_5CH_2Cl$ (b.p. 179°), o-$C_6H_4Cl_2$ (b.p. 180°)

(d) $ClCH_2CH_2OH$ (b.p. 129°), 4-octyne (b.p. 131°), isopentyl alcohol (b.p. 132°), C_6H_5Cl (b.p. 132°), ethylcyclohexane (b.p. 132°), 1-chlorohexane (b.p. 134°)

(e)

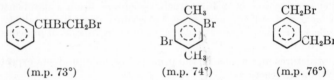

$CHBrCH_2Br$ CH_3 ... Br / Br ... CH_3 CH_2Br ... CH_2Br

(m.p. 73°)   (m.p. 74°)   (m.p. 76°)

13. Treatment of phenol by Br_2 in CS_2 at 0° gives an 80% yield of a product containing 41.6% C, 2.9% H, and 46.2% Br; but when aqueous Br_2 is used, the product, which is formed very rapidly and in quantitative yield, contains 21.8% C, 0.9% H, and 72.5% Br. What are the most likely structures for the two products? Write balanced equations for their formation. (Check your answers in Sec. 22.15.)

Chapter fifteen_____

ETHERS AND EPOXIDES

ETHERS

15.1 Structure and nomenclature of ethers

Ethers are compounds of the general formula R—O—R, Ar—O—R, or Ar—O—Ar.

To name ethers we usually name the two groups that are attached to oxygen, and follow these names by the word *ether:*

$C_2H_5OC_2H_5$

Ethyl ether

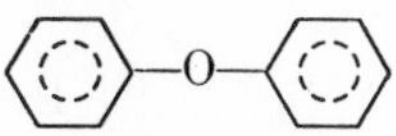

Phenyl ether

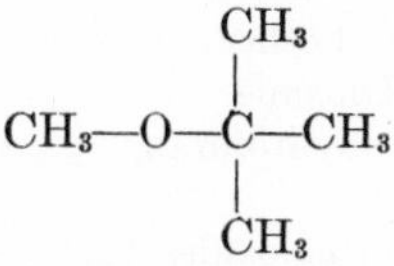

$$CH_3—O—\underset{\underset{CH_3}{|}}{\overset{\overset{CH_3}{|}}{C}}—CH_3$$

Methyl *tert*-butyl ether

$$CH_3—\underset{\underset{H}{|}}{\overset{\overset{CH_3}{|}}{C}}—O—$$

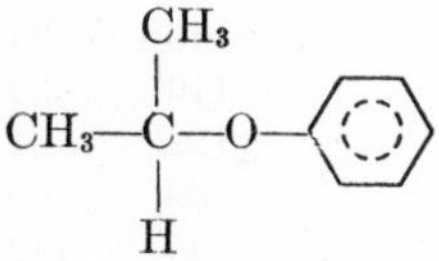

Isopropyl phenyl ether

If one group has no simple name the compound may be named as an *alkoxy* derivative:

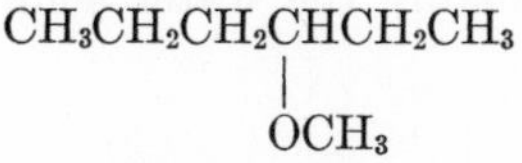

$$CH_3CH_2CH_2\underset{\underset{OCH_3}{|}}{CH}CH_2CH_3$$

3-Methoxyhexane

C_2H_5O⟨ ⟩$COOH$

p-Ethoxybenzoic acid

$$\underset{\underset{HO}{|}}{CH_2}\underset{\underset{OC_2H_5}{|}}{CH_2}$$

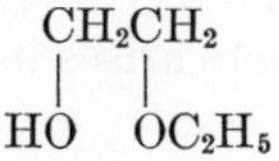

2-Ethoxyethanol

The simplest aryl alkyl ether has the special name of *anisole.*

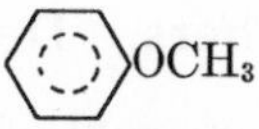

⟨ ⟩OCH_3

Anisole

If the two groups are identical, the ether is said to be *symmetrical* (e.g., *ethyl ether, phenyl ether*), if different, *unsymmetrical* (e.g., *methyl tert-butyl ether, anisole*).

15.2 Physical properties of ethers

Since the C—O—C bond angle is not 180°, the dipole moments of the two C—O bonds do not cancel each other; consequently ethers possess a small net dipole moment (e.g., 1.18 D for ethyl ether).

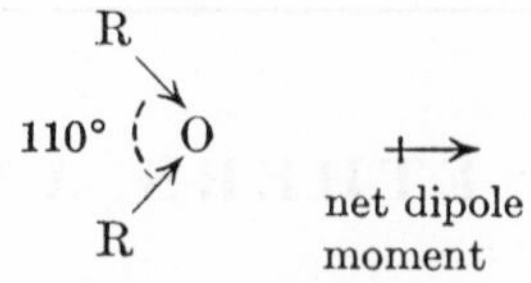

This weak polarity does not appreciably affect the boiling points of ethers, which are about the same as those of alkanes having comparable molecular weights, and much lower than those of isomeric alcohols. Compare, for example, the boiling points of n-heptane (98°), methyl n-pentyl ether (100°), and n-hexyl alcohol (157°). The hydrogen bonding that holds alcohol molecules strongly together is not possible for ethers, since they contain hydrogen bonded only to carbon (Sec. 11.5).

On the other hand, ethers show a solubility in water comparable to that of the alcohols, both ethyl ether and n-butyl alcohol, for example, being soluble to the extent of about 8 g per 100 g of water. We attributed the water solubility of the lower alcohols to hydrogen bonding between

TABLE 15.1

ETHERS AND EPOXIDES

Name	M.p., °C	B.p., °C	Name	M.p., °C	B.p., °C
Methyl ether	−140	− 24	Phenyl ether	27	259
Ethyl ether	−116	34.6	1,4-Dioxane	11	101
n-Propyl ether	−122	91	Tetrahydrofuran	−108	66
Isopropyl ether	− 60	69			
n-Butyl ether	− 95	142	Ethylene oxide	−111	11
Vinyl ether		35	Propylene oxide		34
Allyl ether		94	Cyclohexene oxide		134
Anisole	− 37	154	Styrene oxide		88[23]
Phenetole	− 33	172			
(Ethyl phenyl ether)					

water molecules and alcohol molecules; presumably the water solubility of ethers arises in the same way.

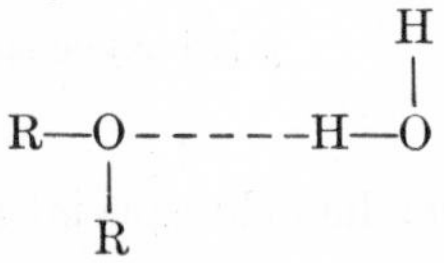

15.3 Industrial source of ethers. Dehydration of alcohols

A number of symmetrical ethers containing the lower alkyl groups are prepared on a large scale, chiefly for use as solvents. The most important of these is **ethyl ether,** the familiar anesthetic and the solvent we use in extractions and in the preparation of Grignard reagents; others include isopropyl ether and n-butyl ether.

These ethers are prepared by reaction of the corresponding alcohols with sulfuric acid. Since a molecule of water is lost for every pair of alcohol molecules, the reaction is a kind of *dehydration*. Dehydration to ethers

$$2R—O—H \xrightarrow{\text{H}_2\text{SO}_4, \text{ heat}} R—O—R + H_2O$$

rather than to alkenes is controlled by the choice of reaction conditions· For example, ethylene is prepared by heating ethyl alcohol with concentrated sulfuric acid to 180°; ethyl ether is prepared by heating a mixture of ethyl alcohol and concentrated sulfuric acid to 140°, continuously adding alcohol to keep it in excess.

The commonly accepted mechanism of ether formation involves the following steps:

(1) $$ROH + H^+ \rightleftharpoons ROH_2^+$$

(2) $$ROH_2^+ \rightleftharpoons R^+ + H_2O$$

(3) $$R^+ + ROH \rightleftharpoons \overset{H}{ROR^+}$$

(4) $$\overset{H}{ROR^+} \rightleftharpoons ROR + H^+$$

As in alkene formation, the protonated alcohol dissociates to yield a carbonium ion. In alkene formation the carbonium ion expels a proton; in ether formation, however, it combines with the basic alcohol molecule to yield the protonated ether. This combining with alcohol is exactly analogous to the combining with water that we encountered in the hydration of alkenes to alcohols (Sec. 5.10).

Problem 15.1 Ether formation by dehydration is an example of nucleophilic substitution. (a) What compound undergoes substitution? (b) What compound is the nucleophilic reagent? (c) As outlined above, is the reaction S_N1 or S_N2? (d) Outline the steps of the mechanism alternative to your answer in (c). (e) As in other cases of substitution, there is a competing elimination reaction. What is this reaction, and what products does it yield?

Dehydration is generally limited to the preparation of symmetrical ethers, because, as we might expect, a combination of two alcohols usually yields a mixture of three ethers.

Problem 15.2 (a) Upon treatment with sulfuric acid a mixture of ethyl and n-propyl alcohols yields a mixture of three ethers. What are they? (b) On the other hand, a mixture of tert-butyl alcohol and ethyl alcohol gives a good yield of a single ether. What ether is this likely to be? How do you account for the good yield?

A number of aryl alkyl ethers occur naturally (see Sec. 22.4). Others are made industrially by the Williamson synthesis described in Sec. 15.7.

15.4 Peroxides in ethers

On standing in contact with air, most aliphatic ethers are converted slowly into unstable peroxides. Although present in only low concentrations, these peroxides are very dangerous, since they can cause violent explosions during the distillations that normally follow extractions with ether.

The presence of peroxides is indicated by formation of a red color when the ether is shaken with an aqueous solution of ferrous ammonium sulfate and potassium thiocyanate; the peroxide oxidizes ferrous ion to ferric ion, which reacts with thiocyanate ion to give the characteristic blood-red color of the complex.

$$\text{peroxide} + Fe^{++} \longrightarrow Fe^{+++} \xrightarrow{SCN^-} Fe(SCN)_n^{-(3-n)} \qquad (n = 1 \text{ to } 6)$$
Red

Peroxides can be removed from ethers in a number of ways, including washing with solutions of ferrous ion (which reduces peroxides), or distillation from concentrated H_2SO_4 (which oxidizes peroxides).

15.5 Absolute ether

For use in the preparation of Grignard reagents, the ether (usually ethyl) must be free of traces of water and alcohol. This so-called **absolute ether** can be prepared by distillation of ordinary ether from concentrated H_2SO_4 (which removes not only water and alcohol but also peroxides), and subsequent storing over metallic sodium. There is available today commercial anhydrous ether of such high quality that only the treatment with sodium is needed to make it ready for the Grignard reaction.

15.6 Hazards of ethyl ether

It is hard to overemphasize the hazards met in using ethyl ether, even when it is free of peroxides: it is highly volatile, and the flammability of its vapors makes explosions and fires ever-present dangers unless proper precautions are observed.

15.7 Preparation of ethers. Williamson synthesis

In the laboratory, the **Williamson synthesis** of ethers is by far the most important, because of its versatility: it can be used to make unsymmetrical ethers as well as symmetrical ethers, and aryl alkyl ethers as well as dialkyl ethers.

In the Williamson synthesis an alkyl halide (or substituted alkyl halide) is allowed to react with a sodium alkoxide or a sodium phenoxide:

$$R\!-\!X + Na^+ \, ^-O\!-\!R' \longrightarrow R\!-\!O\!-\!R' + Na^+X^-$$

$$R\!-\!X + Na^+ \, ^-O\!-\!Ar \longrightarrow R\!-\!O\!-\!Ar + Na^+X^-$$

For the preparation of methyl aryl ethers, *methyl sulfate*, $(CH_3)_2SO_4$, is frequently used instead of the more expensive methyl halides. For example:

$$CH_3Br + Na^+ \, ^-O\!-\!\underset{\underset{\displaystyle CH_3}{|}}{\overset{\overset{\displaystyle CH_3}{|}}{C}}\!-\!CH_3 \longrightarrow CH_3\!-\!O\!-\!\underset{\underset{\displaystyle CH_3}{|}}{\overset{\overset{\displaystyle CH_3}{|}}{C}}\!-\!CH_3$$

Sodium   Methyl *tert*-butyl ether
tert-butoxide

$$\langle\!\bigcirc\!\rangle\text{OH} + \text{CH}_3\text{OSOCH}_3 \xrightarrow{\text{aq. NaOH}} \langle\!\bigcirc\!\rangle\text{OCH}_3 + \text{CH}_3\text{OSO}^-\text{ Na}^+$$

Phenol　　　Methyl sulfate　　　　　　　　　　　　Anisole

$$\langle\!\bigcirc\!\rangle\text{CH}_2\text{Br} + \text{HO}\langle\!\bigcirc\!\rangle\text{NO}_2 \xrightarrow{\text{aq. NaOH}} \langle\!\bigcirc\!\rangle\text{CH}_2\text{O}\langle\!\bigcirc\!\rangle\text{NO}_2$$

Benzyl bromide　　p-Nitrophenol　　　　　　Benzyl p-nitrophenyl ether

The Williamson synthesis involves nucleophilic substitution of alkoxide ion or phenoxide ion for halide ion; it is strictly analogous to the preparation of alcohols by treatment of alkyl halides with aqueous hydroxide (Sec. 11.10). Aryl halides cannot be used, because of their low reactivity toward nucleophilic substitution, unless the ring carries —NO$_2$ groups (or other strongly electron-attracting groups) at positions *ortho* or *para* to the halogen (Sec. 14.10).

Sodium alkoxides are made by direct action of sodium metal on dry alcohols:

$$\text{ROH} + \text{Na} \longrightarrow \text{RO}^-\text{ Na}^+ + \tfrac{1}{2}\text{H}_2$$
An alkoxide

Sodium phenoxides, on the other hand, because of the appreciable acidity of phenols (Sec. 22.8), are made by the action of aqueous sodium hydroxide on phenols:

$$\text{ArOH} + \text{Na}^+\,{}^-\text{OH} \longrightarrow \text{ArO}^-\text{ Na}^+ + \text{H}_2\text{O}$$
Stronger　　　　　　　　　　　A phenoxide　　　Weaker
acid　　　　　　　　　　　　　　　　　　　　　　acid

If we wish to make an unsymmetrical dialkyl ether, we have a choice of two combinations of reagents; one of these is nearly always better than the other. In the preparation of ethyl *tert*-butyl ether, for example, the following combinations are conceivable:

$$\text{CH}_3\text{CH}_2\text{Br} + \text{Na}^+\,{}^-\text{O}-\overset{\overset{\displaystyle\text{CH}_3}{|}}{\underset{\underset{\displaystyle\text{CH}_3}{|}}{\text{C}}}-\text{CH}_3 \qquad \textit{Feasible}$$

$$\text{CH}_3\text{CH}_2-\text{O}-\overset{\overset{\displaystyle\text{CH}_3}{|}}{\underset{\underset{\displaystyle\text{CH}_3}{|}}{\text{C}}}-\text{CH}_3$$

Ethyl *tert*-butyl
ether

$$\text{CH}_3-\overset{\overset{\displaystyle\text{CH}_3}{|}}{\underset{\underset{\displaystyle\text{CH}_3}{|}}{\text{C}}}-\text{Cl} + \text{Na}^+\,{}^-\text{OCH}_2\text{CH}_3 \quad \textit{Not feasible}$$

Which do we choose? As always we must consider the danger of elimination competing with the desired substitution; elimination should be particularly serious here because of the strong basicity of the alkoxide reagent.

$$CH_3CH_2Br + \quad ^-O-\overset{\overset{\displaystyle CH_3}{|}}{\underset{\underset{\displaystyle CH_3}{|}}{C}}-CH_3 \longrightarrow CH_3CH_2-O-\overset{\overset{\displaystyle CH_3}{|}}{\underset{\underset{\displaystyle CH_3}{|}}{C}}-CH_3 + Br^- \quad \textbf{Substitution}$$

Ethyl tert-butyl ether

$$CH_3-\overset{\overset{\displaystyle CH_3}{|}}{\underset{\underset{\displaystyle CH_3}{|}}{C}}-Cl + \quad ^-OC_2H_5 \longrightarrow CH_3-\overset{\overset{\displaystyle CH_3}{|}}{C}=CH_2 + C_2H_5OH + Cl^- \quad \textbf{Elimination}$$

We therefore reject the use of the tertiary halide; which we expect to yield mostly — or all — elimination product; we must use the other combination. The disadvantage of the slow reaction between sodium and *tert*-butyl alcohol (Sec. 12.6) in the preparation of the alkoxide is more than offset by the tendency of the primary halide to undergo substitution rather than elimination. In planning a Williamson synthesis of a dialkyl ether we must always keep in mind that the tendency for alkyl halides to undergo dehydrohalogenation is $3° > 2° > 1°$.

For the preparation of an aryl alkyl ether there are again two combinations to be considered; here, one combination can usually be rejected out of hand. *n*-Propyl phenyl ether, for example, can be prepared only from the alkyl halide and the phenoxide, since the aryl halide is quite unreactive toward alkoxides.

$$CH_3CH_2CH_2Br + Na^+ \, ^-O\langle\bigcirc\rangle \longrightarrow CH_3CH_2CH_2O\langle\bigcirc\rangle + Na^+ \, Br^-$$

n-Propyl   Sodium phenoxide   *n*-Propyl phenyl ether
bromide

$$\langle\bigcirc\rangle Br + Na^+ \, ^-OCH_2CH_2CH_3 \longrightarrow \quad \text{no reaction}$$

Bromobenzene   Sodium *n*-propoxide

Since alkoxides and phenoxides are prepared from the corresponding alcohols and phenols, and since alkyl halides are commonly prepared from the alcohols, the Williamson method ultimately involves the synthesis of an ether from two hydroxy compounds.

Problem 15.3 Outline the synthesis, from alcohols and/or phenols, of:
(a) ethyl *tert*-butyl ether   (c) isobutyl *sec*-butyl ether
(b) *n*-propyl phenyl ether   (d) cyclohexyl methyl ether

15.8 Stereochemistry of the Williamson synthesis. Relating configurations

In our first discussion of optical isomerism, we learned (Sec. 11.22) that the configurations of a few optically active compounds have been determined directly by x-ray diffraction. It was pointed out that the configurations of many other compounds are also known, since these other compounds have been related to the ones whose configurations have been directly determined. Using the Williamson synthesis as an example, let us see how the configurations of two compounds can be related.

When optically active 2-octanol of specific rotation $-9.9°$ is converted into its sodium salt, and the salt is then treated with ethyl bromide, there is obtained the optically active ether, 2-ethoxyoctane, with specific rotation $-17.5°$.

I	II	III
($-$)-2-Octanol		($-$)-2-Ethoxyoctane
$[\alpha] = -9.9°$		$[\alpha] = -17.5°$
Optical purity 100%		Optical purity 100%

Now, ($-$)-2-octanol is known to have the configuration I. What can we say about the configuration of the ($-$)-2-ethoxyoctane that is formed from it? In the reaction of the alcohol with sodium metal, the bond between oxygen and hydrogen is broken to form the salt; since no bonds to the asymmetric carbon have been broken, the —O⁻ group must occupy the same relative position that was previously occupied by the —OH group. The salt therefore has configuration II, which is similar to configuration I.

In the reaction of the salt with ethyl bromide, a bond is formed between oxygen and the carbon of the ethyl bromide, and bromide ion is displaced. Again, no bond to the asymmetric carbon has been broken, so that the ethoxy group must occupy the same relative position that was previously held by the —O⁻ group. The ($-$)-2-ethoxyoctane must therefore have the configuration III, which is similar to that of the ($-$)-2-octanol.

In relating the configuration of the ether to the configuration of the alcohol, care was taken that no step should involve the breaking of a bond to the asymmetric carbon atom, since, if this had happened, there would have been the danger of inversion of configuration. In general, *the configurational relationship between two optically active compounds is determined by converting one into the other by reactions that do not involve breaking of a bond to an asymmetric carbon.*

The conversion of the alcohol into the ether just described can tell us not only the configuration of the ether, but also the specific rotation of the optically pure ether. Since no bonds to the asymmetric carbon are broken, every molecule of alcohol with configuration I is converted into a molecule of ether with configuration III; since 2-octanol of specific rotation $-9.9°$ is optically pure, then 2-ethoxyoctane of specific rotation $-17.5°$ is also optically pure.

Problem 15.4 ($-$)-2-Bromooctane and ($-$)-2-octanol are known to have similar configurations (Sec. 18.8). When 2-bromooctane of specific rotation

$-34.6°$ is treated with ethoxide ion in ethyl alcohol there is obtained 2-ethoxy-octane of specific rotation $+17.5°$. (a) Does this reaction involve complete retention of configuration, complete inversion, or inversion plus racemization? (Check rotation of optically pure 2-bromooctane on page 371.) (b) By what mechanism does this reaction appear to proceed? (c) In view of the reagent and solvent, is this the mechanism you would have expected to operate? (d) What mechanism do you suppose is involved in the alternative synthesis of 2-ethoxyoctane from the salt of 2-octanol and ethyl bromide? (e) Why, then, is the synthesis involving ethyl bromide acceptable for determining configurational relationship, and the synthesis from 2-bromooctane unacceptable?

Problem 15.5 Which of the following reactions could safely be used to relate configurations?

(a) $(-)\text{-}CH_3CH_2CH(CH_3)CH_2OH + KMnO_4 \longrightarrow CH_3CH_2CH(CH_3)COOH$

(b) $(+)\text{-}C_6H_5CH(OH)CH_3 + PBr_3 \longrightarrow C_6H_5CHBrCH_3$

(c) $(+)\text{-}CH_3CH_2CHClCH_3 + C_6H_6 + AlCl_3 \longrightarrow C_6H_5CH(CH_3)CH_2CH_3$

(d) $(-)\text{-}C_6H_5CH(OC_2H_5)CH_2OH + HBr \longrightarrow C_6H_5CH(OC_2H_5)CH_2Br$

(e) $(+)\text{-}CH_3CH(OH)CH_2Br + NaCN \longrightarrow CH_3CH(OH)CH_2CN$

15.9 Preparation of substituted ethers

To get a better idea of how to plan the synthesis of a compound that contains more than one functional group, let us look at the preparation of certain substituted ethers.

Vinyl ether, for example, is used as a general anesthetic. How might

$$CH_2\text{=}CH\text{—}O\text{—}CH\text{=}CH_2$$
Vinyl ether

this compound be made? From its structure we see that we must generate an ether linkage and a carbon–carbon double bond. Following our usual procedure of working backward, what will be the last step of the synthesis: converting some unsaturated alcohol into the unsaturated ether, or converting a saturated ether into the unsaturated one?

We reject the first possibility since the unsaturated compound required is vinyl alcohol, which we know does not exist (Sec. 6.12).

The alternative, introduction of a carbon–carbon double bond into a saturated ether, is essentially a problem of alkene chemistry. Since the best method of making an alkene is dehydrohalogenation of an alkyl halide by alcoholic KOH, we might expect that the best method of making an unsaturated ether would be dehydrohalogenation of a haloether.

We need, then, an ether containing two chloroethyl ($ClCH_2CH_2$—) groups. Again there are two general approaches: chlorination of an ether or conversion of a chloride into an ether. We reject the first possibility when we find, upon looking in the chemical library for an experimental procedure, that chlorination of ethyl ether does not yield the product we want; polychlorination of ether leads to an accumulation of chlorine atoms in only one of the ethyl groups.

The alternative, conversion of a chloro compound into a chloro ether, is a problem in ether chemistry. If ethyl ether is made by dehydration of ethyl alcohol, we might expect chloroethyl ether to be made by dehydration of chloroethyl alcohol. We are already familiar with β-chloro-ethyl alcohol (ethylene chlorohydrin), which is readily made by the addition of chlorine in water to ethylene (Sec. 5.16). We arrive then at the following feasible synthesis, which starts with ethylene:

$$\underset{\text{Vinyl ether}}{CH_2=CH-O-CH=CH_2} \xleftarrow{KOH} \underset{\text{β-Chloroethyl ether}}{\overset{\beta\quad\alpha\quad\quad\alpha\quad\beta}{ClCH_2CH_2-O-CH_2CH_2Cl}} \xleftarrow{H_2SO_4} \underset{\substack{\text{Ethylene chlorohydrin}\\(\beta\text{-Chloroethyl alcohol})}}{\overset{\beta\quad\alpha}{ClCH_2CH_2OH}}$$

$$\Big\uparrow \text{Cl}_2,\ \text{H}_2\text{O}$$

$$\underset{\text{Ethylene}}{CH_2=CH_2}$$

As a second example, let us consider the synthesis of phenyl p-nitro-benzyl ether. Since it is an unsymmetrical ether, it must be prepared by

$$\underset{\text{Phenyl } p\text{-nitrobenzyl ether}}{\langle\ \rangle O-CH_2\langle\ \rangle NO_2}$$

the Williamson synthesis. As usual there are two combinations to consider:

$$\underset{\substack{\text{Sodium}\\\text{phenoxide}}}{\langle\ \rangle O^- Na^+} + \underset{p\text{-Nitrobenzyl chloride}}{ClCH_2\langle\ \rangle NO_2} \qquad \textit{Feasible}$$

$$\underset{\text{Phenyl } p\text{-nitrobenzyl}\\\text{ether}}{\langle\ \rangle OCH_2\langle\ \rangle NO_2} \longleftarrow$$

$$\underset{\text{Bromobenzene}}{\langle\ \rangle Br} + \underset{\text{Sodium } p\text{-nitrobenzoxide}}{Na^+ {}^-OCH_2\langle\ \rangle NO_2} \qquad \textit{Not feasible}$$

Because of the low reactivity of aryl halides, we must reject the reaction between bromobenzene and sodium p-nitrobenzoxide.

The alternative, the reaction of sodium phenoxide with p-nitrobenzyl chloride, is quite feasible. Sodium phenoxide is readily formed from phenol by treatment with aqueous sodium hydroxide. p-Nitrobenzyl chloride can be made by free radical chlorination (Sec. 9.15) of p-nitrotoluene, which in turn is readily prepared by nitration of toluene, a reaction we know to yield the *ortho* and *para* isomers (Sec. 9.12 and Sec. 10.2).

$$\underset{p\text{-Nitrobenzyl chloride}}{ClCH_2\langle\ \rangle NO_2} \xleftarrow{Cl_2,\ \text{heat}} \underset{p\text{-Nitrotoluene}}{CH_3\langle\ \rangle NO_2} \xleftarrow{HNO_3,\ H_2SO_4} \underset{\text{Toluene}}{CH_3\langle\ \rangle}$$

Problem 15.6 (a) Could phenyl p-nitrobenzyl ether be obtained by nitration of phenyl benzyl ether? (b) Could ethyl p-nitrobenzyl ether be made by the nitration of ethyl benzyl ether?

Problem 15.7 Outline a possible synthesis, from readily available materials, of: (a) allyl methyl ether; (b) $CH_2OHCHOHCH_2OCH_3$; (c) 2-(p-methoxyphenyl)-2-propanol.

15.10 Reactions of ethers. Cleavage by acids

Ethers are comparatively unreactive compounds. The ether linkage is quite stable toward bases, oxidizing agents, and reducing agents. In so far as the ether linkage itself is concerned, ethers undergo just one kind of reaction, **cleavage by acids**:

$$R\!-\!O\!-\!R' + HX \longrightarrow R\!-\!X + R'\!-\!OH \xrightarrow{\ HX\ } R'\!-\!X$$

$$Ar\!-\!O\!-\!R + HX \longrightarrow R\!-\!X + Ar\!-\!OH$$

Reactivity of HX: $HI > HBr > HCl$

Cleavage takes place only under quite vigorous conditions: concentrated acids (usually HI or HBr) and high temperatures.

An alkyl ether yields initially an alkyl halide and an alcohol; the alcohol may react further to form a second mole of alkyl halide. Because of the low reactivity at the bond between oxygen and an aromatic ring, an aryl alkyl ether undergoes cleavage of the alkyl–oxygen bond and yields a phenol and an alkyl halide. For example:

$$\underset{\text{Isopropyl ether}}{CH_3\!-\!\underset{\underset{CH_3}{|}}{CH}\!-\!O\!-\!\underset{\underset{CH_3}{|}}{CH}\!-\!CH_3} \xrightarrow[\text{130-140}^\circ]{\text{48\% HBr}} \underset{\text{Isopropyl bromide}}{2CH_3\!-\!\underset{\underset{CH_3}{|}}{CH}\!-\!Br}$$

$$\underset{\text{Anisole}}{\langle\bigcirc\rangle\!OCH_3} \xrightarrow[\text{120-130}^\circ]{\text{57\% HI}} \underset{\text{Phenol \quad Methyl iodide}}{\langle\bigcirc\rangle\!OH + CH_3I}$$

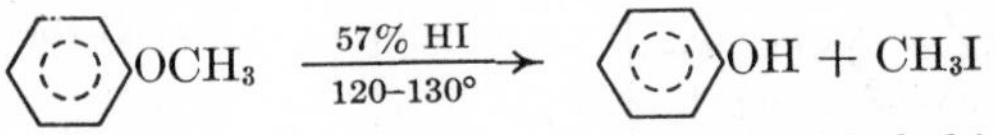

The initial reaction between an ether and an acid is undoubtedly formation of the *protonated ether*:

$$R\!-\!\overset{..}{\underset{..}{O}}\!-\!R' + H^+ \rightleftharpoons R\!-\!\overset{\overset{\displaystyle H}{|}}{\underset{..}{O}}{}^{\oplus}\!-\!R'$$

The basic character of ethers is shown by their solubility in concentrated sulfuric acid, and by actual isolation at low temperatures of crystalline oxonium salts:

$$C_2H_5\overset{..}{\underset{..}{O}}C_2H_5 + \text{conc. } H_2SO_4 \longrightarrow \underset{\substack{\text{Diethyloxonium hydrogen sulfate}\\ \textit{soluble in } H_2SO_4}}{C_2H_5\overset{\overset{\displaystyle H}{\underset{..}{\oplus}}}{O}C_2H_5 \ \ HSO_4^-}$$

$$C_2H_5\overset{..}{\underset{..}{O}}C_2H_5 + \text{dry HCl} \longrightarrow \underset{\substack{\text{Diethyloxonium chloride}\\ \text{m.p. } -92^\circ}}{C_2H_5\overset{\overset{\displaystyle H}{\underset{..}{\oplus}}}{O}C_2H_5 \ \ Cl^-}$$

Ether is the solvent for Grignard reagents because it is able to solvate — and so to dissolve — the reagent by acting as a base toward the acidic magnesium. (The structures involved are actually much more complex than those shown below. See Sec. 3.16.)

$$CH_3I + Mg + C_2H_5\overset{..}{\underset{..}{O}}C_2H_5 \longrightarrow \begin{array}{c} C_2H_5 \quad C_2H_5 \\ \diagdown \quad \diagup \\ \overset{..}{O}: \\ | \\ CH_3 - \overset{..}{M}g - I \\ | \\ \overset{..}{O}: \\ \diagup \quad \diagdown \\ C_2H_5 \quad C_2H_5 \end{array}$$

Soluble in ether

Cleavage involves nucleophilic attack by halide ion on the protonated ether, with displacement of the weakly basic alcohol molecule:

$$R\overset{..}{\underset{..}{O}}R' + HX \rightleftharpoons R\overset{\overset{H}{\underset{..}{\oplus}}}{\underset{..}{O}}R' + X^- \xrightarrow[\text{or}\atop S_N2]{S_N1} RX + R'OH$$

Such a reaction occurs much more readily than displacement of the strongly basic alkoxide ion from the neutral ether.

$$ROR' + X^- \xrightarrow{\;\;\diagup\!\!\!\!\!\backslash\;\;} RX + OR'^-$$

Problem 15.8 (a) Write analogous equations for reaction between an alcohol and HX. (b) Which of these reactions actually occurs, and why?

Reaction of a protonated ether with halide ion, like the corresponding reaction of a protonated alcohol, can proceed by either an S_N1 or S_N2 mechanism, depending upon conditions and the structure of the ether.

S_N1:
$$ROR'^{+}\overset{H}{} \xrightarrow{\text{slow}} R^+ + HOR'$$

$$R^+ + X^- \xrightarrow{\text{fast}} R\!-\!X$$

S_N2:
$$ROR'^{+}\overset{H}{} + X^- \longrightarrow \left[\overset{\delta_-}{X} \cdots R \cdots \overset{\overset{H}{OR'}}{\underset{\delta_+}{}} \right] \longrightarrow RX + HOR'$$

As we might expect, a primary alkyl group tends to undergo S_N2 displacement, whereas a tertiary alkyl group tends to undergo S_N1 displacement.

Problem 15.9 Cleavage of optically active methyl *sec*-butyl ether by anhydrous HBr yields chiefly methyl bromide and *sec*-butyl alcohol; the *sec*-butyl alcohol has the same configuration and optical purity as the starting material. How do you interpret these results?

Problem 15.10 Although most ethers are inert toward bases, 2,4-dinitroanisole is readily cleaved to methanol and 2,4-dinitrophenol when refluxed with dilute aqueous NaOH. (a) How do you account for this? (b) To what general class does this reaction belong?

15.11 Electrophilic substitution in aromatic ethers

The alkoxy group, —OR, was listed (Sec. 10.4) as *ortho,para* directing toward electrophilic aromatic substitution, and moderately activating. It is a much stronger activator than —R, but much weaker than —OH.

The carbonium ions resulting from *ortho* and *para* attack were considered (Sec. 10.10) to be stabilized by contribution from structures I and II.

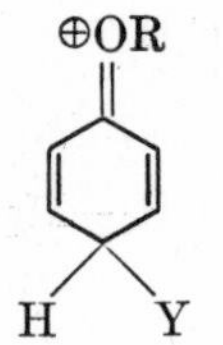

$$\oplus OR \qquad\qquad \oplus OR$$

I 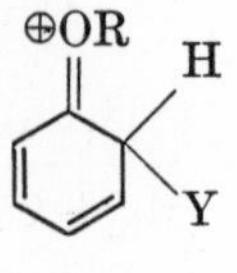   II

These structures are especially stable ones, since in them every atom (except hydrogen, of course) has a complete octet of electrons.

The ability of the oxygen to share more than a pair of electrons with the ring and to accommodate a positive charge is consistent with the basic character of ethers.

Problem 15.11 Predict the principal products of: (a) bromination of *p*-methylanisole; (b) nitration of *m*-nitroanisole; (c) nitration of benzyl phenyl ether.

15.12   Cyclic ethers

In their preparation and properties, most cyclic ethers are just like the ethers we have already studied: the chemistry of the ether linkage is essentially the same whether it forms part of an open chain or of an aliphatic ring.

Problem 15.12   *1,4-Dioxane* is prepared industrially (for use as a water-soluble solvent) by dehydration of an alcohol.   What alcohol is used?

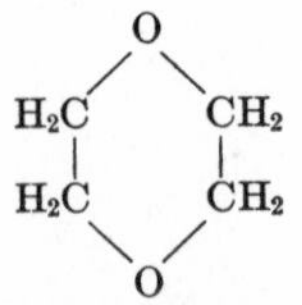

1,4-Dioxane	Furan	Tetrahydrofuran

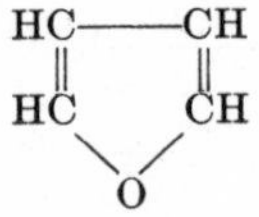

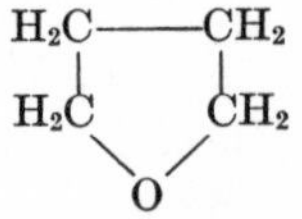

Problem 15.13 The unsaturated cyclic ether *furan* can readily be made from substances isolated from oat hulls and corncobs; one of its important uses involves its conversion into (a) *tetrahydrofuran*, and (b) 1,4-dichlorobutane. Using your knowledge of alkene chemistry and ether chemistry, show how these conversions can be carried out.

Cyclic ethers of one class deserve special attention because of their unusual reactivity; these compounds, the *epoxides*, are taken up in the following sections.

EPOXIDES

15.13   Preparation of epoxides

Epoxides are compounds containing the three-membered ring:

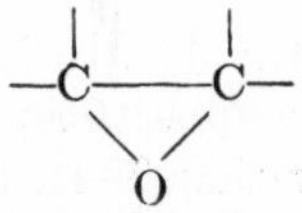

Epoxide ring
(Oxirane ring)

By far the most important epoxide is the simplest one, **ethylene oxide.**
It is prepared on an industrial scale by the action of alkali on ethylene
chlorohydrin, or by catalytic oxidation of ethylene by air.

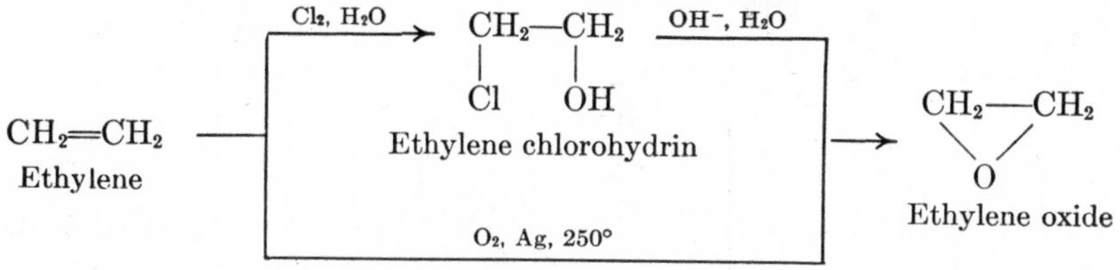

$$CH_2=CH_2 \xrightarrow{\quad} \boxed{\begin{array}{c} \xrightarrow{Cl_2,\ H_2O} \quad \underset{\substack{|\\Cl}}{CH_2}\underset{\substack{|\\OH}}{-CH_2} \xrightarrow{OH^-,\ H_2O} \\ \text{Ethylene chlorohydrin} \\[2ex] O_2,\ Ag,\ 250° \end{array}} \xrightarrow{\quad} \underset{O}{CH_2-CH_2}$$

Ethylene

Ethylene oxide

Other epoxides are prepared by the following methods.

PREPARATION OF EPOXIDES

1. From halohydrins

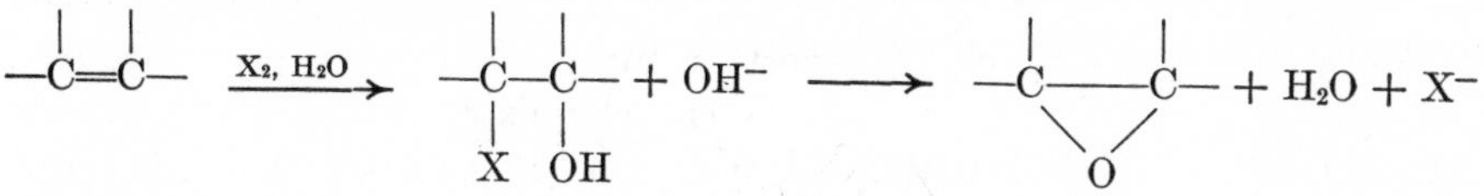

$$-\overset{|}{C}=\overset{|}{C}- \xrightarrow{X_2,\ H_2O} -\underset{\substack{|\\X}}{\overset{|}{C}}-\underset{\substack{|\\OH}}{\overset{|}{C}}- + OH^- \longrightarrow -\underset{O}{\overset{|}{C}\diagdown\diagup\overset{|}{C}}- + H_2O + X^-$$

Example:

$$CH_3-CH=CH_2 \xrightarrow{Br_2,\ H_2O} CH_3-\underset{\substack{|\\OH}}{CH}-\underset{\substack{|\\Br}}{CH_2} \xrightarrow{conc.\ aq.\ OH^-} CH_3-\underset{O}{CH-CH_2}$$

Propylene
bromohydrin

Propylene oxide

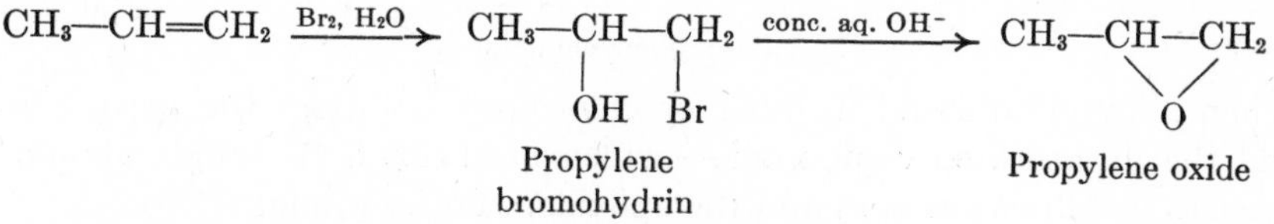

2. Peroxidation of carbon–carbon double bonds

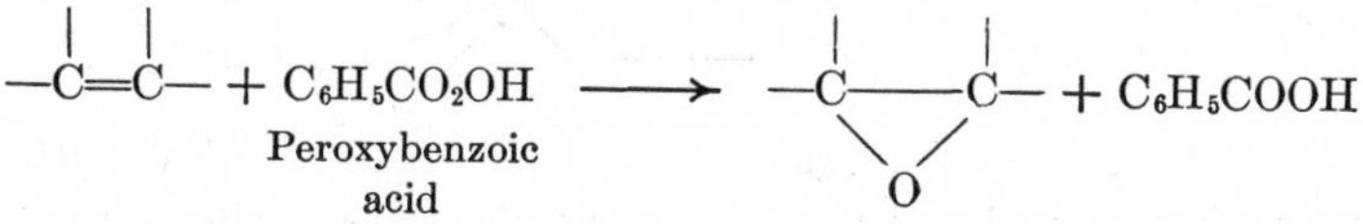

$$-\overset{|}{C}=\overset{|}{C}- + C_6H_5CO_2OH \longrightarrow -\underset{O}{\overset{|}{C}-\overset{|}{C}}- + C_6H_5COOH$$

Peroxybenzoic
acid

Examples:

—CH=CH₂

Styrene

$\xrightarrow{\text{peroxybenzoic acid}}$

—CH—CH₂ over O

Styrene oxide

Cyclohexene

$\xrightarrow{\text{peroxybenzoic acid}}$

Cyclohexene oxide

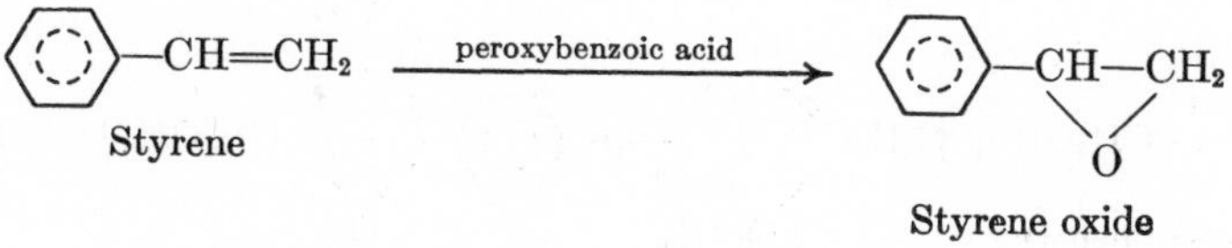

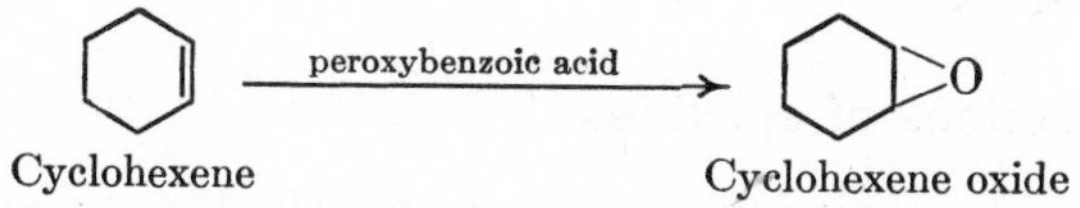

The conversion of halohydrins into epoxides by the action of base is
simply an adaptation of the Williamson synthesis (Sec. 15.7); a cyclic
compound is obtained because both alcohol and halide happen to be part
of the same molecule. In the presence of hydroxide ion a small proportion
of the alcohol exists as alkoxide; this alkoxide displaces halide ion from
another portion of the same molecule to yield the cyclic ether.

(1)

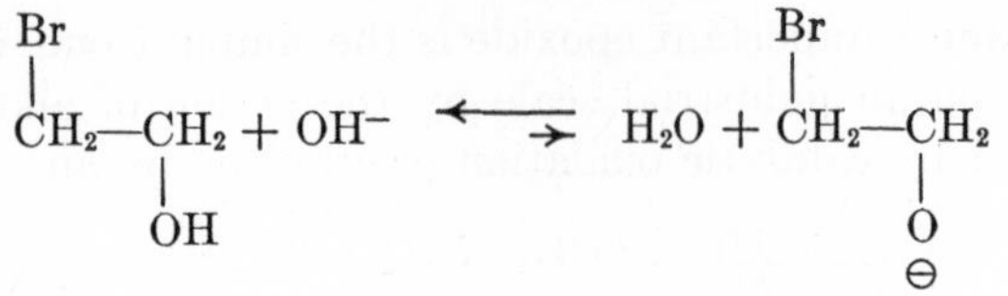

$$CH_2-CH_2 + OH^- \rightleftharpoons H_2O + CH_2-CH_2$$

with Br on first CH₂, OH below; second with Br on CH₂ and O⊖ below.

(2)

$$CH_2-CH_2 \longrightarrow \left[H-C \cdots C-H \right] \longrightarrow CH_2-CH_2 + Br^-$$

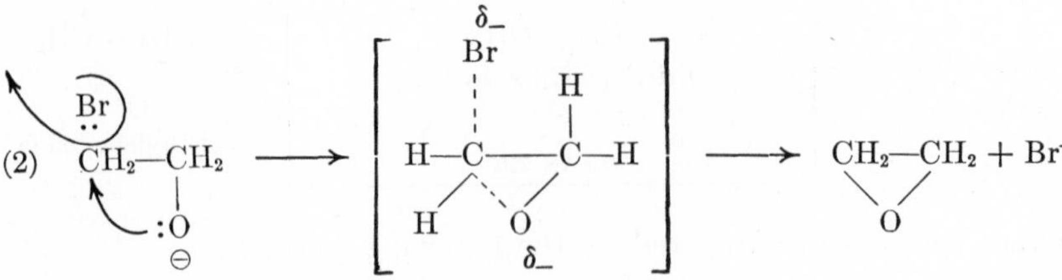

Since halohydrins are nearly always prepared from alkenes by addition of halogen and water to the carbon–carbon double bond (Sec. 5.16), this method amounts to the conversion of an alkene into an epoxide.

Alternatively, the carbon–carbon double bond may be oxidized directly to the epoxide group by peroxybenzoic acid:

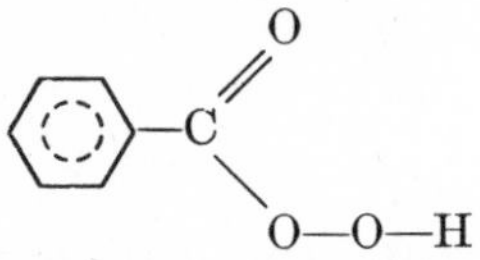

Peroxybenzoic acid

When allowed to stand in ether or chloroform solution, the peroxy acid and the unsaturated compound — which need not be a simple alkene — react to yield benzoic acid and the epoxide. For example:

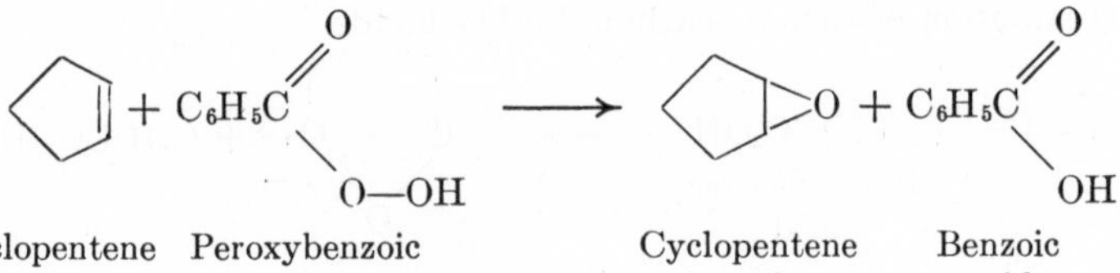

Cyclopentene   Peroxybenzoic   Cyclopentene   Benzoic
                    acid   oxide   acid

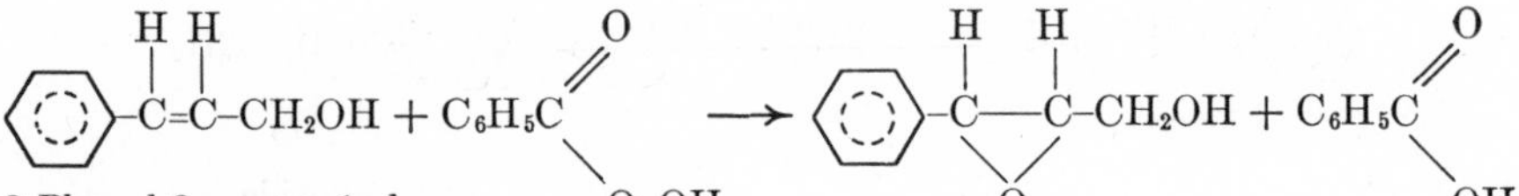

3-Phenyl-2-propen-1-ol
Cinnamyl alcohol

15.14   Reactions of epoxides

Epoxides owe their importance to their high reactivity, which is due to the ease of opening of the highly strained three-membered ring. The bond angles of the ring, which average 60°, are considerably less than the normal tetrahedral carbon angle of 109.5°, or the divalent oxygen angle of 110° for open-chain ethers (Sec. 15.2). Since the atoms cannot be located to permit maximum overlapping of orbitals (Sec. 7.10), the bonds are weaker than in an ordinary ether, and the molecule is less stable.

Epoxides undergo acid-catalyzed reactions with extreme ease, and — unlike ordinary ethers — can even be cleaved by bases. Some of the important reactions are outlined below.

REACTIONS OF EPOXIDES

1. Acid-catalyzed cleavage

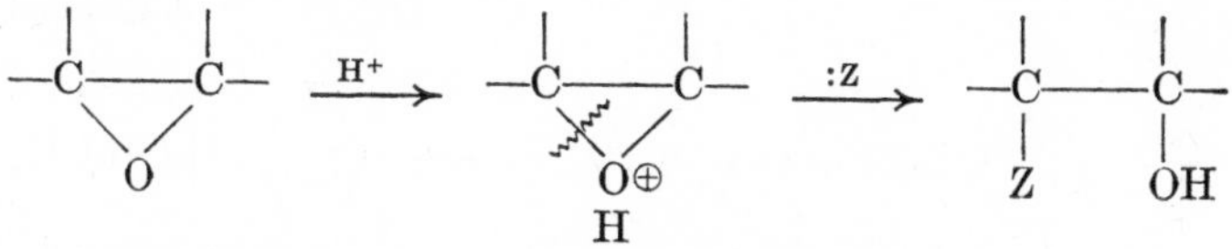

Examples:

$$H_2O + CH_2{-}CH_2 \xrightarrow{H^+} CH_2{-}CH_2$$

$$\underset{OH \quad OH}{|} $$

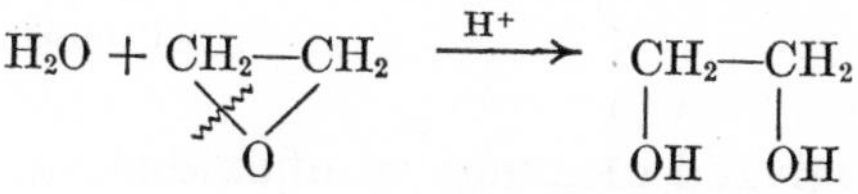

Ethylene glycol
(1,2-Ethanediol)

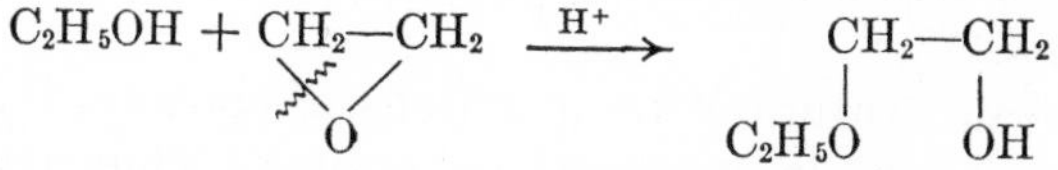

$$C_2H_5OH + CH_2{-}CH_2 \xrightarrow{H^+} CH_2{-}CH_2$$

$$C_2H_5O \qquad OH$$

2-Ethoxyethanol

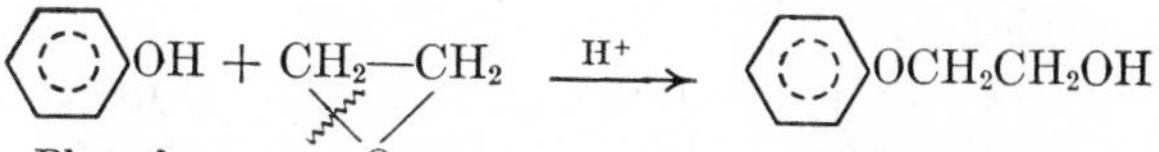

Phenol $\langle \rangle OH + CH_2{-}CH_2 \xrightarrow{H^+} \langle \rangle OCH_2CH_2OH$

2-Phenoxyethanol

$$HBr + CH_2{-}CH_2 \longrightarrow CH_2{-}CH_2$$

$$Br \qquad OH$$

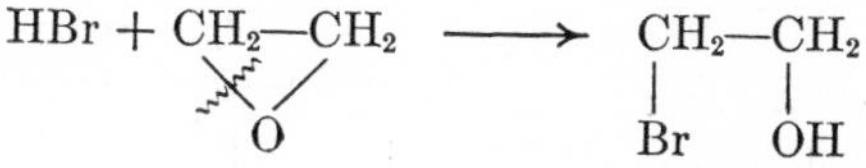

Ethylene bromohydrin
(2-Bromoethanol)

2. Base-catalyzed cleavage

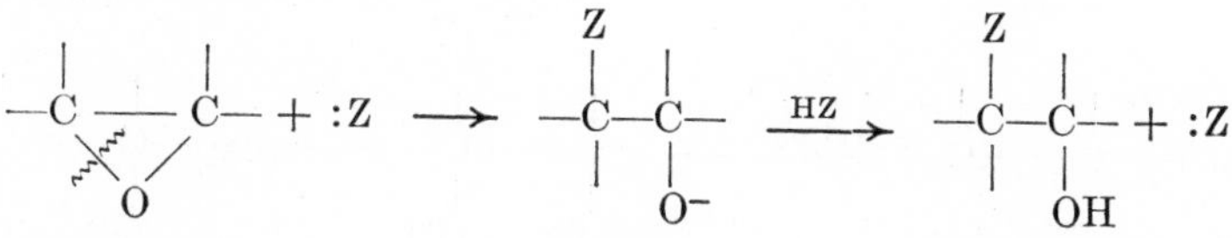

Examples:

$$C_2H_5O^- Na^+ + CH_2{-}CH_2 \longrightarrow C_2H_5OCH_2CH_2OH$$

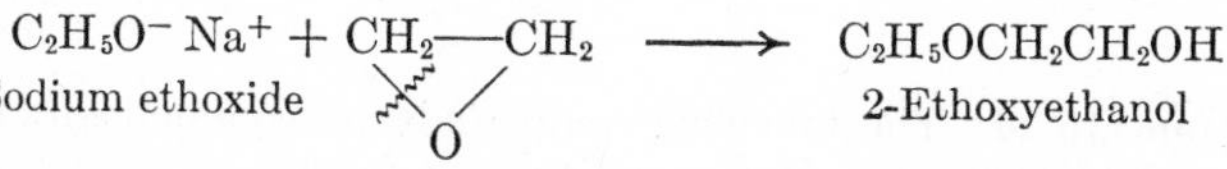

Sodium ethoxide   2-Ethoxyethanol

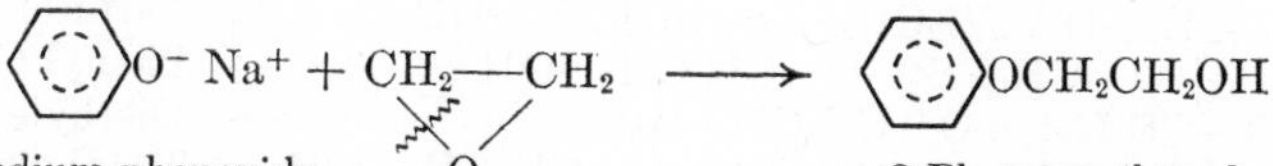

$$\langle \rangle O^- Na^+ + CH_2{-}CH_2 \longrightarrow \langle \rangle OCH_2CH_2OH$$

Sodium phenoxide   2-Phenoxyethanol

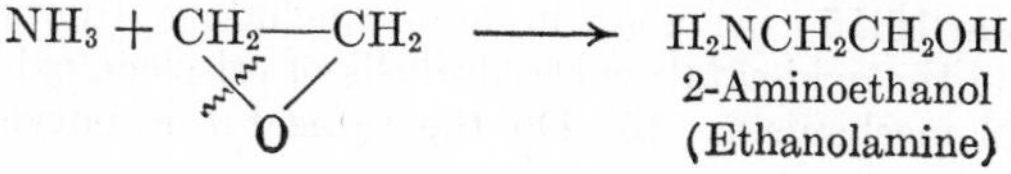

$$NH_3 + CH_2{-}CH_2 \longrightarrow H_2NCH_2CH_2OH$$

2-Aminoethanol
(Ethanolamine)

3. Reaction with Grignard reagents

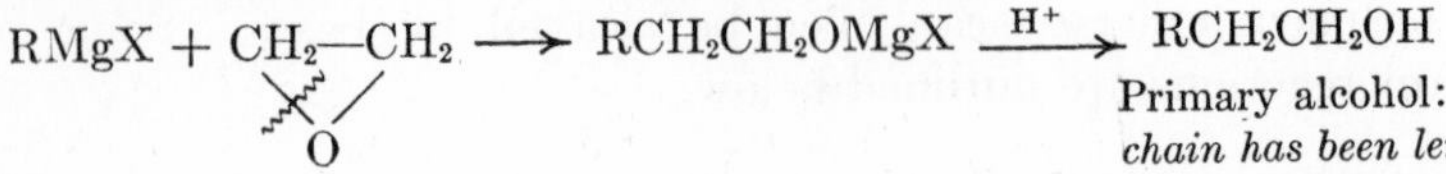

$$RMgX + CH_2\underset{O}{-}CH_2 \longrightarrow RCH_2CH_2OMgX \xrightarrow{H^+} RCH_2CH_2OH$$

Primary alcohol:
chain has been lengthened
by two carbons

Examples:

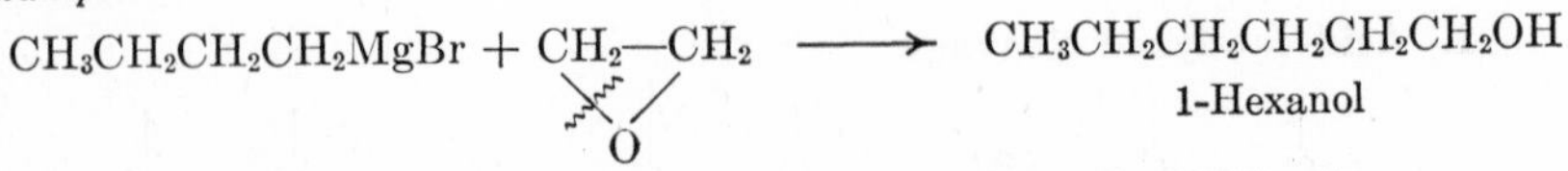

$$CH_3CH_2CH_2CH_2MgBr + CH_2\underset{O}{-}CH_2 \longrightarrow CH_3CH_2CH_2CH_2CH_2CH_2OH$$

1-Hexanol

$$\langle\rangle MgBr + CH_2\underset{O}{-}CH_2 \longrightarrow \langle\rangle CH_2CH_2OH$$

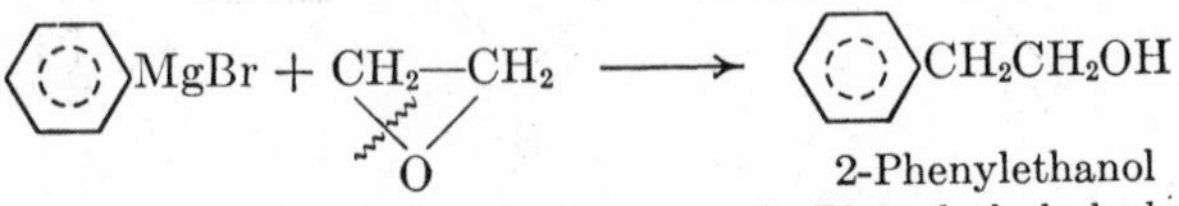

2-Phenylethanol
(β-Phenylethyl alcohol)

15.15 Acid-catalyzed cleavage of epoxides

Like other ethers, an epoxide is converted by acid into the protonated epoxide, which can then undergo attack by any of a number of nucleophilic reagents.

An important feature of the reactions of epoxides is the formation of compounds that contain *two* functional groups. Thus, reaction with water yields a glycol; reaction with an alcohol yields a compound that is both ether and alcohol.

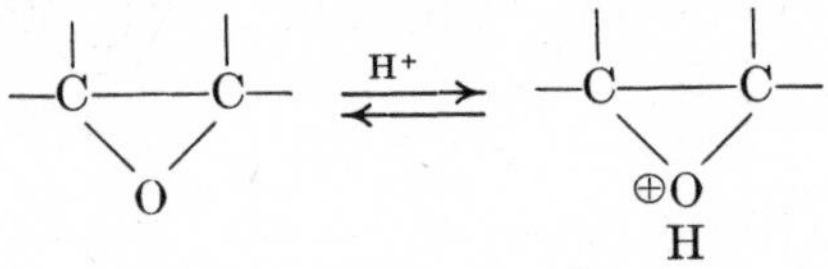

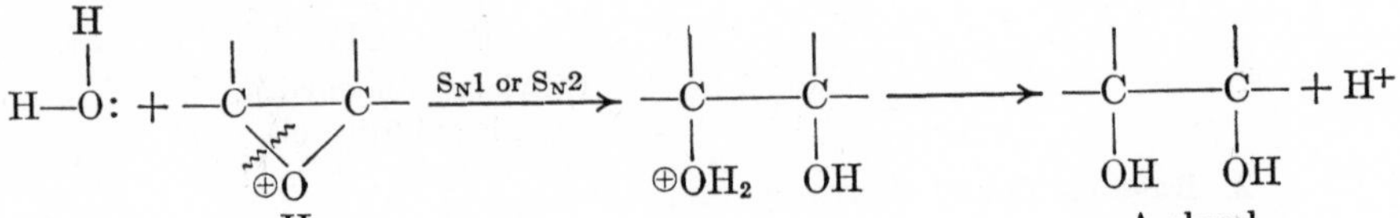

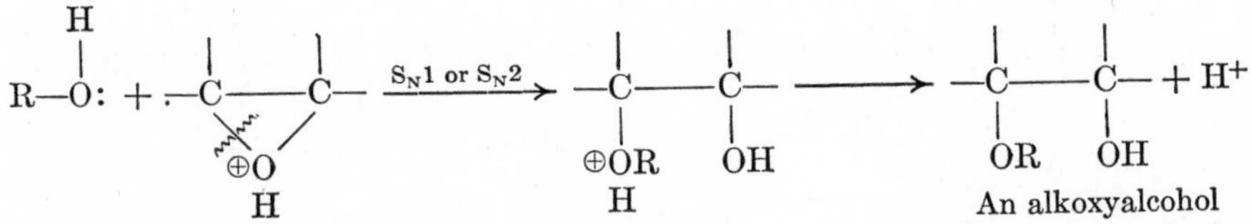

Problem 15.14 The following compounds are commercially available for use as water-soluble solvents. How could each be made?

(a) CH_3CH_2—O—CH_2CH_2—O—CH_2CH_2—OH   Carbitol
(b) C_6H_5—O—CH_2CH_2—O—CH_2CH_2—OH   Phenyl Carbitol
(c) HO—CH_2CH_2--O—CH_2CH_2—OH   Diethylene glycol
(d) HO—CH_2CH_2—O—CH_2CH_2—O—CH_2CH_2—OH   Triethylene glycol

Problem 15.15 (a) Show in detail (including structures and transition states) the steps in the acid-catalyzed hydrolysis of ethylene oxide by an S_N1 mechanism; by an S_N2 mechanism. (b) Do the same for isobutylene oxide. (c) There is evidence that these two epoxides undergo this hydrolysis by different mechanisms. Which epoxide would you expect to react by which mechanism? Why?

In the hydroxylation of an alkene by peroxyformic acid (Secs. 5.19 and 7.14), an epoxide is formed and cleaved in exactly the same manner as described in this chapter. The epoxide is generally not isolated simply because it is rapidly cleaved in the acidic medium, formic acid. Hydroxylation is discussed further in Sec. 15.18.

15.16 Base-catalyzed cleavage of epoxides

Unlike ordinary ethers, epoxides can be cleaved under alkaline conditions. Here it is the epoxide itself, not the protonated epoxide, that undergoes nucleophilic attack. The lower reactivity of the non-protonated epoxide is compensated for by the more basic, more strongly nucleophilic reagent: alkoxide, phenoxide, ammonia, etc.

Let us look, for example, at the reaction of ethylene oxide with phenol. Acid catalyzes reaction by converting the epoxide into the highly reactive protonated epoxide. Base catalyzes reaction by converting the phenol into the more strongly nucleophilic phenoxide ion.

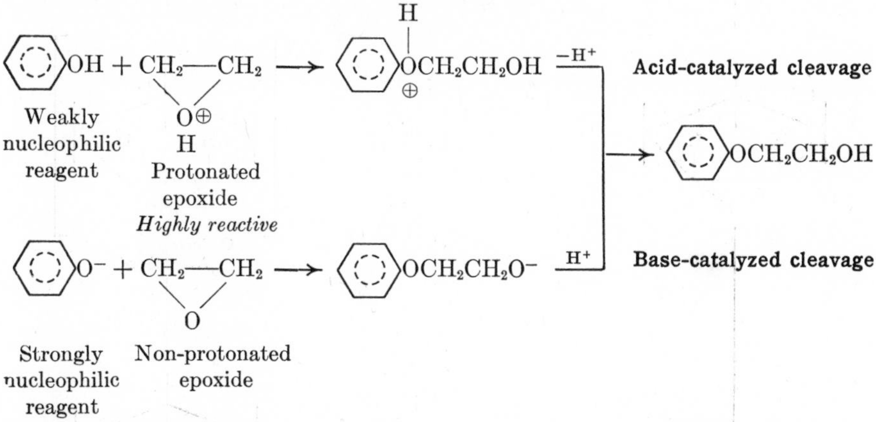

Problem 15.16 Write equations for the reaction of ethylene oxide with (a) methanol in the presence of a little H_2SO_4; (b) methanol in the presence of a little $CH_3O^- Na^+$; (c) aniline, $C_6H_5NH_2$.

Problem 15.17 Using the reaction between phenol and ethylene oxide as an example, show why it is not feasible to bring about reaction between the protonated epoxide and the highly nucleophilic reagent, phenoxide ion. (*Hint:* consider what would happen if one started with a solution of sodium phenoxide and ethylene oxide and added acid to it.)

15.17 Reaction of ethylene oxide with Grignard reagents

Reaction of Grignard reagents with ethylene oxide is an important method of preparing primary alcohols since the product contains two carbons more than the alkyl or aryl group of the Grignard reagent. As in reaction with the carbonyl group (Sec. 11.11) we see the nucleophilic (basic) alkyl or aryl group of the Grignard reagent attach itself to the relatively positive carbon and the electrophilic (acidic) magnesium attach itself to the relatively negative oxygen.

$$\overset{\delta-}{R}-\overset{\delta+}{MgX} + \overset{\delta+}{CH_2}-CH_2 \longrightarrow RCH_2CH_2OMgX \xrightarrow{H^+} RCH_2CH_2OH$$

Use of higher epoxides is complicated by rearrangements and formation of mixtures.

15.18 Stereochemistry of glycol formation. Cyclic compounds

Now that we have learned something about the chemistry of epoxides, let us return to a matter we discussed earlier: hydroxylation of alkenes.

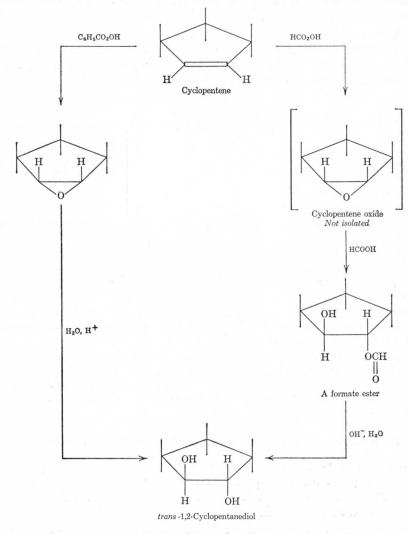

FIGURE 15.1. Hydroxylation of cyclopentene via epoxide.

In particular, let us see how the stereospecificity (Secs. 5.19 and 7.14) of hydroxylation reactions can be accounted for.

We have seen that the action of peroxyformic acid on an alkene results in *trans*-hydroxylation: the glycol obtained has the configuration we would expect from attachment of two —OH groups to opposite faces of the carbon–carbon double bond.

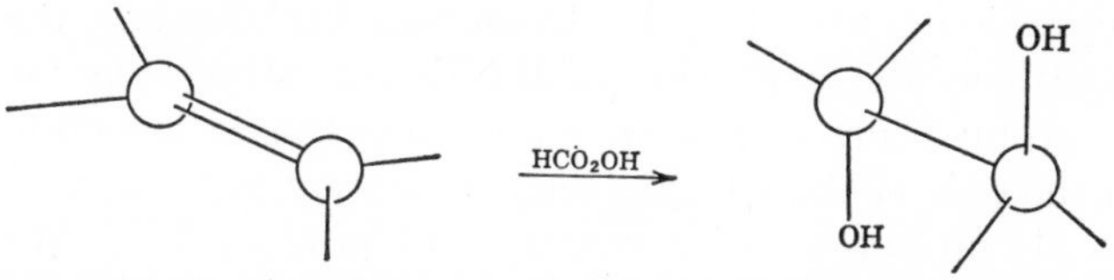

trans-**Hydroxylation**

Exactly the same glycol is obtained if first the alkene is converted into an epoxide and then this epoxide is hydrolyzed, as described earlier in this chapter. Hydrolysis of cyclopentene oxide, for example, yields *trans*-1,2-cyclopentanediol (Figure 15.1).

The two procedures give the same stereochemical results because they actually involve the same reaction: formation and hydrolysis of an epoxide. In the hydroxylation of an alkene by peroxyformic acid, the epoxide is generally not isolated simply because it is rapidly cleaved in the acidic medium, formic acid (Figure 15.1).

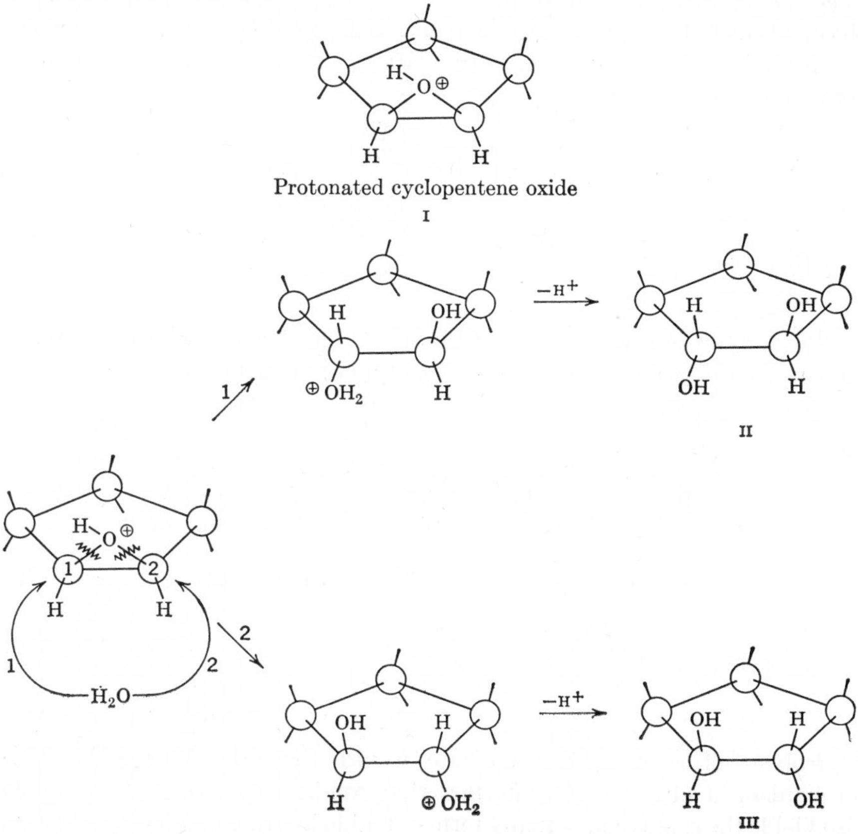

Protonated cyclopentene oxide

I

Let us look at the stereochemistry of the cleavage of an epoxide. As we saw earlier (Sec. 15.15), acid-catalyzed hydrolysis of an epoxide probably involves nucleophilic attack by water on the protonated epoxide. Assuming for the moment that this attack occurs by the S_N2 mechanism, let us make a model of cyclopentene oxide and see what we would expect to obtain.

The protonated epoxide has structure I. In an S_N2 displacement, the nucleophilic reagent attacks the back side of the carbon atom — as far as possible from the group being displaced — and thus causes inversion of configuration. In the case of the epoxide, such attack by water at C–1 would yield product II; attack at C–2 would yield product III. We recognize II and III as enantiomeric forms of the *trans*-glycol. (Although we have not previously mentioned this point, *trans*-1,2-cyclopentanediol is asymmetric.) Since attack is equally likely at either C–1 or C–2, there should be formed racemic *trans*-1,2-cyclopentanediol. This is the product actually obtained.

Thus, the *trans*-glycol would be formed in the hydrolysis of the epoxide because of the inversion that accompanies an S_N2 attack (Sec. 13.10). If hydrolysis were to proceed by an S_N1 mechanism, there would probably be at least some loss of configuration (Sec. 13.13), and, hence, at least some *cis*-glycol would be formed. The fact that only *trans*-glycol is actually obtained strongly suggests that the reaction proceeds by an S_N2 mechanism.

Next, let us consider *cis*-hydroxylation, brought about by action of permanganate.

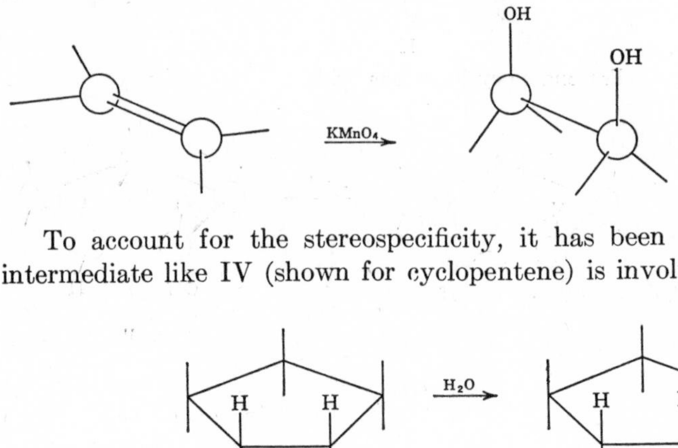

cis-**Hydroxylation**

To account for the stereospecificity, it has been suggested that an intermediate like IV (shown for cyclopentene) is involved:

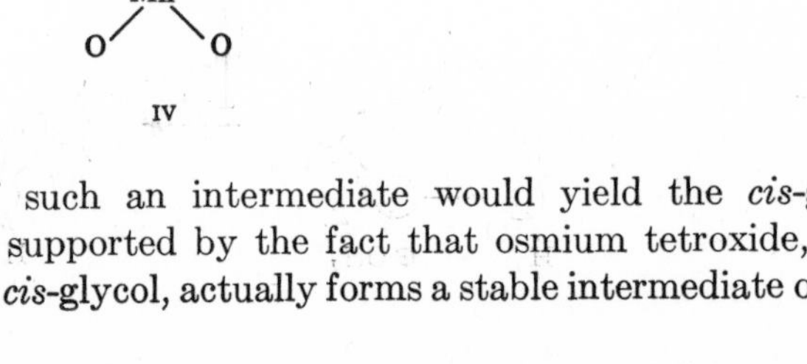

IV

Hydrolysis of such an intermediate would yield the *cis*-glycol. This mechanism is supported by the fact that osmium tetroxide, OsO_4, which also yields the *cis*-glycol, actually forms a stable intermediate of structure V.

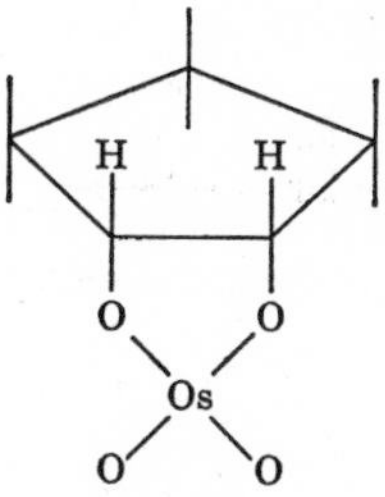

V

The two methods of hydroxylation — by peroxy acids and by permanganate — differ in stereochemistry because they differ in mechanism.
Furthermore, the mechanisms proposed to account for these results are
perfectly consistent with the other chemistry we know.

We shall return to these same ideas when we take up the more complicated — but fundamentally identical — stereochemistry of glycol formation
from open-chain alkenes (Sec. 24.7).

15.19 Stereochemistry of halogen addition

At this point, it is convenient to take up a reaction which — although
seemingly quite different — is actually closely related to the epoxide
chemistry we have just discussed: addition of halogen to the carbon–
carbon double bond.

We saw earlier (Sec. 5.15) that, on the basis of much evidence, this
reaction is believed to proceed by two steps: first, the addition of a positive
halogen ion to form a carbonium ion; then, the combination of this product with a negative halide ion.

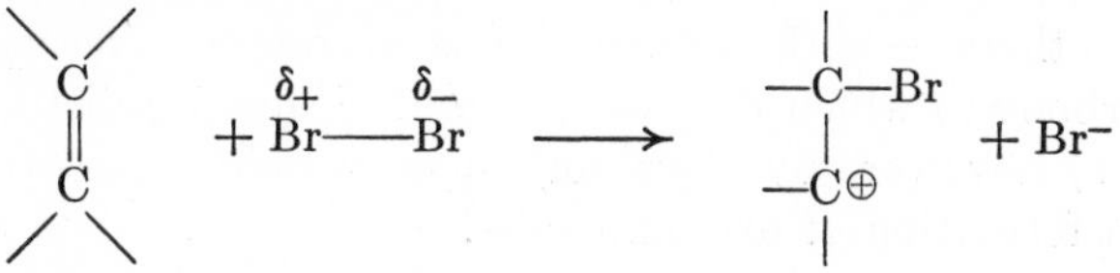

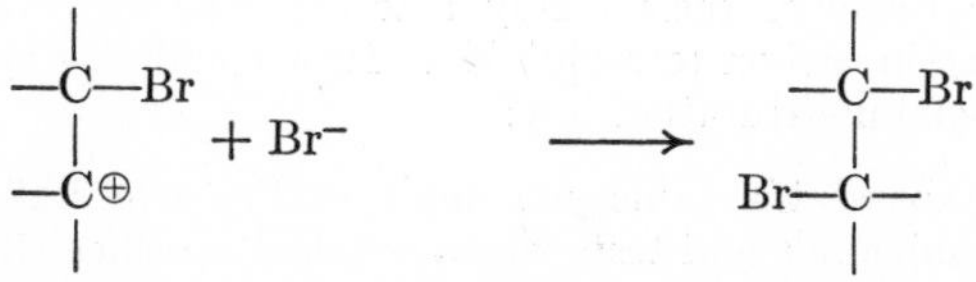

We have also seen (Sec. 7.14) that the reaction is stereospecific, resulting in *trans*-addition. This stereospecificity gives powerful support to
the idea of a two-step mechanism but, at the same time, makes it necessary
to modify the mechanism.

The stereochemistry of halogen addition, we can see, is the same as
that of glycol formation via the epoxide. It has been suggested that the
two reactions proceed by exactly analogous mechanisms. In the first step
of the addition of bromine, for example, positive bromine attaches itself
not to just one of the doubly-bonded carbon atoms, but to both, forming
a cyclic **bromonium ion**, I.

(1)

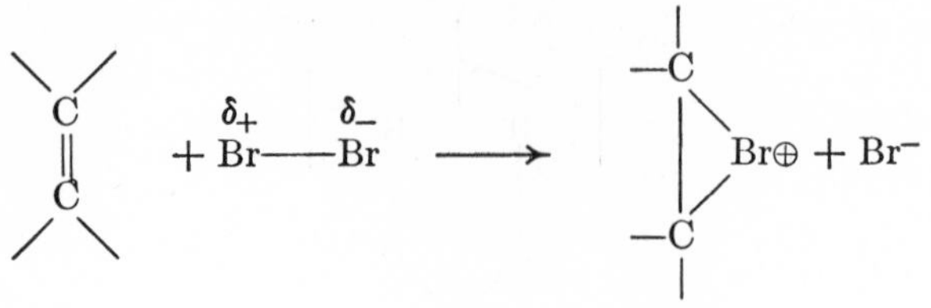

(2)

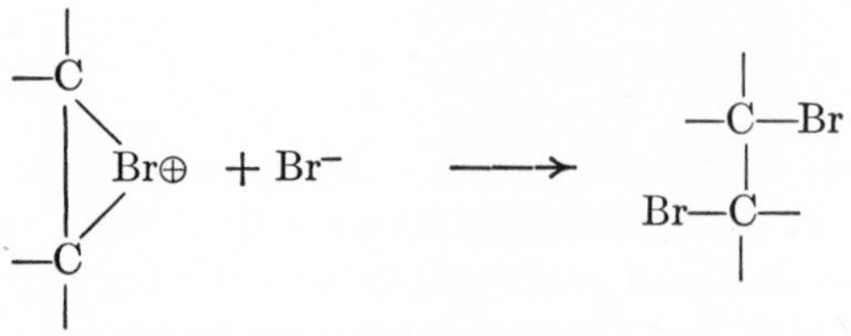

Bromide ion then attacks (step 2), with inversion of configuration. The net result is *trans*-addition.

The idea of a *bromonium* ion (or *chloronium* ion) may appear strange to us, in contrast to the already familiar *oxonium* and *ammonium* ions. It has been proposed as the only reasonable explanation for the observed stereochemistry. The tendency of halogen to share two pairs of electrons and acquire a positive charge is evidently appreciable; the same tendency, we recall, is indicated by the chemistry of vinyl and aryl halides (Secs. 14.8 and 14.9).

Problem 15.18   Using both models and drawings of the kind used in Sec. 15.18, show all steps in the addition of bromine to cyclopentene.

15.20   Analysis of ethers

Because of the low reactivity of the functional group, the chemical behavior of ethers — both aliphatic and aromatic — resembles that of the hydrocarbons to which they are related. They are distinguished from hydrocarbons, however, by their solubility in cold concentrated sulfuric acid through formation of oxonium salts.

Problem 15.19   Because of their highly reactive benzene rings, aryl ethers may decolorize bromine in carbon tetrachloride. How could this behavior be distinguished from the usual unsaturation test?

Problem 15.20   Expand the table you made in Problem 12.8, page 355, to include the kinds of compounds and tests we have taken up since Chapter 12.

Problem 15.21   Describe simple chemical tests (if any) that would distinguish between an aliphatic ether and (a) an alkane; (b) an alkene; (c) an alkyne; (d) an alkyl halide; (e) a primary or secondary alcohol; (f) a tertiary alcohol; (g) an alkyl aryl ether.

Identification as a previously reported ether is accomplished through the usual comparison of physical properties. This can be confirmed by cleavage with hot concentrated hydriodic acid (Sec. 15.10) and identification of one or both products. Aromatic ethers can be converted into solid bromination or nitration products whose melting points can then be compared with those of previously reported derivatives.

Proof of structure of a new ether would involve cleavage by hydriodic acid and identification of the products formed. Cleavage is used quantitatively in the **Zeisel method** to show the number of alkoxyl groups in an alkyl aryl ether.

Problem 15.22 How many methoxyl groups per molecule of papaverine would be indicated by the following results of a Zeisel analysis?

Treatment of *papaverine* ($C_{20}H_{21}O_4N$, one of the opium alkaloids) with hot concentrated hydriodic acid yields CH_3I, indicating the presence of the methoxyl group —OCH_3. When 4.24 mg of papaverine is treated with hydriodic acid and the CH_3I thus formed is passed into alcoholic silver nitrate, 11.62 mg of silver iodide is obtained.

PROBLEMS

1. Write structural formulas for:

(a) methyl ether
(b) isopropyl ether
(c) methyl *n*-butyl ether
(d) isobutyl *tert*-butyl ether
(e) 3-methoxyhexane
(f) vinyl ether
(g) allyl ether
(h) β-chloroethyl ether
(i) anisole
(j) phenetole
(k) phenyl ether
(l) cyclohexene oxide
(m) *p*-nitrobenzyl *n*-propyl ether
(n) 1,2-epoxypentane

2. Name the following structures:

(a) $(CH_3)_2CHCH_2$—O—$CH_2CH(CH_3)_2$
(b) CH_3—O—$CH(CH_3)_2$
(c) $(CH_3)_3C$—O—CH_2CH_3
(d) $CH_3CH_2CH_2CH(OCH_3)CH_2CH_2CH_3$

(e) *p*-$BrC_6H_4OC_2H_5$
(f) *o*-$O_2NC_6H_4CH_2OC_6H_5$
(g) 2,4-$Br_2C_6H_3OCH_3$

3. By means of a diagram summarize the interconversion of ethanol, ethylene, ethyl ether, and ethyl hydrogen sulfate in the presence of H_2SO_4. What is the key intermediate in all these reactions?

4. Outline a possible laboratory synthesis of each of the following compounds from alcohols and phenols:

(a) methyl *tert*-butyl ether
(b) phenetole ($C_6H_5OC_2H_5$)
(c) *n*-butyl cyclohexyl ether
(d) *p*-tolyl benzyl ether
(e) isopropyl isobutyl ether
(f) resorcinol dimethyl ether (1,3-dimethoxybenzene)

5. Arrange the compounds in each set in order of reactivity toward bromine:

(a) anisole, benzene, chlorobenzene, nitrobenzene, phenol
(b) anisole, *m*-hydroxyanisole, *o*-methylanisole, *m*-methylanisole
(c) *p*-$C_6H_4(OH)_2$, *p*-$CH_3OC_6H_4OH$, *p*-$C_6H_4(OCH_2)_2$

6. Write a balanced equation for each of the following. (If no reaction occurs, indicate "no reaction.")

(a) potassium *tert*-butoxide + ethyl iodide
(b) *tert*-butyl iodide + potassium ethoxide
(c) ethyl alcohol + H_2SO_4 (140°)
(d) *n*-butyl ether + boiling aqueous NaOH
(e) methyl ethyl ether + excess HI (hot)
(f) methyl ether + Na
(g) ethyl ether + cold conc. H_2SO_4
(h) ethyl ether + hot conc. H_2SO_4
(i) $C_6H_5OC_2H_5$ + hot conc. HBr
(j) $C_6H_5OC_2H_5$ + HNO_3, H_2SO_4
(k) *p*-$CH_3C_6H_4OCH_3$ + $KMnO_4$ + KOH + heat
(l) $C_6H_5OCH_2C_6H_5$ + Br_2, Fe

7. The oxidation of side chains in aryl alkyl ethers is satisfactory if done under alkaline conditions (say, by $KMnO_4 + KOH$) but not under acidic conditions (say, by $K_2Cr_2O_7 + H_2SO_4$). Can you suggest a reason why this is so?

8. Like other oxygen-containing compounds, *n*-butyl *tert*-butyl ether dissolves in cold concentrated H_2SO_4. On standing, however, an acid-insoluble layer, made up of high-boiling hydrocarbon material, slowly separates from the solution. What is this material likely to be, and how is it formed?

9. When 2,4,6-trinitroanisole is treated with sodium ethoxide a product of formula $C_9H_{10}O_8N_3^- Na^+$ is formed. A product of the same formula is formed by the treatment of trinitrophenetole by sodium methoxide. When treated with acid, both products give the same mixture of trinitroanisole and trinitrophenetole. What structure (or structures) would you assign to these products?

10. Describe simple chemical tests that would distinguish between:

(a) *n*-butyl ether and *n*-pentyl alcohol
(b) ethyl ether and methyl iodide
(c) methyl *n*-propyl ether and 1-pentene
(d) isopropyl ether and allyl ether
(e) anisole and toluene
(f) vinyl ether and ethyl ether
(g) *n*-butyl *tert*-butyl ether and *n*-octane

Tell exactly what you would *do* and *see.*

11. An unknown compound is believed to be one of the following. Describe how you would go about finding out which of the possibilities the unknown actually is. Where possible, use simple chemical tests; where necessary, use more elaborate chemical methods like quantitative hydrogenation, cleavage, etc. Make use of any needed tables of physical constants.

(a) *n*-propyl ether (b.p. 91°) and 2-methylhexane (b.p. 91°)
(b) ethyl benzyl ether (b.p. 188°) and allyl phenyl ether (b.p. 192°)
(c) methyl *p*-tolyl ether (b.p. 176°) and methyl *m*-tolyl ether (b.p. 177°)
(d) ethyl *n*-propyl ether (b.p. 64°), 1-hexene (b.p. 64°), and methanol (b.p. 65°)
(e) anisole (b.p. 154°), bromobenzene (b.p. 156°), *o*-chlorotoluene (b.p. 159°), *n*-propylbenzene (b.p. 159°), and cyclohexanol (b.p. 162°)
(f) ethyl ether (b.p. 35°), *n*-pentane (b.p. 36°), and isoprene (b.p. 34°)
(g) methyl *o*-tolyl ether (b.p. 171°), phenetole (b.p. 172°), and isopentyl ether (b.p. 173°)

12. Three compounds, A, B, and C, have the formula C_8H_9OBr. They are insoluble in water, but are soluble in cold concentrated H_2SO_4. B is the only one of the three that gives a precipitate when treated with $AgNO_3$. The three compounds are unaffected by dilute $KMnO_4$ and Br_2/CCl_4. Further investigation of their chemical properties leads to the following results:

oxidation by hot alkaline KMnO₄:

$$A \longrightarrow D\ (C_8H_7O_3Br),\ \text{an acid}$$
$$B \longrightarrow E\ (C_8H_8O_3),\ \text{an acid}$$
$$C \longrightarrow \text{unaffected}$$

treatment with hot conc. HBr:

$$A \longrightarrow F\ (C_7H_7OBr)$$
$$B \longrightarrow G\ (C_7H_7OBr)$$
$$C \longrightarrow H\ (C_6H_5OBr),\ \text{identified as } o\text{-bromophenol}$$
$$E \longrightarrow I\ (C_7H_6O_3),\ \text{identified as salicylic acid, } o\text{-HOC}_6H_4COOH$$

p-hydroxybenzoic acid $\xrightarrow{(CH_3)_2SO_4,\ NaOH}$ $\xrightarrow{HCl}$ $J\ (C_8H_8O_3)$
$J + Br_2 + Fe \longrightarrow D$

What are the probable structures of A, B, and C? Of compounds D through J? Write equations for all reactions involved.

13. Give the structures and names of the products you would expect from the reaction of ethylene oxide with:

(a) H_2O, H^+

(b) H_2O, OH^-

(c) C_2H_5OH, H^+

(d) product of (c), H^+

(e) $HOCH_2CH_2OH$, H^+

(f) product of (e), H^+

(g) anhydrous HBr

(h) HCN

(i) HCOOH

(j) C_6H_5MgBr

(k) NH_3

(l) diethylamine ($C_2H_5NHC_2H_5$)

(m) phenol, H^+

(n) phenol, OH^-

14. In Sec. 15.13 a mechanism is proposed for the conversion of ethylene bromo-hydrin into ethylene oxide in the presence of base. (a) To what general class does this reaction belong? (b) Using models, show the likely steric course of this reaction. (*Hint:* see Sec. 13.10.) (c) Can you suggest a reason why sodium hydroxide readily converts *trans*-2-chlorocyclohexanol into cyclohexene oxide, but converts the *cis*-isomer into entirely different products?

15. (a) Show in detail (including structures and transition states) the steps in the base-catalyzed cleavage of ethylene oxide by methanol via an S_N1 mechanism; via an S_N2 mechanism. (b) Do the same for propylene oxide; for isobutylene oxide; for styrene oxide. (c) What product would you expect in each case? (d) Actually the chief products are found to be 1-methoxy-2-propanol, 1-methoxy-2-methyl-2-propanol, and 2-methoxy-1-phenylethanol. Which mechanism, S_N1 or S_N2, seems to be more important here?

16. (a) Show in detail (including structures and transition states) the steps in the cleavage of ethylene oxide by hydrogen chloride via an S_N1 mechanism; via an S_N2 mechanism. (b) Do the same for styrene oxide; for trimethylethylene oxide. (c) What product would you expect in each case? (d) Actually the chief products are found to be 2-phenyl-2-chloroethanol and 3-chloro-3-methyl-2-butanol. Which mechanism, S_N1 or S_N2, seems to be more important here?

17. Propylene oxide can be converted into propylene glycol by the action of either dilute acid or dilute base. When optically active propylene oxide is used, the glycol obtained from acidic hydrolysis has a rotation opposite to that obtained from alkaline hydrolysis. What is the most likely interpretation of these facts? (*Hint:* see Problems 15 and 16.)

18. When allyl bromide is treated with dilute H_2SO_4, there is obtained not only 1-bromo-2-propanol, but also 2-bromo-1-propanol. How do you account for this? (*Hint:* see Sec. 15.19.)

19. Give the structures (including configurations where pertinent) of com· pounds A through N:

(a) $ClCH_2CH$—CH_2 + CH_3OH + H_2SO_4 $\longrightarrow$ A ($C_4H_9O_2Cl$)

$\diagdown \diagup$

O

A + NaOCl $\longrightarrow$ $CHCl_3$ + B ($C_3H_6O_3$)

A + NaOH(aq) $\longrightarrow$ C ($C_4H_8O_2$)

(b) $ClCH_2CH_2CH_2OH$ + KOH $\longrightarrow$ D (C_3H_6O)

(c) benzene + ethylene oxide + BF_3 $\longrightarrow$ E ($C_8H_{10}O$)

(d) methyl vinyl ether + dil. H_2SO_4 $\longrightarrow$ CH_3OH + F (C_2H_4O)

(e) anisole + Br_2 $\longrightarrow$ G (C_7H_7OBr)

G + Mg, ether $\longrightarrow$ H (C_7H_7OBrMg)

H + allyl bromide $\longrightarrow$ I ($C_{10}H_{12}O$)

I + hot KOH $\longrightarrow$ J ($C_{10}H_{12}O$)

(f) cyclohexene oxide + anhydrous HCl $\longrightarrow$ K ($C_6H_{11}OCl$)

(g) 1-methylcyclohexene + HCO_2OH $\longrightarrow$ L ($C_7H_{14}O_2$)

(h) ethylene oxide + *n*-butyl alcohol + H^+ $\longrightarrow$ M ($C_6H_{14}O_2$)

M + Cu + heat $\longrightarrow$ N ($C_6H_{12}O_2$)

CARBOXYLIC ACIDS

16.1 Structure

Of the organic compounds that show appreciable acidity, by far the most important are the carboxylic acids. These compounds contain the **carboxyl group**

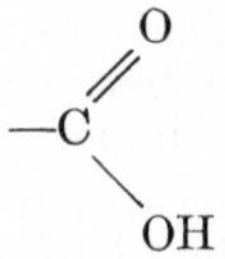

$$-C\diagup\!\!\!\!\diagdown\begin{matrix}O\\OH\end{matrix}$$

attached to either an alkyl group (RCOOH) or an aryl group (ArCOOH). For example:

HCOOH   CH₃COOH   CH₃(CH₂)₁₀COOH   CH₃(CH₂)₇CH=CH(CH₂)₇COOH
Formic acid   Acetic acid   Lauric acid   Oleic acid
                                            (*cis*-9-Octadecenoic acid)

⬡COOH   O₂N⬡COOH   ⬡CH₂COOH
Benzoic acid 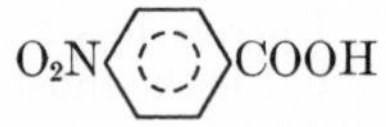   *p*-Nitrobenzoic acid    Phenylacetic acid

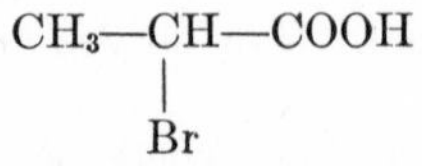

$$CH_3—\underset{\underset{Br}{|}}{CH}—COOH$$

⬡COOH

     α-Bromopropionic acid 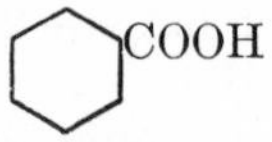   Cyclohexanecarboxylic acid

Whether the group is aliphatic or aromatic, substituted or unsubstituted, the properties of the carboxyl group are essentially the same.

16.2 Nomenclature

The aliphatic carboxylic acids have been known for a long time, and as a result have common names that refer to their sources rather than to their chemical structures. The **common names** of the more important acids are shown in Table 16.1. *Formic acid*, for example, adds the sting to the bite of an ant (Latin, *formica*, ant); *butyric acid* gives rancid butter its typical smell (Latin, *butyrum*, butter); and *caproic, caprylic,* and *capric acids* are all found in goat fat (Latin, *caper*, goat). The student should memorize the names of at least the first six acids and of the C₁₂, C₁₆, and C₁₈ acids.

TABLE 16.1

CARBOXYLIC ACIDS

Name	Formula	M.p., °C	B.p., °C	Solub., g/100 g H_2O
Formic	HCOOH	8	100.5	∞
Acetic	CH_3COOH	16.6	118	∞
Propionic	CH_3CH_2COOH	−22	141	∞
Butyric	$CH_3(CH_2)_2COOH$	− 6	164	∞
Valeric	$CH_3(CH_2)_3COOH$	−34	187	3.7
Caproic	$CH_3(CH_2)_4COOH$	− 3	205	1.0
Caprylic	$CH_3(CH_2)_6COOH$	16	239	0.7
Capric	$CH_3(CH_2)_8COOH$	31	269	0.2
Lauric	$CH_3(CH_2)_{10}COOH$	44	225^{100}	i.
Myristic	$CH_3(CH_2)_{12}COOH$	54	251^{100}	i.
Palmitic	$CH_3(CH_2)_{14}COOH$	63	269^{100}	i.
Stearic	$CH_3(CH_2)_{16}COOH$	70	287^{100}	i.
Oleic	*cis*-9-Octadecenoic	16	223^{10}	i.
Linoleic	*cis,cis*-9,12-Octadecadienoic	−11	230^{16}	i.
Linolenic	*cis,cis,cis*-9,12,15-Octadecatrienoic		232^{17}	i.
Cyclohexanecarboxylic	*cyclo*-$C_6H_{11}COOH$	31	233	0.20
Phenylacetic	$C_6H_5CH_2COOH$	77	266	1.66
Benzoic	C_6H_5COOH	122	250	0.34
o-Toluic	*o*-$CH_3C_6H_4COOH$	106	259	0.12
m-Toluic	*m*-$CH_3C_6H_4COOH$	112	263	0.10
p-Toluic	*p*-$CH_3C_6H_4COOH$	180	275	0.03
o-Chlorobenzoic	*o*-ClC_6H_4COOH	141		0.22
m-Chlorobenzoic	*m*-ClC_6H_4COOH	154		0.04
p-Chlorobenzoic	*p*-ClC_6H_4COOH	242		0.009
o-Bromobenzoic	*o*-BrC_6H_4COOH	148		0.18
m-Bromobenzoic	*m*-BrC_6H_4COOH	156		0.04
p-Bromobenzoic	*p*-BrC_6H_4COOH	254		0.006
o-Nitrobenzoic	*o*-$O_2NC_6H_4COOH$	147		0.75
m-Nitrobenzoic	*m*-$O_2NC_6H_4COOH$	141		0.34
p-Nitrobenzoic	*p*-$O_2NC_6H_4COOH$	242		0.03
Phthalic	*o*-$C_6H_4(COOH)_2$	231		0.70
Isophthalic	*m*-$C_6H_4(COOH)_2$	348		0.01
Terephthalic	*p*-$C_6H_4(COOH)_2$	300*subl.*		0.002
Salicylic	*o*-HOC_6H_4COOH	159		0.22
p-Hydroxybenzoic	*p*-HOC_6H_4COOH	213		0.65
Anthranilic	*o*-$H_2NC_6H_4COOH$	146		0.52
m-Aminobenzoic	*m*-$H_2NC_6H_4COOH$	179		0.77
p-Aminobenzoic	*p*-$H_2NC_6H_4COOH$	187		0.3
o-Methoxybenzoic	*o*-$CH_3OC_6H_4COOH$	101		0.5
m-Methoxybenzoic	*m*-$CH_3OC_6H_4COOH$	110		
p-Methoxybenzoic(Anisic)	*p*-$CH_3OC_6H_4COOH$	184		0.04

The prefix *iso*– is used to designate certain of the branched-chain acids: those with a single branch of a methyl group at the end of the molecule farthest removed from the carboxyl group.

$$CH_3$$
$$|$$
$$CH_3—CH—(CH_2)_n—COOH$$

An *iso* acid

For example:

<table>
<tr><td>CH₃</td><td>CH₃</td><td>CH₃</td></tr>
</table>

$$CH_3—CH—COOH \qquad CH_3—CH—CH_2COOH \qquad CH_3—CH—CH_2CH_2COOH$$

Isobutyric acid   Isovaleric acid   Isocaproic acid

Other branched-chain acids and substituted acids are named as derivatives of the straight-chain acids. To indicate the position of attachment, the Greek letters, α-, β-, γ-, δ-, etc., are used; the α-carbon is the one bearing the carboxyl group.

$$\overset{\delta}{C}—\overset{\gamma}{C}—\overset{\beta}{C}—\overset{\alpha}{C}—COOH \qquad \textit{Used in common names}$$

For example:

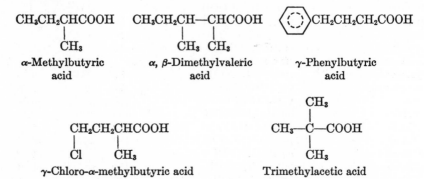

α-Methylbutyric acid   α, β-Dimethylvaleric acid   γ-Phenylbutyric acid

γ-Chloro-α-methylbutyric acid   Trimethylacetic acid

Generally the parent acid is taken as the one of longest carbon chain, although some compounds are named as derivatives of acetic acid.

Aromatic acids, ArCOOH, are usually named as derivatives of the parent acid, **benzoic acid,** C_6H_5COOH. The methylbenzoic acids are given the special name of *toluic acids.*

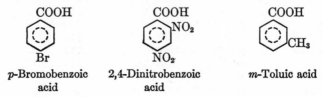

p-Bromobenzoic acid   2,4-Dinitrobenzoic acid   *m*-Toluic acid

The **IUPAC names** follow the usual pattern. The longest chain carrying the carboxyl group is considered the parent structure, and is named by replacing the –*e* of the corresponding alkane with –**oic acid.** For example:

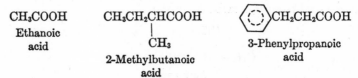

Ethanoic acid   2-Methylbutanoic acid   3-Phenylpropanoic acid

$$\underset{\substack{\\ | \\ \text{Cl}\langle\bigcirc\rangle\text{CHCH}_2\text{COOH}}}{\text{CH}_3}$$

3-(*p*-Chlorophenyl)butanoic
acid

The position of a substituent is indicated as usual by a number. We

$$\underset{5\quad4\quad3\quad2\quad1}{\text{C—C—C—C—COOH}} \qquad \textit{Used in IUPAC names}$$

should notice that the carboxyl carbon is always considered as C–1, and
hence C–2 corresponds to α of the common names, C–3 to β, and so on.
(*Caution:* do not mix Greek letters with IUPAC names, or Arabic numerals
with common names.)

The name of a **salt** of a carboxylic acid consists of the name of the
cation (*sodium, potassium, ammonium*, etc.) followed by the name of the
acid with the ending *–ic acid* changed to **–ate**. For example:

⟨◯⟩COONa   (CH₃COO)₂Ca   HCOONH₄

   Sodium benzoate   Calcium acetate   Ammonium formate

$$\underset{\substack{| \quad | \\ \text{Br} \quad \text{Br}}}{\text{CH}_2\text{—CH—COOK}}$$

Potassium α, β-dibromopropionate
(Potassium 2,3-dibromopropanoate)

16.3 Physical properties of carboxylic acids

As we would expect from their structure, carboxylic acid molecules
are polar, and like alcohol molecules can form hydrogen bonds with each
other and with other kinds of molecules. The aliphatic acids therefore
show very much the same solubility behavior as the alcohols: the first
four are miscible with water, the five-carbon acid is partly soluble, and
the higher acids are virtually insoluble. Water solubility undoubtedly
arises from hydrogen bonding between the carboxylic acid and water.
The simplest aromatic acid, benzoic acid, contains too many carbon atoms
to show appreciable solubility in water.

Carboxylic acids are soluble in less polar solvents like ether, alcohol,
benzene, etc.

We can see from Table 16.1 that as a class the carboxylic acids are
even higher boiling than alcohols. For example, propionic acid (b.p.
141°) boils more than twenty degrees higher than the alcohol of comparable molecular weight, *n*-butyl alcohol (b.p. 118°). These very high
boiling points are due to the fact that a pair of carboxylic acid molecules
are held together not by one but by two hydrogen bonds:

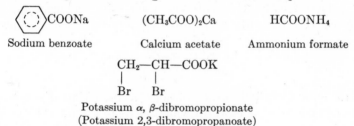

Problem 16.1   At 110° and 454 mm pressure, 0.11 g acetic acid vapor occupies 63.7 cc; at 156° and 458 mm, 0.081 g occupies 66.4 cc.   Calculate the molecular weight of acetic acid in the vapor phase at each temperature.   How do you interpret these results?

The odors of the lower aliphatic acids progress from the sharp, irritating odors of formic and acetic acids to the distinctly unpleasant odors of butyric, valeric, and caproic acids; the higher acids have little odor because of their low volatility.

16.4   Salts of carboxylic acids

Although much weaker than the strong mineral acids (sulfuric, hydrochloric, nitric), the carboxylic acids are tremendously more acidic than the very weak organic acids (alcohols, acetylene) we have so far studied; they are much stronger acids than water.   Aqueous hydroxides therefore readily convert carboxylic acids into their salts; aqueous mineral acids readily convert the salts back into the carboxylic acids.   Since we can

$$\underset{\text{Acid}}{RCOOH} \underset{H^+}{\overset{OH^-}{\rightleftarrows}} \underset{\text{Salt}}{RCOO^-}$$

do little with carboxylic acids without encountering this conversion to and from their salts, it is worth while for us to examine the properties of these salts.

Salts of carboxylic acids — like all salts — are crystalline non-volatile solids made up of positive and negative ions; their properties are what we would expect of such a structure.   The strong electrostatic forces holding the ions in the crystal lattice can be overcome only by heating to a high temperature, or by a very polar solvent.   The temperature required for melting is so high that before it can be reached carbon–carbon bonds break and the molecule decomposes, generally in the neighborhood of 300–400°.   A decomposition point is seldom useful for the identification of a compound, since it usually reflects the rate of heating rather than the identity of the compound.

The alkali metal salts of carboxylic acids (sodium, potassium, ammonium) are soluble in water but insoluble in non-polar solvents; most of the heavy metal salts (iron, silver, copper, etc.) are insoluble in water.

Thus we see that, except for the acids of four carbons or less, which are soluble both in water and in organic solvents, *carboxylic acids and their alkali metal salts show exactly opposite solubility behavior*.   Because of the ready interconversion of acids and their salts, this difference in solubility behavior may be used in two important ways: for *identification* and for *separation*.

A water-insoluble organic compound that dissolves in cold dilute aqueous sodium hydroxide must be either a carboxylic acid or one of the few other kinds of organic compounds more acidic than water; that it is indeed a carboxylic acid can then be shown in other ways.

$$RCOOH + NaOH \longrightarrow RCOONa + H_2O$$

Stronger acid   *Soluble in*   Weaker
Insoluble in H₂O   *H₂O*   acid

Instead of sodium hydroxide, we can use aqueous sodium bicarbonate; even if the unknown is water-soluble, its acidity is shown by the evolution of bubbles of CO_2.

$$RCOOH + NaHCO_3 \longrightarrow RCOONa + H_2O + CO_2 \uparrow$$

Insoluble in H₂O   *Soluble in H₂O*

We can separate a carboxylic acid from non-acidic compounds by taking advantage of its solubility and their insolubility in aqueous base; once the separation has been accomplished, we can regenerate the acid by acidification of the aqueous solution. If we are dealing with solids, we simply stir the mixture with aqueous base and then filter the solution from insoluble, non-acidic materials; addition of mineral acid to the filtrate precipitates the carboxylic acid, which can be collected on a filter. If we are dealing with liquids, we shake the mixture with aqueous base in a separatory funnel and separate the aqueous layer from the insoluble organic layer; addition of acid to the aqueous layer again liberates the carboxylic acid, which can then be separated from the water. For completeness of separation and ease of handling, we often add a water-insoluble solvent like ether to the acidified mixture. The carboxylic acid is extracted from the water by the ether, in which it is more soluble; the volatile ether is readily removed by distillation from the comparatively high-boiling acid.

For example, an aldehyde prepared by the oxidation of a primary alcohol (Sec. 12.7) may very well be contaminated with the carboxylic acid; this acid can be simply washed out with dilute aqueous base. The carboxylic acid prepared by oxidation of an alkylbenzene (Sec. 9.11) may very well be contaminated with unreacted starting material; the carboxylic acid can be taken into solution by aqueous base, separated from the insoluble hydrocarbon, and regenerated by addition of mineral acid.

Since separations of this kind are more clearcut and less wasteful of material, they are preferred wherever possible over recrystallization or distillation.

16.5 Industrial source

As usual, the lowest members of the family are prepared by special methods. **Formic acid** is synthesized on a large scale by the reaction between carbon monoxide and aqueous sodium hydroxide at high temperature and pressure.

$$CO + NaOH \xrightarrow{\text{200°, 100 lb/in.}^2} HCOONa \xrightarrow{\text{H}^+} HCOOH$$

                                       Sodium formate   Formic acid

Acetic acid, by far the most important of all carboxylic acids, is prepared by air oxidation of acetaldehyde, which is readily available from the hydration of acetylene (Sec. 6.12).

$$HC \equiv CH \xrightarrow{H_2O, \ H_2SO_4, \ HgSO_4} \overset{\overset{\displaystyle H}{\displaystyle |}}{CH_3-C}=O \xrightarrow{O_2, \ Mn^{++}} CH_3COOH$$

Acetylene   Acetaldehyde   Acetic acid

Large amounts of acetic acid are also produced as the dilute aqueous solution known as *vinegar*. Here too, the acetic acid is prepared by air oxidation; this time the compound that is oxidized is ethyl alcohol, and the catalyst is the mold known as *mother of vinegar*.

The most important sources of aliphatic carboxylic acids are the animal and vegetable **fats,** which are discussed in the next chapter (Sec. 17.23 through Sec. 17.27). From fats there can be obtained, in purity of over 90%, straight-chain carboxylic acids of even carbon number ranging from six to eighteen carbon atoms. These acids can be converted into the corresponding alcohols (Sec. 16.20), which can then be used, in the ways we have already studied (Sec. 12.10), to make a great number of other compounds containing long, straight-chain units.

The most important of the aromatic carboxylic acids, **benzoic acid** and the **phthalic acids,** are prepared on an industrial scale by a reaction we have already encountered: oxidation of alkylbenzenes (Sec. 9.11). The toluene and xylenes required are readily available from coal tar, and by hydroforming of alkanes (Sec. 9.4), from petroleum; another precursor of phthalic acid (the *ortho* isomer) is the aromatic hydrocarbon *naphthalene*, also found in coal tar. Cheap oxidizing agents like chlorine or even air (in the presence of catalysts) are used.

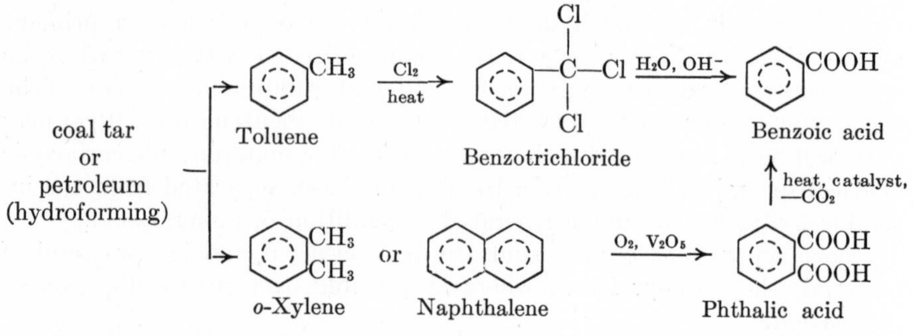

16.6   Preparation

The straight-chain aliphatic acids up to C_6, and those of even carbon number up to C_{18}, are commercially available, as are the simple aromatic acids. Other carboxylic acids are prepared by the methods outlined below.

PREPARATION OF CARBOXYLIC ACIDS

1. Oxidation of primary alcohols

$$RCH_2OH \xrightarrow{KMnO_4} RCOOH$$

Examples:

$$\overset{\overset{\displaystyle CH_3}{\displaystyle |}}{CH_3CH_2CHCH_2OH} \xrightarrow{KMnO_4} \overset{\overset{\displaystyle CH_3}{\displaystyle |}}{CH_3CH_2CHCOOH}$$

2-Methyl-1-butanol   2-Methylbutanoic acid

$$\underset{\text{Isobutyl alcohol}}{\overset{\overset{\displaystyle CH_3}{|}}{CH_3CHCH_2OH}} \xrightarrow{\text{KMnO}_4} \underset{\text{Isobutyric acid}}{\overset{\overset{\displaystyle CH_3}{|}}{CH_3CHCOOH}}$$

2. Oxidation of arenes

$$Ar\text{—}R \xrightarrow{\text{KMnO}_4 \text{ or } K_2Cr_2O_7} Ar\text{—}COOH$$

Examples:

$$O_2N\text{⟨◯⟩}CH_3 \xrightarrow{\text{K}_2\text{Cr}_2\text{O}_7,\ \text{H}_2\text{SO}_4,\ \text{heat}} O_2N\text{⟨◯⟩}COOH$$

p-Nitrotoluene   *p*-Nitrobenzoic acid

$$\text{◯}\overset{CH_3}{\underset{Br}{}} \xrightarrow[\text{heat}]{\text{KMnO}_4,\ OH^-} \text{◯}\overset{COOH}{\underset{Br}{}}$$

o-Bromotoluene   *o*-Bromobenzoic acid

3. Carbonation of Grignard reagents

$$\underset{\text{(or ArX)}}{RX} \xrightarrow{\text{Mg}} RMgX \xrightarrow{CO_2} RCOOMgX \xrightarrow{H^+} \underset{\text{(or ArCOOH)}}{RCOOH}$$

Examples:

$$\underset{\substack{\textit{tert}\text{-Pentyl}\\\text{chloride}}}{\overset{\overset{\displaystyle CH_3}{|}}{\underset{\underset{\displaystyle CH_3}{|}}{C_2H_5\text{–}C\text{–}Cl}}} \xrightarrow{\text{Mg}} \overset{\overset{\displaystyle CH_3}{|}}{\underset{\underset{\displaystyle CH_3}{|}}{C_2H_5\text{–}C\text{–}MgCl}} \xrightarrow{CO_2} \overset{\overset{\displaystyle CH_3}{|}}{\underset{\underset{\displaystyle CH_3}{|}}{C_2H_5\text{–}C\text{–}COOMgCl}} \xrightarrow{H^+} \underset{\substack{\text{Ethyldimethylacetic}\\\text{acid}\\\text{(2,2-Dimethylbutanoic}\\\text{acid)}}}{\overset{\overset{\displaystyle CH_3}{|}}{\underset{\underset{\displaystyle CH_3}{|}}{C_2H_5\text{–}C\text{–}COOH}}}$$

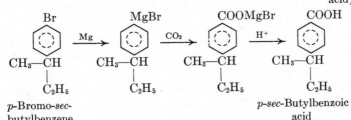

p-Bromo-*sec*-butylbenzene   *p-sec*-Butylbenzoic acid

4. Hydrolysis of nitriles

$$\begin{array}{c} R\text{—}C\equiv N + H_2O \\ \text{or} \\ Ar\text{—}C\equiv N \end{array} \xrightarrow{\text{acid or base}} \begin{array}{c} R\text{—}COOH + NH_3 \\ \text{or} \\ Ar\text{—}COOH \end{array}$$

Examples:

$$\text{◯}CH_2Cl \xrightarrow{\text{NaCN}} \text{◯}CH_2CN \xrightarrow{70\%\ H_2SO_4,\ \text{reflux}} \text{◯}CH_2COOH + NH_4^+$$

Benzyl chloride   Phenylacetonitrile   Phenylacetic acid

$$\underset{n\text{-Butyl bromide}}{n\text{-}C_4H_9Br} \xrightarrow{\text{NaCN}} \underset{\substack{n\text{-Valeronitrile}\\\text{(Pentanenitrile)}}}{n\text{-}C_4H_9CN} \xrightarrow{\text{aq. alc. NaOH, reflux}} n\text{-}C_4H_9COO^- + NH_3$$

$$\downarrow H^+$$

$$\underset{\substack{n\text{-Valeric acid}\\\text{(Pentanoic acid)}}}{n\text{-}C_4H_9COOH + NH_4^+}$$

diazonium salt $\longrightarrow$ [structure: benzene ring with CN and CH₃] $\xrightarrow{\text{75\% H}_2\text{SO}_4,\ 150\text{–}160°}$ [structure: benzene ring with COOH and CH₃] $+ \ NH_4^+$
(Sec. 21.3)

o-Tolunitrile   *o*-Toluic acid

5. Malonic ester synthesis. Discussed in Sec. 25.9.

6. Special methods for phenolic acids. Discussed in Sec. 22.19.

All the methods listed are important; our choice is governed by the availability of starting materials.

Oxidation is the most direct and is generally used when possible, some lower aliphatic acids being made from the available alcohols, and substituted aromatic acids from substituted toluenes.

The **Grignard synthesis** and the **nitrile synthesis** have the special advantage of increasing the length of a carbon chain, and thus extending the range of available starting materials. In the aliphatic series both Grignard reagents and nitriles are prepared from halides which in turn are usually prepared from alcohols. The syntheses thus amount to the preparation of acids from alcohols containing one less carbon atom.

RCH_2OH $-$

$\xrightarrow{\text{KMnO}_4}$ $RCOOH$ *Same carbon number*

Higher carbon number

$\xrightarrow{\text{PBr}_3}$ RCH_2Br $-$ $\xrightarrow{\text{Mg}}$ RCH_2MgBr $\xrightarrow{CO_2}$ $\xrightarrow{H^+}$ RCH_2COOH

$\xrightarrow{CN^-}$ RCH_2CN $\xrightarrow{H_2O}$ RCH_2COOH

Problem 16.2 What carboxylic acid can be prepared from *p*-bromotoluene (a) by direct oxidation? (b) By free radical chlorination followed by the nitrile synthesis?

Aromatic nitriles generally cannot be prepared from the unreactive aryl halides (Sec. 14.7). Instead, they are made from diazonium salts by a reaction we shall discuss later (Sec. 21.6). Diazonium salts are prepared from aromatic amines, which in turn are prepared from nitro compounds. Thus the carboxyl group eventually occupies the position on the ring where a nitro group was originally introduced by direct nitration (Sec. 8.20, Sec. 9.12).

$ArH \longrightarrow ArNO_2 \longrightarrow ArNH_2 \longrightarrow ArN_2^+ \longrightarrow ArC{\equiv}N \longrightarrow ArCOOH$
          Nitro   Amine   Diazonium   Nitrile   Acid
    compound   ion

For the preparation of quite complicated acids, the most versatile method of all is used, the *malonic ester synthesis* (Sec. 25.9).

16.7 Grignard synthesis

The Grignard synthesis of carboxylic acids is carried out by bubbling gaseous CO_2 into the ether solution of the Grignard reagent, or by pouring the Grignard reagent on crushed dry ice (solid CO_2); in the latter method dry ice serves not only as reagent but also as cooling agent.

The Grignard reagent adds to the carbon–oxygen double bond just as in the reaction with aldehydes and ketones (Sec. 11.11). The product is the magnesium salt of the carboxylic acid, from which the free acid is liberated by treatment with mineral acid.

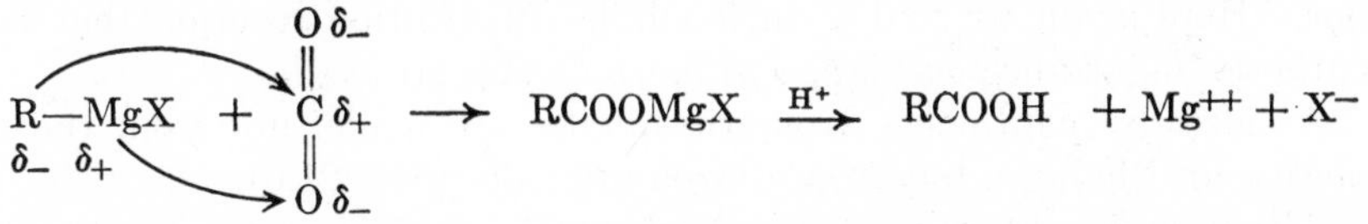

$$R—MgX + C \xrightarrow{} RCOOMgX \xrightarrow{H^+} RCOOH + Mg^{++} + X^-$$

The Grignard reagent can be prepared from primary, secondary, tertiary, or aromatic halides; the method is limited only by the presence of other reactive groups in the molecule (Sec. 11.14). The following syntheses illustrate the application of this method:

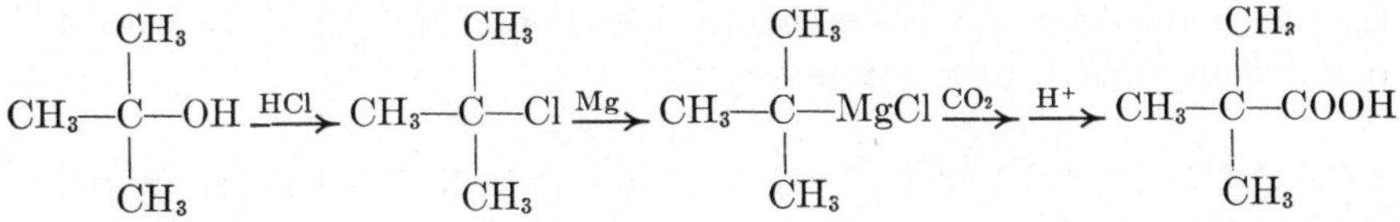

$$CH_3—\overset{\overset{\displaystyle CH_3}{|}}{\underset{\underset{\displaystyle CH_3}{|}}{C}}—OH \xrightarrow{HCl} CH_3—\overset{\overset{\displaystyle CH_3}{|}}{\underset{\underset{\displaystyle CH_3}{|}}{C}}—Cl \xrightarrow{Mg} CH_3—\overset{\overset{\displaystyle CH_3}{|}}{\underset{\underset{\displaystyle CH_3}{|}}{C}}—MgCl \xrightarrow{CO_2} \xrightarrow{H^+} CH_3—\overset{\overset{\displaystyle CH_3}{|}}{\underset{\underset{\displaystyle CH_3}{|}}{C}}—COOH$$

tert-Butyl alcohol   *tert*-Butyl chloride   Trimethylacetic acid

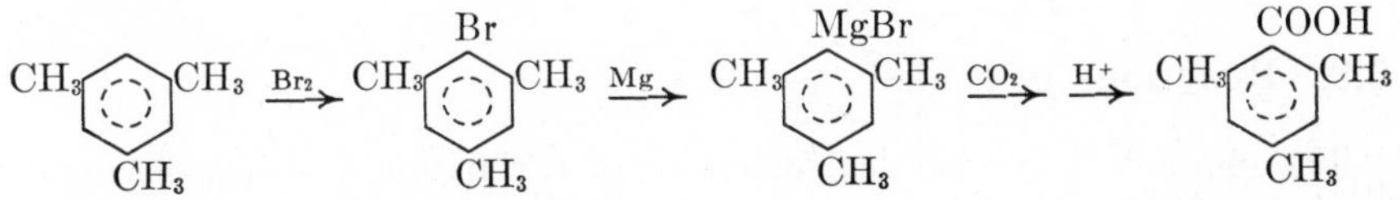

Mesitylene   Bromomesitylene   Mesitoic acid (2,4,6-Trimethyl-benzoic acid)

16.8 Nitrile synthesis

Aliphatic nitriles are prepared by heating alkyl halides with sodium cyanide in a solvent that will dissolve both reactants, generally aqueous alcohol. The resulting nitrile is then hydrolyzed to the acid by boiling aqueous alkali or acid.

$$RX + CN^- \longrightarrow RC\equiv N + X^-$$

$$RC\equiv N + H_2O \quad \begin{cases} \xrightarrow{H^+} RCOOH + NH_4^+ \\ \xrightarrow{OH^-} RCOO^- + NH_3 \end{cases}$$

The reaction of an alkyl halide with cyanide ion involves nucleophilic substitution (Sec. 13.6). The fact that HCN is a very weak acid tells us

$$CH_3CH_2CH_2CH_2Br + CN^- \longrightarrow CH_3CH_2CH_2CH_2CN$$

     n-Butyl bromide   Valeronitrile   1° halide: *substitution*

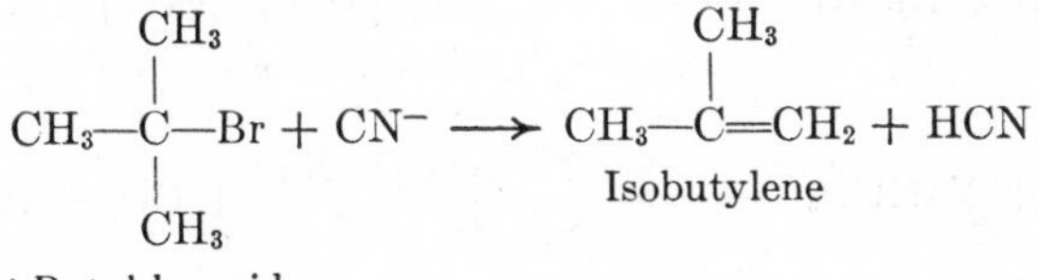

$$CH_3—\overset{\overset{\displaystyle CH_3}{|}}{\underset{\underset{\displaystyle CH_3}{|}}{C}}—Br + CN^- \longrightarrow CH_3—\overset{\overset{\displaystyle CH_3}{|}}{C}=CH_2 + HCN$$

                             Isobutylene   3° halide: *elimination*

tert-Butyl bromide

that cyanide ion is a strong base; as we might expect, this strongly basic ion can abstract hydrogen ion and thus cause elimination as well as substitution. Indeed, with tertiary halides elimination is the principal reaction; even with secondary halides the yield of substitution product is poor. Here again we find a nucleophilic substitution reaction that is of synthetic importance *only when primary halides are used.*

As already mentioned, aromatic nitriles are made, not from the unreactive aryl halides, but from diazonium salts (Sec. 21.6).

Although nitriles are sometimes named as *cyanides* or as *cyano* compounds, they generally take their names from the acids they yield upon hydrolysis. They are named by dropping *–ic acid* from the common name of the acid and adding **–nitrile**; usually for euphony an "o" is inserted between the root and the ending (e.g., *acetonitrile*). In the IUPAC system they are named by adding *–nitrile* to the name of the parent hydrocarbon (e.g., *ethanenitrile*). For example:

$CH_3C \equiv N$	$CH_3(CH_2)_3C \equiv N$	$\langle \bigcirc \rangle C \equiv N$	$CH_3 \langle \bigcirc \rangle C \equiv N$
Acetonitrile	*n*-Valeronitrile		
(Ethanenitrile)	(Pentanenitrile)	Benzonitrile	*p*-Tolunitrile

16.9 Reactions of acids

The characteristic chemical behavior of carboxylic acids is, of course, determined by their functional group, **carboxyl**, –COOH. This group is made up of a carbonyl group (C=O) and a hydroxyl group (—OH). As we shall see, it is the —OH that actually undergoes nearly every reaction — loss of H⁺, or replacement by another group — but *it does so in a way that is possible only because of the effect of the* C=O.

The rest of the molecule undergoes reactions characteristic of its structure; it may be aliphatic or aromatic, saturated or unsaturated, and may contain a variety of other functional groups.

REACTIONS OF CARBOXYLIC ACIDS

1. Acidity. Salt formation

$$RCOOH \rightleftarrows RCOO^- + H^+$$

Examples:

$$2CH_3COOH + Zn \longrightarrow (CH_3COO^-)_2Zn^{++} + H_2$$
$$\text{Acetic acid} \qquad\qquad \text{Zinc acetate}$$

$$CH_3(CH_2)_{10}COOH + NaOH \longrightarrow CH_3(CH_2)_{10}COO^-\ Na^+ + H_2O$$
$$\text{Lauric acid} \qquad\qquad\qquad \text{Sodium laurate}$$

$$\langle \bigcirc \rangle COOH + NaHCO_3 \longrightarrow \langle \bigcirc \rangle COO^-\ Na^+ + CO_2 + H_2O$$
$$\text{Benzoic acid} \qquad\qquad\qquad \text{Sodium benzoate}$$

2. Conversion into functional derivatives

$$R-\overset{\displaystyle O}{\underset{\displaystyle OH}{C}} \longrightarrow R-\overset{\displaystyle O}{\underset{\displaystyle Z}{C}} \qquad (Z = -Cl, \quad -OR', \quad -NH_2)$$

(a) Conversion into acid chlorides

$$R-\overset{\displaystyle O}{\underset{\displaystyle OH}{C}} + \left\{ \begin{array}{l} SOCl_2 \\ PCl_3 \\ PCl_5 \end{array} \right\} \longrightarrow R-\overset{\displaystyle O}{\underset{\displaystyle Cl}{C}}$$

Acid   Acid chloride

Examples:

$$\langle\!\bigcirc\!\rangle COOH + PCl_5 \xrightarrow{100°} \langle\!\bigcirc\!\rangle COCl + POCl_3 + HCl$$

Benzoic acid   Benzoyl chloride

$$n\text{-}C_{17}H_{35}COOH + SOCl_2 \xrightarrow{\text{reflux}} n\text{-}C_{17}H_{35}COCl + SO_2 + HCl$$

Stearic acid   Thionyl   Stearoyl chloride
chloride

$$3CH_3COOH + PCl_3 \xrightarrow{50°} 3CH_3COCl + H_3PO_3$$

Acetic acid   Acetyl chloride

(b) Conversion into esters

$$R-\overset{\displaystyle O}{\underset{\displaystyle OH}{C}} + R'OH \underset{}{\overset{H^+}{\rightleftharpoons}} R-\overset{\displaystyle O}{\underset{\displaystyle OR'}{C}} + H_2O$$

An ester

Reactivity of R'OH: 1° > 2° > 3°

Examples:

$$\langle\!\bigcirc\!\rangle COOH + CH_3OH \underset{}{\overset{H^+}{\rightleftharpoons}} \langle\!\bigcirc\!\rangle COOCH_3 + H_2O$$

Benzoic acid   Methanol   Methyl benzoate

$$CH_3COOH + \langle\!\bigcirc\!\rangle CH_2OH \underset{}{\overset{H^+}{\rightleftharpoons}} CH_3COOCH_2\langle\!\bigcirc\!\rangle + H_2O$$

Acetic acid   Benzyl alcohol   Benzyl acetate

$$\underset{\substack{\text{Isobutyric}\\\text{acid}}}{CH_3\overset{\displaystyle CH_3}{\overset{\displaystyle |}{C}}HCOOH} + \underset{\substack{\text{Isopropyl}\\\text{alcohol}}}{CH_3\overset{\displaystyle CH_3}{\overset{\displaystyle |}{C}}HOH} \underset{}{\overset{H^+}{\rightleftharpoons}} \underset{\text{Isopropyl isobutyrate}}{CH_3\overset{\displaystyle CH_3}{\overset{\displaystyle |}{C}}HCOO\overset{\displaystyle CH_3}{\overset{\displaystyle |}{C}}HCH_3} + H_2O$$

(c) Conversion into amides

$$RCOOH \xrightarrow{NH_3} \underset{\text{An ammonium salt}}{RCOO^-NH_4^+} \xrightarrow[\text{heat}]{-H_2O} \underset{\text{An amide}}{RCONH_2}$$

Example:

$$CH_3COOH \xrightarrow{NH_3} CH_3COO^-NH_4^+ \xrightarrow{heat, -H_2O} CH_3CONH_2$$

Acetic acid   Ammonium acetate   Acetamide

3. Reduction

$$RCOOH \xrightarrow{LiAlH_4} RCH_2OH \qquad \textit{Also reduced via esters, Sec. 17.22}$$
$$1° \text{ alcohol}$$

Examples:

$$4(CH_3)_3CCOOH + 3LiAlH_4 \xrightarrow{ether} [(CH_3)_3CCH_2O]_4AlLi \xrightarrow{H^+} (CH_3)_3CCH_2OH$$

Trimethylacetic
acid
$$+ 2LiAlO_2 + 4H_2$$
Neopentyl alcohol
(2,2-Dimethyl-
1-propanol

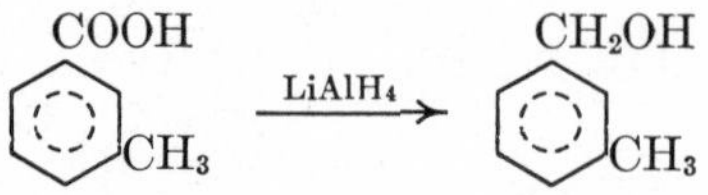

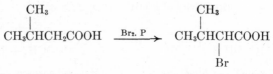

     m-Toluic acid   *m*-Methylbenzyl alcohol

4. Substitution in alkyl or aryl group

(a) Alpha–halogenation of aliphatic acids. Hell-Volhard-Zelinsky reaction

$$RCH_2COOH + X_2 \xrightarrow{P} \underset{\underset{X}{|}}{RCHCOOH} + HX \qquad X_2 = Cl_2, Br_2$$

An α-haloacid

Examples:

$$CH_3COOH \xrightarrow{Cl_2, P} ClCH_2COOH \xrightarrow{Cl_2, P} Cl_2CHCOOH \xrightarrow{Cl_2, P} Cl_3CCOOH$$

Acetic
acid   Chloroacetic
acid   Dichloroacetic
acid   Trichloroacetic
acid

$$\underset{}{\overset{CH_3}{\underset{|}{CH_3CHCH_2COOH}}} \xrightarrow{Br_2, P} \underset{\underset{Br}{|}}{\overset{CH_3}{\underset{|}{CH_3CHCHCOOH}}}$$

     Isovaleric acid   α-Bromoisovaleric acid

(b) Ring substitution in aromatic acids

—COOH: deactivates, and directs *meta* in electrophilic substitution.

Example:

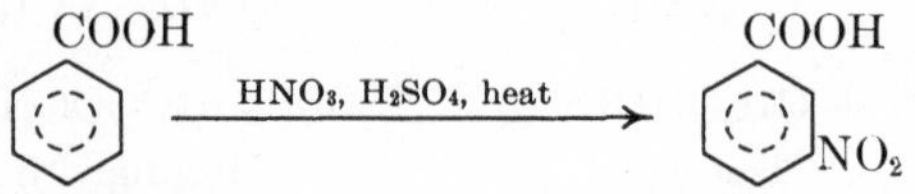

$$\text{COOH} \xrightarrow{HNO_3, H_2SO_4, heat} \text{COOH-NO}_2$$

     Benzoic acid   *m*-Nitrobenzoic acid

5. Decarboxylation

Useful for aromatic acids, and substituted malonic and acetoacetic acids (Secs. 25.9 and 26.4)

Examples:

$$C_6H_5COONa + NaOH(CaO) \xrightarrow{\text{heat}} C_6H_6 + Na_2CO_3$$

| Sodium benzoate | Soda lime | Benzene |

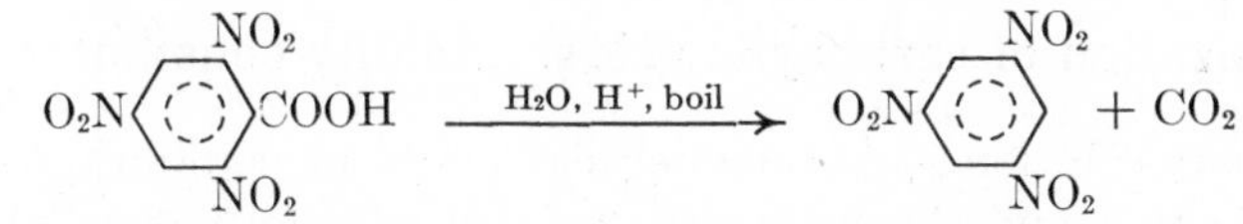

2,4,6-Trinitrobenzoic acid $\xrightarrow{\text{H}_2\text{O, H}^+\text{, boil}}$ 1,3,5-Trinitrobenzene $+ CO_2$

The most characteristic property of the carboxylic acids is the one that gives them their name: **acidity.** Their tendency to give up a hydrogen ion is such that in aqueous solution a measurable equilibrium exists between acid and ions; they are thus much more acidic than any other class of compounds we have studied so far.

$$RCOOH + H_2O \rightleftharpoons RCOO^- + H_3O^+$$

The OH of an acid can be replaced by a number of groups — Cl, OR', NH$_2$ — to yield compounds known as *acid chlorides, esters,* and *amides.* These compounds are called **functional derivatives** of acids; they all contain the **acyl group:**

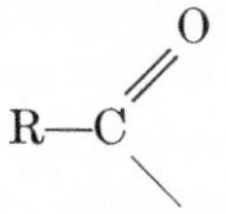

The functional derivatives are all readily reconverted into the acid by simple hydrolysis, and are often converted one into the other.

One of the few reducing agents capable of reducing an acid directly to an alcohol is *lithium aluminum hydride,* LiAlH$_4$.

The hydrocarbon portion of an aliphatic acid can undergo the free radical halogenation characteristic of alkanes, but because of the random nature of the substitution it is seldom used. The presence of a small amount of phosphorus, however, causes halogenation (by an ionic mechanism) to take place *exclusively at the alpha position.* This reaction is known as the **Hell-Volhard-Zelinsky reaction,** and it is of great value in synthesis.

An aromatic ring bearing a carboxyl group undergoes the aromatic electrophilic substitution reactions expected of a ring carrying a deactivating, *meta*-directing group. Deactivation is so strong that the Friedel-Crafts reaction does not take place. We have already accounted for this effect of the —COOH group on the basis of its strong electron-withdrawing tendencies (Sec. 10.8).

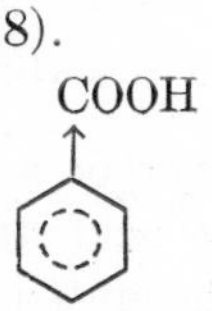

—COOH *withdraws electrons: deactivates, directs meta in electrophilic substitution*

Decarboxylation — elimination of the —COOH group as CO$_2$ — is of limited importance for aromatic acids, and highly important for certain substituted aliphatic acids: malonic acids (Sec. 25.9) and β-keto acids (Sec. 26.4). It is worthless for most simple aliphatic acids, yielding a complicated mixture of hydrocarbons.

16.10 Ionization of carboxylic acids. Acidity constant

In aqueous solution a carboxylic acid exists in equilibrium with the carboxylate anion and the hydrogen ion (actually, of course, the hydronium ion, H_3O^+).

$$RCOOH + H_2O \rightleftharpoons RCOO^- + H_3O^+$$

As for any equilibrium, the concentrations of the components are related by the expression

$$K_a = \frac{[RCOO^-][H_3O^+]}{[RCOOH]}$$

(Since the concentration of water, the solvent, remains essentially constant, this term is usually omitted.) The equilibrium constant is called here the **acidity constant, K_a** (*a* for *acidity*).

Every carboxylic acid has its characteristic K_a, which indicates how strong an acid it is. Since the acidity constant is the ratio of ionized to unionized material, the larger the K_a the greater the extent of the ionization (under a given set of conditions) and the stronger the acid. We use the K_a's, then, to compare in an exact way the strengths of different acids.

We see in Table 16.2 (page 454) that unsubstituted aliphatic and aromatic acids have K_a's of about 10^{-4} to 10^{-5} (0.0001 to 0.00001). This means that they are weakly acidic, with only a slight tendency to release protons.

By the same token, carboxylate anions are moderately basic, with an appreciable tendency to combine with protons. They react with water to increase the concentration of hydroxide ions, a reaction often referred to as *hydrolysis*.

$$RCOO^- + H_2O \rightleftharpoons RCOOH + OH^-$$

As a result aqueous solutions of carboxylate salts are slightly alkaline. (The basicity of an aqueous solution of a carboxylate salt is due chiefly, of course, to the carboxylate anions, not to the comparatively few hydroxide ions they happen to generate.)

We may now expand the series of relative acidities and basicities:

Relative acidities: $RCOOH > HOH > ROH > HC{\equiv}CH > NH_3 \ > RH$

Relative basicities: $RCOO^- < HO^- < RO^- \ < HC{\equiv}C^- < NH_2^- < R^-$

Certain substituted acids are much stronger or weaker than a typical acid like CH_3COOH. We shall see that the acid-strengthening or acid-weakening effect of a substituent can be accounted for in a reasonable way; however, we must first learn a little more about equilibrium in general.

16.11 Equilibrium

So far we have dealt very little with the problem of equilibrium. Under the conditions employed, most of our reactions have been essentially irreversible, that is, they have been one-way reactions. With the exception of 1,4-addition (Sec. 6.17) and Friedel-Crafts alkylation (Sec. 9.14), the products obtained, and their relative yields, have been determined by how fast reactions go and not by how nearly to completion they proceed before equilibrium is reached. Consequently, we have been concerned with the relationship between structure and rate; now we shall turn to the relationship between structure and equilibrium.

Let us consider the reversible reaction between A and B to form C and D.

$$A + B \; \underset{\longleftarrow}{\overset{\longrightarrow}{\rightleftharpoons}} \; C + D$$

The yield of C and D does not depend upon how fast A and B react, but rather upon how completely they have reacted when equilibrium is reached. What factors determine how nearly to completion a reversible reaction proceeds?

Since a system reaches equilibrium when the rates of the opposing reactions become equal, let us apply what we know about rates to the problem of equilibrium. The rate of each reaction depends upon the concentrations of the reactants involved in that reaction; it can be expressed as a product of these concentrations multiplied by the rate constant, k. Thus we have

$$\overset{\longrightarrow}{\text{rate}} \; = \; \overset{\longrightarrow}{k} \; [A][B] \quad \text{and} \quad \overset{\longleftarrow}{\text{rate}} \; = \; \overset{\longleftarrow}{k} \; [C][D]$$

At equilibrium these rates are equal, and so

$$\overset{\longrightarrow}{k} \; [A][B] = \; \overset{\longleftarrow}{k} \; [C][D]$$

Rearranging terms gives

$$K_{eq} = \frac{\overset{\longrightarrow}{k}}{\overset{\longleftarrow}{k}} = \frac{[C][D]}{[A][B]}$$

This is the familiar expression that relates equilibrium constant to the concentrations of the various components. The equilibrium constant, K_{eq}, is thus the ratio of the rate constants of the opposing reactions.

The more nearly a reaction has proceeded to completion when it reaches equilibrium, the larger is $[C][D]$ compared with $[A][B]$, and hence the larger the K_{eq}. The value of K_{eq} is therefore a measure of the tendency of the reaction to go to completion. How is the value of K_{eq} affected by the nature of compounds A, B, C, and D? For example, in the ionization of an acid, how will changes in the structure of the acid and its anion affect the size of K_{eq}?

To see what factors determine the size of K_{eq} we need only to see what factors determine the relative sizes of $\overset{\longrightarrow}{k}$ and $\overset{\longleftarrow}{k}$. Of the factors determining the rate of a reaction (Sec. 2.20), collision frequency is determined largely by the concentrations of the substances. The k's are therefore related to the other two factors, the energy factor and the probability factor; the ratio of the opposing k's must be related to the ratio of the opposing energy and probability factors.

Because of the particular mathematical (logarithmic) relationships involved, it turns out that the ratio of the energy factors is related to the difference between the E_{act}'s of the opposing reactions. From our familiar energy diagram (Figure 16.1) we see that the difference between the E_{act}'s of the opposing reactions is simply the ΔH of the reaction. One quantity, then, that determines the value of K_{eq} is ΔH.

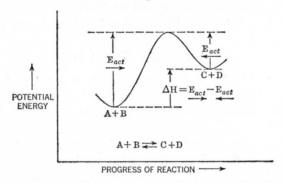

FIGURE 16.1 Potential energy curve for a reversible reaction.

The value of K_{eq} is not determined solely by ΔH, however, since the probability factors of the two opposing reactions usually differ and hence affect the relative rates. In discussing equilibrium we generally do not use the term *probability factor*, but instead we use the related term **entropy change**, ΔS. The standard entropy change, $\Delta S°$, is the quantity that, with ΔH, determines the value of K_{eq}.

Together ΔH (precisely, $\Delta H°$, which is only slightly different) and $\Delta S°$ make up a quantity known as standard **free energy change**, $\Delta F°$.

$$\Delta F° = \Delta H - T\Delta S°$$

It is the $\Delta F°$ that is directly related to K_{eq}, by the expression

$$\Delta F° = -2.303RT \log K_{eq}$$

Under the same experimental conditions, two reactions can proceed at different rates because of a difference in E_{act} or a difference in probability factor. In attempting to understand the effect of structure on rate of reaction, we have found that we can often estimate differences in E_{act}, but not differences in the probability factor; consequently we have been forced to make predictions about relative rates on the basis of E_{act}'s alone. These predictions have generally been good ones, indicating that for closely related reactions the probability factors are not very different, and differences in rate are due chiefly to differences in E_{act}'s.

Under the same experimental conditions, two reversible reactions can have K_{eq}'s of different size because of a difference in ΔH or a difference in $\Delta S°$. In attempting to understand the effect of structure on the position of equilibrium, we shall find that we can often estimate differences in ΔH, but not differences in $\Delta S°$; consequently, we shall be forced to make predictions about relative sizes of K_{eq}'s on the basis of ΔH alone. We shall find that these predictions are generally good ones. *For reactions as similar as ionization of closely related acids the values of $\Delta S°$ are not very different; differences in K_{eq} are due chiefly to differences in ΔH.* (We must keep in mind, however, that our predictions are based on the assumption that differences in $\Delta S°$ are small; this assumption is *not always* justified.)

In dealing with rates, we estimate E_{act} by comparing the stability of the reactants with the stability of the transition state. In dealing with equilibria, we shall estimate ΔH by comparing the stability of the reactants with the stability of the products. For closely related reactions, we are justified in assuming that the more stable the products relative to the reactants, the farther reaction proceeds toward completion.

16.12 Acidity of carboxylic acids

Let us see how the acidity of carboxylic acids is related to structure. In doing this we shall assume that K_a is determined chiefly by ΔH; that is to say, we shall assume that acidity is determined chiefly by the difference in stability between the acid and its anion.

First, and most important, there is the fact that carboxylic acids are acids at all. How can we account for the fact that the —OH of a carboxylic acid tends to release a hydrogen ion so much more readily than the —OH of, say, an alcohol? Let us examine the structures of the reactants and products in these two cases.

We see that the alcohol and alkoxide ion are each represented satisfactorily by a single structure. However, we can draw two reasonable structures (I and II) for the carboxylic acid and two reasonable structures (III and IV) for the carboxylate anion.

$$R\text{—}O\text{—}H \rightleftharpoons H^+ + R\text{—}O^-$$

I II	III IV
Non-equivalent:	Equivalent:
resonance less important	*resonance more important*

Both acid and anion are resonance hybrids. But is resonance equally important in the two cases? By the principles of Sec. 8.7 we know that resonance is much more important between the exactly equivalent structures III and IV than between the non-equivalent structures I and II. As a result, although both acid and anion are stabilized by resonance, stabilization is far greater for the anion than for the acid.

Strictly speaking, resonance is less important for the acid because the contributing structures are of *different stability*, whereas the equivalent structures for the ion must necessarily be of *equal stability*. In structure II two atoms of similar electronegativity carry opposite charges; since energy must be supplied to separate opposite charges, II should contain more energy and hence be less stable than I. Consideration of *separation of charge* is one of the rules of thumb (Sec. 8.15) that can be used to estimate relative stability and hence relative importance of a contributing structure.

Resonance lowers the energy content of the anion more than it lowers the energy content of the acid; this makes ΔH smaller, and K_a larger (see Figure 16.2). The acidity of a carboxylic acid is thus due to the powerful resonance stabilization of its anion. *This stabilization and the resulting acidity are possible only because of the presence of the carbonyl group.*

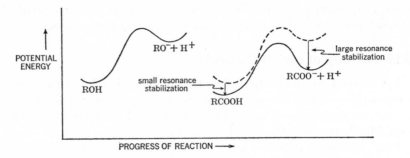

FIGURE 16.2. Molecular structure and position of equilibrium. Carboxylic acid yields resonance-stabilized anion; is stronger acid than alcohol.

16.13 Structure of carboxylate ions

According to the resonance theory, then, a carboxylate ion is a hybrid of two structures which, being of equal stability, contribute equally. Carbon is joined to each oxygen by a "one-and-one-half" bond. The negative charge is evenly distributed over both oxygen atoms.

That the anion is indeed a resonance hybrid is supported by the evidence of bond length. Formic acid, for example, contains a carbon–oxygen double bond and a carbon–oxygen single bond; we would expect these bonds to have different lengths. Sodium formate, on the other hand, if it is a resonance hybrid, ought to contain two equivalent carbon–oxygen bonds; we would expect these to have the same length, intermediate between double and single bonds. X-ray and electron diffraction show that these expectations are correct. Formic acid contains one carbon–oxygen bond of 1.36 A (single bond) and another of 1.23 A (double bond);

sodium formate contains two equal carbon–oxygen bonds, each 1.27 A long.

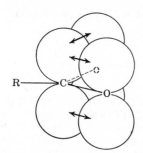

Formic acid   Sodium formate

Problem 16.3 How do you account for the fact that the three carbon–oxygen bonds in $CaCO_3$ have the same length, and that this length (1.31 A) is greater than that found in sodium formate?

What does this resonance mean in terms of orbitals? Carboxyl carbon is joined to the three other atoms by σ bonds (Figure 16.3); since these bonds utilize sp^2 orbitals (Sec. 4.2), they lie in a plane, and are 120° apart. The remaining p orbital of the carbon overlaps equally well p orbitals from *both* of the oxygens, to form hybrid bonds (compare benzene, Sec.

FIGURE 16.3. Carboxylate ion. Overlap of p orbitals in both directions: delocalization of π electrons, and dispersal of charge.

8.12). In this way the electrons are bound not just to one or two nuclei but to *three* nuclei (one carbon and two oxygens); they are therefore held more tightly, the bonds are stronger, and the anion is more stable. This participation of electrons in more than one bond, this smearing-out or delocalization of the electron cloud, is what is meant by representing the anion as a resonance hybrid of two structures.

Problem 16.4 How do you account for the fact that cyclopentadiene, indene, and fluorene are, for hydrocarbons, appreciably acidic? (They are stronger acids than acetylene, for example.)

Cyclopentadiene   Indene   Fluorene

Problem 16.5 How do you account for the fact that the α-hydrogens of an aldehyde (say, n-butyraldehyde) are much more acidic than any other hydrogens in the molecule? (Check your answer in Sec. 23.15.)

$$\overset{\gamma\quad\ \beta\quad\ \alpha\quad\ H}{CH_3CH_2CH_2C\!\!=\!\!O}$$

n-Butyraldehyde

16.14 Effect of substituents on acidity

Next, let us see how changes in the structure of the group bearing the —COOH affect the acidity. Any factor that stabilizes the anion more than it stabilizes the acid should increase the acidity; any factor that makes the anion less stable should decrease acidity. From what we have learned about carbonium ions and carbanions, we can know what to expect. Electron-withdrawing substituents should disperse the negative charge, stabilize the anion, and thus increase acidity. Electron-releasing substituents should intensify the negative charge, destabilize the anion, and thus decrease acidity.

Acid Strength

G withdraws electrons: *stabilizes anion, strengthens acid.*

G releases electrons: *destabilizes anion, weakens acid.*

The K_a's listed in Table 16.2 are in agreement with this prediction.

TABLE 16.2

ACIDITY CONSTANTS OF CARBOXYLIC ACIDS

	K_a			K_a	
HCOOH	18.1	$\times 10^{-5}$	$CH_3CHClCH_2COOH$	8.9	$\times 10^{-5}$
CH_3COOH	1.76	"	$ClCH_2CH_2CH_2COOH$	2.96	"
$ClCH_2COOH$	155	"	FCH_2COOH	219	"
$Cl_2CHCOOH$	5140	"	$BrCH_2COOH$	138	"
Cl_3CCOOH	90000	"	ICH_2COOH	71	"
$CH_3CH_2CH_2COOH$	1.50	"	$C_6H_5CH_2COOH$	4.9	"
$CH_3CH_2CHClCOOH$	139	"	$p\text{-}O_2NC_6H_4CH_2COOH$	14.1	"

K_a of benzoic acid $= 6.3 \times 10^{-5}$

	K_a			K_a			K_a	
$p\text{-}NO_2$	40	$\times 10^{-5}$	$m\text{-}NO_2$	34.5	$\times 10^{-5}$	$o\text{-}NO_2$	656	$\times 10^{-5}$
$p\text{-}Cl$	9.3	"	$m\text{-}Cl$	15.5	"	$o\text{-}Cl$	132	"
$p\text{-}CH_3$	4.2	"	$m\text{-}CH_3$	5.4	"	$o\text{-}CH_3$	12.3	"
$p\text{-}OCH_3$	3.3	"	$m\text{-}OCH_3$	8.2	"	$o\text{-}OCH_3$	8.2	"
$p\text{-}OH$	2.9	"	$m\text{-}OH$	8.3	"	$o\text{-}OH$	105	"
$p\text{-}NH_2$	1.2	"	$m\text{-}NH_2$	1.6	"	$o\text{-}NH_2$	1.0	"

Looking first at the aliphatic acids, we see that the electron-releasing alkyl groups weaken acids: acetic acid, containing —CH₃, is about one-tenth as strong as formic acid, and butyric acid, containing a larger alkyl group, is still weaker. The electron-withdrawing halogens, on the other hand, strengthen acids: chloroacetic acid is 100 times as strong as acetic acid, dichloroacetic acid is still stronger, and trichloroacetic acid is more than 50,000 times as strong as the unsubstituted acid. The other halogens exert similar effects.

Problem 16.6 What do the K_a's of the monohaloacetic acids tell us about the relative strengths of the inductive effects of the different halogens?

α-Chlorobutyric acid is about as strong as chloroacetic acid. As the chlorine is moved away from the —COOH, however, its effect rapidly dwindles: β-chlorobutyric acid is only six times as strong as butyric acid, and γ-chlorobutyric acid is only twice as strong. It is typical of inductive effects that they decrease rapidly with distance, and are seldom important when acting through more than four atoms.

$$Cl \leftarrow CH_2 \leftarrow CH_2 \leftarrow CH_2 \leftarrow C \underset{O}{\overset{O}{\lessgtr}} \Big\} \ominus \qquad \text{Inductive effect: } decreases\ with\ distance$$

The aromatic acids are similarly affected by substituents: —CH₃, —OH, and —NH₂ make benzoic acid weaker, and —Cl and —NO₂ make benzoic acid stronger. We recognize the acid-weakening groups as the ones that activate the ring toward electrophilic substitution (and deactivate toward nucleophilic substitution). The acid-strengthening groups are the ones that deactivate toward electrophilic substitution (and activate toward nucleophilic substitution). Furthermore, the groups that have the largest effects on reactivity — whether activating or deactivating — have the largest effects on acidity.

ortho-Substituted aromatic acids do not fit into the pattern set by their *meta* and *para* isomers, and by aliphatic acids. Nearly all *ortho* substituents exert an effect of the same kind — acid-strengthening — whether they are electron-withdrawing or electron-releasing, and the effect is unusually large. (Compare, for example, the effects of *o*-NO₂ and *o*-CH₃; of *o*-NO₂ and *m*- or *p*-NO₂.) This ortho effect is not understood; it undoubtedly has to do with the *nearness* of the groups involved, but is more than just steric hindrance arising from their bulk.

Thus we see that the same concepts — inductive effect and resonance — that we found so useful in dealing with rates of reaction are also useful in dealing with equilibria. By using these concepts to estimate the stabilities of anions, we are able to predict the relative strengths of acids; in this way we can account not only for the effect of substituents on the acid strength of carboxylic acids but also for the very fact that the compounds are acids.

16.15 Conversion into acid chlorides

A carboxylic acid is perhaps more often converted into the acid chloride than into any other of its functional derivatives. From the highly reactive acid chloride there can then be obtained many other kinds of compounds, including esters and amides (Sec. 17.7).

An acid chloride is prepared by substitution of —Cl for the —OH of a carboxylic acid. Three reagents are commonly used for this purpose: *thionyl chloride*, SOCl₂; *phosphorus trichloride*, PCl₃; and *phosphorus pentachloride,* PCl_5. (Of what inorganic acids might we consider these reagents to be the acid chlorides?) For example:

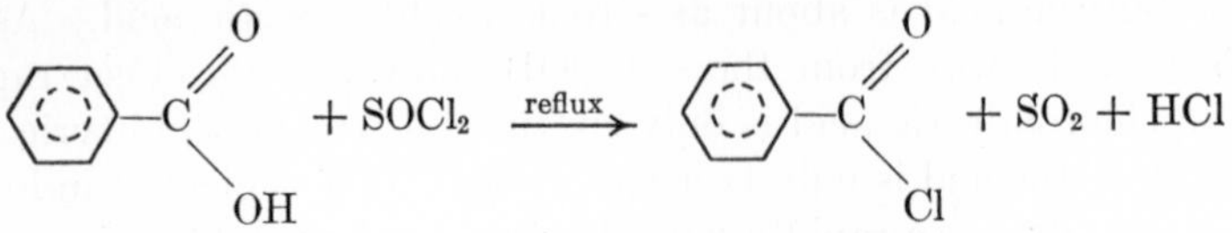

Benzoic acid Benzoyl chloride

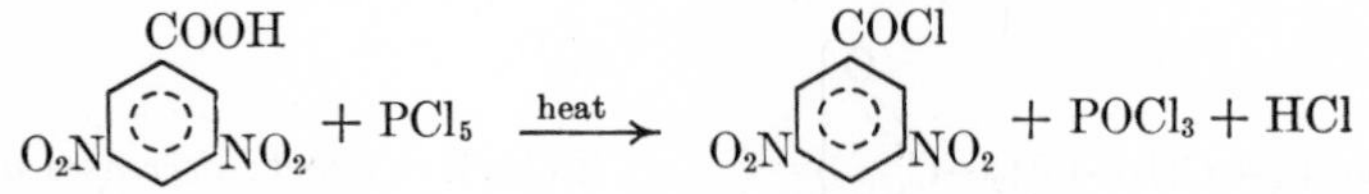

3,5-Dinitrobenzoic 3,5-Dinitrobenzoyl
acid chloride

Thionyl chloride is particularly convenient, since the products formed besides the acid chloride are gases and thus easily separated from the acid chloride; any excess of the low-boiling thionyl chloride (79°) is easily removed by distillation.

16.16 Conversion into esters

Although acids are frequently converted into their esters via the acid chlorides, direct **esterification** is an important and interesting reaction.

A carboxylic acid is converted into an ester when heated with an alcohol in the presence of a little mineral acid, usually concentrated sulfuric

$$RCOOH + R'OH \xrightleftharpoons{H^+} RCOOR' + H_2O$$
Acid Alcohol Ester

acid or dry hydrogen chloride. This reaction is reversible, and generally reaches equilibrium when there are appreciable quantities of both reactants and products. For example, when we allow one mole of acetic acid and one mole of ethyl alcohol to react in the presence of a little sulfuric acid until equilibrium is reached (after several hours), we obtain a mixture of about two-thirds mole each of ester and water, and one-third mole each of acid and alcohol. We obtain this same equilibrium mixture, of course, if we start with one mole of ester and one mole of water, again in the presence of sulfuric acid. *The same catalyst, hydrogen ion, that catalyzes the forward reaction, esterification, necessarily catalyzes the reverse reaction, hydrolysis.*

This reversibility is a disadvantage in the preparation of an ester directly from an acid; the preference for the acid chloride route is due to the fact that both steps — preparation of acid chloride from acid, and preparation of ester from acid chloride — are essentially irreversible and go to completion.

Direct esterification, however, has the advantage of being a single-step synthesis; it can often be made useful by application of our knowledge of equilibria. If either the acid or the alcohol is cheap and readily available, it can be used in large excess to shift the equilibrium toward the products and thus to increase the yield of ester. For example, it is worth while to use eight moles of cheap ethyl alcohol to convert one mole of valuable γ-phenylbutyric acid more completely into the ester:

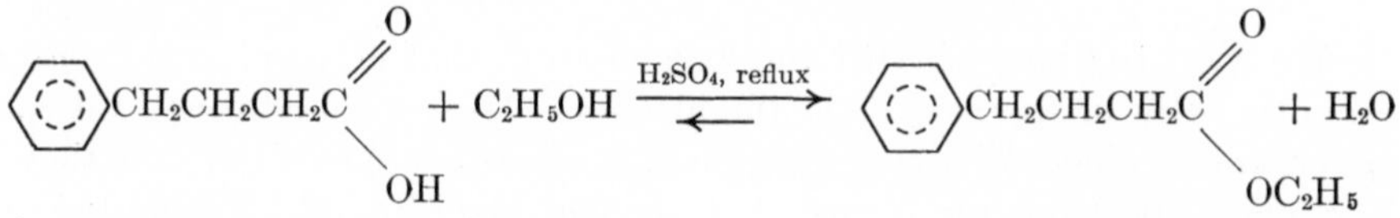

γ-Phenylbutyric acid   Ethyl alcohol   Ethyl γ-phenylbutyrate
        1 mole   *8 moles*   *85–88% yield*

Sometimes the equilibrium is shifted by removing one of the products. An elegant way of doing this is illustrated by the preparation of ethyl adipate. The dicarboxylic acid adipic acid, an excess of ethyl alcohol, and toluene are heated with a little sulfuric acid under a distillation column. The lowest boiling component (b.p. 75°) of the reaction mixture is an azeotrope of water, ethyl alcohol, and toluene (compare Sec. 11.9); consequently, as fast as water is formed it is removed as the azeotrope by distillation. In this way a 95–97% yield of ester is obtained:

$$\text{HOOC(CH}_2)_4\text{COOH} + 2\text{C}_2\text{H}_5\text{OH} \xrightarrow[\text{H}_2\text{SO}_4]{\text{toluene (b.p. 111°),}} \text{C}_2\text{H}_5\text{OOC(CH}_2)_4\text{COOC}_2\text{H}_5$$

Adipic acid   Ethyl alcohol   Ethyl adipate
non-volatile   *b.p. 78°*   *b.p. 245°*

$$+ 2\text{H}_2\text{O}$$

Removed as
azeotrope, b.p. 75°

16.17 Position of cleavage in esterification. Use of isotopic tracers

We have described (Sec. 16.9) conversion of a carboxylic acid into its functional derivatives as reactions in which the —OH of the acid is replaced by —Cl, —OR', or —NH$_2$. Formation of acid chlorides and amides clearly must involve cleavage of the C—OH bond of the acid:

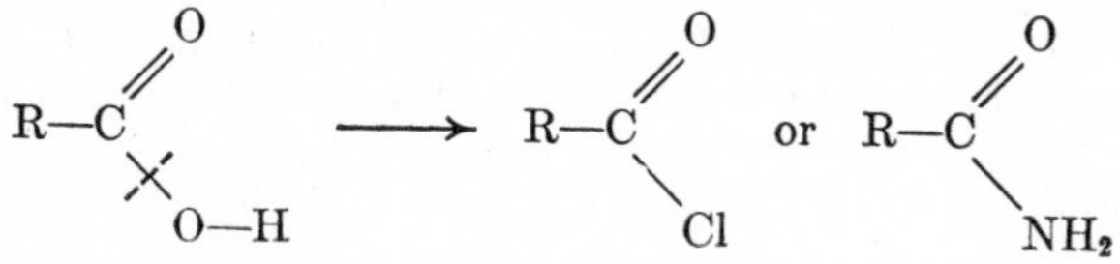

But how do we know that esterification does not involve, instead, cleavage of the O—H bond of the acid? That is, how can we distinguish between these two possible modes of reaction?

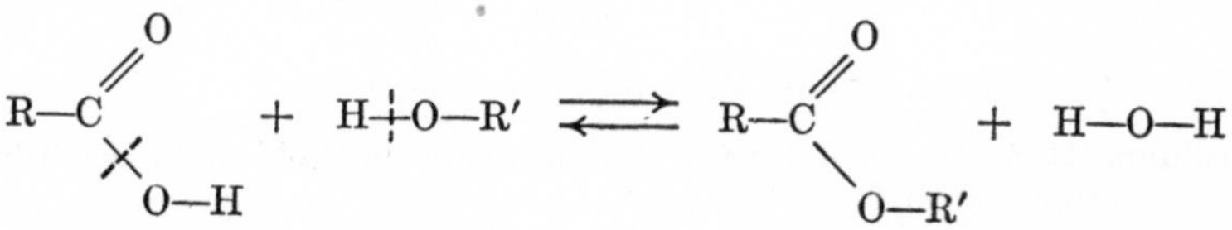

$$\underset{\substack{\text{O} \\ \text{||} \\ \text{R—C} \\ \diagdown \\ \text{O} + \text{H}}}{} \;+\; \text{H—O} + \text{R}' \;\rightleftarrows\; \underset{\substack{\text{O} \\ \text{||} \\ \text{R—C} \\ \diagdown \\ \text{O—R}'}}{} \;+\; \text{H—O—H}$$

We want to know whether the oxygen atom that is found in the water was originally in the acid or in the alcohol. This, we might say, we can never know, since all oxygen atoms are exactly alike — but are they? The mass spectrometer shows that oxygen is ordinarily distributed in nature as a mixture of isotopes: 99.76% O^{16}, 0.04% O^{17}, and 0.20% O^{18}. Modern methods of separating isotopes have made available oxygen compounds containing a high proportion of O^{18}.

Methanol enriched in O^{18} was allowed to react with benzoic acid containing the ordinary distribution of oxygen isotopes, and the water and the methyl benzoate obtained were analyzed by means of the mass spectrometer. The ester was found to be enriched in O^{18}, whereas the water contained only ordinary oxygen. These results show beyond question that the esterification involves cleavage of the C—OH bond of the acid and of the O—H bond of the alcohol.

$$\underset{\text{Methanol}}{\underset{\textit{Enriched in } O^{18}}{\text{H} + \text{O}^{18}\text{CH}_3}} \;\;\xrightarrow{\;\text{H}^+\;}\;\; \underset{\text{Methyl benzoate}}{\underset{\textit{Enriched in } O^{18}}{}} \;+\; \text{H—O—H}$$

Similar studies of the reverse reaction, hydrolysis of esters, have given similar results (Sec. 17.17), showing that this kind of bond cleavage is the usual one for both esterification and hydrolysis.

The solving of this problem illustrates the neat, elegant way in which isotopic tracers can help us to find out what happens during a chemical reaction. We can label a particular atom of a molecule and follow its path through the course of a reaction; in this way we get information that could be gotten in no other way.

Problem 16.7 (a) Show in detail (including structures of transition states) the steps in the acid-catalyzed hydrolysis of ethylene oxide by an S_N1 mechanism; by an S_N2 mechanism. Do the same for isobutylene oxide. (See Sec. 15.15.)

(b) Acid-catalyzed hydrolysis of isobutylene oxide in H_2O^{18} yields almost exclusively:

$$\begin{array}{c} \text{CH}_3 \\ | \\ \text{CH}_2\text{—C—CH}_3 \\ | \quad\quad | \\ \text{OH} \quad \text{O}^{18}\text{H} \end{array}$$

Which mechanism seems to operate here?

Problem 16.8 How could you test your answer to Problem 15.10 on page 419 by use of isotopic tracers?

16.18 Mechanism of esterification. Function of acid

The tracer studies tell us that in esterification the —OH of the carboxylic acid is replaced by —OR'. But just how does this happen? What is the function of hydrogen ion?

Here, as in the matter of acidity, we must turn to the carbonyl group, C=O. Although it is the —OH group that is replaced in esterification, it is the C=O group that makes the replacement possible. The mobile π electrons of the carbon–oxygen double bond are pulled strongly toward the electronegative oxygen. Carbonyl carbon is therefore deficient in electrons and susceptible to nucleophilic attack by bases; carbonyl oxygen is rich in electrons and susceptible to electrophilic attack by acids.

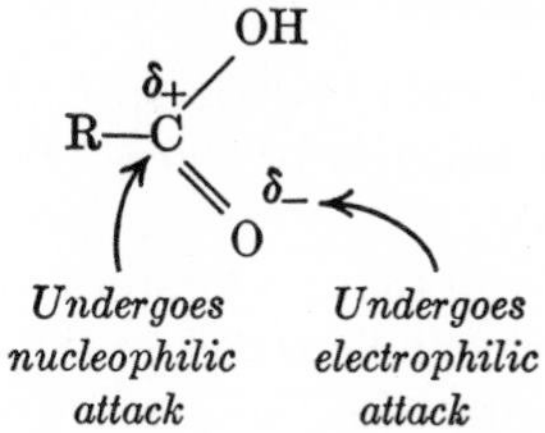

Undergoes   *Undergoes*
nucleophilic   *electrophilic*
attack   *attack*

If acid is present, H^+ becomes attached to carbonyl oxygen, and thus carbonyl carbon becomes even more deficient in electrons and even more susceptible to nucleophilic attack.

Undergoes
nucleophilic attack
more readily

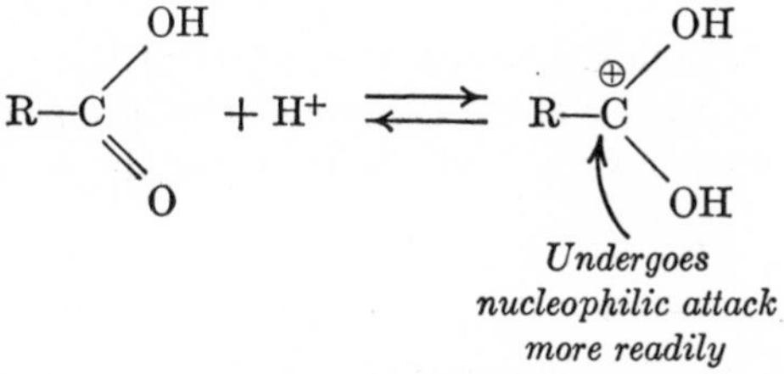

In esterification of acids the nucleophilic reagent is the basic alcohol molecule; in the reverse reaction, hydrolysis of esters, the nucleophilic reagent is the basic water molecule. Mineral acids speed up both processes by protonating carbonyl oxygen. The commonly accepted mechanism for both esterification and hydrolysis, then, is contained in the following equilibria:

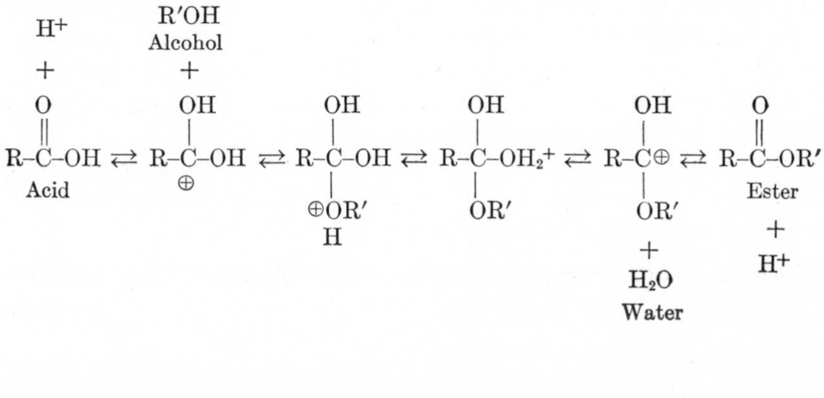

These equilibria amount to nucleophilic substitution of —OR′ for —OH in esterification, and —OH for —OR′ in hydrolysis. Unlike S_N2 reactions, these substitutions involve intermediates that are actual compounds. Here, when carbon bears both entering and leaving groups it is tetrahedral; in the S_N2 reaction it is extremely unstable pentavalent carbon. (This point is discussed further in Sec. 17.4.)

Both esterification and hydrolysis are quite sensitive to steric hindrance. The presence of bulky groups near the site of reaction, whether in the alcohol or in the acid, makes the tetrahedral intermediate less stable and more difficult to form.

Reactivity in esterification

$$CH_3OH > 1° > 2° (> 3°)$$

$$HCOOH > CH_3COOH > RCH_2COOH > R_2CHCOOH > R_3CCOOH$$

These steric effects are so marked that special methods are required to prepare esters of tertiary alcohols or esters of acids like 2,4,6-trimethylbenzoic acid (mesitoic acid).

In summary, we have seen that both esterification of acids and hydrolysis of esters proceed by nucleophilic attack at the electron-deficient carbonyl carbon. Hydrogen ion catalyzes these reactions by attaching itself to carbonyl oxygen and thus making carbon even more electron deficient and even more susceptible to the nucleophilic attack.

16.19 Formation of amides

Amides are compounds in which the —OH of the carboxylic acid has been replaced by —NH₂. These are sometimes prepared by heating the ammonium salts of carboxylic acids, water being driven off by distillation.

$$RCOOH + NH_3 \longrightarrow \underset{\text{An ammonium salt}}{RCOO^- NH_4^+} \xrightarrow{\text{heat}} \underset{\text{An amide}}{R-C\overset{\displaystyle O}{\underset{\displaystyle NH_2}{\Big\backslash}}} + H_2O$$

In the laboratory amides are more likely to be prepared by reaction of ammonia with acid chlorides (Sec. 17.12).

16.20 Reduction of acids to alcohols

Conversion of alcohols into acids (Sec. 16.6) is important because, in general, alcohols are more available than acids. This is not always true, however; long straight-chain acids from fats are more available than are the corresponding alcohols, and here the reverse process becomes important: reduction of acids to alcohols.

Lithium aluminum hydride, LiAlH₄, is one of the few reagents that can reduce an acid to an alcohol; the initial product is an alkoxide from which the alcohol is liberated by hydrolysis:

$$4RCOOH + 3LiAlH_4 \longrightarrow 4H_2 + 2LiAlO_2 + (RCH_2O)_4AlLi \xrightarrow{H_2O} \underset{\text{1° alcohol}}{4RCH_2OH}$$

Because of the excellent yields it gives, LiAlH₄ is widely used in the laboratory for the reduction of not only acids but many other classes of compounds. Since it is somewhat expensive, it can be used in industry only for the reduction of small amounts of valuable raw materials, as in the synthesis of certain drugs and hormones.

As an alternative to direct reduction, acids are often converted into alcohols by a two-step process: esterification, and reduction of the ester. Esters can be reduced in a number of ways (Sec. 17.22) that are adaptable to both laboratory and industry.

We have seen (Sec. 16.5) that in the carboxylic acids obtained from fats we have available long straight-chain units for use in organic synthesis. Reduction to alcohols of these acids (either directly or as esters) is a fundamental step in the utilization of these raw materials, since from the alcohols, as we know, a host of other compounds can be prepared (Sec. 12.10). Although only acids of even carbon number are available, it is possible, of course, to increase the chain length and thus prepare compounds of odd carbon number.

Problem 16.9 Outline the synthesis from lauric acid (n-$C_{11}H_{23}COOH$, dodecanoic acid) of the following compounds: (a) 1-bromododecane, (b) tridecanoic acid (C_{13} acid), (c) 1-tetradecanol, (d) 1-dodecene, (e) dodecane, (f) 1-dodecyne, (g) methyl n-decyl ketone, (h) 2-dodecanol, (i) undecanoic acid, (j) 2-tetradecanol, (k) 2-methyl-2-tetradecanol.

16.21 Halogenation of aliphatic acids. Hell-Volhard-Zelinsky reaction

In the presence of a small amount of phosphorus, aliphatic carboxylic acids react smoothly with chlorine or bromine to yield a compound in which α-hydrogen has been replaced by halogen. This is the **Hell-Volhard-Zelinsky reaction.** Because of its specificity — *only alpha halogenation* — and the readiness with which it takes place, it is of considerable importance in synthesis.

$$CH_3COOH \xrightarrow{Cl_2,\ P} ClCH_2COOH \xrightarrow{Cl_2,\ P} Cl_2CHCOOH \xrightarrow{Cl_2,\ P} Cl_3CCOOH$$

$$CH_3CH_2COOH \xrightarrow{Br_2,\ P} CH_3CHBrCOOH \xrightarrow{Br_2,\ P} CH_3CBr_2COOH$$
$$\downarrow Br_2,\ P$$
$$\text{no further substitution}$$

The halogen of these halogenated acids undergoes *nucleophilic displacement* and *elimination* much as it does in the simpler alkyl halides (Secs. 13.6 and 4.13). Halogenation is therefore the first step in the conversion of a carboxylic acid into many important substituted carboxylic acids:

$$\underset{\substack{| \\ Br}}{RCHCOOH} + \text{large excess of } NH_3 \longrightarrow \underset{\substack{| \\ NH_2}}{RCHCOOH}$$

An α-halogenated acid   An α-amino acid
                                         (See Chapter 33)

$$\underset{\underset{Br}{|}}{RCHCOOH} + NaOH \longrightarrow \underset{\underset{OH}{|}}{RCHCOONa} \xrightarrow{\text{H}^+} \underset{\underset{OH}{|}}{RCHCOOH}$$

An α-hydroxy acid
(See Chapter 27)

$$\underset{\underset{Br}{|}}{RCHCOONa} + NaCN \rightarrow \underset{\underset{CN}{|}}{RCHCOONa} \xrightarrow{\text{H}^+} \underset{\underset{CN}{|}}{RCHCOOH} \xrightarrow{\text{H}_2\text{O}} \underset{\underset{COOH}{|}}{RCHCOOH}$$

An α-cyano   A dicarboxylic acid
acid   (See Chapter 25)

$$\underset{\underset{Br}{|}}{RCH_2CHCOOH} + \text{alc. KOH} \longrightarrow RCH{=}CHCOO^- \xrightarrow{\text{H}^+} RCH{=}CHCOOH$$

An α, β-unsaturated acid
(See Chapter 28)

Problem 16.10 On the basis of the following *known reactions*, what is the function of phosphorus in the Hell-Volhard-Zelinsky reaction?

(a) $P + X_2 \longrightarrow PX_3$

(b) $RCOOH + PX_3 \longrightarrow RCOX$

(c) $RCOX + X_2 \xrightarrow{\text{no P needed}}$ α-halogenation only

(d) $RCOX + R'COOH \rightleftharpoons RCOOH + R'COX$

16.22 Analysis of carboxylic acids. Neutralization equivalent

Carboxylic acids are recognized through their acidity. They dissolve in aqueous sodium hydroxide and in aqueous sodium bicarbonate. The reaction with bicarbonate releases bubbles of carbon dioxide (see Sec. 16.4).

(Phenols, Sec. 22.8, are more acidic than water, but — with certain exceptions — are considerably weaker than carboxylic acids; they dissolve in aqueous sodium hydroxide, but *not* in aqueous sodium bicarbonate. Sulfonic acids, Sec. 18.4, are even more acidic than carboxylic acids, but they contain sulfur, which can be detected by elemental analysis.)

Problem 16.11 Expand the table you made in Problem 15.20, page 430, to include the kinds of compounds and tests we have taken up since then.

Once characterized as a carboxylic acid, an unknown is identified as a particular acid on the usual basis of its physical properties and the physical properties of derivatives. The derivatives commonly used are *amides* (Secs. 17.12 and 20.7) and *esters* (Sec. 17.15).

Particularly useful both in identification of previously studied acids and in proof of structure of new ones is the **neutralization equivalent:** *the equivalent weight of the acid as determined by titration with standard base.* A weighed sample of the acid is dissolved in water or aqueous alcohol, and the volume of standard base needed to neutralize the solution is measured. For example, a 0.224-g sample of an unknown acid (m.p. 139–140°) required 13.6 ml of 0.104 N sodium hydroxide solution for neutralization (to a phenolphthalein end point). Since each 1000 ml of the base contains 0.104 equivalents, and since the number of equivalents of base required equals the number of equivalents of acid present,

$$\frac{13.6}{1000} \times 0.104 \text{ equivalents of acid} = 0.224 \text{ g}$$

and

$$1 \text{ equivalent of acid} = 0.224 \times \frac{1000}{13.6} \times \frac{1}{0.104} = 158 \text{ g}$$

Problem 16.12 Which of the following compounds might the above acid be: (a) *o*-chlorobenzoic acid (m.p. 141°) or (b) 2,6-dichlorobenzoic acid (m.p. 139°)?

Problem 16.13 A 0.187-g sample of an acid (b.p. 203–205°) required 18.7 ml of 0.0972 N NaOH for neutralization. (a) What is the neutralization equivalent? (b) Which of the following acids might it be: *n*-caproic acid (b.p. 205°), methoxy-acetic acid (b.p. 203°), or ethoxyacetic acid (b.p. 206°)?

Problem 16.14 (a) How many equivalents of base would be neutralized by one mole of phthalic acid? What is the neutralization equivalent of phthalic acid? (b) What is the relation between neutralization equivalent and the number of acidic hydrogens per molecule of acid? (c) What is the neutralization equivalent of 1,3,5-benzenetricarboxylic acid? Of mellitic acid, $C_6(COOH)_6$?

A metal salt of a carboxylic acid is recognized through these facts: (a) it leaves a residue when strongly heated (*ignition test*); (b) it decomposes at a fairly high temperature, instead of melting; and (c) it is converted into a carboxylic acid upon treatment with dilute mineral acid.

Problem 16.15 The residue left upon ignition of a sodium salt of a carboxylic acid was white, soluble in water, turned moist litmus blue, and reacted with dilute hydrochloric acid with the formation of bubbles. What was its probable chemical composition?

PROBLEMS

1. Give the common names and IUPAC names for the straight-chain saturated carboxylic acids containing the following numbers of carbon atoms: 1, 2, 3, 4, 5, 6, 8, 10, 12, 16, 18.

2. Give the structural formula and, where possible, a second name (by a different system) for each of the following:

(a) isovaleric acid
(b) trimethylacetic acid
(c) α, β-dimethylcaproic acid
(d) 2-methyl-4-ethyloctanoic acid
(e) phenylacetic acid
(f) γ-phenylbutyric acid
(g) benzoic acid
(h) *p*-toluic acid
(i) phthalic acid
(j) isophthalic acid
(k) terephthalic acid
(l) *p*-hydroxybenzoic acid
(m) potassium α-methylbutyrate
(n) magnesium 2-chloropropanoate
(o) ammonium triethylacetate
(p) sodium *m*-bromobenzoate
(q) isobutyronitrile
(r) 2,4-dinitrobenzonitrile

3. Write equations to show how each of the following compounds could be converted into benzoic acid:

(a) toluene
(b) bromobenzene
(c) benzonitrile
(d) benzyl alcohol
(e) benzotrichloride
(f) acetophenone, $C_6H_5COCH_3$ (*Hint:* see Sec. 12.11.)

4. Write equations to show how each of the following compounds could be converted into *n*-butyric acid:

(a) *n*-butyl alcohol
(b) *n*-propyl alcohol
(c) *n*-propyl alcohol (a second way)
(d) methyl *n*-propyl ketone

Which of the above methods could be used to prepare trimethylacetic acid?

5. Write equations to show the reaction (if any) of benzoic acid with:

(a) KOH
(b) Al
(c) CaO
(d) Na_2CO_3
(e) NH_3(aq)
(f) product of (e) + heat

(g) H_2, Ni, 20°, 1 atm.
(h) $LiAlH_4$
(i) hot $KMnO_4$
(j) PCl_5
(k) PCl_3
(l) $SOCl_2$

(m) Br_2/Fe
(n) $Br_2 + P$
(o) HNO_3/H_2SO_4
(p) fuming sulfuric acid
(q) CH_3Cl, $AlCl_3$
(r) *n*-propyl alcohol, H^+

6. Answer Problem 5 for *n*-valeric acid.

7. Write equations to show how isobutyric acid could be converted into each of the following, using any needed reagents.

(a) ethyl isobutyrate
(b) isobutyryl chloride
(c) isobutyramide

(d) magnesium isobutyrate
(e) isobutyl alcohol

8. Write equations to show all steps in the conversion of benzoic acid into:

(a) sodium benzoate
(b) benzoyl chloride
(c) benzamide
(d) benzene

(e) *n*-propyl benzoate
(f) *p*-tolyl benzoate
(g) *m*-bromophenyl benzoate
(h) benzyl alcohol

9. Write equations to show how phenylacetic acid could be converted into each of the following, using any needed reagents.

(a) sodium phenylacetate
(b) ethyl phenylacetate
(c) phenylacetyl chloride
(d) phenylacetamide
(e) *p*-bromophenylacetic acid
(f) *p*-nitrophenylacetic acid

(g) β-phenylethyl alcohol
(h) α-bromophenylacetic acid P/Br_2
(i) α-aminophenylacetic acid
(j) α-hydroxyphenylacetic acid
(k) phenylmalonic acid, $C_6H_5CH(COOH)_2$

10. Complete the following, giving the structures and names of the principal organic products.

(a) $C_6H_5CH=CHCOOH + KMnO_4 + OH^- +$ heat
(b) $p-CH_3C_6H_4COOH + HNO_3 + H_2SO_4$
(c) $p-CH_3C_6H_4COOH + LiAlH_4$, followed by H^+
(d) $C_6H_5COOH + C_6H_5CH_2OH + H^+$
(e) product (d) $+ HNO_3 + H_2SO_4$
(f) $CH_3COOH + NH_4OH$, followed by heat
(g) cyclo-$C_6H_{11}MgBr + CO_2$, followed by H_2SO_4
(h) product (g) $+ C_2H_5OH + H^+$
(i) product (g) $+ SOCl_2 +$ heat
(j) $m-CH_3C_6H_4OCH_3 + KMnO_4 + OH^-$
(k) mesitylene $+ K_2Cr_2O_7 + H_2SO_4$
(l) isobutyric acid + isobutyl alcohol $+ H^+$
(m) salicylic acid (o-HOC_6H_4COOH) $+ Br_2$, Fe
(n) sodium acetate + *p*-nitrobenzyl bromide (What would you predict?)
(o) linolenic acid + excess H_2, Ni
(p) oleic acid $+ KMnO_4$, heat
(q) linoleic acid $+ O_3$, then H_2O, Zn
(r) benzoic acid ($C_7H_6O_2$) $+ H_2$, Ni, heat, pressure $\longrightarrow$ $C_7H_{12}O_2$
(s) benzoic acid + ethylene glycol $+ H^+$ $\longrightarrow$ $C_{16}H_{14}O_4$
(t) phthalic acid + ethyl alcohol $+ H^+$ $\longrightarrow$ $C_{12}H_{14}O_4$
(u) oleic acid $+ Br_2/CCl_4$
(v) product (u) + KOH (alcoholic)
(w) oleic acid $+ HCO_2OH$

11. (a) Give the structures of compounds A through F.

$$\text{palmitic acid} + \text{LiAlH}_4 \longrightarrow \text{A}$$
$$\text{A} + \text{H}^+ \longrightarrow \text{B}$$
$$\text{B} + \text{PBr}_3 \longrightarrow \text{C}$$
$$\text{C} + \text{Mg, ether} \longrightarrow \text{D}$$
$$\text{D} + \text{CO}_2 \longrightarrow \text{E}$$
$$\text{E} + \text{H}^+ \longrightarrow \text{F}$$

(b) What is another way to get from C to F?

12. Outline a possible laboratory synthesis of the following labeled compounds, using $\text{BaC}^{14}\text{O}_3$ or $\text{C}^{14}\text{H}_3\text{OH}$ as the source of C^{14}.

(a) $\text{CH}_3\text{CH}_2\text{CH}_2\text{C}^{14}\text{OOH}$ (c) $\text{CH}_3\text{C}^{14}\text{H}_2\text{CH}_2\text{COOH}$

(b) $\text{CH}_3\text{CH}_2\text{C}^{14}\text{H}_2\text{COOH}$ (d) $\text{C}^{14}\text{H}_3\text{CH}_2\text{CH}_2\text{COOH}$

13. Outline all steps in a possible laboratory synthesis of each of the following compounds from toluene and any needed aliphatic and inorganic reagents.

(a) benzoic acid   (e) *p*-chlorobenzoic acid
(b) phenylacetic acid   (f) *p*-bromophenylacetic acid
(c) *p*-toluic acid   (g) *α*-chlorophenylacetic acid
(d) *m*-chlorobenzoic acid

14. Outline a possible laboratory synthesis of each of the following compounds from benzene, toluene, and alcohols of four carbons or less, using any needed inorganic reagents.

(a) ethyl *α*-methylbutyrate   (g) *p*-toluamide
(b) 3,5-dinitrobenzoyl chloride   (h) *n*-hexyl benzoate
(c) *α*-amino-*p*-bromophenylacetic acid   (i) 3-bromo-4-methylbenzoic acid
(d) *α*-hydroxypropionic acid   (j) *α*-methylphenylacetic acid
(e) *p*-HO$_3$SC$_6$H$_4$COOH   (k) 2-bromo-4-nitrobenzoic acid
(f) 2-pentenoic acid   (l) 1,2,4-benzenetricarboxylic acid

15. Without referring to tables, arrange the compounds of each set in order of acidity:

(a) butanoic acid, 2-bromobutanoic acid, 3-bromobutanoic acid, 4-bromobutanoic acid
(b) benzoic acid, *p*-chlorobenzoic acid, 2,4-dichlorobenzoic acid, 2,4,6-trichlorobenzoic acid
(c) benzoic acid, *p*-nitrobenzoic acid, *p*-toluic acid
(d) *α*-chlorophenylacetic acid, *p*-chlorophenylacetic acid, phenylacetic acid, *α*-phenylpropionic acid
(e) *p*-nitrobenzoic acid, *p*-nitrophenylacetic acid, *β*-(*p*-nitrophenyl)propionic acid
(f) acetic acid, acetylene, ammonia, ethane, ethanol, sulfuric acid, water

16. Arrange the monosodium salts of the acids in Problem 15(f) in order of basicity.

17. The two water-insoluble solids, benzoic acid and *o*-chlorobenzoic acid, can be separated by treatment with an aqueous solution of sodium formate. What reaction takes place? (*Hint:* look at the K_a's in Table 16.2.)

18. On the basis of Table 16.2, what kind of inductive effect does the phenyl group, C_6H_5—, appear to have?

19. Arrange the compounds of each set in order of reactivity in the indicated reaction:

(a) esterification by benzoic acid: *sec*-butyl alcohol, methanol, *tert*-pentyl alcohol, *n*-propyl alcohol
(b) esterification by ethyl alcohol: benzoic acid, 2,6-dimethylbenzoic acid, *o*-toluic acid
(c) esterification by methanol: acetic acid, formic acid, isobutyric acid, propionic acid, trimethylacetic acid

20. Give structures of compounds G through J:

$$\text{acetylene} + CH_3MgBr \longrightarrow G + CH_4$$
$$G + CO_2 \longrightarrow H \xrightarrow{H^+} I \ (C_3H_2O_2)$$
$$I \xrightarrow{H_2O, \ H_2SO_4, \ HgSO_4} J \ (C_3H_4O_3)$$
$$J + KMnO_4 \longrightarrow CH_2(COOH)_2$$

21. Describe simple chemical tests (other than color change of an indicator) that would serve to distinguish between:

(a) propionic acid and *n*-pentyl alcohol *N+HCO₃ ,CO₂ ↓↑ ⁱ*
(b) isovaleric acid and *n*-octane
(c) ethyl *n*-butyrate and isobutyric acid *Na HCO₃, CO₂ ↓↑²*
(d) propionyl chloride and propionic acid
(e) *p*-aminobenzoic acid and benzamide *Un AcO₃/CO₂ ↓↑ⁱ*
(f) $C_6H_5CH{=}CHCOOH$ and $C_6H_5CH{=}CHCH_3$

Tell exactly what you would do and see.

22. Compare benzoic acid and sodium benzoate with respect to:

(a) volatility *S Higher*   (e) degree of ionization of solid *S*
(b) melting point *S Higher*   (f) degree of ionization in water *S*
(c) solubility in water and (d) in ether   (g) acidity and basicity
   S   *A*   *A*   *s*
Does this comparison hold generally for acids and their salts?

23. Tell how you would separate by chemical means the following mixtures, recovering each component in reasonably pure form:

(a) caproic acid and ethyl caproate   (c) isobutyric acid and 1-hexanol
(b) *n*-butyl ether and *n*-butyric acid   (d) sodium benzoate and triphenylcarbinol

Tell exactly what you would do and see.

24. An unknown compound is believed to be one of the following. Describe how you would go about finding out which of the possibilities the unknown actually is. Where possible, use simple chemical tests; where necessary, use more elaborate chemical methods like quantitative hydrogenation, cleavage, neutralization equivalent, etc. Make use of any needed tables of physical constants.

(a) acrylic acid ($CH_2{=}CHCOOH$, b.p. 142°) and propionic acid (b.p. 141°)
(b) mandelic acid ($C_6H_5CHOHCOOH$, m.p. 120°) and benzoic acid (m.p. 122°)
(c) *o*-chlorobenzoic acid (m.p. 141°), mesotartaric acid (m.p. 140°), *m*-nitrobenzoic acid (m.p. 141°), and suberic acid ($HOOC(CH_2)_6COOH$, m.p. 144°)
(d) chloroacetic acid (b.p. 189°), α-chloropropionic acid (b.p. 186°), dichloroacetic acid (b.p. 194°), and *n*-valeric acid (b.p. 187°)
(e) 3-nitrophthalic acid (m.p. 220°) and 2,4,6-trinitrobenzoic acid (m.p. 220°)
(f) *p*-chlorobenzoic acid (m.p. 242°), *p*-nitrobenzoic acid (m.p. 242°), *o*-nitro-cinnamic acid (o-$O_2NC_6H_4CH{=}CHCOOH$, m.p. 240°)
(g) The following compounds, all of which boil within a few degrees of each other:

o-chloroanisole	isodurene
β-chlorostyrene	linalool (see Problem 19, page 361)
p-cresyl ethyl ether	4-methylpentanoic acid
cis-decalin (see Problem 9, page 216)	α-phenylethyl chloride
2,4-dichlorotoluene	*o*-toluidine (o-$CH_3C_6H_4NH_2$)

25. By use of Table 16.3 tell which acid or acids each of the following is likely to be. Tell what further steps you would take to identify it or to confirm your identification.

K: m.p. 155–7°; positive halogen test; *p*-nitrobenzyl ester, m.p. 104–6°; neutralization equivalent, 158 ± 2
L: m.p. 152–4°; negative tests for halogen and nitrogen
M: m.p. 153–5°; positive chlorine test; neutralization equivalent, 188 ± 4
N: m.p. 72–3°; anilide, m.p. 117–8°; amide, m.p. 155–7°
O: m.p. 79–80°; amide, m.p. 97–9°

P: m.p. 78–80°; negative tests for halogen and nitrogen; positive test with dilute KMnO$_4$

TABLE 16.3

DERIVATIVES OF SOME CARBOXYLIC ACIDS

	Acid M.p., °C	Amide M.p., °C	Anilide M.p., °C	p-Nitrobenzyl ester M.p., °C
trans-Crotonic (CH$_3$CH=CHCOOH)	72	161	118	67
Phenylacetic	77	156	118	65
Arachidic (n-C$_{19}$H$_{39}$COOH)	77	108	92	——
α-Hydroxyisobutyric	79	98	136	80
Glycolic (HOCH$_2$COOH)	80	120	97	107
β-Iodopropionic	82	101	——	——
Iodoacetic	83	95	143	——
Adipic (HOOC(CH$_2$)$_4$COOH)	151	220	241	106
p-Nitrophenylacetic	153	198	198	——
2,5-Dichlorobenzoic	153	155	——	——
m-Chlorobenzoic	154	134	122	107
2,4,6-Trimethylbenzoic	155	——	——	188
m-Bromobenzoic	156	155	136	105
p-Chlorophenoxyacetic	158	133	125	——
Salicylic (o-HOC$_6$H$_4$COOH)	159	142	136	98

26. An unknown acid was believed to be either o-nitrobenzoic acid (m.p. 147°) or anthranilic acid (m.p. 146°). A 0.201-g sample neutralized 12.4 ml of 0.098 N NaOH. Which acid was it?

27. Carboxylic acid Q contained only carbon, hydrogen, and oxygen, and had a neutralization equivalent of 149 ± 3. Vigorous oxidation by KMnO$_4$ converted Q into R, m.p. 345–50°, neutralization equivalent 84 ± 2.

When Q was heated strongly with soda lime a liquid S of b.p. 135–7° distilled. Vigorous oxidation by KMnO$_4$ converted S into T, m.p. 121–2°, neutralization equivalent 123 ± 2.

U, an isomer of Q, gave upon oxidation V, m.p. 375–80°, neutralization equivalent 70 ± 2.

What were compounds Q through V? (Make use of any needed tables of physical constants.)

28. *Nervonic acid* (from cerebrosides of human brain tissue) rapidly decolorizes dilute KMnO$_4$ and Br$_2$/CCl$_4$ solutions. Hydrogenation in the presence of nickel yields tetracosanoic acid, n-C$_{23}$H$_{47}$COOH. Vigorous oxidation of nervonic acid yields one acid of neutralization equivalent 156 ± 3 and another acid of neutralization equivalent 137 ± 2. What structure or structures are possible for nervonic acid?

29. *Tropic acid* (obtained from the alkaloid atropine, found in deadly nightshade, *Atropa belladona*), C$_9$H$_{10}$O$_3$, decolorizes cold dilute KMnO$_4$ and is oxidized by hot KMnO$_4$ to benzoic acid. Tropic acid is converted by the following sequence of reactions into *hydratropic acid:*

tropic acid $\xrightarrow{\text{HBr}}$ C$_9$H$_9$O$_2$Br $\xrightarrow{\text{OH}^-}$ C$_9$H$_8$O$_2$ (atropic acid)

atropic acid $\xrightarrow{\text{H}_2,\text{Ni}}$ hydratropic acid (C$_9$H$_{10}$O$_2$)

(a) What structure or structures are possible at this point for hydratropic acid? For tropic acid?

(b) When α-phenylethyl chloride is treated with magnesium in ether, the resulting solution poured over dry ice, and the mixture then acidified, there is obtained an acid whose amide has the same melting point as the amide of hydratropic acid. A mixed melting point determination shows no depression. Now what is the structure of hydratropic acid? Of tropic acid?

FUNCTIONAL DERIVATIVES
OF CARBOXYLIC ACIDS

17.1 Structure

Closely related to the carboxylic acids and to each other are a number of chemical families known as **functional derivatives of carboxylic acids**: *acid chlorides, anhydrides, amides,* and *esters.* These derivatives are compounds in which the —OH of a carboxyl group has been replaced by —Cl, —OOCR, —NH₂, or —OR'. They all contain the **acyl group**:

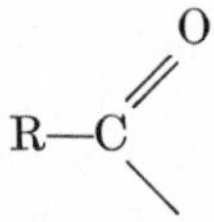

$$R-C\overset{\displaystyle O}{\big\langle}$$

Acyl group

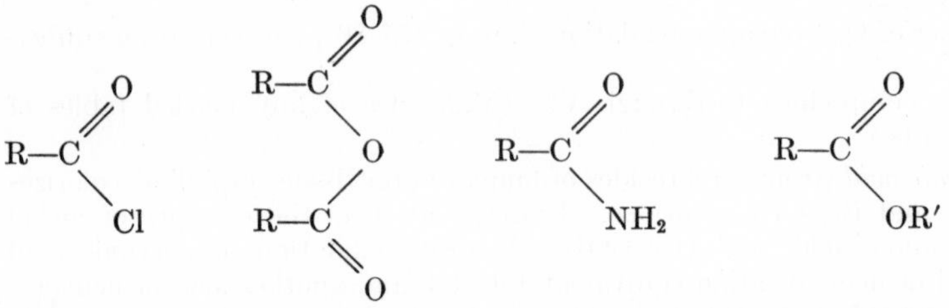

| Acid chloride | Anhydride | Amide | Ester |

R *may be alkyl or aryl*

Like the acid to which it is related, an acid derivative may be aliphatic or aromatic, substituted or unsubstituted; whatever the structure of the rest of the molecule, the properties of the functional group remain essentially the same.

17.2 Nomenclature

The names of acid derivatives are taken in simple ways from either the common name or the IUPAC name of the corresponding carboxylic acid. For example:

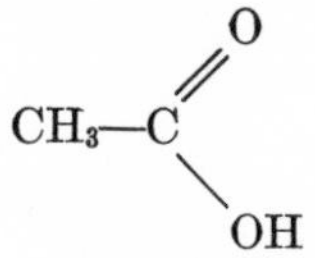

Acetic acid
Ethanoic acid

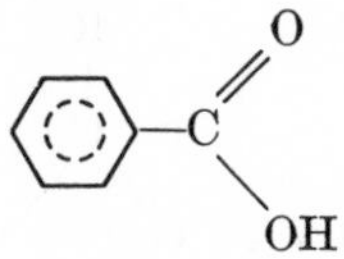

Benzoic acid

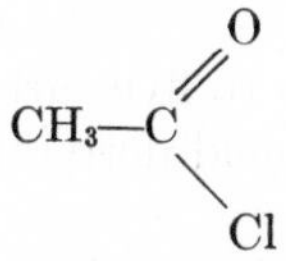

Acetyl chloride
Ethanoyl chloride

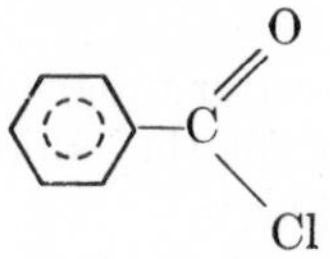

Benzoyl chloride

Change:

−ic acid to *−yl chloride*

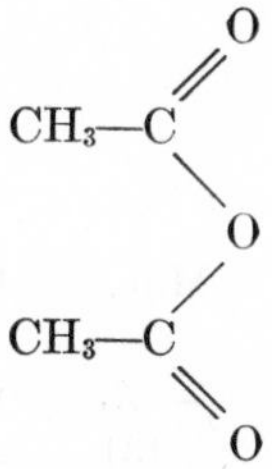

Acetic anhydride
Ethanoic anhydride

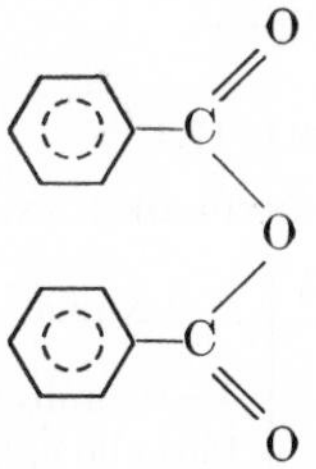

Benzoic anhydride

acid to *anhydride*

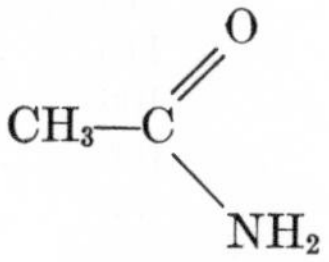

Acetamide
Ethanamide

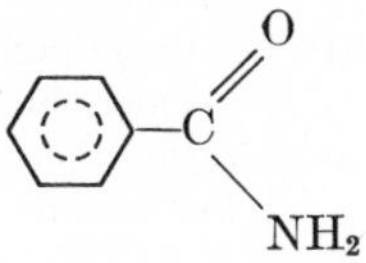

Benzamide

−ic acid of common name
(or *−oic acid* of IUPAC name)
to *−amide*

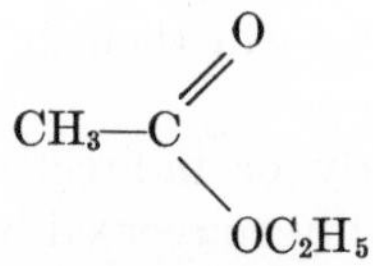

Ethyl acetate
Ethyl ethanoate

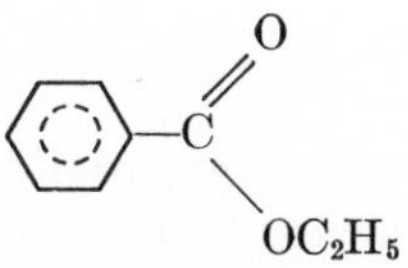

Ethyl benzoate

−ic acid to *−ate*,
preceded by name of
alcohol or phenol group

17.3 Physical properties

The presence of the C=O group makes the acid derivatives polar compounds. Acid chlorides and anhydrides (Table 17.1), and esters (Table 17.2, page 483) have boiling points that are about the same as those of aldehydes or ketones of comparable molecular weight (see Sec. 11.5). Amides (Table 17.1) have quite high boiling points because they are capable of strong intermolecular hydrogen bonding.

$$
\begin{array}{ccccc}
 & & & & R \\
 & & & & | \\
 & H & & & C \\
 & | & & & \diagdown \\
--- O & N{-}H & --- O & & N{-}H --- \\
 \diagdown & \diagup & & & | \\
 & C & & & H \\
 & | & & & \\
 & R & & &
\end{array}
$$

The borderline for solubility in water ranges from three to five carbons for the esters to five or six carbons for the amides. The acid derivatives are soluble in the usual organic solvents.

Volatile esters have pleasant, rather characteristic odors; they are often used in the preparation of perfumes and artificial flavorings. Acid chlorides have sharp, irritating odors, at least partly due to their ready hydrolysis to HCl and carboxylic acids.

TABLE 17.1

ACID CHLORIDES, ANHYDRIDES, AND AMIDES

Name	M.p., °C	B.p., °C	Name	M.p., °C	B.p., °C
Acetyl chloride	−112	51	Acetic anhydride	− 73	140
Propionyl chloride	− 94	80	Phthalic anhydride	131	284
n-Butyryl chloride	− 89	102			
n-Valeryl chloride	−110	128	Formamide	3	200d
Stearoyl chloride	23	215^{15}	Acetamide	82	221
Benzoyl chloride	− 1	197	Propionamide	79	213
p-Nitrobenzoyl chloride	72	154^{15}	n-Butyramide	116	216
			n-Valeramide	106	232
3,5-Dinitrobenzoyl chloride	74	196^{12}	Stearamide	109	251^{12}
			Benzamide	130	290

17.4 Chemistry of acid derivatives. Role of carbonyl group

Before we take up each kind of acid derivative separately, it will be helpful to outline certain general patterns into which we can then fit the rather numerous individual facts.

Each derivative is nearly always prepared — directly or indirectly — from the corresponding carboxylic acid, and can be readily converted back into the carboxylic acid by simple hydrolysis. Much of the chemistry of acid derivatives involves their conversion one into another, and into the parent acid. In addition, each derivative has certain characteristic reactions of its own.

The derivatives of carboxylic acids, like the acids themselves, contain the carbonyl group, C=O. This group is retained in the products of most reactions undergone by these compounds, and does not suffer any permanent changes itself. But by its presence in the molecule it determines the characteristic reactivity of these compounds, and is the key to the understanding of their chemistry.

Carboxylic acids and their derivatives typically undergo nucleophilic substitution in which —OH, —Cl, —OOCR, —NH$_2$, or —OR′ is replaced by some other basic group.

$$W = -OH, -Cl, -OOCR, -NH_2, -OR'$$

Substitution takes place much more readily than at a saturated carbon atom; indeed, many of these substitutions do not usually take place at all in the absence of the carbonyl group, as, for example, replacement of —NH$_2$ by OH⁻. Thus, toward nucleophilic attack acid chlorides are more reactive than alkyl chlorides, amides are more reactive than amines (RNH$_2$), and esters are more reactive than ethers.

Acid chloride   Alkyl chloride

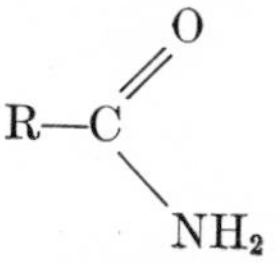

more reactive than   R—NH$_2$ Reactivity in nucleophilic displacement

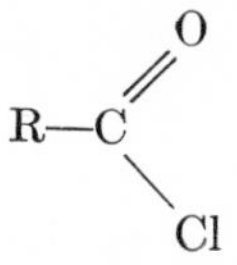

Amide   Amine

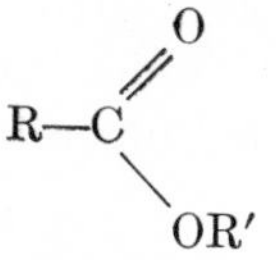

more reactive than   R—OR′

Ester   Ether

The high reactivity of acyl compounds is due to the presence of the carbonyl group, which exerts its activating influence in two ways: (a) by affecting electron distribution, and (b) by affecting the shape of the molecule.

Carbonyl carbon is joined to three other atoms by σ bonds; since these bonds utilize sp^2 orbitals (Sec. 4.2), they lie in a plane and are 120° apart. The remaining p orbital of the carbon overlaps a p orbital of oxygen to form a π bond; carbon and oxygen are thus joined by a double bond. The part of the molecule immediately surrounding carbonyl carbon is *flat*; oxygen, carbonyl carbon, and the two atoms directly attached to carbonyl carbon lie in a plane:

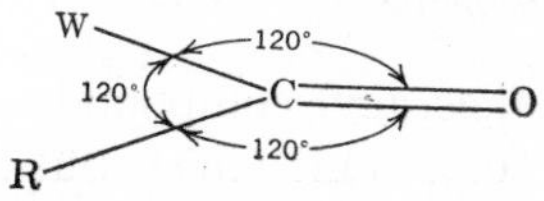

The carbonyl group exerts its electronic effect in the following way. The mobile π electrons of the carbon–oxygen double bond are pulled strongly toward the electronegative oxygen atom; as a result the carbonyl carbon is electron deficient and therefore highly vulnerable to nucleophilic attack:

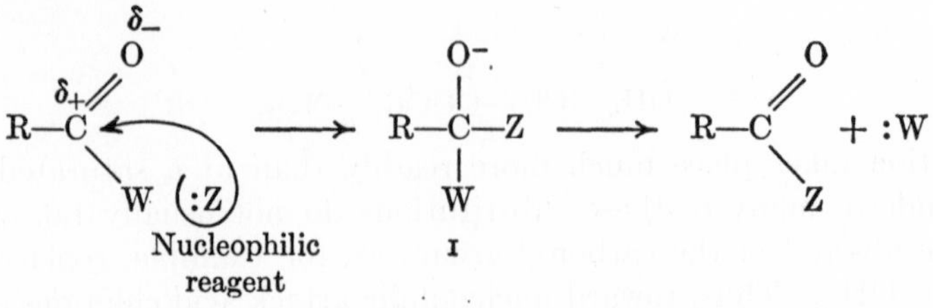

If acid is present, H^+ becomes attached to carbonyl oxygen, thus making carbonyl carbon even more deficient in electrons and even more vulnerable to nucleophilic attack:

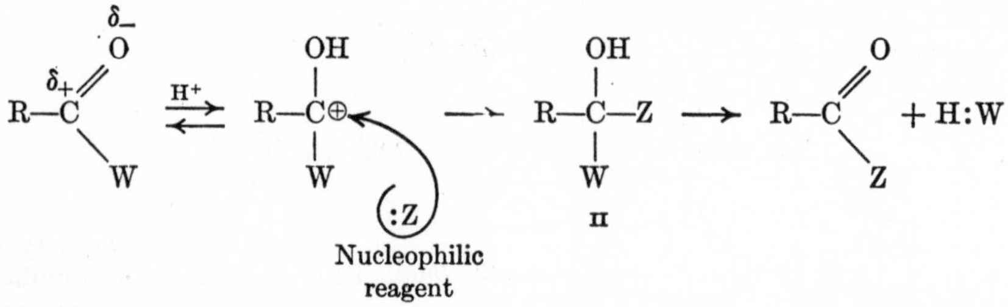

It is understandable that acid derivatives are hydrolyzed more readily in either alkaline or acidic solution than in neutral solution: alkaline solutions provide hydroxide ion, which acts as a strongly nucleophilic reagent; acid solutions provide hydrogen ion, which attaches itself to carbonyl oxygen and thus renders the molecule vulnerable to attack by the weakly nucleophilic reagent, water.

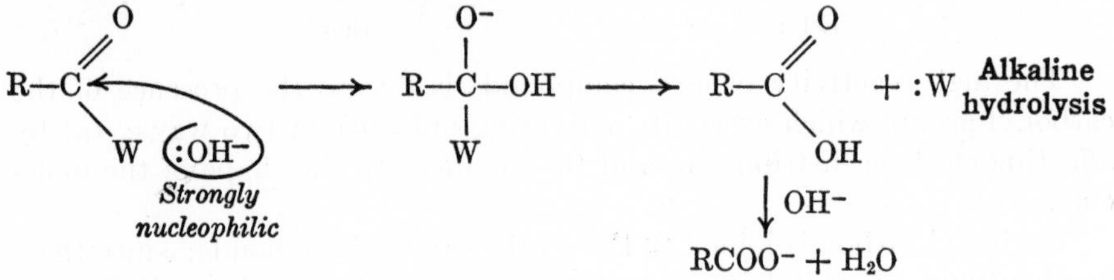

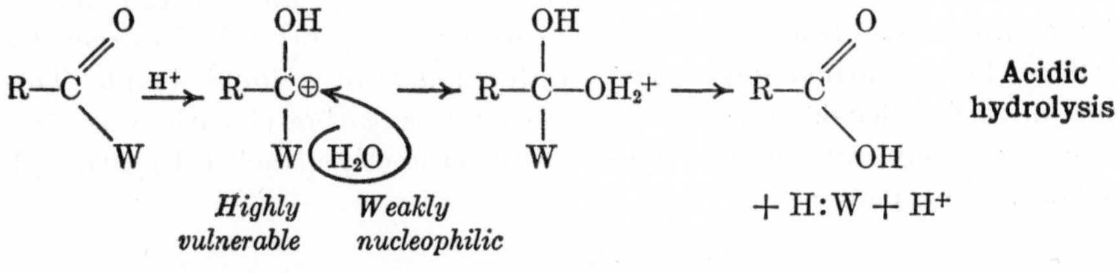

The carbonyl group makes acyl compounds more reactive than alkyl compounds not only by its electronic effect, but also by the way it affects the shape of the molecule. Nucleophilic attack (S_N2) on a tetrahedral alkyl carbon takes place at the crowded back side of the molecule, and is relatively hindered; the transition state contains pentavalent carbon and is highly unstable:

Alkyl nucleophilic substitution

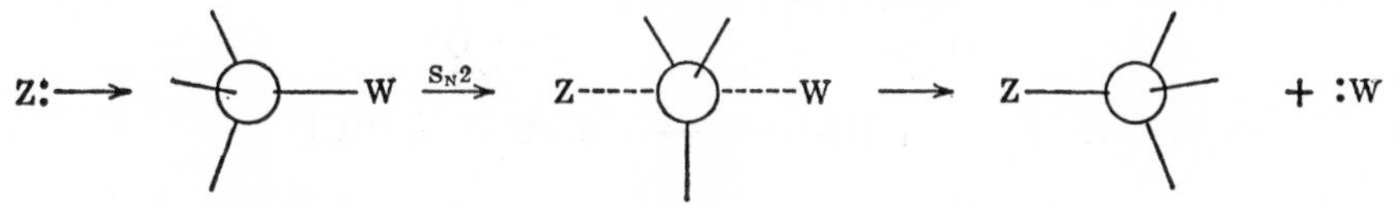

Tetrahedral C: Pentavalent C:
attack hindered   *unstable*

Nucleophilic attack on a flat acyl compound takes place in a direction perpendicular to the plane of the molecule, and is relatively unhindered. The intermediate contains tetrahedral carbon and is comparatively stable; in many cases the intermediate is actually a compound, not a transition state:

Acyl nucleophilic substitution

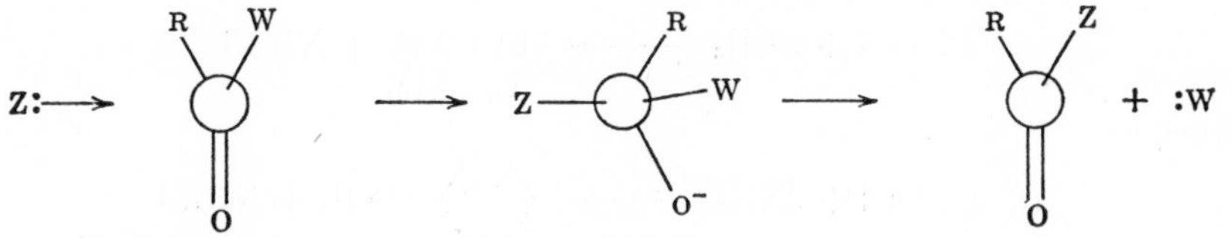

Trigonal C: Tetrahedral C:
attack relatively   *stable*
unhindered

ACID CHLORIDES

17.5 Preparation of acid chlorides

Acid chlorides are prepared from the corresponding acids by reaction with thionyl chloride, phosphorus trichloride, or phosphorus pentachloride, as discussed in Sec. 16.15.

17.6 Reactions of acid chlorides

Like other acid derivatives, acid chlorides typically undergo nucleophilic substitution. Chlorine is expelled as chloride ion or hydrogen chloride, and its place is taken by some other basic group. Because of the carbonyl group these reactions take place much more rapidly than the corresponding nucleophilic substitution reactions of the alkyl halides. Acid chlorides are the most reactive of the derivatives of carboxylic acids.

17.7 Conversion of acid chlorides into acid derivatives

In the laboratory, amides and esters are usually prepared from the acid chloride rather than from the acid itself. Both the preparation of the acid chloride and its reaction with ammonia or an alcohol are rapid, essentially irreversible reactions. It is more convenient to carry out these

REACTIONS OF ACID CHLORIDES

1. Conversion into acids and derivatives

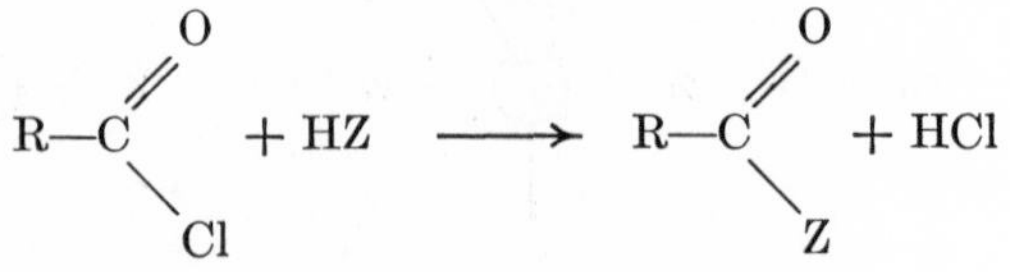

$$R\!-\!\overset{\displaystyle O}{\overset{\|}{C}}\!\!\diagdown_{Cl} + HZ \longrightarrow R\!-\!\overset{\displaystyle O}{\overset{\|}{C}}\!\!\diagdown_{Z} + HCl$$

(a) Conversion into acids. Hydrolysis

$$RCOCl + H_2O \longrightarrow RCOOH + HCl$$
$$\text{An acid}$$

Example:

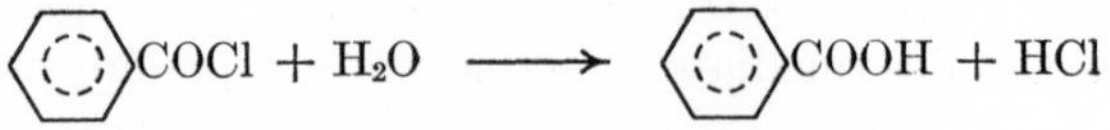

Benzoyl chloride   Benzoic acid

$$C_6H_5COCl + H_2O \longrightarrow C_6H_5COOH + HCl$$

(b) Conversion into amides. Ammonolysis

$$RCOCl + 2NH_3 \longrightarrow RCONH_2 + NH_4Cl$$
$$\text{An amide}$$

Example:

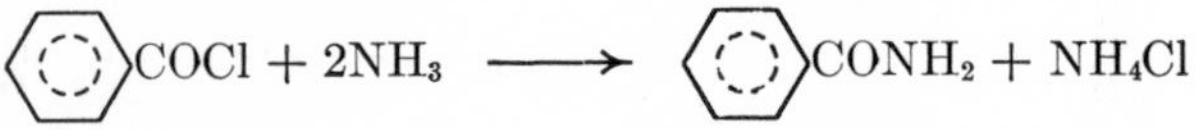

$$C_6H_5COCl + 2NH_3 \longrightarrow C_6H_5CONH_2 + NH_4Cl$$

Benzoyl chloride   Benzamide

(c) Conversion into esters. Alcoholysis

$$RCOCl + R'OH \longrightarrow RCOOR' + HCl$$
$$\text{An ester}$$

Example:

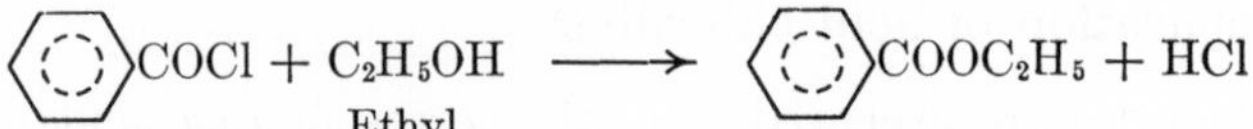

$$C_6H_5COCl + C_2H_5OH \longrightarrow C_6H_5COOC_2H_5 + HCl$$

Benzoyl chloride Ethyl   Ethyl benzoate
alcohol

2. Formation of ketones. Friedel-Crafts acylation

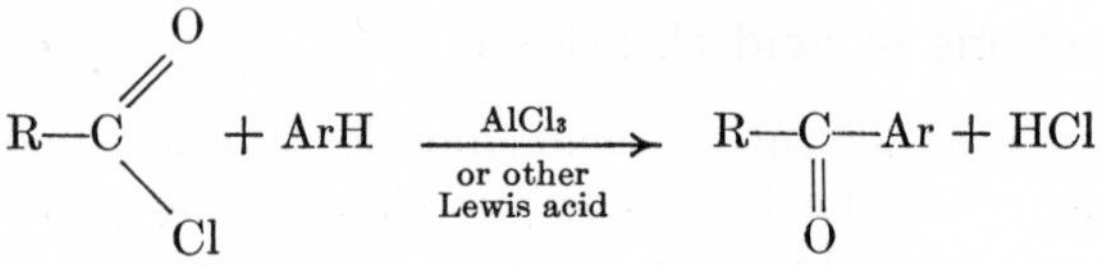

$$R\!-\!\overset{\displaystyle O}{\overset{\|}{C}}\!\!\diagdown_{Cl} + ArH \xrightarrow[\substack{\text{or other}\\ \text{Lewis acid}}]{AlCl_3} R\!-\!\underset{\underset{O}{\|}}{C}\!-\!Ar + HCl$$
$$\text{A ketone}$$

Examples:

$$CH_3COCl + C_6H_6 \xrightarrow{AlCl_3} CH_3\!-\!\underset{\underset{O}{\|}}{C}\!-\!C_6H_5 + HCl$$

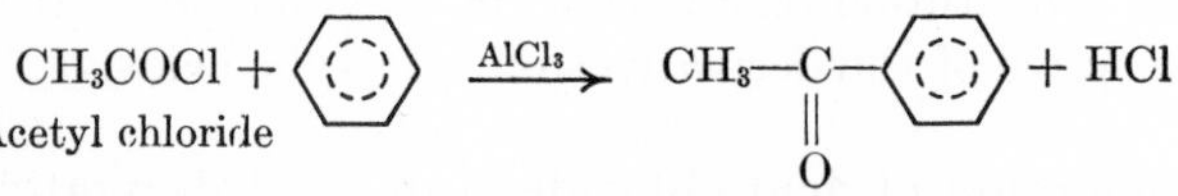

Acetyl chloride

Acetophenone
(Methyl phenyl ketone)

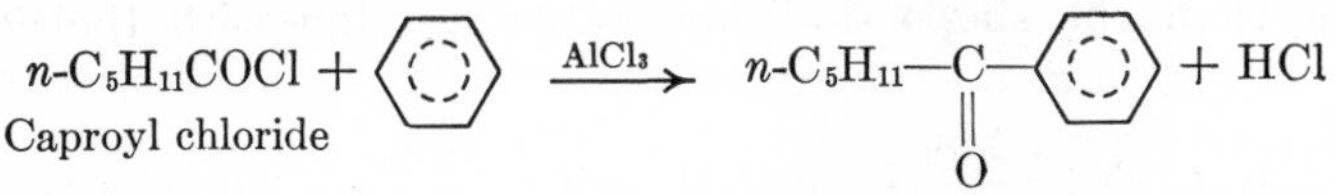

$$n\text{-}C_5H_{11}COCl + \langle \bigcirc \rangle \xrightarrow{\text{AlCl}_3} n\text{-}C_5H_{11}\overset{\displaystyle \|}{\underset{\displaystyle O}{C}}\!\!-\!\!\langle \bigcirc \rangle + HCl$$

Caproyl chloride

n-Pentyl phenyl ketone
No rearrangement of n-pentyl group

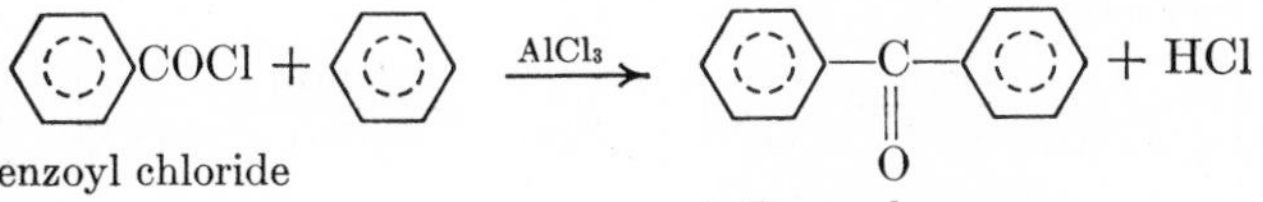

$$\langle \bigcirc \rangle COCl + \langle \bigcirc \rangle \xrightarrow{\text{AlCl}_3} \langle \bigcirc \rangle\!\!-\!\!\overset{\displaystyle \|}{\underset{\displaystyle O}{C}}\!\!-\!\!\langle \bigcirc \rangle + HCl$$

Benzoyl chloride

Benzophenone
(Phenyl ketone)

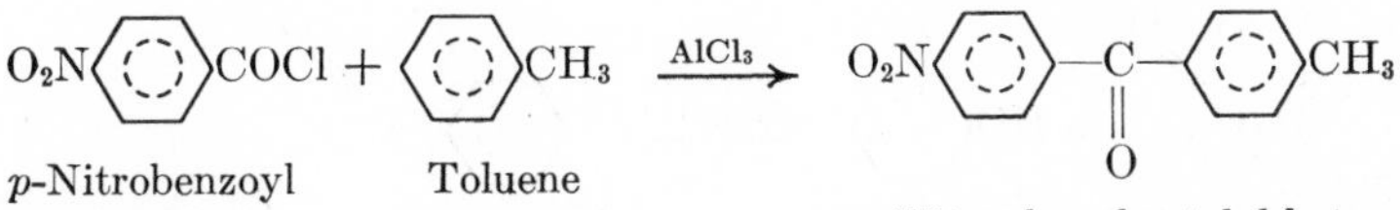

$$O_2N\langle \bigcirc \rangle COCl + \langle \bigcirc \rangle CH_3 \xrightarrow{\text{AlCl}_3} O_2N\langle \bigcirc \rangle\!\!-\!\!\overset{\displaystyle \|}{\underset{\displaystyle O}{C}}\!\!-\!\!\langle \bigcirc \rangle CH_3$$

p-Nitrobenzoyl   Toluene
chloride

p-Nitrophenyl *p*-tolyl ketone

3. Formation of ketones. Reaction with organocadmium compounds

$$2R\!-\!\overset{\displaystyle O}{\overset{\displaystyle \|}{C}}\!\!\underset{\displaystyle Cl}{\diagdown} + R'_2Cd \longrightarrow 2R\!-\!\overset{\displaystyle \|}{\underset{\displaystyle O}{C}}\!\!-\!R' + CdCl_2 \qquad \begin{array}{l}\text{R' \textit{must be aryl or}}\\ \textit{primary alkyl}\end{array}$$

Examples:

$$CH_3CH_2CH_2CH_2MgBr \xrightarrow{\text{CdCl}_2} (CH_3CH_2CH_2CH_2)_2Cd \qquad \overset{\displaystyle CH_3}{\overset{\displaystyle |}{2CH_3CHCOCl}}$$

Di-*n*-butylcadmium   Isobutyryl chloride

$$2CH_3CH_2CH_2CH_2\overset{\displaystyle \|}{\underset{\displaystyle O}{C}}\overset{\displaystyle CH_3}{\overset{\displaystyle |}{CHCH_3}}$$

n-Butyl isopropyl ketone
(2-Methyl-3-heptanone)

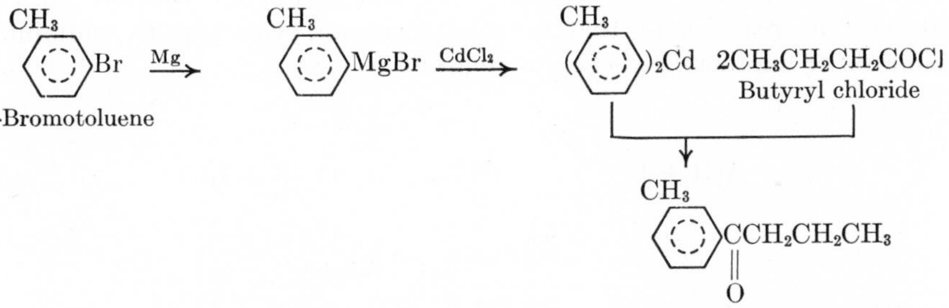

$$\overset{\displaystyle CH_3}{\langle \bigcirc \rangle} Br \xrightarrow{\text{Mg}} \overset{\displaystyle CH_3}{\langle \bigcirc \rangle} MgBr \xrightarrow{\text{CdCl}_2} (\overset{\displaystyle CH_3}{\langle \bigcirc \rangle})_2Cd \quad 2CH_3CH_2CH_2COCl$$

m-Bromotoluene

Butyryl chloride

$$\overset{\displaystyle CH_3}{\langle \bigcirc \rangle}\overset{\displaystyle \|}{\underset{\displaystyle O}{C}}CH_2CH_2CH_3$$

n-Propyl *m*-tolyl ketone

4. Formation of aldehydes by reduction. Discussed in Sec. 23.5.

two steps than the single slow, reversible reaction with the acid. For example:

$$n\text{-}C_{17}H_{35}COOH \xrightarrow[\text{heat}]{\text{SOCl}_2} n\text{-}C_{17}H_{35}COCl \xrightarrow[\text{cold}]{\text{NH}_3} n\text{-}C_{17}H_{35}CONH_2$$

Stearic acid   Stearoyl chloride   Stearamide

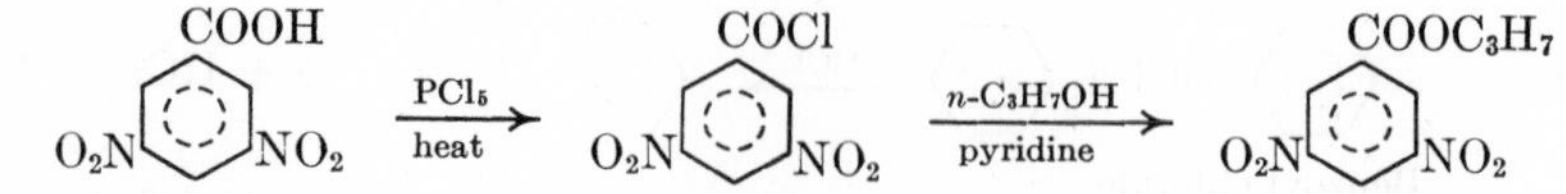

3,5-Dinitrobenzoic acid → 3,5-Dinitrobenzoyl chloride → n-Propyl 3,5-dinitrobenzoate

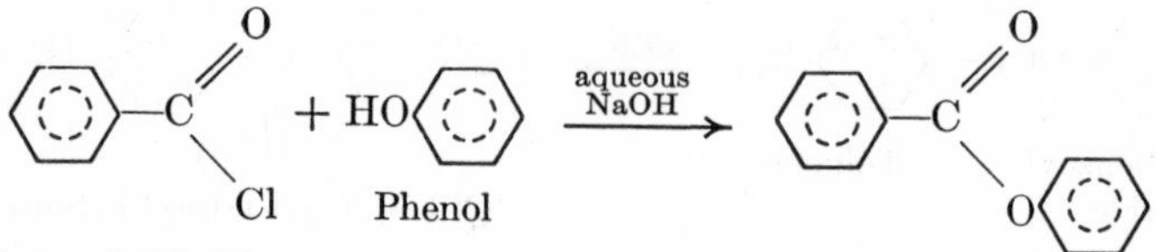

Benzoyl chloride   Phenol   Phenyl benzoate

Aromatic acid chlorides (ArCOCl) are considerably less reactive than the aliphatic acid chlorides. With cold water, for example, acetyl chloride reacts almost explosively, whereas benzoyl chloride reacts only very slowly. The reaction of aromatic acid chlorides with an alcohol or a phenol is often carried out using the **Schotten-Baumann** technique: the acid chloride is added in portions (followed by vigorous shaking) to a mixture of the hydroxy compound and a base, usually aqueous sodium hydroxide or pyridine (an organic base, Sec. 32.11). Although the function of the base is not clear, it seems not only to neutralize the hydrogen chloride that would otherwise be liberated, but also to catalyze the reaction.

17.8 Friedel-Crafts acylation

One of the most important modifications of the Friedel-Crafts reaction involves the use of acid chlorides rather than alkyl halides. An acyl group, RCO—, becomes attached to the aromatic ring, thus forming a ketone; the process is called **acylation**. As usual for the Friedel-Crafts reaction (Sec. 10.12), the aromatic ring undergoing substitution must be at least as reactive as that of a halobenzene; catalysis by aluminum chloride or another Lewis acid is required.

A ketone

The mechanism commonly accepted for Friedel-Crafts acylation is analogous to that proposed for Friedel-Crafts alkylation (Sec. 8.23), and involves the following steps:

(1) $RCOCl + AlCl_3 \longrightarrow R\overset{\oplus}{C}\!\!=\!\!O + AlCl_4^-$

(2) $ArH + R\overset{\oplus}{C}\!\!=\!\!O \longrightarrow Ar\overset{\displaystyle H}{\underset{\displaystyle COR}{\diagup}}$

(3) $Ar\overset{\displaystyle \overset{\oplus}{H}}{\underset{\displaystyle COR}{\diagup}} + AlCl_4^- \longrightarrow Ar\!\!-\!\!\underset{\displaystyle O}{\overset{\parallel}{C}}\!\!-\!\!R + HCl + AlCl_3$

This fits the pattern of electrophilic aromatic substitution, the attacking reagent this time being the **acylium ion,** $R\!\!-\!\!\overset{\oplus}{C}\!\!=\!\!O$. Alternatively, we could consider that the acid chloride undergoes nucleophilic substitution, with the basic aromatic ring (Sec. 8.12) serving as the nucleophilic reagent. If, as shown, prior ionization of the halide actually occurs, acylation is of the S_N1 type. In some cases, it may be that (1) and (2) occur simultaneously; here acylation is of the S_N2 type.

In planning the synthesis of diaryl ketones, ArCOAr′, it is particularly important to select the right combination of ArCOCl and Ar′H. In the preparation of *m*-nitrobenzophenone, for example, the nitro group can be present in the acid chloride but not in the ring undergoing substitution, since as a strongly deactivating group it prevents the Friedel-Crafts reaction (Sec. 10.12).

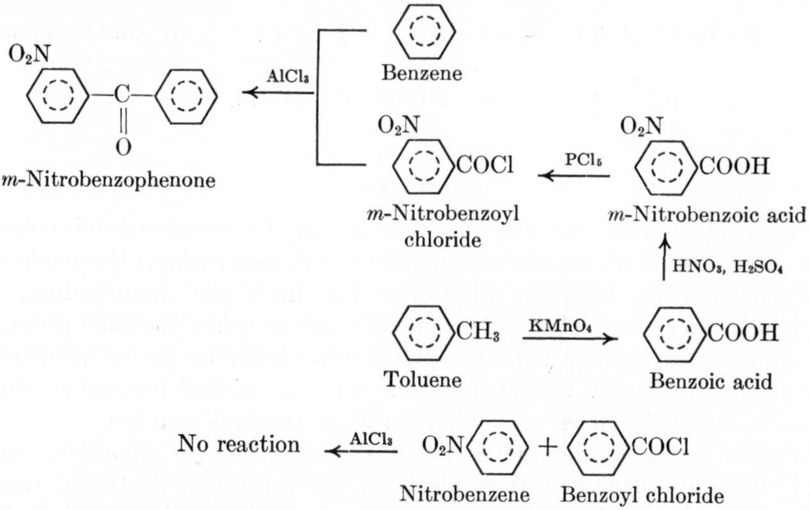

m-Nitrobenzophenone

Benzene

m-Nitrobenzoyl chloride

m-Nitrobenzoic acid

Toluene

Benzoic acid

No reaction

Nitrobenzene   Benzoyl chloride

Friedel-Crafts acylation is one of the most important methods of preparing ketones in which the carbonyl group is attached to an aromatic ring. Once formed, these ketones may be converted into secondary alcohols by reduction, into tertiary alcohols by reaction with Grignard reagents, and into many other important classes of compounds (Sec. 23.7).

Of particular importance is the conversion of the acyl group into an alkyl group, which can be accomplished by the **Clemmensen reduction,** using amalgamated zinc and concentrated hydrochloric acid. For example:

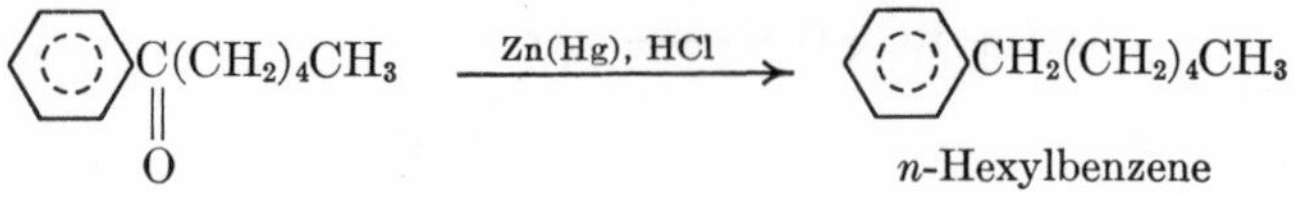

n-Pentyl phenyl ketone   *n*-Hexylbenzene

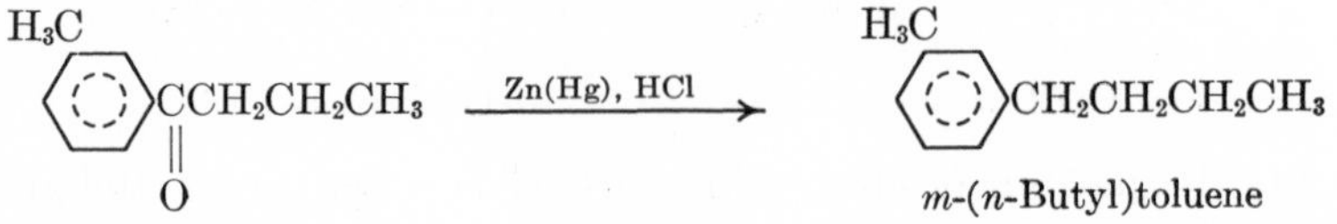

n-Propyl *m*-tolyl ketone   *m*-(*n*-Butyl)toluene

A straight-chain alkyl group longer than ethyl generally cannot be attached to an aromatic ring by Friedel-Crafts alkylation because of rearrangement (Sec. 9.8). Such a group is readily introduced, however, in two steps: (1) formation of a ketone by Friedel-Crafts acylation (or by the reaction of an organocadmium compound with an acyl chloride, described in the following section); (2) Clemmensen reduction of the ketone.

17.9   Reaction of acid chlorides with organocadmium compounds

Grignard reagents react with dry cadmium chloride to yield the corresponding organocadmium compounds, which react with acid chlorides to yield ketones:

$$2R'MgX + CdCl_2 \longrightarrow R'_2Cd + 2MgXCl \qquad \text{R' must be aryl or primary alkyl}$$

$$R'_2Cd + 2RCOCl \longrightarrow 2R\!-\!\underset{\underset{O}{\|}}{C}\!-\!R' + CdCl_2$$

A ketone

Like other reactions of acid chlorides, this one may be considered to involve nucleophilic attack at the electron-deficient carbonyl carbon, the nucleophilic reagent being the basic alkyl or aryl group of the organocadmium compound. (See the addition of Grignard reagents to the carbonyl group, Sec. 11.11.) Only organocadmium compounds containing aryl or primary alkyl groups are stable enough for use. In spite of this limitation, the method is one of the most valuable for the synthesis of ketones.

Grignard reagents themselves react readily with acid chlorides, but the products are usually tertiary alcohols; these presumably result from reaction of initially formed ketones with more Grignard reagent. (If tertiary alcohols are desired, they are better prepared from esters than from acid chlorides, Sec. 17.21.) Organocadmium compounds, being less reactive, do not react with ketones.

The comparatively low reactivity of organocadmium compounds not only makes the synthesis of ketones possible, but in addition widens the application of the method. Organocadmium compounds do not react with many of the functional groups with which the Grignard reagent does react: —NO₂, —CN, —CO—, —COOR, for example. Consequently the presence of one of these groups in the acid chloride molecule does not interfere with the synthesis of a ketone (compare with Sec. 11.14). For example:

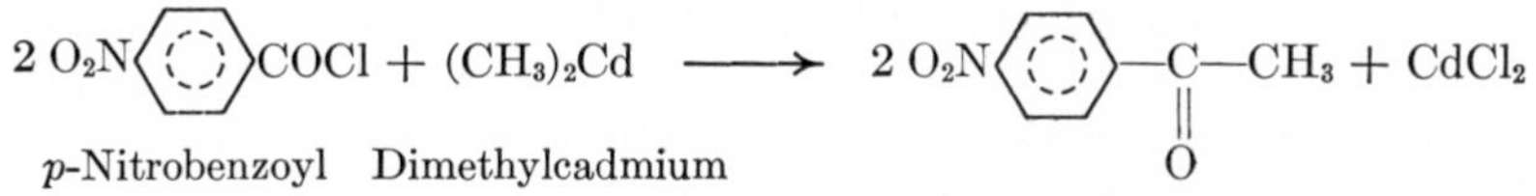

$$2\ O_2N\langle\bigcirc\rangle COCl + (CH_3)_2Cd \longrightarrow 2\ O_2N\langle\bigcirc\rangle -\underset{\underset{O}{\|}}{C}-CH_3 + CdCl_2$$

p-Nitrobenzoyl   Dimethylcadmium
chloride
p-Nitroacetophenone
(Methyl p-nitrophenyl ketone)

$$CH_3O\underset{\underset{O}{\|}}{C}CH_2CH_2\underset{\underset{O}{\|}}{C}Cl + [(CH_3)_2CHCH_2CH_2]_2Cd \longrightarrow$$

Diisopentylcadmium

$$CH_3O\underset{\underset{O}{\|}}{C}CH_2CH_2\underset{\underset{O}{\|}}{C}CH_2CH_2CH(CH_3)_2$$

Methyl 4-oxo-7-methyloctanoate
(A γ–keto ester)

Problem 17.1 Would it be feasible to make p-nitroacetophenone via the reaction between di(p-nitrophenyl)cadmium, $(p\text{-}O_2NC_6H_4)_2Cd$, and acetyl chloride?

ACID ANHYDRIDES

17.10 Preparation of acetic anhydride

Only one monocarboxylic acid anhydride is encountered very often; however, this one, **acetic anhydride,** is immensely important. It is prepared by the reaction of acetic acid with **ketene,** $CH_2{=}C{=}O$, which in turn is prepared by the pyrolysis of acetone, CH_3COCH_3. (Ketene itself is an extremely reactive, interesting compound; it is ordinarily used as soon as it is made.)

$$CH_3COCH_3 \xrightarrow{700\text{--}750°} CH_4 + CH_2{=}C{=}O$$

Acetone   Ketene

$$CH_2{=}C{=}O + CH_3COOH \longrightarrow$$

Ketene   Acetic acid

$$\begin{array}{c} CH_3{-}C\overset{\displaystyle O}{\underset{\displaystyle O}{<}} \\ CH_3{-}C \end{array}$$

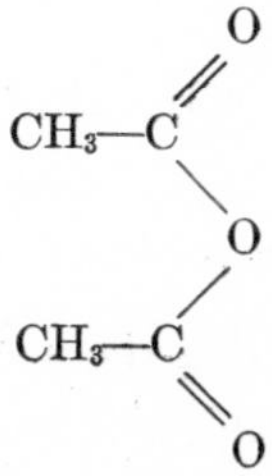

Acetic anhydride

(The exceedingly important anhydrides of dicarboxylic acids are discussed in Chapter 25.)

17.11 Reactions of acid anhydrides

Acid anhydrides undergo the same reactions as acid chlorides, but a little more slowly; where acid chlorides yield a molecule of HCl, anhydrides yield a molecule of carboxylic acid.

REACTIONS OF ACID ANHYDRIDES

1. Conversion into acids and acid derivatives

$$(RCO)_2O + HZ \longrightarrow RCOZ + RCOOH$$

(a) Conversion into acids. Hydrolysis

Example:

$$(CH_3CO)_2O + H_2O \longrightarrow 2CH_3COOH$$
Acetic anhydride   Acetic acid

(b) Conversion into amides. Ammonolysis

Example:

$$(CH_3CO)_2O + 2NH_3 \longrightarrow CH_3CONH_2 + CH_3COO^-NH_4^+$$
Acetic anhydride   Acetamide   Ammonium acetate

(c) Conversion into esters. Alcoholysis

Example:

$$(CH_3CO)_2O + CH_3OH \longrightarrow CH_3COOCH_3 + CH_3COOH$$
Acetic anhydride   Methyl acetate   Acetic acid
                                    (an ester)

2. Formation of ketones. Friedel-Crafts acylation

$$(RCO)_2O + ArH \xrightarrow[\substack{\text{or other}\\\text{Lewis acid}}]{AlCl_3} R-\underset{\underset{O}{\|}}{C}-Ar + RCOOH$$

A ketone

Example:

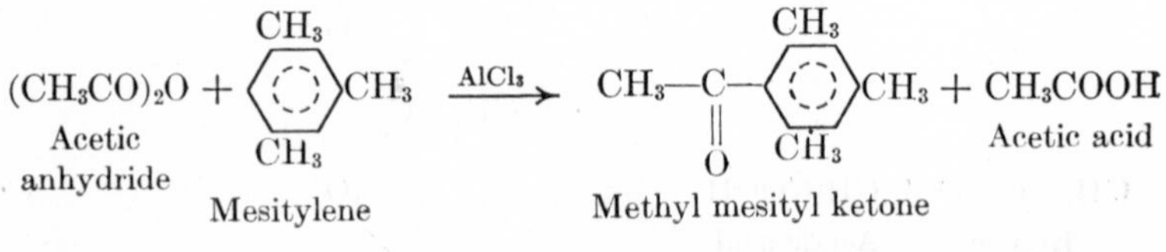

Compounds containing the acetyl group are often prepared from acetic anhydride; it is cheap, readily available, less volatile and more easily handled than acetyl chloride, and it does not form corrosive hydrogen chloride. It is widely used industrially for the esterification of the polyhydroxy compounds known as *carbohydrates*, especially cellulose (Chapter 30).

AMIDES

17.12 Preparation of amides

Amides are prepared from ammonia and an acid or an acid derivative. The most important methods are outlined below.

PREPARATION OF AMIDES

1. From acid chlorides

$$RCOCl + 2NH_3 \longrightarrow RCONH_2 + NH_4Cl$$

Example:

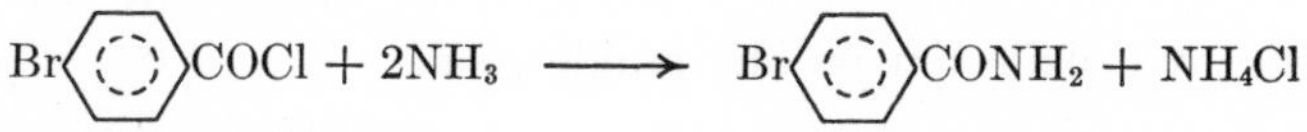

$$Br\langle\bigcirc\rangle COCl + 2NH_3 \longrightarrow Br\langle\bigcirc\rangle CONH_2 + NH_4Cl$$

  p-Bromobenzoyl chloride   *p*-Bromobenzamide

2. From ammonium salts

$$RCOOH + NH_3 \longrightarrow RCOO^- NH_4^+ \xrightarrow{\text{heat}} RCONH_2 + H_2O$$

Example:

$$\text{n-}C_{17}H_{35}COOH + NH_3 \longrightarrow \text{n-}C_{17}H_{35}COO^- NH_4^+ \xrightarrow{\text{heat}} \text{n-}C_{17}H_{35}CONH_2 + H_2O$$

  Stearic acid   Ammonium stearate   Stearamide

In the laboratory most amides are prepared by the convenient reaction of ammonia with acid chlorides (or anhydrides, when available). In industry the cheaper synthesis from ammonium salts is often used.

17.13 Reactions of amides

An amide is hydrolyzed when heated with aqueous acids or aqueous bases. The products are ammonia and the carboxylic acid, although one product or the other is obtained in the form of a salt, depending upon the acidity or basicity of the medium.

Another reaction of importance, the Hofmann degradation of amides, will be discussed later (Sec. 19.13).

REACTIONS OF AMIDES

1. Hydrolysis

$$RCONH_2 + H_2O \quad \begin{cases} \xrightarrow{H^+} RCOOH + NH_4^+ \\ \xrightarrow{OH^-} RCOO^- + NH_3 \end{cases}$$

Examples:

$$\langle\bigcirc\rangle CONH_2 + H_2SO_4 + H_2O \longrightarrow \langle\bigcirc\rangle COOH + NH_4^+ HSO_4^-$$

  Benzamide   Benzoic acid

$$CH_3CH_2CH_2CONH_2 + NaOH + H_2O \longrightarrow CH_3CH_2CH_2COO^- Na^+ + NH_3$$

  Butyramide   Sodium butyrate

2. Hofmann degradation of amides. Discussed in Sec. 19.13.

17.14 Hydrolysis of amides

Hydrolysis of amides is typical of the reactions of carboxylic acid derivatives. It involves nucleophilic substitution, in which the —NH$_2$ group is replaced by —OH. Under acidic conditions hydrolysis involves attack by water on the protonated amide:

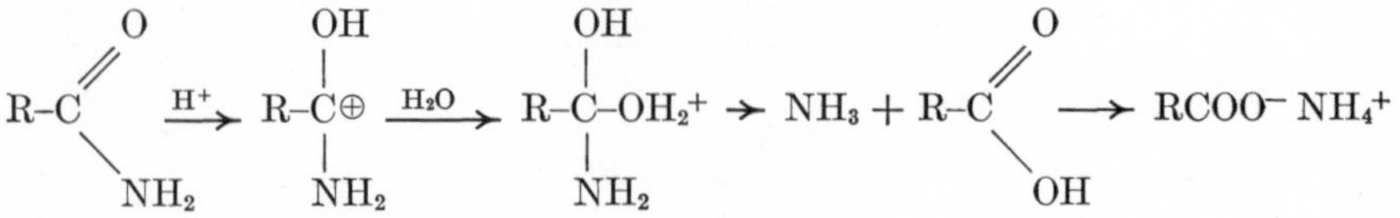

$$
R-C\overset{O}{\underset{NH_2}{\big\backslash}} \xrightarrow{H^+} R\overset{OH}{\underset{NH_2}{-C\oplus}} \xrightarrow{H_2O} R\overset{OH}{\underset{NH_2}{-C-OH_2^+}} \rightarrow NH_3 + R-C\overset{O}{\underset{OH}{\big\backslash}} \longrightarrow RCOO^- NH_4^+
$$

Under alkaline conditions hydrolysis involves attack by the strongly nucleophilic hydroxide ion on the amide itself:

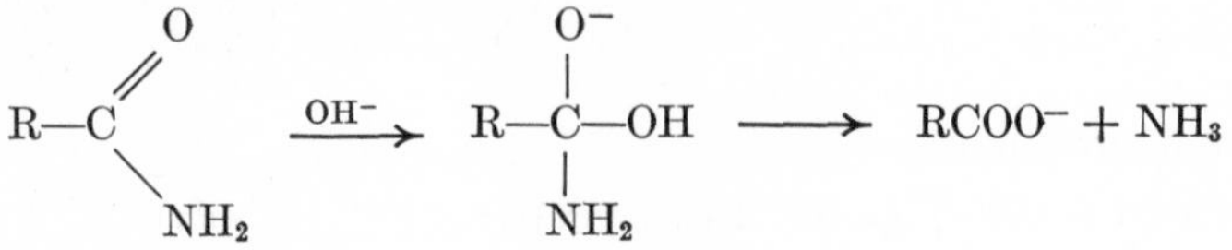

$$
R-C\overset{O}{\underset{NH_2}{\big\backslash}} \xrightarrow{OH^-} R\overset{O^-}{\underset{NH_2}{-C-OH}} \longrightarrow RCOO^- + NH_3
$$

ESTERS

17.15 Preparation of esters

Esters are usually prepared by the reaction of alcohols or phenols with acids or acid derivatives. The most common methods are outlined below.

PREPARATION OF ESTERS

1. From acids

$$
RCOOH + R'OH \underset{\longleftarrow}{\overset{H^+}{\longrightarrow}} RCOOR' + H_2O
$$

<table>
<tr><td>Carboxylic acid</td><td>Alcohol</td><td>Ester</td></tr>
<tr><td>R *may be alkyl or aryl*</td><td>R' *is usually alkyl*</td><td></td></tr>
</table>

Reactivity of R'OH: 1° > 2° (> 3°)

Examples:

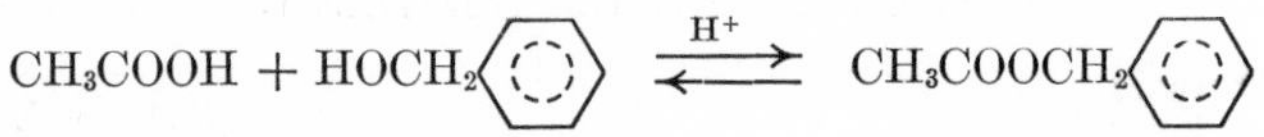

$$
CH_3COOH + HOCH_2{-}\langle\bigcirc\rangle \underset{\longleftarrow}{\overset{H^+}{\longrightarrow}} CH_3COOCH_2{-}\langle\bigcirc\rangle
$$

Acetic acid   Benzyl alcohol   Benzyl acetate

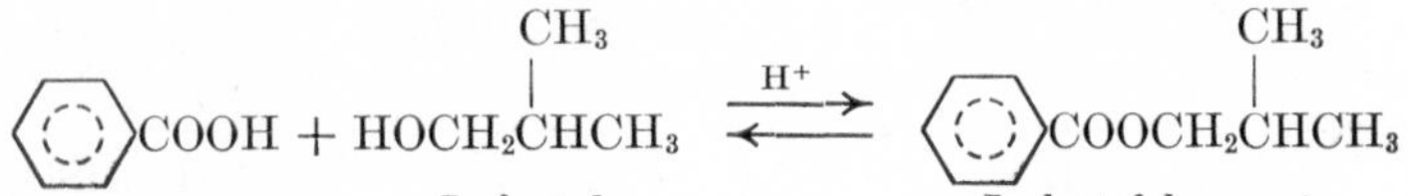

$$
\langle\bigcirc\rangle{-}COOH + HOCH_2\overset{CH_3}{\underset{}{CHCH_3}} \underset{\longleftarrow}{\overset{H^+}{\longrightarrow}} \langle\bigcirc\rangle{-}COOCH_2\overset{CH_3}{\underset{}{CHCH_3}}
$$

Benzoic acid   Isobutyl alcohol   Isobutyl benzoate

2. From acid chlorides or anhydrides

$$
RCOCl + R'OH \text{ (or ArOH)} \longrightarrow RCOOR' \text{ (or RCOOAr)} + HCl
$$

$$
(RCO)_2O + R'OH \text{ (or ArOH)} \longrightarrow RCOOR' \text{ (or RCOOAr)} + RCOOH
$$

Examples:

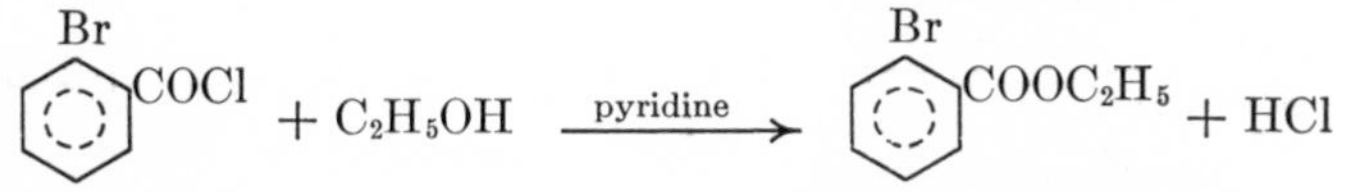

o-Bromobenzoyl
chloride

Ethyl o-bromobenzoate

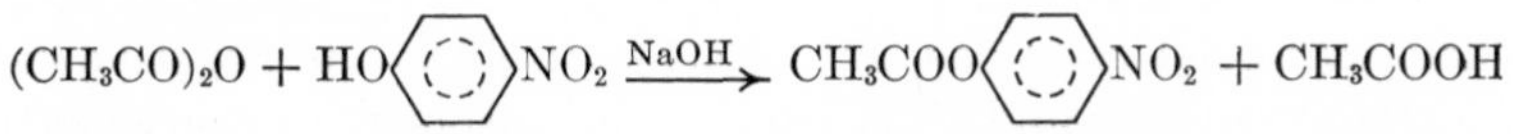

$$(CH_3CO)_2O + HO\langle\rangle NO_2 \xrightarrow{NaOH} CH_3COO\langle\rangle NO_2 + CH_3COOH$$

Acetic   p-Nitrophenol   p-Nitrophenyl acetate
anhydride

3. From esters. Transesterification.   Discussed in Sec. 17.20.

Esters of phenols are usually prepared by the use of acid chlorides or anhydrides, since phenols do not react readily with acids.

Alkyl esters can be prepared by the reaction of alcohols either with acids or with acid derivatives. The direct reaction with acids involves an equilibrium (Sec. 16.16) and requires effort to drive to completion. In the laboratory, reaction with an acid chloride or anhydride is more commonly used.

The effect of the structure of the alcohol and of the acid on ease of esterification has already been discussed (Sec. 16.18).

TABLE 17.2

ESTERS OF CARBOXYLIC ACIDS

Name	M.p., °C	B.p., °C	Name	M.p., °C	B.p., °C
Methyl acetate	−98	57.5	Ethyl formate	−80	54
Ethyl acetate	−84	77	Ethyl acetate	−84	77
n-Propyl acetate	−92	102	Ethyl propionate	−74	99
n-Butyl acetate	−77	126	Ethyl n-butyrate	−93	121
n-Pentyl acetate		148	Ethyl n-valerate	−91	146
Isopentyl acetate	−78	142	Ethyl stearate	34	215^{15}
Benzyl acetate	−51	214	Ethyl phenylacetate		226
Phenyl acetate		196	Ethyl benzoate	−35	213

As was mentioned earlier, esterification using aromatic acid chlorides, ArCOCl, is often carried out in the presence of base (the Schotten-Baumann technique, Sec. 17.7).

Problem 17.2   When benzoic acid is esterified by methanol in the presence of a little sulfuric acid, the final reaction mixture contains five substances: benzoic acid, methanol, water, methyl benzoate, sulfuric acid. Outline a procedure for the separation of the pure ester.

17.16   Reactions of esters

Esters undergo the nucleophilic substitution that is typical of carboxylic acid derivatives. Attack occurs at the electron-deficient carbonyl carbon, and results in the replacement of the —OR′ group by —OH, —OR″, or —NH₂:

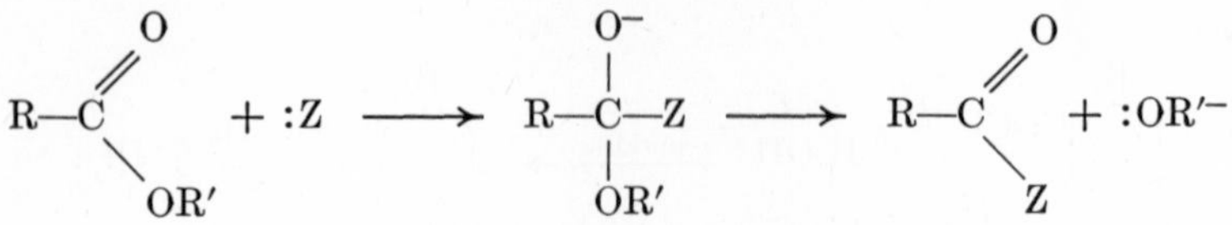

$$R-\overset{\displaystyle O}{\underset{\displaystyle OR'}{C}} + :Z \longrightarrow R-\overset{\displaystyle O^-}{\underset{\displaystyle OR'}{\underset{|}{\overset{|}{C}}}}-Z \longrightarrow R-\overset{\displaystyle O}{\underset{\displaystyle Z}{C}} + :OR'^-$$

$$:Z = :OH^-, \quad :OR''^-, \quad :NH_3$$

These reactions are sometimes carried out in the presence of acid. In these acid-catalyzed reactions, H^+ attaches itself to the negative oxygen of the carbonyl group, and thus renders the carbonyl carbon even more electron deficient and even more reactive toward nucleophilic attack.

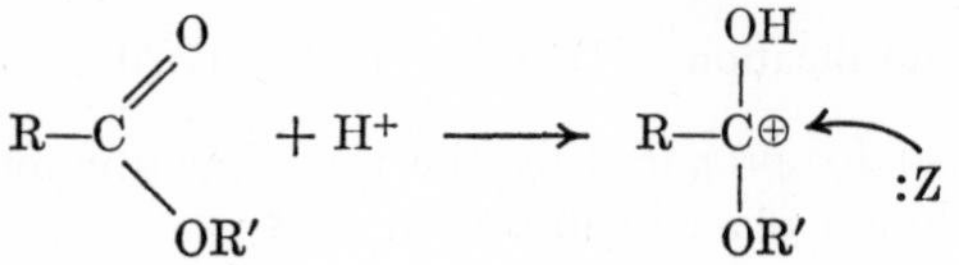

$$R-\overset{\displaystyle O}{\underset{\displaystyle OR'}{C}} + H^+ \longrightarrow R-\overset{\displaystyle OH}{\underset{\displaystyle OR'}{\underset{|}{\overset{|}{C}}}}\oplus \longleftarrow :Z$$

Acid catalysis:
makes carbon more
susceptible to
nucleophilic attack

REACTIONS OF ESTERS

1. Conversion into acids and acid derivatives

(a) Conversion into acids. Hydrolysis

$$RCOOR' + H_2O \overset{H^+}{\underset{OH^-}{\longrightarrow}} \begin{array}{l} RCOOH + R'OH \\ RCOO^- + R'OH \end{array}$$

Example:

$$\langle \bigcirc \rangle COOC_2H_5 + H_2O \begin{array}{l} \overset{H_2SO_4}{\longrightarrow} \langle \bigcirc \rangle COOH + C_2H_5OH \\ \qquad\qquad\qquad \text{Benzoic acid} \quad \text{Ethyl alcohol} \\ \overset{NaOH}{\longrightarrow} \langle \bigcirc \rangle COO^- Na^+ + C_2H_5OH \end{array}$$

Ethyl benzoate

Sodium benzoate   Ethyl alcohol

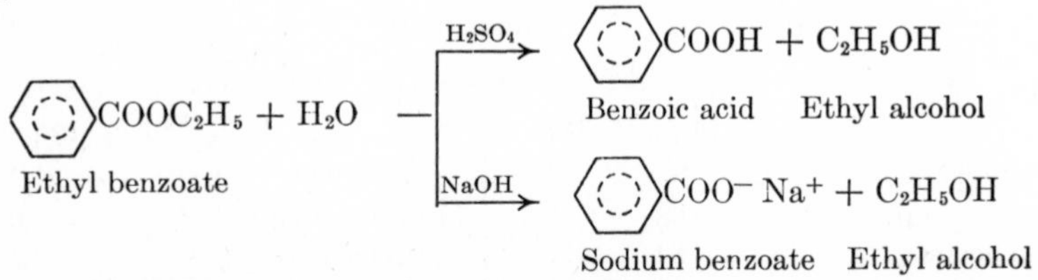

(b) Conversion into amides. Ammonolysis

$$RCOOR' + NH_3 \longrightarrow RCONH_2 + R'OH$$

Example:

$$CH_3COOC_2H_5 + NH_3 \longrightarrow CH_3CONH_2 + C_2H_5OH$$
Ethyl acetate   Acetamide   Ethyl alcohol

(c) Conversion into esters. Transesterification. Alcoholysis

$$RCOOR' + R''OH \underset{\longleftarrow}{\overset{acid\ or\ base}{\longrightarrow}} RCOOR'' + R'OH$$

Example:

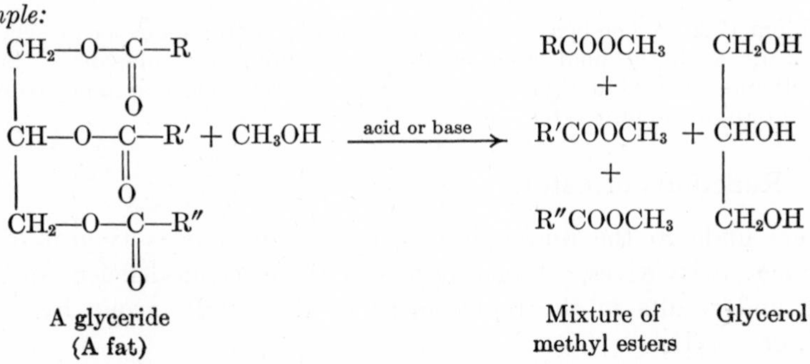

$$\begin{array}{l} CH_2-O-\overset{||}{\underset{O}{C}}-R \\ | \\ CH-O-\overset{||}{\underset{O}{C}}-R' + CH_3OH \overset{acid\ or\ base}{\longrightarrow} \\ | \\ CH_2-O-\overset{||}{\underset{O}{C}}-R'' \end{array} \qquad \begin{array}{ll} RCOOCH_3 & CH_2OH \\ + & | \\ R'COOCH_3 + & CHOH \\ + & | \\ R''COOCH_3 & CH_2OH \end{array}$$

A glyceride   Mixture of   Glycerol
(A fat)   methyl esters

2. Reaction with Grignard reagents

$$RCOOR' + 2R''MgX \longrightarrow \underset{\substack{| \\ OH}}{\overset{\substack{R'' \\ |}}{R-C-R''}}$$

Tertiary alcohol

Examples:

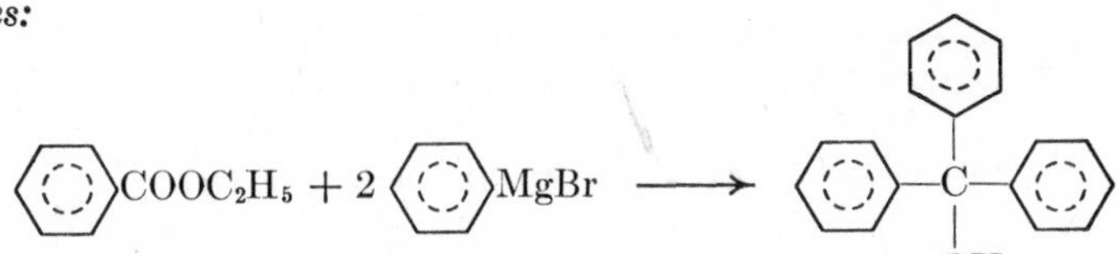

Ethyl benzoate   Phenylmagnesium bromide *2 moles*   Triphenylcarbinol

$$\underset{\substack{| \\ CH_3}}{CH_3CHCOOC_2H_5} + 2CH_3MgI \longrightarrow \underset{\substack{| \\ OH}}{CH_3CH-\overset{\substack{CH_3 \\ |}}{\underset{\substack{| \\ }}{C}}-CH_3}$$

Ethyl isobutyrate   Methylmagnesium iodide *2 moles*   2,3-Dimethyl-2-butanol

3. Reduction to alcohols

(a) Catalytic hydrogenation. Hydrogenolysis

$$RCOOR' + 2H_2 \xrightarrow[\substack{250°, \\ 3000-6000 \text{ lb/in.}^2}]{CuO.CuCr_2O_4} RCH_2OH + R'OH$$

1° alcohol

Example:

$$\underset{\substack{| \\ CH_3}}{CH_3-\overset{\substack{CH_3 \\ |}}{\underset{\substack{| \\ }}{C}}-COOC_2H_5} + 2H_2 \xrightarrow[\substack{250°, 3300 \text{ lb/in.}^2}]{CuO.CuCr_2O_4} \underset{\substack{| \\ CH_3}}{CH_3-\overset{\substack{CH_3 \\ |}}{\underset{\substack{| \\ }}{C}}-CH_2OH} + C_2H_5OH$$

Ethyl trimethylacetate (Ethyl 2,2-dimethylpropanoate)   Neopentyl alcohol (2,2-Dimethylpropanol)   Ethyl alcohol

(b) Chemical reduction

$$RCOOR' \xrightarrow{Na + \text{ an alcohol}} RCH_2OH + R'OH$$

1° alcohol

Bouveault-Blanc method

$$4RCOOR' + 2LiAlH_4 \xrightarrow{\substack{\text{anhyd.} \\ \text{ether}}} \left\{ \begin{array}{c} LiAl(OCH_2R)_4 \\ + \\ LiAl(OR')_4 \end{array} \right\} \xrightarrow{H^+} \left\{ \begin{array}{c} RCH_2OH \\ + \\ R'OH \end{array} \right\}$$

Examples:

$$CH_3(CH_2)_6COOC_2H_5 \xrightarrow{Na, C_2H_5OH} CH_3(CH_2)_6CH_2OH$$

Ethyl octanoate   1-Octanol

$$CH_3(CH_2)_7CH=CH(CH_2)_7COOCH_3 \xrightarrow{LiAlH_4} CH_3(CH_2)_7CH=CH(CH_2)_7CH_2OH$$

Methyl oleate (Methyl *cis*-9-octadecenoate)   Oleyl alcohol (*cis*-9-Octadecen-1-ol)

17.17   Acidic hydrolysis of esters

A carboxylic ester is hydrolyzed to a carboxylic acid and an alcohol or phenol when heated with aqueous acid or aqueous base. Under alkaline conditions, of course, the carboxylic acid is obtained as its salt, from which it can be liberated by addition of mineral acid.

We have already encountered (Sec. 16.16) acidic hydrolysis as the reverse of esterification. The presence of a large amount of water tends to shift the equilibrium toward the hydrolysis products.

$$RCOOR' + H_2O \overset{H^+}{\rightleftharpoons} RCOOH + R'OH$$

The function of hydrogen ion is necessarily the same here as in the esterification reaction: by attaching itself to carbonyl oxygen it renders carbonyl carbon more susceptible to nucleophilic attack, this time by water.

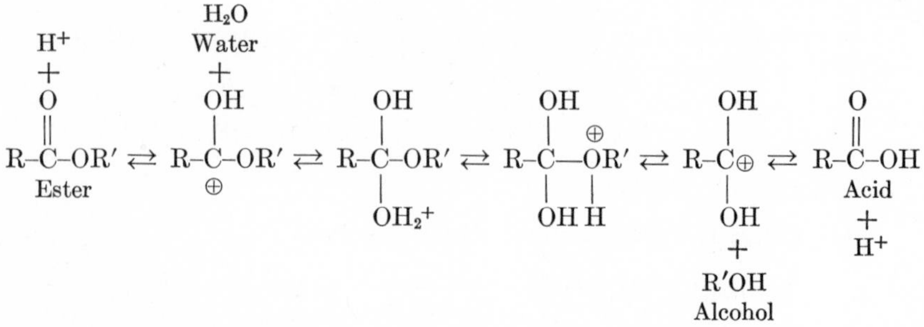

Tracer studies using O^{18} have shown (Sec. 16.17) that the alcohol group retains its oxygen atom in the formation of the ester, indicating cleavage of the hydrogen–oxygen bond, $H\text{--}OR'$. Since hydrolysis is the exact reverse of esterification, we would expect the alcohol group to retain the oxygen during this reaction, too; that is, we would expect cleavage of the bond between oxygen and the acyl group, $RCO\text{--}OR'$. Tracer studies have shown that this is so:

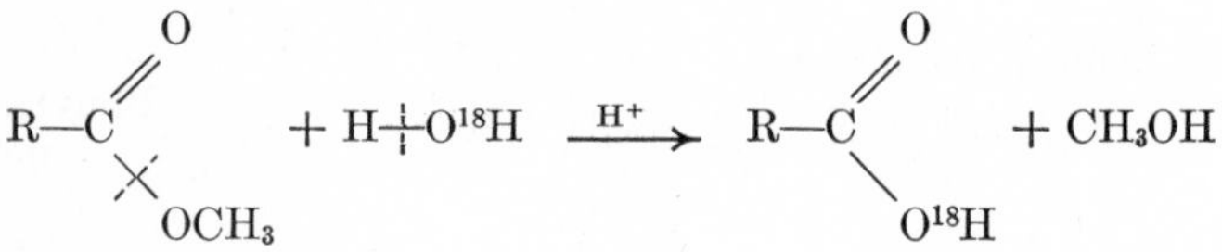

17.18   Alkaline hydrolysis of esters

In alkaline hydrolysis of esters, the absence of acid catalysis is offset by having a more strongly nucleophilic reagent, OH^- instead of H_2O:

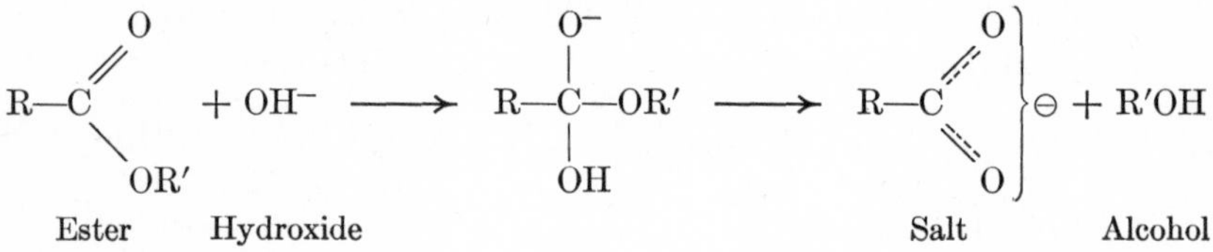

This reaction is essentially irreversible, since a resonance-stabilized carboxylate anion (Sec. 16.13) shows little tendency to react with an alcohol.

As the reaction is written above, alkaline hydrolysis, like acidic hydrolysis, involves cleavage of the bond between oxygen and the acyl group, RCO⋮OR′; that is, the alcohol group retains the oxygen. What evidence is there for this?

First, there are the results of stereochemical studies. Let us consider, for example, the formation and subsequent hydrolysis of an ester of optically active *sec*-butyl alcohol. Reaction of (+)-*sec*-butyl alcohol with benzoyl chloride must involve cleavage of the hydrogen–oxygen bond and hence cannot change the configuration about the asymmetric carbon (see Sec. 15.8). If hydrolysis of this ester involves cleavage of the bond between oxygen and the *sec*-butyl group, we would expect almost certainly inversion (or inversion plus racemization if the reaction goes by an S_N1 type of mechanism):

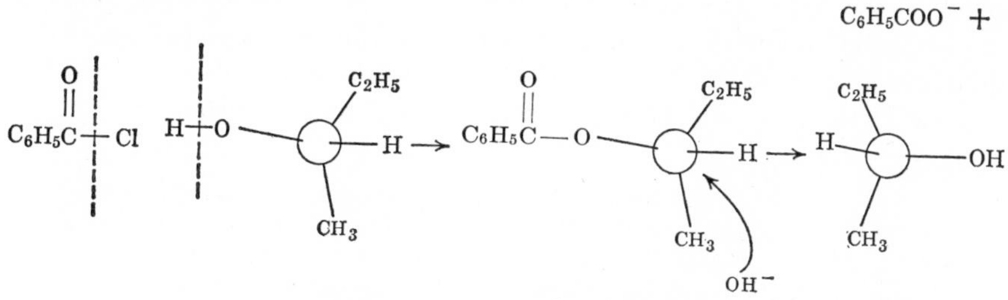
$C_6H_5COO^- +$
C_6H_5C
Cl
H
O
C_2H_5
H
CH_3
OH^-
OH

(+)-*sec*-Butyl alcohol — Cleavage between oxygen and alkyl group: *Inversion* — (−)-*sec*-Butyl alcohol

If, on the other hand, the bond between oxygen and the *sec*-butyl group remains intact during hydrolysis, then we would expect to obtain *sec*-butyl alcohol of the same configuration as the starting material:

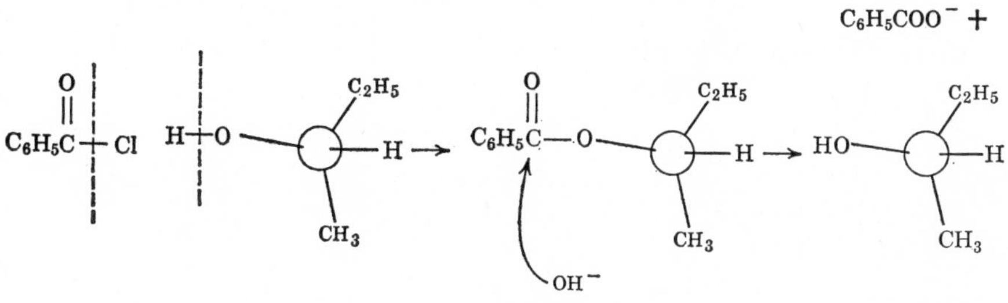
$C_6H_5COO^- +$
C_6H_5C
Cl
H
O
C_2H_5
H
CH_3
OH^-
HO

(+)-*sec*-Butyl alcohol — Cleavage between oxygen and acyl group: *Retention* — (+)-*sec*-Butyl alcohol

When *sec*-butyl alcohol of rotation +13.8° was actually converted into the benzoate and the benzoate was hydrolyzed in alkali, there was obtained *sec*-butyl alcohol of rotation +13.8°. This complete retention of configuration strongly indicates that bond cleavage occurs between oxygen and the acyl group.

Tracer studies have confirmed the kind of bond cleavage indicated by the stereochemical evidence. When *n*-pentyl acetate was hydrolyzed by base in water enriched with O^{18}, the acetic acid produced was found to be enriched in O^{18}; the *n*-pentyl alcohol contained only the ordinary amount of O^{18}:

$$CH_3-\overset{\displaystyle O}{\overset{\|}{C}}\diagdown\kern-1.2em\diagup OC_5H_{11} \quad + O^{18}H^- \longrightarrow \quad CH_3-\overset{\displaystyle O}{\overset{\|}{C}}\diagdown O^{18}H \quad + C_5H_{11}OH$$

The alcohol group retained the oxygen that it held in the ester; cleavage occurred between oxygen and the acyl group.

The study of a number of other hydrolyses by both tracer and stereochemical methods has shown that cleavage between oxygen and the acyl group is the usual one in ester hydrolysis. This behavior indicates that the preferred point of nucleophilic attack is the carbonyl carbon rather than the alkyl carbon; this is, of course, what we might have expected in view of the generally greater reactivity of carbonyl carbon.

Problem 17.3 Acidic hydrolysis of *tert*-butyl acetate in water enriched in O^{18} has been found to yield *tert*-butyl alcohol enriched in O^{18} and acetic acid containing ordinary oxygen. Acidic hydrolysis of the acetate of optically active 3,7-dimethyl-3-octanol has been found to yield alcohol of much lower optical purity than the starting alcohol, and having the opposite sign of rotation. (a) How do you interpret these two sets of results? (b) Is it reasonable that these particular esters should show this kind of behavior?

Problem 17.4 Account for the following observations. (*Hint:* see Sec. 13.13, and Problem 13.8 on page 381.)

$$C_6H_5-\underset{\underset{\displaystyle \text{OCR}}{|}}{CH}-CH=CH-CH_3$$
optically active

$\xrightarrow{\text{5N NaOH}}$ $C_6H_5-\underset{\underset{\displaystyle OH}{|}}{CH}-CH=CH-CH_3$
complete retention

$\xrightarrow{\text{dil. NaOH}}$ $C_6H_5-CH=CH-\underset{\underset{\displaystyle OH}{|}}{CH}-CH_3$
inactive

(where OCR group: $\overset{\displaystyle OCR}{\underset{\displaystyle \overset{\|}{O}}{}}$)

$$C_6H_5-CH=CH-\underset{\underset{\displaystyle \text{OCR}}{|}}{CH}-CH_3$$
optically active

$\xrightarrow{\text{dil. NaOH}}$ $C_6H_5-CH=CH-\underset{\underset{\displaystyle OH}{|}}{CH}-CH_3$
inactive

$\xrightarrow{\text{5N NaOH}}$ $C_6H_5-CH=CH-\underset{\underset{\displaystyle OH}{|}}{CH}-CH_3$
complete retention

17.19 Ammonolysis of esters

Treatment of an ester with ammonia, generally in ethyl alcohol solution, yields the amide. This reaction involves nucleophilic attack by a base, ammonia, on the electron-deficient carbon; the alkoxy group, —OR′, is replaced by —NH_2. For example:

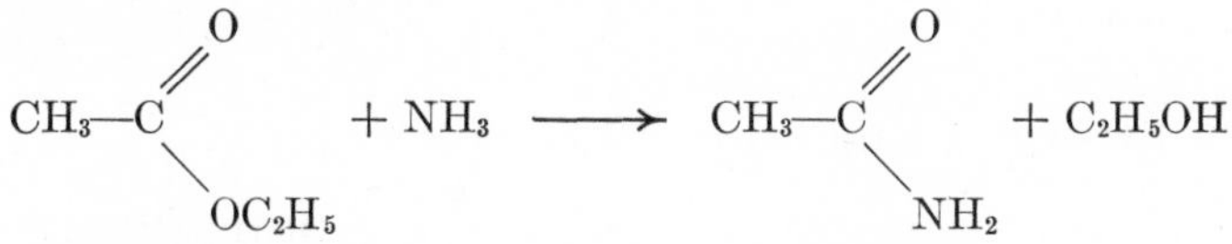

$$CH_3-\overset{\displaystyle O}{\underset{\displaystyle OC_2H_5}{C}} + NH_3 \longrightarrow CH_3-\overset{\displaystyle O}{\underset{\displaystyle NH_2}{C}} + C_2H_5OH$$

Ethyl acetate　　　　　　　　　　Acetamide

17.20 Transesterification

In the esterification of an acid, an alcohol acts as a nucleophilic reagent; in hydrolysis of an ester, an alcohol is displaced by a nucleophilic reagent. Knowing this, we are not surprised to find that one alcohol is capable of displacing another alcohol from an ester. This *alcoholysis* (cleavage by an alcohol) of an ester is called **transesterification.**

$$RCOOR' + R''OH \underset{\longleftarrow}{\overset{H^+ \text{ or } OR''^-}{\longrightarrow}} RCOOR'' + R'OH$$

Transesterification is catalyzed by acid (H_2SO_4 or dry HCl) or base (usually alkoxide ion). The mechanisms of these two reactions are exactly analogous to those we have already studied. For acid-catalyzed transesterification:

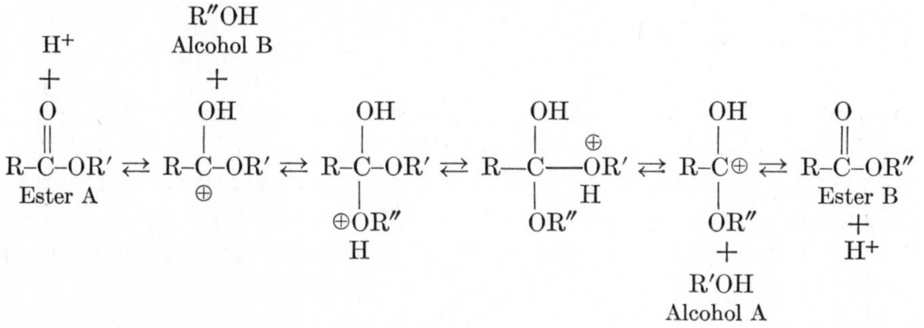

For base-catalyzed transesterification:

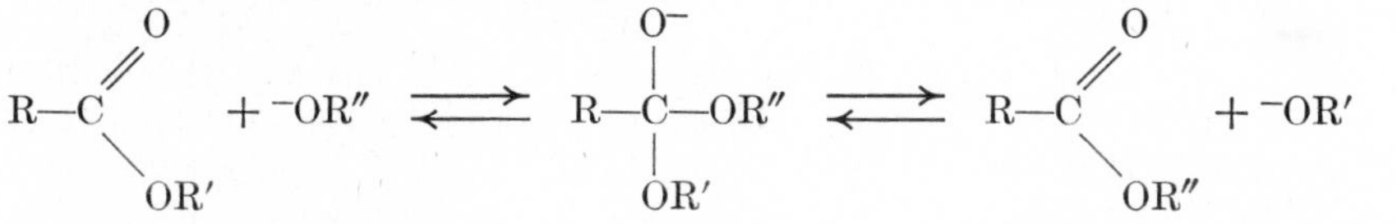

Ester A　　Alkoxide B　　　　　　　　　　　　　　Ester B　　Alkoxide A

Transesterification is an equilibrium reaction. To shift the equilibrium to the right it is necessary to use a large excess of the alcohol whose ester we wish to make, or else to remove one of the products from the reaction mixture. The second approach is the better one when feasible, since in this way the reaction can be driven to completion.

An excellent example of the application of the transesterification reaction is found in the synthesis of the polymer, *polyvinyl alcohol*. Polyvinyl alcohol cannot be made by the polymerization of vinyl alcohol, since that compound does not exist (Sec. 6.12). An ester of vinyl alcohol, *vinyl acetate*, does exist, however; it is prepared by addition of acetic acid to acetylene in the presence of mercuric sulfate:

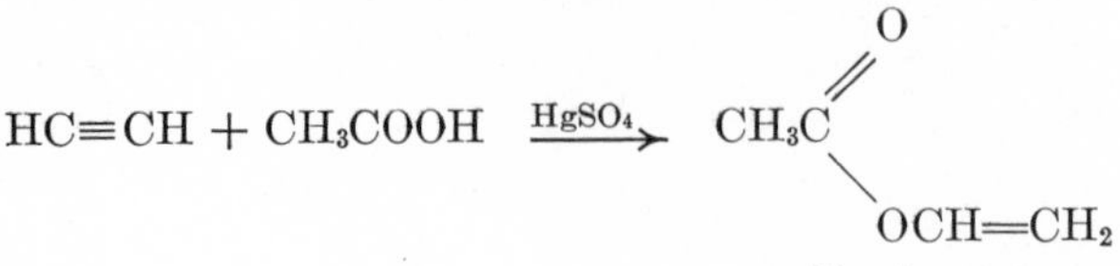

$$HC\equiv CH + CH_3COOH \xrightarrow{HgSO_4} \quad CH_3C\underset{OCH=CH_2}{\overset{O}{<}}$$

Vinyl acetate

(This addition is quite analogous to the addition of water to acetylene that gives rise to vinyl alcohol. Through ionization of hydrogen, vinyl alcohol is rapidly converted into the more stable acetaldehyde; an analogous conversion does not take place with vinyl acetate since it would have to involve separation of the acetyl group.)

Polymerization of vinyl acetate yields the polyester, *polyvinyl acetate:*

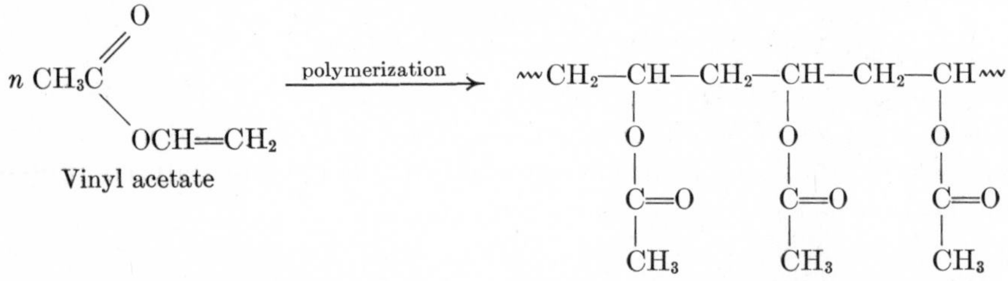

$$n\ CH_3C\underset{OCH=CH_2}{\overset{O}{<}} \xrightarrow{polymerization} \rightsquigarrow CH_2-CH-CH_2-CH-CH_2-CH\rightsquigarrow$$

Vinyl acetate

$$\begin{array}{ccc} O & O & O \\ | & | & | \\ C=O & C=O & C=O \\ | & | & | \\ CH_3 & CH_3 & CH_3 \end{array}$$

Polyvinyl acetate

Although there are hundreds of acetate groups in every molecule of polyvinyl acetate, each of them undergoes the reactions typical of any ester. For example, in the presence of sulfuric acid, polyvinyl acetate and methyl alcohol can exist in equilibrium with methyl acetate and polyvinyl alcohol; if the reaction mixture is held at 57–59°, the lowest boiling component, methyl acetate (b.p. 57°), distills out and the reaction proceeds to completion:

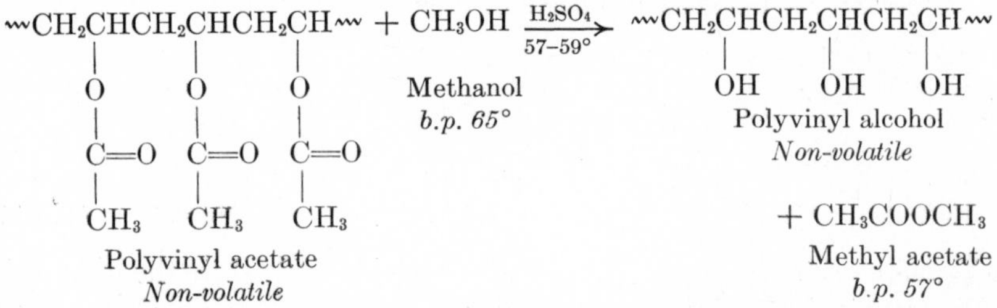

$$\rightsquigarrow CH_2CHCH_2CHCH_2CH\rightsquigarrow + CH_3OH \xrightarrow[57-59°]{H_2SO_4} \rightsquigarrow CH_2CHCH_2CHCH_2CH\rightsquigarrow$$

Methanol
b.p. 65°

$$\begin{array}{ccc} O & O & O \\ | & | & | \\ C=O & C=O & C=O \\ | & | & | \\ CH_3 & CH_3 & CH_3 \end{array}$$

Polyvinyl acetate
Non-volatile

OH   OH   OH
Polyvinyl alcohol
Non-volatile

$$+ CH_3COOCH_3$$

Methyl acetate
b.p. 57°

The polyvinyl alcohol thus obtained is used to form water-soluble coatings and as an intermediate in the formation of certain other polymers (Sec. 23.14).

Polyvinyl acetate itself, and copolymers of vinyl acetate and vinyl chloride, are used to produce tough films, sheets, and fibers.

17.21 Reaction of esters with Grignard reagents

The reaction of carboxylic esters with Grignard reagents is an excellent method for preparing tertiary alcohols. As in the reaction with aldehydes and ketones (Sec. 11.11), the nucleophilic (basic) alkyl or aryl group of the Grignard reagent attaches itself to the electron-deficient carbonyl carbon. Expulsion of the alkoxide group would yield a ketone, and in certain special cases, ketones are indeed isolated from this reaction. However, as we know, ketones themselves readily react with Grignard reagents to yield tertiary alcohols (Sec. 11.12); in the present case the products obtained correspond to the addition of the Grignard reagent to such a ketone:

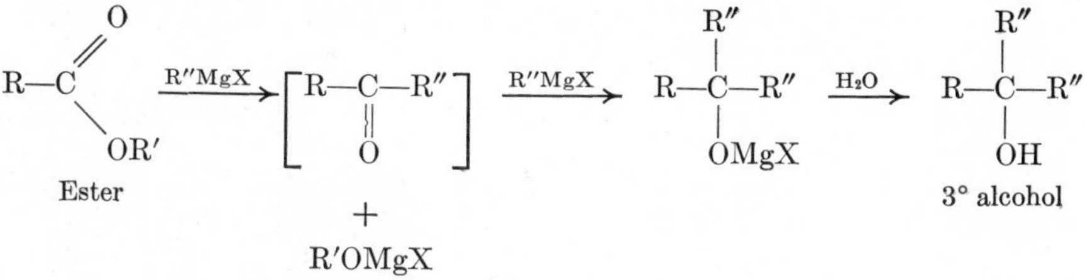

Two of the three groups attached to the carbon bearing the hydroxyl group in the alcohol come from the Grignard reagent and hence must be identical; this, of course, places limits upon the alcohols that can be prepared by this method. Where applicable, reaction of a Grignard reagent with an ester is preferred to reaction with a ketone because of the generally greater availability of the esters. Triphenylcarbinol, for example, could be prepared by the reaction of phenylmagnesium bromide either with the ester, ethyl benzoate, or with the ketone, benzophenone. It is simpler — fewer steps and better yield — to esterify benzoic acid than to convert it into the acid chloride and carry out a Friedel-Crafts acylation of benzene to form the required benzophenone.

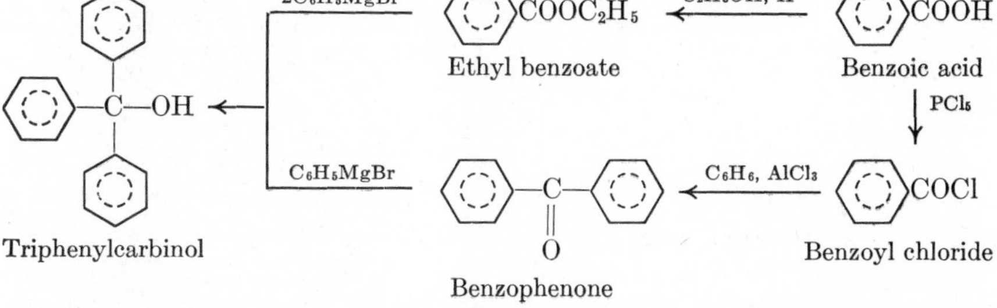

The advantage of an ester over a ketone in this reaction can also be seen in the synthesis of 3-ethyl-3-heptanol shown on the next page.

$$\begin{array}{c} C_2H_5 \\ | \\ n\text{-}C_4H_9\text{-}C\text{-}C_2H_5 \\ | \\ OH \end{array}$$
3-Ethyl-3-heptanol

$\xrightarrow{\;2C_2H_5MgBr\;}$ $n\text{-}C_4H_9COOCH_3$ $\xleftarrow{\;CH_3OH,\ H^+\;}$ $n\text{-}C_4H_9COOH$

Methyl valerate   Valeric acid

$\Big\downarrow SOCl_2$

$\xrightarrow{\;C_2H_5MgBr\;}$ $n\text{-}C_4H_9\text{-}\overset{\displaystyle O}{\overset{||}{C}}\text{-}C_2H_5$ $\xleftarrow{\;(C_2H_5)_2Cd\;}$ $n\text{-}C_4H_9COCl$

Valeroyl chloride

3-Heptanone

Esters of formic acid, HCOOR′, which have hydrogen attached to the carbon of the carboxyl group, necessarily yield secondary alcohols upon reaction with Grignard reagents. This reaction provides an excellent method of making symmetrical secondary alcohols, RCHOHR. For example:

$$\begin{array}{c} O \\ \diagup\!\!\diagup \\ H\!-\!C \\ \diagdown \\ OC_2H_5 \end{array} \;+\; 2CH_3CH_2CH_2MgBr \;\longrightarrow\; CH_3CH_2CH_2\!-\!\overset{\displaystyle H}{\underset{\displaystyle OH}{\overset{|}{\underset{|}{C}}}}\!-\!CH_2CH_2CH_3$$

Ethyl formate n-Propylmagnesium   4-Heptanol
                  bromide
                  2 moles

Problem 17.5 Prepare 4-heptanol by another Grignard sequence from alcohols of four carbons or less.

17.22 Reduction of esters

Like many organic compounds, esters can be reduced in two ways: (a) by catalytic hydrogenation using molecular hydrogen, or (b) by chemical reduction. In either case, the ester is cleaved to yield (in addition to the alcohol or phenol from which it was derived) a primary alcohol corresponding to the acid portion of the ester.

$$RCOOR' \xrightarrow{\;\text{reduction}\;} RCH_2OH + R'OH$$

Ester   1° alcohol

Hydrogenolysis (cleavage by hydrogen) of an ester requires more severe conditions than simple hydrogenation of (addition of hydrogen to) a carbon–carbon double bond. High pressures and elevated temperatures are required; the catalyst used most often is a mixture of oxides known as *copper chromite*, of approximately the composition $CuO.CuCr_2O_4$. For example:

$$CH_3(CH_2)_{10}COOCH_3 \xrightarrow[\;150°,\ 5000\ lb/in.^2\;]{H_2,\ CuO.CuCr_2O_4} CH_3(CH_2)_{10}CH_2OH + CH_3OH$$

Methyl laurate   Lauryl alcohol
(Methyl dodecanoate)   (1-Dodecanol)

Chemical reduction is usually carried out by use of sodium metal and alcohol (the **Bouveault-Blanc** method), or by use of lithium aluminum hydride. For example:

$$CH_3(CH_2)_7CH{=}CH(CH_2)_7C\overset{O}{\underset{OC_2H_5}{\diagdown}} \xrightarrow{\text{Na, C}_2\text{H}_5\text{OH}} CH_3(CH_2)_7CH{=}CH(CH_2)_7CH_2OH$$

Ethyl oleate
(Ethyl *cis*-9-octadecenoate)

Oleyl alcohol
(*cis*-9-Octadecen-1-ol)

$$CH_3(CH_2)_{14}COOC_2H_5 \xrightarrow{\text{LiAlH}_4} CH_3(CH_2)_{14}CH_2OH$$

Ethyl palmitate
(Ethyl hexadecanoate)

1-Hexadecanol

Problem 17.6 Predict the products of the hydrogenolysis of *n*-butyl oleate over copper chromite.

FATS

17.23 Occurrence and composition of fats

In terms of our everyday living, by far the most important esters are those occurring naturally in animal and vegetable **fats.** (Liquid fats are often referred to as *oils*.) Such materials as corn oil, coconut oil, cottonseed oil, palm oil, tallow, bacon grease, and butter are made up largely of esters of carboxylic acids. These esters are derived from a single alcohol, *glycerol*, $HOCH_2CHOHCH_2OH$, and hence are known as **glycerides.**

With very few exceptions, the carboxylic acids from which fats are derived are all straight-chain compounds, ranging in size from three to eighteen carbons; except for the C_3 and C_5 compounds, only acids containing an even number of carbon atoms are present in any substantial amounts. Besides saturated acids, there are unsaturated acids containing one or more double bonds per molecule.

We see in Table 17.3 that each fat is made up of glycerides derived from many different carboxylic acids. The proportions of the various acids vary from fat to fat; each fat has its characteristic composition, which does not differ widely from sample to sample.

Fats make up one of the three major classes of foods (the others being carbohydrates, Chapter 30, and proteins, Chapter 33); they are used in enormous amounts as raw materials for many industrial processes. The specialized chemistry of fats is vast and complicated, particularly the biochemistry and technology. In the following sections we shall examine a tiny fraction of the chemistry of fats so that we may see the application of the fundamental chemistry of esters to these more complicated compounds.

17.24 Hydrolysis of fats. Saponification. Soap

The making of soap is one of the oldest of chemical syntheses. (It is not nearly so old, of course, as the production of ethyl alcohol; man's desire for cleanliness is much newer than his desire for intoxication.) When the German tribesmen of Caesar's time boiled goat tallow with potash leached from the ashes of wood fires, they were carrying out the same

TABLE 17.3

FATTY ACID COMPOSITION OF FATS AND OILS

Fat or oil	Saturated Acids							Unsaturated acids					
									Enoic			Dienoic	Trienoic
	C_8	C_{10}	C_{12}	C_{14}	C_{16}	C_{18}	$> C_{18}$	$< C_{16}$	C_{16}	C_{18}	$> C_{18}$	C_{18}	C_{18}
Beef tallow			0.2	2–3	25–30	21–26	0.4–1	0.5	2–3	39–42	0.3	2	
Butter	1–2[a]	2–3	1–4	8–13	25–32	8–13	0.4–2	1–2	2–5	22–29	0.2–1.5	3	
Coconut	5–9	4–10	44–51	13–18	7–10	1–4				5–8	0–1	1–3	
Corn				0–2	8–10	1–4			1–2	30–50	0–2	34–56	
Cottonseed				0–3	17–23	1–3				23–44	0–1	34–55	
Lard				1	25–30	12–16	0–1	0.2	2–5	41–51	2–3	3–8	
Olive			0–1	0–2	7–20	1–3			1–3	53–86	0–3	4–22	
Palm				1–6	32–47	1–6				40–52		2–11	
Palm kernel	2–4	3–7	45–52	14–19	6–9	1–3	1–2		0–1	10–18		1–2	
Peanut				0.5	6–11	3–6	5–10		1–2	39–66		17–38	
Soybean				0.3	7–11	2–5	1–3		0–1	22–34		50–60	2–10
Cod liver				2–6	7–14	0–1		0–2	10–20	25–31	C_{20} 25–32; $> C_{20}$ 10–20		
Linseed				0.2	5–9	4–7	0.5–1			9–29		8–29	45–67
Tung										4–13		8–15	b

a. 3–4% C_4, 1–2% C_6.
b. 72–82% eleostearic acid, *cis,trans,trans*-9,11,13-octadecatrienoic acid, and 3–6% saturated acids.

chemical reaction as the one carried out on a tremendous scale by modern soap manufacturers: *hydrolysis of glycerides*. Hydrolysis yields salts of the carboxylic acids, and glycerol, $CH_2OHCHOHCH_2OH$.

$$
\begin{array}{c}
CH_2-O-C-R \\
\quad\quad\; \| \\
\quad\quad\; O \\
CH-O-C-R' \\
\quad\quad\; \| \\
\quad\quad\; O \\
CH_2-O-C-R'' \\
\quad\quad\; \| \\
\quad\quad\; O
\end{array}
\xrightarrow{\;NaOH\;}
\begin{array}{c}
CH_2OH \\
| \\
CHOH \\
| \\
CH_2OH
\end{array}
+
\left\{
\begin{array}{c}
RCOO^- \, Na^+ \\
R'COO^- \, Na^+ \\
R''COO^- \, Na^+
\end{array}
\right\}
$$

　　　A glyceride　　　　　　　Glycerol　　　　　Soap
　　　(A fat)

Ordinary soap today is simply a mixture of sodium salts of long-chain fatty acids. It is a mixture because the fat from which it is made is a mixture, and for washing our hands or our clothes a mixture is just as good as a single pure salt. Soap may vary in composition and method of processing: if made from olive oil it is *Castile soap;* alcohol can be added to make it transparent; air can be beaten in to make it float; perfumes, dyes, and germicides can be added; if a potassium salt (instead of a sodium salt) it is *soft soap.* Chemically, however, soap remains pretty much the same, and does its job in the same way.

The cleansing action of a soap is an extremely complicated matter, but we can get some idea of the factors involved from the following simplified picture. A soap molecule has a polar end, —COO⁻ Na⁺, and a non-polar end, the long carbon chain of 12 to 18 carbons; the polar end is water-soluble, the non-polar end is oil-soluble. Ordinarily oil droplets in contact with water tend to coalesce so that there is an oil layer and a water layer; but the presence of soap changes this. The non-polar ends of soap molecules dissolve in the oil droplet, leaving the carboxylate ends

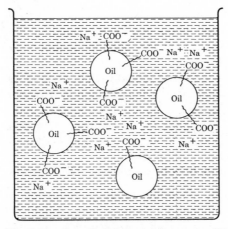

FIGURE 17.1 Emulsification of oil in water by soap. Non-polar hydro- carbon chains dissolve in oil; polar —COO⁻ groups dissolve in water. Similarly charged droplets repel each other.

projecting into the surrounding water layer (Figure 17.1). Due to the presence of the negatively charged carboxylate groups, each oil droplet is surrounded by an ionic atmosphere. Repulsion between similar charges keeps the oil droplets from coalescing, and a stable emulsion of oil in water is thus obtained. Soap cleans by emulsifying the fat and grease that make up and contain the dirt. As we shall see, this emulsifying, and hence cleansing, property is not limited to carboxylic salts, but is possessed by any molecule containing a large non-polar portion and a polar portion (Sec. 17.26).

Hard water contains calcium and magnesium salts, which react with soap to form insoluble calcium and magnesium carboxylates (the "ring" in the bathtub).

17.25   Fats as sources of pure acids

Treatment of the sodium soaps with mineral acid (or hydrolysis of fats under acidic conditions) liberates a mixture of the free carboxylic acids. In recent years, fractional distillation of these mixtures has been developed on a commercial scale to furnish individual carboxylic acids of over 90% purity.

Alternatively, fats are sometimes converted by transesterification into the methyl esters of the carboxylic acids; the glycerides are allowed to react with methanol in the presence of a basic or acidic catalyst.

$$
\begin{array}{ccc}
\text{CH}_2\!-\!\text{O}\!-\!\overset{\|}{\underset{\text{O}}{\text{C}}}\!-\!\text{R} & & \\
\text{CH}\!-\!\text{O}\!-\!\overset{\|}{\underset{\text{O}}{\text{C}}}\!-\!\text{R}' \ + \ \text{CH}_3\text{OH} \ \xrightarrow{\ \text{base}\ } &
\begin{array}{c}\text{CH}_2\text{OH}\\ | \\ \text{CHOH} \\ | \\ \text{CH}_2\text{OH}\end{array} \ +
\left\{\begin{array}{c}\text{RCOOCH}_3\\ \text{R}'\text{COOCH}_3\\ \text{R}''\text{COOCH}_3\end{array}\right\} \\
\text{CH}_2\!-\!\text{O}\!-\!\overset{\|}{\underset{\text{O}}{\text{C}}}\!-\!\text{R}'' & &
\end{array}
$$

A glyceride   Methanol   Glycerol   Mixture of methyl esters

The mixture of methyl esters can be separated by fractional distillation into individual esters, which can then be hydrolyzed to individual carboxylic acids of high purity.

Fats are thus the source of straight-chain acids of even carbon number ranging from six to eighteen carbons; these in turn can be converted into alcohols by reduction (generally via their esters), and from these can be derived a host of compounds (as in Problem 16.9, page 461). Fats thus provide us with long straight-chain units to use in organic synthesis.

17.26   Reduction of fats to alcohols.   Detergents

Like other esters, glycerides undergo reduction at the carboxylate group. There are obtained mixtures of long straight-chain alcohols corresponding to the acid portions of the glycerides.

On an industrial scale reduction of fats has been carried out both catalytically and chemically:

$$CH_2OCR$$
$$|\quad \|$$
$$|\quad O$$
$$CHOCR'$$
$$|\quad \|$$
$$|\quad O$$
$$CH_2OCR''$$
$$\|$$
$$O$$

A glyceride

$\xrightarrow{\text{H}_2,\ \text{CuO.CuCr}_2\text{O}_4,\ 250°,\ 3000-6000\ \text{lb/in.}^2}$

$\xrightarrow{\text{Na, C}_2\text{H}_5\text{OH}}$

$$\left\{ \begin{array}{l} RCH_2OH \\ R'CH_2OH \\ R''CH_2OH \end{array} \right\}$$

Mixture of
primary alcohols

The Bouveault-Blanc reduction with sodium metal and alcohol was used on a large scale during World War II when shortages of materials for the catalyst and for high-pressure equipment prevented use of catalytic hydrogenation. Since the war, chemical reduction has continued to expand and is now one of the major uses of sodium metal in this country.

The fat most commonly reduced is coconut oil, which yields a mixture containing a high proportion of the C_{12} alcohol, lauryl alcohol. Most of the alcohols obtained from fats are used in the synthesis of detergents (cleansing agents), as, for example, the salts of alkyl hydrogen sulfates:

$$n\text{-}C_{11}H_{23}CH_2OH \xrightarrow{\text{H}_2\text{SO}_4} n\text{-}C_{11}H_{23}CH_2OSO_3H \xrightarrow{\text{NaOH}} n\text{-}C_{11}H_{23}CH_2OSO_3^- \ Na^+$$

Lauryl alcohol   Lauryl hydrogen sulfate   Sodium lauryl sulfate

(Alkyl hydrogen sulfates are esters of sulfuric acid.) Although the synthetic detergents vary considerably in their chemical structure, the molecules of all of them have one common feature: a large non-polar hydrocarbon end that is oil-soluble, and a polar end that is water-soluble. In the salts of the alkyl hydrogen sulfates, for example, the non-polar end is the long chain, and the polar end is the $—OSO_3{}^-Na^+$ grouping.

These detergents act in essentially the same way as soap does. They are used because they have certain advantages. For example, sodium alkyl sulfates retain their efficiency in hard water, since the corresponding calcium and magnesium salts are soluble. Being salts of strong acids, the sodium alkyl sulfates yield neutral solutions, in contrast to the soaps, which, being salts of weak acids, yield slightly alkaline solutions (Sec. 16.10).

17.27 Unsaturated fats.   Hardening of oils.   Drying oils

We can see in Table 17.3 that fats contain, in varying proportions, glycerides of certain unsaturated carboxylic acids. The most common of these acids are:

$$CH_3(CH_2)_7CH{=}CH(CH_2)_7COOH \qquad CH_3(CH_2)_4CH{=}CHCH_2CH{=}CH(CH_2)_7COOH$$

Oleic acid   Linoleic acid
(*cis*-isomer)   (*cis,cis*-isomer)

$$CH_3CH_2CH{=}CHCH_2CH{=}CHCH_2CH{=}CH(CH_2)_7COOH$$

Linolenic acid
(*cis,cis,cis*-isomer)

Other things being equal, unsaturation in a fat tends to lower its melting point and thus tends to make it a liquid at room temperature. In the

United States the long established use of lard and butter for cooking purposes has led to a prejudice against the use of the cheaper, equally nutritious oils. Hydrogenation of some of the double bonds in such cheap fats as cottonseed oil, corn oil, and soy bean oil converts these liquids into solids having a consistency comparable to that of lard or butter. This *hardening* of oils is the basis of an important industry that produces cooking fats (e.g., Crisco, Spry) and oleomargarine. Hydrogenation of the carbon–carbon double bonds takes place under such mild conditions (Ni catalyst, 175–190°, 20–40 lb/in.^{2}) that hydrogenolysis of the ester linkage does not occur.

Hydrogenation not only changes the physical properties of a fat, but also — and this is even more important — changes the chemical properties: a hydrogenated fat becomes *rancid* much less readily than does a non-hydrogenated fat. Rancidity is due to the presence of volatile, bad-smelling acids and aldehydes. These compounds result (in part, at least) from attack by oxygen at reactive allylic positions in the fat molecules; hydrogenation slows down the development of rancidity presumably by decreasing the number of double bonds and hence the number of allylic positions.

Linseed oil and tung oil have special importance because of their high content of glycerides derived from acids that contain two or three double bonds. They are known as **drying oils** and are important constituents of paints and varnishes. The "drying" of paint does not involve merely evaporation of a solvent (turpentine, etc.), but rather a chemical reaction in which a tough organic film is formed. Aside from the color due to the pigments present, protection of a surface by this film is the chief purpose of paint. The film is formed by a polymerization of the unsaturated oils that is brought about by oxygen. The polymerization process and the structure of the polymer are extremely complicated and are not well understood. The process seems to involve, in part, free radical attack at reactive allylic hydrogens, free radical addition polymerization similar to that previously described (Sec. 6.20), and cross-linking by oxygen analogous to that by sulfur in vulcanized rubber (Sec. 6.21).

17.28 Analysis of carboxylic acid derivatives. Saponification equivalent

Functional derivatives of carboxylic acids are recognized by their hydrolysis — under more or less vigorous conditions — to carboxylic acids. Just *which kind* of derivative it is is indicated by the other products of the hydrolysis.

Problem 17.7 Which kind (or kinds) of acid derivative: (a) rapidly forms a white precipitate (insoluble in HNO$_3$) upon treatment with alcoholic silver nitrate? (b) reacts with boiling aqueous NaOH to liberate a gas that turns moist litmus paper blue? (c) reacts immediately with cold NaOH to liberate a gas that turns moist litmus blue? (d) yields *only* a carboxylic acid upon hydrolysis? (e) yields an alcohol when heated with acid or base?

Identification or proof of structure of an acid derivative involves the identification or proof of structure of the carboxylic acid formed upon hydrolysis (Sec. 16.22). In the case of an ester, the alcohol that is obtained is also identified (Sec. 12.11). (In the case of a substituted amide, Sec. 20.7, the amine obtained is identified, Sec. 20.14.)

If an ester is hydrolyzed in a known amount of base (taken in excess), the amount of base used up can be measured and used to give the **saponification equivalent:** the equivalent weight of the ester, which is similar to the neutralization equivalent of an acid (see Sec. 16.22).

$$RCOOR' + OH^- \longrightarrow RCOO^- + R'OH$$

one
equivalent   one
equivalent

Problem 17.8 (a) What is the saponification equivalent of n-propyl acetate? (b) There are eight other simple aliphatic esters that have the same saponification equivalent. What are they? (c) In contrast, how many simple aliphatic acids have this equivalent weight? (d) Is saponification equivalent as helpful in identification as neutralization equivalent?

Problem 17.9 (a) How many equivalents of base would be used up by one mole of methyl phthalate, $o\text{-}C_6H_4(COOCH_3)_2$? What is the saponification equivalent of methyl phthalate? (b) What is the relation between saponification equivalent and the number of ester groups per molecule? (c) What is the saponification equivalent of glyceryl stearate (tristearin)?

PROBLEMS

1. Draw structures and give names of:
(a) nine isomeric esters of formula $C_5H_{10}O_2$
(b) six isomeric esters of formula $C_8H_8O_2$
(c) eleven isomeric esters of formula $C_{14}H_{12}O_2$ (*Hint:* three of these are methyl esters.)

2. Write balanced equations, naming all organic products, for the reaction (if any) of n-butyryl chloride with:

(a) H_2O

(b) isopropyl alcohol

(c) p-nitrophenol

(d) ammonia

(e) toluene, $AlCl_3$

(f) nitrobenzene, $AlCl_3$

(g) $NaHCO_3$ (aq)

(h) alcoholic $AgNO_3$

(i) CH_3NH_2

(j) $(CH_3)_2NH$

(k) $(CH_3)_3N$

(l) $C_6H_5NH_2$

(m) $(C_6H_5)_2Cd$

(n) C_6H_5MgBr

(Check your answers to (i) through (l) in Sec. 20.7.)

3. Answer Problem 2, parts (a) through (l) for acetic anhydride.

4. Write balanced equations, naming all organic products, for the reaction (if any) of phenylacetamide with:

(a) hot HCl (aq)

(b) hot NaOH (aq).

5. Answer Problem 4 for phenylacetonitrile.

6. Write balanced equations, naming all organic products, for the reaction (if any) of methyl n-butyrate with:

(a) hot H_2SO_4 (aq)

(b) hot KOH (aq)

(c) isopropyl alcohol + H_2SO_4

(d) benzyl alcohol + $C_6H_5CH_2ONa$

(e) ammonia

(f) phenylmagnesium bromide

(g) isobutylmagnesium bromide

(h) H_2, $CuO.CuCr_2O_4$, heat, pressure

(i) $LiAlH_4$, then acid

(j) Na, C_2H_5OH

7. Outline the synthesis of each of the following labeled compounds, using H_2O^{18} as the source of O^{18}.

(a) $C_6H_5-\overset{\overset{O}{\|}}{C}-O^{18}CH_3$ (b) $C_6H_5-\overset{\overset{O^{18}}{\|}}{C}-OCH_3$ (c) $C_6H_5-\overset{\overset{O^{18}}{\|}}{C}-O^{18}CH_3$

Predict the product obtained from each upon alkaline hydrolysis in ordinary H_2O.

8. Outline the synthesis of each of the following labeled compounds, using $C^{14}O_2$ or $C^{14}H_3OH$ and H_2O^{18} as the source of the "tagged" atoms.

(a) $CH_3CH_2C^{14}CH_3$, with $\overset{\|}{O}$ below

(b) $CH_3CH_2CC^{14}H_3$, with $\overset{\|}{O}$ below

(c) $CH_3C^{14}H_2CCH_3$, with $\overset{\|}{O}$ below

(d) $C^{14}H_3CH_2CCH_3$, with $\overset{\|}{O}$ below

(e) $C_6H_5C^{14}H_2CH_3$

(f) $C_6H_5CH_2C^{14}H_3$

(g) $CH_3CH_2CCH_3$, with $\overset{\|}{O^{18}}$ below

9. The relative rates of alkaline hydrolysis of ethyl p-substituted benzoates, p-$GC_6H_4COOC_2H_5$, are:

$$G = NO_2 > Cl > H > CH_3 > OCH_3$$
$$110 \quad 4 \quad 1 \quad 0.5 \quad 0.2$$

(a) How do you account for this order of reactivity? (b) What kind of effect, activating or deactivating, would you expect from p-Br? from p-NH_2? from p-$C(CH_3)_3$? (c) Predict the order of reactivity toward alkaline hydrolysis of: p-aminophenyl acetate, p-methylphenyl acetate, p-nitrophenyl acetate, phenyl acetate.

10. The relative rates of alkaline hydrolysis of alkyl acetates, CH_3COOR, are:

$$R = CH_3 > C_2H_5 > (CH_3)_2CH > (CH_3)_3C$$
$$1 \quad 0.6 \quad 0.15 \quad 0.008$$

(a) What two factors might be at work here? (b) Predict the order of reactivity toward alkaline hydrolysis of: methyl acetate, methyl formate, methyl isobutyrate, methyl propionate, and methyl trimethylacetate.

11. When heated in methanol solution, *tert*-butyl benzoate yielded not only methyl benzoate and *tert*-butyl alcohol, but also benzoic acid and methyl *tert*-butyl ether. (*tert*-Butyl alcohol and methanol fail to react under these conditions.) (a) What point of cleavage is indicated by the formation of methyl *tert*-butyl ether? (b) Under similar conditions methyl benzoate and methanol do not yield methyl ether. How do you account for the difference in behavior of the two esters? By what mechanism is methyl *tert*-butyl ether most probably formed?

12. Esters can be made by the reaction between alkyl halides and salts of carboxylic acids:

$$RX + R'COO^- M^+ \longrightarrow R'COOR + MX$$

(a) To what general class does this reaction belong? (b) How would you expect the 2-octyl acetate formed from $(-)$-2-bromooctane and sodium acetate to compare with the same ester formed from $(-)$-2-octanol and acetyl chloride? (Refer to the text for any needed configurations and rotations.) (c) What would be the sign of rotation of the 2-octanol obtained by alkaline hydrolysis of each ester in (b)?

13. Describe simple chemical tests that would serve to distinguish between:

(a) propionic acid and methyl acetate
(b) n-butyryl chloride and n-butyl chloride
(c) p-nitrobenzamide and ethyl p-nitrobenzoate
(d) glyceryl tristearate and glyceryl trioleate
(e) benzonitrile and nitrobenzene
(f) acetic anhydride and n-butyl alcohol
(g) glyceryl monopalmitate and glyceryl tripalmitate
(h) ammonium benzoate and benzamide

(i) *p*-bromobenzoic acid and benzoyl bromide

Tell exactly what you would do and see.

14. Tell how you would separate by chemical means the following mixtures, recovering each component in reasonably pure form: (a) benzoic acid and ethyl benzoate; (b) *n*-valeronitrile and *n*-valeric acid; (c) ammonium benzoate and benzamide. Tell exactly what you would do and see.

15. *Spermaceti* (a wax from the head of the sperm whale) resembles high-molecular weight hydrocarbons in physical properties and inertness toward Br_2/CCl_4 and $KMnO_4$; on qualitative analysis it gives positive tests only for carbon and hydrogen. However, its infrared spectrum shows the presence of an ester group, and quantitative analysis gives the empirical formula $C_{16}H_{32}O$.

A solution of the wax and KOH in ethanol is refluxed for a long time. Titration of an aliquot shows that one equivalent of base has been consumed for every 475 ± 10 grams of wax. Water and ether are added to the cooled reaction mixture, and the aqueous and ethereal layers are separated. Acidification of the aqueous layer yields a solid A, m.p. 62–3°, neutralization equivalent 260 ± 5. Evaporation of the ether layer yields a solid B, m.p. 48–9°. (a) What is a likely structure of spermaceti? (b) Reduction by $LiAlH_4$ of either spermaceti or A gives B as the only product. Does this confirm the structure you gave in (a)?

16. An unknown compound is believed to be one of the following, all of which boil within a few degrees of each other. Describe how you would go about finding out which of the possibilities the unknown actually is. Where possible use simple chemical tests; where necessary use more elaborate chemical methods like quantitative hydrogenation, cleavage, neutralization equivalent, saponification equivalent, etc. Make use of any needed tables of physical constants.

benzyl acetate	methyl *o*-toluate
ethyl benzoate	methyl *m*-toluate
isopropyl benzoate	methyl *p*-toluate
methyl phenylacetate	

17. What does each of the following facts tell you about the structure of the compound in question? Suggest a possible structure for each compound. (Where possible, check your answer by use of the index.)

(a) *glucose* ($C_6H_{12}O_6$) + acetic anhydride $\longrightarrow$ $C_{16}H_{22}O_{11}$
(b) *tartaric acid* ($C_4H_6O_6$) + ethyl alcohol + H$^+$ $\longrightarrow$ Compound C ($C_8H_{14}O_6$)
(c) Compound C + benzoyl chloride + OH$^-$ $\longrightarrow$ $C_{22}H_{22}O_8$
(d) *gallic acid* ($C_7H_6O_5$) + acetic anhydride $\longrightarrow$ Compound D ($C_{13}H_{12}O_8$)
(e) Compound D + methanol + H$^+$ $\longrightarrow$ $C_{14}H_{14}O_8$

18. Give the structures (including configurations where pertinent) of compounds E through R.

(a) bromobenzene + Mg, ether $\longrightarrow$ E (C_6H_5MgBr)
E + ethylene oxide, followed by H$^+$ $\longrightarrow$ F ($C_8H_{10}O$)
F + PBr$_3$ $\longrightarrow$ G (C_8H_9Br)
G + NaCN $\longrightarrow$ H (C_9H_9N)
H + H_2SO_4, H_2O, heat $\longrightarrow$ I ($C_9H_{10}O_2$)
I + SOCl$_2$ $\longrightarrow$ J (C_9H_9OCl)
J + anhydrous HF $\longrightarrow$ K (C_9H_8O)
K + H$_2$, catalyst $\longrightarrow$ L ($C_9H_{10}O$)
L + H_2SO_4, warm $\longrightarrow$ M (C_9H_8)
(b) ethyl alcohol + ethylene oxide + H$^+$ $\longrightarrow$ N ($C_4H_{10}O_2$)
N + KMnO$_4$ $\longrightarrow$ O ($C_4H_8O_3$)
O + ethylene glycol + H$^+$ $\longrightarrow$ P ($C_{10}H_{18}O_6$)
(c) *trans*-2-methylcyclohexanol + acetyl chloride $\longrightarrow$ Q
Q + NaOH (aq) + heat $\longrightarrow$ R + sodium acetate

SULFONIC ACIDS AND
THEIR DERIVATIVES

18.1   Structure and nomenclature of sulfonic acids

Besides the carboxylic acids, there is a second important class of organic acids, the **sulfonic acids.**   We shall limit our discussion to the *aromatic* sulfonic acids, since the aliphatic sulfonic acids are of only minor importance.

The aromatic sulfonic acids have the general formula $ArSO_3H$. They are named by adding *–sulfonic acid* to the name of the compound to which the —SO_3H group is attached.

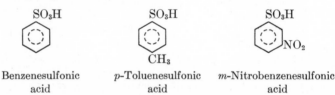

| Benzenesulfonic acid | *p*-Toluenesulfonic acid | *m*-Nitrobenzenesulfonic acid |

It is important to distinguish sulfonic acids, in which carbon is bonded directly to sulfur, from the esters of sulfuric acid, in which carbon is bonded to oxygen.

$$
\underset{\text{A sulfonic acid}}{Ar—\overset{\displaystyle O}{\underset{\displaystyle O}{\overset{|}{\underset{|}{S}}}}—OH}
\qquad\qquad
\underset{\substack{\text{A sulfate}\\\text{(an ester)}}}{Ar—O—\overset{\displaystyle O}{\underset{\displaystyle O}{\overset{|}{\underset{|}{S}}}}—OH}
$$

18.2   Physical properties of sulfonic acids

As we would expect from their structure, sulfonic acids have the physical properties characteristic of highly polar compounds.   As a class they are more soluble in water than any other kind of organic compound.   Indeed, the —SO_3H group is often introduced into large molecules (e.g., those of a drug or a dye) chiefly to bring about water solubility.   Being strong acids, they are completely ionized in these aqueous solutions:

$$ArSO_3H + H_2O \longrightarrow ArSO_3^- + H_3O^+$$

They are also soluble in certain other polar solvents, including the sulfuric acid in which they are prepared, but are insoluble in the usual organic solvents. They are compounds of low volatility and on being heated generally decompose before their boiling points are reached.

Salts are readily prepared from these highly acidic compounds by treatment with bases. Since the sulfonic acids themselves are highly deliquescent and difficult to purify, they are conveniently isolated as their salts, and are often used in this form.

18.3 Preparation of sulfonic acids

Aromatic sulfonic acids are practically always prepared by direct sulfonation, usually by fuming sulfuric acid. If the acid chloride is desired, as is often the case, the —SO₂Cl group can be introduced in one operation by treatment of the aromatic compound with *chlorosulfonic acid*, ClSO₃H.

PREPARATION OF AROMATIC SULFONIC ACIDS

Sulfonation

$$ArH + H_2SO_4 \xrightarrow{SO_3} ArSO_3H + H_2O$$

$$\underset{\substack{\text{Chlorosulfonic} \\ \text{acid}}}{ArH + 2ClSO_3H} \longrightarrow \underset{\substack{\text{A sulfonyl} \\ \text{chloride}}}{ArSO_2Cl} + HCl + H_2SO_4$$

Examples:

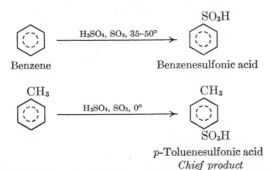

Benzene $\xrightarrow{H_2SO_4,\ SO_3,\ 35\text{–}50°}$ Benzenesulfonic acid (SO₃H)

p-Toluenesulfonic acid
Chief product

A sulfonic acid is most often separated from the sulfonation mixture, purified, and used, in the form of one of its salts. The most generally applicable method of isolation takes advantage of the fact that a calcium or barium sulfonate is appreciably more soluble in water than calcium or barium sulfate.

The sulfonation mixture is poured into water, and the solution is neutralized by the addition of calcium carbonate; insoluble calcium sulfate and excess calcium carbonate are removed by filtration. The resulting solution of the calcium sulfonate is then treated carefully with just the right amount of sodium carbonate; insoluble calcium carbonate is removed by filtration. Evaporation of the filtrate yields the sodium sulfonate. (Calcium hydroxide, barium hydroxide, or barium carbonate can be used in place of calcium carbonate in this procedure.)

Problem 18.1 Write equations for all reactions involved in the isolation of the sodium salt of a sulfonic acid.

Problem 18.2 Outline the preparation of a free sulfonic acid from a solution of its calcium or barium salt.

18.4   Reactions of sulfonic acids

The most important reactions of the aromatic sulfonic acids are summarized below.

REACTIONS OF AROMATIC SULFONIC ACIDS

1. Acidity. Salt formation

$$ArSO_3H + H_2O \longrightarrow ArSO_3^- + H_3O^+ \qquad \textit{Completely ionized}$$

Examples:

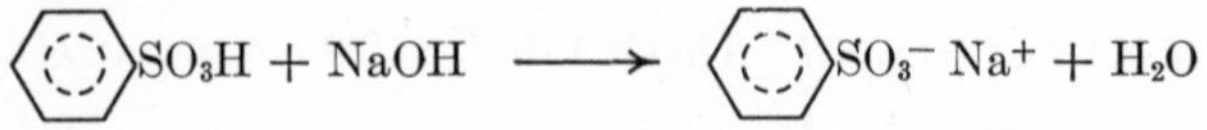

Benzenesulfonic acid → Sodium benzenesulfonate

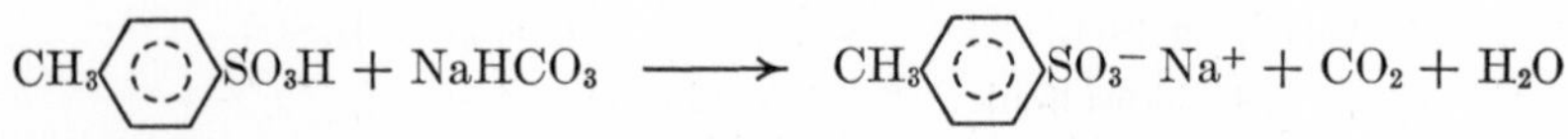

p-Toluenesulfonic acid → Sodium p-toluenesulfonate

2. Conversion into sulfonyl chlorides

$$\text{Ar—S(=O)(=O)—OH} + PCl_5 \longrightarrow \text{Ar—S(=O)(=O)—Cl} + POCl_3 + HCl \text{ (or NaCl)}$$

(or ArSO$_3$Na)

Other derivatives prepared from sulfonyl chlorides

Example:

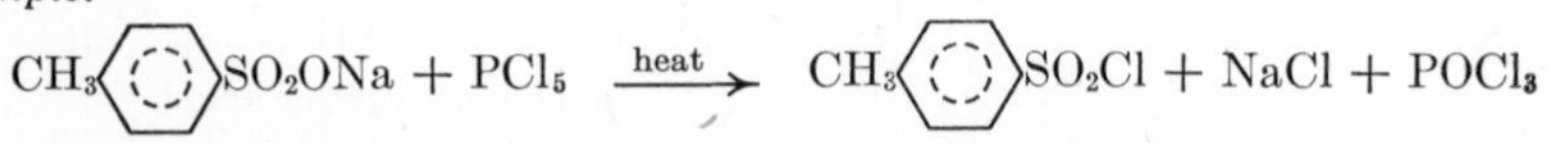

$$CH_3C_6H_4SO_2ONa + PCl_5 \xrightarrow{\text{heat}} CH_3C_6H_4SO_2Cl + NaCl + POCl_3$$

Sodium p-toluenesulfonate → p-Toluenesulfonyl chloride

3. Desulfonation

$$ArSO_3H + H_2O \xrightarrow[\text{heat}]{H^+} ArH + H_2SO_4$$

Example:

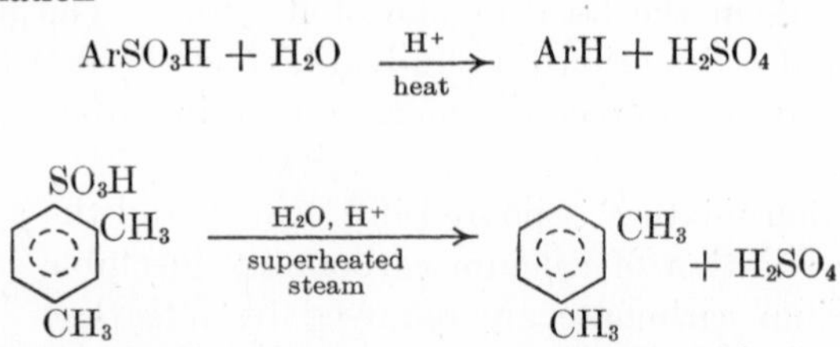

2,4-Dimethylbenzenesulfonic acid
Non-volatile

m-Xylene
Volatile

4. Ring substitution

$-SO_3H$: Deactivates, and directs *meta* in electrophilic aromatic substitution.

Example:

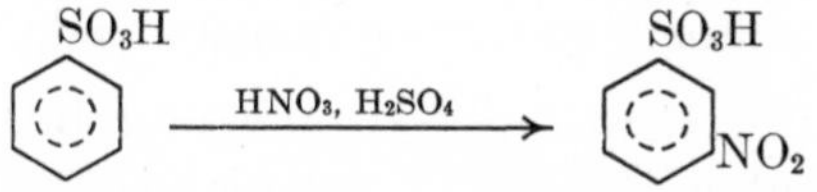

Benzenesulfonic acid　　*m*-Nitrobenzenesulfonic acid
72% yield

5. Fusion with alkali. Preparation of phenols. Discussed in Sec. 22.6.

$$ArSO_3Na + NaOH \xrightarrow{\text{strong heat}} Na_2SO_3 + ArONa \xrightarrow{H^+} \underset{\text{A phenol}}{ArOH}$$

We have seen that carboxylic acids owe their appreciable acidity to the effect of the acyl group, RCO—, on the release of hydrogen ion from the —OH group; the negative charge of the carboxylate anion is dispersed over two oxygen atoms (Sec. 16.13):

$$C_6H_5-C\begin{matrix}\nearrow O\\ \searrow OH\end{matrix} + H_2O \rightleftharpoons H_3O^+ + \left[C_6H_5-C\begin{matrix} O\\ O\end{matrix}\right]^{\ominus} \qquad K_a = 6.3 \times 10^{-5}$$

In the same way, sulfonic acids owe their powerful acidity to the effect of the sulfonyl group, $ArSO_2$—. It is possible that much of the difference between the carbonyl and sulfonyl groups is due to the presence *as such* of carbon in one and sulfur in the other. However, it seems reasonable that a part of the greater acid-strengthening effect of the sulfonyl group should be due to the fact that it contains two oxygen atoms; thus the negative charge of the sulfonate ion is dispersed over *three* oxygen atoms:

$$C_6H_5-\overset{O}{\underset{O}{S}}-OH + H_2O \rightleftharpoons H_3O^+ + \left[C_6H_5-\overset{O}{\underset{O}{S}}-O\right]^{\ominus} \qquad K_a \textit{ very large}$$

Although the two oxygens of the sulfonyl group promote the ionization of hydrogen, they seem to make replacement of the —OH group more difficult. Of the functional derivatives of sulfonic acids, only sulfonyl chlorides can be prepared directly from the acids; esters and amides must be prepared from the sulfonyl chlorides (Sec. 18.6). This point is discussed more fully in Sec. 18.9.

An aromatic ring to which $-SO_3H$ is attached undergoes electrophilic substitution in the way expected of a ring carrying a strongly electron-attracting group: with deactivation and *meta* direction. One particular kind of electrophilic attack, which results in the displacement of the $-SO_3H$ group itself, is discussed in the following section.

18.5   Desulfonation

When an aromatic sulfonic acid is heated to 100–175° with aqueous acid, it is converted into sulfuric acid and an aromatic hydrocarbon. We recognize this *desulfonation* as the exact reverse of the sulfonation process by which the sulfonic acid was originally made.

$$ArH + H_2SO_4 \underset{\longleftarrow}{\overset{H^+}{\longrightarrow}} ArSO_3H + H_2O$$

Hydrocarbon   Sulfonic acid

Volatile   *Non-volatile*

By applying the usual equilibrium principles we can select conditions that will drive the reaction in the direction we want it to go. To sulfonate we use a large excess of concentrated or fuming sulfuric acid; high concentration of sulfonating agent and low concentration of water (or its removal by reaction with SO_3) shift the equilibrium toward sulfonic acid. To desulfonate we use dilute acid and often pass superheated steam through the reaction mixture; high concentration of water and removal of the relatively volatile hydrocarbon by steam distillation shift the equilibrium toward hydrocarbon.

Problem 18.3   In Sec. 8.21 the mechanism of sulfonation is outlined. (a) Write all steps in the mechanism for desulfonation. (b) To what general class of organic reactions does desulfonation belong? What is the attacking reagent?

Problem 18.4   When aniline or phenol is treated with D_2SO_4 in D_2O (deuterium sulfate in heavy water) there is formed aniline or phenol containing deuterium instead of hydrogen at the positions *ortho* and *para* to the —NH_2 or —OH group. Benzene undergoes similar exchange but at a much lower rate; under the same conditions benzenesulfonic acid does not undergo exchange at all. (a) Outline the most probable mechanism for hydrogen–deuterium exchange in aromatic compounds. (b) To what general class of organic reactions does this belong?

Problem 18.5   Treatment of *sulfanilic acid* (p-$H_2NC_6H_4SO_3H$) with 3 moles of bromine yields 2,4,6-tribromoaniline. Treatment of 4-hydroxy-1,3-benzenedisulfonic acid with nitric acid yields picric acid, 2,4,6-trinitrophenol. (a) Outline the most probable mechanism for the replacement of —SO_3H by —Br and by —NO_2. (b) To what general class of organic reactions do these reactions belong?

One practical application of desulfonation is illustrated by the separation of pure *m*-xylene from its isomers. The crude xylene fraction obtained from coal tar distillation contains all three xylenes; further separation of the isomers by distillation is difficult because of the closeness of their boiling points: *ortho*, 144°; *meta*, 139°; *para*, 138°. *m*-Xylene is more reactive toward electrophilic substitution than its isomers. (Why?) It is readily sulfonated by 80% sulfuric acid at room temperature, conditions under which the other two fail to react. The resulting sulfonic acid from *m*-xylene dissolves in the polar reaction medium (H_2SO_4); the non-polar unsulfonated *o*- and *p*-xylene do not dissolve, and can be removed. Dilution of the remaining acidic sulfonation mixture followed by steam distillation regenerates pure *m*-xylene. Here a separation that is difficult by physical means — such as distillation — is accomplished by chemical means.

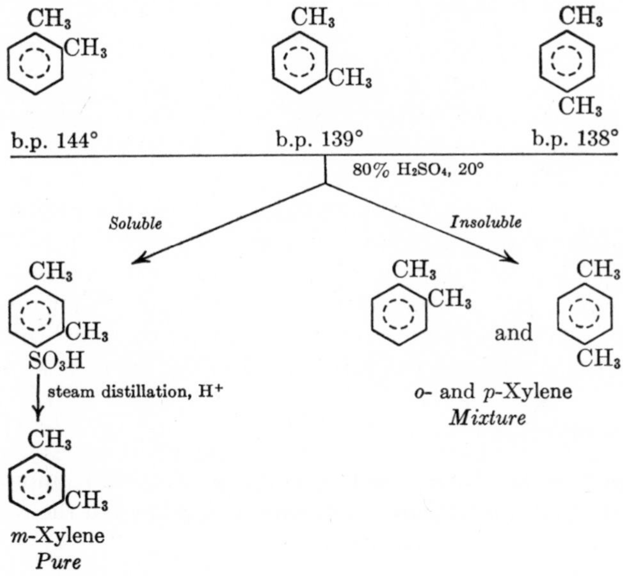

18.6 Sulfonyl chlorides

Sulfonyl chlorides (the acid chlorides of sulfonic acids) are prepared by the action of phosphorus pentachloride or thionyl chloride on sulfonic acids or their salts:

$$ArSO_2OH + PCl_5 \xrightarrow{\text{heat}} ArSO_2Cl + POCl_3 + HCl$$
$$\text{(or } ArSO_3Na) \qquad\qquad \underset{\text{chloride}}{\text{A sulfonyl}} \qquad \text{(or } NaCl)$$

Sometimes aromatic hydrocarbons are converted directly into sulfonyl chlorides by treatment with excess chlorosulfonic acid, $ClSO_3H$:

$$ArH \xrightarrow{ClSO_3H} ArSO_3H \xrightarrow{ClSO_3H} ArSO_2Cl$$
$$+ HCl \qquad\qquad + H_2SO_4$$

For example:

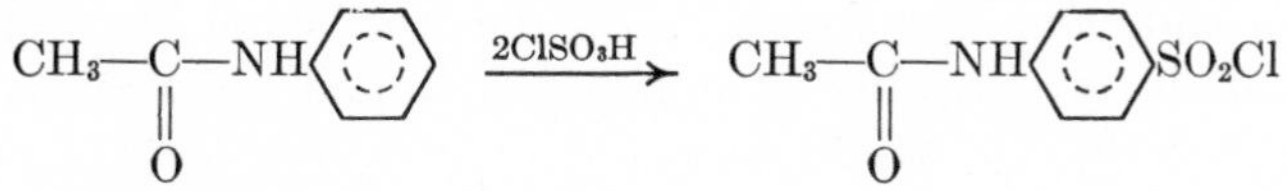

Acetanilide

Sulfonyl chlorides are important as intermediates in the preparation of the other functional derivatives, none of which can be prepared directly from the sulfonic acids. Sulfonyl chlorides react with alcohols or phenols to form esters, and with ammonia to form amides:

$$ArSO_2Cl + ROH \xrightarrow[\text{or pyridine}]{\text{aqueous } OH^-} ArSO_2OR + Cl^- + H_2O$$
$$\text{or} \qquad\qquad\qquad \text{or}$$
$$Ar'OH \qquad\qquad\qquad ArSO_2OAr'$$
$$\text{A sulfonic ester}$$

$$ArSO_2Cl + 2NH_3 \longrightarrow ArSO_2NH_2 + NH_4Cl$$
A sulfonamide

For example:

$$CH_3\text{-}C\text{-}NH\langle\bigcirc\rangle SO_2Cl + 2NH_3 \longrightarrow CH_3\text{-}C\text{-}NH\langle\bigcirc\rangle SO_2NH_2 + NH_4Cl$$

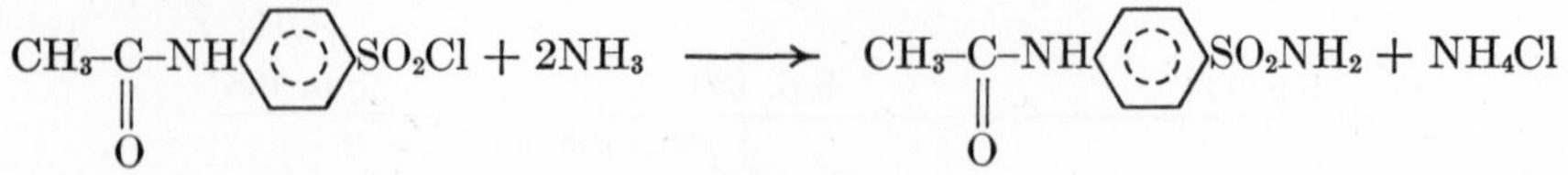

In reactions like these, sulfonyl chlorides are even less reactive than acid chlorides of the aromatic carboxylic acids. To speed up reaction and to prevent formation of by-products, the reaction with alcohols or phenols is carried out in the presence of base (the Schotten-Baumann technique, Sec. 17.7). (The important reaction of sulfonyl chlorides with amines to form substituted sulfonamides is discussed in Sec. 20.14.)

18.7 Sulfonamides

Sulfonamides are hydrolyzed to sulfonic acids and ammonia by hot aqueous acid, but not by base. Reaction is slower than the corresponding hydrolysis of amides of carboxylic acids.

$$ArSO_2NH_2 + H_2O \xrightarrow[\text{heat}]{75\% \ H_2SO_4} ArSO_3H + NH_4^+$$
Sulfonamide   Sulfonic acid

Sulfonic acids are stronger acids than carboxylic acids; the sulfonyl group, $ArSO_2\text{—}$, is more effective than the acyl group, $RCO\text{--}$, in promoting release of hydrogen ion from the —OH group. The sulfonyl group is also more effective in promoting release of hydrogen ion from the —NH group of amides (see Table 18.1). Amides of carboxylic acids are only very weakly acidic, and do not react appreciably with concen-

TABLE 18.1
ACIDITY OF ACYL AND SULFONYL COMPOUNDS

	K_a		K_a
C_6H_5COOH	6.3×10^{-5}	$C_6H_5CONH_2$	$10^{-14}\text{--}10^{-15}$
$C_6H_5SO_3H$	very large	$C_6H_5SO_2NH_2$	10^{-10}

trated hydroxide ion. Sulfonamides, on the other hand, show appreciable acidity, and dissolve readily in aqueous hydroxide solutions; they are weaker than carboxylic acids, however, and do not dissolve in aqueous bicarbonate.

$$\underset{\substack{\text{Insoluble} \\ \text{in water}}}{Ar\text{—}\overset{\overset{O}{|}}{\underset{\underset{O}{|}}{S}}\text{—}NH_2} + OH^- \longrightarrow H_2O + \underset{\substack{\text{Soluble} \\ \text{in water}}}{Ar\text{—}\overset{\overset{O}{|}}{\underset{\underset{O}{|}}{S}}\text{—}NH}^{\ominus}$$

The importance of the acidity of sulfonamides in the Hinsberg test is discussed in Sec. 20.14.

Problem 18.6 Although amides of carboxylic acids are very weakly acidic ($K_a = 10^{-14}$ to 10^{-15}), they are still enormously more acidic than ammonia ($K_a = 10^{-33}$) or amines, RNH_2. How can you account for this? (*Hint:* see Sec. 16.13.)

Problem 18.7 Diacetamide, $(CH_3CO)_2NH$, is much more acidic ($K_a = 10^{-11}$) than acetamide ($K_a = 8.3 \times 10^{-16}$), and roughly comparable to benzenesulfonamide ($K_a = 10^{-10}$). How can you account for this?

18.8 Esters of sulfonic acids. Stereochemical inversion

Esters of sulfonic acids are prepared by the reaction between sulfonyl chlorides and alcohols or phenols, generally in the presence of base (Sec. 18.6); they cannot be prepared directly from the sulfonic acids.

$$ArSO_2Cl + ROH \xrightarrow{\text{base}} ArSO_2OR + H_2O + Cl^-$$
$$\text{or} \qquad\qquad\qquad \text{or}$$
$$Ar'OH \qquad\qquad ArSO_2OAr'$$

They are hydrolyzed to the sulfonic acid and the hydroxy compound when heated with aqueous acid or base.

$$
\begin{array}{l}
ArSO_2OR \\
(\text{or } ArSO_2OAr')
\end{array}
\left\{
\begin{array}{ll}
\xrightarrow{H^+} & ArSO_3H + ROH \quad (\text{or } Ar'OH) \\
\\
\xrightarrow{OH^-} & ArSO_3^- + ROH \quad (\text{or } Ar'O^-)
\end{array}
\right.
$$

Much of the interest in esters of sulfonic acids is due to their use in studying certain theoretical problems. Most commonly used are esters of *p*-toluenesulfonic acid: the *p*-toluenesulfonates. The name of the *p*-toluenesulfonyl group is often shortened to *tosyl* (Ts); *p*-toluenesulfonyl chloride thus becomes *tosyl chloride* (TsCl), and *p*-toluenesulfonates become *tosylates* (TsOR).

$$
CH_3{-}\langle\bigcirc\rangle{-}\overset{\overset{\displaystyle O}{\|}}{\underset{\underset{\displaystyle O}{\|}}{S}}{-} \quad = \quad \textit{Tosyl or Ts}
$$

We shall look at some reactions of alkyl tosylates (alkyl *p*-toluenesulfonates) with two purposes in mind: (a) to see some of the evidence that shows beyond question the occurrence of stereochemical inversion; and (b) to see how the configurations of alkyl halides have been related to the configurations of other compounds. We have seen (Sec. 15.8) that, in general, the configurational relationship between two optically active compounds is established by converting one into the other by reactions in which no bond to an asymmetric carbon is broken. For halides in which the asymmetric carbon bears the halogen, however, this method cannot be used, since it is not possible to make a halide from, or convert a halide into, another compound without involving the carbon–halogen bond.

An alcohol can be converted into its benzoate in two different ways: (a) directly by reaction with benzoyl chloride;

$$ROH + C_6H_5COCl \longrightarrow C_6H_5COOR$$

or (b) indirectly by reaction with tosyl chloride to form the tosylate, followed by reaction with sodium benzoate.

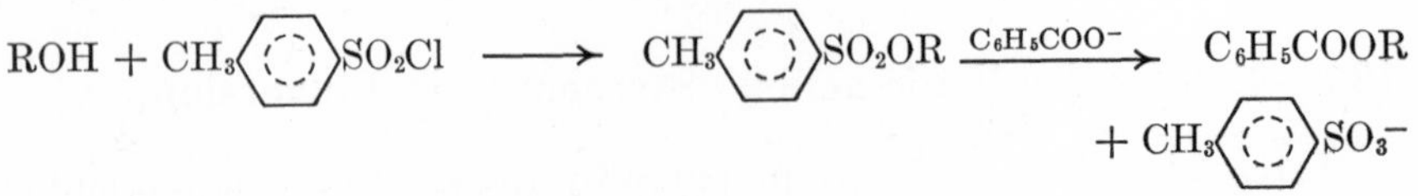

$$ROH + CH_3 \langle \bigcirc \rangle SO_2Cl \longrightarrow CH_3 \langle \bigcirc \rangle SO_2OR \xrightarrow{C_6H_5COO^-} C_6H_5COOR$$
$$+ CH_3 \langle \bigcirc \rangle SO_3^-$$

When these reactions were carried out starting with optically active *sec*-butyl alcohol, the *sec*-butyl benzoates obtained by the two different routes were found to have *opposite signs of rotation:* one ester rotated polarized light to the right, the other ester rotated polarized light almost exactly the same number of degrees to the left.

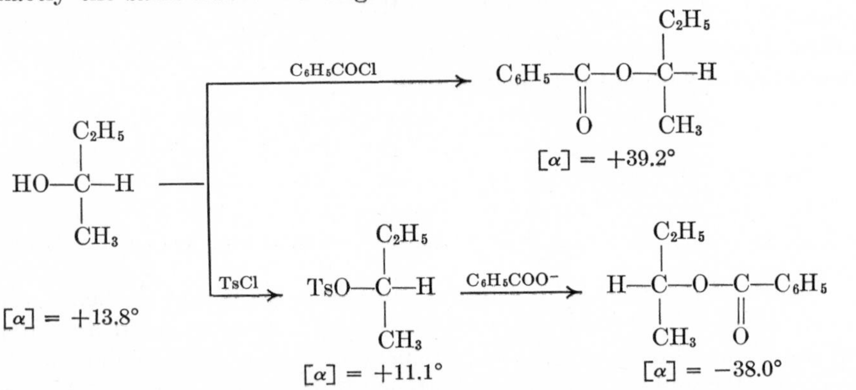

Obviously, both benzoates cannot have the same configuration as the *sec*-butyl alcohol. One of them must have the configuration opposite to that of the alcohol from which it was made, and hence one of the reaction sequences must have brought about an inversion of configuration.

In which reaction did the inversion of configuration take place? In the reaction of the alcohol with benzoyl chloride or with tosyl chloride, the hydrogen–oxygen bond of the alcohol must have been broken to yield hydrogen chloride and the ester; the oxygen–carbon bond of the alcohol must have remained intact. Since no bond to the asymmetric carbon was broken, these steps must have proceeded with retention of configuration.

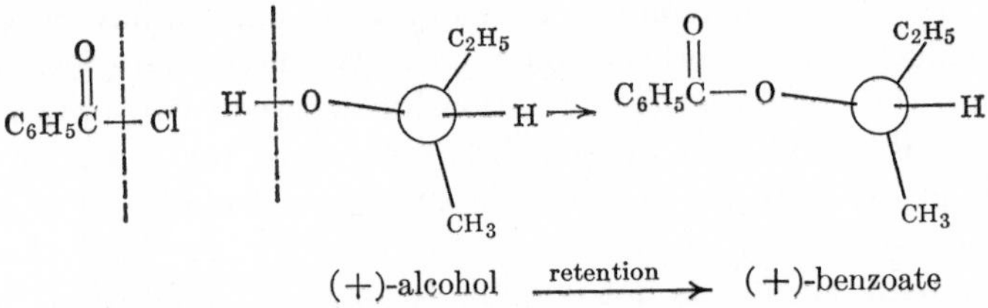

(+)-alcohol $\xrightarrow{\text{retention}}$ (+)-benzoate

Inversion must have occurred, then, in the reaction between *sec*-butyl tosylate and benzoate ion.

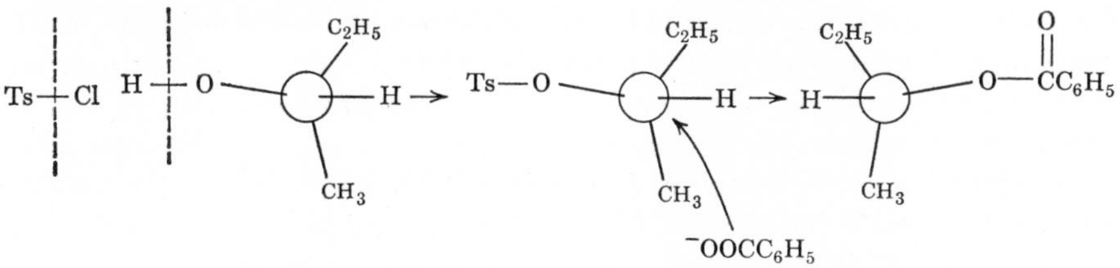

(+)-alcohol $\xrightarrow{\text{retention}}$ (+)-tosylate $\xrightarrow{\text{inversion}}$ (−)-benzoate

Conversion of the (+)-alcohol into both the (+)-benzoate and the (−)-benzoate shows that an inversion must have taken place somewhere; a consideration of the reactions involved shows where it must have occurred.

The benzoate from the benzoyl chloride reaction must have been formed with complete retention of configuration. Since the benzoate from the other reaction sequence has a rotation of almost the same value (although opposite in sign) it must have been formed with almost complete inversion. The reaction of benzoate ion with sec-butyl tosylate is thus a typical S_N2 reaction involving attack at the asymmetric carbon in the sec-butyl group, with displacement of the tosylate ion.

An analogous set of reactions has been carried out in which optically active sec-butyl alcohol was converted into its acetate: in one case directly by reaction with acetic anhydride, and in the other case by reaction of sodium acetate with sec-butyl tosylate. Exactly the same sort of results were obtained; clearly attack by acetate ion on sec-butyl tosylate proceeds with inversion.

Studies similar to these have been made with a number of other optically active alcohols, including 2-octanol and 1-phenyl-2-propanol; similar results were obtained. There can be no doubt about the occurrence of stereochemical inversion.

Most of the inversions that we encountered in previous chapters involved reactions of alkyl halides. Then it was said that those reactions proceeded with inversion, since the products obtained had configurations opposite to the configurations of the halides from which they were made. Let us look at some of the evidence that these configurations are indeed opposite.

Both the benzoate and the acetate obtained from (+)-sec-butyl alcohol by the tosylate reaction have been found to be the (−)-compounds. Since these reactions proceed with inversion, we know that the (−)-benzoate and the (−)-acetate have configurations opposite to that of (+)-sec-butyl alcohol; or conversely, we know that (+)-sec-butyl alcohol, the (+)-benzoate, and the (+)-acetate all have the same configuration.

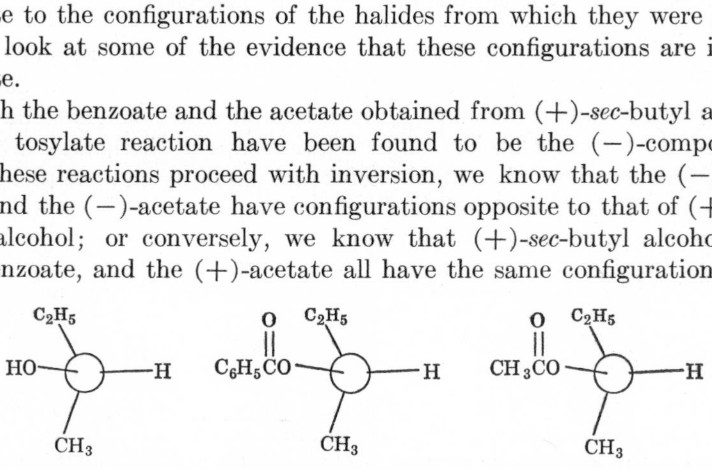

(+)-sec-Butyl alcohol　　(+)-sec-Butyl benzoate　　(+)-sec-Butyl acetate

Now if attack on tosylates by benzoate ion and acetate ion proceeds with inversion, it would seem reasonable that attack by other negative ions, such as chloride, bromide, or iodide, also proceeds with inversion. When the tosylate of (+)-*sec*-butyl alcohol was allowed to react with sodium iodide solution, there was obtained (−)-*sec*-butyl iodide; reaction with bromide ion yielded (−)-*sec*-butyl bromide. If the assumption is valid that halide ion attacks tosylates with inversion, then the (−)-bromide and the (−)-iodide must have configurations opposite to that of the (+)-alcohol; that is, the (+)-alcohol, (+)-bromide, and (+)-iodide all have the same configuration.

$$C_2H_5 \qquad\qquad C_2H_5 \qquad\qquad C_2H_5$$

HO—⟨ ⟩—H   Br—⟨ ⟩—H   I—⟨ ⟩—H

$$CH_3 \qquad\qquad CH_3 \qquad\qquad CH_3$$

(+)-*sec*-Butyl alcohol   (+)-*sec*-Butyl bromide   (+)-*sec*-Butyl iodide

In a similar way relationships between other alcohols and the corresponding halides have been established by reactions with tosylates.

Once it is known that, say, (+)-2-bromooctane has the same configuration as (+)-2-octanol, then the S_N2 reaction in which the (+)-bromide reacts with hydroxide ion to yield the (−)-alcohol is accepted as involving inversion.

$$C_6H_{13} \qquad\qquad\qquad C_6H_{13}$$

Br—⟨ ⟩—H $\xrightarrow[S_N2]{OH^-}$ H—⟨ ⟩—OH

$$CH_3 \qquad\qquad\qquad CH_3$$

(+)-2-Bromooctane   (−)-2-octanol

The configurational relationships between halides and alcohols — and through alcohols to many other compounds — are not so firmly established as are relationships established by reactions in which bonds to an asymmetric carbon are not broken. The relationships of the halides are based upon an assumption: that halide ions react similarly to acetate and benzoate ions. There seems to be no serious doubt as to the validity of this assumption among organic chemists today.

Problem 18.8 The reaction of α-phenylethyl tosylate with acetate ion proceeds with inversion and *much racemization*. (a) Compare this with results obtained using *sec*-butyl tosylate. (b) How can you account for the difference in behavior of the two esters?

Problem 18.9 (a) If *sec*-butyl alcohol of $[\alpha] = +13.8°$ were converted into the tosylate and the resulting ester were then hydrolyzed in alkali, what value of $[\alpha]$ would you predict for the alcohol thus obtained? (b) Compare this prediction with the results found for carboxylic esters (Sec. 17.18).

Problem 18.10 Alkaline hydrolysis of phenyl tosylate in water enriched in O^{18} has been found to yield p-toluenesulfonic acid enriched in O^{18} and phenol containing ordinary oxygen. (a) How do you interpret these results? (b) Do alkyl and aryl sulfonates show similar or different behavior? (c) How does the relationship between alkyl and aryl sulfonates compare with that between alkyl and aryl halides?

18.9 Comparison of sulfonyl compounds with acyl compounds

In summary, let us compare sulfonic acids and their derivatives with carboxylic acids and their derivatives. The differences between the two sets of compounds are due to differences in the effects exerted by the sulfonyl group ($ArSO_2$—) and by the acyl group (RCO— or $ArCO$—). Much of this is undoubtedly due to the fact that the two groups contain different elements, one *sulfur* and the other *carbon*. In addition, however, the differences are consistent with the presence of two oxygens in the sulfonyl group and only one oxygen in the acyl group.

The sulfonyl group exerts a greater acid-strengthening effect upon an attached —OH or —NH_2 group than does an acyl group. Thus sulfonic acids are stronger acids than carboxylic acids, and sulfonamides are stronger acids than amides of carboxylic acids. There are two oxygens in the sulfonyl group to help accommodate the negative charge of the anion, and only one oxygen in the acyl group.

Displacement of —OH, —Cl, —NH_2, —OR, or —OAr' is much harder when the group is attached to sulfonyl than when the group is attached to acyl. The interconversion of sulfonic acids and their derivatives occurs much less readily than interconversion of carboxylic acids and their derivatives. Sulfonic acids cannot be converted directly into amides or esters; sulfonyl chlorides react much more slowly than acyl chlorides with water, ammonia, alcohols, and phenols. Sulfonamides are much more difficult to hydrolyze than amides of carboxylic acids, as is illustrated by the last step in the synthesis of sulfanilamide.

Sulfanilamide
(p-Aminobenzenesulfonamide)

Nucleophilic attack on a trigonal acyl carbon (Sec. 17.4) is relatively unhindered; it involves the temporary attachment of a fourth group, the nucleophilic reagent. Nucleophilic attack on tetrahedral sulfonyl sulfur is relatively hindered; it involves the temporary attachment of a *fifth* group. The tetrahedral carbon of the acyl intermediate makes use of the permitted octet of electrons; although sulfur may be able to use more than eight electrons in covalent bonding, this is a less stable system than the octet.

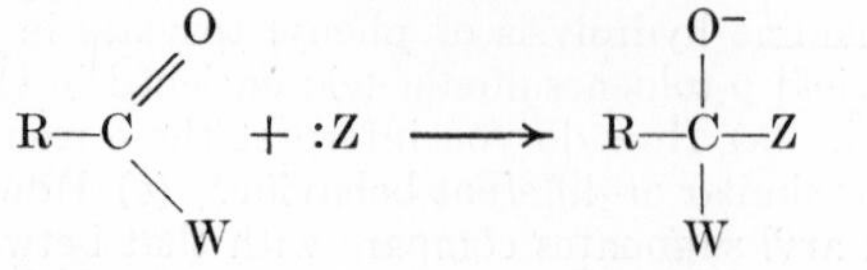

$$R-\overset{\overset{O}{\|}}{C}\overset{\diagdown}{\underset{W}{}} + :Z \longrightarrow R-\overset{\overset{O^-}{|}}{\underset{W}{C}}-Z$$

Trigonal C:
*attack relatively
unhindered*

Tetrahedral C:
stable octet

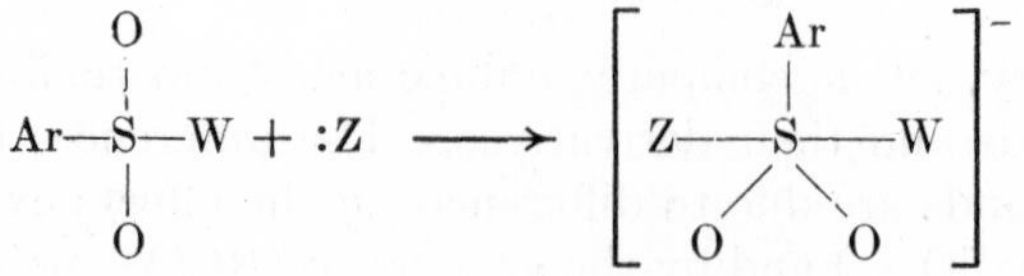

Acyl
nucleophilic
substitution

$$Ar-\overset{\overset{O}{|}}{\underset{O}{S}}-W + :Z \longrightarrow \left[Z\underset{\diagup \diagdown}{\overset{\overset{Ar}{|}}{S}}W \atop O \quad O \right]^-$$

Tetrahedral S:
attack hindered

Pentavalent S:
unstable decet

Sulfonyl
nucleophilic
substitution

Thus both steric and electronic factors tend to make sulfonyl compounds less reactive than acyl compounds.

We have seen that in their nucleophilic reactions, esters of carboxylic acids generally undergo cleavage between oxygen and the acyl group:

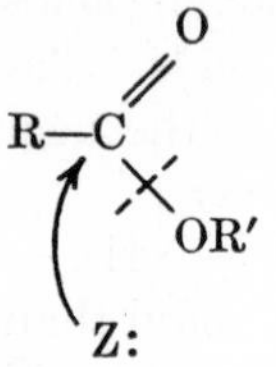

$$R-\overset{\overset{O}{\|}}{C}\overset{\diagup \times}{\underset{\underset{Z:}{\uparrow}}{OR'}}$$

Esters of sulfonic acids, on the other hand, generally undergo cleavage between oxygen and the alkyl group:

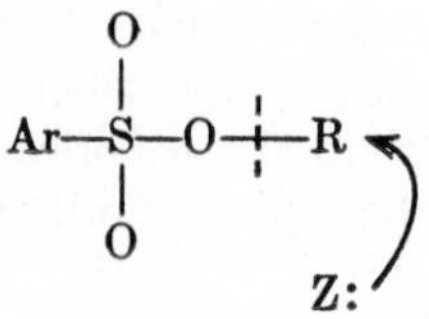

$$Ar-\overset{\overset{O}{|}}{\underset{\underset{Z:}{O}}{S}}-O\!\!\!+\!\!\!R$$

This is illustrated by the inversion of configuration described in the last section. The sulfonate ion is displaced from alkyl sulfonates in much the same way as halide ion is displaced from alkyl halides.

Two factors are at work here. Not only (a) is attack at sulfur more difficult than attack at carbonyl carbon, but also (b) attack at the alkyl carbon of a sulfonic acid ester is easier than attack at the alkyl carbon of a carboxylic acid ester. Displacement of the less basic sulfonate ion is easier than displacement of the carboxylate ion. Just as sulfonate separates with a pair of electrons from hydrogen more readily than does carboxylate (as shown by the relative acidities of the two kinds of acid), so sulfonate separates with a pair of electrons from an alkyl group more readily than does carboxylate.

It is generally true that the less basic of two groups is displaced more readily. We have seen a good example of this in the reactions of alcohols

(Sec. 12.5): the weak base H_2O is displaced from the protonated alcohol, whereas the strong base OH^- cannot be displaced from the alcohol itself. The similarity in behavior of alkyl sulfonates and alkyl halides is reasonable in view of the low basicity of both sulfonate ions and halide ions.

Problem 18.11 Arrange ethyl acetate, acetyl chloride, and acetic anhydride in order of their reactivity toward nucleophilic substitution (e.g., hydrolysis). What is one factor that might account for this order of reactivity? (*Hint:* what group is displaced in each case?)

Problem 18.12 The alkyl sulfates, $ROSO_2OR$, are good alkylating agents, often serving the same purpose as alkyl halides; for example, *methyl sulfate*, $CH_3OSO_2OCH_3$, reacts with phenol in alkaline solution to form the ether, anisole, $C_6H_5OCH_3$. Is this behavior of the alkyl sulfates reasonable?

18.10 Analysis of sulfonic acids

Sulfonic acids are characterized by the presence of sulfur, high acidity, and solubility in water. They are identified by conversion into sulfonyl chlorides and sulfonamides.

Functional derivatives of sulfonic acids are handled in much the same manner as derivatives of carboxylic acids (see Sec. 17.28).

PROBLEMS

1. Write the structural formulas for:
(a) *m*-benzenedisulfonic acid
(b) *p*-toluenesulfonamide
(c) benzenesulfonyl chloride
(d) sodium *m*-bromobenzenesulfonate
(e) sulfanilic acid
(f) isopropyl tosylate

2. Give structures and names of the principal products from the sulfonation of:
(a) toluene
(b) chlorobenzene
(c) nitrobenzene
(d) *m*-xylene
(e) *p*-xylene
(f) *o*-nitrophenol
(g) anisole
(h) *p*-cresol (p-$CH_3C_6H_4OH$)
(i) *p*-nitrotoluene
(j) benzenesulfonic acid

3. How do you account for the fact that *m*-xylene is more rapidly sulfonated than either of its isomers?

4. Give structures and names of the principal organic products of the reaction (if any) of benzenesulfonic acid with:
(a) H_2O
(b) NaOH(aq), cold
(c) product of (b) fused with NaOH
(d) NaCN(aq)
(e) $NaHCO_3$(aq)
(f) $Ba(OH)_2$ (aq)
(g) PCl_5
(h) NH_3 (aq)
(i) C_2H_5OH
(j) fuming sulfuric acid, heat
(k) dilute H_2SO_4, heat
(l) HNO_3, H_2SO_4
(m) Br_2, Fe
(n) CH_3Cl, $AlCl_3$
(o) $ClSO_3H$

5. Answer Problem 4 for sodium benzenesulfonate.

6. Answer Problem 4 for benzenesulfonyl chloride.

7. Outline all steps in the conversion of *p*-toluenesulfonic acid into:
(a) sodium *p*-toluenesulfonate
(b) calcium *p*-toluenesulfonate
(c) *p*-toluenesulfonyl chloride
(d) *p*-toluenesulfonamide
(e) ethyl *p*-toluenesulfonate
(f) *p*-cresol (p-$CH_3C_6H_4OH$)

(g) toluene

(h) 4-methyl-3-nitrobenzenesulfonic acid

(i) o-bromotoluene

(j) p-methylanisole

(k) p-HO$_3$SC$_6$H$_4$COOH

(l) p-cresyl p-toluenesulfonate

8. Outline all steps in a possible laboratory synthesis of the following from benzene and/or toluene, using any needed inorganic or aliphatic reagents.

(a) m-chlorobenzenesulfonyl chloride

(b) p-bromobenzenesulfonamide

(c) p-cresol (p-CH$_3$C$_6$H$_4$OH)

(d) m-HO$_3$SC$_6$H$_4$COOH

(e) resorcinol (m-C$_6$H$_4$(OH)$_2$)

(f) phenyl p-toluenesulfonate

(g) p-carbethoxybenzenesulfonic acid

(p-C$_2$H$_5$OOCC$_6$H$_4$SO$_3$H)

9. The isomeric xylenes have been separated by the following procedure, an alternative to the one described in Sec. 18.5. (a) The mixture is treated with concentrated H$_2$SO$_4$ under conditions that result in sulfonation of all three xylenes. Give the structures of the chief products expected. (b) The mixture of sulfonic acids is then heated with dilute acid under such conditions that only one of the xylenes is liberated. Which xylene is this likely to be? Why do you think this is so? (c) The remaining sulfonic acids are separated by fractional crystallization. Which is obtained in purer form?

10. When benzene is treated with fuming sulfuric acid and the reaction product poured slowly into water, a small amount of an insoluble white solid separates. This solid, *diphenylsulfone*, has the formula C$_{12}$H$_{10}$O$_2$S. (a) What is the most likely structure for diphenylsulfone? (b) How is it probably formed?

11. Treatment of o-chloronitrobenzene by aqueous sodium sulfite yields sodium o-nitrobenzenesulfonate. (a) To what general class does this reaction belong? (b) Give the structure of the reagent involved. How does this reagent compare with the one in ordinary sulfonations? (c) Would you expect this to be a general method for preparation of sulfonic acids? Could it be used, for example, to prepare benzenesulfonic acid? (d) Washing crude m-dinitrobenzene with aqueous sodium sulfite removes contaminating o- and p-dinitrobenzene. How do you account for this?

12. (a) Predict the product of monobromination of p-toluenesulfonic acid followed by treatment with acid and superheated steam. (b) Using the principle of (a), suggest a synthesis of o-dibromobenzene; of o-bromophenol.

13. When benzenesulfonyl chloride is treated either with zinc and sulfuric acid or with lithium aluminum hydride, there is obtained *thiophenol*, C$_6$H$_6$S. Treatment of thiophenol with Cl$_2$/H$_2$O reconverts it into benzenesulfonic acid. (a) What is the structure of thiophenol? (b) The interconversion just described proved an important point about the structure of sulfonic acids. What point was this? (*Hint:* see Sec. 18.1.)

14. Referring to the text for configurations and signs of rotation, predict the configurations (and, where possible, signs of rotation) of the products of the following reactions.

(a) benzenesulfonyl chloride + (+)-2-octanol

(b) product of (a) + hot aqueous NaOH

(c) product of (a) + sodium acetate

(d) product of (a) + sodium bromide

(e) acetyl chloride + (+)-2-octanol

(f) product of (e) + hot aqueous NaOH

(g) benzenesulfonyl chloride + CH$_3$O^{18}H

(h) product of (g) + hot aqueous NaOH

(i) acetyl chloride + CH$_3$O^{18}H

(j) product of (i) + hot aqueous NaOH

15. Give the structures of the principal products expected from the reaction of ethyl benzoate with each of the following reagents:

(a) ammonia

(b) methanol + sodium methoxide

(c) benzylmagnesium chloride

On the basis of Sec. 18.9, predict the product expected in each case if ethyl benzenesulfonate were used instead of ethyl benzoate.

16. Acid-catalyzed hydrolysis of neopentyl methylphosphonate,

$$OCH_2C(CH_3)_3$$
$$CH_3PO$$
$$OCH_2C(CH_3)_3$$

yields 2-methyl-2-butene but no neopentyl alcohol. (a) What position of cleavage and what mechanism are indicated by these results? (*Hint:* see Sec. 12.5.) (b) How does this behavior compare with the acid-catalyzed hydrolysis of esters of carboxylic acids? (c) Account for this behavior on the basis of structure. (*Hint:* see Sec. 18.9.)

17. The following steps are involved in the synthesis of *saccharin*, a compound some 500 times sweeter than sugar. Assign a structure to each compound.

toluene + ClSO₃H $\longrightarrow$ liquid A (C₇H₇O₂SCl) + solid B (C₇H₇O₂SCl)

A + NH₃ $\longrightarrow$ C (C₇H₉O₂NS)

C + KMnO₄ $\longrightarrow$ D (C₇H₇O₄NS)

D + heat $\longrightarrow$ saccharin (C₇H₅O₃NS)

saccharin + dilute NaOH $\longrightarrow$ soluble saccharin (C₇H₄O₃NSNa)

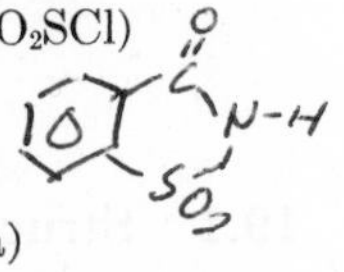

18. *Chloramine T*, a compound used as a water disinfectant, is prepared by the action of sodium hypochlorite on *p*-toluenesulfonamide. It has the formula C₇H₇O₂NSClNa, dissolves readily in water, and upon treatment with dilute acid is converted into *p*-toluenesulfonamide and hypochlorous acid. What is the most likely structure for Chloramine T?

AMINES I. PREPARATION AND PHYSICAL PROPERTIES

19.1 Structure

Nearly all the organic compounds that we have studied so far are bases, although very weak ones. Much of the chemistry of alcohols, ethers, esters, and even of alkenes and aromatic hydrocarbons is understandable in terms of the basicity of these compounds.

Of the organic compounds that show appreciable basicity (strong enough to turn litmus blue, for example), by far the most important are the **amines.** An amine has the general formula RNH_2, R_2NH, or R_3N, where R is any alkyl or aryl group. For example:

CH_3NH_2	$(CH_3)_2NH$	$(CH_3)_3N$	$H_2NCH_2CH_2NH_2$
Methylamine	Dimethylamine	Trimethylamine	Ethylenediamine
(1°)	(2°)	(3°)	(1°)

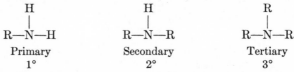

Aniline	N-Methylaniline	N,N-Dimethylaniline
(1°)	(2°)	(3°)

19.2 Classification

Amines are classified as **primary, secondary,** or **tertiary** according to the number of groups attached to the nitrogen atom:

H	H	R
|	|	|
R—N—H	R—N—R	R—N—R
Primary	Secondary	Tertiary
1°	2°	3°

In certain of their properties, particularly basicity, amines of different classes are very much the same. Many of their properties, however, depend upon the number of hydrogen atoms attached to the nitrogen atom, and hence are different for amines of different classes.

19.3   Nomenclature

Aliphatic amines are named by naming the alkyl group or groups attached to nitrogen, and following these by the word *–amine*.   More complicated ones are often named by prefixing *amino–* (or *N-methylamino–*, *N,N-diethylamino–*, etc.) to the name of the parent chain.   For example:

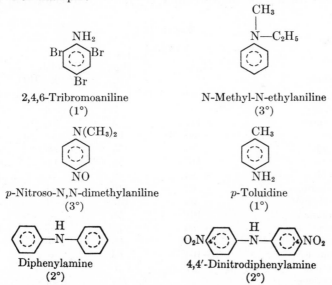

$$CH_3-\underset{\underset{NH_2}{|}}{\overset{\overset{CH_3}{|}}{C}}-CH_3 \qquad CH_3CH_2-\overset{\overset{H}{|}}{N}-CH_3 \qquad CH_3-\overset{\overset{CH_3}{|}}{N}-\underset{\underset{CH_3}{|}}{C}HCH_2CH_3$$

tert-Butylamine   Methylethylamine   Dimethyl-*sec*-butylamine
       (1°)   (2°)   (3°)

$$H_2NCH_2CH_2CH_2COOH \qquad H_2NCH_2CH_2OH \qquad CH_3-\overset{\overset{H}{|}}{N}-\underset{\underset{CH_3}{|}}{C}H(CH_2)_4CH_3$$

γ-Aminobutyric acid   2-Aminoethanol   2-(N-Methylamino)heptane
                                        (Ethanolamine)
       (1°)   (1°)   (2°)

Aromatic amines — those in which nitrogen is attached directly to an aromatic ring — are generally named as derivatives of the simplest aromatic amine, **aniline**.   An aminotoluene is given the special name of *toluidine*.   For example:

2,4,6-Tribromoaniline   N-Methyl-N-ethylaniline
       (1°)   (3°)

p-Nitroso-N,N-dimethylaniline   *p*-Toluidine
       (3°)   (1°)

Diphenylamine   4,4′-Dinitrodiphenylamine
       (2°)   (2°)

Salts of amines are generally named by replacing *–amine* by *–ammonium* (or *–aniline* by *–anilinium*), and adding the name of the anion (*chloride, nitrate, sulfate*, etc.).   For example:

$(C_2H_5NH_3{}^+)_2SO_4{}^=$ $(CH_3)_3NH^+ \ NO_3{}^-$ $C_6H_5NH_3{}^+ \ Cl^-$

Ethylammonium   Trimethylammonium   Anilinium
     sulfate   nitrate   chloride

19.4   Physical properties of amines

Like ammonia, amines are polar compounds and, except for tertiary amines, can form intermolecular hydrogen bonds.

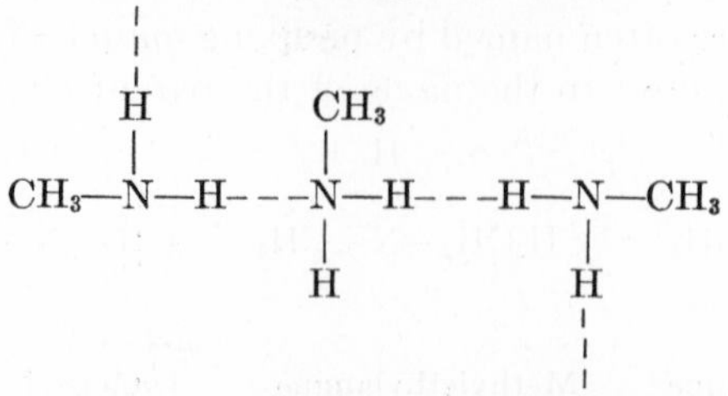

$$CH_3-\overset{\displaystyle\overset{\vdots}{\underset{\textstyle H}{N}}}{}-H---\overset{\displaystyle\overset{CH_3}{\underset{\textstyle H}{N}}}{}-H---H-\overset{\displaystyle\underset{\textstyle\underset{\vdots}{H}}{N}}{}-CH_3$$

Amines have higher boiling points than non-polar compounds of the same molecular weight, but lower boiling points than alcohols or carboxylic acids.

Amines of all three classes are capable of forming hydrogen bonds with water.   As a result, smaller amines are quite soluble in water, with border-line solubility being reached at about six carbon atoms.   Amines are soluble in less polar solvents like ether, alcohol, benzene, etc.   The methyl-amines and ethylamines smell very much like ammonia; the higher alkyl-amines have decidedly "fishy" odors.

Aromatic amines are generally very toxic; they are readily absorbed through the skin, often with fatal results.

Aromatic amines are very easily oxidized by air, and although most are colorless when pure, they are often encountered discolored by oxidation products.

TABLE 19.1

AMINES

Name	M.p., °C	B.p., °C	Solub., g/100 g H_2O	K_b
Methylamine	− 92	−7.5	v.sol.	4.4×10^{-4}
Dimethylamine	− 96	7.5	v.sol.	5.1
Trimethylamine	−117	3	91	0.6
Ethylamine	− 80	17	∞	4.7
Diethylamine	− 39	55	v.sol.	9.5
Triethylamine	−115	89	14	5.5
n-Propylamine	− 83	49	∞	3.8
Di-n-propylamine	− 63	110	s.sol.	8.1
Tri-n-propylamine	− 93	157	s.sol.	4.5
Isopropylamine	−101	34	∞	
n-Butylamine	− 50	78	v.sol.	4.1
Isobutylamine	− 85	68	∞	
sec-Butylamine	−104	63	∞	
tert-Butylamine	− 67	46	∞	
Cyclohexylamine		134	s.sol.	
Benzylamine		185	∞	0.23
α-Phenylethylamine		187	4.2	
β-Phenylethylamine		195	s.	
Ethylenediamine	8	117	s.	
Tetramethylenediamine [$H_2N(CH_2)_4NH_2$]	27	158	v.sol.	
Hexamethylenediamine	39	196	v.sol.	
Tetramethylammonium hydroxide	63	135d	220	strong base

TABLE 19.1 (*Continued*)

Name	M.p., °C	B.p., °C	Solub., g/100 g H₂O	K_b
Aniline	− 6	184	3.7	4.2×10^{-10}
Methylaniline	− 57	196	v.sl.sol.	7.1
Dimethylaniline	3	194	1.4	11
Diphenylamine	53	302	i.	0.0007
Triphenylamine	127	365	i.	
o-Toluidine	− 28	200	1.7	2.5
m-Toluidine	− 30	203	s.sol.	4.9
p-Toluidine	44	200	0.7	12
o-Anisidine (o-CH₃OC₆H₄NH₂)	5	225	s.sol.	3
m-Anisidine		251	s.sol.	
p-Anisidine	57	244	v.sl.sol.	15
o-Chloroaniline	− 2	209	i.	0.05
m-Chloroaniline	− 10	236		0.3
p-Chloroaniline	70	232		1.5
o-Bromoaniline	32	229	s.sol.	
m-Bromoaniline	19	251	v.sl.sol.	
p-Bromoaniline	66	d	i.	1
o-Nitroaniline	71	284	0.1	0.00035
m-Nitroaniline	114	307d	0.1	0.032
p-Nitroaniline	148	332	0.05	0.001
2,4-Dinitroaniline	187		s.sol.	
2,4,6-Trinitroaniline (picramide)	188		0.1	
o-Phenylenediamine	104	252	3	3.2×10^{-10}
m-Phenylenediamine	63	287	25	7.6
p-Phenylenediamine	142	267	3.8	110
Benzidine	127	401	0.05	0.0074
p-Aminobenzoic acid	187		0.3	0.023
Sulfanilic acid	288d		1	0.16
Sulfanilamide	163		0.4	

Name	Formula	M.p., °C
Acetanilide	C₆H₅NHCOCH₃	114
Benzanilide	C₆H₅NHCOC₆H₅	163
Aceto-o-toluidide	o-CH₃C₆H₄NHCOCH₃	110
Aceto-m-toluidide	m-CH₃C₆H₄NHCOCH₃	66
Aceto-p-toluidide	p-CH₃C₆H₄NHCOCH₃	147
o-Nitroacetanilide	o-O₂NC₆H₄NHCOCH₃	93
m-Nitroacetanilide	m-O₂NC₆H₄NHCOCH₃	154
p-Nitroacetanilide	p-O₂NC₆H₄NHCOCH₃	216

19.5 Salts of amines

Aliphatic amines are about as basic as ammonia; aromatic amines are considerably less basic. Although amines are much weaker bases than hydroxide ion or ethoxide ion, they are much stronger bases than alcohols, ethers, esters, etc.; they are much stronger bases than water. Aqueous mineral acids or carboxylic acids readily convert amines into their salts; aqueous hydroxide ion readily converts the salts back into the free amines.

$$
\left.\begin{array}{l}
\text{RNH}_2 \\
1^\circ \text{ amine} \\[8pt]
\text{R}_2\text{NH} \\
2^\circ \text{ amine} \\[8pt]
\text{R}_3\text{N} \\
3^\circ \text{ amine}
\end{array}\right\}
\underset{\text{OH}^-}{\overset{\text{H}^+}{\rightleftarrows}}
\left\{\begin{array}{l}
\text{RNH}_3^+ \\
\text{salt} \\[8pt]
\text{R}_2\text{NH}_2^+ \\
\text{salt} \\[8pt]
\text{R}_3\text{NH}^+ \\
\text{salt}
\end{array}\right.
$$

Insoluble   *Soluble*
in water   *in water*

As with the carboxylic acids, we can do little with amines without encountering this conversion to and from their salts; it is therefore worth while to look at the properties of these salts.

In Sec. 16.4 we contrasted physical properties of carboxylic acids with those of their salts; amines and their salts show the same contrast. Amine salts are typical ionic compounds. They are non-volatile solids, and when heated generally decompose before the high temperature required for melting is reached. The halides, nitrates, and sulfates are soluble in water but are insoluble in non-polar solvents.

The difference in solubility behavior between amines and their salts can be used both to detect amines and to separate them from non-basic compounds. A water-insoluble organic compound that dissolves in cold, dilute aqueous hydrochloric acid must be appreciably basic, which means almost certainly that it is an amine. An amine can be separated from non-basic compounds by its solubility in acid; once separated, the amine can be regenerated by making the aqueous solution alkaline. (See Sec. 16.4 for a comparable situation for carboxylic acids.)

Problem 19.1   Describe exactly how you would go about separating a mixture of the three water-insoluble liquids, aniline (b.p. 184°), n-butylbenzene (b.p. 183°), and n-valeric acid (b.p. 187°), recovering each compound pure and in essentially quantitative yield. Do the same for a mixture of the three water-insoluble solids, p-toluidine, o-bromobenzoic acid, and p-nitroanisole.

19.6   Stereochemistry of nitrogen

So far in our study of organic chemistry, we have devoted considerable time to the spatial arrangement of atoms and groups attached to carbon atoms, that is, to the stereochemistry of carbon. Now let us look briefly at the stereochemistry of nitrogen.

Spectroscopic evidence shows that the ammonia molecule is pyramidal, with nitrogen at the apex of a pyramid and a hydrogen atom at each corner of its triangular base (Figure 19.1). We have seen (Sec. 1.9) that this arrangement of atoms is consistent with the quantum mechanical picture of the molecule. In forming ammonia, nitrogen uses sp^3 orbitals, which are directed to the corners of a tetrahedron. Three of these orbitals overlap s orbitals of hydrogen atoms; the fourth contains an unshared pair of electrons.

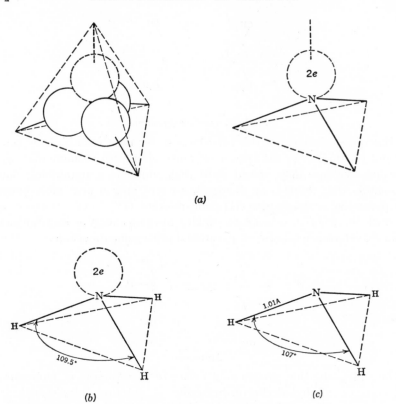

FIGURE 19.1. Ammonia molecule. (a) Tetrahedral sp^3 orbitals. (b) Predicted shape, showing unshared pair: H nuclei located for maximum overlap. (c) Shape and size.

Since amines are simply ammonia in which one or more hydrogen atoms have been replaced by alkyl groups, we might expect that amines, too, would be pyramidal. This is the case: electron diffraction of trimethylamine has shown that its molecules are pyramidal with C—N—C angles (about 108°) very nearly the same as the H—N—H angles (107°) in ammonia.

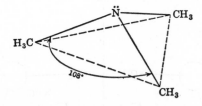

From an examination of models, it at first appears that a molecule in which nitrogen carries three different groups is not superimposable on its mirror image, and should exist in two enantiomeric, optically active forms. For example, methylethyl-*n*-propylamine (I and II):

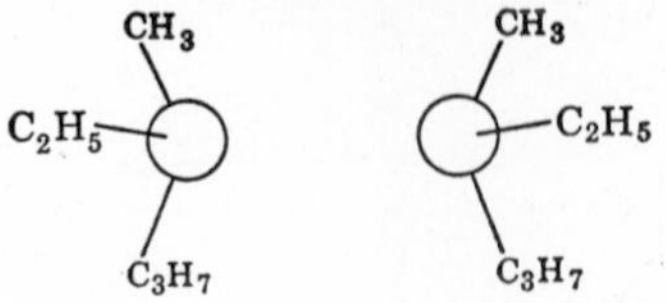

CH₃ structures:

$$CH_3 \quad C_2H_5 \quad C_3H_7$$

I   II

Methylethyl-*n*-propylamine

But optical isomers of this kind have never been found. How can we account for this? For the answer we must again turn to ammonia. Spectroscopic evidence does indeed show that ammonia is pyramidal; but it also shows that there is an energy barrier of only 6 kcal/mole between one pyramidal arrangement (III) and another (IV); even at room temperature the fraction of collisions with sufficient energy is so large that a rapid transformation between pyramidal arrangements occurs.

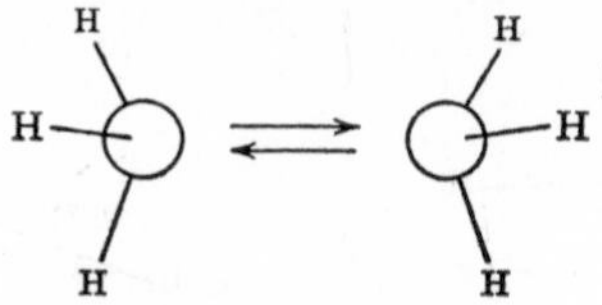

III   IV

Ammonia

The same situation presumably exists for derivatives of ammonia: a molecule of methylethyl-*n*-propylamine is rapidly transformed from arrangement I to arrangement II. Thus, although a molecule of the amine is not identical with its mirror image, it can be *made* identical without breaking bonds and is thus *superimposable* on its mirror image (Sec. 11.18). Because of this ready superimposability, there cannot be optical isomerism or optical activity. An unshared pair of electrons on nitrogen evidently cannot serve as a fourth group to maintain configuration.

Next, let us consider the quaternary ammonium salts, compounds in which four alkyl groups are attached to nitrogen. Here all four sp^3 orbitals are used to form bonds, and quaternary nitrogen should be tetrahedral. If this is so, a quaternary ammonium salt in which nitrogen holds four

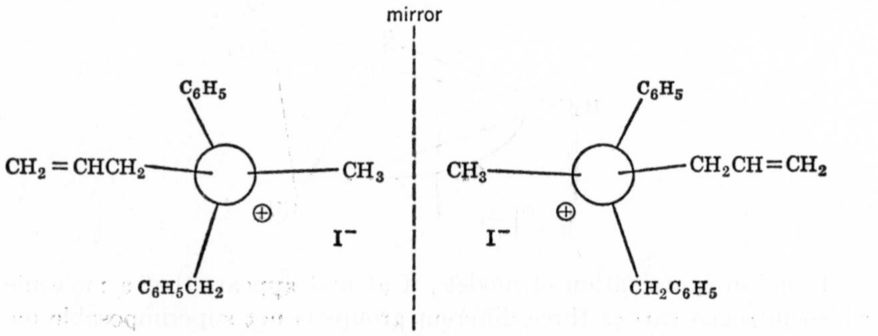

mirror

$CH_2=CHCH_2$, C_6H_5, CH_3, $C_6H_5CH_2$, I^-

V   VI

(+)- and (−)-Methylallylphenylbenzylammonium iodide

different groups should show optical isomerism and optical activity. This has been found to be the case. Methylallylphenylbenzylammonium iodide, for example, exists in two enantiomeric forms, V and VI, each of which is optically active.

Problem 19.2 Consideration of orbitals led us to conclude that the methyl carbonium ion, CH_3^+, is probably flat. (a) On the same basis, account for the generally accepted view that the methyl carbanion, $CH_3:^-$, is pyramidal. (b) The shape of the methyl free radical, $CH_3\cdot$, is in doubt. Suggest two possibilities.

Problem 19.3 Racemization in an S_N1 reaction is accounted for (Sec. 13.13) by loss of configuration in an intermediate carbonium ion. Account for the fact that intermediate carbanions and free radicals often seem to lose configuration.

19.7 Industrial source

Some of the simplest and most important amines are prepared on an industrial scale by processes that are not practicable as laboratory methods.

The most important of all amines, **aniline,** is prepared in two ways: (a) reduction of nitrobenzene by the cheap reagents, iron and dilute hydrochloric acid; (b) treatment of chlorobenzene with ammonia at high temperatures and high pressures in the presence of a catalyst. We recognize

Nitrobenzene $\xrightarrow{\text{Fe, 30\% HCl, heat}}$ Anilinium chloride $\xrightarrow{\text{Na}_2\text{CO}_3}$ Aniline

Chlorobenzene $\xrightarrow{\text{NH}_3,\ \text{Cu}_2\text{O, 200}^\circ,\ 900\ \text{lb/in.}^2}$ Aniline

the second process as involving nucleophilic aromatic substitution. In the laboratory only aryl halides containing electron-attracting groups (Sec. 14.12) are reactive enough to make nucleophilic substitution feasible; on an industrial scale, it is worth while to construct equipment that will withstand the more severe conditions necessary for reaction of simple unsubstituted chlorobenzene. (Compare the synthesis of phenol, Sec. 22.4.)

Methylamine, dimethylamine, and trimethylamine are synthesized on an industrial scale from methanol and ammonia:

$$NH_3 \xrightarrow[\substack{Al_2O_3,\\450^\circ}]{CH_3OH} CH_3NH_2 \xrightarrow[\substack{Al_2O_3,\\450^\circ}]{CH_3OH} (CH_3)_2NH \xrightarrow[\substack{Al_2O_3,\\450^\circ}]{CH_3OH} (CH_3)_3N$$

Ammonia   Methylamine   Dimethylamine   Trimethylamine

For higher alkylamines the more expensive alkyl halides must be used, just as in the laboratory (Sec. 19.10).

19.8 Preparation

Some of the many methods that are used to prepare amines in the laboratory are outlined on the following pages.

PREPARATION OF AMINES

1. Reduction of nitro compounds

$$\begin{array}{c} \text{ArNO}_2 \\ \text{or} \\ \text{RNO}_2 \end{array} \xrightarrow{\text{metal, H}^+;\ \text{or H}_2,\ \text{catalyst}} \begin{array}{c} \text{ArNH}_2 \\ \text{or} \\ \text{RNH}_2 \end{array}$$

$\quad$ Nitro compound $\qquad\qquad\qquad\qquad$ 1° amine

Chiefly for aromatic amines

Examples:

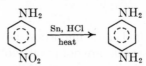

Ethyl *p*-nitrobenzoate $\quad$ Ethyl *p*-aminobenzoate

p-Nitroaniline $\qquad$ *p*-Phenylenediamine

m-Dinitrobenzene $\qquad$ *m*-Nitroaniline

$$\text{CH}_3\text{CH}_2\text{CH}_2\text{NO}_2 \xrightarrow{\text{Fe, HCl}} \text{CH}_3\text{CH}_2\text{CH}_2\text{NH}_2$$

$\quad$ 1-Nitropropane $\qquad\qquad\qquad$ *n*-Propylamine

2. Reaction of halides with ammonia or amines

$$\text{NH}_3 \xrightarrow{\text{RX}} \text{RNH}_2 \xrightarrow{\text{RX}} \text{R}_2\text{NH} \xrightarrow{\text{RX}} \text{R}_3\text{N} \xrightarrow{\text{RX}} \text{R}_4\text{N}^+\text{X}^-$$

$\qquad\quad$ 1° amine $\quad$ 2° amine $\quad$ 3° amine $\quad$ Quaternary
$\qquad\qquad\qquad\qquad\qquad\qquad\qquad\qquad$ ammonium salt
$\qquad\qquad\qquad\qquad\qquad\qquad\qquad\qquad$ (4°)

RX must be alkyl, or aryl with electron-attracting substituents

Examples:

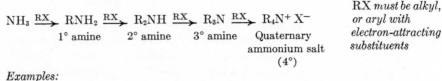

$$\text{CH}_3\text{COOH} \xrightarrow[\text{P}]{\text{Cl}_2} \underset{\underset{\text{Cl}}{|}}{\text{CH}_2\text{COOH}} \xrightarrow{\text{NH}_3} \underset{\underset{\text{NH}_2}{|}}{\text{CH}_2\text{COO}^-\,\text{NH}_4{}^+} \xrightarrow{\text{H}^+} \underset{\underset{\text{NH}_2}{|}}{\text{CH}_2\text{COOH}}\ (\text{or } \underset{\underset{^+\text{NH}_3}{|}}{\text{CH}_2\text{COO}^-})$$

$\quad$ Acetic $\qquad$ Chloroacetic $\qquad\qquad\qquad\qquad$ Aminoacetic acid
$\quad$ acid $\qquad\qquad$ acid $\qquad\qquad\qquad\qquad$ (Glycine; an amino acid)
$\qquad\qquad\qquad\qquad\qquad\qquad\qquad\qquad\qquad\qquad$ (1°)

$$\text{C}_2\text{H}_5\text{Cl} \xrightarrow{\text{NH}_3} \text{C}_2\text{H}_5\text{NH}_2 \xrightarrow{\text{CH}_3\text{Cl}} \text{C}_2\text{H}_5\!-\!\overset{\text{H}}{\underset{}{\text{N}}}\!-\!\text{CH}_3$$

$\quad$ Ethyl chloride $\qquad$ Ethylamine $\qquad$ Methylethylamine
$\qquad\qquad\qquad\qquad\qquad$ (1°) $\qquad\qquad\qquad$ (2°)

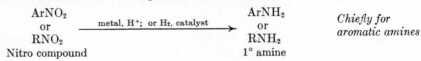

Benzyl chloride $\qquad$ Benzylamine $\qquad\qquad$ Benzyldimethylamine
$\qquad\qquad\qquad\qquad\qquad$ (1°) $\qquad\qquad\qquad\qquad$ (3°)

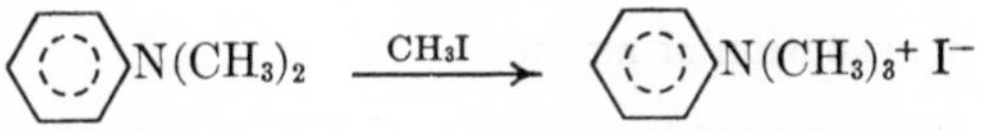

$$\langle\bigcirc\rangle N(CH_3)_2 \xrightarrow{CH_3I} \langle\bigcirc\rangle N(CH_3)_3^+ \; I^-$$

N,N-Dimethylaniline   Phenyltrimethylammonium iodide
(3°)   (4°)

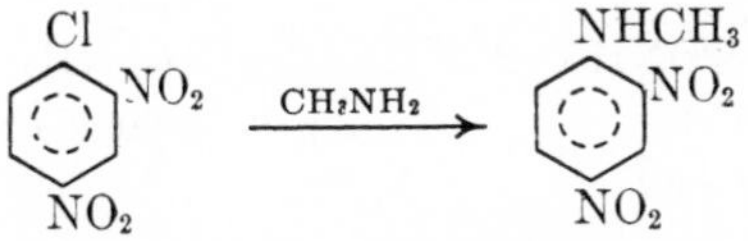

2,4-Dinitrochlorobenzene   N-Methyl-2,4-dinitroaniline
(2°)

with reagent CH_2NH_2 converting Cl/NO₂/NO₂ ring to NHCH₃/NO₂/NO₂ ring

3. Reductive amination

$$\diagdown C=O + NH_3 + H_2 \xrightarrow{Ni} \diagdown CH-NH_2 \qquad 1° \text{ amine}$$

$$+ RNH_2 + H_2 \xrightarrow{Ni} \diagdown CH-NHR \qquad 2° \text{ amine}$$

$$+ R_2NH + H_2 \xrightarrow{Ni} \diagdown CH-NR_2 \qquad 3° \text{ amine}$$

Examples:

$$CH_3-\underset{\underset{O}{\|}}{C}-CH_3 + NH_3 + H_2 \xrightarrow{Ni} CH_3-\underset{\underset{NH_2}{|}}{CH}-CH_3$$

Acetone   Isopropylamine
                       (1°)

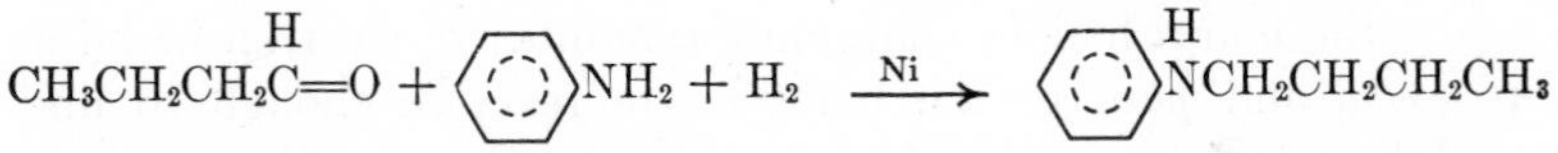

$$CH_3CH_2CH_2\overset{H}{C}=O + \langle\bigcirc\rangle NH_2 + H_2 \xrightarrow{Ni} \langle\bigcirc\rangle \overset{H}{N}CH_2CH_2CH_2CH_3$$

n-Butyraldehyde   Aniline   N-*n*-Butylaniline
                    (1°)   (2°)

$$CH_3\overset{H}{C}=O + (CH_3)_2NH + H_2 \xrightarrow{Ni} CH_3CH_2-\underset{}{\overset{\overset{CH_3}{|}}{N}}-CH_3$$

Acetaldehyde   Dimethylamine   Dimethylethylamine
               (2°)   (3°)

4. Reduction of nitriles

$$RC\equiv N \xrightarrow{2H_2, \text{ catalyst}} RCH_2NH_2$$

Nitrile   1° amine

Examples:

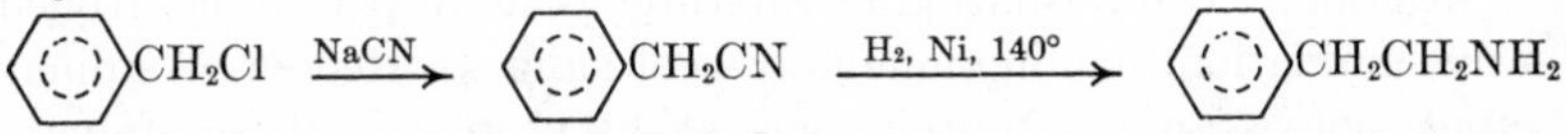

$$\langle\bigcirc\rangle CH_2Cl \xrightarrow{NaCN} \langle\bigcirc\rangle CH_2CN \xrightarrow{H_2, \text{ Ni}, 140°} \langle\bigcirc\rangle CH_2CH_2NH_2$$

Benzyl chloride   Phenylacetonitrile   β-Phenylethylamine
                  (Benzyl cyanide)   (1°)

$$ClCH_2CH_2CH_2CH_2Cl \xrightarrow{NaCN} NC(CH_2)_4CN \xrightarrow{H_2, \text{ Ni}} H_2NCH_2(CH_2)_4CH_2NH_2$$

1,4-Dichlorobutane   Adiponitrile   Hexamethylenediamine
                     (see adipic acid,   (1,6-Diaminohexane)
                     Chapter 25)   (1°)

5. Hofmann degradation of amides

$$\text{RCONH}_2 \text{ or ArCONH}_2 \xrightarrow{\text{OBr}^-} \text{RNH}_2 \text{ or ArNH}_2 + \text{CO}_3^=$$

Amide   1° amine

Examples:

$$\text{CH}_3(\text{CH}_2)_4\text{CONH}_2 \xrightarrow{\text{KOBr}} \text{CH}_3(\text{CH}_2)_4\text{NH}_2$$

Caproamide   *n*-Pentylamine
(Hexanamide)

m-Bromobenzamide   *m*-Bromoaniline

6. Gabriel synthesis of pure primary amines. Discussed in Sec. 25.8.

Reduction of aromatic nitro compounds is by far the most useful method of preparing amines, since it uses readily available starting materials, and yields the most important kind of amines, *primary aromatic amines*. These amines can be converted into aromatic diazonium salts, which are perhaps the most versatile class of organic compounds known (see Chapter 21). The sequence

Nitro compound   ⟶   Amine   ⟶   Diazonium salt

provides the best possible route to dozens of kinds of aromatic compounds.

Reduction of aliphatic nitro compounds is limited by the availability of the starting materials.

Ammonolysis of halides is generally limited to the aliphatic series, since only those aryl halides containing a number of electron-withdrawing groups *ortho* and *para* to the halogen are reactive enough to undergo nucleophilic substitution (Sec. 14.12). Ammonolysis has the disadvantage of yielding a mixture of different classes of amines. It is important to us as one of the most general methods of introducing the amino (—NH$_2$) group into molecules of all kinds; it can be used, for example, to convert bromoacids into amino acids. The exactly analogous reaction of halides with amines permits the preparation of every class of amine (as well as quaternary ammonium salts, R$_4$N$^+$ X$^-$).

Reductive amination, the catalytic reduction of aldehydes (RCHO) and ketones (R$_2$CO) in the presence of ammonia or an amine, accomplishes much the same purpose as the reaction of halides. It too can be used to prepare any class of amine, and has certain advantages over the halide reaction. The formation of mixtures is more readily controlled in reductive amination than in ammonolysis of halides. Reductive amination of ketones yields amines containing a *sec*-alkyl group; these amines are difficult to prepare by ammonolysis because of the tendency of *sec*-alkyl halides to undergo elimination rather than substitution.

The **reduction of nitriles** has the special feature of *increasing the length of a carbon chain*, producing a primary amine that has one more carbon atom than the alkyl halide from which the nitrile was made. The **Hof-**

mann degradation of amides has the feature of *decreasing the length of a carbon chain* by one carbon atom; it is also of interest as an example of an important class of reactions involving rearrangement.

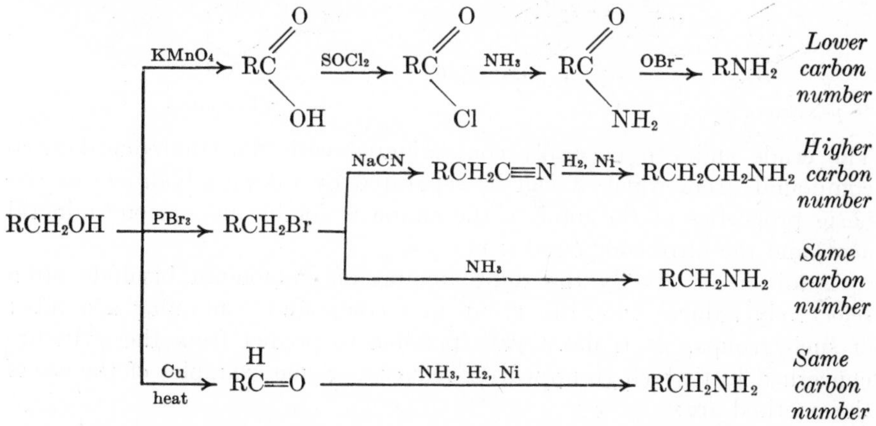

Problem 19.4 Show how *n*-pentylamine can be synthesized from available materials by the four routes just outlined.

The Gabriel synthesis, which is designed to prepare primary amines free of secondary and tertiary amines, will be discussed later (Sec. 25.8).

19.9 Reduction of nitro compounds

Like many organic compounds, nitro compounds can be reduced in two general ways: (a) by catalytic hydrogenation using molecular hydrogen, or (b) by chemical reduction, usually by a metal and acid. When the reduction of only one of several nitro groups in a compound is desired, ammonium bisulfide (NH_4SH) is often used.

Hydrogenation of a nitro compound to an amine takes place smoothly when a solution of the nitro compound in alcohol is shaken with finely divided nickel or platinum under hydrogen gas. For example:

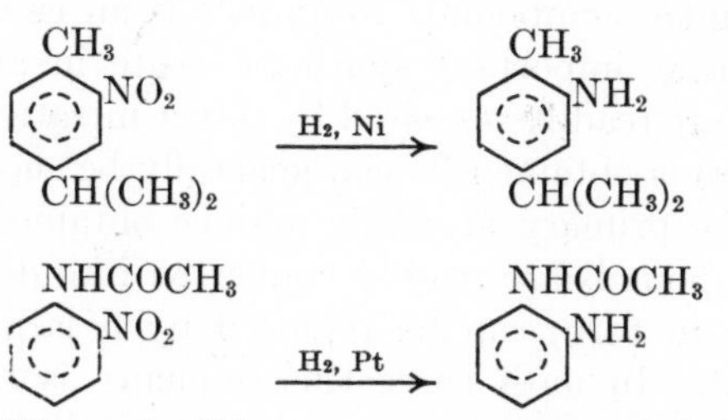

o-Nitroacetanilide   *o*-Aminoacetanilide

This method cannot be used when the molecule also contains some other easily hydrogenated group, such as a carbon–carbon double bond.

Chemical reduction in the laboratory is most often carried out by adding hydrochloric acid to a mixture of the nitro compound and a metal, usually granulated tin. In the acidic solution, the amine is obtained as its salt; the free amine is liberated by the addition of base, and is steam-distilled from the reaction mixture.

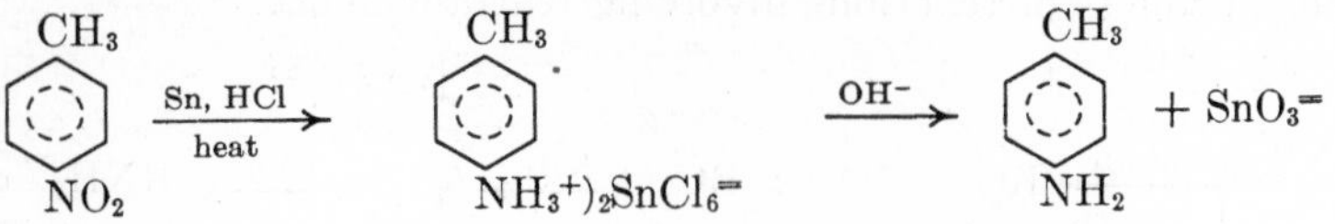

p-Nitrotoluene $NH_3^+)_2SnCl_6^=$ *p*-Toluidine

The crude amine is generally contaminated with some unreduced nitro compound, from which it can be separated by taking advantage of the basic properties of the amine; the amine is soluble in aqueous mineral acid, and the nitro compound is not.

Addition of exactly the right amount of ammonium bisulfide often selectively reduces one nitro group in a compound containing a number of such groups. It is not always possible to predict from the structure concerned just which group will be reduced. Some examples of the use of this method are:

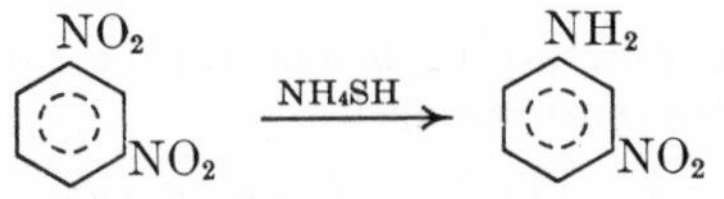

m-Dinitrobenzene   *m*-Nitroaniline

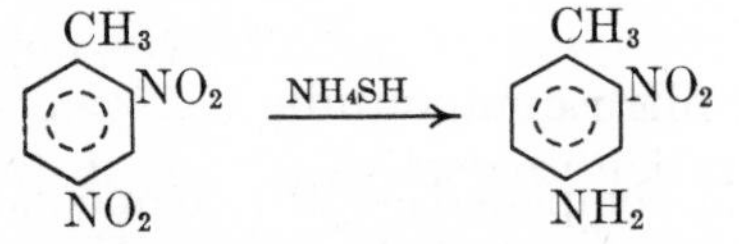

2,4-Dinitrotoluene   4-Amino-2-nitrotoluene

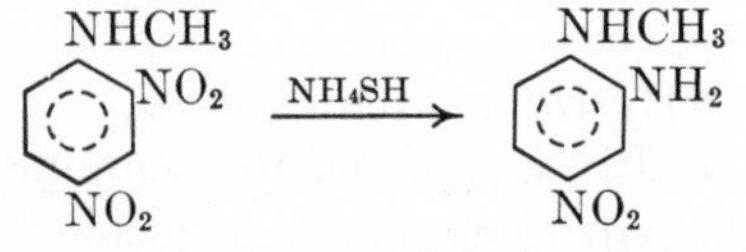

2,4-Dinitro-N-methylaniline   2-Amino-4-nitro-N-methylaniline

Reduction of nitro compounds to amines is an essential step in what is probably the most important synthetic route in aromatic chemistry. Nitro compounds are readily prepared by direct nitration; when a mixture of *o*- and *p*-isomers is obtained, it can generally be separated to yield the pure isomers. The primary aromatic amines obtained by the reduction of these nitro compounds are readily converted into diazonium salts; the diazonium group, in turn, can be replaced by a large number of other groups (Sec. 21.4). In most cases this sequence is the best method of introducing these other groups into the aromatic ring. In addition, diazonium salts can be used to prepare the extremely important class of compounds, the *azo dyes*.

$$ArH \longrightarrow ArNO_2 \longrightarrow ArNH_2 \longrightarrow ArN_2^+ \quad \begin{array}{l} \longrightarrow ArX \\ \longrightarrow ArOH \\ \longrightarrow ArCN \\ \longrightarrow \text{azo dyes} \end{array}$$

19.10   Ammonolysis of halides

Many organic halogen compounds are converted into amines by treatment with aqueous or alcoholic solutions of ammonia. The reaction is generally carried out either by allowing the reactants to stand together at room temperature or by heating them under pressure. Displacement of halogen by NH_3 yields the amine salt, from which the free amine can be liberated by treatment with hydroxide ion.

$$RX + NH_3 \longrightarrow RNH_3^+ X^-$$

$$RNH_3^+ X^- + OH^- \longrightarrow RNH_2 + H_2O + X^-$$

Ammonolysis of halides belongs to the class of reactions that we have called nucleophilic substitution. The organic halide is attacked by the nucleophilic ammonia molecule in the same way that it is attacked by hydroxide ion, alkoxide ion, cyanide ion, acetylide ion, and water:

$$H_3N: + R{-}X \longrightarrow \left[\overset{\delta_+}{H_3N} {\text{---}} R {\text{---}} \overset{\delta_-}{X} \right] \longrightarrow H_3\overset{+}{N}{-}R + X^-$$

Like these other nucleophilic substitution reactions, ammonolysis is limited chiefly to alkyl halides or substituted alkyl halides. As with other reactions of this kind, elimination tends to compete with substitution: ammonia can attack hydrogen to form alkene as well as attack carbon to form amine. Ammonolysis thus gives the highest yields with primary halides (where substitution predominates) and is virtually worthless with tertiary halides (where elimination predominates).

$$CH_3CH_2CH_2CH_2Br \xrightarrow{NH_3} CH_3CH_2CH_2CH_2NH_3^+ Br^- \qquad \textit{Substitution}$$

$$\underset{\underset{Br}{\overset{|}{}}}{\overset{\overset{CH_3}{\overset{|}{}}}{CH_3{-}C{-}CH_3}} \xrightarrow{NH_3} \overset{\overset{CH_3}{\overset{|}{}}}{CH_3{-}C{=}CH_2} + NH_4Br \qquad \textit{Elimination}$$

Because of their low reactivity, aryl halides are not generally used in the laboratory unless the ring carries —NO_2 groups, or other strongly electron-attracting groups, at positions *ortho* and *para* to the halogen (Sec. 14.12).

Some examples of the application of ammonolysis to synthesis are:

Toluene   Benzyl chloride   Benzylamine

$$CH_3CH_2COOH \xrightarrow[P]{Br_2} \underset{\underset{Br}{\overset{|}{}}}{CH_3CHCOOH} \xrightarrow{NH_3} \underset{\underset{NH_2}{\overset{|}{}}}{CH_3CHCOOH}$$

Propionic acid   α-Bromopropionic acid   Alanine   (α-Aminopropionic acid)

$$CH_2{=}CH_2 \xrightarrow{Cl_2} ClCH_2CH_2Cl \xrightarrow{2NH_3} H_2NCH_2CH_2NH_2$$

Ethylene   Ethylene chloride   Ethylenediamine

A serious disadvantage to the synthesis of amines by ammonolysis is the formation of more than one class of amine. The primary amine salt,

$$RX + NH_3 \longrightarrow RNH_3^+ X^-$$
1° amine salt

formed by the initial substitution, reacts with the reagent ammonia to yield the ammonium salt and the free primary amine; the following equilibrium thus exists:

$$RNH_3^+ + NH_3 \rightleftharpoons RNH_2 + NH_4^+$$
1° amine

The free primary amine, like the ammonia from which it was made, is a nucleophilic reagent; it too can attack the alkyl halide, to yield the salt of a secondary amine:

$$RNH_2 + RX \longrightarrow R_2NH_2^+ X^- \overset{NH_3}{\rightleftharpoons} R_2NH$$
1° amine   2° amine

The secondary amine, which is in equilibrium with its salt, can in turn attack the alkyl halide to form the salt of a tertiary amine:

$$R_2NH + RX \longrightarrow R_3NH^+ X^- \overset{NH_3}{\rightleftharpoons} R_3N$$
2° amine   3° amine

Finally, the tertiary amine can attack the alkyl halide to form a compound of the formula $R_4N^+ X^-$ called a *quaternary ammonium salt* (discussed in Sec. 20.6):

$$R_3N + RX \longrightarrow R_4N^+ X^-$$
3° amine   Quaternary ammonium salt
(4°)

The presence of a large excess of ammonia lessens the importance of these last reactions and increases the yield of primary amine; under these conditions, a molecule of alkyl halide is more likely to encounter, and be attacked by, one of the numerous ammonia molecules rather than one of the relatively few amine molecules. At best, the yield of primary amine is always cut down by the formation of the higher classes of amines. Except in the special case of methylamine, the primary amine can be separated from these by-products by distillation.

19.11   Reductive amination

Many aldehydes (RCHO) and ketones (R_2CO) are converted into amines by treatment with hydrogen and ammonia in the presence of a catalyst; this process is known as **reductive amination**. Although the mechanism is not clear, the reaction may involve hydrogenation of an intermediate compound (an *imine*, $RCH{=}NH$ or $R_2C{=}NH$) that contains a carbon–nitrogen double bond.

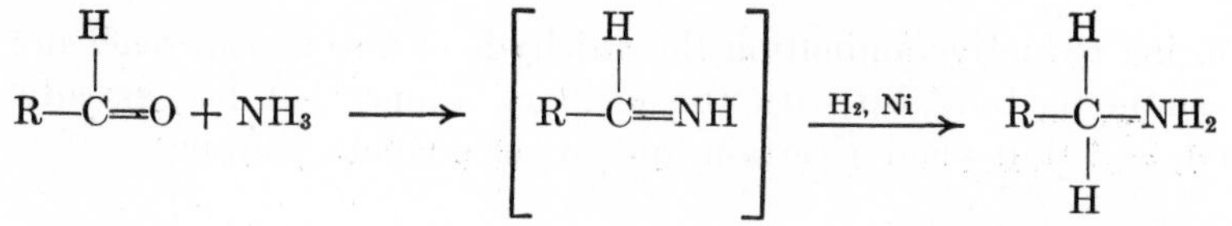

$$R-\underset{\underset{H}{|}}{C}=O + NH_3 \longrightarrow \left[R-\underset{\underset{H}{|}}{C}=NH \right] \xrightarrow{H_2,\ Ni} R-\underset{\underset{H}{\overset{H}{|}}}{C}-NH_2$$

An aldehyde   An imine   A 1° amine

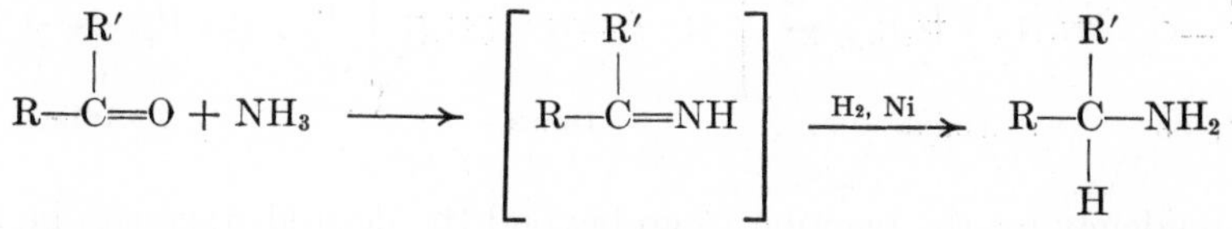

$$R-\underset{\underset{R'}{|}}{C}=O + NH_3 \longrightarrow \left[R-\underset{\underset{R'}{|}}{C}=NH \right] \xrightarrow{H_2,\ Ni} R-\underset{\underset{H}{\overset{R'}{|}}}{C}-NH_2$$

A ketone   An imine   A 1° amine

Reductive amination has been used successfully with a wide variety of aldehydes and ketones, both aliphatic and aromatic. For example:

$$CH_3(CH_2)_5CHO \xrightarrow{NH_3,\ H_2,\ Ni} CH_3(CH_2)_5CH_2NH_2$$

Heptaldehyde   *n*-Heptylamine

(Heptanal)   (1-Aminoheptane)

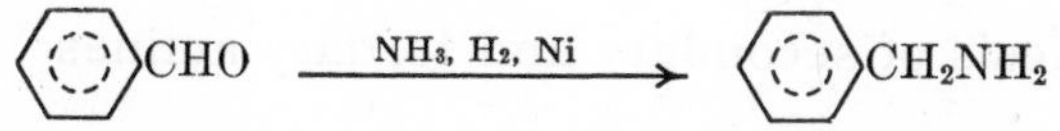

Benzaldehyde $\xrightarrow{NH_3,\ H_2,\ Ni}$ Benzylamine

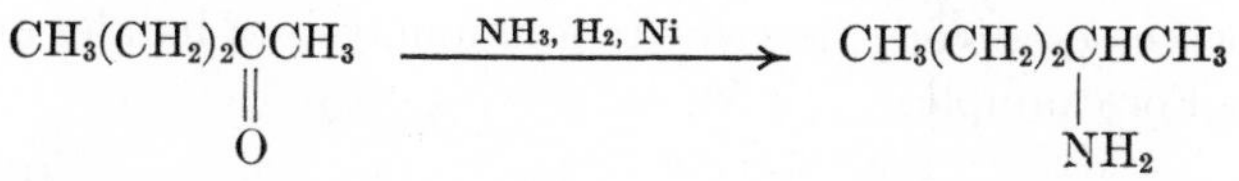

$$CH_3(CH_2)_2\underset{\underset{O}{\|}}{C}CH_3 \xrightarrow{NH_3,\ H_2,\ Ni} CH_3(CH_2)_2\underset{\underset{NH_2}{|}}{C}HCH_3$$

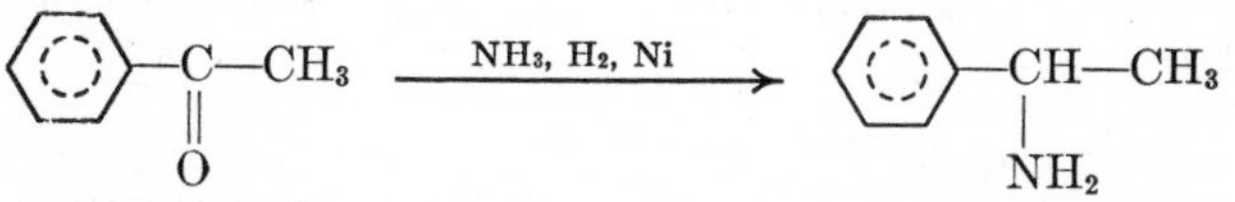

2-Pentanone   2-Aminopentane

(Methyl *n*-propyl ketone)

Acetophenone   α-Phenylethylamine

(Methyl phenyl ketone)

Reductive amination of ketones yields amines containing a *sec*-alkyl group; such amines are difficult to obtain by ammonolysis because of the tendency for *sec*-alkyl halides to undergo elimination. For example, cyclo-hexanone is converted into cyclohexylamine in good yield, whereas am-monolysis of bromocyclohexane yields only cyclohexene.

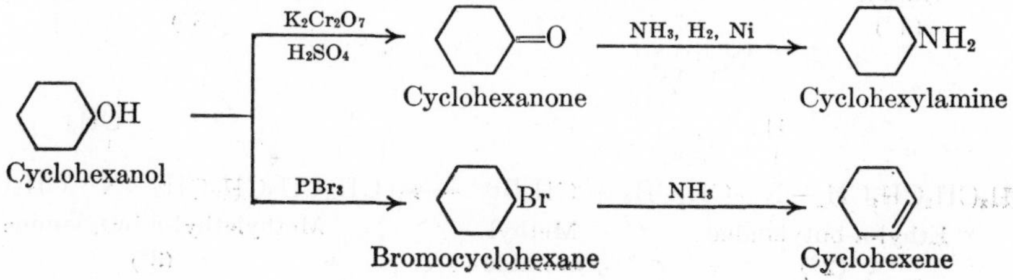

During reductive amination the aldehyde or ketone can react not only with ammonia but also with the primary amine that has already been formed, and thus yield a certain amount of secondary amine.

$$R—\overset{H}{\underset{|}{C}}=O + H_2N—CH_2R \longrightarrow \left[R—\overset{H}{\underset{|}{C}}=N—CH_2R \right] \xrightarrow[Ni]{H_2} RCH_2—\overset{H}{\underset{|}{N}}—CH_2R$$

Aldehyde   1° Amine   Imine   2° Amine

The tendency for the reaction to go beyond the desired stage can be fairly well limited by the proportions of reactants employed and is seldom a serious handicap.

Although we have not yet taken up the chemistry of aldehydes and ketones, we already know some of the ways in which they can be made: oxidation of alcohols (Sec. 12.7), Friedel-Crafts acylation (Sec. 17.8), and the reaction of acid chlorides with organocadmium compounds (Sec. 17.9).

19.12 Synthesis of secondary and tertiary amines

So far we have been chiefly concerned with the synthesis of primary amines. Secondary and tertiary amines are prepared by adaptations of one of the processes already described: ammonolysis of halides or reductive amination. For example:

$$CH_3CH_2CH_2CH_2NH_2 + CH_3CH_2Br \longrightarrow CH_3CH_2CH_2CH_2—\overset{H}{\underset{|}{N}}—CH_2CH_3$$

n-Butylamine   Ethyl bromide   Ethyl-*n*-butylamine
(1°)   (2°)

$$CH_3CH_2\overset{}{\underset{\overset{\|}{O}}{C}}CH_3 + CH_3NH_2 \xrightarrow{H_2,\ Ni} CH_3CH_2\overset{}{\underset{\overset{|}{NHCH_3}}{CH}}CH_3$$

Butanone   Methylamine   Methyl-*sec*-butylamine
(Methyl ethyl ketone)   (1°)   (2°)

$$⟨○⟩NH_2 \xrightarrow{CH_3Cl} ⟨○⟩NHCH_3 \xrightarrow{CH_3Cl} ⟨○⟩N(CH_3)_2$$

Aniline   N-Methylaniline   N,N-Dimethylaniline
(1°)   (2°)   (3°)

$$CH_3CH_2CH_2CH_2—\overset{H}{\underset{|}{N}}—CH_2CH_3 + CH_3Br \longrightarrow CH_3CH_2CH_2CH_2—\overset{CH_3}{\underset{|}{N}}—CH_2CH_3$$

Ethyl-*n*-butylamine   Methyl   Methylethyl-*n*-butylamine
(2°)   bromide   (3°)

Where ammonia has been used to produce a primary amine, a primary amine can be used to produce a secondary amine, or a secondary amine can be used to produce a tertiary amine. In each of these syntheses there is a tendency for reaction to proceed beyond the first stage and to yield an amine of a higher class than the one that is wanted.

Problem 19.5 Outline the syntheses of the following from benzene or toluene and any aliphatic reagents, using a different method in each case.

(a) *p*-nitrobenzylamine   (c) β-phenylethylamine
(b) N,N-dimethyl-*p*-toluidine   (d) 1-phenyl-2-aminopropane

    (e) 1-aminoundecane (n-$C_{11}H_{23}NH_2$) from available compounds

19.13   Hofmann degradation of amides

In addition to its importance as a method of synthesis of amines, the Hofmann degradation of amides is of considerable theoretical interest. Whatever the mechanism of the reaction, it is clear that a rearrangement occurs, since the group joined to carbonyl carbon in the amide is found joined to nitrogen in the product. The reaction is one of a number of quite similar rearrangements in which a group migrates from carbon to an adjacent nitrogen atom.

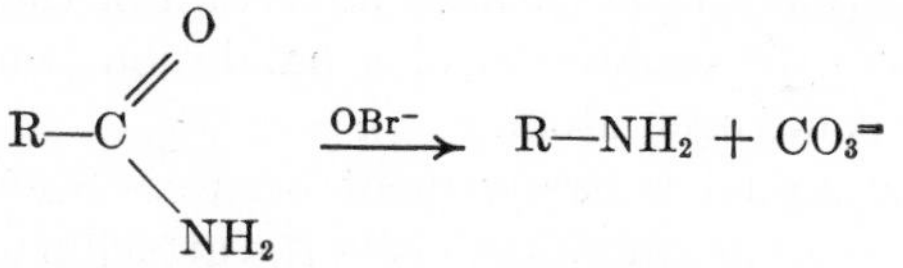

$$R-C\!\!\begin{array}{c} \nearrow O \\ \searrow NH_2 \end{array} \xrightarrow{\ OBr^- \ } R-NH_2 + CO_3^=$$

An amide   A 1° amine

Like the rearrangement of carbonium ions that we have already encountered (Sec. 9.8), the Hofmann degradation of amides involves a 1,2-shift. In the rearrangement of carbonium ions a group migrates with its electrons to an electron-deficient carbon; in the present reaction the group migrates with its electrons to an electron-deficient *nitrogen*.

The reaction is believed to proceed by the following steps:

$$(1) \qquad R-C\!\!\begin{array}{c} \nearrow O \\ \searrow \ddot{N}H_2 \end{array} + OBr^- \longrightarrow R-C\!\!\begin{array}{c} \nearrow O \\ \searrow \overset{\displaystyle \ddot{}}{N}-Br \\ | \\ H \end{array} + OH^-$$

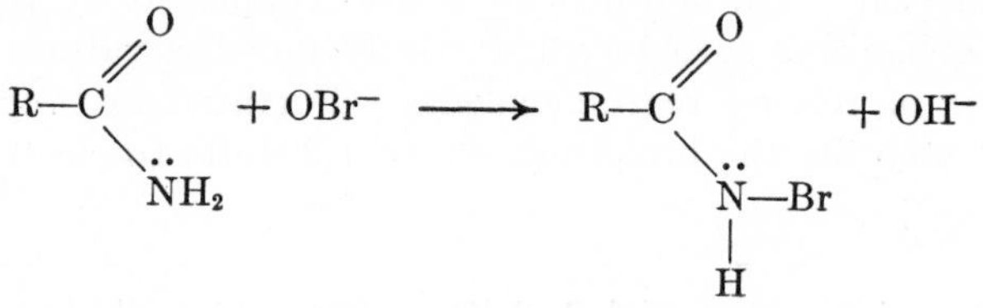

$$(2) \qquad R-C\!\!\begin{array}{c} \nearrow O \\ \searrow \overset{\displaystyle \ddot{}}{N}-Br \\ | \\ H \end{array} + OH^- \longrightarrow R-C\!\!\begin{array}{c} \nearrow O \\ \searrow \overset{\displaystyle \ddot{}}{N}-Br \\ \ominus \end{array} + H_2O$$

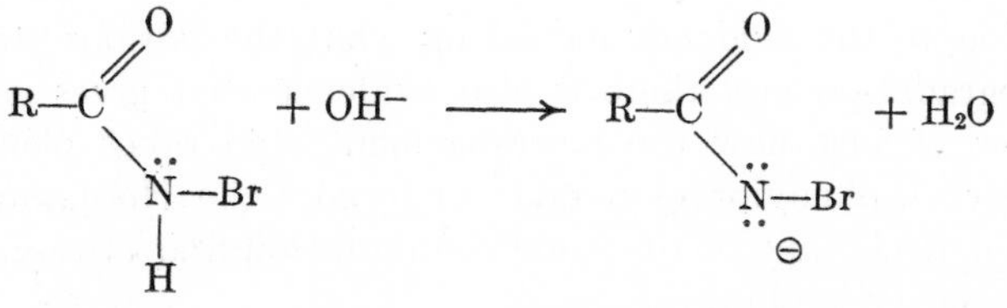

$$(3)\qquad R-C\underset{\underset{\ominus}{\overset{..}{N}-Br}}{\overset{\overset{O}{\|}}{\Big\langle}} \longrightarrow R-C\underset{\overset{..}{\underset{..}{N}}}{\overset{\overset{O}{\|}}{\Big\langle}} + Br^-$$

Simultaneous

$$(4)\qquad \overset{\overset{O}{\|}}{\underbrace{R}-C}\underset{\to \overset{..}{N}}{\Big\langle} \longrightarrow R-\overset{..}{N}=C=O$$

$$(5)\qquad R-\overset{..}{N}=C=O + 2OH^- \xrightarrow{\ H_2O\ } R-\overset{..}{N}H_2 + CO_3^-$$

Step (1) is the halogenation of an amide. This is a known reaction, an N-haloamide being isolated if no base is present. Furthermore, if the N-haloamide isolated in this way is then treated with base, it is converted into the amine.

Step (2) is the abstraction of a hydrogen ion by hydroxide ion. This is reasonable behavior for hydroxide ion, especially since the presence of the electron-attracting bromine increases the acidity of the amide. Unstable salts have actually been isolated in certain of these reactions.

Step (3) involves the separation of a halide ion, which leaves behind an electron-deficient nitrogen atom.

In Step (4) the actual rearrangement occurs. Steps (3) and (4) are generally believed to occur simultaneously, the attachment of R to nitrogen helping to push out halide ion.

Step (5) is the hydrolysis of an isocyanate (R—N=C=O) to form an amine and carbonate ion. This is a known reaction of isocyanates (Sec. 25.14). If the Hofmann degradation is carried out in the absence of water, an isocyanate can actually be isolated.

The strongest support for the mechanism just outlined is the fact that many of the proposed intermediates have been isolated, and that these intermediates have been shown to yield the products of the Hofmann degradation. The mechanism is also supported by the fact that analogous mechanisms account satisfactorily for observations made on a large number of related rearrangements. Furthermore, the actual rearrangement step fits the broad pattern of 1,2-shifts to electron-deficient atoms.

19.14 Stereochemistry of 1,2-shifts. The migrating group

In addition to the evidence indicating what the various steps in the Hofmann degradation are, there is also evidence that gives us a rather intimate view of just how the rearrangement step takes place. When optically active α-phenylpropionamide undergoes the Hofmann degradation, α-phenylethylamine of the same configuration and of essentially the same optical purity is obtained:

$$
\underset{\text{(+)-}\alpha\text{-Phenylpropionamide}}{
\begin{array}{c}
CH_3 \\
| \\
H-C-C \\
| \quad\ \ \diagdown NH_2 \\
C_6H_5 \quad \parallel O
\end{array}}
\quad \xrightarrow{\ OBr^-\ } \quad
\underset{\text{(-)-}\alpha\text{-Phenylethylamine}}{
\begin{array}{c}
CH_3 \\
| \\
H-C-NH_2 \\
| \\
C_6H_5
\end{array}}
$$

Retention of configuration

Rearrangement proceeds *with complete retention of configuration* about the asymmetric carbon.

These results tell us two things. First, nitrogen takes the same relative position on the asymmetric carbon that was originally occupied by the carbonyl carbon. Second, the asymmetric carbon does not break away from the carbonyl carbon until it has started to attach itself to nitrogen; if the group had actually become free during its migration, we would expect considerable racemization. (Why?) We may picture the migrating group as moving from carbon to nitrogen in the following way:

$$
\begin{array}{ccc}
\underset{\substack{\| \\ O}}{\overset{\substack{H \\ |}}{C_6H_5 \diagdown C \diagup CH_3}}{-N\!:}
& \longrightarrow &
\underset{\substack{\| \\ O}}{\overset{\substack{H \\ |}}{C_6H_5 \diagdown C \diagup CH_3}}{\cdots N\!:}
\qquad \longrightarrow \qquad
\underset{\substack{\| \\ O}}{\overset{\substack{H \\ |}}{C_6H_5 \diagdown C \diagup CH_3}}{=N\!:}
\end{array}
$$

There is much evidence to suggest that the stereochemistry of all 1,2-shifts has this common feature: *complete retention of configuration in the migrating group.*

Problem 19.6 Many years before the Hofmann degradation of optically active α-phenylpropionamide was studied, the following observations were made: when the cyclopentane derivative I, in which the —COOH and —CONH₂ groups are *cis* to each other, was treated with hypobromite, compound II was obtained; compound II could be converted by heat into the amide III (called a *lactam*). What do these results show about the mechanism of the rearrangement? (*Use models.*)

$$
\underset{I}{HOOC-\!\!\!\overset{\overset{\displaystyle CH_3 \quad CH_3}{\diagdown\ \ \diagup}}{\bigcirc}\!\!\!-CONH_2}
\quad \xrightarrow{\ OBr^-\ } \quad
\underset{II}{HOOC-\!\!\!\overset{\overset{\displaystyle CH_3 \quad CH_3}{\diagdown\ \ \diagup}}{\bigcirc}\!\!\!-NH_2}
\quad \xrightarrow{\ heat\ } \quad
\underset{III}{
\begin{array}{c}
CH_3 \quad CH_3 \\
\diagdown\ \ \diagup \\
\bigcirc \\
C-NH \\
\parallel \\
O
\end{array}}
$$

19.15 Migration of aryl groups

When the migrating group is aryl, the rate of the Hofmann degradation is increased by the presence of electron-releasing substituents on the aromatic ring; thus substituted benzamides show the following order of reactivity:

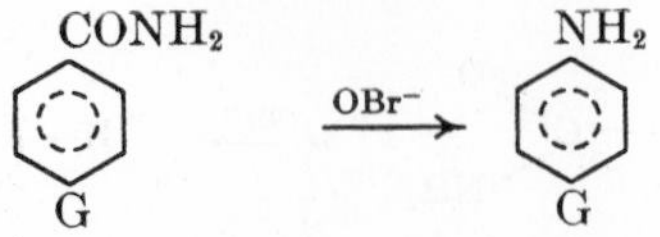

$$G: \quad -OCH_3 > -CH_3 > -H > -Cl > -NO_2$$

It is believed that electron-releasing substituents speed up reaction by speeding up the rearrangement step; it is generally observed in rearrangements of this kind that the *migratory aptitude* of a group is increased by electron-releasing substituents.

From one point of view, migration of an aryl group is just a special instance of electrophilic aromatic substitution, with electron-deficient nitrogen acting as the attacking reagent. There may even be an intermediate compound like IV, analogous to the intermediate proposed for other electrophilic aromatic substitutions (Sec. 10.7).

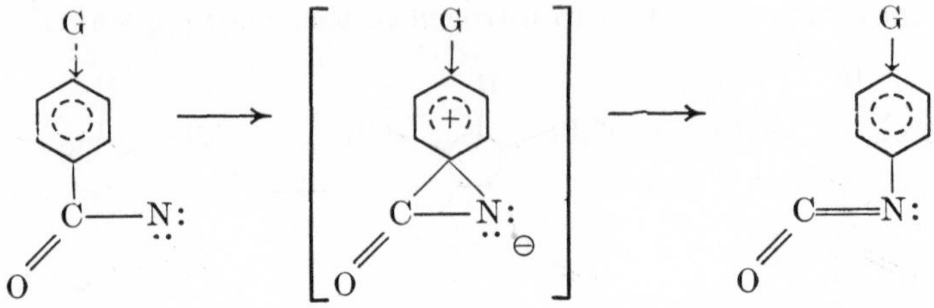

IV

Electron-releasing groups would disperse the developing positive charge on the aromatic ring and thus speed up formation of intermediate IV. Viewed in this way, substituents affect the rate of the Hofmann degradation (and many related rearrangements) in exactly the same way as they affect the rate of aromatic nitration, halogenation, or sulfonation.

PROBLEMS

1. Draw structures, give names, and classify as primary, secondary, or tertiary:
(a) the eight isomeric amines of formula $C_4H_{11}N$
(b) the five isomeric amines of formula C_7H_9N that contain a benzene ring

2. Give the structural formulas of the following compounds:

(a) *sec*-butylamine
(b) *o*-toluidine
(c) anilinium chloride
(d) diethylamine
(e) *p*-aminobenzoic acid
(f) benzylamine
(g) isopropylammonium benzoate
(h) *o*-phenylenediamine
(i) N,N-dimethylaniline
(j) ethanolamine (2-aminoethanol)
(k) β-phenylethylamine
(l) N,N-dimethylaminocyclohexane
(m) diphenylamine
(n) 2,4-dimethylaniline
(o) tetra-*n*-butylammonium iodide
(p) *p*-anisidine

3. Show how *n*-propylamine could be prepared from each of the following:

(a) *n*-propyl bromide
(b) *n*-propyl alcohol
(c) propionaldehyde
(d) 1-nitropropane
(e) propionitrile
(f) *n*-butyramide
(g) *n*-butyl alcohol
(h) ethyl alcohol

Which of these methods can be applied to the preparation of aniline? Of benzylamine?

4. Outline all steps in a possible laboratory synthesis of each of the following compounds from benzene, toluene, and alcohols of four carbons or less, using any needed inorganic reagents.

(a) n-pentylamine
(b) p-toluidine
(c) m-nitroaniline
(d) α-phenylethylamine
(e) β-phenylethylamine
(f) m-chloroaniline

(g) p-aminobenzoic acid
(h) 3-aminoheptane
(i) N-ethylaniline
(j) 2,4-dinitroaniline
(k) the drug *benzedrine* (2-amino-1-phenylpropane)
(l) 2-(N,N-diethylamino)ethanol (*Hint:* see Sec. 15.14.)

5. Outline all steps in a possible laboratory synthesis from palmitic acid, n-$C_{15}H_{31}COOH$, of:

(a) n-$C_{16}H_{33}NH_2$
(b) n-$C_{17}H_{35}NH_2$

(c) n-$C_{15}H_{31}NH_2$
(d) n-$C_{15}H_{31}CH(NH_2)$-n-$C_{16}H_{33}$

6. On the basis of the following syntheses give the structures of *putrescine* and *cadaverine*, found in rotting flesh:

(a) ethylene bromide $\xrightarrow{\text{KCN}}$ $C_4H_4N_2$ $\xrightarrow{\text{Na, }C_2H_5OH}$ putrescine ($C_4H_{12}N_2$)
(b) $Br(CH_2)_5Br$ $\xrightarrow{\text{NH}_3}$ cadaverine ($C_5H_{14}N_2$)

7. Using models and then drawing formulas, show the stereoisomeric forms in which each of the following compounds can exist. Tell which stereoisomers when separated from all others would be optically active and which would be optically inactive.

(a) α-phenylethylamine
(b) N-methyl-N-ethylaniline
(c) methylethyl-n-propylphenylammonium bromide

(d)

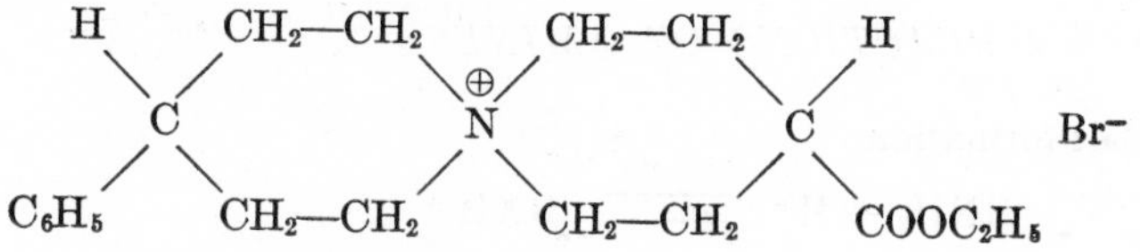

(e)

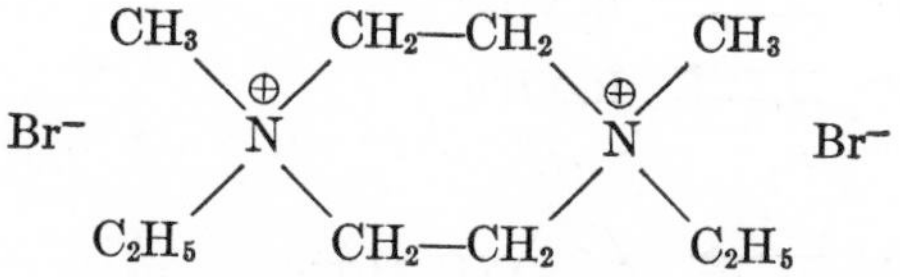

(f) methylethylphenylamine oxide, $(CH_3)(C_2H_5)(C_6H_5)N$—O

8. Two geometric isomers of benzaldoxime, C_6H_5CH=NOH, are known. (a) Draw their structures, showing the geometry of the molecules. (b) Show how this geometry results from their electronic configurations. (c) Would you predict geometric isomerism for benzophenoneoxime, $(C_6H_5)_2C$=NOH? For acetophenoneoxime, $C_6H_5C(CH_3)$=NOH? For azobenzene, C_6H_5N=NC_6H_5?

9. Account for the fact that benzylmethylphenylphosphine oxide, $(C_6H_5CH_2)(CH_3)(C_6H_5)P$—$O$, has been resolved (separated into enantiomeric forms), but benzylmethylphenylphosphine, $(C_6H_5CH_2)(CH_3)(C_6H_5)P$, has not been resolved.

Chapter twenty

AMINES II. REACTIONS

20.1 Reactions

Like ammonia, the three classes of amines contain nitrogen that bears an unshared pair of electrons. Much of the chemical behavior of amines resembles very closely the chemical behavior of ammonia, and is due to the tendency for nitrogen to share this pair of electrons. This tendency is responsible for the basicity of amines, for their action as nucleophilic reagents, and for the unusually high reactivity of aromatic rings bearing amino or substituted amino groups.

REACTIONS OF AMINES

1. Basicity. Salt formation

$$RNH_2 + H^+ \rightleftharpoons RNH_3^+$$
$$R_2NH + H^+ \rightleftharpoons R_2NH_2^+$$
$$R_3N + H^+ \rightleftharpoons R_3NH^+$$

Examples:

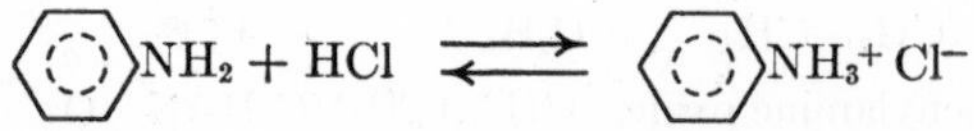

$$\langle \bigcirc \rangle NH_2 + HCl \rightleftharpoons \langle \bigcirc \rangle NH_3^+ Cl^-$$

Aniline

Anilinium chloride
(Aniline hydrochloride)

$$(CH_3)_2NH + HNO_3 \rightleftharpoons (CH_3)_2NH_2^+ NO_3^-$$

Dimethylamine

Dimethylammonium nitrate

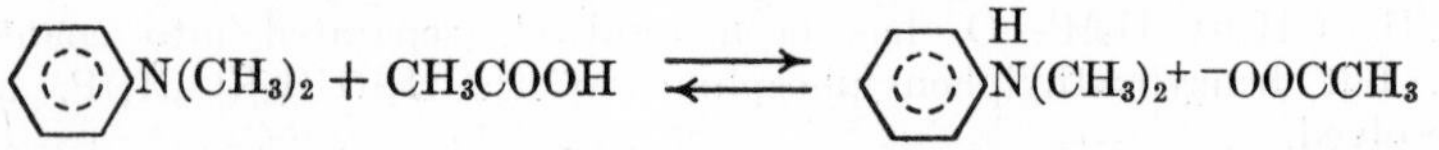

$$\langle \bigcirc \rangle N(CH_3)_2 + CH_3COOH \rightleftharpoons \langle \bigcirc \rangle \overset{H}{N}(CH_3)_2^+ {}^-OOCCH_3$$

N,N-Dimethylaniline

N,N-Dimethylanilinium acetate

2. Alkylation

$$RNH_2 \xrightarrow{RX} R_2NH \xrightarrow{RX} R_3N \xrightarrow{RX} R_4N^+ X^-$$
$$ArNH_2 \xrightarrow{RX} ArNHR \xrightarrow{RX} ArNR_2 \xrightarrow{RX} ArNR_3^+ X^-$$

Examples:

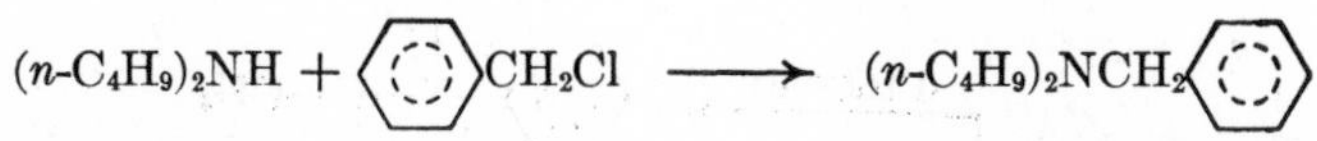

$$(n\text{-}C_4H_9)_2NH + \langle \bigcirc \rangle CH_2Cl \longrightarrow (n\text{-}C_4H_9)_2NCH_2\langle \bigcirc \rangle$$

Di-*n*-butylamine Benzyl chloride Benzyldi(*n*-butyl)amine
(2°) (3°)

$$n\text{-}C_3H_7NH_2 \xrightarrow{CH_3I} n\text{-}C_3H_7\overset{\overset{\displaystyle H}{|}}{N}CH_3 \xrightarrow{CH_3I} n\text{-}C_3H_7\overset{\overset{\displaystyle CH_3}{|}}{N}CH_3 \xrightarrow{CH_3I} n\text{-}C_3H_7\overset{\overset{\displaystyle CH_3}{|}}{\underset{\underset{\displaystyle CH_3}{|}}{N}}CH_3^+\ I^-$$

n-Propylamine *n*-Propylmethylamine *n*-Propyltrimethylammonium
(1°) (2°) iodide
(4°)

n-Propyldimethylamine
(3°)

3. Conversion into amides

Primary: RNH_2 —

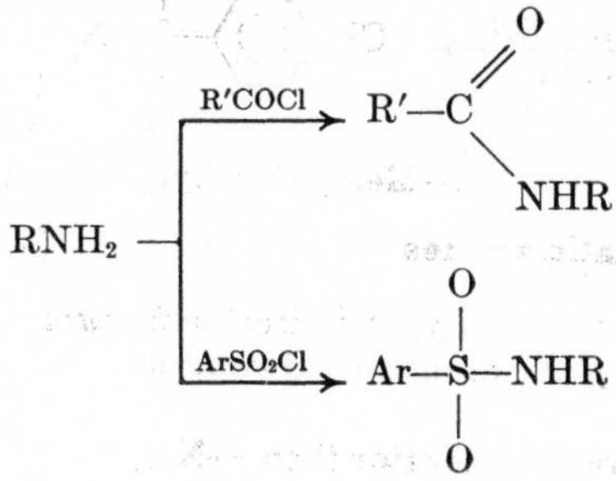

$$\xrightarrow{R'COCl} \quad R'\!-\!\overset{\overset{\displaystyle O}{\|}}{C}\diagdown_{NHR} \qquad \text{An N-substituted amide}$$

$$\xrightarrow{ArSO_2Cl} \quad Ar\!-\!\overset{\overset{\displaystyle O}{|}}{\underset{\underset{\displaystyle O}{|}}{S}}\!-\!NHR \qquad \text{An N-substituted sulfonamide}$$

Secondary: R_2NH —

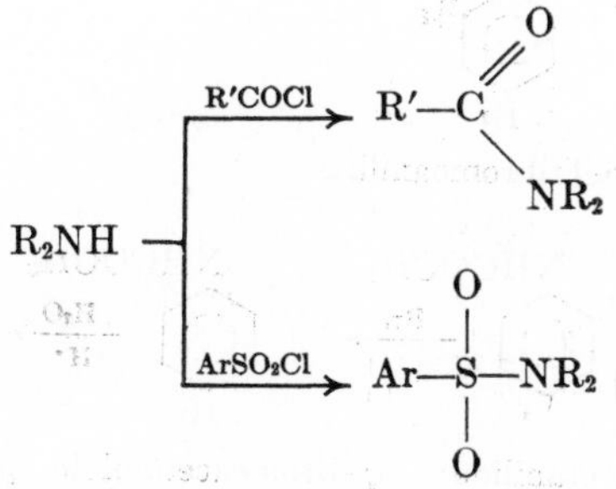

$$\xrightarrow{R'COCl} \quad R'\!-\!\overset{\overset{\displaystyle O}{\|}}{C}\diagdown_{NR_2} \qquad \text{An N,N-disubstituted amide}$$

$$\xrightarrow{ArSO_2Cl} \quad Ar\!-\!\overset{\overset{\displaystyle O}{|}}{\underset{\underset{\displaystyle O}{|}}{S}}\!-\!NR_2 \qquad \text{An N,N-disubstituted sulfonamide}$$

Tertiary: R_3N —

$$\xrightarrow{R'COCl} \text{No reaction}$$

$$\xrightarrow{ArSO_2Cl} \text{No reaction}$$

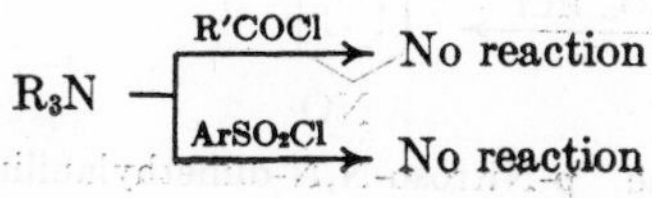

Examples:

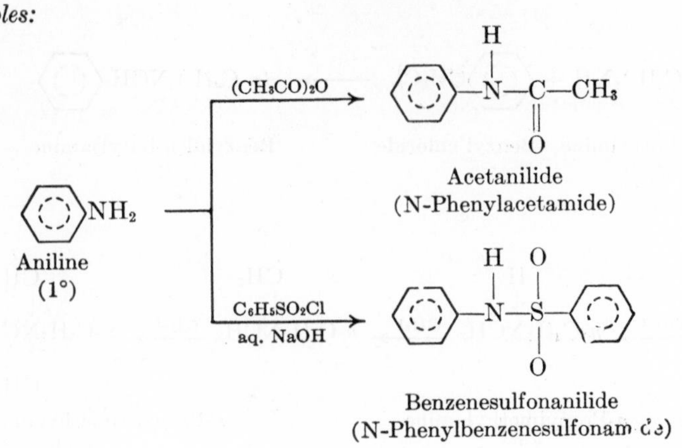

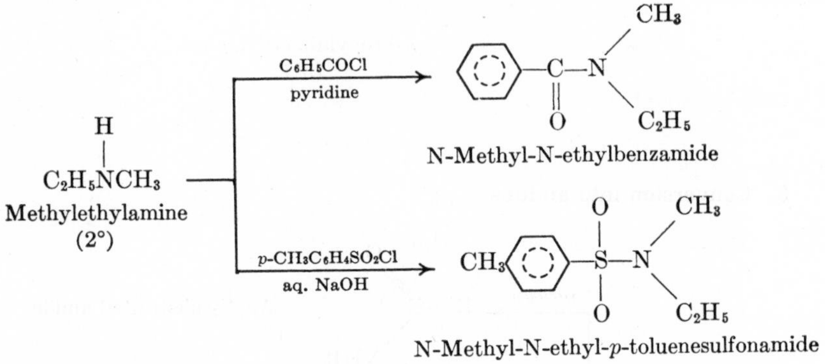

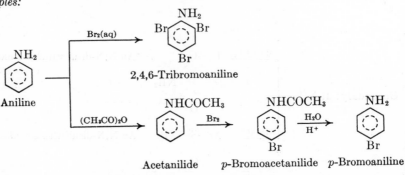

$$\text{Aniline} \atop (1°)$$

$\xrightarrow{\text{(CH}_3\text{CO)}_2\text{O}}$ Acetanilide (N-Phenylacetamide)

$\xrightarrow[\text{aq. NaOH}]{\text{C}_6\text{H}_5\text{SO}_2\text{Cl}}$ Benzenesulfonanilide (N-Phenylbenzenesulfonam de)

$$\text{C}_2\text{H}_5\text{NCH}_3 \atop \text{Methylethylamine} \atop (2°)$$

$\xrightarrow[\text{pyridine}]{\text{C}_6\text{H}_5\text{COCl}}$ N-Methyl-N-ethylbenzamide

$\xrightarrow[\text{aq. NaOH}]{p\text{-CH}_3\text{C}_6\text{H}_4\text{SO}_2\text{Cl}}$ N-Methyl-N-ethyl-*p*-toluenesulfonamide

4. Ring substitution in aromatic amines

—NH$_2$
—NHR Activate powerfully, and direct *ortho,para*
—NR$_2$ in electrophilic aromatic substitution

—NHCOR: Less powerful activator than —NH$_2$

Examples:

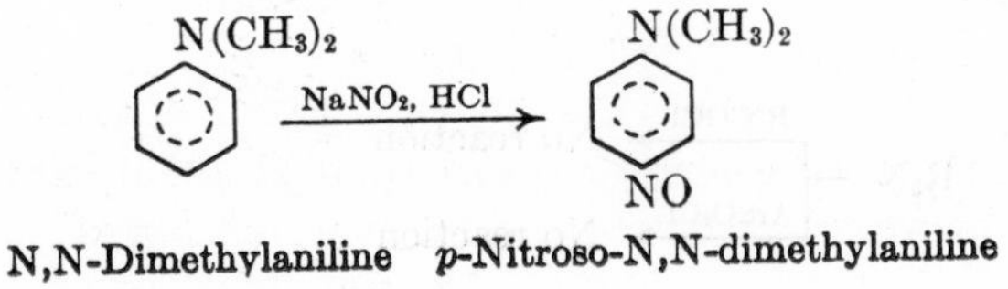

Aniline

$\xrightarrow{\text{Br}_2\text{(aq)}}$ 2,4,6-Tribromoaniline

$\xrightarrow{\text{(CH}_3\text{CO)}_2\text{O}}$ Acetanilide $\xrightarrow{\text{Br}_2}$ *p*-Bromoacetanilide $\xrightarrow[\text{H}^+]{\text{H}_2\text{O}}$ *p*-Bromoaniline

N,N-Dimethylaniline $\xrightarrow{\text{NaNO}_2\text{, HCl}}$ *p*-Nitroso-N,N-dimethylaniline

$$(CH_3)_2N\langle\bigcirc\rangle + \langle\bigcirc\rangle N_2^+ \, Cl^- \xrightarrow{\text{acid}} (CH_3)_2N\langle\bigcirc\rangle\text{-N}=\text{N-}\langle\bigcirc\rangle + HCl$$

N,N-Dimethylaniline
         Benzenediazonium chloride
                              An azo compound
                           (Discussed in Chap. 21)

5. Reaction with nitrous acid

Primary aromatic: $ArNH_2 \xrightarrow{\text{HONO}} Ar\text{-}N\equiv N^+$ Diazonium salt
                                                    (Discussed in Chap. 21)

Primary aliphatic: $RNH_2 \xrightarrow{\text{HONO}} [R\text{-}N\equiv N^+] \xrightarrow{H_2O} N_2 +$ mixture of
                                                               alcohols and
                                                               alkenes

Secondary aromatic ArNHR $\overset{\overset{\textstyle R}{|}}{Ar\text{-}N\text{-}N=O}$

or aliphatic: or $\xrightarrow{\text{HONO}}$ or   N-Nitrosoamine
                 R_2NH $R_2N\text{-}N=O$

Tertiary aromatic: $\langle\bigcirc\rangle NR_2 \xrightarrow{\text{HONO}} O=N\langle\bigcirc\rangle NR_2$ *p*-Nitroso
                                                                compound

Tertiary aliphatic: $R_3N \xrightarrow{\text{HONO}} R_3NH^+$

20.2 Basicity of amines. Basicity constant

The fact that ammonia is converted into ammonium salts by aqueous solutions of mineral acids tells us that ammonia is a stronger base than water:

$$NH_3 + H_3O^+ \longrightarrow NH_4^+ + H_2O$$

       Stronger   Weaker
        base   base

The fact that ammonia is liberated from ammonium salts by aqueous hydroxides tells us that ammonia is a weaker base than hydroxide ion:

$$NH_4^+ + OH^- \longrightarrow NH_3 + H_2O$$

          Stronger   Weaker
            base   base

Like ammonia, amines are converted into their salts by mineral acids and are liberated from their salts by hydroxide ion; amines, too, are more basic than water and less basic than hydroxide ion:

$$RNH_2 + H_3O^+ \longrightarrow RNH_3^+ + H_2O$$

       Stronger   Weaker
        base   base

$$RNH_3^+ + OH^- \longrightarrow RNH_2 + H_2O$$

         Stronger   Weaker
            base   base

We found it convenient to compare acidities of carboxylic acids by measuring the extent to which they give up hydrogen ion to water; the equilibrium constant for this reaction was called the acidity constant, K_a. In the same way, it is convenient to compare basicities of amines by measuring the extent to which they accept hydrogen ion from water; the equilibrium constant for this reaction is called a **basicity constant**, K_b.

$$RNH_2 + H_2O \;\xrightleftharpoons{}\; RNH_3^+ + OH^-$$

$$K_b = \frac{[RNH_3^+][OH^-]}{[RNH_2]}$$

(As in the analogous expression for an acidity constant, the concentration of the solvent, water, is omitted.) Each amine has its characteristic K_b; the larger the K_b, the stronger is the base.

We must not lose sight of the fact that the principal base in an aqueous solution of an amine (or of ammonia, for that matter) is the *amine* itself, not hydroxide ion. Measurement of $[OH^-]$ is simply a convenient way to compare basicities.

We see in Table 19.1 (page 520) that aliphatic amines of all three classes have K_b's of about 10^{-3} to 10^{-4} (0.001 to 0.0001); they are thus somewhat stronger bases than ammonia ($K_b = 1.8 \times 10^{-5}$). Aromatic amines, on the other hand, are considerably weaker bases than ammonia, having K_b's of 10^{-9} or less. Substituents on the ring have a marked effect on the basicity of aromatic amines, p-nitroaniline, for example, being only 1/4000 as basic as aniline (Table 20.1).

TABLE 20.1

BASICITY CONSTANTS OF SUBSTITUTED ANILINES

K_b of aniline = 4.2×10^{-10}

	K_b		K_b		K_b
p-NH$_2$	110×10^{-10}	m-NH$_2$	7.6×10^{-10}	o-NH$_2$	3.2×10^{-10}
p-OCH$_3$	15	m-OCH$_3$	—	o-OCH$_3$	3
p-CH$_3$	12	m-CH$_3$	4.9	o-CH$_3$	2.5
p-Cl	1.5	m-Cl	.3	o-Cl	.05
p-NO$_2$	.001	m-NO$_2$	.032	o-NO$_2$	.00035

20.3 Structure and basicity

Let us see how basicity of amines is related to structure. In doing this we shall assume (as we did in dealing with the acidity of carboxylic acids, Sec. 16.12) that differences in basicity, that is, differences in K_b, are due chiefly to differences in ΔH of ionization. This means that we shall compare the stabilities of amines with the stabilities of their ions; the more stable the ion relative to the amine from which it is formed, the more basic is the amine.

First of all, amines are more basic than alcohols, ethers, esters, etc., for the same reason that ammonia is more basic than water: nitrogen is less electronegative than oxygen, and can better accommodate the positive charge of the ion

An aliphatic amine is more basic than ammonia because the electron-releasing alkyl groups tend to disperse the positive charge of the substituted ammonium ion, and therefore stabilize it in a way that is not possible for the unsubstituted ammonium ion. Thus an *ammonium* ion is stabilized by electron release in the same way as a *carbonium* ion (Sec. 4.17). From another point of view, we can consider that an alkyl group pushes electrons toward nitrogen, and thus makes the fourth pair more available for sharing with an acid. (The differences in basicity among primary, secondary, and tertiary aliphatic amines are due to a combination of solvation and electronic factors, and are difficult to interpret.)

$$
\begin{array}{ccc}
\overset{\displaystyle H}{\underset{\displaystyle H}{R{\rightarrow}N:}} + H^+ & \rightleftharpoons & \overset{\displaystyle H}{\underset{\displaystyle H}{R{\rightarrow}N{-}H^+}}
\end{array}
$$

R *releases electrons:*　　　R *releases electrons:*
makes unshared pair　　　*stabilizes ion,*
more available　　　　　　*increases basicity*

How can we account for the fact that aromatic amines are weaker bases than ammonia? Let us compare the structures of aniline and the anilinium ion with the structures of ammonia and the ammonium ion. We see that ammonia and the ammonium ion are each represented satisfactorily by a single structure:

$$
\begin{array}{cc}
\overset{\displaystyle H}{H\!:\!\overset{..}{\underset{..}{N}}\!:\!H} & \overset{\displaystyle H}{\underset{\displaystyle H}{H\!:\!\overset{..}{N}\!:\!H^+}}
\end{array}
$$

Ammonia　　　　　　Ammonium ion

Aniline and anilinium ion contain the benzene ring and therefore are hybrids of the Kekulé structures I and II, and III and IV.

Aniline　　　　　　　　　　　Anilinium ion

This resonance presumably stabilizes both amine and ion to the same extent. It lowers the energy content of each by the same number of kcal/mole, and hence does not affect the *difference* in their energy contents, that is, does not affect ΔH of ionization. If there were no other factors involved, then, we might expect the basicity of aniline to be about the same as the basicity of ammonia.

However, there are additional structures to be considered. To account for the powerful activating effect of the —NH$_2$ group on electrophilic aromatic substitution (Sec. 10.10), we considered that the intermediate carbonium ion is stabilized by structures in which there is a double bond between nitrogen and the ring; contribution from these structures is simply a way of indicating the tendency for nitrogen to share its fourth pair of electrons and to accept a positive charge. It is generally believed that the —NH$_2$ group tends to share electrons with the ring, not only in the carbonium ion which is the intermediate in electrophilic aromatic substitution, but also in the aniline molecule itself.

Thus aniline is a hybrid not only of structures I and II but also of structures V, VI, and VII.

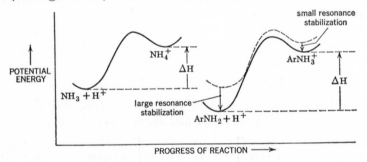

<table>
<tr><td align="center">V</td><td align="center">VI</td><td align="center">VII</td></tr>
</table>

We cannot draw comparable structures for the anilinium ion. Contribution from the three structures V, VI, and VII stabilizes the amine in a way that is not possible for the ammonium ion; resonance thus lowers the energy content of aniline more than it lowers the energy content of the anilinium ion. The net effect is to make ΔH of ionization larger and K_b smaller (see Figure 20.1).

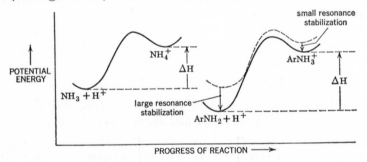

FIGURE 20.1 Molecular structure and position of equilibrium. Resonance-stabilized aromatic amine is weaker base than ammonia.

The low basicity of aromatic amines is thus due to the fact that the amine is stabilized by resonance to a greater extent than is the ion.

From another point of view, we can say that aniline is a weaker base than ammonia because the fourth pair of electrons is partly shared with the ring and is thus less available for sharing with a hydrogen ion. The tendency (through resonance) for the —NH$_2$ group to release electrons to the aromatic ring makes the ring more reactive toward electrophilic attack; at the same time this tendency necessarily makes the amine less basic. Similar considerations apply to other aromatic amines.

Problem 20.1 How can you account for the following? Diphenylamine, C$_6$H$_5$NHC$_6$H$_5$, has a K_b of 7×10^{-14} and thus is a much weaker base than aniline; triphenylamine, (C$_6$H$_5$)$_3$N, has essentially no basic properties at all in aqueous solutions.

20.4 Effect of substituents on basicity of aromatic amines

How is the basicity of an aromatic amine affected by substituents on the ring?

In Table 20.1 (page 544) we see that an electron-releasing substituent like —CH_3 increases the basicity of aniline, and an electron-withdrawing substituent like —X or —NO_2 decreases the basicity. These effects are reasonable ones. Electron release tends to disperse the positive charge of the anilinium ion, and thus stabilizes the ion relative to the amine. Electron withdrawal tends to intensify the positive charge of the anilinium ion, and thus destabilizes the ion relative to the amine.

Basicity of Aromatic Amines

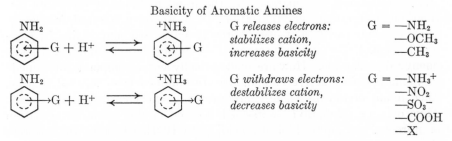

We notice that the base-strengthening substituents are the ones that activate an aromatic ring toward electrophilic substitution; the base-weakening substituents are the ones that deactivate an aromatic ring toward electrophilic substitution (see Sec. 10.4). Basicity depends upon position of equilibrium, and hence on relative stabilities of reactants and products. Reactivity in electrophilic aromatic substitution depends upon rate, and hence on relative stabilities of reactants and transition state. The effect of a particular substituent is the same in both cases, however, since the controlling factor is accommodation of a positive charge.

A given substituent affects the basicity of an amine and the acidity of a carboxylic acid in opposite ways (compare Sec. 16.14). This is to be expected, since basicity depends upon ability to accommodate a positive charge, and acidity depends upon ability to accommodate a negative charge.

Once again we see the operation of the **ortho effect** (Sec. 16.14). Even electron-releasing substituents weaken basicity when they are *ortho* to the amino group, and electron-withdrawing substituents do so to a much greater extent from the *ortho* position than from the *meta* or *para* position.

From another point of view, we can consider that an electron-releasing group pushes electrons toward nitrogen and makes the fourth pair more available for sharing with an acid, whereas an electron-attracting group helps pull electrons away from nitrogen and thus makes the fourth pair less available for sharing.

Problem 20.2 (a) Besides destabilizing the anilinium ion, how else might a nitro group affect basicity? (*Hint:* see structures V–VII on page 546.) (b) Why does the nitro group exert a larger base-weakening effect from the *para* position than from the nearer *meta* position?

Problem 20.3 Draw the structural formula of the product expected (if any) from the reaction of trimethylamine and boron trifluoride (BF_3).

20.5 Amine salts and resolution of racemates

As bases, amines react with acids to form salts. Let us examine one of the most important applications of such salt formation: **resolution of a racemate,** that is, *the separation of a racemate into enantiomers.*

We know (Sec. 11.23) that when optically inactive reactants form a compound containing one asymmetric carbon atom, the product is a racemate. We know that the enantiomers making up a racemate have identical physical properties (except for direction of rotation of polarized light) and hence cannot be separated by the usual methods of fractional distillation or fractional crystallization. Yet we have referred frequently to experiments carried out using optically active compounds like (+)-*sec*-butyl alcohol, (−)-2-bromooctane, (−)-α-phenylethyl chloride, (+)-α-phenylpropionamide. How are such optically active compounds obtained?

Some optically active compounds are obtained from natural sources, since living organisms usually produce only one enantiomer of a pair. Thus only (−)-2-methyl-1-butanol is formed in the yeast fermentation of starches, and only (+)-lactic acid, $CH_3CHOHCOOH$, in the contraction of muscles; only (−)-malic acid, $HOOCCH_2CHOHCOOH$, is obtained from fruit juices, only (−)-quinine from the bark of the cinchona tree. Indeed, we deal with optically active substances to an extent that we may not realize. We eat optically active bread and optically active meat, live in houses, wear clothes, and read books made of optically active cellulose. The proteins that make up our muscles and other tissues, the glycogen in our liver and in our blood, the enzymes and hormones that enable us to grow, and that regulate our bodily processes — all these are optically active. Naturally occurring compounds are optically active because the enzymes that bring about their formation — and often the raw materials from which they are made — are themselves optically active. As to the origin of the optically active enzymes, we can only speculate.

(+)-1-Bromo-2-methylbutane

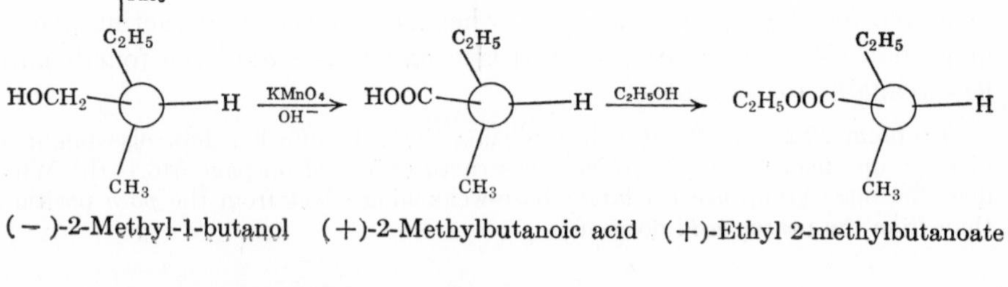

(−)-2-Methyl-1-butanol   (+)-2-Methylbutanoic acid   (+)-Ethyl 2-methylbutanoate

From these naturally occurring compounds, other optically active compounds can be made. For example, (−)-2-methyl-1-butanol can be converted without loss of configuration into the corresponding bromide, acid, ester, and many other compounds.

Problem 20.4   Outline the synthesis of the following *optically active* compounds starting from (−)-2-methyl-1-butanol:

(a) 4-methyl-3-hexanone   (d) 2-methyl-1-aminobutane
(b) β-methylvaleric acid   (e) 3-methyl-1-aminopentane
(c) 2,4-dimethyl-2-hexanol   (f) *sec*-butylamine

Most optically active compounds are obtained by the **resolution** of a racemate, that is, by the *separation of a racemate into enantiomers.* The separation of enantiomers can be accomplished only through the use of reagents that are themselves optically active; these reagents are generally obtained from natural sources.

The first resolution was carried out in 1848 at the École normale in Paris by Louis Pasteur, who mechanically separated left-handed and right-handed crystals of sodium ammonium tartrate. Although this method is limited to the very few racemates that happen to crystallize in a particular way, Pasteur's discovery was of great theoretical importance, since it led him to the fundamental idea that optical activity is related to molecular geometry. Pasteur also developed the method of resolution by conversion into diastereoisomers (discussed below), and was the first to observe that living organisms often preferentially destroy only one enantiomer of a pair.

Although popularly known chiefly for his great work in bacteriology and medicine, Pasteur was by training a chemist, and his work in chemistry alone would have earned him a position as an outstanding scientist.

The majority of resolutions that have been carried out depend upon the reaction of amines with acids to yield salts. Although most of these resolutions involve rather complicated organic compounds, the principle can be illustrated by a few simple examples.

Let us consider first the resolution of an amine, for example, *sec*-butylamine. As ordinarily prepared by the reductive amination of methyl ethyl ketone, *sec*-butylamine would be obtained as a racemate. (*Problem:* using models, show why this should be so.) If this racemic *sec*-butylamine is mixed with the (−)-malic acid obtained from fruit juice, *sec*-butylammonium hydrogen malate will be formed. The amine is present in two different configurations, but the acid is present in only one configuration; there will result therefore crystals of two different salts, (+)-*sec*butylammonium hydrogen (−)-malate and (−)-*sec*-butylammonium hydrogen (−)-malate (shown on the next page).

What is the relationship between these two salts? They are not superimposable, since the ammonium portions are not superimposable. They are not mirror images, since the malate portions are not mirror images. The salts are optical isomers but are not enantiomers. *Optical isomers that are not enantiomers are called* **diastereomers.**

Diastereomers have different physical properties: different melting point, boiling point, solubility in a given solvent, density, refractive index, etc. Diastereomers differ in specific rotation; they may have the same

Unresolved enantiomers
(Racemate)

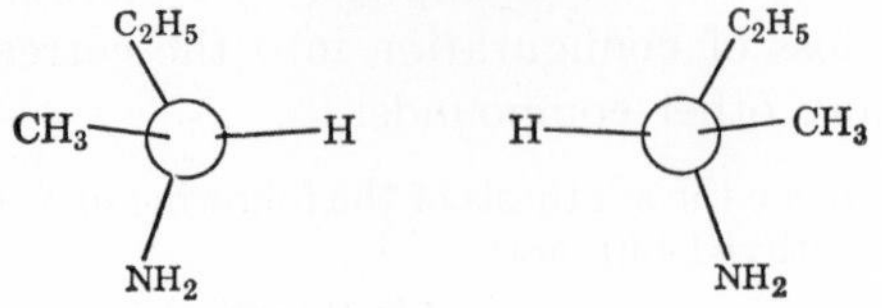

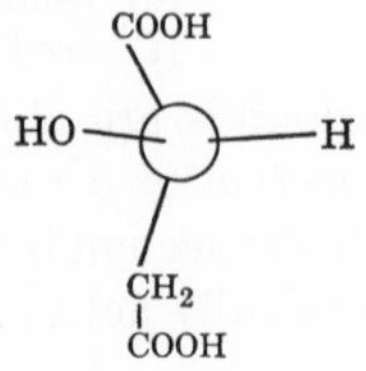

C_2H_5

CH_3——————H   H——————CH_3

NH_2 NH_2

COOH

HO——————H

CH_2
|
COOH

(−)-Malic acid

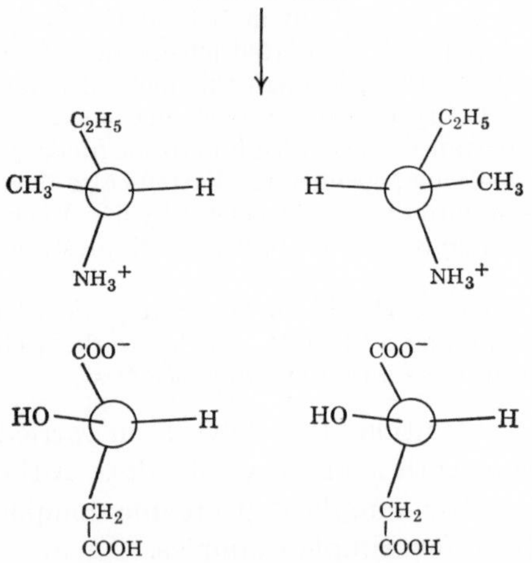

C_2H_5 C_2H_5

CH_3——————H   H——————CH_3

$NH_3{}^+$ $NH_3{}^+$

COO^- COO^-

HO——————H   HO——————H

CH_2 CH_2
| |
COOH   COOH

Salt of   Salt of
(−)-amine   (+)-amine

Diastereomers
(*Separable*)

or opposite signs of rotation, or some may be inactive. Diastereomers contain the same functional groups, and hence show similar chemical properties; the chemical properties are not identical, however, for each diastereomer reacts with a given reagent at a different rate. In so far as chemical and physical properties are concerned, therefore, diastereomers show the same relationship to each other as do geometric isomers.

The diastereomeric salts formed from racemic *sec*-butylamine and (−)-malic acid have different physical properties, including solubility in a given solvent. They can therefore be separated by fractional crystallization. Once the two salts are separated, optically active *sec*-butylamine can be recovered from each salt by addition of the strong base hydroxide ion which displaces the weaker base, the amine. If the salt has been carefully purified by repeated crystallizations to remove all traces of its diastereomer, then the amine obtained from it is *optically pure*.

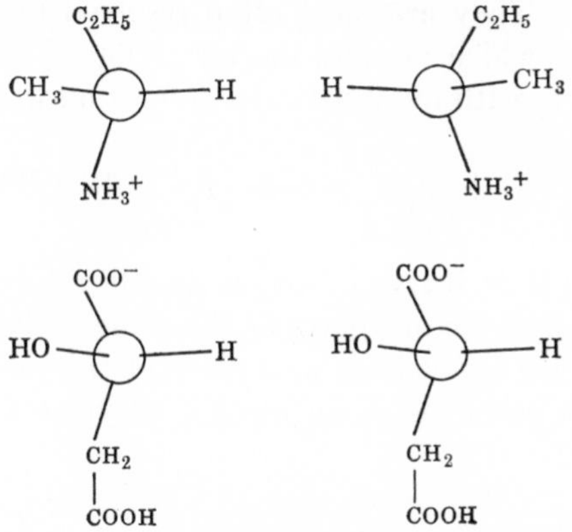

Separated diastereomers

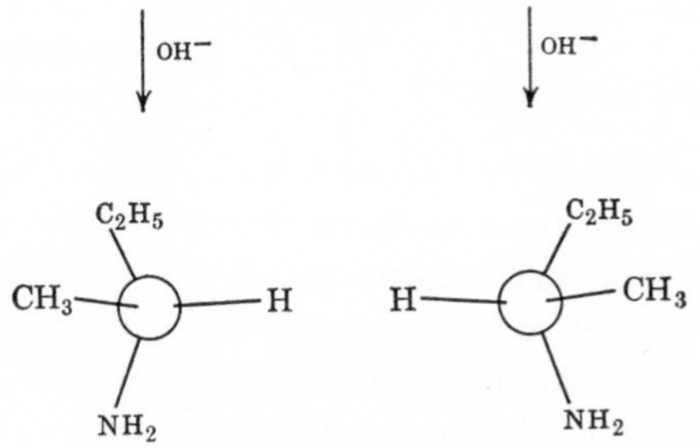

Resolved enantiomers

Resolution of an acid — α-bromopropionic acid, for example, or α-phenylpropionic acid — is carried out by reversing the process just described. There are isolated from various plants certain very complicated amines called *alkaloids* (that is, *alkali-like*), among which are cocaine, morphine, strychnine, and quinine. Most alkaloids are produced by plants in only one of two possible enantiomeric forms, and hence they are optically active. They can be used in the resolution of racemic acids, just as optically active acids are used in the resolution of racemic amines. Diastereomeric salts are formed, and are separated by fractional crystallization; each enantiomeric acid is then regenerated by addition of mineral acid.

$$\left.\begin{matrix}(+)\text{-RCOOH}\\(-)\text{-RCOOH}\end{matrix}\right\} + (+)\text{-B} \longrightarrow \left\{\begin{matrix}(+)\text{-RCOO}^-(+)\text{-BH}^+ \xrightarrow{H^+} (+)\text{-RCOOH} + (+)\text{-BH}^+\\(-)\text{-RCOO}^-(+)\text{-BH}^+ \xrightarrow{H^+} (-)\text{-RCOOH} + (+)\text{-BH}^+\end{matrix}\right.$$

Enantiomers *in a racemate*	Alkaloid *base*	Diastereomers *separable*	Resolved enantiomers	Alkaloid *as a salt*

Among the alkaloids commonly used for this purpose are (−)-brucine, (−)-quinine, (−)-strychnine, and (+)-cinchonine.

Resolution of alcohols poses a special problem: since alcohols are neither appreciably basic nor acidic, they cannot be resolved by direct formation of salts. They are most often resolved by attaching to them an acidic "handle," which permits the formation of salts.

An alcohol reacts with an anhydride to form a molecule of ester and a molecule of acid:

$$\underset{\text{Anhydride}}{(R'CO)_2O} + \underset{\text{Alcohol}}{ROH} \longrightarrow \underset{\text{Ester}}{R'COOR} + \underset{\text{Acid}}{R'COOH}$$

When the anhydride is derived from a dicarboxylic acid, so that both "halves" of the anhydride are parts of the same molecule, then the ester and the acid that are formed are also parts of the same molecule. Thus phthalic anhydride reacts with an alcohol to yield a compound that is both ester and acid.

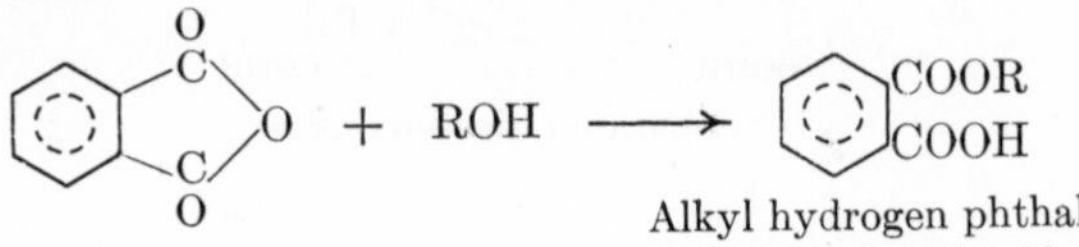

Phthalic anhydride

Alkyl hydrogen phthalate
Both ester and acid

The alkyl hydrogen phthalate formed from a racemic alcohol reacts readily with an optically active base to form diastereomeric salts, which can be separated by fractional crystallization. Once separated, each ester can be hydrolyzed to an optically active alcohol. Since hydrolysis of a carboxylic ester does not usually involve cleavage of the alkyl–oxygen bond there is no loss of activity in the hydrolysis step.

Enantiomers
racemate

Enantiomers
racemate

Diastereomers
separable

Resolved enantiomers

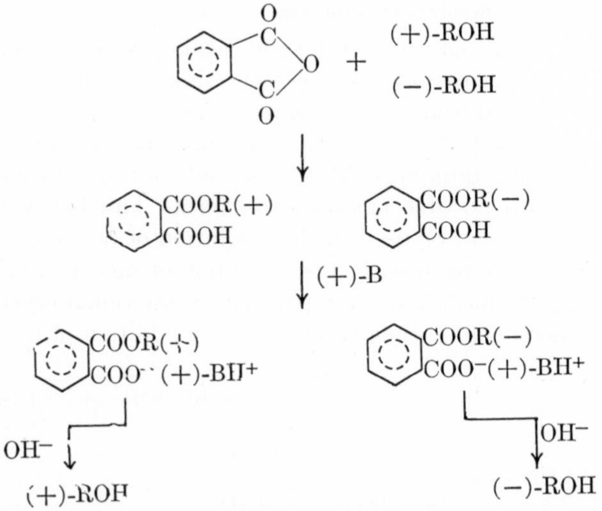

Compounds other than amines, acids, or alcohols can also be resolved. Although the particular chemistry may differ from the salt formation just described, the principle remains the same: **a racemate is converted by an optically active reagent into a mixture of diastereomers, which can then be separated.**

Problem 20.5 Outline a procedure for the resolution of racemic mandelic acid, $C_6H_5CHOHCOOH$, using (−)-menthol, a naturally occurring optically active secondary alcohol

20.6 Quaternary ammonium salts. Exhaustive methylation. Hofmann elimination

Like ammonia, an amine can react with an alkyl halide; the product is an amine of the next higher class. The alkyl halide undergoes nucleophilic substitution, with the basic amine serving as the nucleophilic reagent.

$$RNH_2 \xrightarrow{RX} R_2NH \xrightarrow{RX} R_3N \xrightarrow{RX} R_4N^+ X^-$$
$$1° \qquad\qquad 2° \qquad\qquad 3° \qquad\qquad 4°$$

We see that one of the hydrogens attached to nitrogen has been replaced by an alkyl group; the reaction is therefore often referred to as *alkylation of amines*. The amine can be aliphatic or aromatic, primary, secondary, or tertiary; the halide is generally an alkyl halide.

We have already encountered alkylation of amines as a side reaction in the preparation of primary amines by the ammonolysis of halides (Sec. 19.10), and as a method of synthesis of secondary and tertiary amines (Sec. 19.12). Let us look at one further aspect of this reaction, the formation of quaternary ammonium salts.

Quaternary ammonium salts are the products of the final stage of alkylation of nitrogen. They have the formula $R_4N^+X^-$. Four organic groups are covalently bonded to nitrogen, and the positive charge of this ion is balanced by some negative ion. When the salt of a primary, secondary, or tertiary amine is treated with hydroxide ion, nitrogen gives up a hydrogen ion and the free amine is liberated. The quaternary ammonium ion, having no proton to give up, is not affected by hydroxide ion.

$$
\begin{array}{ccc}
R & & R \\
\cdot\cdot & & \cdot\cdot \\
R:N:R^+ X^- & \xrightarrow{Ag_2O} & R:N:R^+ OH^- \quad + \quad AgX \\
\cdot\cdot & & \cdot\cdot \\
R & & R
\end{array}
$$

Quaternary	Quaternary	*Insoluble*
ammonium salt	ammonium hydroxide	

When a solution of a quaternary ammonium halide is treated with silver oxide, silver halide precipitates. When the mixture is filtered and the filtrate is evaporated to dryness, there is obtained a solid which is free of halogen. An aqueous solution of this substance is strongly alkaline, and is comparable to a solution of sodium hydroxide or potassium hydroxide. A compound of this sort is called a **quaternary ammonium hydroxide.** It has the structure $R_4N^+ OH^-$. Its aqueous solution is basic for the same reason that solutions of sodium or potassium hydroxide are basic: the solution contains hydroxide ions.

When a quaternary ammonium hydroxide is heated strongly (to 125° or higher), it decomposes to yield water, a tertiary amine, and an alkene. Trimethyl-*n*-propylammonium hydroxide, for example, yields trimethylamine and propylene:

$$
\begin{array}{ccc}
CH_3 & & CH_3 \\
| & & | \\
CH_3{-}N^+{-}CH_2CH_2CH_3 \; OH^- & \xrightarrow{heat} & CH_3{-}N \quad + CH_2{=}CHCH_3 + H_2O \\
| & & | \\
CH_3 & & CH_3
\end{array}
$$

Trimethyl-*n*-propylammonium hydroxide	Trimethylamine	Propylene

This reaction, called the **Hofmann elimination,** is quite analogous to the dehydrohalogenation of an alkyl halide (Sec. 4.13). Hydroxide ion abstracts a hydrogen ion from carbon; a molecule of tertiary amine is expelled, and the double bond is generated.

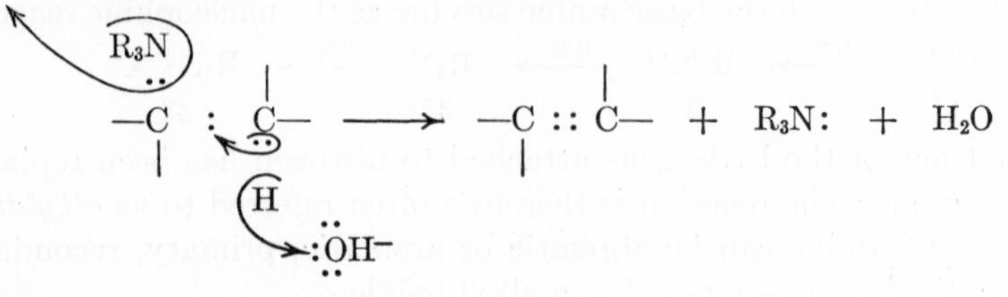

Problem 20.6 When tetramethylammonium hydroxide is heated strongly, it yields methanol and trimethylamine. (a) How is the methanol formed? To what general class of reaction does this belong? (b) Why should this particular quaternary ammonium hydroxide behave differently from the others? (c) Predict the products of heating tetramethylammonium chloride.

The formation of quaternary ammonium salts, followed by an elimination of the kind just described, is very useful in the determination of the structures of certain complicated nitrogen-containing compounds. The compound, which may be a primary, secondary, or tertiary amine, is converted into the quaternary ammonium hydroxide by treatment with excess methyl iodide and silver oxide. The number of methyl groups taken up by nitrogen depends upon the class of the amine; a primary amine will take up three methyl groups, a secondary amine will take up two, and a tertiary amine only one. This process is known as **exhaustive methylation of amines.**

When heated, a quaternary ammonium hydroxide undergoes elimination to an alkene and a tertiary amine. From the structures of these products it is often possible to deduce the structure of the original amine. As a simple example, contrast the products (I, II, III) obtained from the following isomeric cyclic amines:

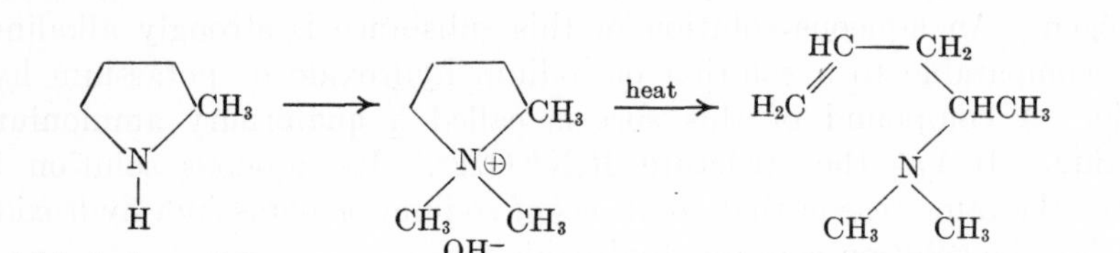

2-Methylpyrrolidine

4-(Dimethylamino)-1-pentene

I

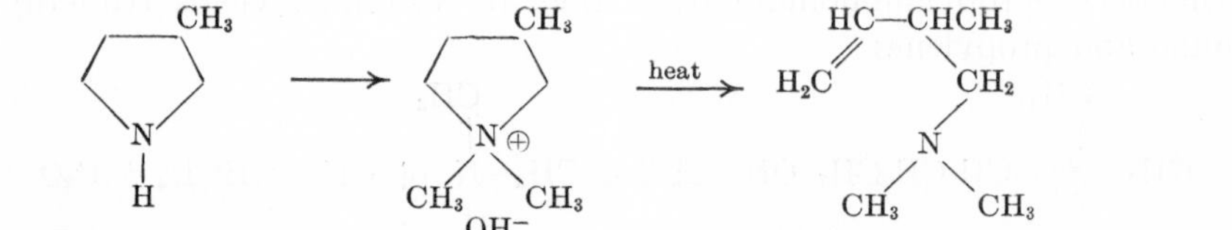

3-Methylpyrrolidine

4-(Dimethylamino)-3-methyl-1-butene

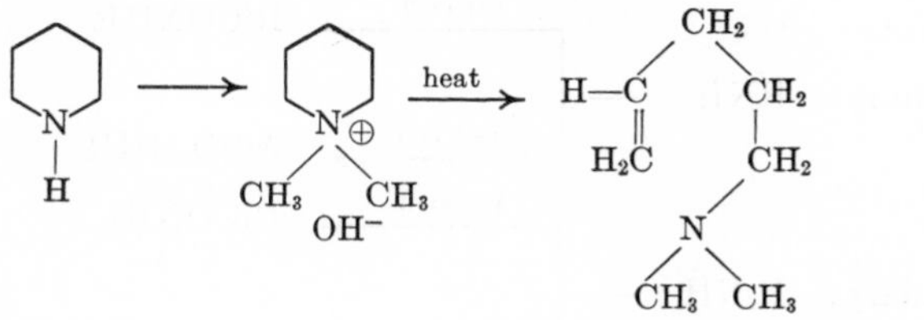

Piperidine   5-(Dimethylamino)-1-pentene

III

Problem 20.7 (a) What products would be expected from the hydrogenation of I, II, and III? (b) How could you prepare an authentic sample of each of these expected hydrogenation products?

Problem 20.8 What products would be expected if I, II, and III were subjected to exhaustive methylation and elimination?

A newer, somewhat more reliable way of getting the same kind of information about structure makes use of the sequence:

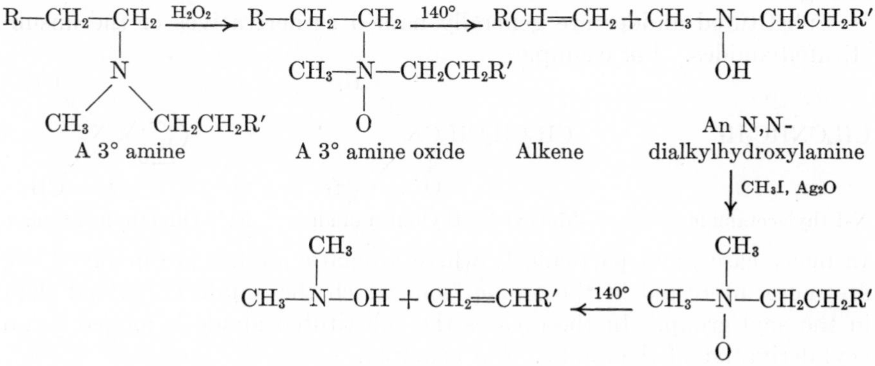

Because of the high yields, pyrolysis of tertiary amine oxides has been used in the synthesis of alkenes.

20.7 Conversion of amines into substituted amides

We have learned (Sec. 17.12 and Sec. 18.6) that ammonia reacts with the acid chlorides of both carboxylic and sulfonic acids to yield amides, compounds in which —Cl has been replaced by the —NH_2 group.

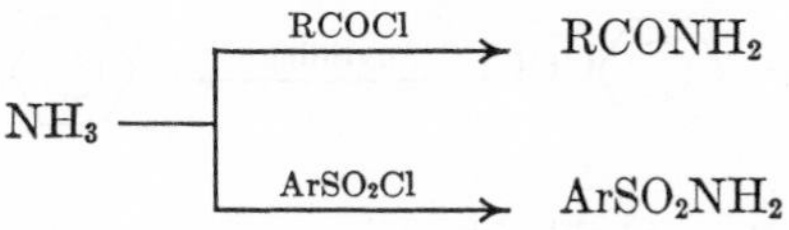

In these reactions ammonia serves as a nucleophilic reagent, attacking the carbonyl carbon or sulfur and displacing chloride ion. In the process nitrogen loses a proton to a second molecule of ammonia.

In a similar way primary and secondary amines can react with acid chlorides to form **substituted amides,** compounds in which —Cl has been replaced by the —NHR or —NR_2 group:

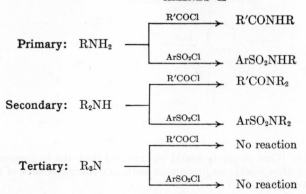

Tertiary amines, although basic, fail to react, presumably because they cannot lose a proton (to stabilize the product) after attaching themselves to carbon or to sulfur. Here is a reaction which requires not only that amines be basic, but also that they possess a hydrogen atom attached to nitrogen.

Substituted amides are generally named as derivatives of the unsubstituted amides. For example:

$$CH_3CNHC_2H_5 \qquad CH_3CH_2CH_2CN{\overset{CH_3}{\underset{C_2H_5}{}}} \qquad \langle\bigcirc\rangle CN{\overset{CH_3}{\underset{CH_3}{}}}$$
$$\overset{\|}{O} \qquad\qquad\qquad \overset{\|}{O} \qquad\qquad\qquad\qquad \overset{\|}{O}$$

N-Ethylacetamide   N-Methyl-N-ethylbutyramide   N,N-Dimethylbenzamide

In many cases, and particularly where aromatic amines are involved, we are more interested in the amine from which the amide is derived than in the acyl group. In these cases the substituted amide is named as an acyl derivative of the amine. For example:

$$\langle\bigcirc\rangle NHCCH_3 \qquad \langle\bigcirc\rangle NHC\langle\bigcirc\rangle \qquad CH_3\langle\bigcirc\rangle NHCCH_3$$
$$\overset{\|}{O} \qquad\qquad\qquad \overset{\|}{O} \qquad\qquad\qquad\qquad \overset{\|}{O}$$

Acetanilide   Benzanilide   Aceto-*p*-toluidide

Substituted amides of aromatic carboxylic acids or of sulfonic acids are prepared by the Schotten-Baumann technique: the acid chloride is added to the amine in the presence of a base, either aqueous sodium hydroxide or pyridine. For example:

$$\langle\bigcirc\rangle NH_2 \; + \; \langle\bigcirc\rangle COCl \; \xrightarrow{\text{pyridine}} \; \langle\bigcirc\rangle NHC\langle\bigcirc\rangle$$
$$\overset{\|}{O}$$

Aniline   Benzoyl chloride   Benzanilide

$$(n\text{-}C_4H_9)_2NH \; + \; \langle\bigcirc\rangle SO_2Cl \; \xrightarrow{\text{NaOH}} \; \langle\bigcirc\rangle SO_2N{\overset{C_4H_9}{\underset{C_4H_9}{}}}$$

Di-*n*-butylamine   Benzenesulfonyl   N,N-di-*n*-butylbenzenesulfonamide
                   chloride

Acetylation is generally carried out using acetic anhydride rather than acetyl chloride. For example:

NH₂ CH₃ + (CH₃CO)₂O —CH₃COONa→ NHCOCH₃ CH₃ + CH₃COOH

o-Toluidine   Acetic anhydride   Aceto-o-toluidide

Like simple amides, substituted amides undergo hydrolysis; the products are the acid and the amine, although one or the other is obtained as its salt, depending upon the acidity or alkalinity of the medium.

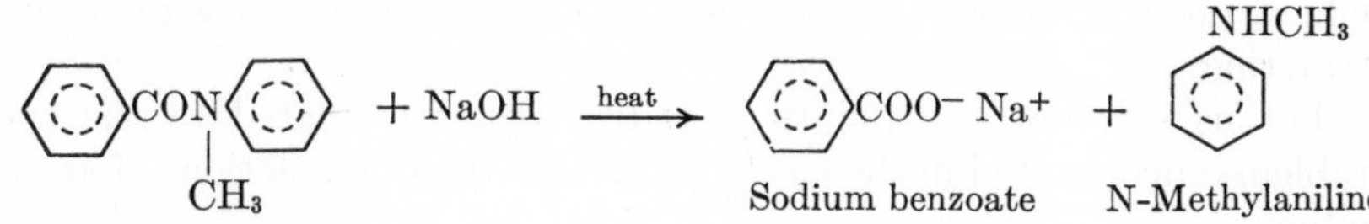

⟨⟩CON⟨⟩ + NaOH —heat→ ⟨⟩COO⁻ Na⁺ + NHCH₃⟨⟩
  |
  CH₃
N-Methylbenzanilide   Sodium benzoate   N-Methylaniline

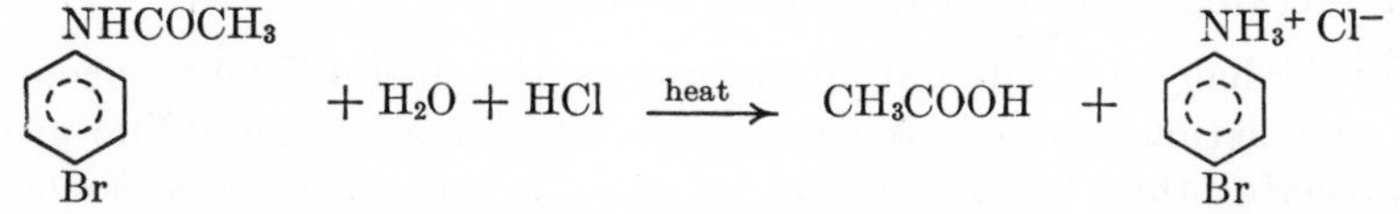

NHCOCH₃ Br + H₂O + HCl —heat→ CH₃COOH + NH₃⁺ Cl⁻ Br

p-Bromoacetanilide   Acetic acid   p-Bromoanilinium chloride

The conversion of an amine into a sulfonamide is used in determining the class of the amine; this is discussed in the section on analysis (Sec. 20.14).

20.8 Ring substitution in aromatic amines

We have already seen that the —NH₂, —NHR, and —NR₂ groups act as powerful activators and *ortho,para* directors in electrophilic aromatic substitution. These effects were accounted for by assuming that the intermediate carbonium ion is stabilized by structures like I and II in

which nitrogen bears a positive charge and is joined to the ring by a double bond. Such structures are especially stable since in them every atom (except hydrogen) has a complete octet of electrons.

Contribution by such structures is simply a way of indicating that nitrogen can share more than a pair of electrons with the ring and help disperse the charge of the carbonium ion. Thus the basicity of nitrogen accounts for one more characteristic of aromatic amines.

The acetamido group, —NHCOCH₃, is also activating and *ortho,para*-directing, but less powerfully so than a free amino group. Electron withdrawal by oxygen of the carbonyl group makes the nitrogen of an amide a much poorer source of electrons than the nitrogen of an amine. Electrons are less available for sharing with a hydrogen ion, and therefore amides are much weaker bases than amines: amides of carboxylic acids do not dissolve in dilute aqueous acids. Electrons are less available for sharing with an aromatic ring, and therefore an acetamido group activates an aromatic ring less strongly than an amino group.

We have seen (Sec. 10.4) that the —NR$_3$$^+$ group is a powerful deactivator and *meta* director. In a quaternary ammonium salt, nitrogen no longer has electrons to share with the ring; on the contrary, the full-fledged positive charge on nitrogen makes the group strongly electron-attracting.

Let us see how the points just discussed are related to the special problems encountered in the electrophilic substitution reactions of aromatic amines.

20.9   Halogenation of aromatic amines

In the halogenation of aromatic amines, the chief difficulty encountered is that reaction proceeds too readily. Activation by the amino group is so powerful that halogen tends to enter every available *ortho* or *para* position. Thus aniline yields 2,4,6-tribromoaniline, and *p*-toluidine yields 3,5-dibromo-4-aminotoluene.

Aniline   2,4,6-Tribromoaniline

p-Toluidine   3,5-Dibromo-4-aminotoluene

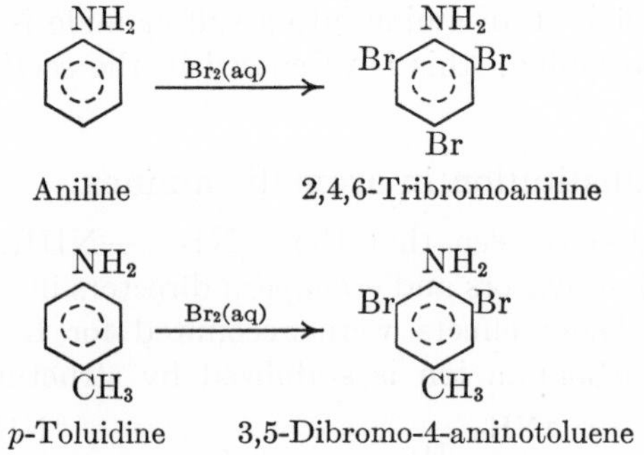

Introduction of a single halogen atom is quite feasible, however, if the amino group is acetylated before halogenation is carried out. After halogenation is complete, the amide can be hydrolyzed to yield the desired halogenated amine. For example:

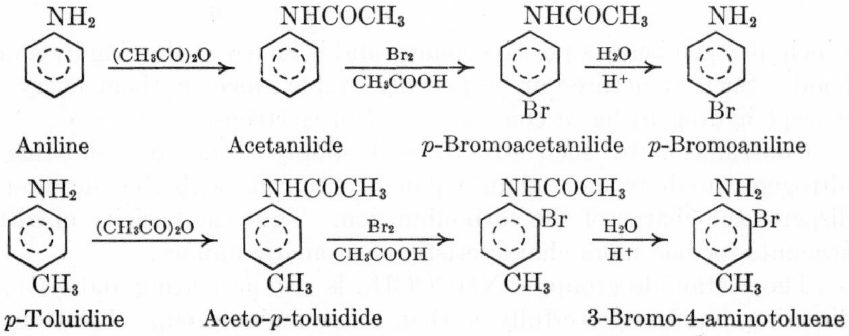

Aniline   Acetanilide   *p*-Bromoacetanilide   *p*-Bromoaniline

p-Toluidine   Aceto-*p*-toluidide   3-Bromo-4-aminotoluene

Acetylation is thus a useful way to moderate the activating effect of an amino group.

20.10 Nitration of aromatic amines

Like halogenation, nitration is best carried out using an acetylated amine rather than the free amine itself. There are two reasons for this preference.

First, acetylation lowers the reactivity of the ring. Nitric acid is not only a nitrating agent, but also an oxidizing agent; the reactive ring of aromatic amines is highly susceptible to oxidation, so that under ordinary nitrating conditions much material is lost in the formation of tarry oxidation products. Nitration of acetylated amines, however, proceeds smoothly. For example:

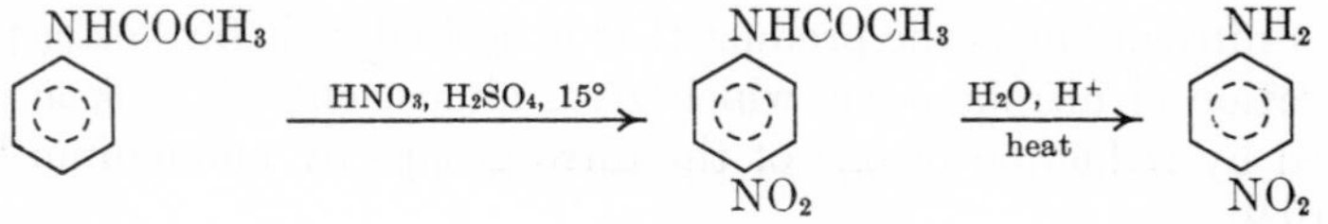

$$\text{NHCOCH}_3 \xrightarrow[\text{}]{\text{HNO}_3,\ \text{H}_2\text{SO}_4,\ 15^\circ} \text{NHCOCH}_3 \text{—NO}_2 \xrightarrow[\text{heat}]{\text{H}_2\text{O, H}^+} \text{NH}_2 \text{—NO}_2$$

| Acetanilide | p-Nitroacetanilide | p-Nitroaniline |

The use of acetylation in this way is often referred to as "protecting the amino group"; actually it is a matter of protecting the entire molecule from oxidation.

Problem 20.9 Amides can be hydrolyzed by either aqueous acid or aqueous alkali. Hydrolysis of p-nitroacetanilide is best carried out in acidic solution, as shown above. Why is this so? (*Hint:* see Sec. 14.12.)

The second reason for acetylating prior to nitration is found in the following observations. If aniline is treated very carefully with a mixture of nitric acid and sulfuric acid at a low temperature, it is possible to obtain nitroanilines without undue oxidation. The product is found to consist of about 50% p-nitroaniline and 50% m-nitroaniline. How can we account for the formation of such a mixture from a compound containing an *ortho,para* director? The —NH₂ group is indeed an *ortho,para* director, but we can readily see that it is not the —NH₂ group alone with which we are dealing. In the highly acidic nitration mixture, even weakly basic aniline must exist almost entirely in the form of anilinium ion; substitution in most of the rings, therefore, is controlled not by the —NH₂ group but by

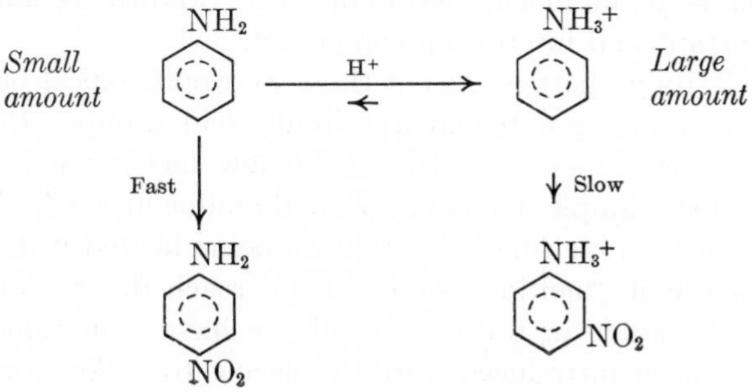

$$\text{NH}_2 \underset{\xleftarrow{}}{\xrightarrow{\text{H}^+}} \text{NH}_3^+$$

Small amount   *Large amount*

Fast ↓   ↓ Slow

$$\text{NH}_2 \text{—NO}_2 \qquad \text{NH}_3^+ \text{—NO}_2$$

the —NH$_3$+ group, which, because of its positive charge, must be a powerful deactivator and *meta* director. The *m*-nitroaniline obtained is a product of nitration of the anilinium ion.

Now the question arises, if most of the aniline exists as its salt, how can there be so much *p*-isomer in the product? We must remember that the —NH$_2$ group is a powerful activator, whereas the —NH$_3$+ group is a powerful deactivator. Even though there are relatively few molecules of free aniline present, each of these is many times as reactive as each of the anilinium ions. The few aniline molecules are nitrated very rapidly, the many anilinium ions are nitrated very slowly. The two factors, relative concentrations and relative reactivities, are very nearly balanced, since equal amounts of the two products are obtained. The acetylation of an amine prior to nitration prevents salt formation, and permits clean-cut *ortho,para* orientation.

If *m*-nitroaniline is the product that is desired, it is far better prepared by nitration of nitrobenzene, which gives almost entirely a *meta* product, followed by reduction of one of the nitro groups by ammonium bisulfide (Sec. 19.9).

20.11 Sulfonation of aromatic amines. Dipolar ions

Aniline is usually sulfonated by "baking" the salt, anilinium hydrogen sulfate, at 180–200°; the chief product is the *p*-isomer. In this case we cannot discuss orientation on our usual basis of which isomer is formed

| NH$_2$ | | NH$_3$+ HSO$_4$$^-$ | | NH$_3$+ |
| Aniline | $\xrightarrow{\text{H}_2\text{SO}_4}$ | Anilinium hydrogen sulfate | $\xrightarrow{180-200°}$ | SO$_3$$^-$ Sulfanilic acid |

faster. Sulfonation is known to be reversible, and the *p*-isomer is known to be the most stable isomer; it may well be that the product obtained, the *p*-isomer, is determined by the position of an equilibrium and not by relative rates of formation (see Sec. 6.17 and Sec. 9.14). It also seems likely that, in some cases at least, sulfonation of amines proceeds by a mechanism that is entirely different from ordinary aromatic substitution.

Whatever the mechanism by which it is formed, the chief product of this reaction is *p*-aminobenzenesulfonic acid, known as **sulfanilic acid**; it is an important and interesting compound.

First of all, its properties are not those we would expect of a compound containing an amino group and a sulfonic acid group. Both aromatic amines and aromatic sulfonic acids have low melting points; benzenesulfonic acid, for example, melts at 66°, and aniline at −6°. Yet sulfanilic acid has such a high melting point that on being heated it decomposes (at 280–300°) before its melting point can be reached. Sulfonic acids are generally very soluble in water; indeed, we have seen that the sulfonic acid group is often introduced into a molecule to make it water-soluble.

Yet sulfanilic acid is not only insoluble in organic solvents, but also nearly insoluble in water. Amines dissolve in aqueous mineral acids because of their conversion into water-soluble salts. Sulfanilic acid is soluble in aqueous bases but insoluble in aqueous acids.

These properties of sulfanilic acid are understandable when we realize that sulfanilic acid actually has the structure I which contains the —NH$_3$+ and —SO$_3$- groups. Sulfanilic acid is a salt, but of a rather special kind,

I   II
Insoluble in water   *Soluble in water*

called a **dipolar ion** (sometimes called a *zwitterion*, from the German, *Zwitter*, hermaphrodite). It is the product of reaction between an acidic group and a basic group that are part of the same molecule. The hydrogen ion is attached to nitrogen rather than oxygen simply because the —NH$_2$ group is a stronger base than the —SO$_3$- group. A high melting point and insolubility in organic solvents are properties we would expect of a salt. Insolubility in water is not surprising, since many salts are insoluble in water. In alkaline solution, the strongly basic hydroxide ion pulls hydrogen ion away from the weakly basic —NH$_2$ group to yield the *p*-aminobenzenesulfonate ion (II), which, like most sodium salts, is soluble in water. In aqueous acid, however, the sulfanilic acid structure is not changed, and therefore the compound remains insoluble; sulfonic acids are strong acids and their anions (very weak bases) show little tendency to accept hydrogen ion from H$_3$O+.

We can expect to encounter dipolar ions whenever we have a molecule containing both an amino group and an acid group, providing the amine is more basic than the anion of the acid.

Problem 20.10 *p*-Aminobenzoic acid is not a dipolar ion, whereas glycine (aminoacetic acid) is a dipolar ion. How can you account for this?

20.12 Sulfonamides. The sulfa drugs

The amide of sulfanilic acid (*sulfanilamide*) and certain related substituted amides are of considerable medical importance as the *sulfa drugs*. Although they have been supplanted to a wide extent by the antibiotics (such as penicillin, terramycin, chloromycetin, and aureomycin), the sulfa drugs still have their medical uses, and make up a considerable portion of the output of the pharmaceutical industry.

Sulfonamides are prepared by the reaction of a sulfonyl chloride with ammonia or an amine. The presence in a sulfonic acid molecule of an amino group, however, poses a special problem: if sulfanilic acid were converted to the acid chloride, the sulfonyl group of one molecule could attack the amino group of another to form an amide linkage. This problem is solved by acetylating the amino group prior to the preparation of the sulfonyl chloride. Sulfanilamide and related compounds are generally prepared in the following way:

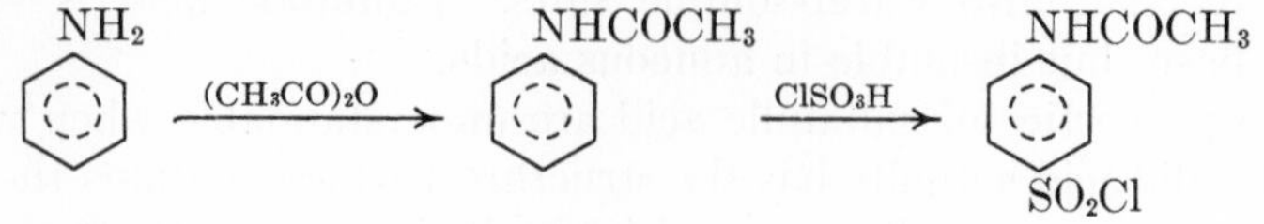

Aniline   Acetanilide   p-Acetamidobenzenesulfonyl chloride

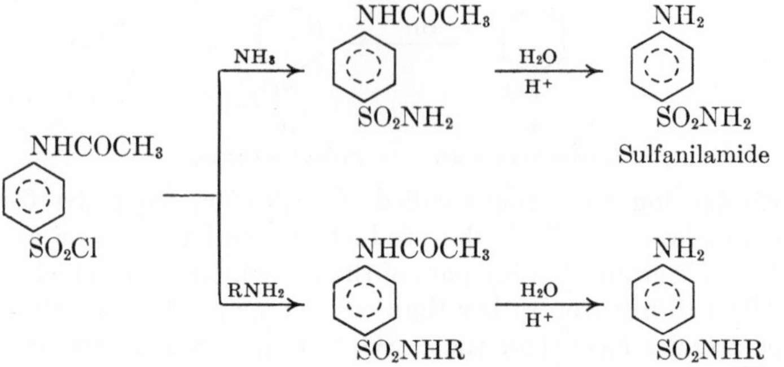

Sulfanilamide

Substituted sulfanilamide

The selective removal of the acetyl group in the final step is consistent with the general observation that amides of carboxylic acids are more easily hydrolyzed than amides of sulfonic acids (Sec. 18.9).

The antibacterial activity and toxicity of the substituted sulfanilamides depend upon the nature of the group R attached to amido nitrogen. Of the hundreds of such compounds that have been synthesized, only a half dozen or so have had the proper combination of high antibacterial activity and low toxicity to human beings that is necessary for an effective drug; in nearly all these effective compounds the group R contains a heterocyclic ring (Chapter 32).

Sulfamerazine 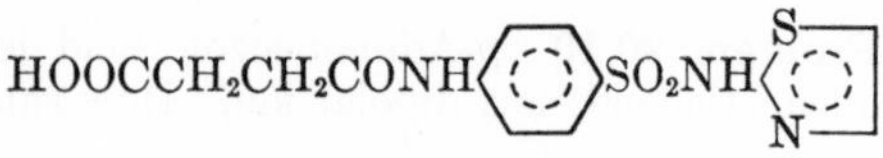   Succinoylsulfathiazole

20.13 Reaction of amines with nitrous acid

Each class of amine shows different behavior toward nitrous acid, HONO. This unstable reagent is generated in the presence of the amine by the action of mineral acid on sodium nitrite.

Primary aromatic amines react with nitrous acid to yield **diazonium salts;** this is one of the most important reactions in organic chemistry.

$$\underset{\substack{\text{1}^\circ \text{ aromatic} \\ \text{amine}}}{ArNH_2} + NaNO_2 + 2HX \xrightarrow{\text{cold}} \underset{\text{A diazonium salt}}{ArN_2^+ X^-} + NaX + 2H_2O$$

The following chapter (Chapter 21) is devoted entirely to the preparation and properties of aromatic diazonium salts.

Primary aliphatic amines also react with nitrous acid to yield diazonium salts; but since aliphatic diazonium salts are quite unstable and break down to yield a complicated mixture of organic products (see the following Problem), this reaction is of little synthetic value. The fact that nitrogen

$$RNH_2 + NaNO_2 + HX \longrightarrow [RN_2^+] \xrightarrow{H_2O} N_2 + \text{mixture of alcohols}$$

1° aliphatic amine   *Unstable*   and alkenes

is evolved quantitatively is of some importance in analysis, however, particularly of amino acids and proteins.

Problem 20.11 The reaction of *n*-butylamine with sodium nitrite and hydrochloric acid yields nitrogen and the following mixture: *n*-butyl alcohol, 25%; *sec*-butyl alcohol, 13%; 1-butene and 2-butene, 37%; *n*-butyl chloride, 5%; *sec*-butyl chloride, 3%. (a) What is the most likely intermediate common to all of these products? (b) Outline reactions that account for the various products.

Problem 20.12 Predict the organic products of the reaction of: (a) isobutylamine with nitrous acid; (b) neopentylamine with nitrous acid.

Secondary amines, both aliphatic and aromatic, react with nitrous acid to yield N-nitrosoamines. The N-nitrosoamines are generally yellow and, unlike the parent amines, are neutral compounds, insoluble in dilute aqueous mineral acids.

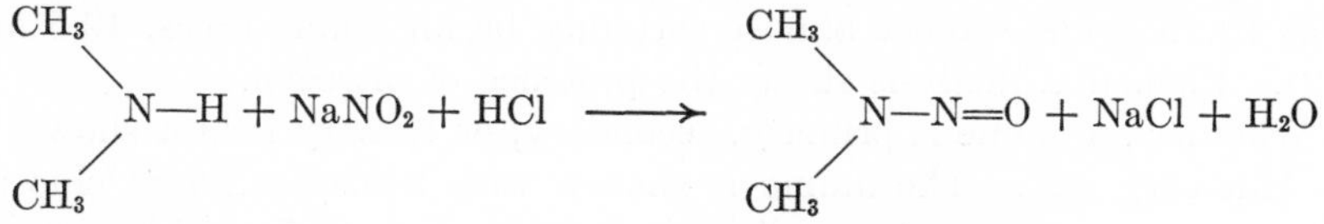

Dimethylamine → N-Nitrosodimethylamine *Yellow Insoluble in acid*

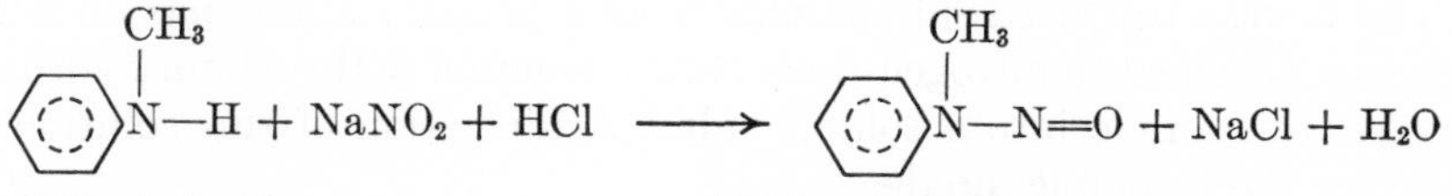

N-Methylaniline → N-Nitroso-N-methylaniline *Yellow Insoluble in acid*

Tertiary aliphatic amines do not react with nitrous acid except to form salts in the acidic medium. Tertiary aromatic amines, however, undergo ring substitution, to yield compounds in which a nitroso group, —N=O, is joined to carbon; thus N,N-dimethylaniline yields chiefly *p*-nitroso-N,N-dimethylaniline.

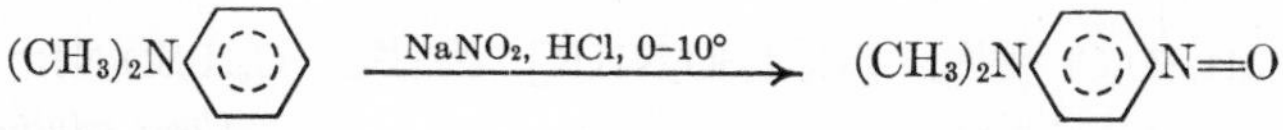

N,N-Dimethylaniline → *p*-Nitroso-N,N-dimethylaniline *Green*

Ring nitrosation is an electrophilic aromatic substitution reaction, in which the nitrosonium ion, ^+NO, is believed to be the attacking reagent. The nitrosonium ion is very weakly electrophilic compared with the reagents involved in nitration, sulfonation, halogenation, and the Friedel-Crafts reaction; nitrosation ordinarily occurs only in rings bearing the powerfully activating dialkylamino ($-NR_2$) or hydroxy ($-OH$) group.

Despite the differences in final product, the reaction of nitrous acid with all amines involves the same initial step: *electrophilic attack by ^+NO with displacement of H^+*. This attack occurs at the position of highest electron availability in primary and secondary amines: at nitrogen. Tertiary aromatic amines, which have no hydrogen on nitrogen, are attacked at the next best place: the highly reactive ring.

Problem 20.13 When *p*-nitroso-N,N-dimethylaniline is heated with aqueous KOH, dimethylamine is evolved; this reaction is sometimes used to prepare pure dimethylamine, free from methylamine and trimethylamine. (a) What are the other products of the reaction? (b) To what class of organic reactions does this belong? (c) Upon what property of the nitroso group does this reaction depend? (d) Outline all steps in the preparation of pure diethylamine starting from nitrobenzene and ethyl alcohol.

20.14 Analysis of amines. Hinsberg test

Amines are characterized chiefly through their basicity. A water-insoluble compound that dissolves in cold dilute hydrochloric acid — or a water-soluble compound (not a salt, Sec. 16.22) whose aqueous solution turns litmus blue — must almost certainly be an amine (Secs. 19.5 and 20.2). Elemental analysis shows the presence of nitrogen.

Whether an amine is primary, secondary, or tertiary is best shown by the **Hinsberg test.** The amine is shaken with benzenesulfonyl chloride in the presence of aqueous sodium hydroxide (Sec. 20.7). Primary and secondary amines form substituted sulfonamides; tertiary amines do not react.

The monosubstituted sulfonamide from a primary amine has an acidic hydrogen attached to nitrogen (Sec. 18.7); reaction with sodium hydroxide converts this amide into a soluble salt. Acidification of this solution regenerates the insoluble amide.

The disubstituted sulfonamide from a secondary amine has no acidic hydrogen and remains insoluble in the alkaline reaction mixture.

What do we observe when we treat an amine with benzenesulfonyl chloride and excess sodium hydroxide? A *primary amine* yields a clear solution, from which, upon acidification, an insoluble material separates. A *secondary amine* yields an insoluble compound, which is unaffected by acid. A *tertiary amine* yields an insoluble compound (the unreacted amine itself) which dissolves upon acidification of the mixture.

$$RNH_2 + C_6H_5SO_2Cl \xrightarrow{OH^-} [C_6H_5SO_2NHR] \xrightarrow{NaOH} C_6H_5SO_2NR^- Na^+ \xrightarrow{H^+}$$
1° Amine $\qquad\qquad\qquad\qquad\qquad\qquad\qquad\qquad\qquad$ *Clear solution*

$$C_6H_5SO_2NHR$$
$\qquad\qquad\qquad\qquad\qquad\qquad\qquad\qquad\qquad\qquad\qquad$ *Insoluble*

$$R_2NH + C_6H_5SO_2Cl \xrightarrow{OH^-} C_6H_5SO_2NR_2 \xrightarrow{NaOH \text{ or } H^+} \text{No reaction}$$
2° Amine $\qquad\qquad\qquad\qquad$ *Insoluble*

$$R_3N + C_6H_5SO_2Cl \xrightarrow{OH^-} R_3N \xrightarrow{HCl} R_3NH^+ Cl^-$$

3° Amine   *Insoluble*   *Clear solution*

Although less reliable than the Hinsberg method, behavior toward nitrous acid (Sec. 20.13) is of some use in determining the class of an amine. In particular, the behavior of primary aromatic amines is quite characteristic: treatment with nitrous acid converts them into diazonium salts, which yield highly colored azo compounds upon treatment with β-naphthol (a phenol, see Sec. 21.10).

Among the numerous derivatives useful in identifying amines are: amides (e.g., acetamides, benzamides, or sulfonamides) for primary and secondary amines; quaternary ammonium salts (e.g., those from benzyl chloride or methyl iodide) for tertiary amines.

We have already discussed proof of structure by use of exhaustive methylation and elimination (Sec. 20.6).

20.15 Analysis of substituted amides

A substituted amide of a carboxylic acid is characterized by the presence of nitrogen, insolubility in dilute acid and dilute base, and hydrolysis to a carboxylic acid and an amine. It is generally identified through identification of its hydrolysis products (Secs. 16.22 and 20.14).

PROBLEMS

1. Write complete equations, naming all organic products, for the reaction (if any) of *n*-butylamine with:

(a) dilute HCl
(b) dilute H_2SO_4
(c) acetic acid
(d) product (c) + heat
(e) dilute NaOH
(f) acetic anhydride
(g) isobutyryl chloride
(h) *p*-nitrobenzoyl chloride + pyridine
(i) benzenesulfonyl chloride + NaOH (aq)
(j) ethyl bromide
(k) bromobenzene
(l) excess methyl iodide, then Ag_2O
(m) product (l) + strong heat
(n) $CH_3COCH_3 + H_2 + Ni$
(o) HONO ($NaNO_2 + HCl$)
(p) phthalic anhydride
(q) ethylene oxide
(r) sodium chloroacetate
(s) 2,4,6-trinitrochlorobenzene

2. Without referring to tables, arrange the compounds of each set in order of basicity:
(a) ammonia, aniline, cyclohexylamine
(b) ethylamine, 2-aminoethanol, 3-amino-1-propanol
(c) aniline, *p*-methoxyaniline, *p*-nitroaniline
(d) benzylamine, *m*-chlorobenzylamine, *m*-ethylbenzylamine
(e) *p*-chloro-N-methylaniline, 2,4-dichloro-N-methylaniline, 2,4,6-trichloro-N-methylaniline

3. Which is the more strongly basic, an aqueous solution of trimethylamine or an aqueous solution of tetramethylammonium hydroxide? Why? (*Hint:* what is the principal base in each solution?)

4. Compare the behavior of the three amines, aniline, N-methylaniline, and N,N-dimethylaniline, toward each of the following reagents:

(a) dilute HCl
(b) $NaNO_2 + HCl$ (aq)
(c) methyl iodide
(d) benzenesulfonyl chloride + NaOH (aq)
(e) acetic anhydride
(f) benzoyl chloride + pyridine
(g) bromine water

5. Answer Problem 4 for ethylamine, diethylamine, and triethylamine.

6. Give structures and names of the principal organic products expected from the reaction (if any) of nitrous acid with:

(a) *p*-toluidine
(b) N,N-diethylaniline
(c) *n*-propylamine
(d) N-ethyl-N-methyl-*p*-bromoaniline
(e) methyl-*n*-butylamine
(f) sulfanilic acid
(g) N-methylaniline
(h) 2-amino-3-methylbutane
(i) benzidine (4,4'-diaminobiphenyl)
(j) benzylamine
(k) benzylmethylamine
(l) dimethyl-*sec*-butylamine

7. How does each of the following groups affect electrophilic substitution in an aromatic ring to which it is attached? How do you account for these effects?

(a) —NH₂
(b) —N(CH₃)₂
(c) —NHCOCH₃
(d) —N(CH₃)₃⁺

What effect would you expect —NHSO₂C₆H₅ to have? Why? How would it compare with —NHCOCH₃?

8. Write balanced equations, naming all organic products, for the following reactions:

(a) *n*-butyryl chloride + methylamine
(b) acetic anhydride + N-methylaniline
(c) tetra-*n*-propylammonium hydroxide + heat
(d) isovaleryl chloride + diethylamine
(e) tetramethylammonium hydroxide + heat
(f) trimethylamine + acetic acid
(g) N,N-dimethylacetamide + boiling dilute HCl
(h) benzanilide + boiling aqueous NaOH
(i) methyl formate + aniline
(j) excess methylamine + phosgene (COCl₂)
(k) *m*-O₂NC₆H₄NHCH₃ + NaNO₂ + H₂SO₄
(l) aniline + Br₂ (aq) in excess
(m) *m*-toluidine + Br₂ (aq) in excess
(n) *p*-toluidine + Br₂ (aq) in excess
(o) *p*-toluidine + NaNO₂ + HCl
(p) C₆H₅NHCOCH₃ + HNO₃ + H₂SO₄
(q) *p*-CH₃C₆H₄NHCOCH₃ + HNO₃ + H₂SO₄
(r) *p*-C₂H₅C₆H₄NH₂ + large excess of CH₃I
(s) benzanilide + Br₂ + Fe

9. (a) What structure would you expect *p*-N,N-dimethylaminobenzenesulfonic acid to have? (b) What properties (melting point, boiling point, solubility behavior) would you expect it to have?

10. Outline all steps in a possible laboratory synthesis of each of the following compounds from benzene, toluene, and alcohols of four carbons or less, using any needed inorganic reagents.

(a) 4-amino-2-bromotoluene
(b) 4-amino-3-bromotoluene
(c) *p*-aminobenzenesulfonanilide (*p*-H₂NC₆H₄SO₂NHC₆H₅)
(d) monoacetyl *p*-phenylenediamine (*p*-aminoacetanilide)
(e) *p*-nitroso-N,N-diethylaniline
(f) 4-amino-3-nitrobenzoic acid
(g) 2,6-dibromo-4-isopropylaniline
(h) *p*-aminobenzylamine
(i) N-nitroso-N-isopropylaniline
(j) trimethylamine oxide
(k) N-ethyl-N-methyl-*n*-valeramide
(l) *n*-hexylamine
(m) 1-amino-1-phenylbutane
(n) aminoacetamide
(o) hippuric acid (C₆H₅CONHCH₂COOH)

11. Describe simple chemical tests (other than color reactions with indicators) that would serve to distinguish between:

(a) N-methylaniline and *o*-toluidine

(b) aniline and cyclohexylamine

(c) *n*-C₄H₉NH₂ and (*n*-C₄H₉)₂NH

(d) (*n*-C₄H₉)₂NH and (*n*-C₄H₉)₃N

(e) (CH₃)₃NHCl and (CH₃)₄NCl

(f) C₆H₅NH₃Cl and *o*-ClC₆H₄NH₂

(g) (C₂H₅)₂NCH₂CH₂OH and (C₂H₅)₄NOH

(h) aniline and acetanilide

(i) $(C_6H_5NH_3)_2SO_4$ and $p\text{-}H_3\overset{+}{N}C_6H_4SO_3^-$

(j) ClCH₂CH₂NH₂ and CH₃CH₂NH₃Cl

(k) 2,4,6-trinitroaniline and aniline

(l) C₆H₅NHSO₂C₆H₅ and C₆H₅NH₃HSO₄

Tell exactly what you would do and see.

12. Describe simple chemical methods for the separation of the following mixtures, recovering each component in essentially pure form:

(a) triethylamine and *n*-heptane

(b) aniline and anisole

(c) stearamide and octadecylamine

(d) $o\text{-}O_2NC_6H_4NH_2$ and $p\text{-}H_3\overset{+}{N}C_6H_4SO_3^-$

(e) C₆H₅NHCH₃ and C₆H₅N(CH₃)₂

(f) *n*-caproic acid, tri-*n*-propylamine, and cyclohexane

(g) *o*-nitrotoluene and *o*-toluidine

(h) *p*-ethylaniline and propionanilide

Tell exactly what you would do and see.

13. The compounds in each of the following sets boil (or melt) within a few degrees of each other. Describe simple chemical tests that would serve to distinguish among the members of each set.

(a) aniline, benzylamine, and N,N-dimethylbenzylamine

(b) *o*-chloroacetanilide and 2,4-diaminochlorobenzene

(c) N-ethylbenzylamine, N-ethyl-N-methylaniline, β-phenylethylamine, and *o*-toluidine

(d) acetanilide and ethyl oxamate (C₂H₅OOCCONH₂)

(e) benzonitrile, N,N-dimethylaniline, and formamide

(f) N,N-dimethyl-*m*-toluidine, nitrobenzene, and *m*-tolunitrile

(g) N-(*sec*-butyl)benzenesulfonamide

    p-chloroaniline   *o*-nitroaniline

    N,N-dibenzylaniline   *p*-nitrobenzyl chloride

    2,4-dinitroaniline   *p*-toluenesulfonyl chloride

    N-ethyl-N-(*p*-tolyl)-*p*-toluenesulfonamide

Tell exactly what you would do and see.

14. An unknown amine is believed to be one of those in Table 20.2. Describe how you would go about finding out which of the possibilities the unknown actually is. Where possible use simple chemical tests.

TABLE 20.2

DERIVATIVES OF SOME AMINES

Amine	B.p., °C	Benzene-sulfonamide M.p., °C	Acetamide M.p., °C	Benzamide M.p., °C	*p*-Toluene-sulfonamide M.p., °C
m-Toluidine	203	95	66	125	114
N-Ethylaniline	205		54	60	87
N-Methyl-*m*-toluidine	206		66		
N,N-Diethyl-*o*-toluidine	206				
N-Methyl-*o*-toluidine	207		55	66	120
N-Methyl-*p*-toluidine	207	64	83	53	60
N,N-Dimethyl-*o*-chloroaniline	207				
o-Chloroaniline	209	129	87	99	105

15. *Choline*, a constituent of *lecithins* (fat-like phosphate esters of great physiological importance), has the formula $C_5H_{15}O_2N$. It dissolves readily in water to form a strongly basic solution. It can be prepared by the reaction of ethylene oxide with trimethylamine in the presence of water.

(a) What is a likely structure for choline? (b) What is a likely structure for its acetyl derivative, *acetylcholine*, $C_7H_{17}O_3N$, important in nerve action?

16. *Novocaine*, a local anesthetic, is a compound of formula $C_{13}H_{20}O_2N_2$. It is insoluble in water and dilute NaOH, but soluble in dilute HCl. Upon treatment with $NaNO_2$ and HCl and then with β-naphthol, a highly colored solid is formed.

When Novocaine is boiled with aqueous NaOH, it slowly dissolves. The alkaline solution is shaken with ether and the layers are separated.

Acidification of the aqueous layer causes the precipitation of a white solid A; continued addition of acid causes A to redissolve. Upon isolation A is found to have a melting point of 185–6° and the formula $C_7H_7O_2N$.

Evaporation of the ether layer leaves a liquid B of formula $C_6H_{15}ON$. B dissolves in water to give a solution that turns litmus blue. Treatment of B with acetic anhydride gives C, $C_8H_{17}O_2N$, which is insoluble in water and dilute base, but soluble in dilute HCl.

B is found to be identical with the compound formed by the action of diethylamine on ethylene oxide.

(a) What is the structure of Novocaine? (b) Outline all steps in a complete synthesis of Novocaine from toluene and readily available aliphatic and inorganic reagents.

17. Compound D of formula C_7H_9N dissolved readily in dilute HCl. When this acidic solution was cooled, treated with sodium nitrite and then with an alkaline solution of β-naphthol, a red solid separated.

When D was treated with bromine water, a solid E immediately precipitated. Quantitative analysis showed that E contained 70.0% bromine.

(a) What was the molecular formula of E? (b) What was the structure of D?

18. A solid compound, F, of formula $C_{15}H_{15}ON$, was insoluble in water, dilute HCl, or dilute NaOH. After prolonged heating of F with aqueous NaOH, a liquid, G, was observed floating on the surface of the alkaline mixture. G did not solidify upon cooling to room temperature; it was steam-distilled and separated. Acidification of the alkaline mixture with hydrochloric acid caused precipitation of a white solid, H.

Compound G was soluble in dilute HCl, and reacted with benzenesulfonyl chloride and excess NaOH to give a base-insoluble solid, I.

Compound H, m.p. 180°, was soluble in aqueous $NaHCO_3$, and contained no nitrogen.

What were compounds F, G, H, and I?

19. Give the structures of compounds J through S:

$$\text{J + heat} \longrightarrow \text{K } (C_9H_{15}N)$$
$$\text{K + CH}_3\text{I, then Ag}_2\text{O} \longrightarrow \text{L } (C_{10}H_{19}ON)$$
$$\text{L + heat} \longrightarrow \text{M } (C_{10}H_{17}N)$$
$$\text{M + CH}_3\text{I, then Ag}_2\text{O} \longrightarrow \text{N } (C_{11}H_{21}ON)$$
$$\text{N + heat} \longrightarrow \text{O } (C_8H_{10})$$
$$\text{O + Br}_2 \longrightarrow \text{P } (C_8H_{10}Br_2)$$
$$\text{P + (CH}_3)_2\text{NH} \longrightarrow \text{Q } (C_{12}H_{22}N_2)$$
$$\text{Q + CH}_3\text{I, then Ag}_2\text{O} \longrightarrow \text{R } (C_{14}H_{30}O_2N_2)$$
$$\text{R + heat} \longrightarrow \text{S}(C_8H_8)$$

20. Compound T gave positive tests for nitrogen, sulfur, and bromine. Quantitative analysis gave the formula $C_{12}H_{10}O_2NSBr$. T was insoluble in water and dilute acid, but was soluble in dilute NaOH, from which it could be regenerated upon acidification even after prolonged heating.

Prolonged heating with concentrated hydrochloric acid finally brought about dissolution of T. When the acidic solution was made alkaline by NaOH, a solid U separated. U contained nitrogen and bromine but not sulfur. U melted at 66°; it reacted rapidly with bromine water to yield V, $C_6H_4NBr_3$. V was soluble with difficulty in acid, and was insoluble in base.

Evaporation of the alkaline solution from which U had been isolated gave a residue that contained sulfur. Recrystallization of this residue yielded a compound of formula $C_6H_5O_3SNa$ that had no definite melting point.

(a) What were T, U, and V? (b) Why was V so difficultly soluble in acid?
(c) Outline a synthesis of T from benzene and any needed inorganic reagents.

21. An unknown compound W contained chlorine and nitrogen. It dissolved readily in water to give a solution that turned litmus red. Titration of W with standard base gave a neutralization equivalent of 131 ± 2.

When a sample of W was treated with aqueous NaOH a liquid X separated. X contained nitrogen but not chlorine. Treatment of X with nitrous acid followed by β-naphthol gave a red precipitate.

What was W? Write equations for all reactions.

Chapter twenty-one _____

DIAZONIUM SALTS

21.1   Structure and nomenclature

The reaction of primary aromatic amines with nitrous acid yields the important class of compounds known as **diazonium salts.** These salts have the general formula $ArN_2^+ X^-$, where X^- is any of a large number of anions, such as Cl^-, Br^-, NO_3^-, HSO_4^-, BF_4^-, etc.

$$Ar—N\equiv N:^+ X^-$$
A diazonium salt

Diazonium salts are named by adding *–diazonium* to the name of the aromatic compound to which they are related, and following this by the name of the anion.   For example:

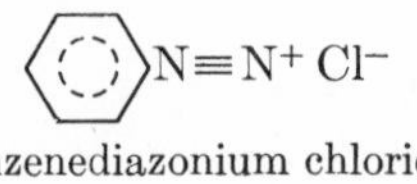

Benzenediazonium chloride

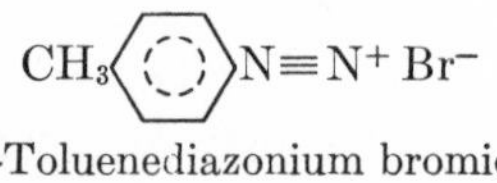

p-Toluenediazonium bromide

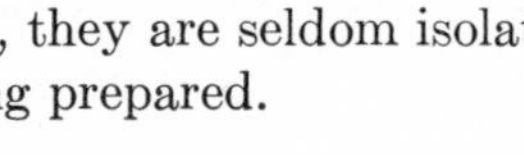

p-Nitrobenzenediazonium fluoborate

21.2   Physical properties

Dry diazonium salts are crystalline solids; many of them are explosive. Because of their instability, they are seldom isolated, but are used in solution immediately after being prepared.

21.3   Preparation

Since nitrous acid is an unstable compound, it is generated in the presence of the amine by the reaction between sodium nitrite and a mineral acid, usually hydrochloric acid or sulfuric acid.   The over-all equation for diazotization is

$$ArNH_2 + NaNO_2 + 2HX \xrightarrow{\text{cold}} ArN_2^+ X^- + NaX + 2H_2O$$
1° aromatic   A diazonium salt
amine

Diazotization is generally carried out in the following way. The amine is dissolved or suspended in an aqueous solution of the mineral acid. More acid is used than the two equivalents per mole of amine that are required by the equation; the excess acid serves to keep the mixture strongly acidic, which, as we shall see, is necessary to prevent undesirable side reactions (see Problem 21.5, page 579). The mixture of amine and acid is cooled in an ice-salt mixture to a temperature between $0°$ and $-10°$. An aqueous solution of sodium nitrite is then added at such a rate that the temperature does not rise above $5-10°$ (diazotization is an exothermic reaction). Although the amount of sodium nitrite theoretically required for reaction can be calculated, there is some loss of nitrous acid as NO and NO_2; consequently it is necessary to test the reaction mixture to see when enough sodium nitrite has been added. This is done with starch–potassium iodide paper. Excess sodium nitrite forms nitrous acid that is not consumed by the amine; nitrous acid, being an oxidizing agent, converts iodide ion into free iodine which reacts with starch to yield a characteristic deep blue color. Since this excess nitrous acid interferes with subsequent reactions of the diazonium salt, it is destroyed by the addition of a small amount of urea, H_2NCONH_2, which reacts with nitrous acid to form nitrogen, carbon dioxide, and water (Sec. 25.12). Any excess urea does not interfere with subsequent reactions.

Since diazonium salts slowly decompose even at ice-bath temperatures, the solution is used immediately after preparation.

21.4 Reactions of diazonium salts

The large number of reactions undergone by diazonium salts may be divided into two classes: **replacement,** in which nitrogen is lost as N_2, and some other atom or group becomes attached to the ring in its place; and **coupling,** in which the nitrogen is retained in the product.

REACTIONS OF DIAZONIUM SALTS

1. Replacement of nitrogen

$$ArN_2^+ + :Z \longrightarrow ArZ + N_2$$

(a) Replacement by —Cl, —Br, and —CN. Sandmeyer reaction

$$ArN_2^+ \quad \begin{cases} \xrightarrow{CuCl} & ArCl + N_2 \\ \xrightarrow{CuBr} & ArBr + N_2 \\ \xrightarrow{CuCN} & ArCN + N_2 \end{cases}$$

Examples:

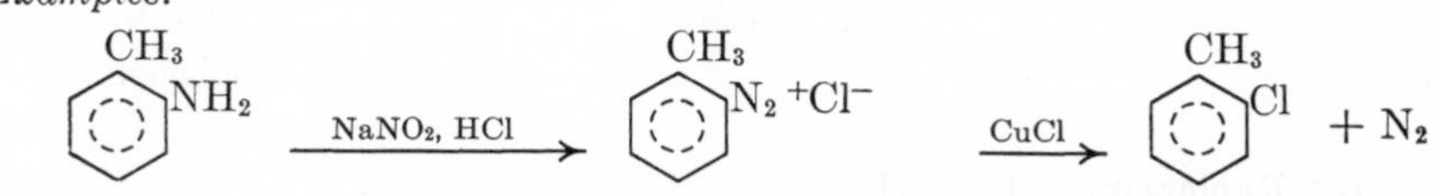

o-Toluidine $\xrightarrow{NaNO_2, HCl}$ o-Toluenediazonium chloride $\xrightarrow{CuCl}$ o-Chlorotoluene $+ N_2$

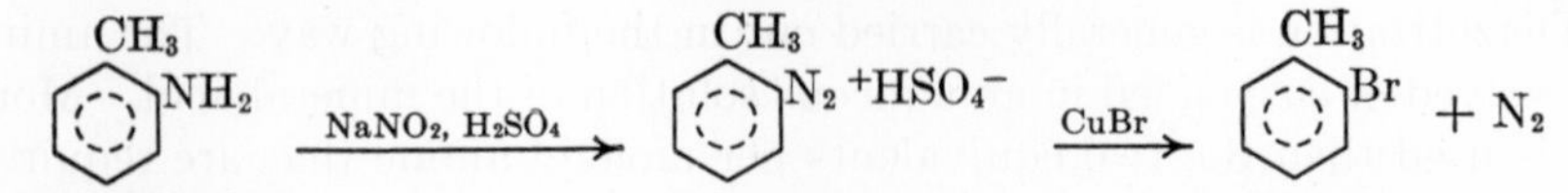

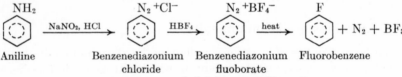

o-Toluidine $\xrightarrow{\text{NaNO}_2,\ \text{H}_2\text{SO}_4}$ (CH$_3$, N$_2^+$HSO$_4^-$) $\xrightarrow{\text{CuBr}}$ o-Bromotoluene (CH$_3$, Br) $+$ N$_2$

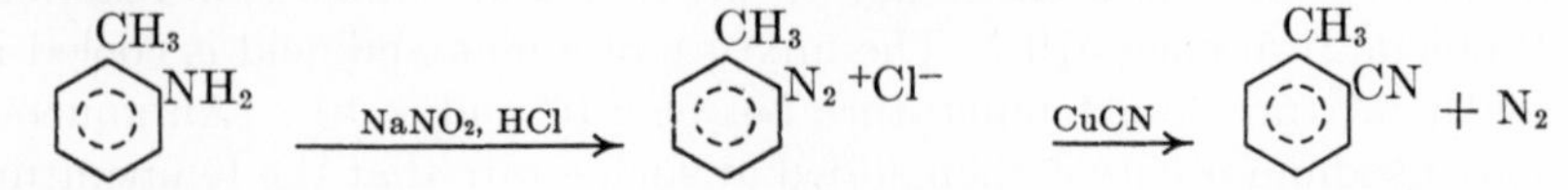

o-Toluidine $\xrightarrow{\text{NaNO}_2,\ \text{HCl}}$ (CH$_3$, N$_2^+$Cl$^-$) $\xrightarrow{\text{CuCN}}$ o-Tolunitrile (CH$_3$, CN) $+$ N$_2$

(b) Replacement by —I

$$\text{ArN}_2^+ + \text{I}^- \longrightarrow \text{ArI} + \text{N}_2$$

Example:

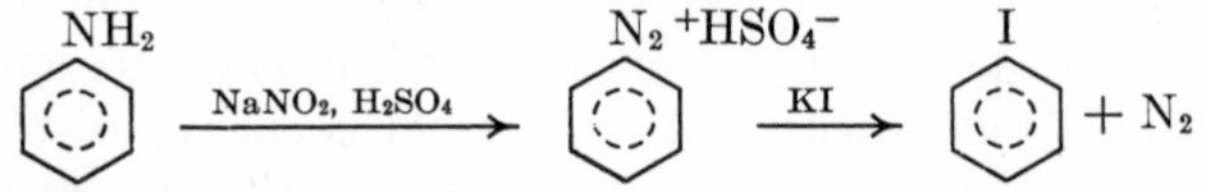

Aniline (NH$_2$) $\xrightarrow{\text{NaNO}_2,\ \text{H}_2\text{SO}_4}$ (N$_2^+$HSO$_4^-$) $\xrightarrow{\text{KI}}$ Iodobenzene (I) $+$ N$_2$

(c) Replacement by —F

$$\text{ArN}_2^+ \text{BF}_4^- \xrightarrow{\text{heat}} \text{ArF} + \text{N}_2 + \text{BF}_3$$

Example:

Aniline (NH$_2$) $\xrightarrow{\text{NaNO}_2,\ \text{HCl}}$ Benzenediazonium chloride (N$_2^+$Cl$^-$) $\xrightarrow{\text{HBF}_4}$ Benzenediazonium fluoborate (N$_2^+$BF$_4^-$) $\xrightarrow{\text{heat}}$ Fluorobenzene (F) $+$ N$_2$ + BF$_3$

Isolated as crystalline salt

(d) Replacement by —OH

$$\text{ArN}_2^+ + \text{H}_2\text{O} \xrightarrow{\text{H}^+} \text{ArOH} + \text{N}_2$$
A phenol

Examples:

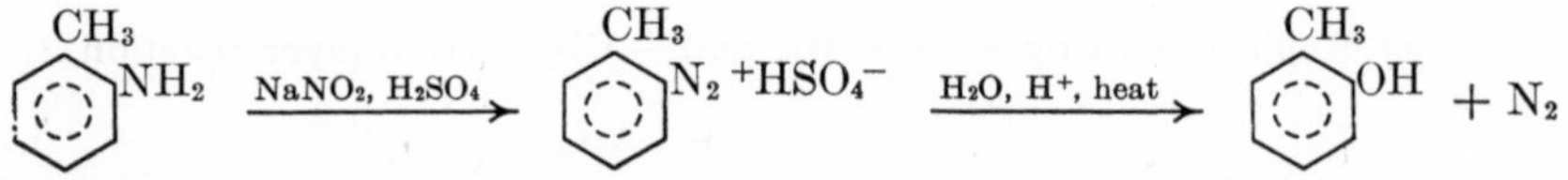

o-Toluidine (CH$_3$, NH$_2$) $\xrightarrow{\text{NaNO}_2,\ \text{H}_2\text{SO}_4}$ (CH$_3$, N$_2^+$HSO$_4^-$) $\xrightarrow{\text{H}_2\text{O, H}^+,\ \text{heat}}$ o-Cresol (CH$_3$, OH) $+$ N$_2$

m-Nitroaniline (NH$_2$, NO$_2$) $\xrightarrow{\text{NaNO}_2,\ \text{H}_2\text{SO}_4}$ (N$_2^+$HSO$_4^-$, NO$_2$) $\xrightarrow{\text{H}_2\text{O, H}^+,\ \text{heat}}$ m-Nitrophenol (OH, NO$_2$) $+$ N$_2$

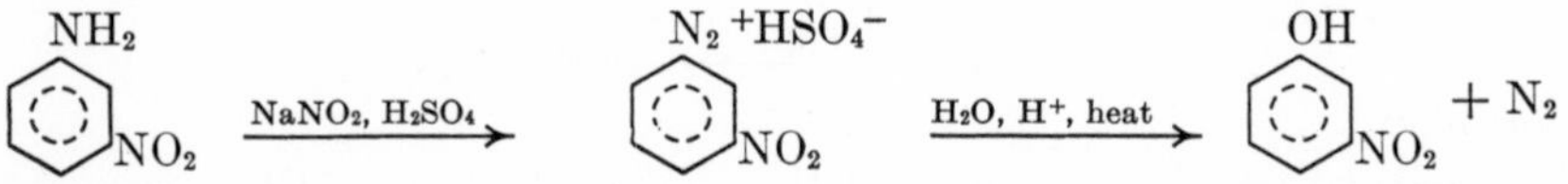

(e) Replacement by —H

$$\text{ArN}_2^+ + \text{H}_3\text{PO}_2 \xrightarrow{\text{H}_2\text{O}} \text{ArH} + \text{H}_3\text{PO}_3 + \text{N}_2$$

Examples:

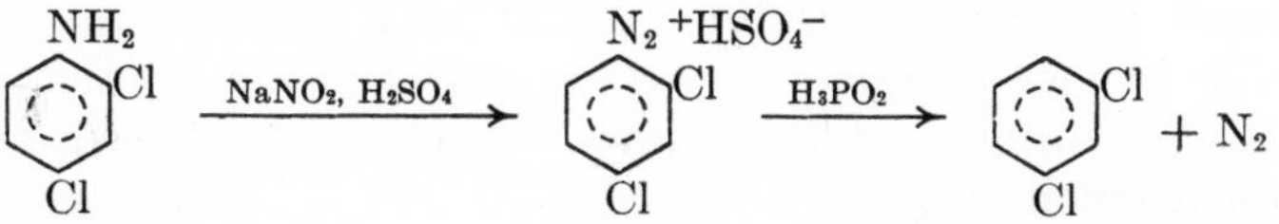

2,4-Dichloroaniline m-Dichlorobenzene

2. Coupling

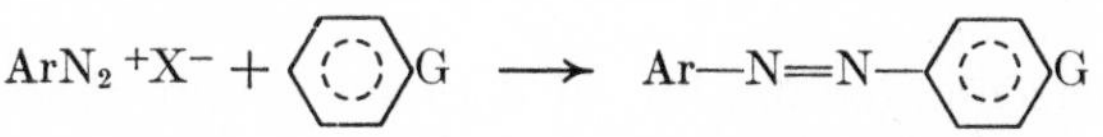

An azo compound

G must be a strongly electron-releasing group: OH, NR_2, NHR, NH_2

Example:

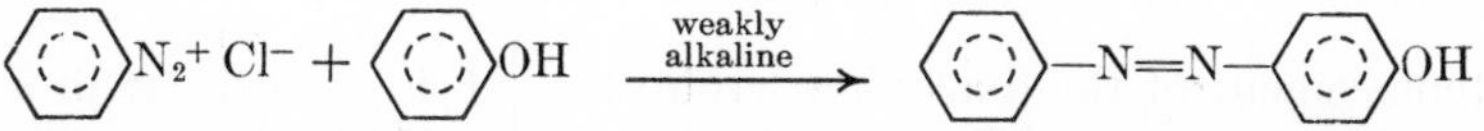

Benzenediazonium chloride Phenol *p*-Hydroxyazobenzene *p*-(Phenylazo)phenol

Replacement of the diazonium group is the best general way of introducing F, Cl, Br, I, CN, OH, and H into an aromatic ring. Diazonium salts are valuable in synthesis not only because they react to form so many classes of compounds, but also because they can be prepared from nearly all primary aromatic amines. There are few groups whose presence in the molecule interferes with diazotization; in this respect, diazonium salts are quite different from Grignard reagents (Sec. 11.14). The amines from which diazonium compounds are prepared are readily obtained from the corresponding nitro compounds, which are prepared by direct nitration. Diazonium salts are thus the most important link in the sequence:

$$ArH \longrightarrow ArNO_2 \longrightarrow ArNH_2 \longrightarrow ArN_2^+ \longrightarrow \begin{cases} Ar{-}F \\ Ar{-}Cl \\ Ar{-}Br \\ Ar{-}I \\ Ar{-}CN \longrightarrow Ar{-}COOH \\ Ar{-}OH \\ Ar{-}H \end{cases}$$

In addition to the atoms and groups just listed, there are dozens of other groups that can be attached to an aromatic ring by replacement of the diazonium nitrogen, as, for example, —Ar, —NO_2, —OR, —SH, —SR, —NCS, —NCO, —PO_3H_2, —AsO_3H_2, —SbO_3H_2; the best way to introduce most of these groups is via diazotization.

The coupling of diazonium salts with aromatic phenols and amines yields *azo compounds*, which are of tremendous importance to the dye industry.

21.5 Replacement by halogen. Sandmeyer reaction

Replacement of the diazonium group by —Cl or —Br is carried out by mixing the solution of freshly prepared diazonium salt with cuprous chloride or cuprous bromide. At room temperature, or occasionally at elevated temperatures, nitrogen is steadily evolved, and after several hours the aryl chloride or aryl bromide can be isolated from the reaction mixture. This procedure, using cuprous halides, is generally referred to as the **Sandmeyer reaction.**

$$ArN_2^+ X^- \xrightarrow{CuX} ArX + N_2$$

Sometimes the synthesis is carried out by a modification known as the *Gattermann reaction,* in which copper powder and hydrogen halide are used in place of the cuprous halide.

Replacement of the diazonium group by —I does not require the use of a cuprous halide or copper; the diazonium salt and potassium iodide are simply mixed together and allowed to react.

$$ArN_2^+ X^- + I^- \longrightarrow ArI + N_2 + X^-$$

Replacement of the diazonium group by —F is carried out in a somewhat different way. Addition of fluoboric acid, HBF_4, to the solution of diazonium salt causes the precipitation of the diazonium fluoborate, $ArN_2^+ BF_4^-$, which can be collected on a filter, washed, and dried. The diazonium fluoborates are unusual among diazonium salts in being fairly stable compounds. On being heated, the dry diazonium fluoborate decomposes to yield the aryl fluoride, boron trifluoride, and nitrogen.

$$ArN_2^+ X^- \xrightarrow{HBF_4} ArN_2^+ BF_4^- \xrightarrow{heat} ArF + BF_3 + N_2$$

The advantages of the synthesis of aryl halides from diazonium salts have already been discussed (Sec. 14.5). Aryl fluorides and iodides cannot generally be prepared by direct halogenation. Aryl chlorides and bromides can be prepared by direct halogenation, but, when a mixture of *o*- and *p*-isomers is obtained, it is difficult to isolate the pure compounds because of their similarity in boiling point. Diazonium salts ultimately go back to nitro compounds, which are usually obtainable in pure form.

21.6   Replacement by —CN.   Synthesis of carboxylic acids

Replacement of the diazonium group by —CN is carried out by allowing the diazonium salt to react with cuprous cyanide. To prevent loss of cyanide as HCN, the diazonium solution is neutralized with sodium carbonate before being mixed with the cuprous cyanide.

$$ArN_2^+ X^- \xrightarrow{CuCN} ArCN + N_2$$

Hydrolysis of nitriles yields carboxylic acids. The synthesis of nitriles from diazonium salts thus provides us with an excellent route from nitro compounds to carboxylic acids. For example:

p-Toluic   *p*-Tolunitrile   *p*-Toluenediazonium   *p*-Toluidine   *p*-Nitrotoluene   Toluene
acid   chloride

This way of making aromatic carboxylic acids is more generally useful than either carbonation of a Grignard reagent or oxidation of side chains. We have just seen that pure bromo compounds, which are needed to prepare the Grignard reagent, are themselves most often prepared via diazonium salts; furthermore, there are many groups that interfere with the preparation and use of the Grignard reagent (Sec. 11.14). The nitro group can generally be introduced into a molecule more readily than an alkyl side chain; furthermore, conversion of a side chain into a carboxyl group cannot be carried out on molecules that contain other groups sensitive to oxidation.

21.7   Replacement by —OH.   Synthesis of phenols

Diazonium salts react with water to yield phenols.

$$ArN_2^+ X^- + H_2O \longrightarrow ArOH + N_2 + H^+$$

This reaction takes place slowly in the ice-cold solutions of diazonium salts, and is the reason diazonium salts are used immediately upon preparation; at elevated temperatures it can be made the chief reaction of diazonium salts.

As we shall see, phenols can couple with diazonium salts to form azo compounds (Sec. 21.10); they do so only slowly, however, in acidic solution. To minimize coupling during the synthesis of a phenol, therefore, the diazonium solution is added slowly to a large volume of boiling dilute sulfuric acid.

This is the best general way to make the important class of compounds, the phenols.

21.8   Replacement by —H

Replacement of the diazonium group by —H can be brought about by a number of reducing agents; perhaps the most useful of these is *hypophosphorous acid*, H_3PO_2. The diazonium salt is simply allowed to stand in the presence of the hypophosphorous acid; nitrogen is lost, and hypophosphorous acid is oxidized to phosphorous acid:

$$ArN_2^+ X^- + H_3PO_2 + H_2O \longrightarrow ArH + N_2 + H_3PO_3 + HX$$

An especially elegant way of carrying out this replacement is to use hypophosphorous acid as the diazotizing acid. The amine is dissolved in hypophosphorous acid, and sodium nitrite is added; the diazonium salt is reduced as fast as it is formed.

This reaction of diazonium salts provides a method of removing an —NH$_2$ or —NO$_2$ group from an aromatic ring. This process can be extremely useful in synthesis, as is shown in some of the examples in the following section.

21.9   Syntheses using diazonium salts

Let us look at a few examples of how diazonium salts can be used in organic synthesis.

To begin with, we might consider some rather simple compounds, the three isomeric bromotoluenes. The best synthesis of each employs diazotization, but not for the same purpose in the three cases. The *o-* and *p-*bromotoluenes are prepared from the corresponding *o-* and *p-*nitrotoluenes:

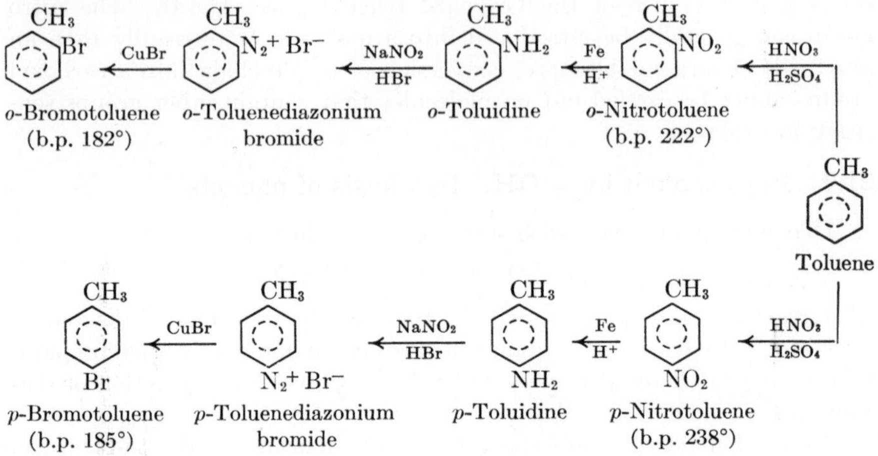

$$\text{CH}_3\text{C}_6\text{H}_4\text{Br} \xleftarrow{\text{CuBr}} \text{CH}_3\text{C}_6\text{H}_4\text{N}_2^+\text{Br}^- \xleftarrow[\text{HBr}]{\text{NaNO}_2} \text{CH}_3\text{C}_6\text{H}_4\text{NH}_2 \xleftarrow[\text{H}^+]{\text{Fe}} \text{CH}_3\text{C}_6\text{H}_4\text{NO}_2 \xleftarrow[\text{H}_2\text{SO}_4]{\text{HNO}_3} \text{C}_6\text{H}_5\text{CH}_3$$

o-Bromotoluene (b.p. 182°)   *o*-Toluenediazonium bromide   *o*-Toluidine   *o*-Nitrotoluene (b.p. 222°)   Toluene

p-Bromotoluene (b.p. 185°)   *p*-Toluenediazonium bromide   *p*-Toluidine   *p*-Nitrotoluene (b.p. 238°)

The advantage of these many-step syntheses over direct bromination is, as we have seen, that a pure product is obtained. Separation of the *o-* and *p-*bromotoluenes obtained by direct bromination is not feasible.

Synthesis of *m-*bromotoluene is a more complicated matter. The problem here is one of preparing a compound in which two *ortho,para-* directing groups are situated *meta* to each other. Bromination of toluene or methylation of bromobenzene would not yield the correct isomer. *m-*Bromotoluene is obtained by the following sequence of reactions:

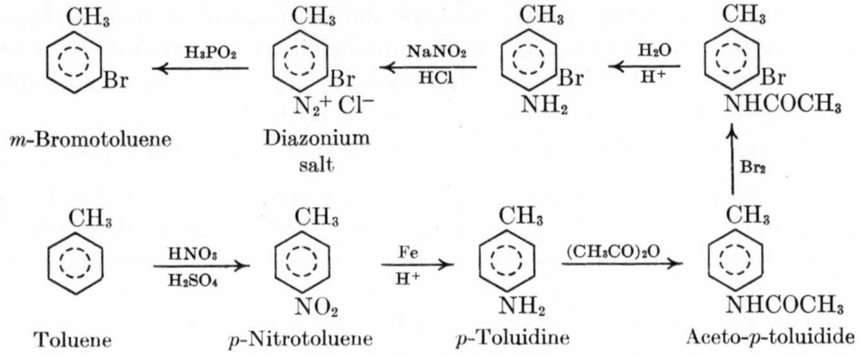

m-Bromotoluene   Diazonium salt   Toluene   *p*-Nitrotoluene   *p*-Toluidine   Aceto-*p*-toluidide

The key to the synthesis is the introduction of a group that is a much stronger *ortho,para* director than —CH₃, and that can be easily removed after it has done its job of directing bromine to the correct position. Such a group is the —NHCOCH₃ group: it is introduced into the *para* position of toluene via nitration, reduction, and acetylation; it is readily removed by hydrolysis, diazotization, and reduction.

Problem 21.1 Outline the synthesis from benzene or toluene of the following compounds: m-nitrotoluene, m-iodotoluene, 3,5-dibromotoluene, 1,3,5-tribromobenzene, the three toluic acids ($CH_3C_6H_4COOH$), the three methylphenols (cresols).

In the synthesis of m-bromotoluene, advantage was taken of the fact that the diazonium group is prepared from a group that is strongly ortho,para-directing. Ultimately, however, the diazonium group is prepared from the —NO₂ group, which is a strongly meta-directing group. Advantage can be taken of this fact, too, as in the preparation of m-bromophenol:

OH   N₂⁺ Cl⁻   NH₂   NO₂   NO₂

m-Bromophenol   m-Bromoaniline   Nitrobenzene
        m-Bromobenzenediazonium   m-Bromonitrobenzene
                     chloride

Here again there is the problem of preparing a compound with two ortho,para directors situated meta to each other. Bromination at the nitro stage gives the necessary meta orientation.

Problem 21.2 Outline the synthesis from benzene or toluene of the following compounds: m-dibromobenzene, m-iodonitrobenzene, m-fluoroaniline, m-difluorobenzene, m-fluoroiodobenzene.

As a final example, let us consider the preparation of 1,2,3-tribromobenzene:

Br   Br   Br   Br

1,2,3-Tribromobenzene   3,4,5-Tribromoaniline
        3,4,5-Tribromobenzenediazonium   3,4,5-Tribromonitrobenzene
                     chloride

                                          Br   Br
                    NH₂   NH₂   N₂⁺HSO₄⁻

p-Nitroaniline   2,6-Dibromo-4-   2,6-Dibromo-4-nitro-
                                       nitroaniline   benzenediazonium
                                                                     hydrogen sulfate

In this synthesis advantage is taken of the fact that the —NO₂ group is a meta director, that the —NH₂ group is an ortho,para director, and that each of them can be converted into a diazonium group. One diazonium group is replaced by —Br, the other by —H.

Problem 21.3 Outline the synthesis from benzene or toluene of the following compounds: 2,6-dibromotoluene, 3,5-dibromonitrobenzene.

21.10 Coupling. Synthesis of azo compounds

Under the proper conditions, diazonium salts react with certain aromatic compounds to yield products of the general formula Ar—N=N—Ar′, called **azo compounds.** In this reaction, known as **coupling,** the nitrogen of the diazonium group is retained in the product, in contrast to the replacement reactions we have studied up to this point, in which nitrogen is lost.

$$ArN_2^+ + Ar'H \longrightarrow Ar-N=N-Ar' + H^+$$
An azo compound

The aromatic ring (Ar'H) undergoing attack by the diazonium ion must contain a powerfully electron-releasing group, generally —OH, —NR$_2$, —NHR, or —NH$_2$. Substitution usually occurs *para* to the activating group. Coupling with phenols is carried out in weakly alkaline solution; with amines in weakly acidic solution.

Activation by electron-releasing groups, as well as the evidence of kinetics studies, indicates that coupling is electrophilic aromatic substitution in which the diazonium ion is the attacking reagent:

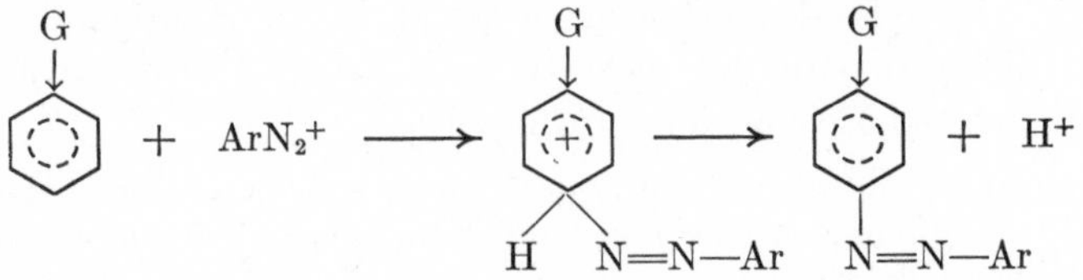

It is significant that the aromatic compounds which undergo coupling are also the ones which undergo nitrosation. Like the nitrosonium ion, ^+NO, the diazonium ion, ArN_2^+, is evidently very weakly electrophilic, and is capable of attacking only very reactive rings.

Problem 21.4　Benzenediazonium chloride couples with phenol, but not with the less reactive anisole. 2,4-Dinitrobenzenediazonium chloride, however, couples with anisole; 2,4,6-trinitrobenzenediazonium chloride even couples with the hydrocarbon mesitylene (1,3,5-trimethylbenzene). (a) How can you account for these differences in behavior? (b) Would you expect *p*-toluenediazonium chloride to be more or less reactive as a coupling reagent than benzenediazonium chloride?

In the laboratory we find that coupling involves more than merely mixing together a diazonium salt and a phenol or amine. Competing with any other reaction of diazonium salts is the reaction with water to yield a phenol. If coupling proceeds slowly because of unfavorable conditions, phenol formation may very well become the major reaction. Furthermore, the phenol formed from the diazonium salt can itself undergo coupling; even a relatively small amount of this undesired coupling product could contaminate the desired material — usually a dye whose color should be as pure as possible — to such an extent that the product would be worthless. Conditions under which coupling proceeds as rapidly as possible must therefore be selected.

It is most important that the coupling medium be adjusted to the right degree of acidity or alkalinity. This is accomplished by addition of the proper amount of hydroxide or salts like sodium acetate or sodium carbonate. It will be well to examine this matter in some detail, since it illustrates a problem that is frequently encountered in organic chemical practice.

The electrophilic reagent is the diazonium ion, ArN_2^+. In the presence of hydroxide ion, the diazonium ion exists in equilibrium with an unionized compound, $Ar-N=N-OH$, and salts $(Ar-N=N-O^- Na^+)$ derived from it:

$$Ar-N\equiv N^+ OH^- \underset{H^+}{\overset{NaOH}{\rightleftarrows}} Ar-N=N-OH \underset{H^+}{\overset{NaOH}{\rightleftarrows}} Ar-N=N-O^- Na^+$$

Couples   Does not couple   Does not couple

For our purpose we need only know that hydroxide tends to convert diazonium ion, which couples, into compounds which do not couple. In so far as the electrophilic reagent is concerned, then, coupling will be favored by a low concentration of hydroxide ion, that is, by high acidity.

But what is the effect of high acidity on the amine or phenol with which the diazonium salt is reacting? Acid converts an amine into its ion, which, as we have seen (Sec. 20.10), is unreactive toward electrophilic aromatic substitution. The higher the acidity, the higher the proportion of amine that exists as its ion, and the lower is the rate of coupling.

NH_2 $\underset{OH^-}{\overset{H^+}{\rightleftarrows}}$ NH_3^+

Couples   Does not couple

An analogous situation exists for a phenol. A phenol is appreciably acidic; in aqueous solutions it exists in equilibrium with phenoxide ion:

O^- $\underset{OH^-}{\overset{H^+}{\rightleftarrows}}$ OH

Couples   Couples
rapidly   slowly

The fully developed negative charge makes $-O^-$ much more powerfully electron-releasing than $-OH$; the phenoxide ion is therefore much more reactive than the un-ionized phenol toward electrophilic aromatic substitution. The higher the acidity of the medium, the higher the proportion of phenol that is un-ionized, and the lower is the rate of coupling. In so far as the amine or phenol is concerned, then, coupling is favored by low acidity.

The conditions under which coupling proceeds most rapidly are the result of a compromise. The solution must not be so alkaline that the concentration of diazonium ion is too low; it must not be so acidic that the concentration of free amine or phenoxide ion is too low. It turns out that amines couple best in weakly acidic solutions, and phenols couple best in weakly alkaline solutions.

Problem 21.5 Suggest a reason for the use of *excess* mineral acid in the diazotization process.

Problem 21.6 (a) Coupling of diazonium salts with primary or secondary aromatic amines (but not with tertiary aromatic amines) is complicated by a side-reaction that yields an isomer of the azo compound. Judging from the reaction of secondary aromatic amines with nitrous acid (Sec. 20.13), suggest a possible structure for this by-product.

(b) Upon treatment with mineral acid, this by-product regenerates the original reactants which recombine to form the azo compound. What do you think is the function of the acid in this regeneration? (*Hint:* see Sec. 4.16.)

21.11 Azo compounds

Azo compounds, Ar—N=N—Ar', can be named in two ways. The less complicated ones are named as derivatives of *azobenzene*. Positions of substituents in the rings are usually indicated by numbers, primes being used to distinguish between positions on the two rings. For example:

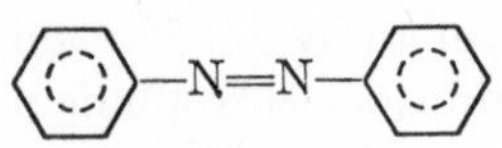

Azobenzene

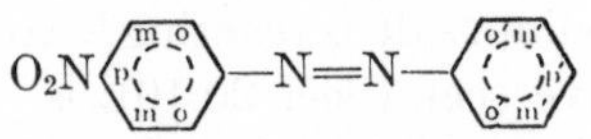

p-Nitroazobenzene

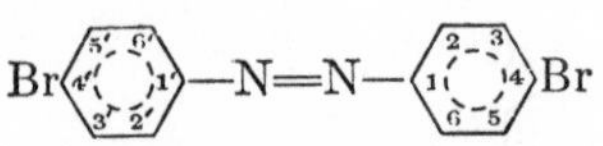

4,4'-Dibromoazobenzene

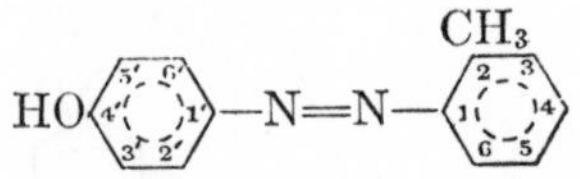

2-Methyl-4'-hydroxyazobenzene

(The use of primed numbers to distinguish substituents in two or more equivalent parts of a molecule is common in organic nomenclature.)

More complicated azo compounds can be named by considering the *arylazo* group, Ar—N=N—, as a substituent. For example:

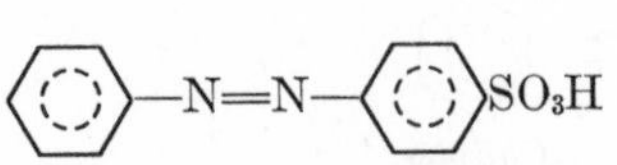

p-(Phenylazo)benzenesulfonic acid

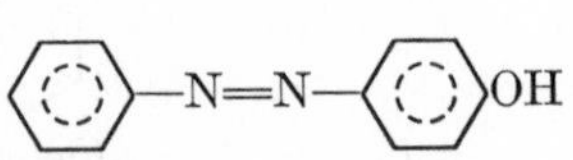

p-(Phenylazo)phenol

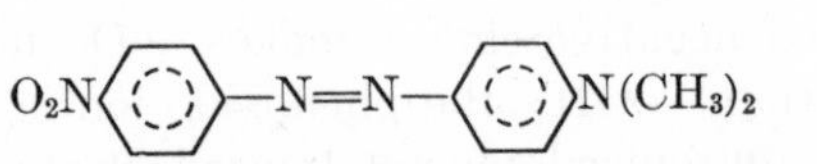

p-(*p*-Nitrophenylazo)-N,N-dimethylaniline

The azo compounds are the first compounds we have encountered that as a class are strongly colored. They can be intensely yellow, orange, red, blue, or even green, depending upon the exact structure of the molecule. Because of their color, the azo compounds are of tremendous importance as dyes; about half of the dyes in industrial use today are azo dyes. Some of the acid-base indicators with which the student is already familiar are azo compounds.

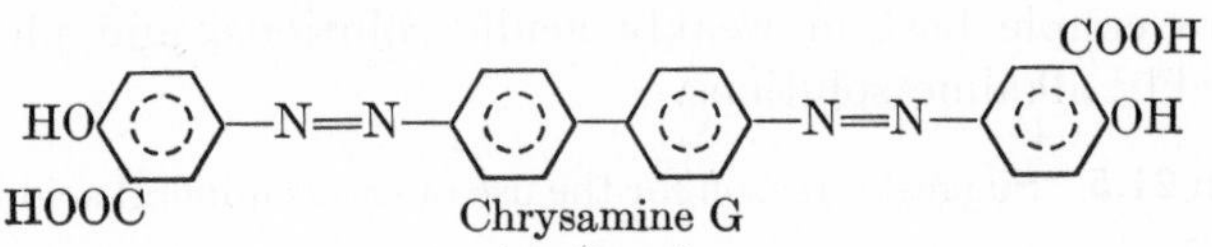

Chrysamine G
A yellow dye

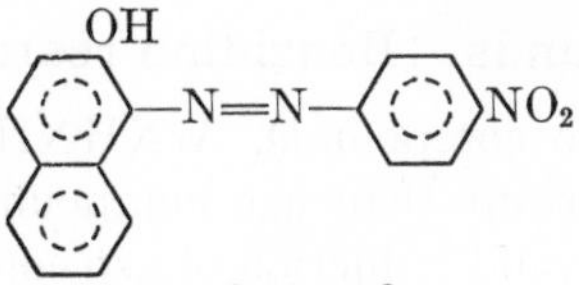

Para red
A red dye

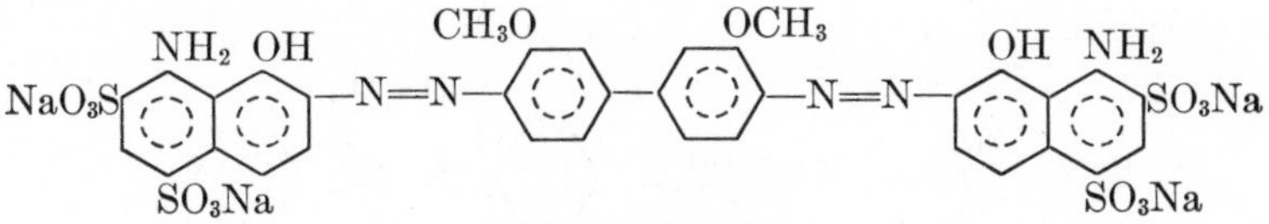

Chicago blue 6B
A blue dye

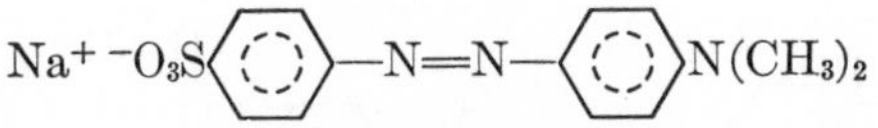

Methyl orange
An acid-base indicator:
red in acid, *yellow* in base

Mild oxidation (with H_2O_2, for example) converts azo compounds into **azoxy compounds**:

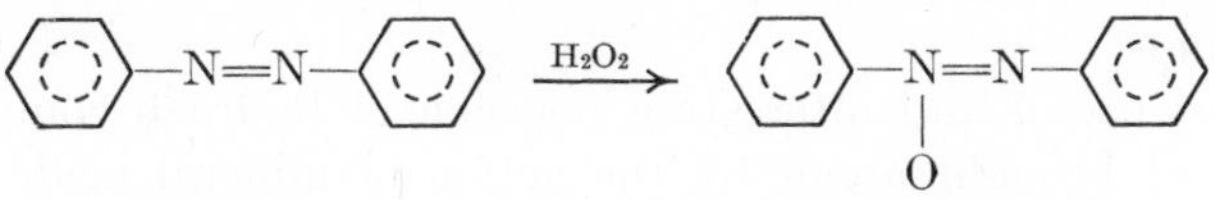

Azobenzene   Azoxybenzene
Orange-red   *Yellow*

Mild alkaline reduction (with zinc and sodium hydroxide, for example) converts azo compounds into **hydrazo compounds**:

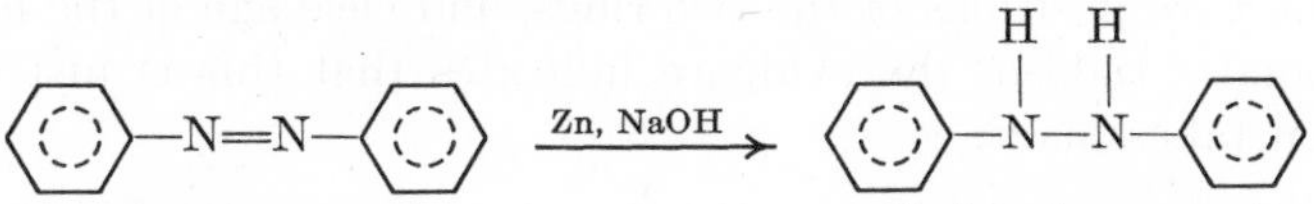

Azobenzene   Hydrazobenzene
Orange-red   *Colorless*

The most important reaction of azo compounds is cleavage, which is generally accomplished by a strong reducing agent like stannous chloride. This reaction yields two amines, and is very useful in determining the structure of an azo compound.

$$Ar-N=N-Ar' \xrightarrow{\text{SnCl}_2,\ \text{H}^+} ArNH_2 + H_2NAr'$$
Azo compound   Amine   Amine

Problem 21.7 Treatment of an azo compound with stannous chloride yields 3-bromo-4-aminotoluene and 2-methyl-4-aminophenol. (a) What is the structure of the azo compound? (b) Outline a synthesis of this azo compound, starting with benzene and toluene.

Problem 21.8 Show how an azo compound can be used in the preparation of *p*-amino-N,N-dimethylaniline.

21.12 Hydrazo compounds. Benzidine rearrangement

As a class, the hydrazo compounds, ArNHNHAr', are colorless, and hence are much less important than azo compounds. They can be prepared, as we have seen, by mild reduction of azo compounds. Symmetrical hydrazo compounds are more conveniently prepared by direct reduction of a nitro compound; zinc and sodium hydroxide are used in the laboratory for this purpose.

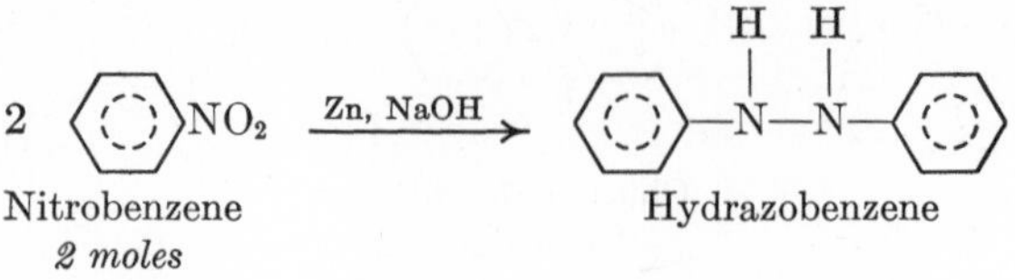

Nitrobenzene
2 moles

Hydrazobenzene

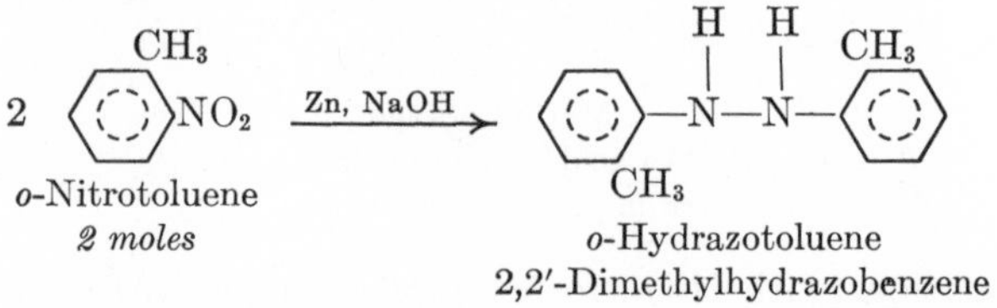

o-Nitrotoluene
2 moles

o-Hydrazotoluene
2,2'-Dimethylhydrazobenzene

Hydrazo compounds are readily oxidized (even by air) to the corresponding azo compounds.

The most useful and interesting reaction of hydrazo compounds is a rearrangement brought about by the action of mineral acid. As shown below, hydrazobenzene itself yields 4,4'-diaminobiphenyl, known commonly as **benzidine**; the rearrangement is therefore given the general name of **benzidine rearrangement.** The product obtained in each case is the one expected from a "folding" of the molecule, formation of a bond between the *para* positions of the two rings, and cleavage of the nitrogen-nitrogen bond. Indeed, the evidence indicates that this is just the way the reaction takes place.

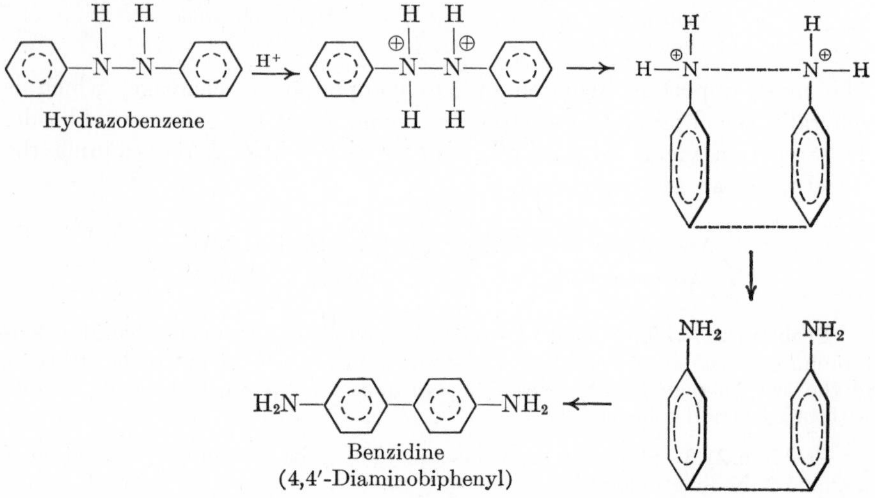

Hydrazobenzene

Benzidine
(4,4'-Diaminobiphenyl)

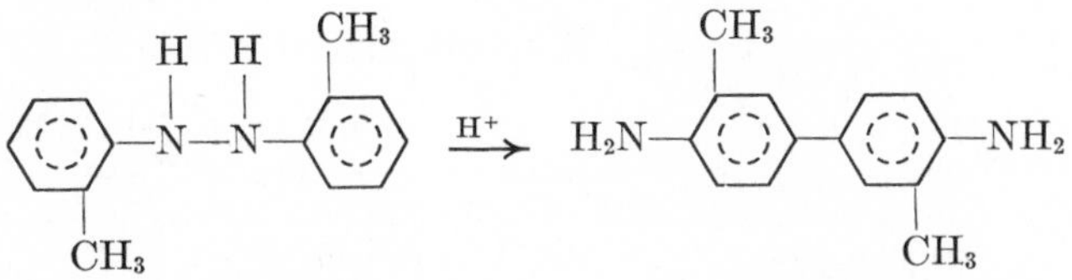

o-Hydrazotoluene
(2,2'-Dimethylhydrazobenzene)

o-Tolidine
(3,3'-Dimethyl-4,4'-diaminobiphenyl)

Benzidine and substituted benzidines are aromatic diamines, and as such are extremely valuable in the preparation of azo dyes. On treatment with nitrous acid both amino groups are diazotized, so that coupling can occur at both ends of the molecule. For example:

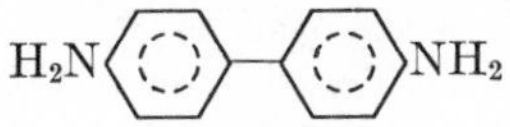

Benzidine

| HONO

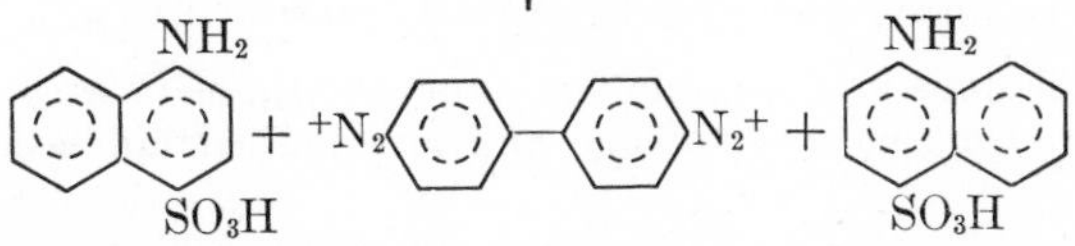

Naphthionic acid   coupling   Naphthionic acid

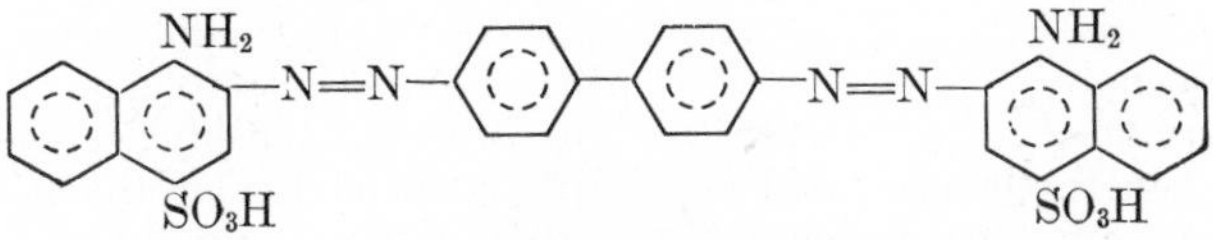

Congo red
An acid-base indicator:
blue in acid, *red* in base

PROBLEMS

1. Give the structures of the following:

(a) benzenediazonium nitrate
(b) p-nitrobenzenediazonium sulfate
(c) azobenzene
(d) p-aminoazobenzene
(e) p-(phenylazo)aniline
(f) benzidine
(g) 2,4-dihydroxy-4'-(N,N-dimethylamino)azobenzene

2. Give the names of the following:

(a) 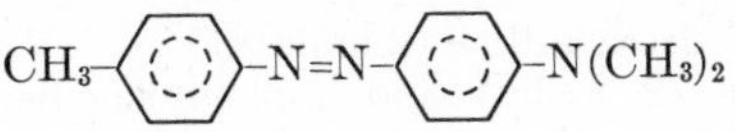 CH_3—⟨ ⟩—N=N—⟨ ⟩—$N(CH_3)_2$

(c) 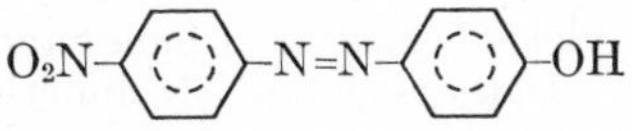 O_2N—⟨ ⟩—N=N—⟨ ⟩—OH

(b) 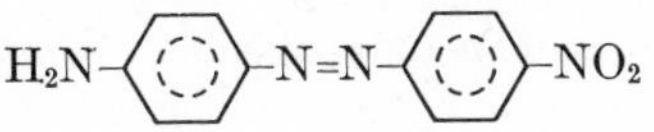 H_2N—⟨ ⟩—N=N—⟨ ⟩—NO_2

(d) 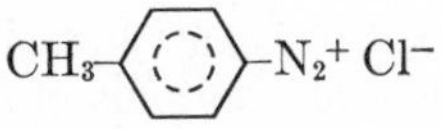 CH_3—⟨ ⟩—N_2^+ Cl$^-$

(e) 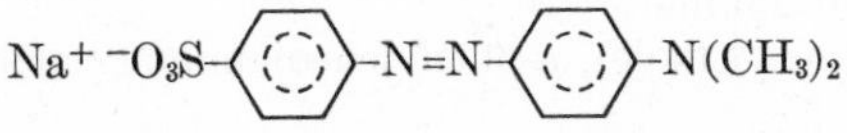 Na^+ ^-O_3S—⟨ ⟩—N=N—⟨ ⟩—$N(CH_3)_2$

3. Give the reagents and any special conditions necessary to convert p-toluene diazonium chloride into:

(a) toluene
(b) p-cresol, p-CH$_3$C$_6$H$_4$OH
(c) p-chlorotoluene
(d) p-bromotoluene

(e) p-iodotoluene
(f) p-fluorotoluene
(g) p-tolunitrile, p-CH$_3$C$_6$H$_4$CN

(h) 4-methyl-4'-(N,N-dimethylamino)azobenzene
(i) 2,4-dihydroxy-4'-methylazobenzene

4. Write equations for the reaction of p-nitrobenzenediazonium sulfate with:

(a) m-phenylenediamine
(b) hot dilute H$_2$SO$_4$
(c) HBr + Cu

(d) p-cresol
(e) KI
(f) CuCl

(g) CuCN
(h) HBF$_4$, then heat
(i) H$_3$PO$_2$

5. Outline all steps in a possible laboratory synthesis from benzene, toluene, and any needed inorganic reagents of:

(a) the six isomeric dibromotoluenes, CH$_3$C$_6$H$_3$Br$_2$. (*Note:* one may be more difficult to make than any of the others.)
(b) the three isomeric chlorobenzoic acids, free of the others
(c) the three isomeric chlorofluorobenzenes
(d) the three isomeric iodophenols

Review the instructions of Problem 17, page 160. Assume that an *ortho,para* mixture of isomeric nitro compounds can be separated by distillation (see Sec. 10.6.)

6. Outline all steps in a possible laboratory synthesis of each of the following compounds from benzene and toluene and any needed aliphatic and inorganic reagents.

(a) p-fluorotoluene
(b) m-fluorotoluene
(c) p-iodobenzoic acid
(d) m-nitrophenol
(e) m-fluorophenol
(f) m-bromoaniline
(g) 3-bromo-4-methylbenzoic acid
(h) 2-bromo-4-methylbenzoic acid
(i) m-ethylphenol

(j) 3,5-dibromoaniline
(k) 3-bromo-4-iodotoluene
(l) 2-amino-4-methylphenol
(m) 2,6-dibromoiodobenzene
(n) 4-iodo-3-nitrotoluene
(o) p-hydroxyphenylacetic acid
(p) 2-bromo-4-chlorotoluene
(q) p,p'-dihydroxybiphenyl
(r) 4,4'-difluorobiphenyl

7. Outline the synthesis from benzene, toluene, and any needed aliphatic and inorganic reagents of:

(a)–(d) the four azo compounds in Problem 2
(e) 2-methyl-4'-hydroxyazobenzene
(f) 2,4-diaminoazobenzene

(g) O$_2$N—⟨ ⟩—N=N—⟨ ⟩N(CH$_2$CH$_2$OH)$_2$
      Cl   H$_3$C

8. Give the structures of the azo compounds A through E, and list the reactants from which each was probably made.

Upon cleavage by SnCl$_2$ or Zn + HCl:

(a) A yields benzidine (1 mole) and 2,4-dihydroxyaniline (2 moles).
(b) B yields p-amino-N,N-dimethylaniline (2 moles) and p-phenylenediamine (1 mole)
(c) C (C$_{12}$H$_9$O$_3$N$_3$) yields p-phenylenediamine and p-aminophenol. (*Caution:* note the molecular formula of C.)
(d) D yields only o-toluidine.
(e) E yields benzidine (1 mole), p-phenylenediamine (2 moles), and p-aminophenol (2 moles).

Chapter twenty-two_____

PHENOLS

22.1 Structure and nomenclature

Phenols are compounds of the general formula ArOH, where Ar is phenyl, substituted phenyl, or one of the other aryl groups we shall study later (e.g., naphthyl, Chapter 31). *Phenols differ from alcohols in having the —OH group attached directly to an aromatic ring.*

Phenols are generally named as derivatives of the simplest member of the family, **phenol.** The methylphenols are given the special name of *cresols.* Occasionally phenols are named as *hydroxy–* compounds.

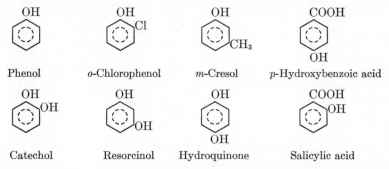

Phenol	*o*-Chlorophenol	*m*-Cresol	*p*-Hydroxybenzoic acid
Catechol	Resorcinol	Hydroquinone	Salicylic acid

Both phenols and alcohols contain the —OH group, and as a result the two families resemble each other to a limited extent. We have already seen, for example, that both alcohols and phenols can be converted into ethers and esters. In most of their properties, however, and in their preparations, the two kinds of compound differ so greatly that they well deserve to be classified as different families.

22.2 Physical properties

The simplest phenols are liquids or low-melting solids; because of hydrogen bonding, they have quite high boiling points. Phenol itself is somewhat soluble in water (9 g per 100 g of water), presumably because of hydrogen bonding with the water; most other phenols are essentially insoluble in water. Unless some group capable of producing color is present, phenols themselves are colorless. However, like aromatic amines they are easily oxidized; unless carefully purified, many phenols are colored by oxidation products.

TABLE 22.1

PHENOLS

Name	M.p., °C	B.p., °C	Solub., g/100 g H_2O at 25°	K_a
Phenol	41	182	9.3	1.1×10^{-10}
o-Cresol	31	191	2.5	.63
m-Cresol	11	201	2.6	.98
p-Cresol	35	202	2.3	.67
o-Fluorophenol	16	152		15
m-Fluorophenol	14	178		5.2
p-Fluorophenol	48	185		1.1
o-Chlorophenol	9	173	2.8	77
m-Chlorophenol	33	214	2.6	16
p-Chlorophenol	43	220	2.7	6.3
o-Bromophenol	5	194		41
m-Bromophenol	33	236		14
p-Bromophenol	64	236	1.4	5.6
o-Iodophenol	43			34
m-Iodophenol	40			13
p-Iodophenol	94			6.3
o-Aminophenol	174		1.7^0	2.0
m-Aminophenol	123		2.6	69
p-Aminophenol	186		1.1^0	
o-Nitrophenol	45	217	0.2	600
m-Nitrophenol	96		1.4	50
p-Nitrophenol	114		1.7	690
2,4-Dinitrophenol	113		0.6	1000000
2,4,6-Trinitrophenol (picric acid)	122		1.4	very large
Catechol	104	246	45	1
Resorcinol	110	281	123	3
Hydroquinone	173	286	8	2

An important point emerges from a comparison of the physical properties of the isomeric nitrophenols (Table 22.2).

TABLE 22.2

PROPERTIES OF THE NITROPHENOLS

	B.p., °C at 70 mm	Solub., g/100 g H_2O	
o-Nitrophenol	100	0.2	Volatile in steam
m-Nitrophenol	194	1.35	Non-volatile in steam
p-Nitrophenol	dec.	1.69	Non-volatile in steam

We notice that o-nitrophenol has a much lower boiling point and much lower solubility in water than its isomers; it is the only one of the three that is readily steam-distillable. How can these differences be accounted for?

Let us consider first the m- and p-isomers. They have very high boiling points because of intermolecular hydrogen bonding:

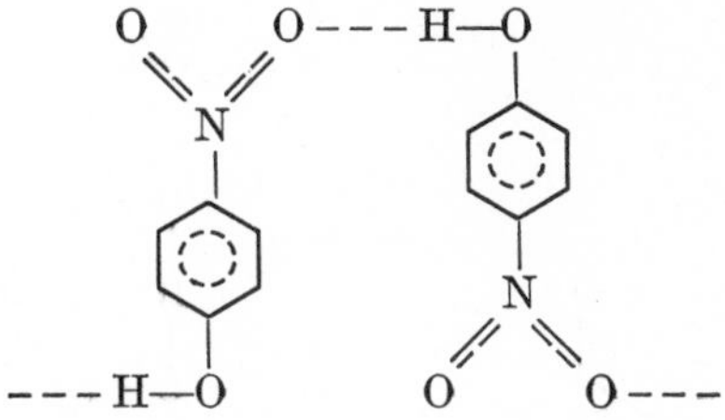

Intermolecular
hydrogen bonding

Their solubility in water is due to hydrogen bonding with water molecules:

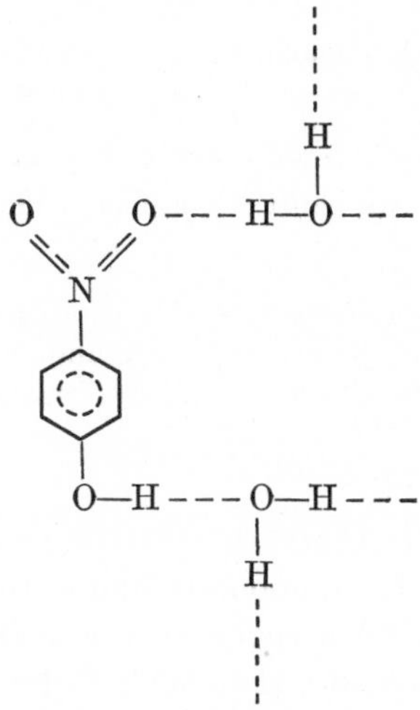

Steam distillation depends upon a substance having an appreciable vapor pressure at the boiling point of water; by lowering the vapor pressure, intermolecular hydrogen bonding inhibits steam distillation of the *m*- and *p*-isomers.

What is the situation for the *o*-isomer? Examination of models shows that the —NO_2 and —OH groups are located exactly right for the formation of a hydrogen bond *within a single molecule.*

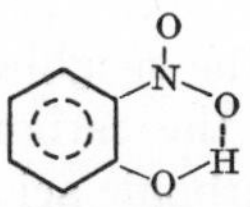

o-Nitrophenol

Intramolecular
hydrogen bonding:
chelation

This **intramolecular hydrogen bonding** takes the place of *inter*molecular hydrogen bonding with other phenol molecules and with water molecules; therefore *o*-nitrophenol does not have the low volatility of an associated liquid, nor does it have the solubility characteristic of a compound that forms hydrogen bonds with water.

The holding of a hydrogen or metal atom between two atoms of a single molecule is called **chelation** (from the Greek, *chele*, claw). Some examples are shown on the next page. Two others, fundamental to plant and animal life, are *chlorophyll* (page 836) and *hemin* (page 876).

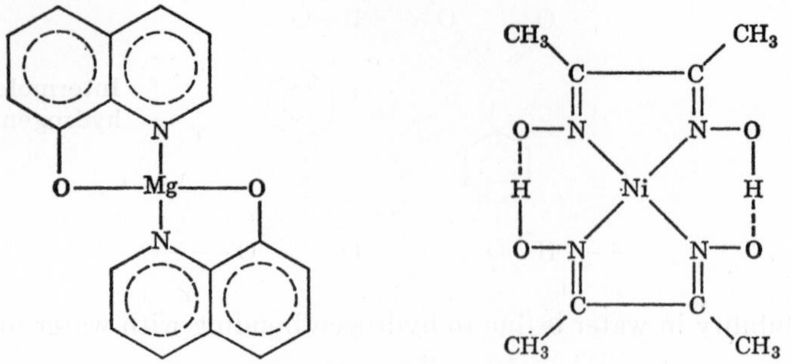

Magnesium 8-hydroxyquinolinate   Nickel dimethylglyoxime
Used in inorganic analysis

Intramolecular hydrogen bonding seems to occur whenever the structure of a compound permits; we shall encounter other examples of its effect on physical properties.

Problem 22.1 In which of the following compounds would you expect intramolecular hydrogen bonding to occur: *o*-nitroaniline, *o*-cresol, *o*-hydroxybenzoic acid (salicylic acid), *o*-hydroxybenzaldehyde (salicylaldehyde), *o*-fluorophenol, *o*-hydroxybenzonitrile.

22.3 Salts of phenols

Phenols are fairly acidic compounds, and in this respect differ markedly from alcohols, which are even more weakly acidic than water. Aqueous hydroxides convert phenols into their salts; aqueous mineral acids convert the salts back into the free phenols. As we might expect, phenols and their salts have opposite solubility properties, the salts being soluble in water and insoluble in organic solvents.

$$\text{ArOH} \underset{\text{H}^+}{\overset{\text{OH}^-}{\rightleftarrows}} \text{ArO}^-$$

A phenol	A phenoxide ion
(acid)	(salt)
Insoluble	*Soluble*
in water	*in water*

Most phenols have K_a's in the neighborhood of 10^{-10}, and are thus considerably weaker acids than the carboxylic acids (K_a's about 10^{-5}). Most phenols are weaker than carbonic acid, and hence, unlike carboxylic acids, do not dissolve in aqueous bicarbonate solutions. Indeed, phenols are conveniently liberated from their salts by the action of carbonic acid.

$$\text{CO}_2 + \text{H}_2\text{O} \rightleftarrows \text{H}_2\text{CO}_3 + \text{ArO}^-\text{Na}^+ \longrightarrow \text{ArOH} + \text{Na}^+\text{HCO}_3^-$$

Stronger acid	Weaker acid
Soluble in water	*Insoluble in water*

The acid strength of phenols and the solubility of their salts in water are useful both in analysis and in separations. A water-insoluble substance that dissolves in aqueous hydroxide but not in aqueous bicarbonate must be more acidic than water, but less acidic than a carboxylic acid; most compounds in this range of acidity are phenols. A phenol can be separated from non-acidic compounds by means of its solubility in base; it can be separated from carboxylic acids by means of its insolubility in bicarbonate.

Problem 22.2 Outline the separation by chemical methods of a mixture of *p*-cresol, *p*-toluic acid, *p*-toluidine, and *p*-nitrotoluene. Describe exactly what you would *do* and *see*.

22.4 Industrial source

Most phenols are made industrially by the same methods that are used in the laboratory; these are described in Sec. 22.6. There are, however, special ways of obtaining certain of these compounds on a commercial scale, including the most important one, phenol. In quantity produced, phenol ranks near the top of the list of synthetic aromatic compounds. Its principal use is in the manufacture of the phenol-formaldehyde polymers (Sec. 22.21).

A certain amount of phenol, as well as the cresols, is obtained from coal tar (Sec. 9.4). Most of it (probably over 90%) is synthesized. One of the synthetic processes used is the fusion of sodium benzenesulfonate with alkali (Sec. 22.6); another is the Dow process, in which chlorobenzene is allowed to react with aqueous sodium hydroxide at a temperature of about 360°. Like the synthesis of aniline from chlorobenzene (Sec. 19.7), this second reaction involves nucleophilic substitution of a kind that is not generally feasible in the laboratory (Sec. 14.6). (Another, increasingly

Chlorobenzene $\xrightarrow[\text{4500 lb/in}^2]{\text{NaOH, 360°}}$ Sodium phenoxide $\xrightarrow{\text{HCl}}$ Phenol

important process for making phenol is discussed in the following section.)

Certain phenols and their ethers are isolated from the *essential oils* of various plants (so called because they contain the *essence* — odor or flavor — of the plants). A few of these are:

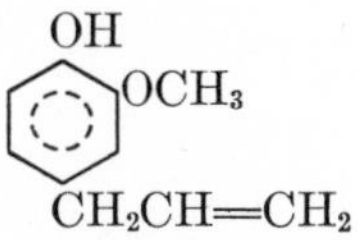

OH
OCH$_3$
CH$_2$CH=CH$_2$
Eugenol
Oil of cloves

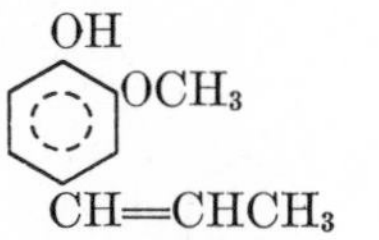

OH
OCH$_3$
CH=CHCH$_3$
Isoeugenol
Oil of nutmeg

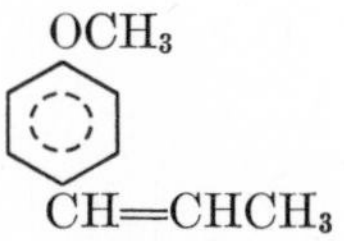

OCH$_3$
CH=CHCH$_3$
Anethole
Oil of aniseed

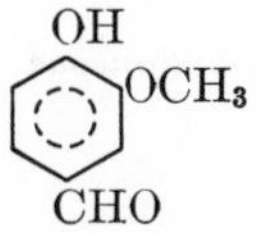

OH
OCH$_3$
CHO
Vanillin
Vanilla bean

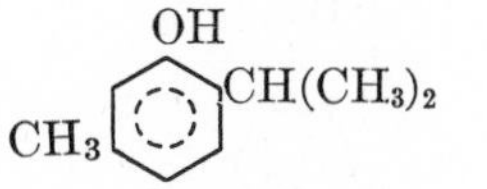

OH
CH(CH$_3$)$_2$
CH$_3$
Thymol
Oil of thyme and mint

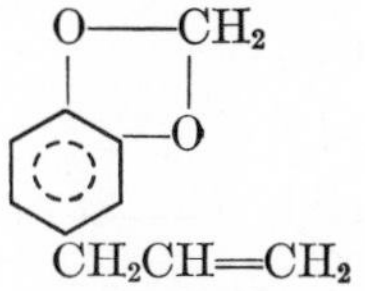

O—CH$_2$
—O
CH$_2$CH=CH$_2$
Safrole
Oil of sassafras

22.5 Phenol from cumene hydroperoxide. Migration to electron-deficient oxygen

Recently a process has been developed for the synthesis of phenol from *cumene*, isopropylbenzene; eventually, this process may become the principal source of phenol. Cumene is converted by air oxidation into cumene hydroperoxide, which is converted by aqueous acid into phenol and acetone.

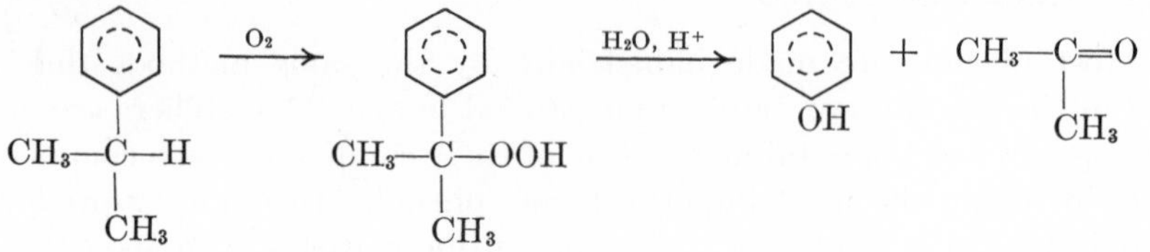

| Cumene | Cumene hydroperoxide | Phenol | Acetone |

Problem 22.3 Outline a synthesis of cumene from cheap, readily available hydrocarbons.

The conversion of cumene hydroperoxide into phenol clearly involves a rearrangement, since the phenyl group is joined to carbon in the peroxide and to oxygen in the phenol. We have encountered 1,2-shifts to electron-deficient carbon atoms (Sec. 9.8) and to electron-deficient nitrogen atoms (Sec. 19.13); study has shown that the rearrangement of cumene hydroperoxide involves a 1,2-shift to an electron-deficient *oxygen* atom. It is believed that the following steps are involved:

(1)

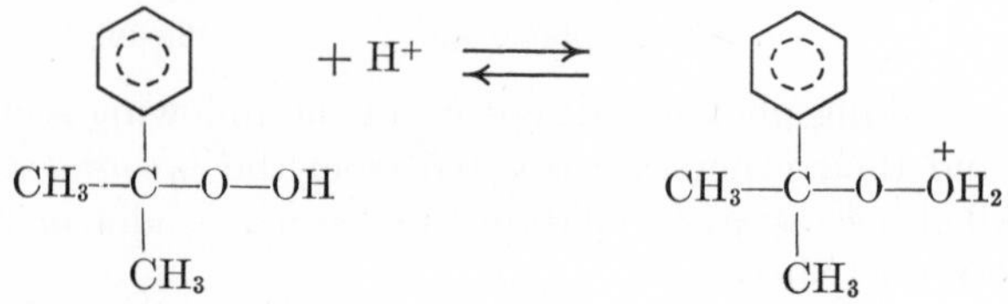

Cumene hydroperoxide
I

(2)

(3)

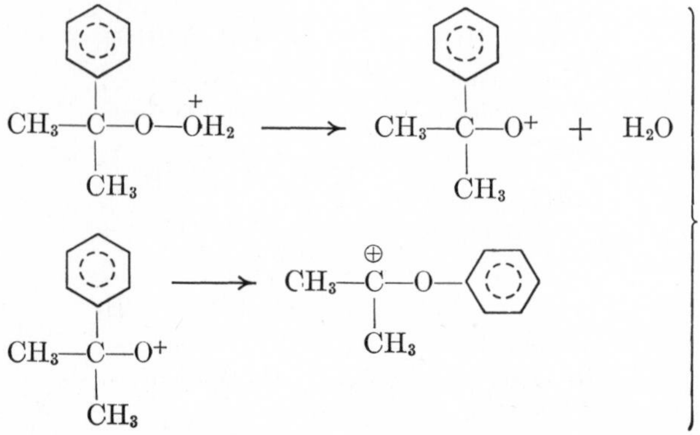

Simultaneous

$$\text{(4)} \quad CH_3\text{-}\overset{\oplus}{\underset{\underset{CH_3}{|}}{C}}\text{-}O\text{-}\langle\bigcirc\rangle + H_2O \longrightarrow CH_3\text{-}\overset{\overset{+OH_2}{|}}{\underset{\underset{CH_3}{|}}{C}}\text{-}O\text{-}\langle\bigcirc\rangle \rightleftharpoons CH_3\text{-}\overset{\overset{OH}{|}}{\underset{\underset{CH_3}{|}}{C}}\text{-}O\text{-}\langle\bigcirc\rangle + H^+$$

II

$$\text{(5)} \quad CH_3\text{-}\overset{\overset{OH}{|}}{\underset{\underset{CH_3}{|}}{C}}\text{-}O\langle\bigcirc\rangle \xrightarrow{H^+} CH_3\text{-}\overset{\overset{O}{\diagup\!\diagdown}}{\underset{\underset{CH_3}{|}}{C}} + HO\langle\bigcirc\rangle$$

II   Acetone   Phenol

Acid converts (step 1) the peroxide I into the protonated peroxide, which loses (step 2) a molecule of water to form an intermediate in which oxygen bears only six electrons. A 1,2-shift of the phenyl group from carbon to electron-deficient oxygen yields (step 3) the carbonium ion, which reacts with water to yield (step 4) the hydroxy compound II. Compound II is a hemi-acetal (Sec. 23.14) which breaks down (step 5) to give phenol and acetone. It is believed that steps (2) and (3) are simultaneous, the migrating phenyl group helping to push out the molecule of water. As before, we may view the rearrangement as a special instance of electrophilic attack on the aromatic ring, in this case by electron-deficient oxygen.

Except for step (5), the reaction involves chemistry with which we are already quite familiar: protonation of a hydroxy compound with subsequent ionization to leave an electron-deficient particle; a 1,2-shift to an electron-deficient atom; reaction of a carbonium ion with water to yield a hydroxy compound. In studying organic chemistry we encounter many new things; but much of what seems new is found to fit into old familiar patterns of behavior.

Problem 22.4 When p-nitrotriphenylmethyl hydroperoxide (III) is treated with mineral acids, it yields exclusively phenol and p-nitrobenzophenone (IV). (a) Outline all steps in the mechanism of this reaction.

$$O_2N\langle\bigcirc\rangle\text{-}\overset{\overset{C_6H_5}{|}}{\underset{\underset{C_6H_5}{|}}{C}}\text{-}O\text{-}OH \qquad\qquad O_2N\langle\bigcirc\rangle\text{-}\overset{}{\underset{\underset{O}{\|}}{C}}\text{-}C_6H_5$$

III   IV

(b) What can you say about the relative migrating tendencies of the phenyl and the p-nitrophenyl groups? How do you account for this?

22.6 Preparation

In the laboratory, phenols are generally prepared by one of the two methods outlined below.

PREPARATION OF PHENOLS

1. Hydrolysis of diazonium salts. Discussed in Sec. 21.7.

$$ArN_2^+ + H_2O \longrightarrow ArOH + H^+ + N_2$$

Example:

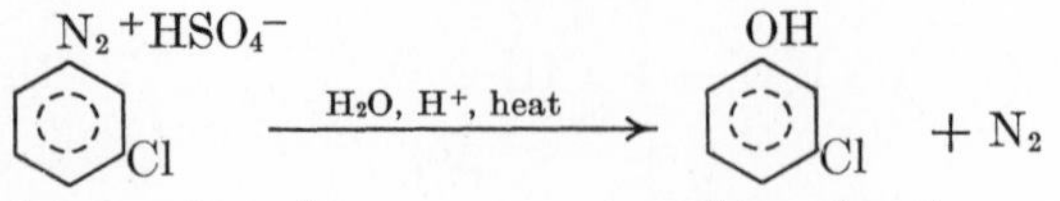

$$N_2{}^+HSO_4{}^- \xrightarrow[\text{H}_2\text{O, H}^+\text{, heat}]{} \text{OH} + N_2$$

m-Chlorobenzenediazonium
hydrogen sulfate   *m*-Chlorophenol

2. Alkali fusion of sulfonates

$$\text{ArSO}_3\text{Na} + \text{NaOH} \xrightarrow{\text{strong heat}} \text{Na}_2\text{SO}_3 + \text{ArONa} \xrightarrow{\text{H}^+} \text{ArOH}$$

Examples:

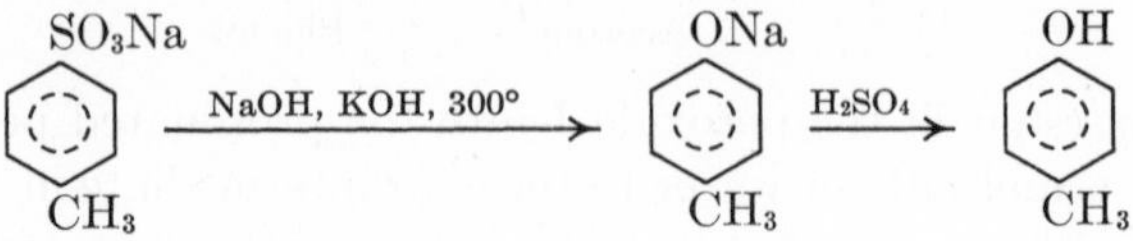

Sodium *p*-toluenesulfonate   *p*-Cresol

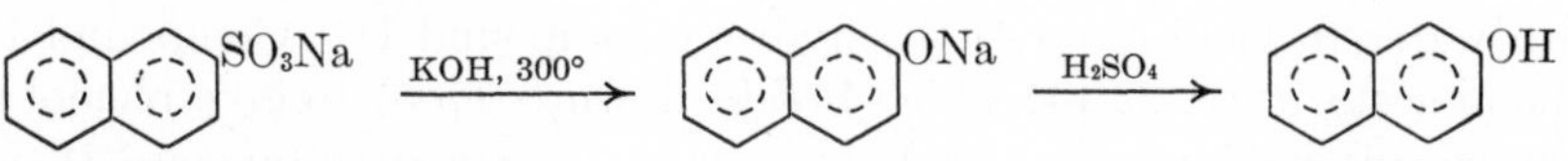

Sodium 2-naphthalenesulfonate   2-Naphthol
Sodium β-naphthalenesulfonate   β-Naphthol

Phenols are most often prepared from diazonium salts because of the mild conditions under which this process is carried out. The action of alkali at high temperatures generally brings about undesired reactions — substitution or oxidation, for example — if the sulfonic acid molecule contains —COOH, —Cl, —NO₂, or almost any other group.

Of limited use is the hydrolysis of aryl halides containing strongly electron-withdrawing groups *ortho* and *para* to the halogen (Sec. 14.10); 2,4-dinitrophenol and 2,4,6-trinitrophenol (*picric acid*) are produced in this way on a large scale:

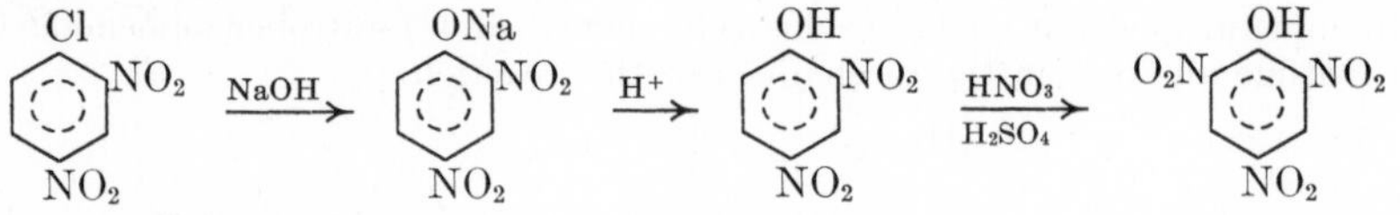

2,4-Dinitrochlorobenzene   2,4-Dinitrophenol
Sodium 2,4-dinitrophenoxide   2,4,6-Trinitrophenol
Picric acid

Problem 22.5 2,4,6-Trinitrochlorobenzene is more easily hydrolyzed than 2,4-dinitrochlorobenzene. What is the advantage, then, of the synthesis of picric acid just outlined over one involving the preparation and hydrolysis of 2,4,6-trinitrochlorobenzene?

22.7 Reactions

Aside from acidity, the most striking chemical property of a phenol is the extremely high reactivity of its ring toward electrophilic substitution. Even in ring substitution, acidity plays an important part; ionization of a phenol yields the —O⁻ group, which, because of its full-fledged negative charge, is even more strongly electron-releasing than the —OH group.

Phenols undergo not only those electrophilic substitution reactions that are typical of most aromatic compounds, but also many others that are possible only because of the unusual reactivity of the ring. We shall have time to take up only a few of these reactions.

REACTIONS OF PHENOLS

1. Acidity. Salt formation

$$ArOH + H_2O \rightleftharpoons ArO^- + H_3O^+$$

Example:

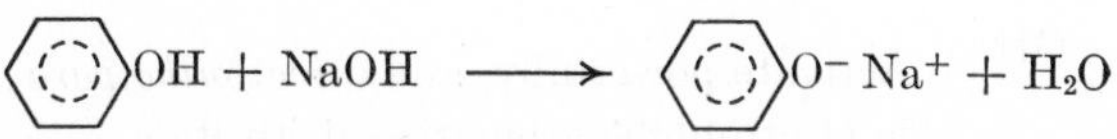

$OH + NaOH \longrightarrow$ $O^- Na^+ + H_2O$

2. Ether formation. Williamson synthesis. Discussed in Sec. 15.7.

$$ArO^- + RX \longrightarrow ArOR + X^-$$

Examples:

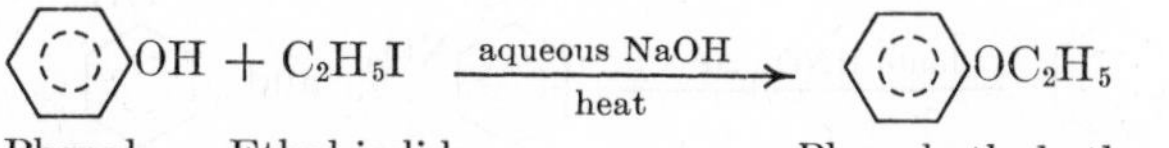

$OH + C_2H_5I \xrightarrow[\text{heat}]{\text{aqueous NaOH}}$ OC_2H_5

Phenol　　Ethyl iodide　　　　　　　Phenyl ethyl ether
　　　　　　　　　　　　　　　　　　　(Phenetole)

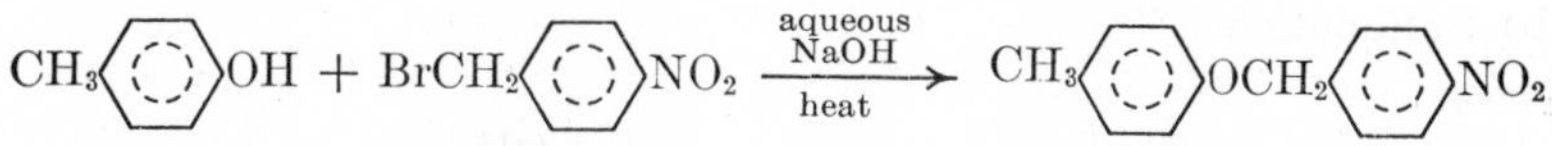

$CH_3$$OH + BrCH_2$$NO_2 \xrightarrow[\text{heat}]{\text{aqueous NaOH}} CH_3$$OCH_2$$NO_2$

p-Cresol　　　*p*-Nitrobenzyl　　　　　　*p*-Tolyl *p*-nitrobenzyl ether
　　　　　　　　bromide

$+ (CH_3)_2SO_4 \xrightarrow[\text{heat}]{\text{aqueous NaOH}}$ $+ CH_3SO_4Na$

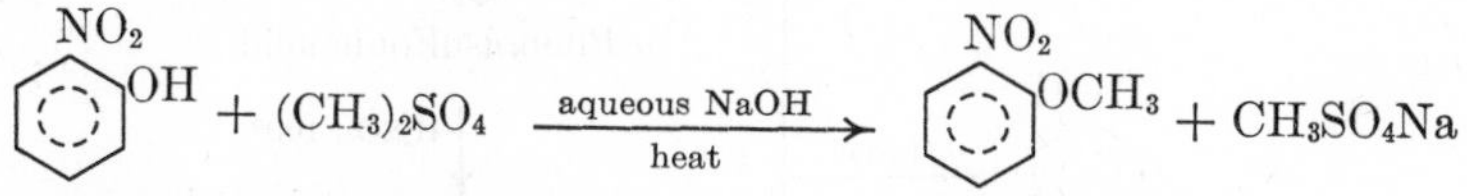

o-Nitrophenol　Methyl sulfate　　　　　　*o*-Nitroanisole
　　　　　　　　　　　　　　　　　(*o*-Nitrophenyl methyl ether)

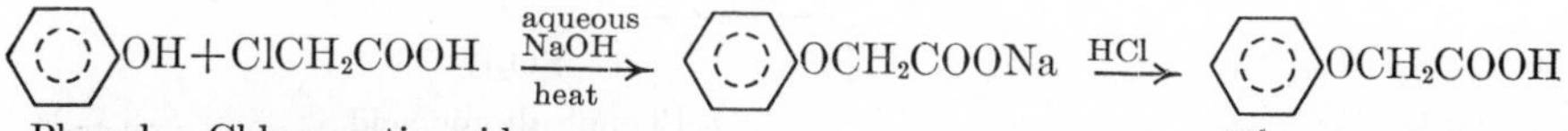

$OH + ClCH_2COOH \xrightarrow[\text{heat}]{\substack{\text{aqueous} \\ \text{NaOH}}}$ $OCH_2COONa \xrightarrow{HCl}$ OCH_2COOH

Phenol　　Chloroacetic acid　　　　　　　　　　　　　　　　　Phenoxyacetic acid

3. Ester formation

$$ArOH \begin{cases} \xrightarrow{RCOCl} RCOOAr \\ \xrightarrow{Ar'SO_2Cl} Ar'SO_2OAr \end{cases}$$

Examples:

$OH +$ $COCl \xrightarrow{NaOH}$ $O-C$

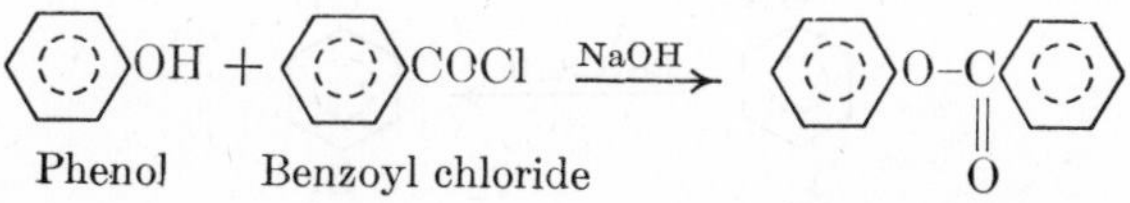

　　Phenol　　　Benzoyl chloride　　　　　　　　　　　O

Phenyl benzoate

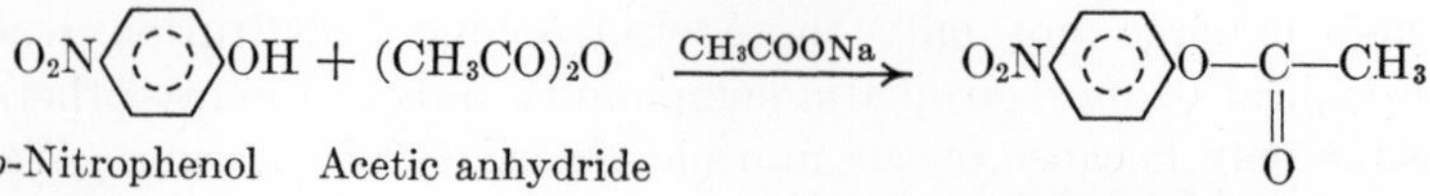

O2N OH + (CH3CO)2O
CH3COONa
O2N O—C—CH3
O

p-Nitrophenol   Acetic anhydride   p-Nitrophenyl acetate

Br
OH
+ CH3 SO2Cl
pyridine
CH3 SO2O
Br

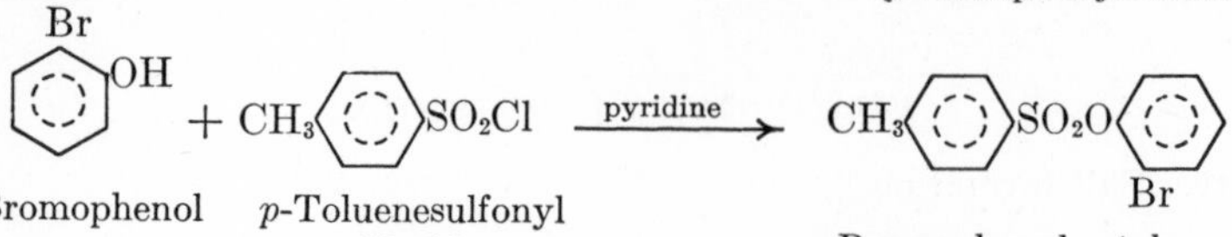

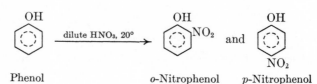

o-Bromophenol   p-Toluenesulfonyl chloride   o-Bromophenyl p-toluenesulfonate

4. Ring substitution

—OH, —O⁻ } Activate powerfully, and direct *ortho,para* in electrophilic aromatic substitution.

—OR: Less powerful activator than —OH.

(a) Nitration

Example:

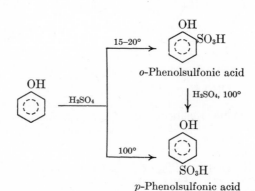

OH
dilute HNO3, 20°
OH
NO2
and
OH
NO2

Phenol   o-Nitrophenol   p-Nitrophenol

(b) Sulfonation

Example:

OH
SO3H
15–20°
o-Phenolsulfonic acid
H2SO4, 100°
OH
H2SO4
OH
100°
SO3H

p-Phenolsulfonic acid

(c) Halogenation

Examples:

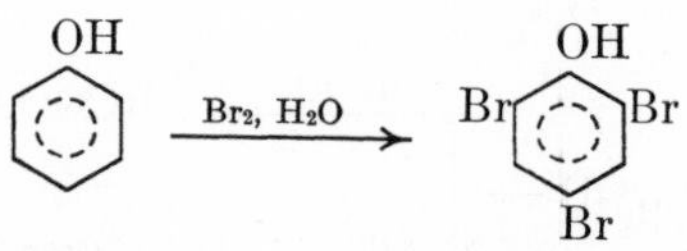

OH
Br2, H2O
OH
Br
Br
Br

Phenol   2,4,6-Tribromophenol

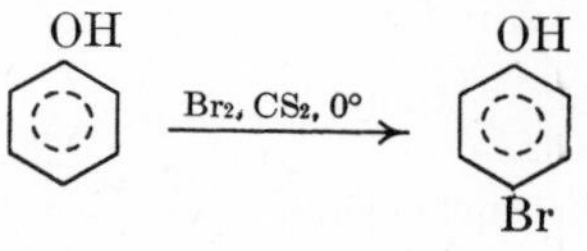

OH
Br2, CS2, 0°
OH
Br

Phenol   p-Bromophenol

(d) **Friedel-Crafts alkylation**

Example:

OH
Phenol
CH3
CH3—C—CH3
Cl
tert-Butyl chloride
HF
OH
CH3—C—CH3
CH3
p-tert-Butylphenol

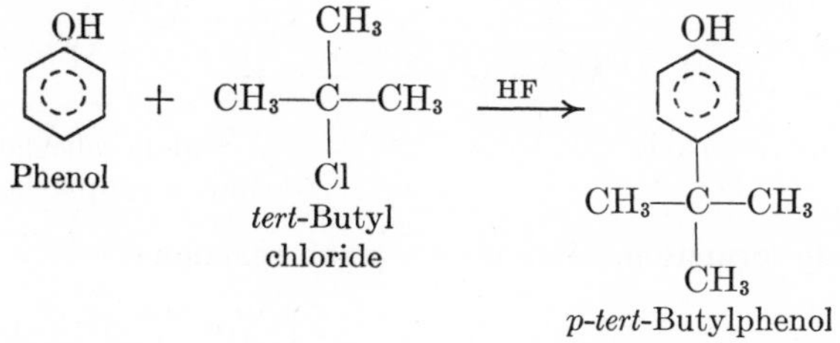

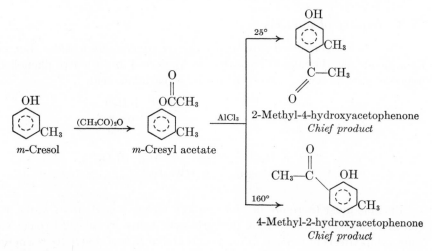

(e) **Friedel-Crafts acylation. Fries rearrangement**

Examples:

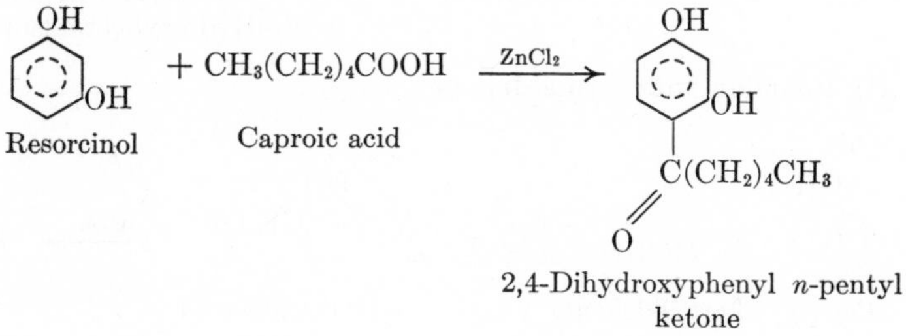

OH
OH
Resorcinol
+ CH3(CH2)4COOH
Caproic acid
ZnCl2
OH
OH
C(CH2)4CH3
O
2,4-Dihydroxyphenyl n-pentyl ketone

OH
CH3
m-Cresol
(CH3CO)2O
O
OCCH3
CH3
m-Cresyl acetate
AlCl3
25°
OH
CH3
C—CH3
O
2-Methyl-4-hydroxyacetophenone
Chief product
160°
O
CH3—C
OH
CH3
4-Methyl-2-hydroxyacetophenone
Chief product

(f) **Nitrosation**

Example:

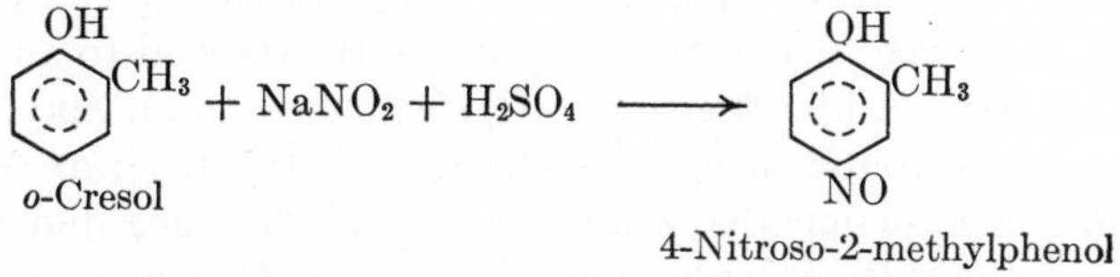

OH
CH3
+ NaNO2 + H2SO4
o-Cresol
OH
CH3
NO
4-Nitroso-2-methylphenol

(g) **Coupling with diazonium salts.** Discussed in Sec. 21.10.

(h) Carbonation. Kolbe reaction

Example:

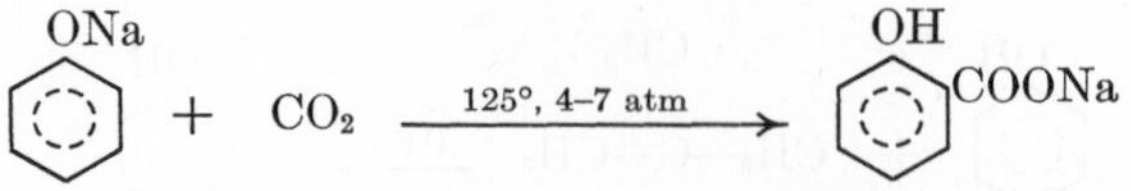

Sodium phenoxide   Sodium salicylate
(Sodium *o*-hydroxybenzoate)

ONa + CO$_2$ $\xrightarrow{125°, 4-7 \text{ atm}}$ (OH)(COONa)

(i) Aldehyde formation. Reimer-Tiemann reaction

Example:

OH + CHCl$_3$ $\xrightarrow{\text{aqueous NaOH}}$ (OH)(CHO)

Phenol   Chloroform   Salicylaldehyde
(*o*-Hydroxybenzaldehyde)

(j) Reaction with formaldehyde

Example:

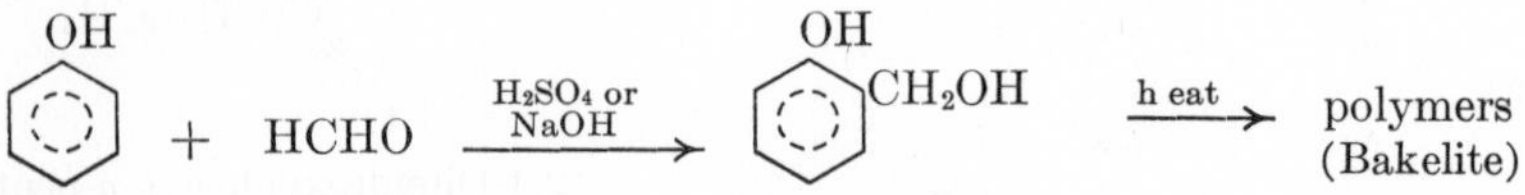

OH + HCHO $\xrightarrow[\text{NaOH}]{\text{H}_2\text{SO}_4 \text{ or}}$ (OH)(CH$_2$OH) $\xrightarrow{\text{heat}}$ polymers (Bakelite)

Phenol   Formaldehyde   *o*-Hydroxybenzyl
alcohol

22.8 Acidity of phenols

Phenols are converted into their salts by aqueous hydroxides, but not by aqueous bicarbonates. The salts are converted into the free phenols by aqueous mineral acids, carboxylic acids, or carbonic acid.

$$\text{ArOH} + \text{OH}^- \longrightarrow \text{ArO}^- + \text{H}_2\text{O}$$

Stronger   Weaker
acid   acid

$$\text{ArO}^- + \text{H}_2\text{CO}_3 \longrightarrow \text{ArOH} + \text{HCO}_3^-$$

Stronger   Weaker
acid   acid

Phenols must therefore be considerably stronger acids than water, but considerably weaker acids than the carboxylic acids. Table 22.1 (page 586) shows that this is indeed so: most phenols have K_a's of about 10^{-10} whereas carboxylic acids have K_a's of about 10^{-5}.

Although weaker than carboxylic acids, phenols are tremendously more acidic than alcohols, which have K_a's in the neighborhood of 10^{-16} to 10^{-18}. How does it happen that an —OH attached to an aromatic ring is so much more acidic than an —OH attached to an alkyl group? The answer is to be found in an examination of the structures involved. As usual we shall assume that differences in acidity are due chiefly to differences in the ΔH of ionization, that is, to differences in stabilities of reactants and products (Sec. 16.12).

Let us examine the structures of reactants and products in the ionization of an alcohol and of phenol. We see that the alcohol and the alkoxide ion are each represented satisfactorily by a single structure.

$$R\text{—}\overset{..}{\underset{..}{O}}{:}H \rightleftharpoons H^+ + R\text{—}\overset{..}{\underset{..}{O}}{:}^-$$

Alcohol   Alkoxide ion

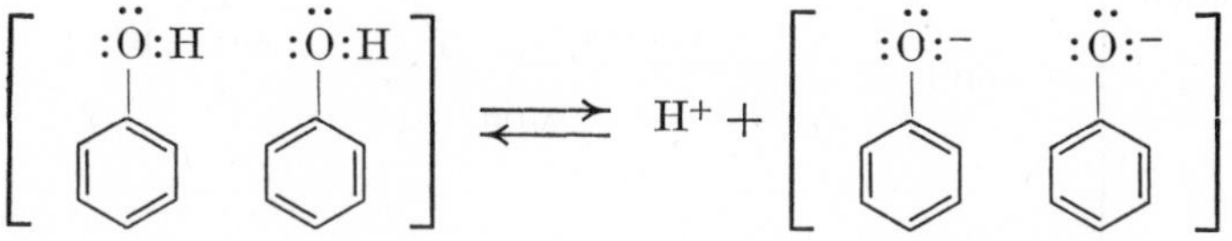

I   II   III   IV

Phenol   Phenoxide ion

Phenol and the phenoxide ion contain a benzene ring and therefore must be hybrids of the Kekulé structures I and II, and III and IV. This resonance presumably stabilizes both molecule and ion to the same extent. It lowers the energy content of each by the same number of kcal/mole, and hence does not affect the *difference* in their energy contents, that is, does not affect the ΔH of ionization. If there were no other factors involved, then, we might expect the acidity of a phenol to be about the same as the acidity of an alcohol.

However, there are additional structures to be considered. Being basic, oxygen can share more than a pair of electrons with the ring; this is indicated by contribution from structures V–VII for phenol, and VIII–X for the phenoxide ion. Now, are these two sets of structures equally im-

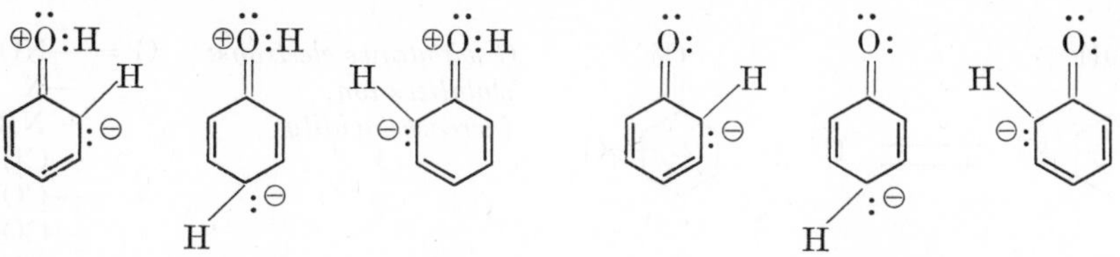

V   VI   VII   VIII   IX   X

Phenol   Phenoxide ion

portant? Structures V–VII for phenol carry both positive and negative charges; structures VIII–X for phenoxide ion carry only a negative charge. Since energy must be supplied to separate opposite charges, the structures for the phenol should contain more energy and hence be less stable than the structures for phenoxide ion. (We have already encountered the effect of *separation of charge* on stability in Sec. 16.12.) The net effect of resonance is therefore to stabilize the phenoxide ion to a greater extent than the phenol, and thus to make the ΔH of ionization less than for ionization of an alcohol (see Figure 22.1 on the next page).

We have seen (Sec. 20.3) that aromatic amines are weaker bases than aliphatic amines, since resonance stabilizes the free amine to a greater extent than it does the ion. Here we have exactly the opposite situation, phenols being stronger acids than their aliphatic counterparts, the alcohols, because resonance stabilizes the ion to a greater extent than it does the free phenol.

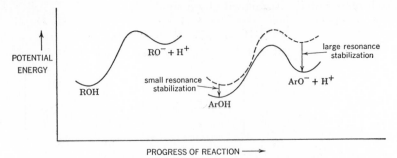

FIGURE 22.1. Molecular structure and position of equilibrium. Phenol yields resonance-stabilized anion; is stronger acid than alcohol.

22.9 Effect of substituents on acidity

In Table 22.1 (page 586) we see that electron-attracting substituents like —X or —NO_2 increase the acidity of phenols, and electron-releasing substituents like —CH_3 decrease acidity. Thus substituents affect acidity of phenols in the same way that they affect acidity of carboxylic acids (Sec. 16.14); it is, of course, opposite to the way these groups affect basicity of amines (Sec. 20.4). Electron-attracting substituents tend to disperse the negative charge of the phenoxide ion, whereas electron-releasing substituents tend to intensify the charge:

G withdraws electrons: stabilizes ion, increases acidity

$G =$ —NO_2
—X
—NR_3^+
—CHO
—COR
—COOR
—CN

G releases electrons: destabilizes ion, decreases acidity

$G =$ —CH_3
—C_2H_5

Problem 22.6 How do you account for the fact that, unlike most phenols, 2,4-dinitrophenol and 2,4,6-trinitrophenol are soluble in aqueous sodium bicarbonate?

We can see that a group attached to an aromatic ring affects *position of equilibrium* in reversible reactions in the same way that it affects *rate* in irreversible reactions. An electron-releasing group favors reactions in which the ring becomes more positive, as in electrophilic substitution or in the conversion of an amine into its salt. An electron-withdrawing group favors reactions in which the ring becomes more negative, as in nucleophilic substitution or in the conversion of a phenol or an acid into its salt.

22.10   Formation of ethers.   Williamson synthesis

As already discussed (Sec. 15.7), phenols are converted into ethers by reaction in alkaline solution with alkyl halides; methyl ethers can also be prepared by reaction with methyl sulfate.   In alkaline solutions a phenol exists as the phenoxide ion which, acting as a nucleophilic reagent, attacks the halide (or the sulfate) and displaces halide ion (or sulfate ion).

$$\text{ArOH} \xrightarrow{\ \text{OH}^-\ } \text{ArO}^- \ \Bigg[\begin{array}{l} \xrightarrow{\ \text{RX}\ } \ \text{Ar—O—R} + \text{X}^- \\ \xrightarrow{\ \text{(CH}_3)_2\text{SO}_4\ } \ \text{Ar—O—CH}_3 + \text{CH}_3\text{OSO}_3{}^- \end{array}$$

Certain ethers can be prepared by the reaction of unusually active aryl halides with sodium alkoxides.   For example:

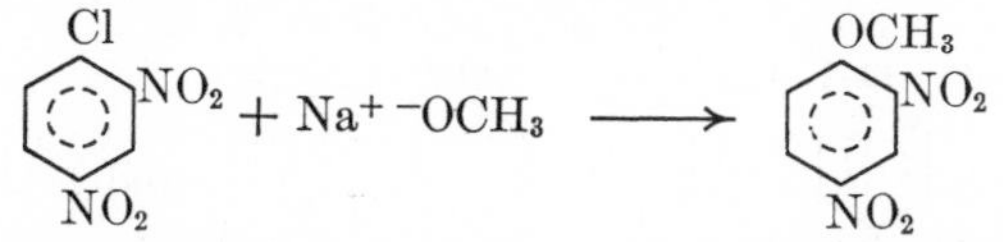

2,4-Dinitrochlorobenzene	2,4-Dinitroanisole
	(2,4-Dinitrophenyl methyl ether)

While alkoxy groups are activating and *ortho,para*-directing in electrophilic aromatic substitution, they are considerably less so than the —OH group.   As a result, ethers do not generally undergo those reactions (Secs. 22.17–22.21) which require the especially high reactivity of phenols: coupling, Kolbe reaction, Reimer-Tiemann reaction, etc.   This difference in reactivity is probably due to the fact that, unlike a phenol, an ether cannot ionize to form the extremely reactive phenoxide ion.

As a consequence of the lower reactivity of the ring, an aromatic ether is less sensitive to oxidation than a phenol.   For example:

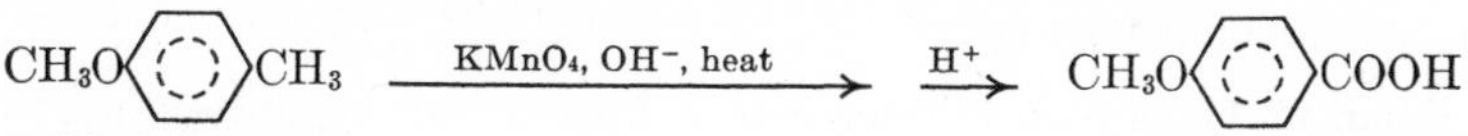

p-Methylanisole	Anisic acid

We have already discussed the cleavage of ethers by acids (Sec. 15.10). Cleavage of methyl aryl ethers by concentrated hydriodic acid is the basis of an important analytical procedure (the *Zeisel procedure*, Sec. 15.20).

Problem 22.7   2,4-Dichlorophenoxyacetic acid is the important weed-killer known as 2,4-D.   Outline the synthesis of this compound starting from benzene or toluene and acetic acid.

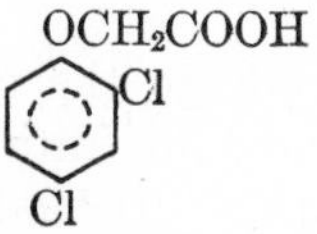

2,4-Dichlorophenoxyacetic acid
(2,4-D)

Problem 22.8   The *n*-propyl ether of 2-amino-4-nitrophenol is one of the sweetest compounds ever prepared, being about 5000 times as sweet as the common sugar sucrose.   It can be made from the dinitro compound by reduction with ammonium bisulfide.   Outline the synthesis of this material starting from benzene or toluene and any aliphatic reagents.

22.11   Ester formation.   Fries rearrangement

Phenols are usually converted into their esters by the action of acid chlorides or anhydrides as discussed in Sec. 17.7 and Sec. 18.8.

Problem 22.9   Predict the products of the reaction between phenyl benzoate and one mole of bromine in the presence of iron.

When esters of phenols are heated with aluminum chloride, the acyl group migrates from the phenolic oxygen to an *ortho* or *para* position of the ring, thus yielding a ketone.   This reaction, called the *Fries rearrangement*, is often used instead of direct acylation for the synthesis of phenolic ketones.   For example:

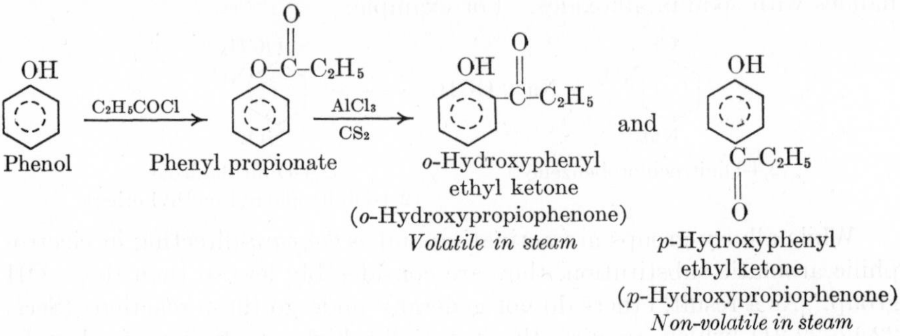

Although the mechanism is not well understood, the rearrangement may involve separation of an acylium ion, RCO^+, which then attacks the ring as in ordinary Friedel-Crafts acylation.

Problem 22.10   A mixture of *o*- and *p*-isomers obtained by the Fries rearrangement can often be separated by steam distillation, only the *o*-isomer distilling. How do you account for this?

Problem 22.11   4-*n*-Hexylresorcinol is used in certain antiseptics.   Outline its preparation starting with resorcinol and any aliphatic reagents.

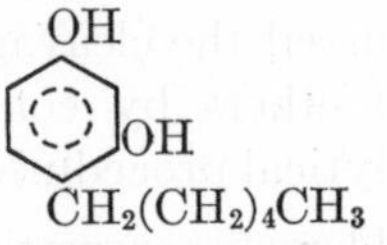

4-*n*-Hexylresorcinol

22.12   Ring substitution

Like amines, phenols undergo the ordinary electrophilic substitution reactions so readily that special precautions must often be taken to prevent polysubstitution and oxidation.   In addition, phenols undergo a number of other reactions that also involve electrophilic substitution, and that are possible only because of the especially high reactivity of the ring.

22.13   Nitration

Phenol is converted by concentrated nitric acid into 2,4,6-trinitrophenol (*picric acid*).   The nitration is accompanied by considerable oxidation.

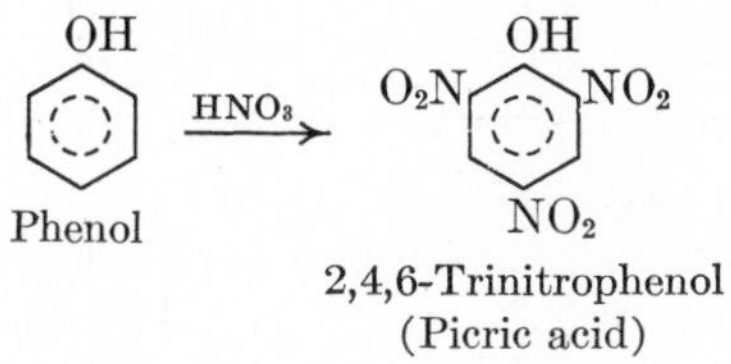

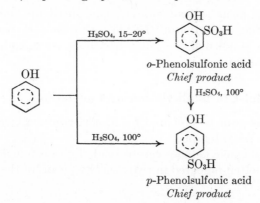

OH

Phenol

HNO₃ →

OH

O₂N$\quad$NO₂

NO₂

2,4,6-Trinitrophenol
(Picric acid)

To obtain mononitrophenols it is necessary to use dilute nitric acid at a low temperature; even then the yield is poor.

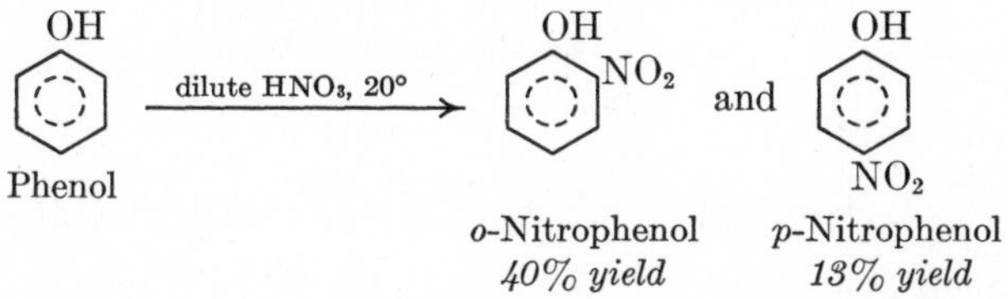

OH

Phenol

dilute HNO₃, 20° →

OH $\quad$ NO₂

o-Nitrophenol
40% yield

and

OH

NO₂

p-Nitrophenol
13% yield

The isomeric products are readily separated by steam distillation, since, as we have seen, the o-nitrophenol is more volatile than its isomer.

Problem 22.12 Picric acid can be prepared by treatment of 2,4-phenoldisulfonic acid with nitric acid. (a) Upon what property of sulfonic acids does this depend? (b) What advantage does this method of synthesis have over the direct nitration of phenol?

22.14 Sulfonation

Sulfonation of phenol occurs readily, to yield chiefly the o-isomer or chiefly the p-isomer, depending upon the temperature.

OH

H₂SO₄, 15–20° →

OH $\quad$ SO₃H

o-Phenolsulfonic acid
Chief product

H₂SO₄, 100°

OH

SO₃H

p-Phenolsulfonic acid
Chief product

H₂SO₄, 100° →

Problem 22.13 o-Phenolsulfonic acid is converted into the p-isomer by sulfuric acid at 100°. How do you account for the effect of temperature upon the orientation in the sulfonation of phenol? (*Hint:* see Sec. 6.17 and Sec. 9.14.)

22.15 Halogenation

Because of the high reactivity of phenols, treatment with aqueous solutions of bromine results in replacement of every hydrogen *ortho* or *para* to the —OH group, and may even cause displacement of certain other groups. For example:

Phenol + 3Br₂(aq) → 2,4,6-Tribromophenol + 3HBr

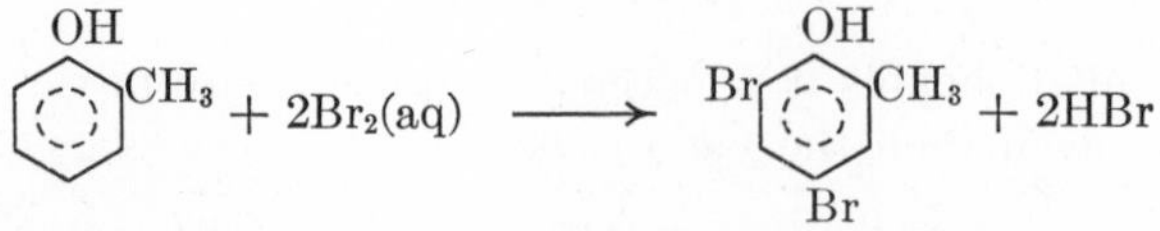

o-Cresol + 2Br₂(aq) → 4,6-Dibromo-2-methylphenol + 2HBr

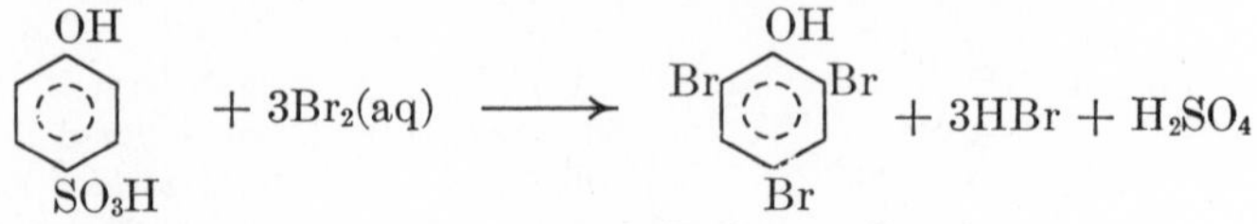

p-Phenolsulfonic acid + 3Br₂(aq) → 2,4,6-Tribromophenol + 3HBr + H₂SO₄

If halogenation is carried out in a solvent of low polarity, such as chloroform, carbon tetrachloride, or carbon disulfide, reaction can be limited to monohalogenation. For example:

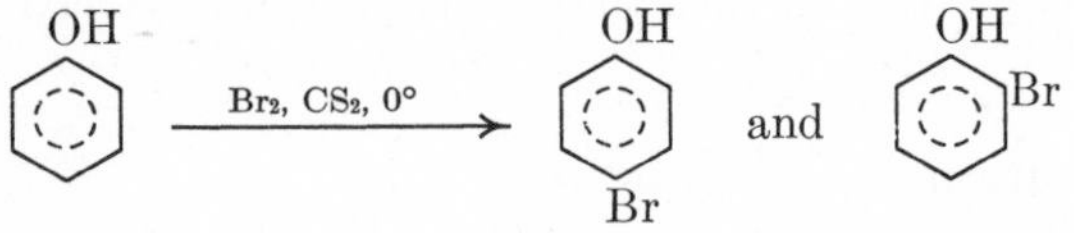

Phenol → (Br₂, CS₂, 0°) p-Bromophenol *Chief product* and o-Bromophenol

The highly polar solvent, water, may speed up halogenation either (a) by promoting ionization of the phenol to the very reactive phenoxide ion, or (b) by stabilizing the polar transition state leading to the intermediate carbonium ion.

22.16 Friedel-Crafts alkylation and acylation

Alkylphenols can be prepared by Friedel-Crafts alkylation of phenols, but the yields are often poor.

Although phenolic ketones can be made by direct acylation of phenols, they are more often prepared in two steps by means of the Fries rearrangement (Sec. 22.11).

22.17 Nitrosation

Nitrous acid converts phenols into nitrosophenols:

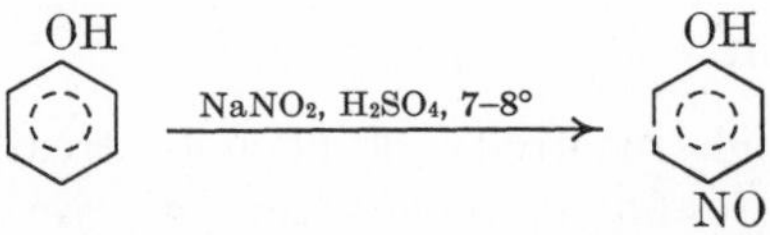

Phenol → (NaNO₂, H₂SO₄, 7–8°) p-Nitrosophenol *80% yield*

Phenols are one of the few classes of compounds reactive enough to undergo attack by the weakly electrophilic nitrosonium ion, $^+$NO.

Problem 22.14   The —NO group is readily oxidized to the —NO$_2$ group by nitric acid. Suggest a better way to synthesize *p*-nitrophenol than the one given in Sec. 22.13.

22.18   Coupling with diazonium salts

As we have seen, the ring of a phenol is reactive enough to undergo attack by diazonium salts, with the formation of azo compounds. This reaction is discussed in detail in Sec. 21.10.

22.19   Kolbe reaction.   Synthesis of phenolic acids

Treatment of the salt of a phenol with carbon dioxide brings about substitution of the carboxyl group, —COOH, for hydrogen of the ring. This reaction is known as the **Kolbe reaction**; its most important application is in the conversion of phenol itself into *o*-hydroxybenzoic acid, known as *salicylic acid*.

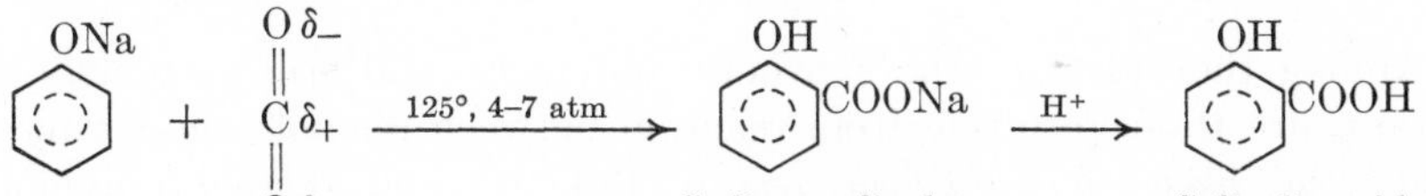

Sodium salicylate
Chief product

Salicylic acid

Although some *p*-hydroxybenzoic acid is formed as well, the separation of the two isomers can be carried out readily by steam distillation, the *o*-isomer being the more volatile. (Why?)

It seems likely that CO$_2$ attaches itself initially to phenoxide oxygen rather than to the ring. In any case, the final product almost certainly results from electrophilic attack by electron-deficient carbon on the highly reactive ring.

Problem 22.15   *Aspirin* is the sodium salt of acetylsalicylic acid (*o*-acetoxy-benzoic acid, *o*-CH$_3$COOC$_6$H$_4$COOH); *oil of wintergreen* is the ester, methyl salicylate. Outline the synthesis of these two compounds from phenol.

22.20   Reimer–Tiemann reaction.   Synthesis of phenolic aldehydes

Treatment of a phenol with chloroform and aqueous hydroxide introduces an aldehyde group, —CHO, into the aromatic ring, generally *ortho* to the —OH. This reaction is known as the **Reimer–Tiemann reaction.** For example:

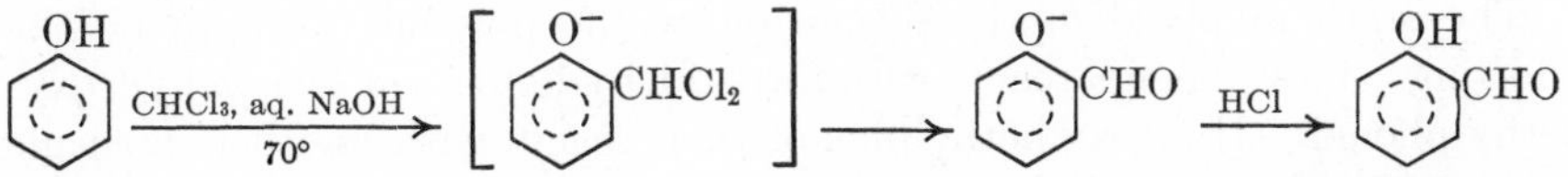

Phenol

Salicylaldehyde
Chief product

A substituted benzal chloride is initially formed, but is hydrolyzed by the alkaline reaction medium.

The Reimer-Tiemann reaction involves electrophilic substitution on the highly reactive phenoxide ring. There is evidence that the electrophilic reagent is *carbon dichloride*, CCl_2, generated from chloroform by the action of base. Although electrically neutral, carbon dichloride contains a carbon atom with only a sextet of electrons and hence is strongly electrophilic.

$$OH^- + CHCl_3 \rightleftharpoons H_2O + {}^-:CCl_3 \longrightarrow Cl^- + Cl:\overset{..}{C}:Cl$$

Chloroform   Carbon dichloride

Electrophilic reagent

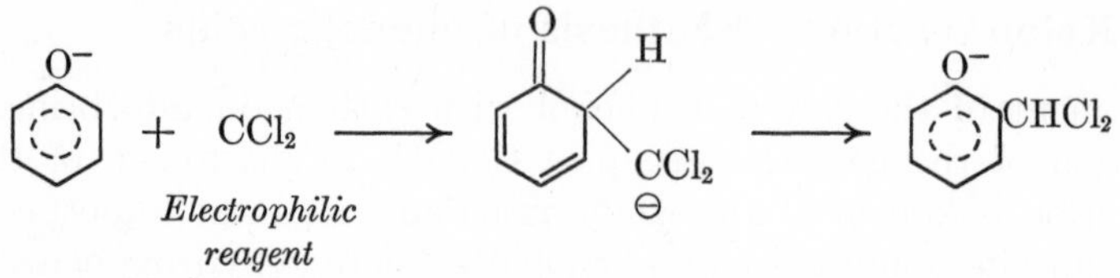

22.21 Reaction with formaldehyde. Phenol–formaldehyde resins

Among the oldest of the synthetic polymers, and still extremely important, are those resulting from reaction between phenols and formaldehyde: the *phenol-formaldehyde resins* (Bakelite and related polymers). When phenol is treated with formaldehyde in the presence of alkali or acid there is obtained a high molecular weight substance in which many phenol rings are held together by $—CH_2—$ groups:

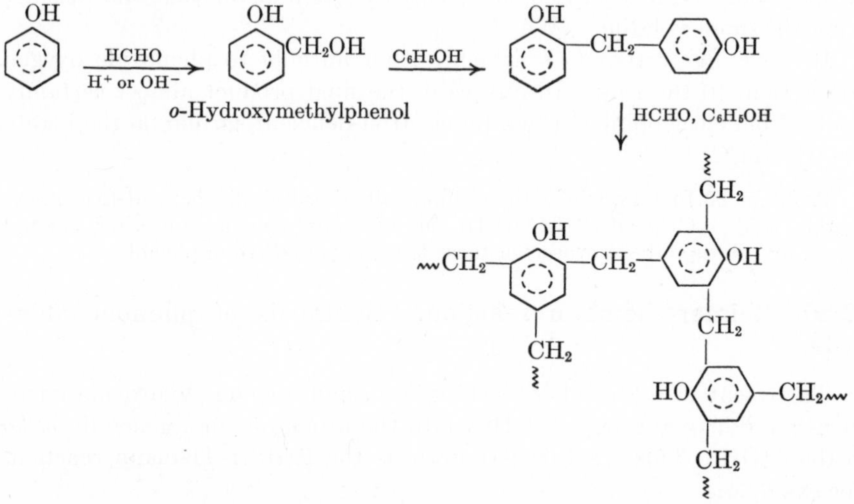

o-Hydroxymethylphenol

The steps involved in the formation of the polymer seem to be the following. First, phenol reacts with formaldehyde to form *o*- or *p*-hydroxymethylphenol. Hydroxymethylphenol then reacts with another molecule of phenol, with the loss of water, to form a compound in which two rings are joined by a $—CH_2—$ link. This process then continues, to yield a product of high molecular weight. Since three positions in each phenol molecule are susceptible to attack, the final product contains many cross-links and hence has a rigid structure.

Reaction can be viewed as both electrophilic substitution on the ring by the electron-deficient carbon of formaldehyde, and nucleophilic addition of the aromatic ring to the carbonyl group. Base catalyzes reaction by converting phenol into the more reactive (more nucleophilic) phenoxide ion. Acid catalyzes reaction by protonating formaldehyde and increasing the electron deficiency of the carbonyl carbon.

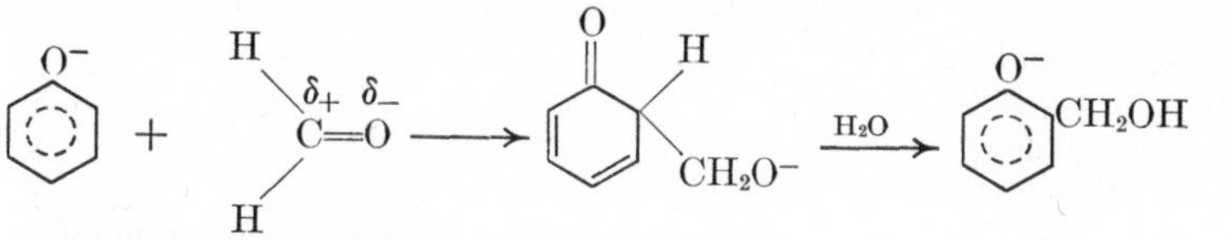

Nucleophilic   Electrophilic
reagent   reagent

Basic catalysis

Nucleophilic   Electrophilic
reagent   reagent

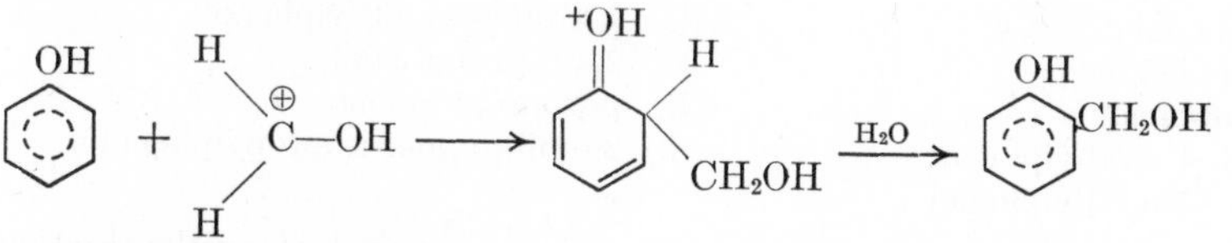

Acidic catalysis

22.22 Analysis of phenols

The most characteristic property of phenols is their particular degree of acidity. Most of them (Secs. 22.3 and 22.8) are stronger acids than water but weaker acids than carbonic acid. Thus, a water-insoluble compound that dissolves in aqueous sodium hydroxide but *not* in aqueous sodium bicarbonate is most likely a phenol.

Many (but not all) phenols form colored complexes (ranging from green through blue and violet to red) with ferric chloride. (This test is also given by *enols*, Sec. 26.6.)

Phenols are often identified through bromination products and certain esters and ethers.

Problem 22.16 Phenols are often identified as their aryloxyacetic acids, $ArOCH_2COOH$. Suggest a reagent and a procedure for the preparation of these derivatives. (*Hint:* see Sec. 22.10.) Aside from melting point, what other property of the aryloxyacetic acids would be useful in identifying phenols? (*Hint:* see Sec. 16.22.)

PROBLEMS

1. Write structural formulas for:

(a) 2,4-dinitrophenol
(b) *m*-cresol
(c) hydroquinone
(d) resorcinol
(e) 4-*n*-hexylresorcinol
(f) catechol

(g) picric acid
(h) phenyl acetate
(i) anisole
(j) salicylic acid
(k) ethyl salicylate

2. Give the reagents and any critical conditions necessary to prepare phenol from:

(a) aniline
(b) benzenesulfonic acid

(c) chlorobenzene
(d) cumene (isopropylbenzene)

(e) Outline the steps in the synthesis of phenol from benzene via each of the above compounds.
(f) Which of these methods are used in industrial manufacture of phenol?
(g) Which of these methods is the most versatile in the laboratory preparation of phenols?

3. Outline the steps in a possible industrial synthesis of:

(a) catechol from *guaiacol*, o-CH$_3$OC$_6$H$_4$OH, found in beech-wood tar
(b) catechol from phenol
(c) resorcinol from benzene
(d) picric acid from chlorobenzene
(e) *veratrole*, o-C$_6$H$_4$(OCH$_3$)$_2$, from catechol

4. Outline a possible laboratory synthesis of each of the following compounds from benzene and/or toluene, using any needed aliphatic and inorganic reagents.

(a)–(c) the three cresols
(d) p-iodophenol
(e) m-fluorophenol
(f) o-bromophenol
(g) 3-bromo-4-methylphenol
(h) 2-bromo-4-methylphenol

(i) 2-bromo-5-methylphenol
(j) 5-bromo-2-methylphenol
(k) 2,4-dinitrophenol
(l) p-isopropylphenol
(m) 2,6-dibromo-4-isopropylphenol

5. Give structures and names of the principal organic products of the reaction (if any) of o-cresol with:

(a) aqueous NaOH
(b) aqueous NaHCO$_3$
(c) hot conc. HBr
(d) methyl sulfate, aqueous NaOH
(e) benzyl bromide, aqueous NaOH
(f) bromobenzene, aqueous NaOH
(g) 2,4-dinitrochlorobenzene, aqueous NaOH
(h) acetic acid, H$_2$SO$_4$
(i) acetic anhydride
(j) phthalic anhydride
(k) p-nitrobenzoyl chloride, pyridine
(l) benzenesulfonyl chloride, aqueous NaOH

(m) product (i) + AlCl$_3$
(n) thionyl chloride
(o) ferric chloride solution
(p) H$_2$, Ni, 200°, 20 atm.
(q) cold dilute HNO$_3$
(r) H$_2$SO$_4$, 15°
(s) H$_2$SO$_4$, 100°
(t) bromine water
(u) Br$_2$, CS$_2$
(v) NaNO$_2$, dilute H$_2$SO$_4$
(w) product (v) + HNO$_3$
(x) p-nitrobenzenediazonium chloride
(y) CO$_2$, NaOH, 125°, 5 atm.
(z) CHCl$_3$, aqueous NaOH, 70°

6. Answer Problem 5 for anisole.

7. Answer Problem 5, parts (a) through (o), for benzyl alcohol.

8. Without referring to tables, arrange the compounds of each set in order of acidity:

(a) benzenesulfonic acid, benzoic acid, benzyl alcohol, phenol
(b) carbonic acid, phenol, sulfuric acid, water
(c) m-bromophenol, m-cresol, m-nitrophenol, phenol
(d) p-chlorophenol, 2,4-dichlorophenol, 2,4,6-trichlorophenol

9. Describe simple chemical tests that would serve to distinguish between:

(a) phenol and o-xylene
(b) p-ethylphenol, p-methylanisole, and p-methylbenzyl alcohol
(c) 2,5-dimethylphenol, phenyl benzoate, m-toluic acid
(d) anisole and o-toluidine

(e) acetylsalicylic acid, ethyl acetylsalicylate, ethyl salicylate, and salicylic acid
(f) *m*-dinitrobenzene, *m*-nitroaniline, *m*-nitrobenzoic acid, and *m*-nitrophenol
Tell exactly what you would do and see.

10. Describe simple chemical methods for the separation of the compounds of Problem 9, parts (a), (c), (d), and (f), recovering each component in essentially pure form.

11. Outline all steps in a possible laboratory synthesis of each of the following compounds starting from the aromatic source given, and using any needed aliphatic and inorganic reagents:

(a) 2,4-diaminophenol (Amidol, used as a photographic developer) from chlorobenzene
(b) 4-amino-1,2-dimethoxybenzene from catechol
(c) 2-nitro-1,3-dihydroxybenzene from resorcinol (*Hint:* see Problem 12, page 516)
(d) 2,4,6-trimethylphenol (mesitol) from mesitylene
(e) *p-tert*-butylphenol from phenol
(f) 4-(*p*-hydroxyphenyl)-2,2,4-trimethylpentane from phenol
(g) 2-phenoxy-1-bromoethane from phenol (*Hint:* together with $C_6H_5OCH_2CH_2OC_6H_5$)
(h) phenyl vinyl ether from phenol
(i) What will phenyl vinyl ether give when heated with acid?
(j) 2,6-dinitro-4-*tert*-butyl-3-methylanisole (synthetic musk) from *m*-cresol

12. The cresols obtained from coal tar have been separated in the following way: careful distillation separates one cresol, b.p. 191°, from a mixture of the other two, b.p. about 201°. The higher boiling fraction is sulfonated and the resulting mixture is treated with dilute acid at 130°. One cresol distills out of the reaction mixture, leaving the other cresol behind as a sulfonic acid. This latter sulfonic acid is then decomposed under more vigorous conditions to give the third cresol.
Which cresol do you think is obtained at each stage? Why?

13. Give structures of all compounds below:

(a) *p*-nitrophenol + C_2H_5Br + NaOH (aq) $\longrightarrow$ A ($C_8H_9O_3N$)
A + Sn + HCl $\longrightarrow$ B ($C_8H_{11}ON$)
B + $NaNO_2$ + HCl, then phenol $\longrightarrow$ C ($C_{14}H_{14}O_2N_2$)
C + ethyl sulfate + NaOH (aq) $\longrightarrow$ D ($C_{16}H_{18}O_2N_2$)
D + $SnCl_2$ $\longrightarrow$ E ($C_8H_{11}ON$)
E + acetyl chloride $\longrightarrow$ *phenacetin* ($C_{10}H_{13}O_2N$), an analgesic ("pain-killer") and antipyretic ("fever-killer")

(b) β-(*o*-hydroxyphenyl)ethyl alcohol + HBr $\longrightarrow$ F (C_8H_9OBr)
F + KOH $\longrightarrow$ *coumarane* (C_8H_8O), insoluble in NaOH

(c) phenol + $ClCH_2COOH$ + NaOH (aq), then HCl $\longrightarrow$ G ($C_8H_8O_3$)
G + $SOCl_2$ $\longrightarrow$ H ($C_8H_7O_2Cl$)
H + $AlCl_3$ $\longrightarrow$ *3-cumaranone* ($C_8H_6O_2$)

(d) *p*-cymene (*p*-isopropyltoluene) + conc. H_2SO_4 $\longrightarrow$ I + J (both $C_{10}H_{14}O_3S$)
I + KOH + heat, then H^+ $\longrightarrow$ *carvacrol* ($C_{10}H_{14}O$), found in some essential oils
J + KOH + heat, then H^+ $\longrightarrow$ *thymol* ($C_{10}H_{14}O$), from oil of thyme
I + HNO_3 $\longrightarrow$ K ($C_8H_8O_5S$)
p-toluic acid + fuming sulfuric acid $\longrightarrow$ K

(e) anethole (page 589) + HBr $\longrightarrow$ L ($C_{10}H_{13}OBr$)
L + Mg $\longrightarrow$ M ($C_{20}H_{26}O_2$)
M + HBr, heat $\longrightarrow$ *hexestrol* ($C_{18}H_{22}O_2$), a synthetic estrogen (female sex hormone)

14. Compound N, C_7H_8O, is insoluble in water, dilute HCl, and aqueous $NaHCO_3$; it dissolves in dilute NaOH. When N is treated with bromine water it is converted rapidly into a compound of formula $C_7H_5OBr_3$. What is the structure of N?

15. *Saligenin*, o-$HOC_6H_4CH_2OH$, is obtained from willow bark and leaves. One hydroxyl group is esterified by benzoyl chloride more easily than the other. (a) Which one would you predict this to be, the alcoholic or the phenolic –OH group? Why? (b) How could you determine experimentally which –OH group had been esterified? Tell exactly what you would do and see.

16. Two isomeric compounds, O and P, are isolated from oil of bay leaf; both are found to have the formula $C_{10}H_{12}O$. Both are insoluble in water, dilute acid, and dilute base. Both give positive tests with dilute $KMnO_4$ and Br_2/CCl_4. Upon vigorous oxidation, both yield anisic acid, p-$CH_3OC_6H_4COOH$.
(a) At this point what structures are possible for O and P?
(b) Catalytic hydrogenation converts O and P into the same compound, $C_{10}H_{14}O$. Now what structures are possible for O and P?
(c) Describe chemical procedures (other than synthesis) by which you could assign structures to O and P.
(d) Compound O can be synthesized as follows:

$$p\text{-bromoanisole} + Mg + \text{ether, then allyl bromide} \longrightarrow O$$

What is the structure of O?
(e) O is converted into P when heated strongly with concentrated base. What is the most likely structure for P?
(f) Suggest a synthetic sequence starting with p-bromoanisole that would independently confirm the structure assigned to P.

17. Compound Q ($C_{10}H_{12}O_3$) was insoluble in water, dilute HCl, and dilute aqueous $NaHCO_3$; it was soluble in dilute NaOH. A solution of Q in dilute NaOH was boiled, and the distillate was collected in a solution of NaOI, where a yellow precipitate formed.
The alkaline residue in the distillation flask was acidified with dilute H_2SO_4; a solid, R, precipitated. When this mixture was boiled, R steam-distilled and was collected. R was found to have the formula $C_7H_6O_3$; it dissolved in aqueous $NaHCO_3$ with evolution of a gas.
(a) Give structures and names for Q and R. (b) Write complete equations for all the above reactions.

18. The parent compound of the dyes found in litmus is *orcinol*, 5-methylresorcinol (5-methyl-1,3-dihydroxybenzene). Suggest a synthesis of orcinol from toluene and any needed inorganic reagents.

19. *Chavibetol*, $C_{10}H_{12}O_2$, is found in betel-nut leaves. It is soluble in aqueous NaOH but not in aqueous $NaHCO_3$.
Treatment of chavibetol (a) with methyl sulfate and aqueous NaOH gives compound S, $C_{11}H_{14}O_2$; (b) with hot hydriodic acid gives methyl iodide; (c) with hot concentrated base gives compound T, $C_{10}H_{12}O_2$.
Compound S is insoluble in aqueous NaOH, and readily decolorizes dilute $KMnO_4$ and Br_2/CCl_4. Treatment of S with hot concentrated base gives U, $C_{11}H_{14}O_2$.
Ozonolysis of T gives a compound that is isomeric with vanillin (page 589).
Ozonolysis of U gives a compound that is identical with the one obtained from the treatment of vanillin with methyl sulfate.
What is the structure of chavibetol?

20. The following reactions have been carried out:

nitrobenzene + Zn + NH_4Cl $\longrightarrow$ V (C_6H_7ON), *N-phenylhydroxylamine*

V $\xrightarrow{\text{acid}}$ W (C_6H_7ON)

V $\xrightarrow{\text{reduction}}$ aniline

V $\xrightarrow{\text{oxidation}}$ nitrosobenzene

W $\xrightarrow{\text{acetic anhydride}}$ X ($C_8H_9O_2N$) $\xrightarrow{\text{acetic anhydride}}$ Y ($C_{10}H_{11}O_3N$)

X $\xrightarrow{(CH_3)_2SO_4,\ OH^-}$ Z ($C_9H_{11}O_2N$) $\xrightarrow{OH^-,\ \text{heat}}$ AA (C_7H_9ON)

AA $\xrightarrow{NaNO_2,\ H_2SO_4}$ $\xrightarrow{CuBr}$ p-bromoanisole

	dil. HCl	dil. NaOH	aq. NaHCO₃
W	sol.	sol.	insol.
X	insol.	sol.	insol.
Y	insol.	insol.	insol.
Z	insol.	insol.	insol.
AA	sol.	insol.	insol.

(a) What is the structure of W? Of X through AA? (b) What is the most likely structure for V? (c) What kind of reaction must have taken place in the conversion of V into W? (d) Predict what you would get instead of W if you started with *m*-nitrotoluene. (e) Outline a possible synthesis of 3-methyl-4-aminophenol starting from toluene.

21. The structure of the terpene *α-terpineol* (found in oils of cardamom and marjoram) was proved in part by the following synthesis:

p-toluic acid + fuming sulfuric acid $\longrightarrow$ BB ($C_8H_8O_5S$)

BB + KOH $\xrightarrow{\text{fusion}}$ CC ($C_8H_8O_3$)

CC + Na, alcohol $\longrightarrow$ DD ($C_8H_{14}O_3$)

DD + HBr $\longrightarrow$ EE ($C_8H_{13}O_2Br$)

EE + base, heat $\longrightarrow$ FF ($C_8H_{12}O_2$)

FF + C_2H_5OH, HCl $\longrightarrow$ GG ($C_{10}H_{16}O_2$)

GG + CH_3MgI, then H_2O $\longrightarrow$ *α*-terpineol ($C_{10}H_{18}O$)

What is the most likely structure for *α*-terpineol?

22. *Coniferyl alcohol*, $C_{10}H_{12}O_3$, is obtained from the sap of conifers. It is soluble in aqueous NaOH but not in aqueous NaHCO₃.

Treatment of coniferyl alcohol (a) with benzoyl chloride and pyridine gives compound HH, $C_{24}H_{20}O_5$; (b) with cold HBr gives $C_{10}H_{11}O_2Br$; (c) with hot hydriodic acid gives a volatile compound identified as methyl iodide; (d) with methyl iodide and aqueous base gives compound II, $C_{11}H_{14}O_3$.

Both HH and II are insoluble in dilute NaOH, and rapidly decolorize dilute $KMnO_4$ and Br_2/CCl_4.

Ozonolysis of coniferyl alcohol gives vanillin.

What is the structure of coniferyl alcohol?

Write equations for all the above reactions.

23. *Hordinene*, $C_{10}H_{15}ON$, is an alkaloid found in germinating barley. It is soluble in dilute HCl and in dilute NaOH; it reprecipitates from the alkaline solution when CO_2 is bubbled in. It reacts with benzenesulfonyl chloride to yield a product JJ that is soluble in dilute acids.

When hordinene is treated with methyl sulfate and base, a product, KK, is formed. When KK is oxidized by alkaline $KMnO_4$, there is obtained anisic acid, *p*-$CH_3OC_6H_4COOH$. When KK is heated strongly there is obtained *p*-methoxy-styrene.

(a) What structure or structures are consistent with this evidence? (b) Outline a synthesis or syntheses that would prove the structure of hordinene.

24. In the production of phenol from chlorobenzene a by-product LL of formula $C_{12}H_{10}O$ is obtained. LL is insoluble in dilute acid and dilute base, and gives negative tests with $KMnO_4$ and Br_2/CCl_4.

LL can also be synthesized by the high-temperature reaction between potassium phenoxide and bromobenzene in the presence of copper.

What is the structure and name of LL?

25. Upon reduction with $SnCl_2$, azo compound MM gave 2-amino-4-methylphenol and *p*-aminoacetanilide; azo compound NN gave one mole each of *p*-phenylenediamine, 2,4-dihydroxyaniline, and *p*-amino-N,N-dimethylaniline; azo compound OO gave 4-amino-3-bromotoluene and 4-amino-2-methylphenol.

(a) Give the structures of MM, NN, and OO.

(b) Outline a possible synthesis of MM, NN, and OO from benzene, toluene, and any needed aliphatic and inorganic reagents.

(c) Outline a synthesis that would confirm the structure of each of the above reduction products.

26. When a bright yellow solid, PP, was treated with $SnCl_2$ the color disappeared. The reaction mixture was made strongly alkaline and was extracted with ether. Evaporation of the ether layer left a solid residue QQ. When CO_2 was bubbled into the aqueous layer a precipitate RR formed and was collected on a filter. When dilute HCl was added to the filtrate, a solid precipitated and then redissolved upon further addition of acid to give solution SS.

After recrystallization QQ was found to have a melting point of 126–7° and the formula $C_{12}H_{12}N_2$. It dissolved readily in aqueous HCl; treatment of this acidic solution with sodium nitrite and then H_3PO_2 gave a solid of m.p. 69–70° and formula $C_{12}H_{10}$.

Compound RR was found to have a melting point of 185–6° and formula C_6H_7ON. It was soluble in aqueous acid.

When solution SS was treated with sodium nitrite and then H_3PO_2, a solid TT separated and was collected on a filter. TT had a melting point of 157–9° and formula $C_7H_6O_3$; it gave a violet color with ferric chloride.

(a) What was the probable structure of PP? (Use any necessary tables.)
(b) Outline a possible synthesis of PP from benzene, toluene, and any needed aliphatic and inorganic reagents.

Chapter twenty-three

ALDEHYDES AND KETONES

23.1 Structure

Aldehydes are compounds of the general formula RCHO; ketones are compounds of the general formula RR'CO. The groups R and R' may be aliphatic or aromatic.

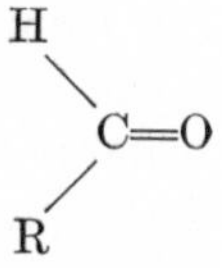

$$\begin{array}{ccc}
H & & R' \\
\diagdown & & \diagdown \\
& C{=}O & \quad\quad\quad\quad & C{=}O \\
\diagup & & \diagup \\
R & & R
\end{array}$$

An aldehyde 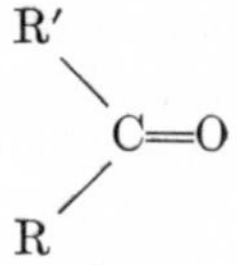   A ketone

Both aldehydes and ketones contain the carbonyl group, $C{=}O$, and are often referred to collectively as **carbonyl compounds.** *It is the carbonyl group that largely determines the chemistry of aldehydes and ketones.*

It is not surprising to find that aldehydes and ketones resemble each other closely in most of their properties. However, there is a hydrogen atom attached to the carbonyl group of aldehydes, and there are two organic groups attached to the carbonyl group of ketones. This difference in structure affects their properties in two ways: (a) aldehydes are quite easily oxidized, whereas ketones are oxidized only with difficulty; (b) aldehydes are usually more reactive than ketones toward nucleophilic addition, the characteristic reaction of carbonyl compounds.

Let us look again at the structure of the carbonyl group (Sec. 17.4). Carbonyl carbon is joined to three other atoms by σ bonds; since these bonds utilize sp^2 orbitals (Sec. 4.2), they lie in a plane, and are 120° apart. The remaining p orbital of the carbon overlaps a p orbital of oxygen to form a π bond; carbon and oxygen are thus joined by a double bond. The part of the molecule immediately surrounding carbonyl carbon is *flat;* oxygen, carbonyl carbon, and the two atoms directly attached to carbonyl carbon lie in a plane:

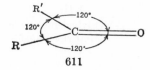

The electrons of the carbonyl double bond hold together atoms of quite different electronegativity, and hence the electrons are not equally shared; in particular, the mobile π cloud is pulled strongly toward the more electronegative atom, oxygen.

The facts are consistent with the orbital picture of the carbonyl group. Electron diffraction and spectroscopic studies of aldehydes and ketones show that carbon, oxygen, and the two other atoms attached to carbonyl carbon lie in a plane; the three bond angles of carbon are very close to 120°. The large dipole moments (2.3–2.8 D) of aldehydes and ketones indicate that the electrons of the carbonyl group are quite unequally shared.

Polarity of carbonyl group

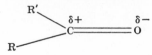

We shall see how the physical and chemical properties of aldehydes and ketones are determined by the structure of the carbonyl group.

23.2　Nomenclature

The common names of aldehydes are derived from the names of the corresponding carboxylic acids by replacing *–ic acid* by *–aldehyde.*

The IUPAC names of aldehydes follow the usual pattern. The longest chain carrying the —CHO group is considered the parent structure and is named by replacing the *–e* of the corresponding alkane by *–al.* The position of a substituent is indicated by a number, the carbonyl carbon always being considered as C-1. Here, as with the carboxylic acids, we notice that C-2 of the IUPAC name corresponds to *alpha* of the common name.

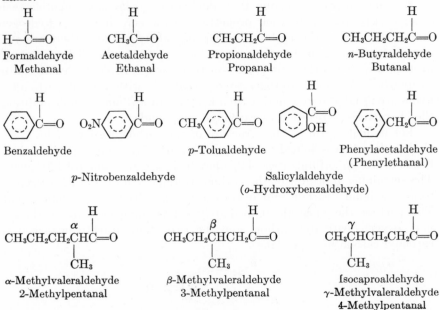

The simplest aliphatic ketone has the common name of *acetone*. For most other aliphatic ketones we name the two groups that are attached to carbonyl carbon, and follow these names by the word *ketone*. A ketone in which the carbonyl group is attached to a benzene ring is named as a –*phenone*, as illustrated below.

According to the IUPAC system, the longest chain carrying the carbonyl group is considered the parent structure, and is named by replacing the –*e* of the corresponding alkane with –*one*. The positions of various groups are indicated by numbers, the carbonyl carbon being given the lowest possible number.

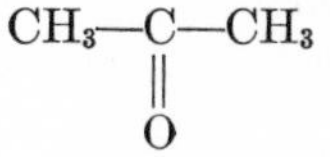

CH₃—C—CH₃　　　　　CH₃CH₂—C—CH₃　　　　　CH₃CH₂CH₂—C—CH₃
    ‖　　　　　 ‖　　　　　 ‖
    O　　　　　 O　　　　　 O

Acetone　　　　　Methyl ethyl ketone　　　　　Methyl *n*-propyl ketone
Propanone　　　　　Butanone　　　　　2-Pentanone

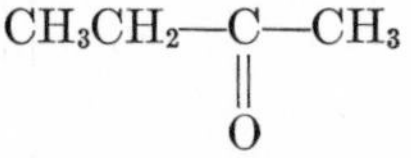

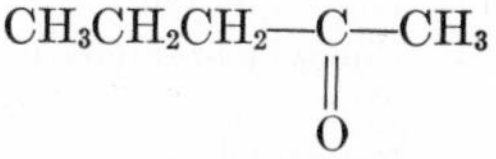

                                CH₃
                                |
CH₃CH₂—C—CH₂CH₃　　　　　CH₃CH—C—CH₃　　　　　⟨◯⟩CH₂—C—CH₃
        ‖　　　　　 ‖　　　　　 ‖
        O　　　　　 O　　　　　 O

Ethyl ketone　　　　　Methyl isopropyl ketone　　　　　Benzyl methyl ketone
3-Pentanone　　　　　3-Methyl-2-butanone　　　　　1-Phenyl-2-propanone

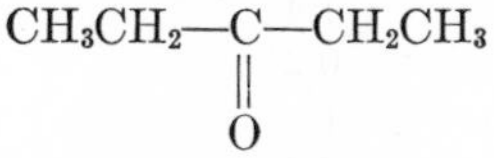

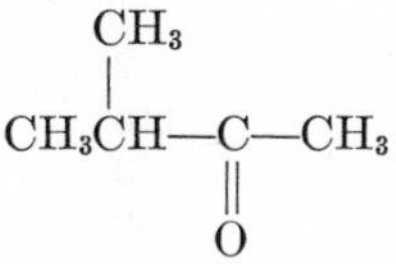

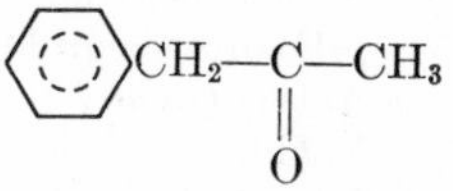

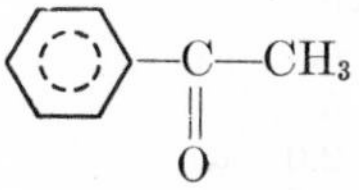

⟨◯⟩—C—CH₃　　　　　⟨◯⟩—C—CH₂CH₂CH₃　　　　　⟨◯⟩—C—⟨◯⟩
     ‖　　　　　 ‖　　　　　 ‖
     O　　　　　 O　　　　　 O

Acetophenone 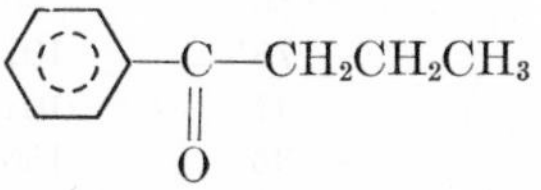　　　　　*n*-Butyrophenone 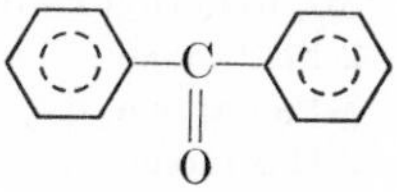　　　　　Benzophenone

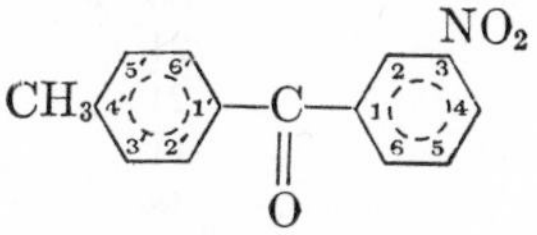

                                         NO₂
CH₃⟨5′ 6′/4′ 1′\3′ 2′⟩—C—⟨2 3/1 4\6 5⟩
                                 ‖
                                 O

3-Nitro-4′-methylbenzophenone

23.3　Physical properties

The polar carbonyl group makes aldehydes and ketones polar compounds, and hence they have higher boiling points than non-polar compounds of comparable molecular weight. By themselves, they are not capable of intermolecular hydrogen bonding since they contain hydrogen bonded only to carbon; as a result they have lower boiling points than comparable alcohols or carboxylic acids. For example, compare *n*-butyraldehyde (b.p. 76°) and methyl ethyl ketone (b.p. 80°) with *n*-pentane (b.p. 36°) and ethyl ether (b.p. 35°) on the one hand, and with *n*-butyl alcohol (b.p. 118°) and propionic acid (b.p. 141°) on the other.

The lower aldehydes and ketones are appreciably soluble in water, presumably because of hydrogen bonding between solute and solvent molecules; borderline solubility is reached at about five carbons. Aldehydes and ketones are soluble in the usual organic solvents.

TABLE 23.1

ALDEHYDES AND KETONES

	M.p., °C	B.p., °C	Solub., g/100 g H_2O
Formaldehyde	− 92	− 21	v.sol.
Acetaldehyde	−121	20	∞
Propionaldehyde	− 81	49	16
n-Butyraldehyde	− 99	76	7
n-Valeraldehyde	− 91	103	sl.s
Caproaldehyde		131	sl.s.
Heptaldehyde	− 42	155	0.1
Phenylacetaldehyde		194	sl.s
Benzaldehyde	− 26	178	0.3
o-Tolualdehyde		196	
m-Tolualdehyde		199	
p-Tolualdehyde		205	
Salicylaldehyde	2	197	1.7
p-Hydroxybenzaldehyde	116		1.4
Anisaldehyde	3	248	0.2
Vanillin	82	285	1
Piperonal	37	263	0.2
Acetone	− 94	56	∞
Methyl ethyl ketone	− 86	80	26
2-Pentanone	− 78	102	6.3
3-Pentanone	− 41	101	5
2-Hexanone	− 35	150	2.0
3-Hexanone		124	sl.s
Methyl isobutyl ketone	− 85	119	1.9
Acetophenone	21	202	
Propiophenone	21	218	
n-Butyrophenone	11	232	
Benzophenone	48	306	

23.4   Industrial source

Formaldehyde is made by oxidation of methanol by air in the presence of a catalyst:

$$CH_3OH + O_2 \xrightarrow{\text{Cu, 550–600°}} HCHO + H_2O$$

Methanol   Formaldehyde

Formaldehyde is a gas (b.p. −21°), and is handled either as an aqueous solution (*Formalin*), or as one of its solid polymers: *paraformaldehyde*, $(CH_2O)_n$, or *trioxane*, $(CH_2O)_3$.

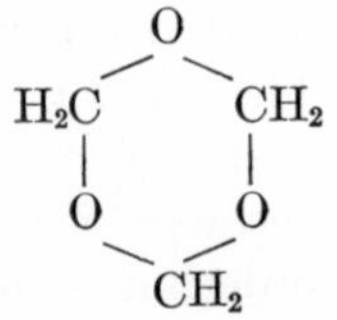

~~~CH₂OCH₂OCH₂O~~~

Paraformaldehyde

</div>

Trioxane

When dry formaldehyde is desired, as, for example, in reaction with a Grignard reagent, it is obtained by heating paraformaldehyde or trioxane.

Acetaldehyde, we have already seen (Sec. 6.12), is made by hydration of acetylene:

$$HC\equiv CH + H_2O \xrightarrow{\text{H}_2\text{SO}_4,\ \text{HgSO}_4} CH_3CHO$$

Acetylene   Acetaldehyde

The chief use of acetaldehyde is in the manufacture of acetic acid (Sec. 16.5). Acetaldehyde is often available in the form of its trimer, *paraldehyde,* $(CH_3CHO)_3$. The low-boiling monomer can be obtained by heating the trimer with acid:

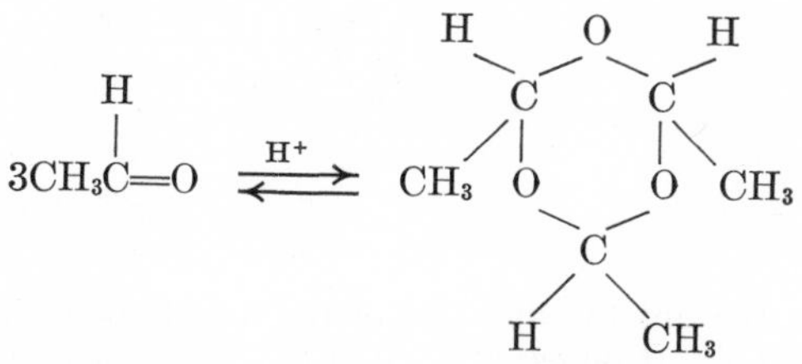

Acetaldehyde
B.p. 20°

Paraldehyde
B.p. 125°

Benzaldehyde is made from toluene by side-chain chlorination (Sec. 9.15), followed by hydrolysis of the benzal chloride:

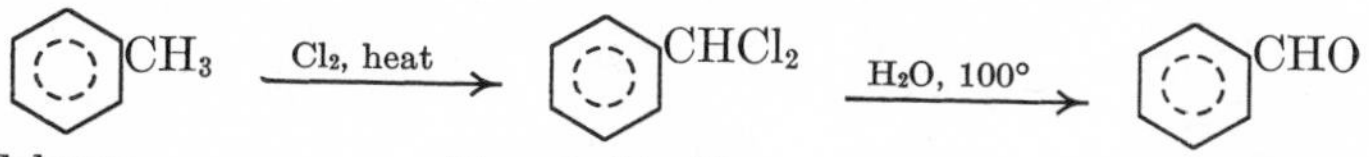

Toluene   Benzal chloride   Benzaldehyde

This method is of some use in the laboratory preparation of aromatic aldehydes.

Salicylaldehyde and other phenolic aldehydes are prepared by the Reimer-Tiemann reaction (Sec. 22.20).

A number of aromatic aldehydes that are used in flavorings and perfumes are prepared by careful oxidation of unsaturated side chains of naturally occurring compounds (Sec. 22.4). For example:

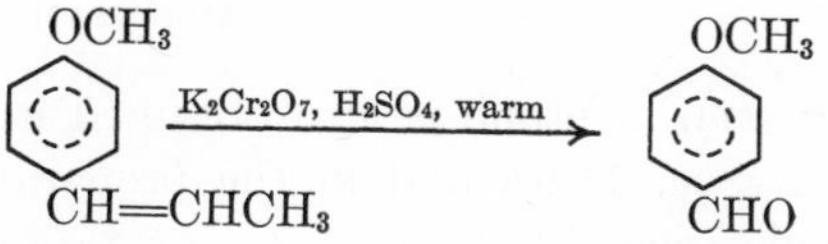

Anethole
Oil of aniseed

Anisaldehyde

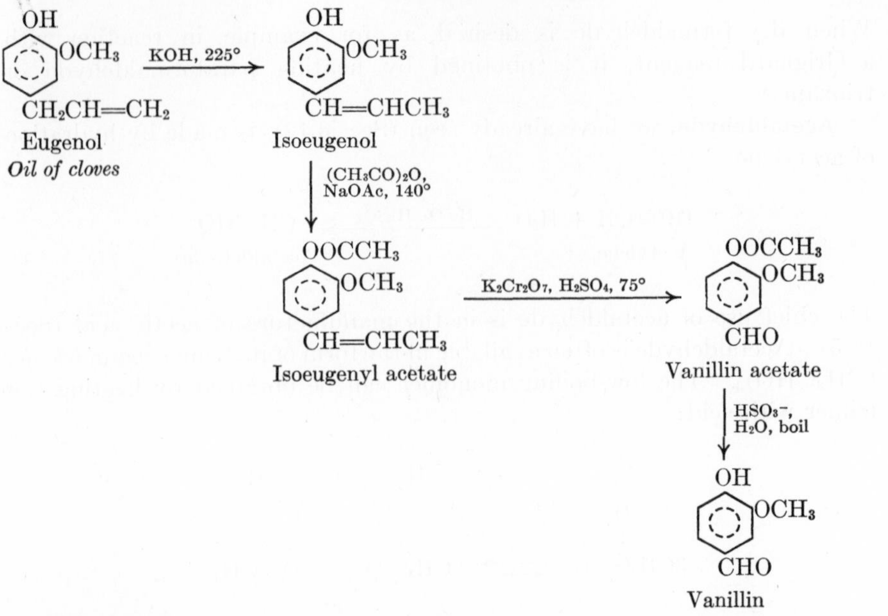

OH
⬡OCH₃   KOH, 225°   →   OH
⬡OCH₃
CH₂CH=CH₂   CH=CHCH₃
Eugenol   Isoeugenol
Oil of cloves

↓ (CH₃CO)₂O,
  NaOAc, 140°

OOCCH₃
⬡OCH₃   K₂Cr₂O₇, H₂SO₄, 75°   →   OOCCH₃
⬡OCH₃
CH=CHCH₃   CHO
Isoeugenyl acetate   Vanillin acetate

↓ HSO₃⁻,
  H₂O, boil

OH
⬡OCH₃
CHO
Vanillin

Problem 23.1   Account for the shift of the double bond in the synthesis of isoeugenol from eugenol.   (Compare Sec. 9.21.)

Problem 23.2   Suggest a way to convert safrole (page 589) into *piperonal*.

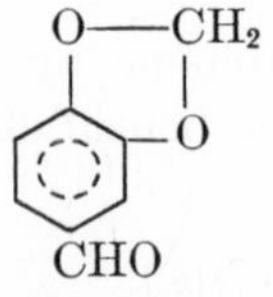

O——CH₂
⬡   O
CHO
Piperonal

The important solvents, **acetone** and **methyl ethyl ketone,** are prepared by dehydrogenation of the corresponding alcohols:

$$CH_3CHOHCH_3 \xrightarrow{\text{Cu, } 250\text{--}300°} CH_3\text{—}\underset{\underset{O}{\|}}{C}\text{—}CH_3 + H_2$$
Isopropyl alcohol   Acetone

$$CH_3CH_2CHOHCH_3 \xrightarrow{\text{Cu, } 250\text{--}300°} CH_3CH_2\text{—}\underset{\underset{O}{\|}}{C}\text{—}CH_3 + H_2$$
sec-Butyl alcohol   Methyl ethyl ketone

As we have already seen, acetone is also obtained in the Weizmann fermentation of starch (Sec. 11.6), and in the preparation of phenol from cumene hydroperoxide (Sec. 22.5).

Many aldehydes and ketones are manufactured by the laboratory methods outlined in the next section.

23.5 Preparation

A few of the many laboratory methods of preparing aldehydes and ketones are outlined below; most of these are already familiar to us. Some of the methods involve oxidation or reduction in which an alcohol, hydrocarbon, or acid chloride is converted into an aldehyde or ketone of the same carbon number. Other methods involve the formation of new carbon–carbon bonds, and yield aldehydes or ketones of higher carbon number than the starting materials.

PREPARATION OF ALDEHYDES

1. Oxidation of primary alcohols. (See also Sec. 12.7.)

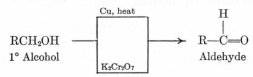

Examples:

$$CH_3CH_2CH_2CH_2CH_2OH \xrightarrow{\text{Cu, 250–300°}} CH_3CH_2CH_2CH_2CHO$$

n-Pentyl alcohol   n-Valeraldehyde
(1-Pentanol)   (Pentanal)

$$CH_3CH_2CH_2CH_2OH \xrightarrow{\text{K}_2\text{Cr}_2\text{O}_7\text{, H}_2\text{SO}_4\text{, warm}} CH_3CH_2CH_2CHO$$

n-Butyl alcohol   n-Butyraldehyde
(1-Butanol)   (Butanal)
B.p. 118°   *B.p. 76°*

2. Oxidation of methylbenzenes

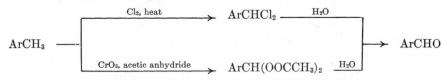

Examples:

p-Bromotoluene   p-Bromobenzaldehyde

p-Nitrotoluene   p-Nitrobenzaldehyde

3. Reduction of acid chlorides

$$RCOCl \text{ or } ArCOCl \xrightarrow[\text{or LiAlH(O-}t\text{-C}_4\text{H}_9)_3]{\text{H}_2\text{, Pd–BaSO}_4\text{, catalyst moderator}} RCHO \text{ or } ArCHO$$

Acid chloride   Aldehyde

Examples:

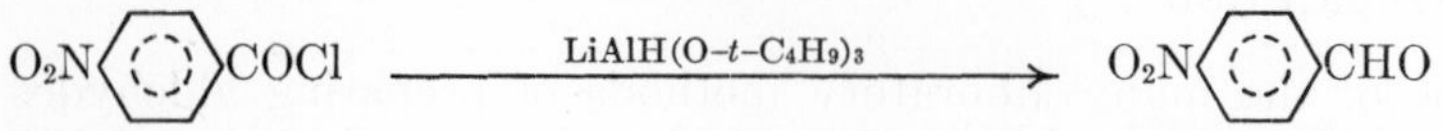

$$O_2N-C_6H_4-COCl \xrightarrow{\text{LiAlH}(O-t-C_4H_9)_3} O_2N-C_6H_4-CHO$$

p-Nitrobenzoyl chloride   *p*-Nitrobenzaldehyde

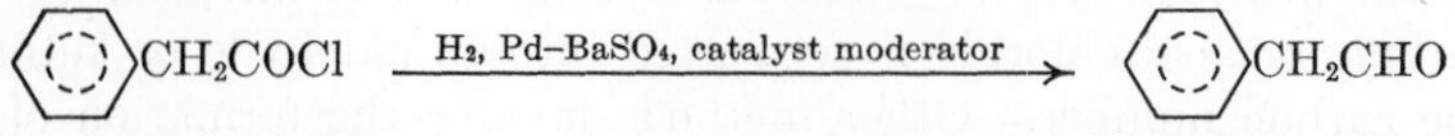

$$C_6H_5-CH_2COCl \xrightarrow{\text{H}_2,\ \text{Pd-BaSO}_4,\ \text{catalyst moderator}} C_6H_5-CH_2CHO$$

Phenylacetyl chloride   Phenylacetaldehyde

4. Reimer-Tiemann reaction. Phenolic aldehydes. Discussed in Sec. 22.20.

PREPARATION OF KETONES

1. Oxidation of secondary alcohols. (See also Sec. 12.7.)

$$\text{RCHOHR'} \xrightarrow[\text{KMnO}_4\ \text{or}\ \text{K}_2\text{Cr}_2\text{O}_7]{\text{Cu, heat}} R-\underset{\underset{O}{\|}}{C}-R'$$

2° Alcohol   Ketone

Examples:

$$\text{CH}_3\text{CH}_2\text{CH}_2\text{CH}_2\underset{\underset{\text{OH}}{|}}{\text{CH}}\text{CH}_2\text{CH}_3 \xrightarrow{\text{Cu, 250°}} \text{CH}_3\text{CH}_2\text{CH}_2\text{CH}_2\underset{\underset{\text{O}}{\|}}{\text{C}}\text{CH}_2\text{CH}_3$$

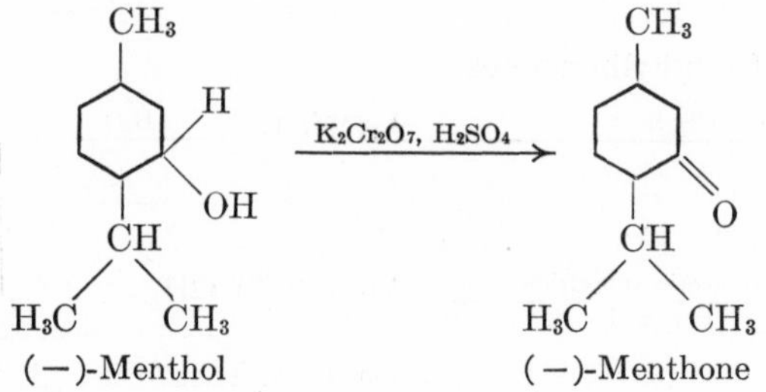

3-Heptanol   3-Heptanone

                                                   (Ethyl *n*-butyl ketone)

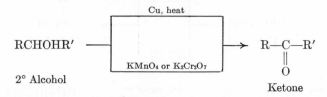

(−)-Menthol   (−)-Menthone

2. Friedel-Crafts acylation. Discussed in Sec. 17.8 and Sec. 22.11.

$$\text{ArH} + \text{RCOCl or Ar'COCl} \xrightarrow{\text{Lewis acid}} \text{Ar}-\underset{\underset{O}{\|}}{C}-R \text{ or } \text{Ar}-\underset{\underset{O}{\|}}{C}-\text{Ar'}$$

3. Reaction of acid chlorides with organocadmium compounds. Discussed in Sec. 17.9.

$$\text{R'MgX} \xrightarrow{\text{CdCl}_2} \text{R'}_2\text{Cd}$$

$$\left.\begin{matrix}\text{RCOCl}\\ \text{or}\\ \text{ArCOCl}\end{matrix}\right\} \longrightarrow R-\underset{\underset{O}{\|}}{C}-R' \text{ or } \text{Ar}-\underset{\underset{O}{\|}}{C}-R'$$

                                                  *R' must be aryl

                                                  or primary alkyl*

4. Acetoacetic ester synthesis. To be discussed in Sec. 26.4.

5. Decarboxylation of acids. To be discussed in Sec. 25.6.

Depending upon the availability of starting materials, **aliphatic aldehydes** can be prepared from alcohols or acid chlorides of the same carbon skeleton, and **aromatic aldehydes** can be prepared from methylbenzenes or aromatic acid chlorides.

$$RCOOH \longrightarrow RCOCl$$
$$RCH_2OH \\ RCOCl \Big\} \longrightarrow RCHO \qquad \textit{Preparation of aliphatic aldehydes}$$

$$ArCOOH \longrightarrow ArCOCl$$
$$ArCH_3 \\ ArCOCl \Big\} \longrightarrow ArCHO \qquad \textit{Preparation of aromatic aldehydes}$$

There are, in addition, a number of methods by which the aldehyde group is introduced into an aromatic ring; of these methods we have already encountered the Reimer-Tiemann synthesis of phenolic aldehydes (Sec. 22.20).

Problem 23.3 Formyl chloride, HCOCl, the acid chloride of formic acid, is not known, but a mixture of carbon monoxide and hydrogen chloride acts as its equivalent. Predict the product when benzene is treated with this mixture in the presence of $AlCl_3$; when toluene is so treated. (This is known as the **Gattermann-Koch reaction.**)

Aliphatic ketones are readily prepared from the corresponding secondary alcohols, if these are available. More complicated aliphatic ketones can be prepared by the reaction of acid chlorides with organocadmium compounds (Sec. 17.9).

$$RCOOH \longrightarrow RCOCl$$
$$RR'CHOH \\ RCOCl \xrightarrow{R'_2Cd} \Big\} \longrightarrow \underset{\underset{O}{\|}}{R-C-R'} \qquad \textit{Preparation of aliphatic ketones}$$

A particularly useful method for making complicated aliphatic ketones, the acetoacetic ester synthesis, will be discussed later (Sec. 26.4). **Aromatic ketones** containing a carbonyl group attached directly to an aromatic ring are conveniently prepared by Friedel-Crafts acylation or by the modification known as the Fries rearrangement (Sec. 17.8 and Sec. 22.11).

$$ArH \xrightarrow{RCOCl\ (Ar'COCl),\ AlCl_3}$$
$$ArBr \rightarrow ArMgBr \rightarrow Ar_2Cd \xrightarrow{RCOCl\ (Ar'COCl)} \Big\} \longrightarrow \underset{\underset{O}{\|}}{ArCR}\ (\underset{\underset{O}{\|}}{ArCAr'}) \qquad \textit{Preparation of aromatic ketones}$$
$$ArCOOH \rightarrow ArCOCl \xrightarrow{R_2Cd\ (Ar'_2Cd)}$$

23.6 Preparation of aldehydes by oxidation methods

As we shall see (Sec. 23.8), aldehydes are more easily oxidized than any other class of organic compounds we have studied; indeed, it is by their ease of oxidation that aldehydes are most readily recognized. How is it possible, then, to stop the oxidation of a primary alcohol or a methylbenzene (Sec. 23.5) at the aldehyde stage? An oxidizing agent that can oxidize an alcohol or a methylbenzene certainly ought to be able to oxidize an aldehyde.

One way — and possibly the best — is to use catalytic dehydrogenation over hot copper. Another way takes advantage of a particular physical property of an aldehyde: it always has a lower boiling point than the alcohol from which it is formed. (Why?) Acetaldehyde, for example, has a boiling point of 20°; ethyl alcohol has a boiling point of 78°. When a solution of dichromate and sulfuric acid is dripped into boiling ethyl alcohol, acetaldehyde is formed in a medium whose temperature is some 60 degrees above its boiling point; before it can undergo appreciable oxidation it escapes from the reaction medium. Reaction is carried out under a fractionating column that allows aldehyde to pass but returns alcohol to the reaction vessel.

Problem 23.4 Give a detailed experimental procedure (including apparatus) for: (a) Dehydration of cyclohexanol to cyclohexene. (Remember that dehydration is reversible and that alkenes are polymerized by acid.) (b) Formation of *o*-cresol by the hydrolysis of *o*-toluenediazonium chloride. (Remember that phenols couple readily with diazonium salts.)

Problem 23.5 Optically active alcohols in which the asymmetric carbon carries the —OH undergo racemization in acidic solutions. (Why?) Give a detailed experimental procedure (including apparatus) for studying the stereochemistry of acidic hydrolysis of *sec*-butyl benzoate that would prevent racemization of the alcohol subsequent to hydrolysis. *sec*-Butyl benzoate has a boiling point of 234°; an azeotrope of 68% *sec*-butyl alcohol and 32% water has a boiling point of 88.5°.

23.7 Reactions

The carbonyl group, C=O, governs the chemistry of aldehydes and ketones. It does this in two ways: (a) by providing a site for nucleophilic addition, and (b) by increasing the acidity of the hydrogen atoms attached to the *alpha* carbon. Both these effects are quite consistent with the structure of the carbonyl group.

The carbonyl group contains a carbon–oxygen double bond; since the π electrons are pulled strongly toward oxygen, carbonyl carbon is electron-deficient and carbonyl oxygen is electron-rich. Because it is flat, this part of the molecule is open to relatively unhindered attack from above or below, in a direction perpendicular to the plane of the group. It is not surprising that this accessible, polarized group is highly reactive.

What kind of reagents will attack such a group? Since the important step in these reactions is the formation of a bond to the electron-deficient carbonyl carbon, the carbonyl group is most susceptible to attack by electron-rich, nucleophilic reagents, that is, by bases. **The typical reaction of aldehydes and ketones is nucleophilic addition.**

Carbonyl addition

Attack perpendicular to plane of group

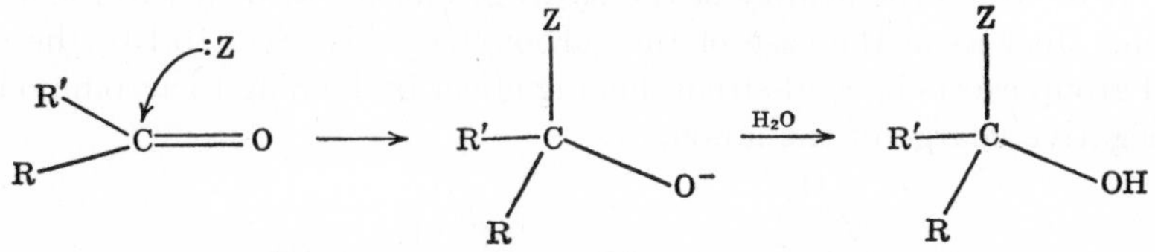

$$R' \diagdown \atop R \diagup \!\! C = O \quad \xrightarrow{\;:Z\;} \quad R'-\underset{R}{\overset{Z}{C}}-O^- \quad \xrightarrow{\;H_2O\;} \quad R'-\underset{R}{\overset{Z}{C}}-OH$$

Planar   Tetrahedral

We already know a great deal about the carbonyl group from our study of acyl compounds, carboxylic acids and their derivatives (Chapters 16 and 17). The chemical behavior of these compounds, too, is determined by the carbonyl group, and by the susceptibility of carbonyl carbon to nucleophilic attack. Nucleophilic attack on acyl compounds is followed by expulsion of a group and hence leads to *substitution*. Nucleophilic attack on aldehydes and ketones, on the other hand, results in *addition*.

We have seen (Sec. 17.4) that acid catalysis can be employed to speed up nucleophilic attack on acyl compounds, the attachment of hydrogen ion to carbonyl oxygen rendering carbonyl carbon even more electron-deficient. Nucleophilic addition to aldehydes and ketones can also be catalyzed by acids, and for the same reason.

Acid-catalyzed carbonyl addition

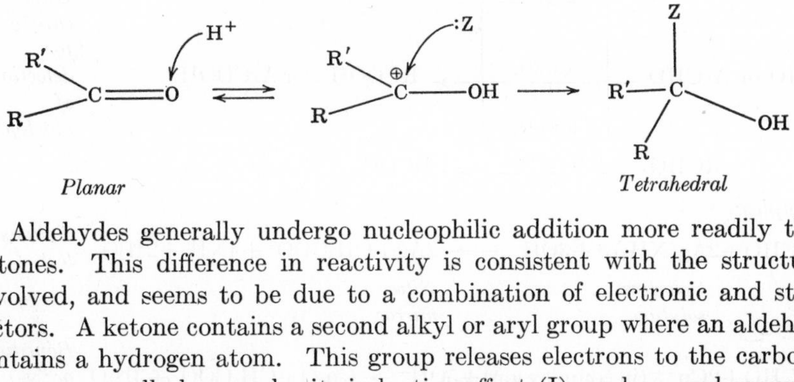

$$R' \diagdown \atop R \diagup \!\! C = O \quad \underset{\longleftarrow}{\overset{H^+}{\rightleftharpoons}} \quad R' \diagdown \atop R \diagup \!\! \overset{\oplus}{C}-OH \quad \xrightarrow{\;:Z\;} \quad R'-\underset{R}{\overset{Z}{C}}-OH$$

Planar   Tetrahedral

Aldehydes generally undergo nucleophilic addition more readily than ketones. This difference in reactivity is consistent with the structures involved, and seems to be due to a combination of electronic and steric factors. A ketone contains a second alkyl or aryl group where an aldehyde contains a hydrogen atom. This group releases electrons to the carbonyl oxygen — an alkyl group by its inductive effect (I), and an aryl group by resonance (II) — and thus makes carbonyl carbon less vulnerable to nucleophilic attack.

$$R' \longrightarrow \underset{R}{\overset{}{C}} = \ddot{O}: \qquad\qquad \underset{II}{\overset{}{\langle + \rangle}} = \underset{R}{\overset{}{C}} - \ddot{O}:^-$$

I   II

The second alkyl or aryl group of a ketone is larger than the hydrogen of an aldehyde, and offers more hindrance to the approach of the nucleophilic reagent.

Besides providing a site for nucleophilic addition, the carbonyl group affects the properties of aldehydes and ketones in a second very important way: it increases the acidity of the hydrogen atoms attached to the *alpha* carbon. Just as in the case of the carboxylic acids (Sec. 16.13), the carbonyl group exerts its acid-strengthening effect by helping to accommodate the negative charge of the anion.

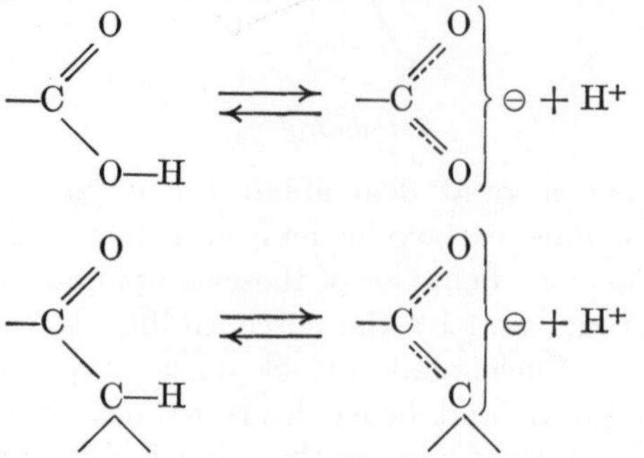

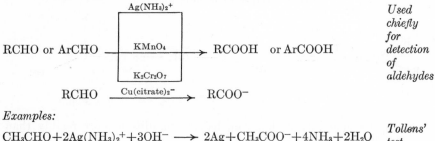

The acidity of *alpha* hydrogens is the basis of an extremely important group of reactions: the aldol condensation and its variations.

REACTIONS OF ALDEHYDES AND KETONES

1. Oxidation   Discussed in Sec. 23.8.

(a) Aldehydes

$$
\text{RCHO or ArCHO} \xrightarrow[\substack{\text{K}_2\text{Cr}_2\text{O}_7}]{\substack{\text{Ag(NH}_3)_2{}^+ \\ \text{KMnO}_4}} \text{RCOOH}\quad\text{or ArCOOH}
$$

Used chiefly for detection of aldehydes

$$
\text{RCHO} \xrightarrow{\text{Cu(citrate)}_2{}^-} \text{RCOO}^-
$$

Examples:

$$
\text{CH}_3\text{CHO}+2\text{Ag(NH}_3)_2{}^++3\text{OH}^- \longrightarrow 2\text{Ag}+\text{CH}_3\text{COO}^-+4\text{NH}_3+2\text{H}_2\text{O}
$$

Colorless solution   Silver mirror

Tollens' test

$$
\text{CH}_3\text{CHO}+2\text{Cu}^{++}\ (\text{in complex ion})+5\text{OH}^- \rightarrow \text{Cu}_2\text{O}+\text{CH}_3\text{COO}^-+3\text{H}_2\text{O}
$$

Deep blue solution   Brick-red precipitate

Benedict's or Fehling's test

(b) Methyl ketones

$$
\underset{\substack{\text{O}}}{\text{R}-\overset{\|}{\text{C}}-\text{CH}_3}\ \text{or}\ \underset{\substack{\text{O}}}{\text{Ar}-\overset{\|}{\text{C}}-\text{CH}_3} \xrightarrow{\text{OX}^-} \text{RCOO}^-\ \text{or ArCOO}^- + \text{CHX}_3
$$

Haloform reaction

Examples:

$$
\underset{\substack{\text{O}}}{\text{C}_2\text{H}_5-\overset{\|}{\text{C}}-\text{CH}_3} + 3\text{OI}^- \longrightarrow \text{C}_2\text{H}_5\text{COO}^- + \text{CHI}_3 + 2\text{OH}^-
$$

Iodoform
Yellow; m.p. 119°

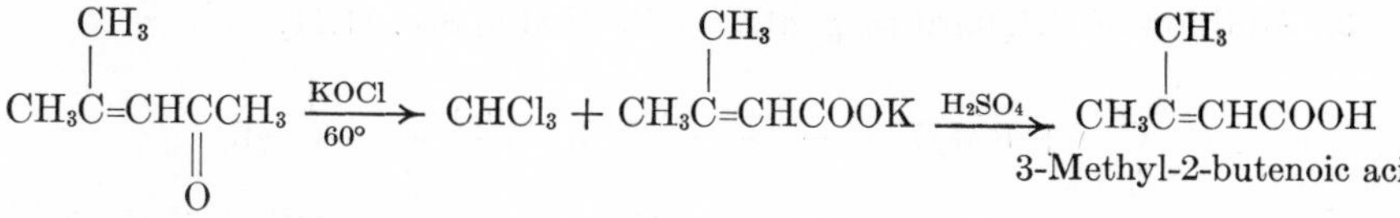

$$\underset{\substack{\text{Mesityl oxide}\\ \text{(4-Methyl-3-penten-2-one)}}}{\underset{\displaystyle \|}{\underset{\displaystyle O}{CH_3\overset{\displaystyle CH_3}{\overset{\displaystyle |}{C}}=CHCCH_3}}} \xrightarrow[60°]{KOCl} CHCl_3 + CH_3\overset{\displaystyle CH_3}{\overset{\displaystyle |}{C}}=CHCOOK \xrightarrow{H_2SO_4} \underset{\text{3-Methyl-2-butenoic acid}}{CH_3\overset{\displaystyle CH_3}{\overset{\displaystyle |}{C}}=CHCOOH}$$

2. Reduction. Discussed in Sec. 23.9.

    (a) Reduction to alcohols

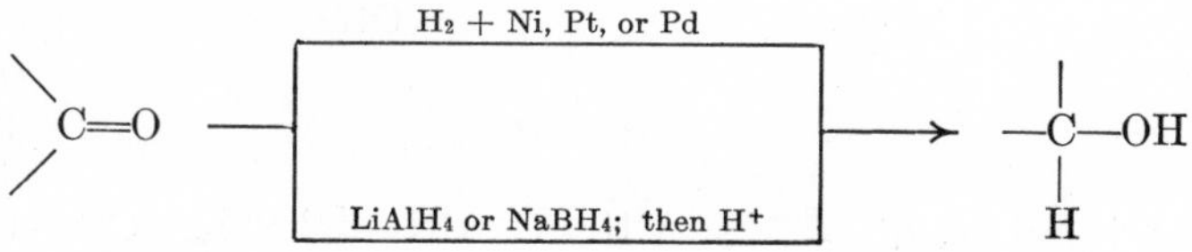

Examples:

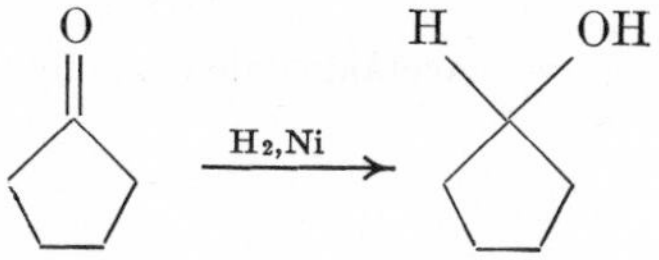

Cyclopentanone   Cyclopentanol

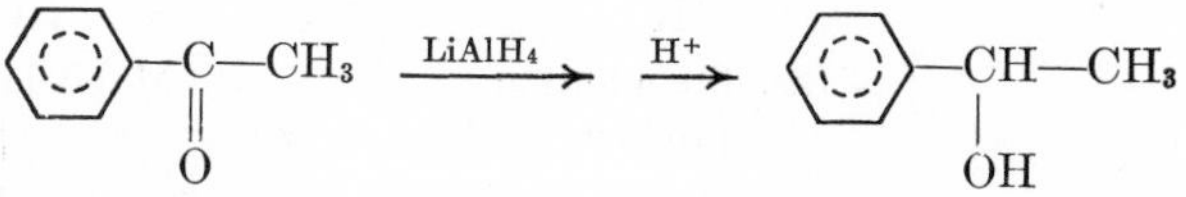

    Acetophenone   α-Phenylethyl alcohol

    (b) Reduction to hydrocarbons. Clemmensen reduction

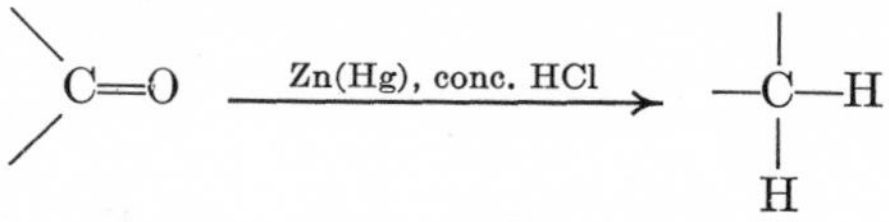

Examples:

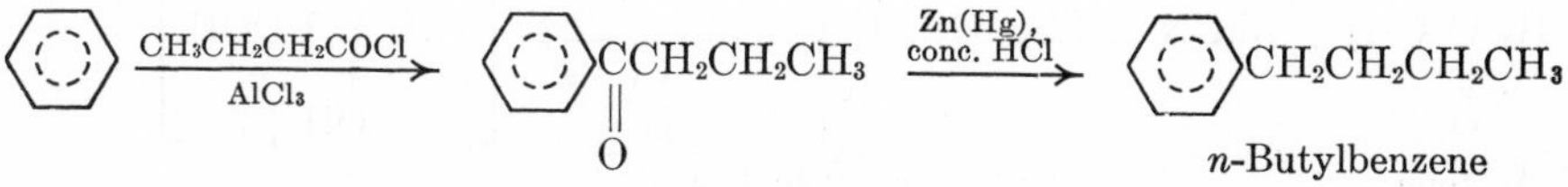

n-Butyrophenone   n-Butylbenzene
(Phenyl n-propyl ketone)

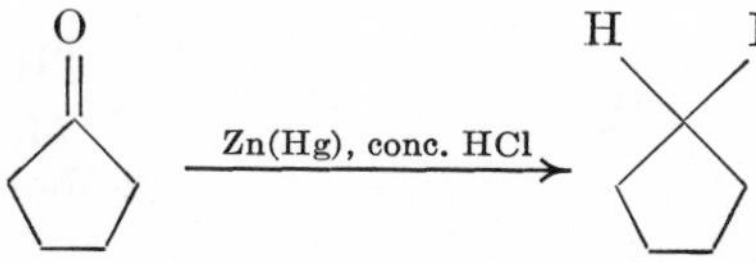

    Cyclopentanone   Cyclopentane

    (c) Reduction to pinacols. Discussed in Sec. 24.4.

    (d) Reductive amination. Discussed in Sec. 19.11.

3. Addition of Grignard reagents. Discussed in Sec. 11.11.

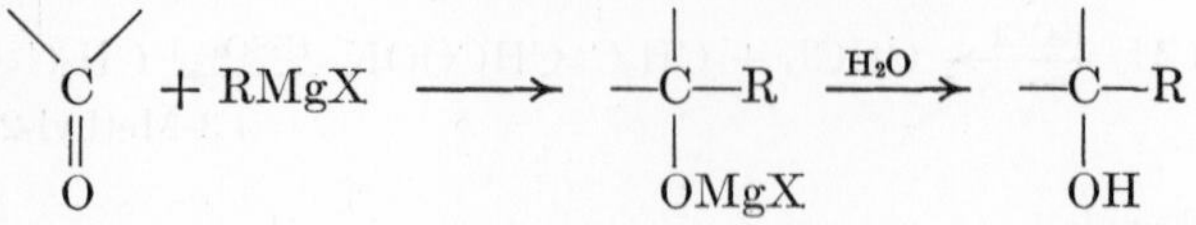

$$\underset{O}{\overset{\diagdown}{\underset{\|}{C}}} + RMgX \longrightarrow \underset{OMgX}{\overset{|}{\underset{|}{-C-R}}} \xrightarrow{H_2O} \underset{OH}{\overset{|}{\underset{|}{-C-R}}}$$

4. Addition of cyanide. Cyanohydrin formation. Discussed in Sec. 23.11.

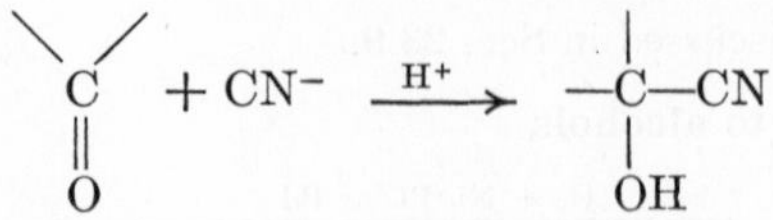

$$\underset{O}{\overset{\diagdown}{\underset{\|}{C}}} + CN^- \xrightarrow{H^+} \underset{OH}{\overset{|}{\underset{|}{-C-CN}}}$$

Examples:

$$CH_3-\overset{H}{\underset{}{C}}=O + NaCN(aq) \xrightarrow{H_2SO_4} CH_3-\overset{H}{\underset{OH}{\underset{|}{C}}}-CN \xrightarrow{H_2O,\ HCl} CH_3-\overset{H}{\underset{OH}{\underset{|}{C}}}-COOH$$

Acetaldehyde　　　　　　Acetaldehyde cyanohydrin　　　Lactic acid
　　　　　　　　　　　　　　　　　　　　　　　　　　　(α-Hydroxypropionic acid)

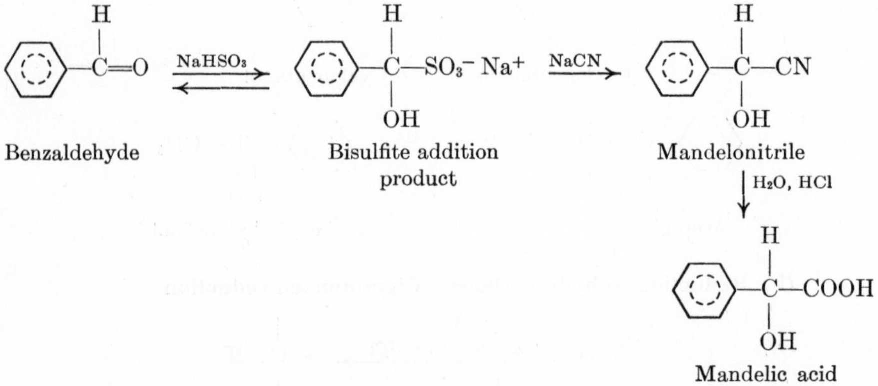

Benzaldehyde $\overset{H}{\underset{}{C}}=O \xrightarrow{NaHSO_3} \overset{H}{\underset{OH}{\underset{|}{C}}}-SO_3^-\ Na^+ \xrightarrow{NaCN} \overset{H}{\underset{OH}{\underset{|}{C}}}-CN$

Benzaldehyde　　　　　　Bisulfite addition　　　　Mandelonitrile
　　　　　　　　　　　　　　product　　　　　　　　│ H₂O, HCl
　　　　　　　　　　　　　　　　　　　　　　　　　　↓

$$\overset{H}{\underset{OH}{\underset{|}{C}}}-COOH$$

Mandelic acid

$$CH_3-\underset{O}{\overset{\|}{C}}-CH_3 + NaCN \xrightarrow{H_2SO_4} CH_3-\overset{CH_3}{\underset{OH}{\underset{|}{\overset{|}{C}}}}-CN \xrightarrow{H_2O,\ H_2SO_4} \left[CH_3-\overset{CH_3}{\underset{OH}{\underset{|}{\overset{|}{C}}}}-COOH \right]$$

Acetone　　　　　　　Acetone cyanohydrin

$$\downarrow$$

$$CH_2=\overset{CH_3}{\underset{}{\overset{|}{C}}}-COOH$$

Methacrylic acid
(2-Methylpropenoic acid)

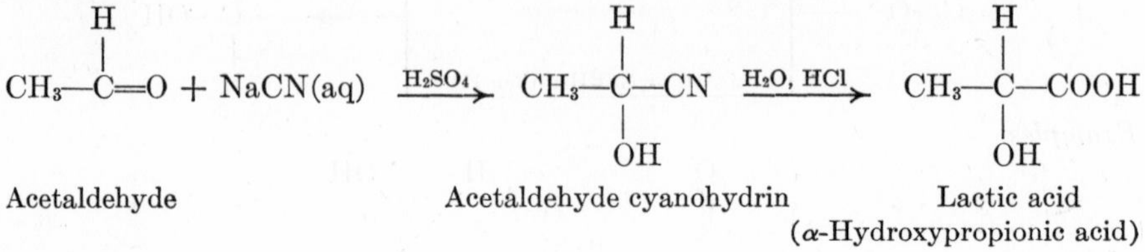

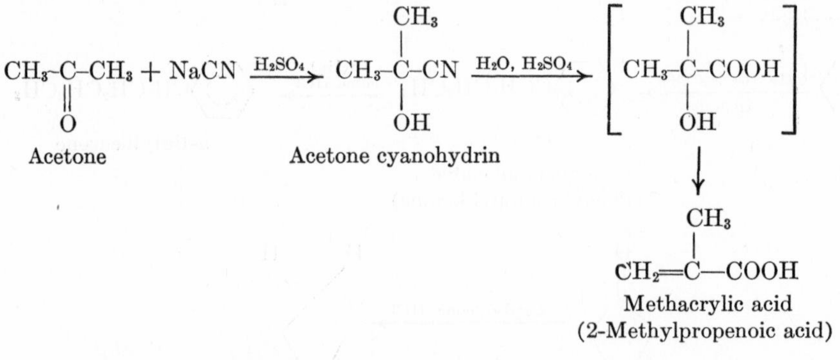

5. Addition of bisulfite. Discussed in Sec. 23.12.

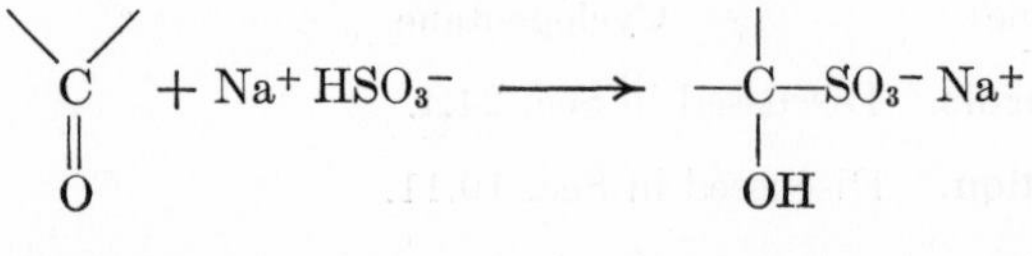

$$\underset{O}{\overset{\diagdown}{\underset{\|}{C}}} + Na^+\ HSO_3^- \longrightarrow \underset{OH}{\overset{|}{\underset{|}{-C-SO_3^-\ Na^+}}} \qquad \textit{Used in purification}$$
$$\textit{Not for hindered ketones}$$

Examples:

$$\langle\bigcirc\rangle\text{-}\overset{\overset{\text{H}}{|}}{\text{C}}{=}\text{O} + \text{Na}^+\,\text{HSO}_3^- \longrightarrow \langle\bigcirc\rangle\text{-}\overset{\overset{\text{H}}{|}}{\underset{\underset{\text{OH}}{|}}{\text{C}}}\text{-SO}_3^-\,\text{Na}^+ \left[\xrightarrow{\text{H}^+\text{ or OH}^-} \langle\bigcirc\rangle\text{CHO}\right]$$

Benzaldehyde

$$\text{CH}_3\text{CH}_2\overset{\overset{}{\underset{\underset{\text{O}}{\|}}{\text{C}}}}{\text{C}}\text{CH}_3 + \text{Na}^+\,\text{HSO}_3^- \longrightarrow \text{CH}_3\text{CH}_2\overset{\overset{\text{CH}_3}{|}}{\underset{\underset{\text{OH}}{|}}{\text{C}}}\text{-SO}_3^-\,\text{Na}^+$$

Methyl ethyl ketone
2-Butanone

$$\text{CH}_3\overset{\overset{\text{CH}_3}{|}}{\text{CH}}\text{-}\overset{\overset{}{\underset{\underset{\text{O}}{\|}}{\text{C}}}}{\text{C}}\text{-}\overset{\overset{\text{CH}_3}{|}}{\text{CH}}\text{CH}_3 + \text{Na}^+\,\text{HSO}_3^- \longrightarrow \text{ no reaction}$$

Isopropyl ketone
2,4-Dimethyl-3-pentanone

6. Addition of derivatives of ammonia. Discussed in Sec. 23.13.

$$\overset{\diagdown}{\underset{\diagup}{\text{C}}}\underset{\underset{\text{O}}{\|}}{} + \text{H}_2\text{N}\text{-G} \longrightarrow \left[\overset{|}{\underset{\underset{\text{OH}}{|}}{\text{-C-NH-G}}}\right] \longrightarrow \overset{\diagdown}{\underset{\diagup}{\text{C}}}{=}\text{N}\text{-G} + \text{H}_2\text{O} \quad \textit{Used for identification}$$

H₂N—G		**Product**	
$\text{H}_2\text{N}\text{-OH}$	Hydroxylamine	$\overset{\diagdown}{\underset{\diagup}{\text{C}}}{=}\text{NOH}$	Oxime
$\text{H}_2\text{N}\text{-NH}_2$	Hydrazine	$\overset{\diagdown}{\underset{\diagup}{\text{C}}}{=}\text{NNH}_2$	Hydrazone
$\text{H}_2\text{N}\text{-NHC}_6\text{H}_5$	Phenylhydrazine	$\overset{\diagdown}{\underset{\diagup}{\text{C}}}{=}\text{NNHC}_6\text{H}_5$	Phenylhydrazone
$\text{H}_2\text{N}\text{-NHCONH}_2$	Semicarbazide	$\overset{\diagdown}{\underset{\diagup}{\text{C}}}{=}\text{NNHCONH}_2$	Semicarbazone

Examples:

$$\text{CH}_3\overset{\overset{\text{H}}{|}}{\text{C}}{=}\text{O} + \text{H}_2\text{N}\text{-OH} \xrightarrow{\text{H}^+} \text{CH}_3\overset{\overset{\text{H}}{|}}{\text{C}}{=}\text{NOH} + \text{H}_2\text{O}$$

    Acetaldehyde   Hydroxylamine   Acetaldoxime

$$\langle\bigcirc\rangle\text{-}\overset{\overset{\text{H}}{|}}{\text{C}}{=}\text{O} + \text{H}_2\text{N}\text{-NHC}_6\text{H}_5 \xrightarrow{\text{H}^+} \langle\bigcirc\rangle\text{-}\overset{\overset{\text{H}}{|}}{\text{C}}{=}\text{NNHC}_6\text{H}_5 + \text{H}_2\text{O}$$

Benzaldehyde   Phenylhydrazine   Benzaldehyde phenylhydrazone

$$\text{CH}_3\text{COCH}_3 + \text{H}_2\text{N}\text{-NHCONH}_2 \xrightarrow{\text{H}^+} \text{CH}_3\overset{\overset{\text{CH}_3}{|}}{\text{C}}{=}\text{NNHCONH}_2 + \text{H}_2\text{O}$$

   Acetone   Semicarbazide   Acetone semicarbazone

7. Addition of alcohols. Acetal formation. Discussed in Sec. 23.14.

$$\underset{\text{O}}{\overset{\diagdown\diagup}{\text{C}}}\ +\ 2ROH \rightleftharpoons \underset{\text{OR}}{\overset{|}{-}\text{C}\text{--}OR}\ +\ H_2O$$

An acetal

Example:

$$CH_3\text{--}\overset{\text{H}}{\underset{}{\text{C}}}{=}O + 2C_2H_5OH \underset{}{\overset{HCl}{\rightleftharpoons}} CH_3\text{--}\overset{\text{H}}{\underset{OC_2H_5}{\text{C}}}\text{--}OC_2H_5 + H_2O$$

Acetaldehyde   Acetal
                                 (Acetaldehyde
                                 diethyl acetal)

8. Addition of carbanions

    (a) Aldol condensation. Discussed in Secs. 23.15 through 23.18.

$$\underset{\text{O}}{\overset{\diagdown\diagup}{\text{C}}}\ +\ \underset{\text{H}}{\overset{|\ \ |}{-}\text{C}\text{--}\text{C}{=}O} \xrightarrow{\text{base or acid}} \underset{\text{OH}}{\overset{|\ \ |\ \ |}{-}\text{C}\text{--}\text{C}\text{--}\text{C}{=}O}$$

An aldol
(A β-hydroxy carbonyl compound)

Examples:

$$CH_3\overset{\text{H}}{\underset{}{\text{C}}}{=}O + CH_2\overset{\text{H}}{\underset{\text{H}}{\text{C}}}{=}O \xrightarrow{OH^-} CH_3\overset{\text{H}}{\underset{OH}{\text{C}}}\text{--}CH_2\overset{\text{H}}{\underset{}{\text{C}}}{=}O \xrightarrow[\text{heat}]{NaHSO_4,} CH_3\text{--}\overset{\text{H}}{\underset{}{\text{C}}}{=}\overset{\text{H}}{\underset{}{\text{C}}}\text{--}\overset{\text{H}}{\underset{}{\text{C}}}{=}O + H_2O$$

Acetaldehyde   Acetaldol   Crotonaldehyde
2 moles   (3-Hydroxybutanal)   (2-Butenal)

$$CH_3\overset{CH_3}{\underset{\text{H}}{\text{C}}}{=}O + CH_2\overset{CH_3}{\underset{}{\text{C}}}{=}O \xrightarrow{OH^-} CH_3\overset{CH_3}{\underset{OH}{\text{C}}}\text{--}CH_2\overset{}{\underset{O}{\text{C}}}CH_3 \xrightarrow[\text{heat}]{NaHSO_4,} CH_3\overset{CH_3}{\underset{}{\text{C}}}{=}CH\underset{O}{\text{C}}CH_3 + H_2O$$

Acetone   Diacetone alcohol   Mesityl oxide
2 moles   (4-Methyl-3-penten-2-one)

$$\text{C}_6\text{H}_5\text{--}\overset{\text{H}}{\underset{}{\text{C}}}{=}O + CH_2\overset{\text{H}}{\underset{\text{H}}{\text{C}}}{=}O \xrightarrow{OH^-} \left[\text{C}_6\text{H}_5\text{--}\overset{\text{H}}{\underset{OH}{\text{C}}}\text{--}CH_2\overset{\text{H}}{\underset{}{\text{C}}}{=}O\right] \rightarrow \text{C}_6\text{H}_5\text{--}\overset{\text{H}}{\underset{}{\text{C}}}{=}\overset{\text{H}}{\underset{}{\text{C}}}\text{--}\overset{\text{H}}{\underset{}{\text{C}}}{=}O + H_2O$$

Benzaldehyde   Acetaldehyde   Cinnamaldehyde
                                                (3-Phenyl-2-propenal)

$$\underset{\text{Benzaldehyde}}{\left\langle\bigcirc\right\rangle\overset{\text{H}}{\underset{}{\text{C}}}\text{=O}} + \underset{\text{Acetone}}{\underset{\text{H}\quad\text{O}}{\text{CH}_2\text{CCH}_3}} \xrightarrow{\text{OH}^-} \left[\left\langle\bigcirc\right\rangle\overset{\text{H}}{\underset{\text{OH}}{\text{C}}}\text{-CH}_2\underset{\text{O}}{\text{CCH}_3}\right] \longrightarrow \left\langle\bigcirc\right\rangle\overset{\text{H H}}{\text{C=C-C}}\underset{\text{O}}{\text{-CH}_3}$$

Benzaldehyde   Acetone

Benzalacetone
(*Benzal* is $C_6H_5CH=$)
(4-Phenyl-3-buten-2-one)

$$\underset{\text{Benzaldehyde}}{\left\langle\bigcirc\right\rangle\overset{\text{H}}{\text{C}}\text{=O}} + \underset{\text{Acetophenone}}{\underset{\text{H}\quad\text{O}}{\text{CH}_2\text{-C-}\left\langle\bigcirc\right\rangle}} \xrightarrow{\text{OH}^-} \underset{\text{Benzalacetophenone}}{\left\langle\bigcirc\right\rangle\overset{\text{H H}}{\text{C=C-C}}\underset{\text{O}}{\text{-}\left\langle\bigcirc\right\rangle}} + H_2O$$

Benzaldehyde   Acetophenone

Benzalacetophenone
(1,3-Diphenyl-2-propen-1-one)

(b) Perkin condensation.   Discussed in Sec. 23.20.

$$\underset{}{\text{Ar}\overset{\text{H}}{\text{C}}\text{=O}} + (\text{RCHCO})_2\text{O} \xrightarrow{\text{base}} \text{Ar}\overset{\text{H R}}{\text{C=C}}\text{-COOH} \qquad \text{R } may\ be\ \text{H}$$

Examples:

$$\underset{\text{Benzaldehyde}}{\left\langle\bigcirc\right\rangle\overset{\text{H}}{\text{C}}\text{=O}} + \underset{\text{Acetic anhydride}}{\begin{array}{c}\text{CH}_3\text{C}\diagdown^{\text{O}}\\ \diagup\text{O}\\ \text{CH}_2\text{C}\diagdown\\ \underset{\text{H}}{\quad}\diagdown\text{O}\end{array}} \xrightarrow{\text{CH}_3\text{COONa, }175°} \underset{\substack{\text{Cinnamic acid}\\(\text{3-Phenylpropenoic acid})}}{\left\langle\bigcirc\right\rangle\overset{\text{H H}}{\text{C=C}}\text{-COOH}} + \text{CH}_3\text{COOH}$$

Benzaldehyde   Acetic anhydride

Cinnamic acid
(3-Phenylpropenoic acid)

$$\underset{\text{Benzaldehyde}}{\left\langle\bigcirc\right\rangle\overset{\text{H}}{\text{C}}\text{=O}} + \underset{\text{Propionic anhydride}}{\begin{array}{c}\text{CH}_3\text{CH}_2\text{C}\diagdown^{\text{O}}\\ \diagup\text{O}\\ \text{CH}_3\text{CHC}\diagdown\\ \underset{\text{H}}{\quad}\diagdown\text{O}\end{array}} \xrightarrow[135°]{\text{CH}_3\text{CH}_2\text{COONa,}} \underset{\substack{\alpha\text{-Methylcinnamic acid}\\(\text{3-Phenyl-2-methylpropenoic acid})}}{\left\langle\bigcirc\right\rangle\overset{\text{H CH}_3}{\text{C=C}}\text{-COOH}} + \text{CH}_3\text{CH}_2\text{COOH}$$

Benzaldehyde   Propionic anhydride

α-Methylcinnamic acid
(3-Phenyl-2-methylpropenoic acid)

$$\underset{\substack{p\text{-Nitro-}\\\text{benzaldehyde}}}{\text{O}_2\text{N}\left\langle\bigcirc\right\rangle\overset{\text{H}}{\text{C}}\text{=O}} + \underset{\text{Acetic anhydride}}{\begin{array}{c}\text{CH}_3\text{C}\diagdown^{\text{O}}\\ \diagup\text{O}\\ \text{CH}_2\text{C}\diagdown\\ \underset{\text{H}}{\quad}\diagdown\text{O}\end{array}} \xrightarrow{\text{CH}_3\text{COONa, }175°} \underset{p\text{-Nitrocinnamic acid}}{\text{O}_2\text{N}\left\langle\bigcirc\right\rangle\overset{\text{H H}}{\text{C=C}}\text{-COOH}} + \text{CH}_3\text{COOH}$$

p-Nitro-
benzaldehyde

Acetic anhydride

p-Nitrocinnamic acid

9. Cannizzaro reaction. Discussed in Sec. 23.21.

$$2 \overset{\overset{\displaystyle H}{|}}{-C}{=}O \xrightarrow{\text{strong base}} -COO^- \ + \ -CH_2OH$$

An aldehyde with   Acid   Alcohol
no α-hydrogens   salt

Examples:

$$2HCHO \xrightarrow{\text{50\% NaOH, room temperature}} HCOO^- \ + \ CH_3OH$$

Formaldehyde   Formate ion   Methanol

$$2\ CH_3{-}\overset{\overset{\displaystyle CH_3}{|}}{\underset{\underset{\displaystyle CH_3}{|}}{C}}{-}CHO \xrightarrow{\text{50\% alcoholic KOH}} CH_3{-}\overset{\overset{\displaystyle CH_3}{|}}{\underset{\underset{\displaystyle CH_3}{|}}{C}}{-}COO^- \ + \ CH_3{-}\overset{\overset{\displaystyle CH_3}{|}}{\underset{\underset{\displaystyle CH_3}{|}}{C}}{-}CH_2OH$$

Trimethylacetaldehyde   Trimethylacetate ion   Neopentyl alcohol

$$2\ \underset{m\text{-Chlorobenzaldehyde}}{\overset{CHO}{\bigcirc}\!Cl} \xrightarrow{\text{50\% KOH}} \underset{m\text{-Chlorobenzoate ion}}{\overset{COO^-}{\bigcirc}\!Cl} + \underset{m\text{-Chlorobenzyl alcohol}}{\overset{CH_2OH}{\bigcirc}\!Cl}$$

$$\underset{\substack{\text{Veratraldehyde (cf. Sec. 22.4)}\\ \text{3,4-Dimethoxybenzaldehyde}}}{\overset{CHO}{\underset{OCH_3}{\bigcirc}\!OCH_3}} + HCHO \xrightarrow{\text{50\% NaOH,65°}} \underset{\substack{\text{3,4-Dimethoxybenzyl alcohol}}}{\overset{CH_2OH}{\underset{OCH_3}{\bigcirc}\!OCH_3}} + HCOO^-$$

Crossed Cannizzaro reaction

10. Halogenation. Discussed in Sec. 26.8.

$$\overset{\overset{\displaystyle O}{\|}}{-C}{-}\overset{\underset{\underset{\displaystyle H}{|}}{|}}{C}{-} + X_2 \longrightarrow \overset{\overset{\displaystyle O}{\|}}{-C}{-}\overset{\underset{\underset{\displaystyle X}{|}}{|}}{C}{-} + HX$$

$$X_2 = Cl_2,\ Br_2,\ I_2$$

23.8 Oxidation

Of all the organic compounds we have studied, aldehydes as a class are the most easily oxidized. They are converted into carboxylic acids not only by reagents like permanganate and dichromate, but even by such weak oxidizing agents as silver ion or cupric ion. Oxidation by silver or cupric ion requires an alkaline medium; to prevent precipitation of the insoluble metal oxide or hydroxide, complexing agents are added.

Tollens' reagent contains the silver ammonia ion, $Ag(NH_3)_2^+$. In **Benedict's solution** cupric ion is complexed with citrate ion; in the older **Fehling's solution** it is complexed with tartrate ion. Oxidation of the aldehyde is accompanied by reduction of silver ion to free silver (in the form of a *mirror* under the proper conditions), or reduction of cupric ion to cuprous oxide (a brick-red precipitate).

$$RCHO + Ag(NH_3)_2^+ \longrightarrow RCOO^- + Ag$$

Colorless
solution

Silver
mirror

$$RCHO + Cu(citrate)_2^= \longrightarrow RCOO^- + Cu_2O$$

Deep blue
solution

Brick-red
precipitate

The extreme ease with which aldehydes undergo oxidation is useful chiefly for detecting these compounds, and in particular for differentiating them from ketones (see Sec. 23.22). The reaction is of value in synthesis in those cases where aldehydes are more readily available than the corresponding acids: in particular, for the synthesis of unsaturated acids from the unsaturated aldehydes obtained from the aldol condensation (Sec. 23.16), where advantage is taken of the fact that neither Tollens' nor Benedict's reagent attacks carbon–carbon double bonds.

$$\overset{\beta}{R}CH=\overset{\alpha}{C}H-\overset{\overset{\displaystyle H}{|}}{C}=O \xrightarrow{\text{Tollens' or Benedict's reagent}} \overset{\beta}{R}CH=\overset{\alpha}{C}H-COOH$$

α,β-Unsaturated aldehyde α,β-Unsaturated acid

Oxidation of ketones requires the breaking of carbon–carbon bonds, and hence (with the exception noted below of the haloform reaction) takes place only under rather severe conditions. The reaction is seldom of value in synthesis; many ketones can be cleaved on either side of the carbonyl group to yield a mixture of acids. For example:

$$\underset{O}{\overset{6 \quad 5 \quad 4 \quad 3 \; 2 \quad 1}{CH_3CH_2CH_2CCH_2CH_3}} \xrightarrow[\text{heat}]{KMnO_4, \, H^+} \begin{cases} \xrightarrow{C_2-C_3 \text{ cleavage}} \overset{6 \quad 5 \quad 4 \quad 3}{CH_3CH_2CH_2COOH} + \overset{2 \; 1}{HOOCCH_3} \\ \xrightarrow{C_3-C_4 \text{ cleavage}} \overset{6 \quad 5 \quad 4}{CH_3CH_2COOH} + \overset{3 \; 2 \quad 1}{HOOCCH_2CH_3} \end{cases}$$

The reaction is, however, important in the case of cyclic ketones, which yield dicarboxylic acids (Sec. 25.3).

Problem 23.6 Predict the product of vigorous oxidation of cyclohexanone.

Methyl ketones are oxidized smoothly by means of hypohalite in the haloform reaction (Sec. 12.11). Although most commonly used to detect these ketones (Sec. 23.22), this reaction is often useful in synthesis, hypohalite having the special advantage of not attacking carbon–carbon double bonds. For example:

$$\langle\!\!\bigcirc\!\!\rangle\!-\!\overset{\overset{\displaystyle H}{|}}{C}=\overset{\overset{\displaystyle CH_3}{|}}{C}-\underset{O}{\overset{}{C}}-CH_3 \xrightarrow{KOCl} \langle\!\!\bigcirc\!\!\rangle\!-\!\overset{\overset{\displaystyle H}{|}}{C}=\overset{\overset{\displaystyle CH_3}{|}}{C}-COOH + CHCl_3$$

(Available by aldol condensation) α-Methylcinnamic acid

23.9 Reduction

Aldehydes can be reduced to primary alcohols, and ketones to secondary alcohols, either by catalytic hydrogenation or by use of chemical reducing agents like lithium aluminum hydride, LiAlH₄. Such reduction is useful for the preparation of certain alcohols that are less available than the corresponding carbonyl compounds, in particular those that can be obtained by the aldol condensation (Sec. 23.17). For example:

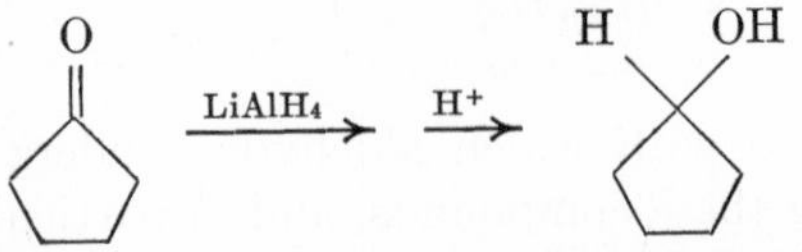

Cyclopentanone → Cyclopentanol

$$CH_3CH{=}CHCHO \xrightarrow{H_2,\ Ni} CH_3CH_2CH_2CH_2OH$$

Crotonaldehyde (from aldol condensation of acetaldehyde) → n-Butyl alcohol

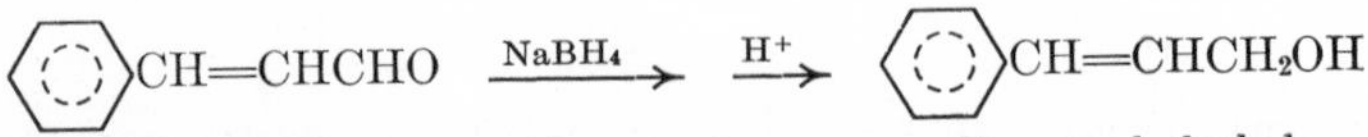

Cinnamaldehyde (from aldol condensation of benzaldehyde and acetaldehyde) → Cinnamyl alcohol

Sodium borohydride, NaBH₄, does not reduce carbon–carbon double bonds, not even those conjugated with carbonyl groups, and is thus useful for the reduction of such unsaturated carbonyl compounds to unsaturated alcohols.

Aldehydes and ketones can be reduced to hydrocarbons by the action of amalgamated zinc and concentrated hydrochloric acid, the **Clemmensen reduction**. The Clemmensen reduction is particularly important when applied to the alkyl aryl ketones obtained from Friedel-Crafts acylation, since this reaction sequence permits, indirectly, the attachment of straight alkyl chains to the benzene ring. For example:

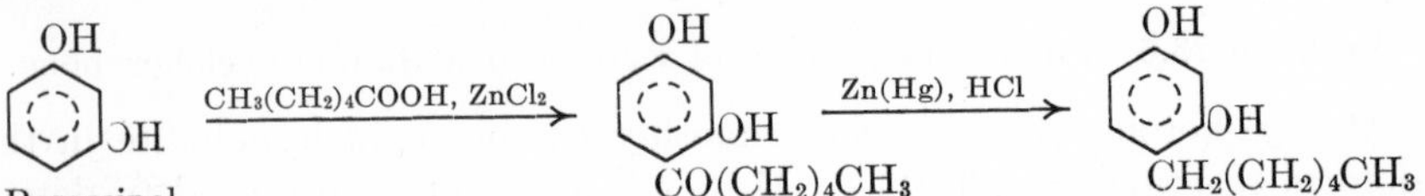

Resorcinol → ... → 4-n-Hexylresorcinol *Used as an antiseptic*

The *bimolecular reduction* of carbonyl compounds to pinacols will be discussed in Sec. 24.4.

A special sort of oxidation and reduction, the *Cannizzaro reaction*, will be discussed in Sec. 23.21.

23.10 Addition of Grignard reagents

The addition of Grignard reagents to aldehydes and ketones has already been discussed as one of the most important methods of preparing complicated alcohols (Sec. 11.13).

23.11   Addition of cyanide

The elements of HCN add to the carbonyl group of aldehydes and ketones to yield compounds known as **cyanohydrins**:

$$\underset{\underset{\displaystyle O}{\|}}{C} + CN^- \xrightarrow{\;H^+\;} \underset{\displaystyle OH}{-\overset{|}{\underset{|}{C}}-CN}$$

A cyanohydrin

The reaction is often carried out by adding mineral acid to a mixture of the carbonyl compound and aqueous sodium cyanide. In a useful modification, cyanide is added to the bisulfite addition product (Sec. 23.12), of the carbonyl compound, the bisulfite ion serving as the necessary acid:

$$-\overset{|}{\underset{\underset{\displaystyle OH}{|}}{C}}-SO_3^- Na^+ \;\rightleftharpoons\; \underset{\underset{\displaystyle O}{\|}}{C} + Na^+ HSO_3^- \xrightarrow{\;CN^-\;} -\overset{|}{\underset{\underset{\displaystyle OH}{|}}{C}}-CN + SO_3^= + Na^+$$

Addition appears to involve nucleophilic attack on carbonyl carbon by the strongly basic cyanide ion; subsequently (or possibly simultaneously) oxygen accepts a hydrogen ion to form the cyanohydrin product:

$$\underset{\underset{\displaystyle :CN^-}{\underset{\displaystyle O}{\|}}}{C} \longrightarrow -\overset{|}{\underset{\underset{\displaystyle O_-}{|}}{C}}-CN \xrightarrow{\;H^+\;} -\overset{|}{\underset{\underset{\displaystyle OH}{|}}{C}}-CN$$

Nucleophilic reagent   Cyanohydrin

Although it is the elements of HCN that become attached to the carbonyl group, a highly acidic medium — in which the concentration of un-ionized HCN is highest — actually retards reaction. This is reasonable, since the very weak acid HCN is a poor source of cyanide ion.

Cyanohydrins are nitriles, and their principal use is based on the fact that, like other nitriles, they undergo hydrolysis; in this case the products are α-hydroxyacids or unsaturated acids. For example:

$$O_2N\text{—}\underset{\displaystyle}{\text{(ring)}}\text{—}\overset{\displaystyle H}{\underset{}{C}}{=}O \xrightarrow{CN^-, H^+} O_2N\text{—}\underset{\displaystyle}{\text{(ring)}}\text{—}\overset{\displaystyle H}{\underset{\displaystyle OH}{C}}\text{—}CN \xrightarrow{HCl,\ heat} O_2N\text{—}\underset{\displaystyle}{\text{(ring)}}\text{—}\overset{\displaystyle H}{\underset{\displaystyle OH}{C}}\text{—}COOH$$

m-Nitrobenzaldehyde   *m*-Nitromandelic acid

$$CH_3CH_2\text{—}\overset{\displaystyle CH_3}{\underset{}{C}}{=}O \xrightarrow{CN^-, H^+} CH_3CH_2\text{—}\overset{\displaystyle CH_3}{\underset{\displaystyle OH}{C}}\text{—}CN \xrightarrow{H_2SO_4,\ heat} \left[\ CH_3CH_2\text{—}\overset{\displaystyle CH_3}{\underset{\displaystyle OH}{C}}\text{—}COOH\ \right]$$

Methyl ethyl ketone
2-Butanone

$$\downarrow$$

$$CH_3CH{=}\overset{\displaystyle CH_3}{\underset{}{C}}\text{—}COOH$$

2-Methyl-2-butenoic acid

Problem 23.7   Discuss the stereochemistry (active? resolvable?) of the cyanohydrin prepared from acetaldehyde; from benzaldehyde; from acetone. Of the α-hydroxyacid obtained by hydrolysis of each of these.

23.12   Addition of bisulfite

Sodium bisulfite adds to most aldehydes and to many ketones (especially methyl ketones) to form bisulfite addition products:

$$\underset{O}{\overset{\diagdown \diagup}{C}} + Na^+ HSO_3^- \rightleftharpoons -\underset{OH}{\overset{|}{C}}-SO_3^- Na^+$$

A bisulfite
addition product

The reaction is carried out by mixing the aldehyde or ketone with a concentrated aqueous solution of sodium bisulfite; the product separates as a crystalline solid. Ketones containing bulky groups usually fail to react with bisulfite, presumably for steric reasons.

Addition involves nucleophilic attack by bisulfite ion on carbonyl carbon, followed by attachment of a hydrogen ion to carbonyl oxygen:

$$\overset{\diagdown \diagup}{\underset{O}{C}} \rightleftharpoons -\underset{O_-}{\overset{|}{C}}-SO_3^- \overset{H^+}{\rightleftharpoons} -\underset{OH}{\overset{|}{C}}-SO_3^-$$

$:SO_3H^-$

*Nucleophilic
reagent*

Like other carbonyl addition reactions, this one is reversible. Addition of acid or base destroys the bisulfite ion in equilibrium with the addition product, and regenerates the carbonyl compound.

$$-\underset{OH}{\overset{|}{C}}-SO_3^- Na^+ \rightleftharpoons \overset{\diagdown \diagup}{\underset{O}{C}} + HSO_3^- - \begin{cases} \overset{H^+}{\longrightarrow} SO_2 + H_2O \\ \overset{OH^-}{\longrightarrow} SO_3^= + H_2O \end{cases}$$

Bisulfite addition products are generally prepared for the purpose of separating a carbonyl compound from non-carbonyl compounds. The carbonyl compound can be purified by conversion into its bisulfite addition product, separation of the crystalline addition product from the non-carbonyl impurities, and subsequent regeneration of the carbonyl compound. A non-carbonyl compound can be freed of carbonyl impurities by washing it with aqueous sodium bisulfite; any contaminating aldehyde or ketone is converted into its bisulfite addition product which, being somewhat soluble in water, dissolves in the aqueous layer.

Problem 23.8   Suggest a practical situation that might arise in the laboratory in which you would need to (a) separate an aldehyde from undesired non-carbonyl materials; (b) remove an aldehyde that is contaminating a non-carbonyl compound. Describe how you could carry out the separations, telling exactly what you would do and see.

23.13 Addition of derivatives of ammonia

Certain compounds related to ammonia add to the carbonyl group to form derivatives that are important chiefly for the characterization and identification of aldehydes and ketones (Sec. 23.22). The products contain a carbon–nitrogen double bond resulting from elimination of a molecule of water from the initial addition products. Some of these reagents and their products are:

$$\underset{O}{\overset{}{\underset{\|}{C}}} + :NH_2OH \xrightarrow{H^+} \left[-\underset{OH}{\overset{|}{\underset{|}{C}}}-NHOH \right] \longrightarrow \underset{}{\overset{}{C}}=NOH + H_2O$$

Hydroxylamine   Oxime

$$\underset{O}{\overset{}{\underset{\|}{C}}} + :NH_2NHC_6H_5 \xrightarrow{H^+} \left[-\underset{OH}{\overset{|}{\underset{|}{C}}}-NHNHC_6H_5 \right] \longrightarrow \underset{}{\overset{}{C}}=NNHC_6H_5 + H_2O$$

Phenylhydrazine   Phenylhydrazone

$$\underset{O}{\overset{}{\underset{\|}{C}}} + :NH_2NHCONH_2 \xrightarrow{H^+} \left[-\underset{OH}{\overset{|}{\underset{|}{C}}}-NHNHCONH_2 \right] \longrightarrow$$

Semicarbazide

$$\underset{}{\overset{}{C}}=NNHCONH_2 + H_2O$$

Semicarbazone

Like ammonia, these derivatives of ammonia are basic, and therefore react with acids to form salts: hydroxylamine hydrochloride, $HONH_3^+ Cl^-$; phenylhydrazine hydrochloride, $C_6H_5NHNH_3^+ Cl^-$; and semicarbazide hydrochloride, $NH_2CONHNH_3^+ Cl^-$. The salts are less easily oxidized by air than the free bases, and it is in this form that the reagents are best preserved and handled. When needed, the basic reagents are liberated from their salts in the presence of the carbonyl compound by addition of a base, usually sodium acetate.

$$C_6H_5NHNH_3^+ Cl^- + CH_3COO^-Na^+ \rightleftarrows C_6H_5NHNH_2 + CH_3COOH + Na^+Cl^-$$

Phenylhydrazine hydrochloride	Sodium acetate	Phenylhydrazine	Acetic acid
Stronger acid	Stronger base	Weaker base	Weaker acid

As in the coupling of diazonium salts (Sec. 21.10) — and for exactly the same reason — it is often necessary to adjust the reaction medium to just the right acidity. Addition involves nucleophilic attack by the basic nitrogen compound on carbonyl carbon (as shown on the next page). Protonation of carbonyl oxygen makes carbonyl carbon more susceptible to nucleophilic attack; in so far as the carbonyl compound is concerned, then, addition will be favored by high acidity. But the ammonia derivative, $H_2N—G$, can also undergo protonation to form the ion, $^+H_3N—G$, which lacks unshared electrons and is no longer nucleophilic; in so far

$$\underset{O}{\overset{\diagdown}{\underset{\diagup}{C}}}= \underset{\overset{H^+}{\rightleftarrows}}{} \quad -\overset{|}{\underset{\underset{OH}{|}}{C}}^{\oplus}, \longrightarrow \left[-\overset{|}{\underset{\underset{OH}{|}}{C}}-\overset{\overset{H}{|}\overset{|\oplus}{}}{\underset{\underset{H}{|}}{N}}-G \right] \longrightarrow \overset{\diagdown}{\underset{\diagup}{C}}=N-G + H_2O + H^+$$

$$H_2\overset{..}{N}-G \underset{\overset{H^+}{\rightleftarrows}}{} {}^+H_3N-G$$

Free base: Salt:
nucleophilic   *not nucleophilic*

as the nitrogen compound is concerned, then, addition is favored by low acidity. The conditions under which addition proceeds most rapidly are thus the result of a compromise: the solution must be acidic enough for an appreciable fraction of the carbonyl compound to be protonated, but not so acidic that the concentration of the free nitrogen compound is too low. The exact conditions used depend upon the basicity of the reagent, and upon the reactivity of the carbonyl compound.

Problem 23.9 Semicarbazide (1 mole) is added to a mixture of cyclohexanone (1 mole) and benzaldehyde (1 mole). If the product is isolated immediately, it consists almost entirely of the semicarbazone of cyclohexanone; if the product is isolated after several hours, it consists almost entirely of the semicarbazone of benzaldehyde. How do you account for these observations? (*Hint:* see Sec. 6.17.)

23.14 Addition of alcohols. Acetal formation

Alcohols add to the carbonyl group of aldehydes in the presence of anhydrous acids to yield **acetals**:

$$R'-\overset{\overset{H}{|}}{C}=O + 2ROH \underset{\overset{\text{dry HCl}}{\longrightarrow}}{} R'-\overset{\overset{H}{|}}{\underset{\underset{OR}{|}}{C}}-OR + 2H_2O$$

Aldehyde   Alcohol   Acetal

The reaction is carried out by allowing the aldehyde to stand with an excess of the anhydrous alcohol and a little anhydrous acid, usually hydrogen chloride. In the preparation of ethyl acetals the water is often removed as it is formed by means of the azeotrope of water, benzene, and ethyl alcohol (b.p. 64.9°, Sec. 11.9). (Simple *ketals* are usually difficult to prepare by reaction of ketones with alcohols, and are made in other ways.)

$$\langle \bigcirc \rangle-\overset{\overset{H}{|}}{C}=O + 2C_2H_5OH \underset{\overset{\text{dry HCl}}{\longrightarrow}}{} \langle \bigcirc \rangle-\overset{\overset{H}{|}}{\underset{\underset{OC_2H_5}{|}}{C}}-OC_2H_5 + H_2O$$

Benzaldehyde   Ethyl alcohol   Diethyl acetal of benzaldehyde

$$\text{\textasciitilde}CHCH_2CHCH_2\text{\textasciitilde} + CH_3CH_2CH_2\overset{\overset{\displaystyle H}{|}}{C}=O \rightleftharpoons \text{\textasciitilde}CHCH_2CHCH_2\text{\textasciitilde} + H_2O$$

$$\underset{OH \quad\quad OH}{|} \qquad\qquad\qquad\qquad\qquad\qquad \underset{O \quad\quad O}{|}$$

Poylvinyl alcohol   Butyraldehyde

(see Sec. 17.20)

Polyvinyl butyral

Used in safety glass

There is good evidence that in alcoholic solution an aldehyde exists in equilibrium with a compound called a **hemiacetal**:

$$\overset{\overset{\displaystyle H}{|}}{R'-C}=O + ROH \underset{}{\overset{H^+}{\rightleftharpoons}} R'-\overset{\overset{\displaystyle H}{|}}{\underset{\underset{\displaystyle OH}{|}}{C}}-OR$$

A hemiacetal

A hemiacetal is formed by the addition of the nucleophilic alcohol molecule to the carbonyl group; it is both an ether and an alcohol. With a few exceptions, hemiacetals are too unstable to be isolated.

In the presence of acid the hemiacetal, acting as an alcohol, reacts with more of the solvent alcohol to form the acetal, an ether:

$$R'-\overset{\overset{\displaystyle H}{|}}{\underset{\underset{\displaystyle OH}{|}}{C}}-OR + ROH \overset{H^+}{\rightleftharpoons} R'-\overset{\overset{\displaystyle H}{|}}{\underset{\underset{\displaystyle OR}{|}}{C}}-OR + H_2O$$

Hemiacetal   Acetal

(an alcohol)   (an ether)

The mechanism of this reaction is probably the one we have previously encountered (Sec. 15.3) for the formation of ethers.

Problem 23.10 Account for the fact that anhydrous acids bring about formation of acetals whereas aqueous acids bring about hydrolysis of acetals.

Problem 23.11 Outline the steps (all must be equilibria) in the probable mechanism for transformation of a hemiacetal into an acetal.

Acetal formation thus involves (1) nucleophilic addition to a carbonyl group, and (2) ether formation via a carbonium ion.

Acetals have the structure of ethers and, like ethers, are cleaved by acids and are stable toward bases. Acetals differ from ethers, however, in the extreme *ease* with which they undergo acidic cleavage; they are rapidly converted even at room temperature into the aldehyde and alcohol by dilute mineral acids.

$$R'-\overset{\overset{\displaystyle H}{|}}{\underset{\underset{\displaystyle OR}{|}}{C}}-OR + H_2O \underset{fast}{\overset{H^+}{\longrightarrow}} R'-\overset{\overset{\displaystyle H}{|}}{C}=O + 2ROH$$

Acetal   Aldehyde   Alcohol

We shall find the chemistry of hemiacetals and acetals to be fundamental to the study of carbohydrates (Chapters 29 and 30).

Problem 23.12   (a) The following reaction is an example of what familiar
synthesis?

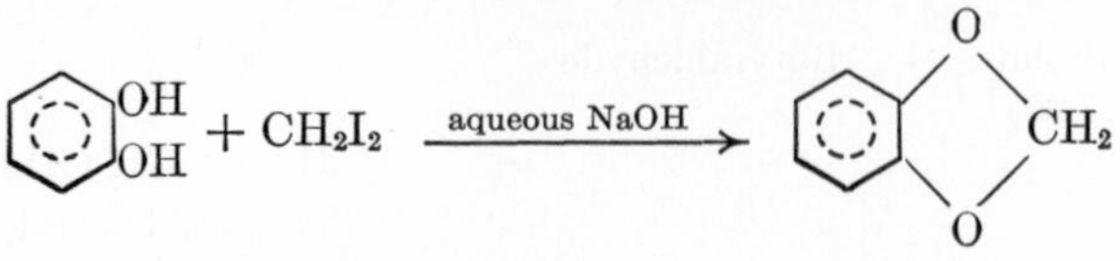

(b) To what family of compounds does I belong?   (c) What will I yield upon
treatment with acid?   With base?

Problem 23.13   Suggest a convenient chemical method for separating unreacted benzaldehyde from benzaldehyde diethyl acetal.   (Compare Problem 23.8,
page 632.)

Problem 23.14   *Glyceraldehyde,* $CH_2OHCHOHCHO$, is commonly made from
the acetal of acrolein, $CH_2{=}CH{-}CHO$.   Show how this could be done.   Why is
acrolein itself not used?

23.15   Aldol condensation.   Addition of aldehydes and ketones

Under the influence of dilute base or dilute acid, two molecules of an
aldehyde or a ketone may combine to form a β-hydroxyaldehyde or
β-hydroxyketone.   This reaction is called the **aldol condensation.**   In
every case the product results from addition of one molecule of aldehyde
(or ketone) to a second molecule in such a way that the α-carbon of the
first becomes attached to the carbonyl carbon of the second.   For example:

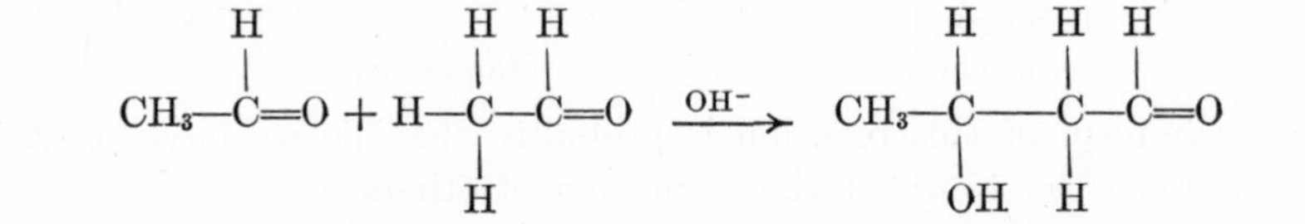

Acetaldehyde
2 moles

Aldol
(β-Hydroxybutyraldehyde)
(3-Hydroxybutanal)

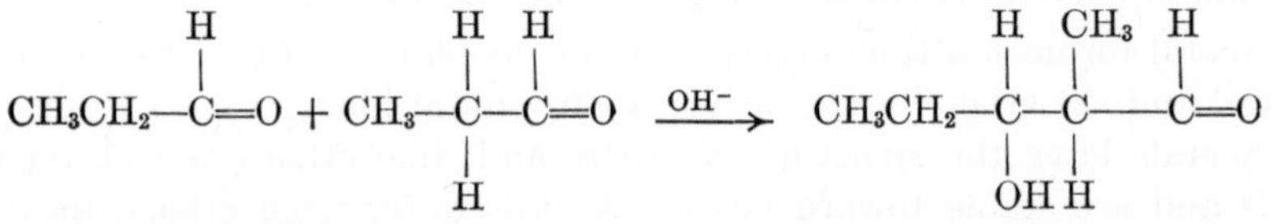

Propionaldehyde
2 moles

β-Hydroxy-α-methylvaleraldehyde
(3-Hydroxy-2-methylpentanal)

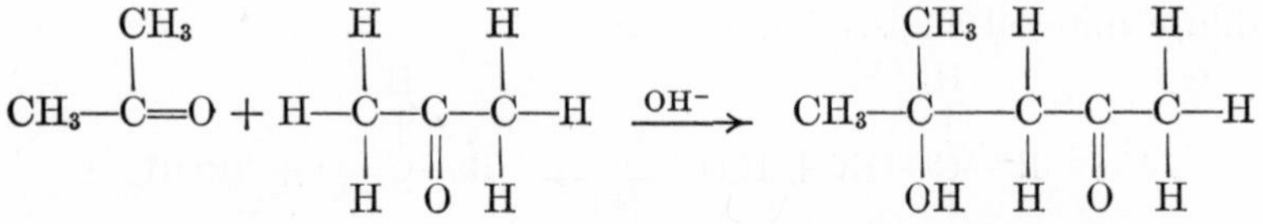

Acetone
2 moles

4-Hydroxy-4-methyl-2-pentanone
(Diacetone alcohol)

If the aldehyde or ketone does not contain an α-hydrogen, a simple aldol condensation cannot take place. For example:

$$
\left.
\begin{matrix}
\text{ArCHO} \\
\text{HCHO} \\
\text{(CH}_3\text{)}_3\text{CCHO} \\
\text{ArCOAr} \\
\text{ArCOCR}_3
\end{matrix}
\right\}
\xrightarrow{\text{dilute OH}^-} \quad \text{no reaction}
$$

No
α-hydrogen
atoms

The generally accepted mechanism for the base-catalyzed condensation involves the following steps, acetaldehyde being used as an example.

(1) $\qquad\qquad$ $CH_3CHO + OH^- \; \underset{\substack{\text{Basic} \\ \text{catalyst}}}{\overset{\longrightarrow}{\longleftarrow}} \; H_2O + [CH_2CHO]^-$
$\qquad\qquad\qquad\qquad\qquad\qquad\qquad\qquad\qquad\qquad\qquad$ I

(2) $\quad$ $\underset{\text{I}}{CH_3{-}\overset{\displaystyle H}{\underset{}{C}}{=}O} + [CH_2CHO]^- \; \overset{\longrightarrow}{\longleftarrow} \; \underset{\text{II}}{CH_3{-}\overset{\displaystyle H}{\underset{\displaystyle O_-}{C}}{-}CH_2CHO}$

$\qquad\qquad\qquad\qquad$ *Nucleophilic*
$\qquad\qquad\qquad\qquad\quad$ *reagent*

(3) $\quad$ $\underset{\text{II}}{CH_3{-}\overset{\displaystyle H}{\underset{\displaystyle O_-}{C}}{-}CH_2CHO} + H_2O \; \overset{\longrightarrow}{\longleftarrow} \; \underset{\text{III}}{CH_3{-}\overset{\displaystyle H}{\underset{\displaystyle OH}{C}}{-}CH_2CHO} + OH^-$

Hydroxide ion abstracts (step 1) a hydrogen ion from the α-carbon of the aldehyde to form carbanion I, which attacks (step 2) carbonyl carbon to form ion II. II (an alkoxide) abstracts (step 3) a hydrogen ion from water to form the β-hydroxyaldehyde III, regenerating hydroxide ion. The purpose of hydroxide ion is thus to produce the carbanion I, which is the actual nucleophilic reagent.

Problem 23.15   Illustrate these steps for:

(a) propionaldehyde $\qquad\qquad$ (d) cyclohexanone
(b) acetone $\qquad\qquad\qquad\qquad$ (e) phenylacetaldehyde
(c) acetophenone

Problem 23.16   The aldol condensation of unsymmetrical ketones (methyl ethyl ketone, for example) is usually of little value in synthesis. Why do you think this is so?

The carbonyl group plays two roles in the aldol condensation. It not only provides the unsaturated linkage at which addition (step 2) occurs, but also makes the α-hydrogens acidic enough for carbanion formation (step 1) to take place. The carbanion formed by ionization of an α-hydrogen is stabilized by resonance between structures IV and V:

$$
\left[\begin{matrix} \; | \quad\; | \quad\; .. \\ -\overset{|}{\underset{..}{C}}{-}\overset{|}{C}{=}\overset{..}{O}: \end{matrix} \quad\quad \begin{matrix} \; | \quad\; | \quad\; .. \\ -\overset{|}{C}{=}\overset{|}{C}{-}\overset{..}{\underset{..}{O}}:^- \end{matrix} \right] \quad \textit{equivalent to} \quad \left[\begin{matrix} \; | \quad\; | \\ -\overset{|}{C}{\cdots}\overset{|}{C}{\cdots}O \\ \underbrace{\qquad\qquad}_{\ominus} \end{matrix} \right]
$$

$\qquad$ IV $\qquad\qquad\qquad$ V $\qquad\qquad\qquad\qquad\qquad\qquad$ VI

Resonance of this kind is not possible for carbanions formed by ionization of β-hydrogens, γ-hydrogens, etc., from saturated carbonyl compounds.

The carbonyl group affects the acidity of α-hydrogens in just the way it affects the acidity of carboxylic acids: by helping to accommodate the negative charge of the anion.

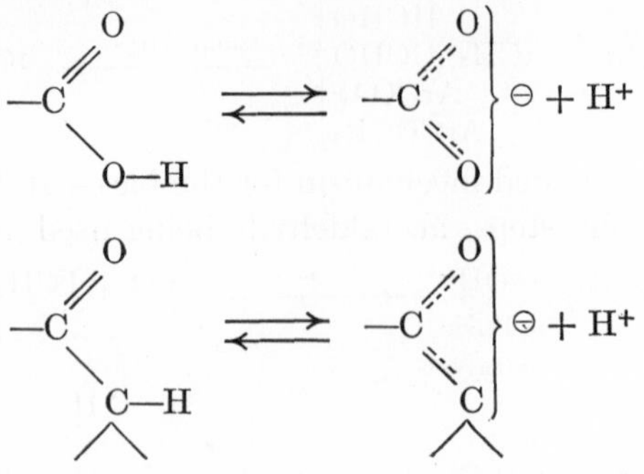

VI

Resonance in VI involves structures (IV and V) of quite different stabilities, and hence is much less important than the resonance involving equivalent structures in a carboxylate ion. Compared with the hydrogen of a —COOH group, the α-hydrogen atoms of an aldehyde or ketone are very weakly acidic; the important thing is that they are considerably more acidic than hydrogen atoms anywhere else in the molecule, and that they are acidic enough for the aldol condensation to take place.

Problem 23.17 Which structure, IV or V, would you expect to make the larger contribution to the carbanion VI? Why?

Problem 23.18 Account for the fact that the diketone acetylacetone (2,4-pentanedione) is about as acidic as phenol, and much more acidic than, say, acetone. Which hydrogens are the most acidic?

23.16 Dehydration of aldol products

The β-hydroxyaldehydes and β-hydroxyketones obtained from aldol condensations are very easily dehydrated; the major products have the carbon–carbon double bond between the α- and β-carbon atoms. For example:

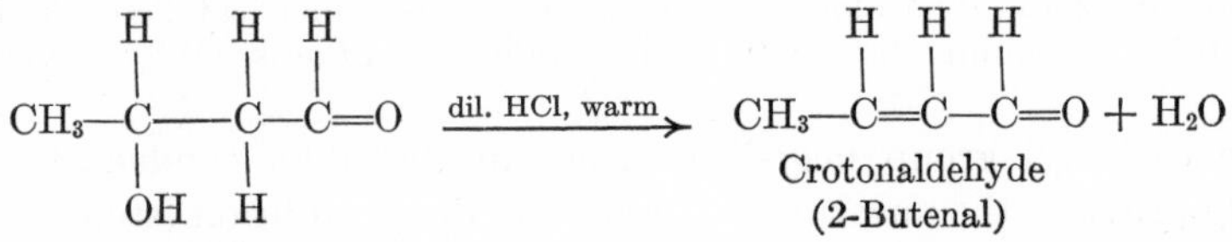

Aldol — Crotonaldehyde (2-Butenal)

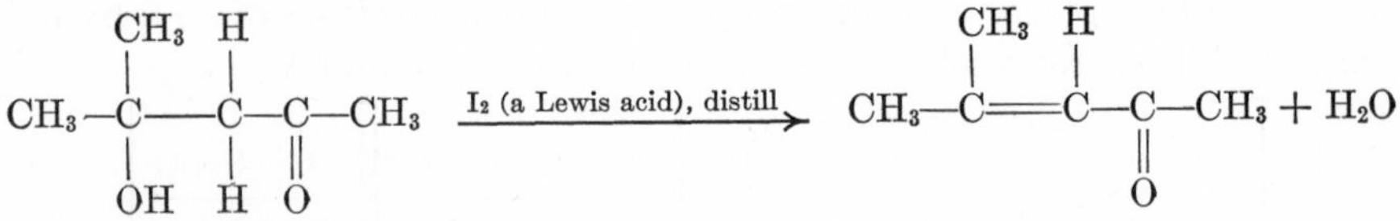

Diacetone alcohol (4-Hydroxy-4-methyl-2-pentanone) — Mesityl oxide (4-Methyl-3-penten-2-one)

Both the ease and the orientation of elimination are related to the fact that the alkene obtained is a particularly stable one, since the carbon–

carbon double bond is conjugated with the carbon–oxygen double bond of the carbonyl group (compare Sec. 6.15).

Problem 23.19 Draw resonance structures to account for the unusual stability of an α,β-unsaturated aldehyde or ketone. What is the significance of these structures in terms of orbitals? (See Sec. 8.16.)

As we know, an alkene in which the carbon–carbon double bond is conjugated with an aromatic ring is particularly stable (Sec. 9.21); in those cases where elimination of water from the aldol product can form such a conjugated alkene, the unsaturated aldehyde or ketone is the product actually isolated from the reaction. For example:

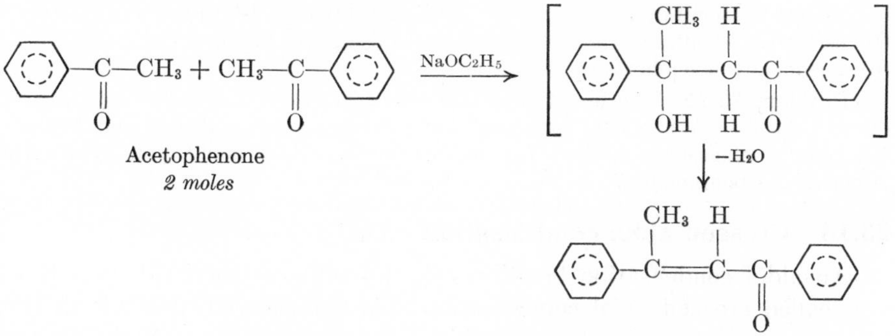

Acetophenone
2 moles

1,3-Diphenyl-2-buten-1-one

23.17 Use of aldol condensation in synthesis

Catalytic hydrogenation of α,β-unsaturated aldehydes and ketones yields saturated alcohols, addition of hydrogen occurring both at carbon–carbon and at carbon–oxygen double bonds. It is for the purpose of ultimately preparing saturated alcohols that the aldol condensation is often carried out. For example, *n*-butyl alcohol and 2-ethyl-1-hexanol are both prepared on an industrial scale in this way:

$$2CH_3CHO \xrightarrow{OH^-} CH_3CHOHCH_2CHO \xrightarrow{-H_2O} CH_3CH{=}CHCHO$$

Acetaldehyde — Aldol — Crotonaldehyde (2-Butenal)

$$CH_3CH{=}CHCHO \xrightarrow{H_2,\ Ni} CH_3CH_2CH_2CH_2OH$$

n-Butyl alcohol

$$CH_3CH_2CH_2CH_2OH \xrightarrow{Cu,\ 250^\circ} CH_3CH_2CH_2CHO$$

n-Butyl alcohol — *n*-Butyraldehyde

$$CH_3CH_2CH_2CHO \xrightarrow{OH^-} CH_3CH_2CH_2CHOHCH(C_2H_5)CHO \xrightarrow{-H_2O} CH_3CH_2CH_2CH{=}C(C_2H_5)CHO \xrightarrow{H_2,\ Ni} CH_3CH_2CH_2CH_2CH(C_2H_5)CH_2OH$$

2-Ethyl-1-hexanol

Unsaturated alcohols can be prepared if a reagent is selected that reduces only the carbonyl group and leaves the carbon–carbon double bond untouched; one such reagent is sodium borohydride, $NaBH_4$.

$$\overset{\beta}{R}CH=\overset{\alpha}{CH}-\underset{\underset{O}{\|}}{C}-R' \xrightarrow{NaBH_4} \xrightarrow{H^+} RCH=CH-\underset{\underset{OH}{|}}{CH}-R'$$

α,β-Unsaturated carbonyl compound   Unsaturated alcohol

Problem 23.20 Outline the synthesis of the following alcohols starting from alcohols of smaller carbon number.

(a) 2-methyl-1-pentanol
(b) 4-methyl-2-pentanol
(c) 2-cyclohexylcyclohexanol
(d) 2,4-diphenyl-1-butanol
(e) 1,3-diphenyl-2-buten-1-ol

Problem 23.21 The insect repellant "6-12" (2-ethyl-1,3-hexanediol) is produced by the same chemical company that produces *n*-butyl alcohol and 2-ethyl-1-hexanol; suggest a method for its synthesis. How could you synthesize 2-methyl-2,4-pentanediol?

23.18 Crossed aldol condensation

An aldol condensation between two different carbonyl compounds — a so-called **crossed aldol condensation** — is not generally feasible in the laboratory, since a mixture of the four possible products is obtained. On a commercial scale, however, such a synthesis may be worth while if the mixture can be separated and the components marketed.

Problem 23.22 *n*-Butyl alcohol, *n*-hexyl alcohol, 2-ethyl-1-hexanol, and 2-ethyl-1-butanol are marketed by the same chemical concern; how might they be prepared from cheap, readily available compounds?

Under certain conditions, a good yield of a single product can be obtained from a crossed aldol condensation: (a) one reactant contains no α-hydrogens and therefore is incapable of condensing with itself (e.g., aromatic aldehydes or formaldehyde); (b) this reactant is mixed with the

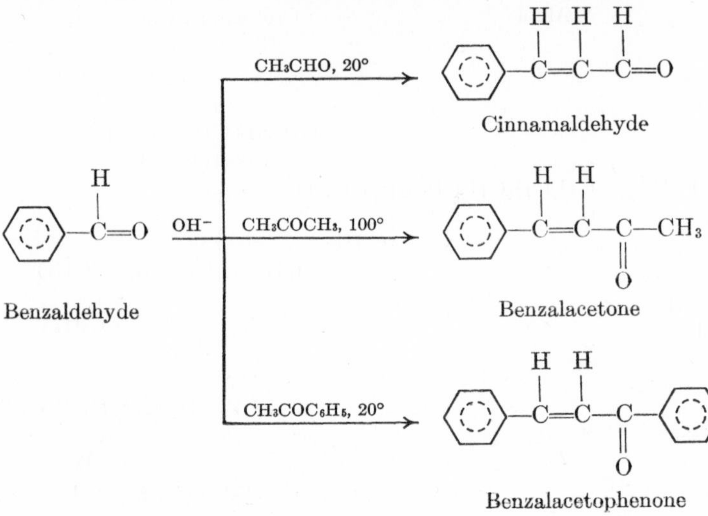

Crossed aldol condensations

Benzaldehyde

CH₃CHO, 20° → Cinnamaldehyde

CH₃COCH₃, 100° → Benzalacetone

CH₃COC₆H₅, 20° → Benzalacetophenone

catalyst; and then (c) a carbonyl compound that contains α-hydrogens is added slowly to this mixture. There is thus present at any time only a very low concentration of the ionizable carbonyl compound, and the carbanion it forms reacts almost exclusively with the other carbonyl compound, which is present in large excess.

Problem 23.23　Outline the synthesis of each of the following from benzene or toluene and any readily available alcohols:

(a) 4-phenyl-2-butanol
(b) 1,3-diphenyl-1-propanol
(c) 1,3-diphenylpropane

(d) 2,3-diphenyl-1-propanol
(e) 1,5-diphenyl-1,4-pentadien-3-one
　　(dibenzalacetone)

Problem 23.24　(a) What prediction can you make about the acidity of the γ-hydrogens of α,β-unsaturated carbonyl compounds,

$$\overset{\gamma\quad\ \beta\quad\ \alpha}{-\overset{|}{C}-\overset{|}{C}=\overset{|}{C}-\overset{|}{C}=O}$$
$$\overset{|}{\underset{H}{}}$$

as, for example, in crotonaldehyde?

(b) In view of your answer to (a), suggest a way to synthesize 5-phenyl-2,4-pentadienal, $C_6H_5CH{=}CH-CH{=}CH-CHO$.

23.19　Reactions related to the aldol condensation

There are a large number of condensations that are closely related to the aldol condensation. Each of these reactions has its own name — *Perkin, Knoevenagel, Doebner, Claisen, Dieckmann*, for example — and at first glance each may seem quite different from the others. Closer examination shows, however, that like the aldol condensation each of these involves attack by a carbanion on a carbonyl group. In each case the carbanion is generated in very much the same way: the abstraction by base of a hydrogen ion *alpha* to a carbonyl group. Different bases may be used — sodium hydroxide, sodium ethoxide, sodium acetate, amines — and the carbonyl group to which the hydrogen is *alpha* may vary — aldehyde, ketone, anhydride, ester — but the chemistry is essentially the same as that of the aldol condensation. We shall take up a few of these condensations in following sections and following chapters; in doing this, we must not lose sight of the fundamental resemblance of each of them to the aldol condensation.

23.20　Perkin condensation.　Addition of anhydrides

Acid anhydrides add to aromatic aldehydes in the presence of bases to yield α,β-unsaturated acids. This reaction is given the special name of **Perkin condensation**; it closely resembles the aldol condensation. The base most commonly used is the sodium salt of the carboxylic acid from which the anhydride is derived. Only aromatic aldehydes are used in the Perkin condensation, since they are incapable of undergoing self-condensation (aldol condensation) in the presence of the basic catalyst.

Addition occurs in such a way that the α-carbon of the anhydride becomes attached to the carbonyl carbon of the aromatic aldehyde. In the reaction mixture the β-hydroxy anhydride thus formed undergoes two reactions: (a) loss of water, and (b) hydrolysis of the anhydride. For example:

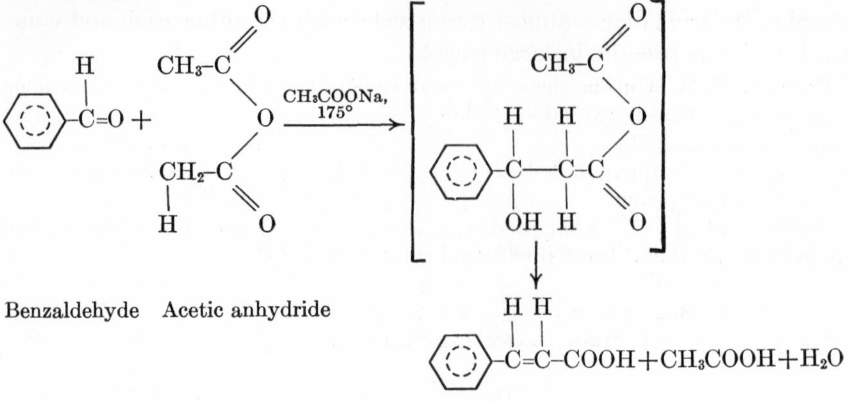

Benzaldehyde   Acetic anhydride

Cinnamic acid
(3-Phenylpropenoic acid)

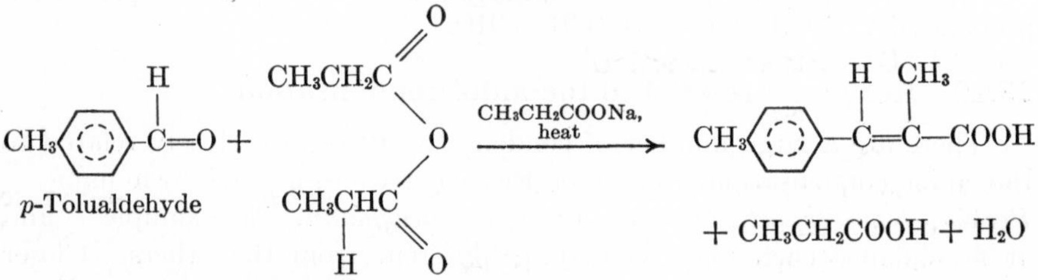

p-Tolualdehyde

Propionic anhydride

The Perkin condensation proceeds by the same mechanism as the aldol condensation.

Problem 23.25 (a) Considering it a modified aldol condensation, show the steps in the mechanism of the Perkin condensation involving benzaldehyde, acetic anhydride, and sodium acetate. (b) Why are the α-hydrogens of an anhydride acidic?

Problem 23.26 Esters can be condensed with aromatic aldehydes in the presence of alkoxides; thus benzaldehyde and ethyl acetate, in the presence of sodium ethoxide, give ethyl cinnamate, $C_6H_5CH{=}CHCOOC_2H_5$. Show all steps in the most likely mechanism for this condensation.

Problem 23.27 Account for the following reactions:

(a) $C_6H_5CHO + CH_3NO_2 \xrightarrow{\text{KOH}} C_6H_5CH{=}CHNO_2 + H_2O$

(b) $C_6H_5CHO + C_6H_5CH_2CN \xrightarrow{\text{NaOC}_2\text{H}_5} C_6H_5CH{=}C{-}CN + H_2O$

$\qquad\qquad\qquad\qquad\qquad\qquad\qquad\qquad\qquad\quad |$
$\qquad\qquad\qquad\qquad\qquad\qquad\qquad\qquad\quad C_6H_5$

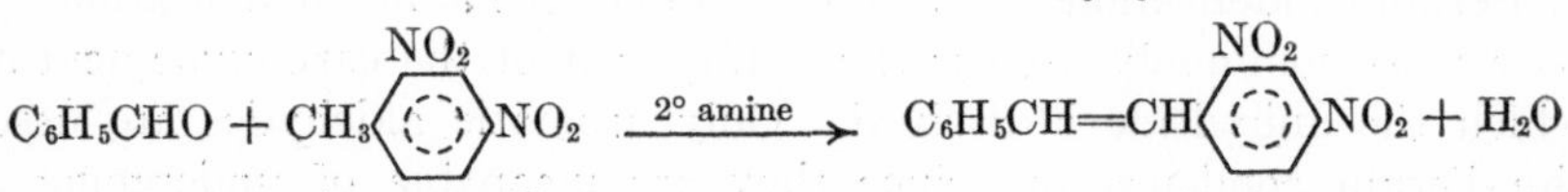

(d) $CH_3CHO + NaC{\equiv}CH \xrightarrow{\text{NH}_3(l)} CH_3CHC{\equiv}CH \xrightarrow{\text{NH}_4\text{Cl}} CH_3CHC{\equiv}CH$

$\qquad\qquad\qquad\qquad\qquad\qquad\qquad\qquad |\qquad\qquad\qquad\qquad\qquad |$
$\qquad\qquad\qquad\qquad\qquad\qquad\qquad\quad ONa\qquad\qquad\qquad\qquad OH$

By varying the substituents in the aromatic aldehyde, it is possible to make a wide variety of substituted cinnamic acids by the Perkin condensation. The corresponding saturated acids, if desired, can be readily prepared by hydrogenation of the carbon–carbon double bond.

$$ArCH\!\!=\!\!CHCOOH + H_2 \xrightarrow{\text{Ni}} ArCH_2CH_2COOH$$

A cinnamic acid   A hydrocinnamic acid

Problem 23.28 Show how hydrocinnamic acid, $C_6H_5CH_2CH_2COOH$, can be transformed into:

(a) hydrocinnamyl alcohol

(b) 4-phenyl-2-butanone

(c) 4-phenyl-2-methyl-2-butanol

(d) 5-phenyl-3-ethyl-3-pentanol

Problem 23.29 Prepare phenylpropiolic acid, $C_6H_5C\!\!\equiv\!\!CCOOH$, from cheap, readily available materials.

Problem 23.30 *Coumarin* is used in perfumes and flavorings. Outline its synthesis from cheap, readily available materials. (*Hint:* coumarin is an ester.)

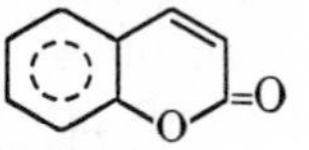

Coumarin

23.21 Cannizzaro reaction

In the presence of concentrated alkali, aldehydes containing no α-hydrogens undergo self-oxidation and -reduction to yield a mixture of an alcohol and a salt of a carboxylic acid. This reaction, known as the **Cannizzaro reaction,** is generally brought about by allowing the aldehyde to stand at room temperature with concentrated aqueous or alcoholic hydroxide. (Under these conditions an aldehyde containing α-hydrogens would, of course, undergo aldol condensation.)

$$2HCHO \xrightarrow{\text{50\% NaOH}} CH_3OH + HCOO^- Na^+$$

Formaldehyde   Methanol   Sodium formate

$$O_2N\!\!-\!\!\langle\bigcirc\rangle\!\!-\!\!CHO \xrightarrow{\text{35\% NaOH}} O_2N\!\!-\!\!\langle\bigcirc\rangle\!\!-\!\!CH_2OH + O_2N\!\!-\!\!\langle\bigcirc\rangle\!\!-\!\!COO^- Na^+$$

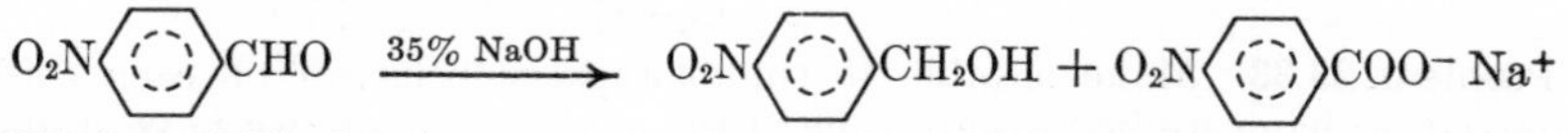

p-Nitrobenzaldehyde   *p*-Nitrobenzyl alcohol   Sodium *p*-nitrobenzoate

In general, a mixture of two aldehydes undergoes a Cannizzaro reaction to yield all possible products. If one of the aldehydes is formaldehyde, however, reaction yields almost exclusively sodium formate and the alcohol corresponding to the other aldehyde:

$$ArCHO + HCHO \xrightarrow{\text{conc. NaOH}} ArCH_2OH + HCOO^- Na^+$$

The high tendency for formaldehyde to undergo oxidation makes this **crossed Cannizzaro reaction** a useful synthetic tool. For example:

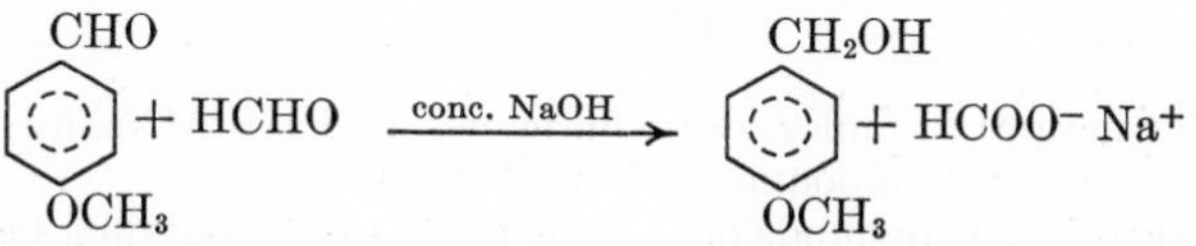

Anisaldehyde   *p*-Methoxybenzyl alcohol
(*p*-Methoxybenzaldehyde)

Problem 23.31   The compound *pentaerythritol*, $C(CH_2OH)_4$, used in making explosives, is obtained from the reaction of acetaldehyde and formaldehyde in the presence of calcium hydroxide.   Outline the probable steps in this synthesis.

Problem 23.32   Outline a synthesis of 3,4-dimethoxybenzyl alcohol (*veratryl alcohol*) starting from the naturally occurring compound *guaiacol*, $o\text{-}C_6H_4(OH)OCH_3$.

23.22   Analysis of aldehydes and ketones

Aldehydes and ketones are characterized through the addition to the carbonyl group of nucleophilic reagents, especially derivatives of ammonia (Sec. 23.13).   An aldehyde or ketone will, for example, react with 2,4-dinitrophenylhydrazine to form an insoluble yellow or red solid.

Aldehydes are characterized, and in particular are differentiated from ketones, through their ease of oxidation.   Aliphatic aldehydes give positive tests with Tollens' reagent and Benedict's solution; aromatic aldehydes give positive tests with Tollens' reagent (see Sec. 23.8).   A positive Tollens' test is also given by a few other kinds of easily oxidized compounds, e.g., certain phenols and amines; these compounds do not, however, give positive tests with 2,4-dinitrophenylhydrazine.

A highly sensitive test for aldehydes is the *Schiff test*.   An aldehyde reacts with the fuchsin-aldehyde reagent to form a characteristic magenta color.

Aliphatic aldehydes and ketones having α-hydrogens react with Br_2 in CCl_4 (Sec. 26.8).   This reaction is generally too slow to be confused with a test for unsaturation, and moreover it liberates HBr.

Aldehydes and ketones are generally identified through the melting points of derivatives like 2,4-dinitrophenylhydrazones, oximes, and semi-carbazones (Sec. 23.13).

Methyl ketones are characterized through the iodoform test (see Sec. 12.11).

Problem 23.33   Make a table to summarize the behavior of each class of compound we have studied toward each of the oxidizing agents we have studied.

Problem 23.34   A convenient test for aldehydes and most ketones depends upon the fact that a carbonyl compound generally causes a change in color when it is added to a solution of hydroxylamine hydrochloride and acid-base indicator. What is the basis of this test?

Problem 23.35   Expand the table you made in Problem 16.11, page 462, to include aldehydes and ketones, and, in particular, emphasize oxidizing agents.

PROBLEMS

1. Give structural formulas, common names, and IUPAC names for:
(a) the seven carbonyl compounds of formula $C_5H_{10}O$
(b) the five carbonyl compounds of formula C_8H_8O that contain a benzene ring

2. Give the structural formula of:

(a) acetone
(b) benzaldehyde
(c) methyl isobutyl ketone
(d) trimethylacetaldehyde
(e) acetophenone
(f) cinnamaldehyde
(g) 4-methylpentanal
(h) phenylacetaldehyde
(i) benzophenone
(j) α,γ-dimethylcaproaldehyde

(k) 3-methyl-2-pentanone
(l) 2-butenal
(m) 4-methyl-3-penten-2-one (mesityl oxide)
(n) 1,3-diphenyl-2-propen-1-one (benzalaceto-phenone)
(o) 3-hydroxypentanal
(p) benzyl phenyl ketone
(q) salicylaldehyde
(r) p,p'-dihydroxybenzophenone

3. (a) Make a list of the ways in which a carbonyl group can be introduced into a compound. (b) Which of the methods in (a) could be used to make *n*-butyr-aldehyde? Write equations for the reactions involved. (c) Answer (b) for methyl ethyl ketone. (d) Answer (b) for benzaldehyde. (e) Answer (b) for acetophenone.

4. Write balanced equations, naming all organic products, for the reaction (if any) of phenylacetaldehyde with:

(a) Tollens' reagent
(b) Benedict's solution
(c) cold dilute $KMnO_4$
(d) $KMnO_4$, H^+, heat
(e) H_2, Ni, 20 lb/in^2, 30°
(f) NH_3, H_2, Ni
(g) $LiAlH_4$
(h) $NaBH_4$
(i) C_6H_5MgBr, then H_2O
(j) isopropylmagnesium chloride, then H_2O
(k) $NaHSO_3$

(l) CN^-, H^+
(m) CN^-, H^+, then H_2, Ni, 20 lb/in^2, 30°
(n) hydroxylamine
(o) phenylhydrazine
(p) 2,4-dinitrophenylhydrazine
(q) semicarbazide
(r) ethyl alcohol, dry $HCl(g)$
(s) dilute NaOH
(t) dilute HCl
(u) aqueous Na_2CO_3
(v) Br_2, CCl_4

5. Answer Problem 4 for cyclohexanone.

6. Write balanced equations, naming all organic products, for the reaction (if any) of benzaldehyde with:

(a) dilute NaOH
(b) conc. NaOH
(c) CN^-, H^+; then H_2O, H^+, heat
(d) CN^-, H^+; then H_2, Ni
(e) acetaldehyde, dilute NaOH
(f) propionaldehyde, dilute NaOH
(g) acetone, dilute NaOH

(h) product (g), dilute NaOH
(i) acetophenone, NaOH
(j) acetic anhydride, sodium acetate, heat
(k) ethyl acetate, sodium ethoxide
(l) ethyl phenylacetate, sodium ethoxide
(m) formaldehyde, conc. NaOH
(n) crotonaldehyde, NaOH

7. Write equations for all steps in the synthesis of the following from propion-aldehyde, using any other needed reagents:

(a) *n*-propyl alcohol
(b) propionic acid
(c) *n*-propylamine
(d) α-hydroxybutyric acid
(e) 1-amino-2-butanol
(f) *sec*-butyl alcohol
(g) 1-phenyl-1-propanol
(h) methyl ethyl ketone

(i) *n*-propyl propionate
(j) α-methyl-β-hydroxyvaleraldehyde
(k) 2-methyl-1-pentanol
(l) 2-methyl-2-pentenal
(m) 2-methyl-2-penten-1-ol
(n) 2-methyl-1,3-pentanediol
(o) α-methylvaleric acid
(p) 2-methyl-3-phenylpropenal

8. Write equations for all steps in the synthesis of the following from acetone, using any other needed reagents:

(a) 2-propanol
(b) isopropylamine
(c) α-methyl-α-hydroxypropionic acid
(d) *tert*-butyl alcohol

(e) 2-phenyl-2-propanol
(f) 4-methyl-4-hydroxy-2-pentanone
(g) 4-methyl-2-pentanol

9. Write equations for all steps in the synthesis of the following from aceto-phenone, using any other needed reagents:

(a) ethylbenzene
(b) benzoic acid
(c) α-phenylethyl alcohol
(d) α-phenylethylamine
(e) 2-phenyl-2-butanol
(f) diphenylmethylcarbinol

(g) α-hydroxy-α-phenylpropionic acid
(h) 1-amino-2-phenyl-2-propanol
(i) 1,3-diphenyl-2-buten-1-one
(j) 1,3-diphenyl-1-butanol
(k) 1,3-diphenyl-2-buten-1-ol
(l) 1,3-diphenyl-2-propen-1-one

10. Outline all steps in a possible laboratory synthesis of each of the following from benzene, toluene, and alcohols of four carbons or less, using any needed inorganic reagents:

(a) isobutyraldehyde
(b) phenylacetaldehyde
(c) p-fluorobenzaldehyde
(d) methyl ethyl ketone
(e) 2,4-dinitrobenzaldehyde
(f) p-nitrobenzophenone
(g) 2-methyl-3-pentanone
(h) benzyl methyl ketone
(i) m-nitrobenzophenone

(j) n-propyl m-tolyl ketone
(k) 2-hydroxy-5-methylbenzaldehyde
(l) α-methylbutyraldehyde
(m) n-butyl tert-butyl ketone
(n) p-hydroxyacetophenone
(o) o-methoxybenzaldehyde
(p) 3-nitro-4'-methoxybenzophenone
(q) p-nitropropiophenone

11. Outline all steps in a possible laboratory synthesis of each of the following from benzene, toluene, and alcohols of four carbons or less, using any needed inorganic reagents:

(a) n-butylbenzene
(b) α-hydroxy-n-valeric acid
(c) 2-methylheptane
(d) 1-amino-1-phenylpropane
(e) p-amino-α-hydroxyphenylacetic acid
(f) crotyl alcohol, $CH_3CH{=}CHCH_2OH$
(g) 2,3,5-trimethyl-3-hexanol
(h) 1,2-diphenyl-2-propanol
(i) cinnamyl alcohol, $C_6H_5CH{=}CHCH_2OH$
(j) p-nitrocinnamaldehyde
(k) o-methoxybenzyl alcohol
(l) ethylphenyl-p-bromophenylcarbinol
(m) 2,3-dihydroxy-3-phenylpropanoic acid
(n) 1,3-butanediol
(o) 3-methyl-2-butenoic acid
(p) 3-methyl-1-pentyn-3-ol (*Oblivon*, a hypnotic)

(q) indanone

12. The insecticide DDT, 1,1,1-trichloro-2,2-bis-(p-chlorophenyl)ethane, $(p\text{-}ClC_6H_4)_2CHCCl_3$, is manufactured by the reaction between chlorobenzene and trichloroacetaldehyde in the presence of sulfuric acid. Outline the series of steps by which this synthesis most probably takes place; make sure you show the function of the H_2SO_4. Label each step according to its fundamental reaction type.

13. Account for the fact that cyclobutanecarboxaldehyde, cyclobutyl–CHO, gives cyclopentanone when heated with acid.

14. Vigorous sulfonation of benzene finally yields compound A of formula $C_6H_6O_9S_3$. Fusion of A with alkali followed by acidification yields B, $C_6H_6O_3$.

As expected, compound B gives a color with $FeCl_3$ and on methylation yields compound C, $C_9H_{12}O_3$. Yet treatment of B with hydroxylamine yields D, $C_6H_9O_3N_3$.

What can you say about the structure of B? (*Hint:* see Sec. 6.12.)

15. Benzophenone oxime, $C_{13}H_{11}ON$, m.p. 141°, like other oximes, is soluble in aqueous NaOH and gives a color with ferric chloride. When heated with acids it is transformed into a solid E, $C_{13}H_{11}ON$, m.p. 163°, which is insoluble in aqueous NaOH and in aqueous HCl.

After prolonged heating of E with aqueous NaOH, a liquid F separates and is collected by steam distillation. Acidification of the aqueous residue causes precipitation of a white solid G, m.p. 120–1°.

Compound F, b.p. 184°, is soluble in dilute HCl. When this acidic solution is chilled and then treated successively with $NaNO_2$ and β-naphthol, a red solid is formed. F reacts with acetic anhydride to give a compound that melts at 112.5–114°.

(a) What is the structure of E? (b) To what general class of reactions does the transformation of benzophenone oxime into E belong? (c) Can you suggest a likely series of steps for this transformation? (*Hint:* see Secs. 12.5, 5.10, and 6.12.)

(d) What product or products corresponding to E would you expect from similar transformation of acetone oxime; of acetophenone oxime; of p-nitrobenzophenone oxime; of methyl n-propyl ketoxime? (e) How would you go about identifying each of the products in (d)?

16. Describe a simple chemical test that would serve to distinguish between:

(a) n-valeraldehyde and ethyl ketone
(b) phenylacetaldehyde and benzyl alcohol
(c) cyclohexanone and methyl n-caproate
(d) 2-pentanone and 3-pentanone
(e) propionaldehyde and ethyl ether
(f) diethyl acetal and n-valeraldehyde
(g) diethyl acetal and n-propyl ether
(h) methyl m-tolyl ketone and propiophenone
(i) 2-pentanone and 2-pentanol
(j) diacetone alcohol and mesityl oxide
(k) paraldehyde and isobutyl ether
(l) dioxane and trioxane
(m) salicylaldehyde and benzaldehyde

Tell exactly what you would do and see.

17. An unknown compound is believed to be one of the following, all of which boil within a few degrees of each other. Describe how you would go about finding out which of the possibilities the unknown actually is. Where possible use simple chemical tests; where necessary use more elaborate chemical methods such as quantitative hydrogenation, cleavage, neutralization equivalent, saponification equivalent, etc. Make use of any needed tables of physical constants.

(a) phenylacetaldehyde
salicylaldehyde
m-tolualdehyde
o-tolualdehyde
acetophenone
p-tolualdehyde

(b) methyl β-phenylethyl ketone
cyclohexylbenzene
benzyl n-butyrate
γ-phenylpropyl alcohol
n-caprylic acid

(c) isophorone (3,5,5-trimethyl-2-cyclohexen-1-one)
n-dodecane
benzyl n-butyl ether
ethyl benzoate
m-cresyl acetate
n-nonyl alcohol

(d) p-chloroacetophenone
methyl o-chlorobenzoate
o-chlorobenzoyl chloride
m-chloronitrobenzene

18. Outline a possible synthesis of each of the following from benzene, toluene, or any of the natural products shown in Sec. 22.4, using any other needed reagents.
(a) *benzedrine*, a vasoconstrictor and pressor compound
(b) *caffeic acid*, from coffee beans
(c) *tyramine*, found in ergot (*Hint:* see Problem 23.27a, page 642.)
(d) *noradrenaline*, an adrenal hormone

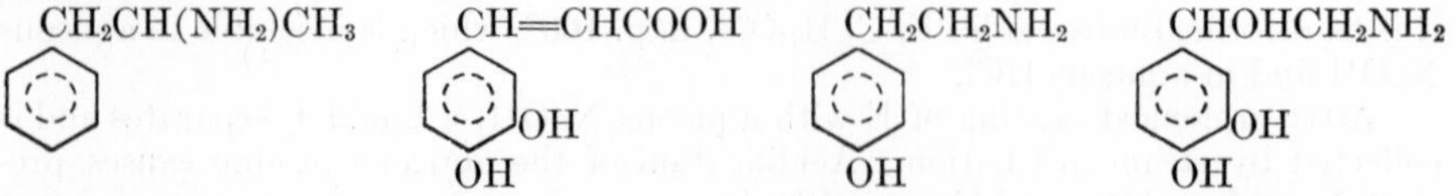

$CH_2CH(NH_2)CH_3$ $CH{=}CHCOOH$ $CH_2CH_2NH_2$ $CHOHCH_2NH_2$

Benzedrine   Caffeic acid   Tyramine   Noradrenaline

19. The adrenal hormone $(-)$-*adrenaline* was the first hormone isolated and the first synthesized. Its structure was proved by the following synthesis:

catechol + $ClCH_2COCl$ $\xrightarrow{POCl_3}$ H $(C_8H_7O_3Cl)$
H + CH_3NH_2 $\longrightarrow$ I $(C_9H_{11}O_3N)$
I + H_2, Pd $\longrightarrow$ $(\pm)$-adrenaline $(C_9H_{13}O_2N)$
H + NaOI, then H^+ $\longrightarrow$ 3,4-dihydroxybenzoic acid

What is the structure of adrenaline?

20. *Citral*, $C_{10}H_{16}O$, is a terpene that is the major constituent of lemongrass oil. It reacts with hydroxylamine to yield a compound of formula $C_{10}H_{17}ON$, and with Tollens' reagent to give a silver mirror and a compound of formula $C_{10}H_{16}O_2$. Upon vigorous oxidation citral yields acetone, oxalic acid (HOOC—COOH), and levulinic acid ($CH_3COCH_2CH_2COOH$).

(a) Propose a structure for citral that is consistent with these facts and with the isoprene rule (Sec. 6.21).

(b) Actually citral seems to consist of two isomers, citral *a* (*geranial*) and citral *b* (*neral*), which yield the same oxidation products. What is the most likely structural difference between these two isomers?

(c) Citral *a* is obtained by mild oxidation of geraniol (Problem 18, page 360); citral *b* is obtained in a similar way from nerol. On this basis assign structures to citral *a* and citral *b*.

(d) Upon treatment with dilute NaOH, β-methylcrotonaldehyde, $(CH_3)_2C{=}CHCHO$, yields a product of formula $C_{10}H_{14}O$, called *dehydrocitral*. What is a likely structure for this product, and how is it formed? (*Hint:* see Problem 23.24, page 641.)

21. $(+)$-*Carvotanacetone*, $C_{10}H_{16}O$, is a terpene found in thuja oil. It reacts with hydroxylamine and semicarbazide to form crystalline derivatives. It gives negative tests with Tollens' reagent and Benedict's solution, but rapidly decolorizes cold dilute $KMnO_4$.

Carvotanacetone can be reduced successively to *carvomenthone*, $C_{10}H_{18}O$, and *carvomenthol*, $C_{10}H_{20}O$. Carvomenthone reacts with hydroxylamine but not with cold dilute $KMnO_4$. Carvomenthol does not react with hydroxylamine but decolorizes cold dilute $KMnO_4$.

One set of investigators found that oxidation of carvotanacetone gave isopropylsuccinic acid, HOOCCHCH$_2$COOH, and pyruvic acid, $CH_3COCOOH$;

$|$
$CH(CH_3)_2$

another set of investigators isolated acetic acid and β-isopropylglutaric acid, $HOOCCH_2CHCH_2COOH$.

$|$
$CH(CH_3)_2$

What single structure for carvotanacetone is consistent with all these facts?

22. $(-)$-*Phellandral*, $C_{10}H_{16}O$, is a terpene found in eucalyptus oils. It is oxidized by Tollens' reagent to $(-)$-phellandric acid, $C_{10}H_{16}O_2$, which readily absorbs only one mole of hydrogen, yielding dihydrophellandric acid, $C_{10}H_{18}O_2$. $(\pm)$-Phellandral has been synthesized as follows:

isopropylbenzene $+ H_2SO_4 + SO_3 \longrightarrow$ J $(C_9H_{12}O_3S)$
J $+$ KOH, fuse $\longrightarrow$ K $(C_9H_{12}O)$
K $+ H_2$, Ni $\longrightarrow$ L $(C_9H_{18}O)$
L $+ K_2Cr_2O_7, H_2SO_4 \longrightarrow$ M $(C_9H_{16}O)$
M $+$ KCN $+ H^+ \longrightarrow$ N $(C_{10}H_{17}ON)$
N $+$ acetic anhydride $\longrightarrow$ O $(C_{12}H_{19}O_2N)$
O $+$ heat $(600°) \longrightarrow$ P $(C_{10}H_{15}N) + CH_3COOH$
P $+ H_2SO_4 + H_2O \longrightarrow$ Q $(C_{10}H_{16}O_2)$
Q $+ SOCl_2 \longrightarrow$ R $(C_{10}H_{15}OCl)$
R $\xrightarrow{\text{reduction}}$ $(\pm)$-phellandral

(a) What is the most likely structure of phellandral? (b) Why is synthetic phellandral optically inactive? At what stage in the synthesis does inactivity of this sort first appear? (c) Dihydrophellandric acid is actually a mixture of two optically inactive isomers. Give the structures of these isomers and account for their optical inactivity.

23. *Piperine*, $C_{17}H_{19}O_3N$, is an alkaloid found in black pepper. It is insoluble in water, dilute acid, and dilute base. When heated with aqueous alkali it yields *piperic acid*, $C_{12}H_{10}O_4$, and the cyclic secondary amine *piperidine* (see page 850), $C_5H_{11}N$.

Piperic acid is insoluble in water, but soluble in aqueous NaOH and aqueous NaHCO$_3$. Titration gives an equivalent weight of 215 ± 6. It reacts readily with Br_2/CCl_4, without evolution of HBr, to yield a compound of formula $C_{12}H_{10}O_4Br_4$. Careful oxidation of piperic acid yields *piperonylic acid*, $C_8H_6O_4$, and *tartaric acid*, HOOCCHOHCHOHCOOH.

When piperonylic acid is heated with aqueous HCl at 200° it yields formaldehyde and *protocatechuic acid*, 3,4-dihydroxybenzoic acid.

(a) What kind of compound is piperine? (b) What is the structure of piperonylic acid? Of piperic acid? Of piperine?

(c) Does the following synthesis confirm your structure?

catechol $+ CHCl_3 + NaOH \longrightarrow$ S $(C_7H_6O_3)$
S $+ CH_2I_2 + NaOH \longrightarrow$ T $(C_8H_6O_3)$
T $+ CH_3CHO + NaOH \longrightarrow$ U $(C_{10}H_8O_3)$
U $+$ acetic anhydride $+$ sodium acetate $\longrightarrow$ piperic acid $(C_{12}H_{10}O_4)$
piperic acid $+ PCl_5 \longrightarrow$ V $(C_{12}H_9O_3Cl)$
V $+$ piperidine $\longrightarrow$ piperine

24. "Heavy rubber" has been synthesized by the following sequence of reactions:

$CD_3COCD_3 + KC{\equiv}CD \longrightarrow$ W (C_5D_7OK)
W $+ D_2O \longrightarrow$ X (C_5D_8O)
X $+ D_2$, Pd $\longrightarrow$ Y $(C_5D_{10}O)$
Y $+ Al_2O_3$, heat $\longrightarrow$ Z (C_5D_8)
Z $+ [(CH_3)_2CHCH_2]_3Al, TiCl_4 \longrightarrow$ "heavy rubber," $(C_5D_8)_n$, all *cis*

(a) What is the structure of "heavy rubber"? (b) What are the intermediates W through Z?

Chapter twenty-four

GLYCOLS

24.1 Polyfunctional compounds

So far our work has emphasized the properties of individual functional groups, although we have, of course, been concerned with the way these properties are modified by other substituents.

Now we shall take up some of the more important classes of *polyfunctional compounds*. In these, the functional groups interact to such an extent as to produce certain properties characteristic not of one group or another but of a *particular combination of groups*. It is to these special properties that we shall devote most of our time.

In all this, however, we must not forget that we already know most of the chemistry of these compounds, which is essentially the sum of the chemistry of the individual groups.

24.2 Structure and nomenclature

Glycols are alcohols containing two hydroxyl groups. We shall be chiefly concerned with the ones in which the —OH groups are attached to adjacent carbon atoms, the 1,2-*glycols*. Glycols have both common names and IUPAC names:

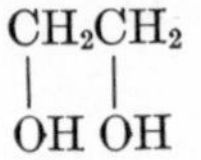

$$CH_2CH_2 \quad\quad CH_3CH—CH_2 \quad\quad CH_2—CH_2—CH_2 \quad\quad CH_2—CH—CH_2$$
$$| \ | \quad\quad\quad | \quad | \quad\quad\quad\quad | \quad\quad\quad\quad | \quad\quad\quad\quad | \quad\quad | \quad\quad |$$
$$OH \ OH \quad\quad OH \quad OH \quad\quad\quad OH \quad\quad\quad OH \quad\quad OH \quad OH \quad OH$$

Ethylene glycol Propylene glycol Trimethylene glycol Glycerol
1,2-Ethanediol 1,2-Propanediol 1,3-Propanediol 1,2,3-Propanetriol

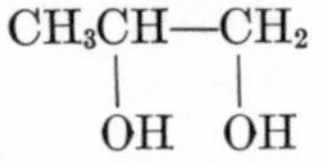

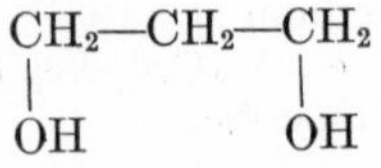

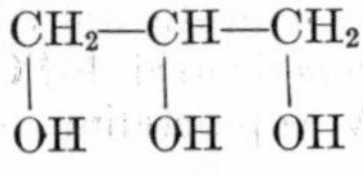

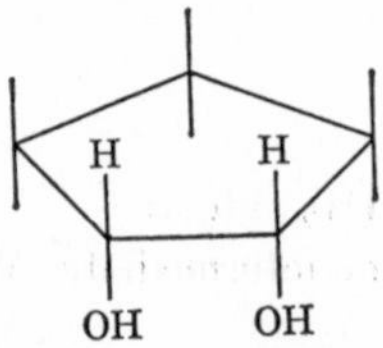

$$CH_3 \quad CH_3$$
$$\quad\quad\quad | \quad\quad\quad |$$
$$CH_3—C\!\!\!—\!\!\!—C—CH_3$$
$$\quad\quad\quad | \quad\quad\quad |$$
$$OH \quad OH$$

H H

OH OH
cis-1,2-Cyclopentanediol 2,3-Dimethyl-2,3-butanediol

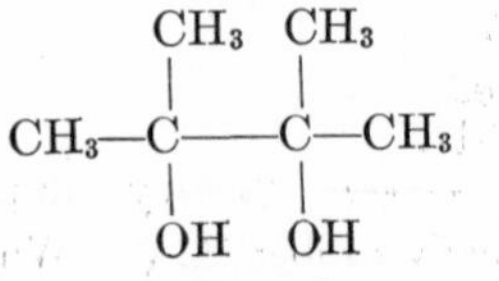

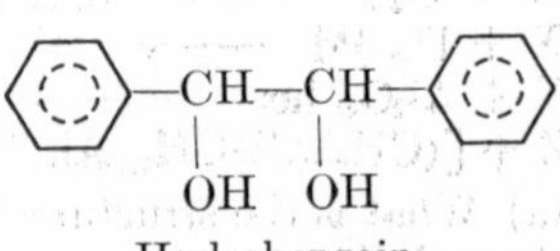

Pinacol

$$⟨◯⟩—CH—CH—⟨◯⟩$$
$$\quad\quad\quad | \quad\quad |$$
$$\quad\quad\quad OH \quad OH$$

Hydrobenzoin
1,2-Diphenyl-1,2-ethanediol

24.3 Physical properties

As we might expect from their structure, with more than one site for hydrogen bonding, glycols have high boiling points, even the simplest

650

member, **ethylene glycol,** boiling at 197°. The lower glycols are miscible with water, and those containing as many as seven carbon atoms show appreciable solubility in water.

Ethylene glycol owes its use as an anti-freeze (e.g., Prestone) to its high boiling point, low freezing point, and high solubility in water. We have already encountered certain commercially available glycols in Sec. 15.15.

TABLE 24.1

POLYHYDROXY ALCOHOLS AND RELATED COMPOUNDS

Name	Formula	M.p., °C	B.p., °C	Solub., g/100 g H_2O
Ethylene glycol	CH_2OHCH_2OH	− 16	197	∞
Propylene glycol	$CH_3CHOHCH_2OH$		187	∞
1,3-Propanediol	$HOCH_2CH_2CH_2OH$		215	∞
1,2-Butanediol	$CH_3CH_2CHOHCH_2OH$		192	sl.s.
meso-2,3-Butanediol	$CH_3CHOHCHOHCH_3$	34	183	∞
1,4-Butanediol	$HOCH_2CH_2CH_2CH_2OH$	16	230	∞
Pinacol	$(CH_3)_2COHC(CH_3)_2OH$	45	174	s.cold
Glycerol	$HOCH_2CHOHCH_2OH$	18	290	∞
Pentaerythritol	$C(CH_2OH)_4$	260		6
meso-Hydrobenzoin	$C_6H_5CHOHCHOHC_6H_5$	137		0.3
cis-1,2-Cyclopentanediol		30	118^{22}	
trans-1,2-Cyclopentanediol		55	136^{22}	
cis-1,2-Cyclohexanediol		98		
trans-1,2-Cyclohexanediol		104		

24.4 Preparation

Glycols are generally prepared by one of the methods outlined below.

PREPARATION OF GLYCOLS

1. Hydroxylation of alkenes

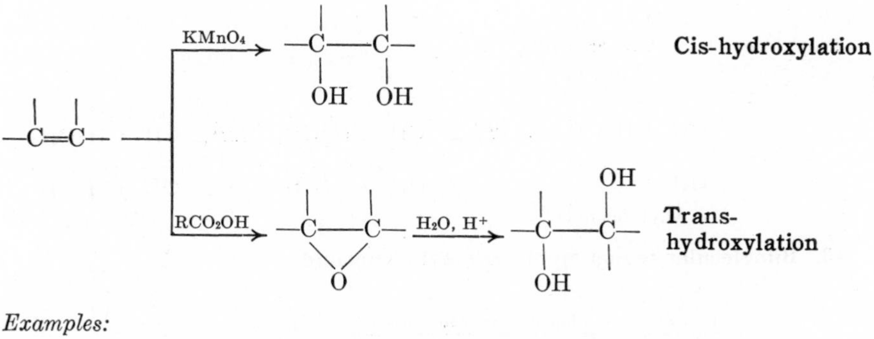

Cis-hydroxylation

Trans-hydroxylation

Examples:

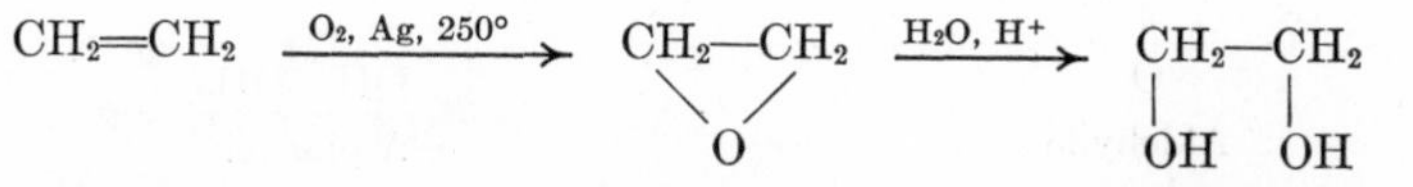

Ethylene   Ethylene oxide   Ethylene glycol

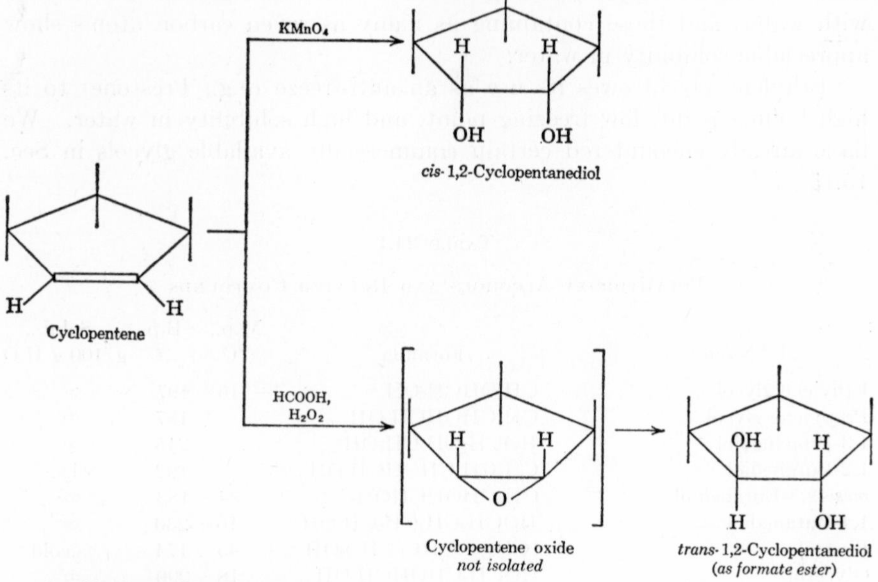

cis-1,2-Cyclopentanediol

Cyclopentene

Cyclopentene oxide
not isolated

trans-1,2-Cyclopentanediol
(*as formate ester*)

2. Hydrolysis of halides

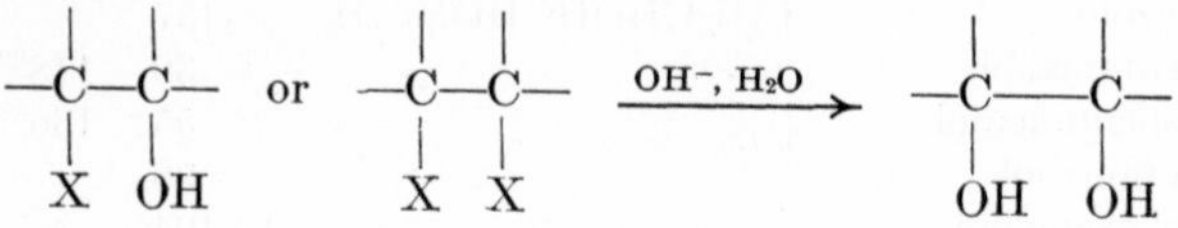

$$
\begin{array}{cc}
\overset{|}{\underset{X}{C}}-\overset{|}{\underset{OH}{C}}- & \text{or} & \overset{|}{\underset{X}{C}}-\overset{|}{\underset{X}{C}}- \xrightarrow{\text{OH}^-,\ \text{H}_2\text{O}} & \overset{|}{\underset{OH}{C}}-\overset{|}{\underset{OH}{C}}-
\end{array}
$$

Examples:

$$
\text{CH}_2{=}\text{CH}_2 \xrightarrow{\text{Cl}_2,\ \text{H}_2\text{O}} \underset{\text{Cl} \quad \text{OH}}{\text{CH}_2{-}\text{CH}_2} \xrightarrow{\text{Na}_2\text{CO}_3,\ \text{H}_2\text{O}} \underset{\text{OH} \quad \text{OH}}{\text{CH}_2{-}\text{CH}_2}
$$

Ethylene   Ethylene chlorohydrin   Ethylene glycol

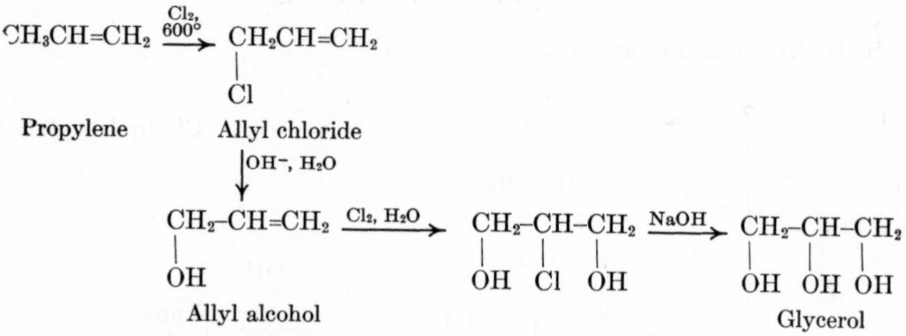

$$
\text{CH}_3\text{CH}{=}\text{CH}_2 \xrightarrow[600°]{\text{Cl}_2,} \underset{\text{Cl}}{\text{CH}_2\text{CH}{=}\text{CH}_2}
$$

Propylene   Allyl chloride

$$\downarrow \text{OH}^-,\ \text{H}_2\text{O}$$

$$
\underset{\text{OH}}{\text{CH}_2{-}\text{CH}{=}\text{CH}_2} \xrightarrow{\text{Cl}_2,\ \text{H}_2\text{O}} \underset{\text{OH} \quad \text{Cl} \quad \text{OH}}{\text{CH}_2{-}\text{CH}{-}\text{CH}_2} \xrightarrow{\text{NaOH}} \underset{\text{OH} \quad \text{OH} \quad \text{OH}}{\text{CH}_2{-}\text{CH}{-}\text{CH}_2}
$$

Allyl alcohol   Glycerol

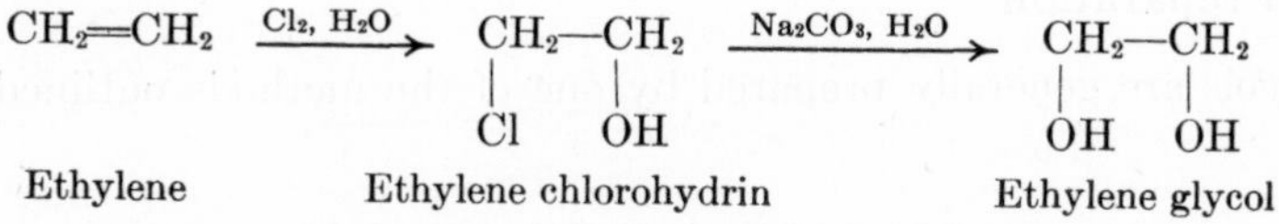

3. Bimolecular reduction of carbonyl compounds

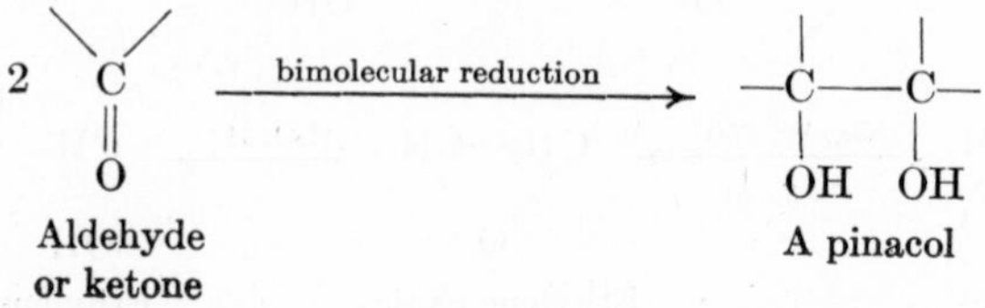

$$
2 \underset{\text{O}}{\overset{\diagdown}{\underset{\|}{\text{C}}}\diagup} \xrightarrow{\text{bimolecular reduction}} \overset{|}{\underset{\text{OH}}{\text{C}}}{-}\overset{|}{\underset{\text{OH}}{\text{C}}}{-}
$$

Aldehyde   A pinacol
or ketone

Examples:

$$2CH_3CCH_3 \xrightarrow{\text{Mg, benzene}} \underset{\substack{|\\O}}{CH_3C}\!-\!-\!-\!\underset{\substack{|\\O}}{CCH_3} \xrightarrow{\text{H}_2\text{O}} \underset{\substack{|\\OH}}{CH_3C}\!-\!-\!-\!\underset{\substack{|\\OH}}{CCH_3}$$

Acetone   Mg

Pinacol
2,3-Dimethyl-1,3-butanediol

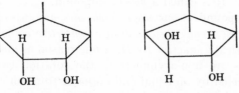

Benzophenone

Benzopinacol
1,1,2,2-Tetraphenyl-1,2-ethanediol

Glycols are often prepared by **hydroxylation of carbon–carbon double bonds,** either directly or via the epoxide, by methods we have already encountered (Sec. 5.19). Being alcohols, they can also be made by adaptations of methods used for the preparation of monohydroxy alcohols, in particular, **hydrolysis of halides;** the halohydrins used for this purpose are themselves obtained by additions to carbon–carbon double bonds.

Symmetrical glycols can often be prepared by **bimolecular reduction of aldehydes and ketones,** that is, reduction under conditions that bring about formation of a bond between two carbonyl carbons. Such glycols are often referred to as *pinacols.*

Problem 24.1 Predict the major by-product in the preparation of ethylene glycol by the action of aqueous NaOH on ethylene bromide. Account for the fact that a much better yield of ethylene glycol can be obtained by treatment of ethylene bromide with aqueous sodium acetate and subsequent hydrolysis of the diacetate.

Problem 24.2 Ethylene glycol has been prepared industrially not only from ethylene but also from methyl glycolate, $CH_2OHCOOCH_3$. How could this be done?

24.5   Stereoisomerism of cyclic glycols.   Meso compounds

In our study of cycloalkenes (Sec. 7.13), we found that cyclopentene can be converted into two stereoisomeric glycols. Oxidation with permanganate yields a glycol of m.p. 30°: the *cis*-glycol. Oxidation to the epoxide, and subsequent hydrolysis, yields a glycol of m.p. 55°: the *trans*-glycol. In Sec. 15.18 we saw the mechanisms that have been proposed to account for the stereochemistry of these reactions.

Let us look more closely at the stereoisomerism of these compounds.

cis-1,2-Cyclopentanediol   *trans*-1,2-Cyclopentanediol

In particular, let us see why we can be confident that the glycol of m.p. 30° is indeed the *cis*-isomer, and that the glycol of m.p. 55° is the *trans*-isomer.

If we examine models of *cis*- and *trans*-1,2-cyclopentanediol, we find that each compound contains two asymmetric carbon atoms. We have learned (Sec. 11.21) that compounds containing asymmetric carbon atoms are often optically active. Are these glycols optically active? As always, to test for possible optical activity, we construct a model of the molecule and a model of its mirror image, and see if the two are superimposable.

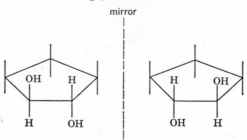

Not superimposable
trans-1,2-Cyclopentanediol

When we do this for the *trans*-glycol, we find that the models are *not* superimposable. The two models we have constructed therefore correspond to enantiomeric *trans*-1,2-cyclopentanediols, each of which is optically active.

Next let us look at *cis*-1,2-cyclopentanediol. This, too, contains two asymmetric carbons; is it, too, capable of showing optical activity? This time we find that a model of the molecule and a model of its mirror image *are* superimposable.

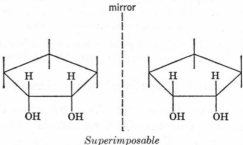

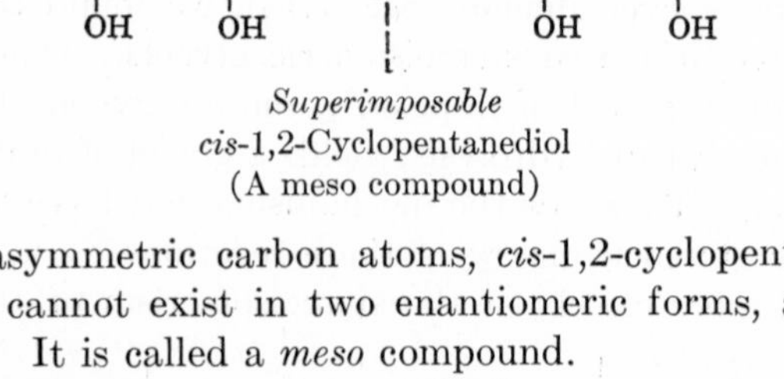

Superimposable
cis-1,2-Cyclopentanediol
(A meso compound)

In spite of its asymmetric carbon atoms, *cis*-1,2-cyclopentanediol is not asymmetric; it cannot exist in two enantiomeric forms, and cannot be optically active. It is called a *meso* compound.

A **meso compound** *is one whose molecules are superimposable on their mirror images even though they contain asymmetric carbon atoms.* A *meso* compound is optically inactive for the same reason as any other compound whose molecules are non-asymmetric: the rotation caused by any one molecule is canceled by an equal and opposite rotation caused by another molecule that is the mirror image of the first. (See Sec. 11.20.)

We can often recognize a *meso* structure on sight by the fact that it is symmetrical. This can be seen for *cis*-1,2-cyclopentanediol by imagining the molecule to be cut by a plane lying where the dotted line is drawn:

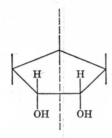

cis-1,2-Cyclopentanediol
(A meso compound)

The two halves thus formed are mirror images. The molecule has what is called a *plane of symmetry*; being symmetrical, it must be superimposable on its mirror image. However, the optical inactivity of a *meso* structure is most safely predicted by the usual method of superimposing molecule and mirror image.

Thus, of the two 1,2-cyclopentanediols obtainable from cyclopentene, one should be separable into enantiomers, that is, should be *resolvable*; this must necessarily be the *trans*-glycol. It has been found experimentally that the glycol of m.p. 55°, obtained by hydrolysis of the epoxide, is a racemate that is separable by the methods described in Sec. 20.5 into two optically active isomers; hence this glycol must have the *trans* configuration. The other glycol (m.p. 30°, resulting from the permanganate oxidation) is a single, inactive, nonresolvable compound; hence it must have the *cis* configuration.

Problem 24.3 Given the alkaloid (−)-brucine, tell exactly how you would attempt to resolve *trans*-1,2-cyclopentanediol; write equations for each step. (*Hint:* See Sec. 20.5.)

What is the relationship between the *meso cis*-glycol and either of the enantiomeric *trans*-glycols? They are *diastereomers*, since they are optical isomers that are not enantiomers. Like other diastereomers (see Sec. 20.5) they differ appreciably in their physical and chemical properties, in much the way geometric isomers do. Indeed, in the present case we use the same designations of *cis* and *trans* that we have previously applied to geometric isomers.

Turning to models of 1,2-cyclohexanediol, we find that here, too, the *trans*-isomer can exist as a pair of enantiomers, and the *cis*-isomer must be a *meso* compound. Experimentally the product of hydrolysis of cyclohexene oxide is a resolvable racemate, and hence must be the *trans*-glycol. The product of permanganate oxidation of cyclohexene is an inactive, nonresolvable material, and hence must be the *cis*-glycol.

The importance of using models is especially evident in dealing with these cyclohexane derivatives. The *cis*-glycol and its mirror image are *not identical*, since they have different conformations; they can, however, *be made* identical without breaking any bonds — that is, are *superimposable* — and the compound is optically inactive.

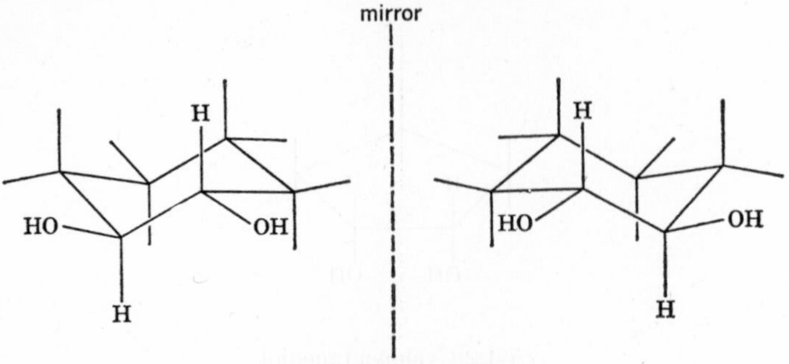

Not superimposable
trans-1,2-Cyclohexanediol
(A resolvable racemate)

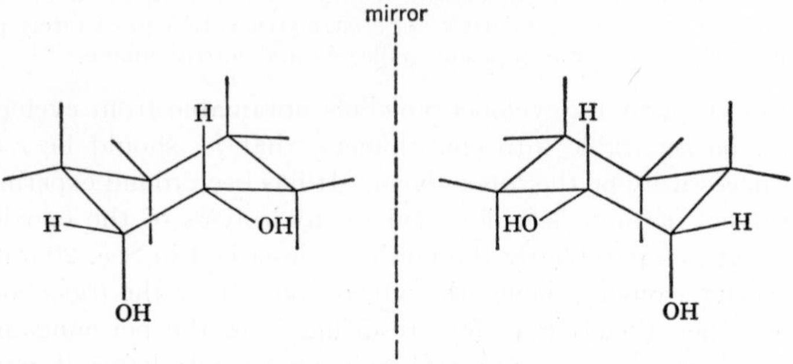

Superimposable
cis-1,2-Cyclohexanediol
(A non-resolvable meso compound)

Problem 24.4   Make a model of *cis*-1,2-cyclohexanediol in a chair conformation.   Make a model of its mirror image.   (a) Are the two models identical?   (b) Flip one model into the other chair conformation.   Now are the two models identical?   (c) and (d) Do the same for the *trans*-isomer.

Because of the ready interconvertibility of chair conformations, it is possible to use planar drawings to predict the stereoisomerism of cyclohexane derivatives:

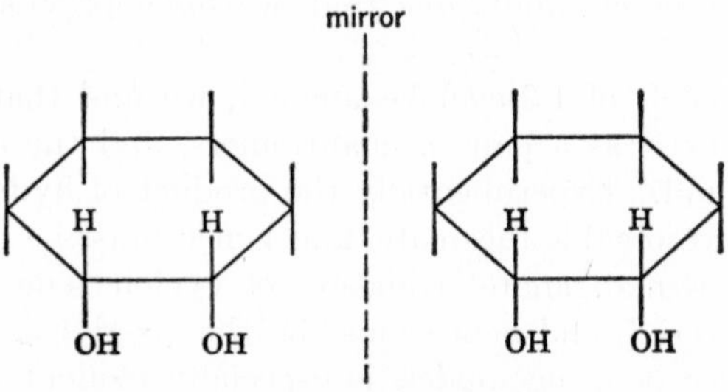

Superimposable
cis-1,2-Cyclohexanediol

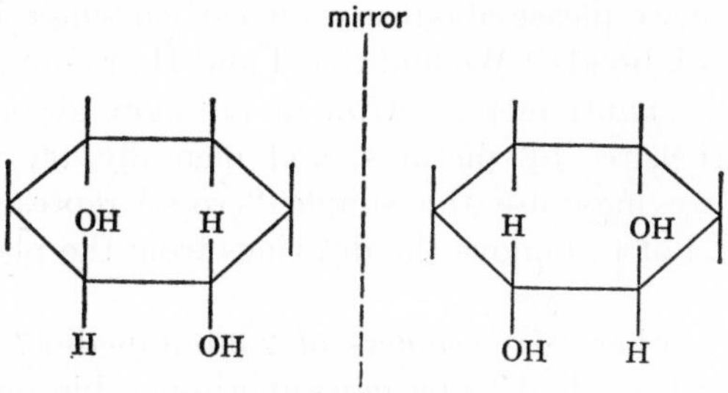

Not superimposable
trans-1,2-Cyclohexanediol

Problem 24.5 Which of the following compounds are resolvable and which are nonresolvable? Use models as well as drawings.

(a) *cis*-1,3-cyclohexanediol   (c) *cis*-1,4-cyclohexanediol
(b) *trans*-1,3-cyclohexanediol   (d) *trans*-1,4-cyclohexanediol

Problem 24.6 Draw structural formulas for all stereoisomers of the following, labeling any *meso* compounds, and indicating pairs of enantiomers:

(a) *cis*-2-chlorocyclohexanol   (d) *trans*-3-chlorocyclopentanol
(b) *trans*-2-chlorocyclohexanol   (e) *cis*-4-chlorocyclohexanol
(c) *cis*-3-chlorocyclopentanol   (f) *trans*-4-chlorocyclohexanol

24.6 Stereoisomerism of open-chain glycols

Let us turn next to the stereoisomerism of the open-chain glycols. A molecule of 2,3-butanediol, for example, contains two asymmetric carbon atoms; how many stereoisomeric 2,3-butanediols are there?

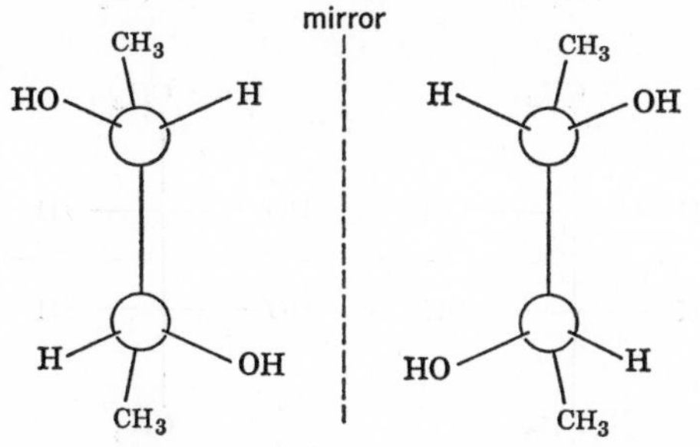

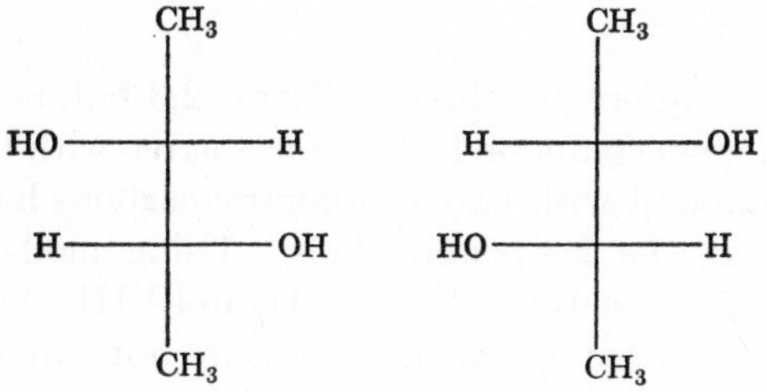

Using models let us first make structures I and II, and see if these are superimposable. In doing this, we may twist and turn the models, and make any rotation we please about carbon–carbon single bonds; we may not, of course, break bonds. We find that I and II are not superimposable, and hence must be enantiomers. (After we are more experienced, we may represent the structures by pictures, and mentally try to superimpose these. Finally, we may use the simple "cross" representations, being careful, as before, not to remove the drawings from the plane of the paper or blackboard.)

Are there any other stereoisomers of 2,3-butanediol? We can make structure III, which we find to be non-superimposable on either I or II; it is not, of course the mirror image of either. Then III must be a di-astereomer of I and of II. Can III be optically active? No, because we find it to be superimposable on its mirror image IV; turned end-for-end IV coincides in every respect with III. Structure III is a *meso* compound. (We might have recognized III as a *meso* structure from the fact that it is a symmetrical molecule; in the conformation shown, the top half of the molecule is the mirror image of the bottom half.)

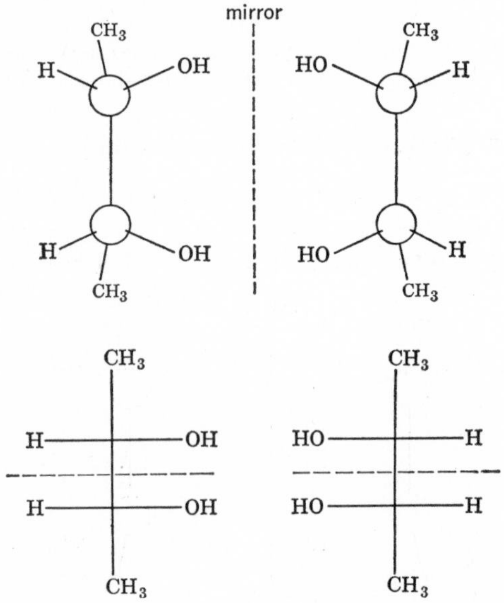

III   IV

There should therefore be three isomeric 2,3-butanediols: a pair of enantiomers and a *meso* compound. The facts agree with these predictions.

Can every compound with two asymmetric carbons have a *meso* form? Let us look next at the 2,3-pentanediols. Using models as before, we arrive at four possible structures, V, VI, VII, and VIII, shown on page 659. Structures V and VI are mirror images that are not superimposable; they are therefore enantiomers, and each should be optically active. What can we say about VII and its mirror image VIII? We also find that VII and VIII are not superimposable. When we turn VIII end-for-end its —OH groups coincide with those of VII, but where VII has a —CH₃

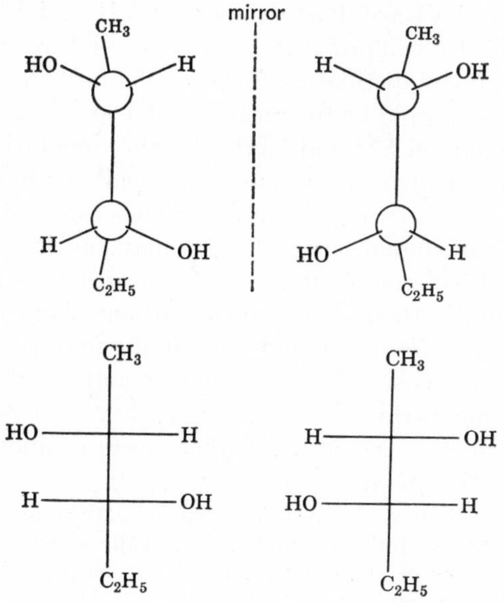

mirror

CH_3
HO— —H | H— —OH
            | CH_3

H— —OH | HO— —H
C_2H_5 | C_2H_5

CH_3 CH_3
HO———H   H———OH

H———OH   HO———H

C_2H_5 C_2H_5
V   VI

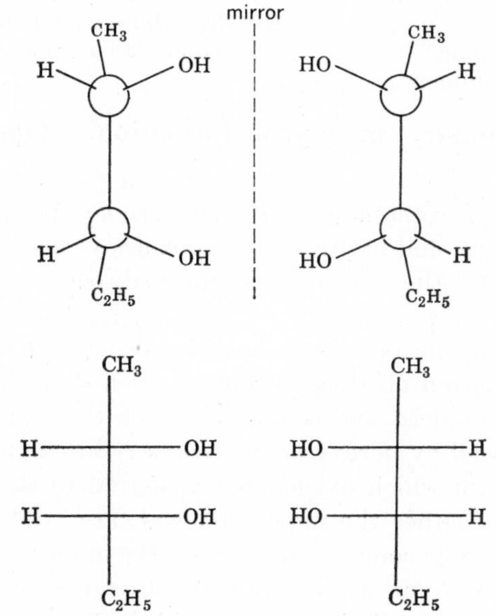

mirror

CH_3 CH_3
H— —OH   HO— —H

H— —OH   HO— —H
C_2H_5 C_2H_5

CH_3 CH_3
H———OH   HO———H

H———OH   HO———H

C_2H_5 C_2H_5
VII   VIII

group VIII has a —C_2H_5 group, and where VII has —C_2H_5 VIII has —CH_3. This time we do not have a *meso* structure, but instead another pair of enantiomers.

In agreement with prediction, four 2,3-pentanediols are known: two pairs of enantiomers. (V and VI are designated *threo* isomers and VII and VIII as *erythro* isomers, the names being derived from the carbohydrates *threose* and *erythrose*.)

Structures V and VI are diastereomers of VII and VIII, and as such differ from them in physical properties. Given a mixture of all four isomers, we could separate it, by distillation for example, into two fractions but no further; one fraction would be the racemate of V and VI, the other fraction would be the racemate of VII and VIII. Further separation would require resolution of the racemates with the use of optically active reagents.

Thus the presence of two asymmetric carbons can lead to the existence of as many as four stereoisomers; there may, as with 2,3-butanediol, actually be only three stereoisomers if a *meso* structure is possible. For compounds containing three asymmetric carbons there can be as many as eight stereoisomers, for compounds containing four asymmetric carbons there can be as many as sixteen stereoisomers, and so on. The maximum number of stereoisomers that can exist is equal to 2^n, where n is the number of asymmetric carbons. In any case where *meso* compounds exist, there will be fewer than this maximum number.

Problem 24.7 Draw stereochemical formulas for all the possible stereoisomers of the following compounds. Indicate which are optically active, which are optically inactive, which are pairs of enantiomers, which are *meso* compounds. Pick out several examples of diastereomers.

(a) 1,2-propanediol
(b) 3,4-dimethyl-3,4-hexanediol
(c) 2,4-pentanediol
(d) *p*-di-*sec*-butylbenzene
(e) 2,3,4-trihydroxybutanal

(f) 1,2,3,4-tetrahydroxybutane
(g) 2,3-dihydroxy-1,4-butanedioic acid
(h) the sodium ammonium salt of (g)
(i) 3-amino-2-butanol

24.7 Stereochemistry of glycol formation. Open-chain compounds

Hydroxylation of cyclic alkenes is *stereospecific:* permanganate oxidation yields *cis*-glycols, and hydrolysis of epoxides yields *trans*-glycols. We have seen (Sec. 15.18) the mechanisms proposed to account for this stereospecificity.

If these mechanisms operate, what stereochemical results would we expect in the formation of glycols from an open-chain alkene, say, from 2-butene? Using models, let us first consider the conversion of *trans*-2-butene into a glycol by peroxy acids. *trans*-2-Butene is a flat molecule. Whatever the way in which oxygen is transferred to the alkene, it must become attached to either the upper or lower face. Let us see what we would get if oxygen becomes attached to the upper face. When this happens, the carbon atoms of the double bond tend to become tetrahedral, and the hydrogens and methyls are displaced downward:

trans-2-Butene   *trans*-Epoxide

The methyl groups, however, are still located across the molecule from each other, as they were in the alkene. In this way, epoxide I is formed.

Now epoxide I becomes protonated and undergoes nucleophilic attack by water. As shown in path (A), water becomes attached to carbon on the side opposite to oxygen, a carbon–oxygen bond breaks, and inversion occurs. This yields structure II.

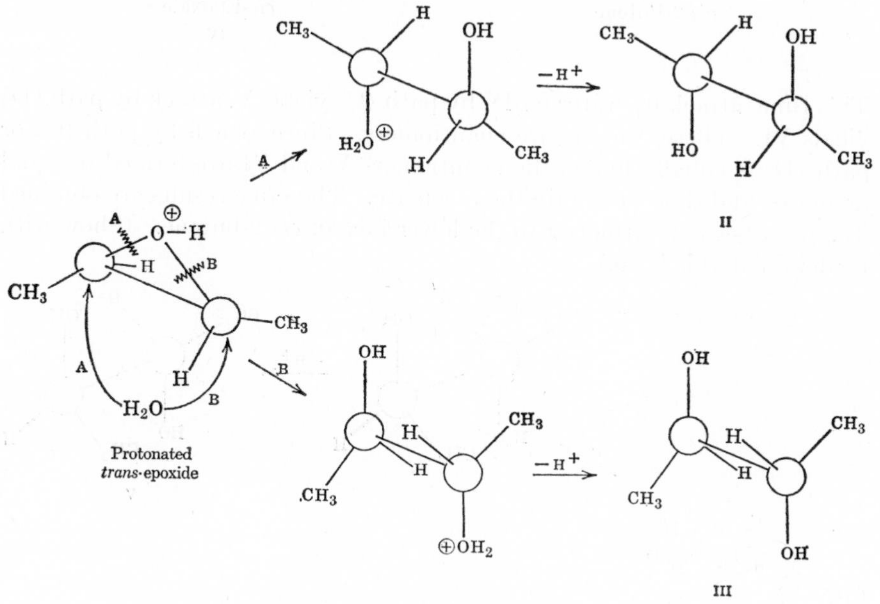

II *and* III *are the same as*

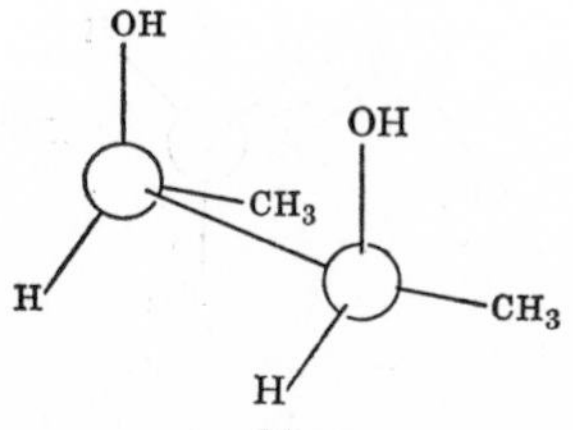

Meso

But attack can equally well occur at the other carbon by path (B). This again involves inversion and yields structure III. If we simply rotate the two ends of either structure, II or III, about the carbon–carbon bond, we can readily recognize the symmetry of the compound. It is *meso*-2,3-butanediol; II and III are identical. The same results are obtained if oxygen becomes attached to the lower face of *trans*-2-butene. (Show with models that this is so.)

Next, let us carry through the same operations on *cis*-2-butene.

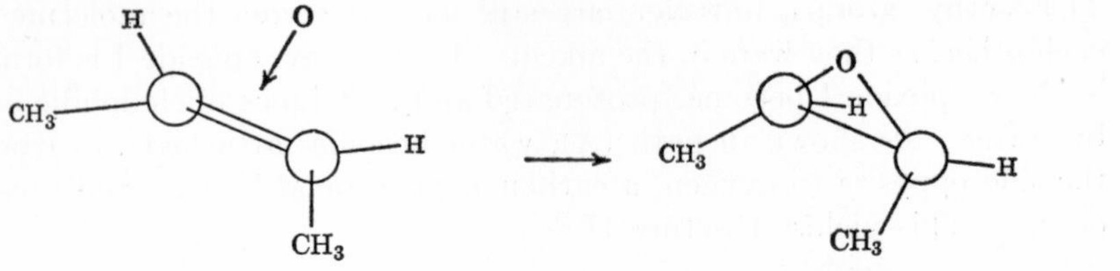

cis-2-Butene

cis-Epoxide
IV

This time, attack by water on **IV** by path (C) yields **V**, attack by path (D) yields **VI**. These, we see, are enantiomers. Since attack by path (C) or path (D) is equally likely, the enantiomers **V** and **VI** are formed in equal amounts, and thus we obtain the racemate. The same results are obtained if oxygen becomes attached to the lower face of cis-2-butene. (Show with models that this is so.)

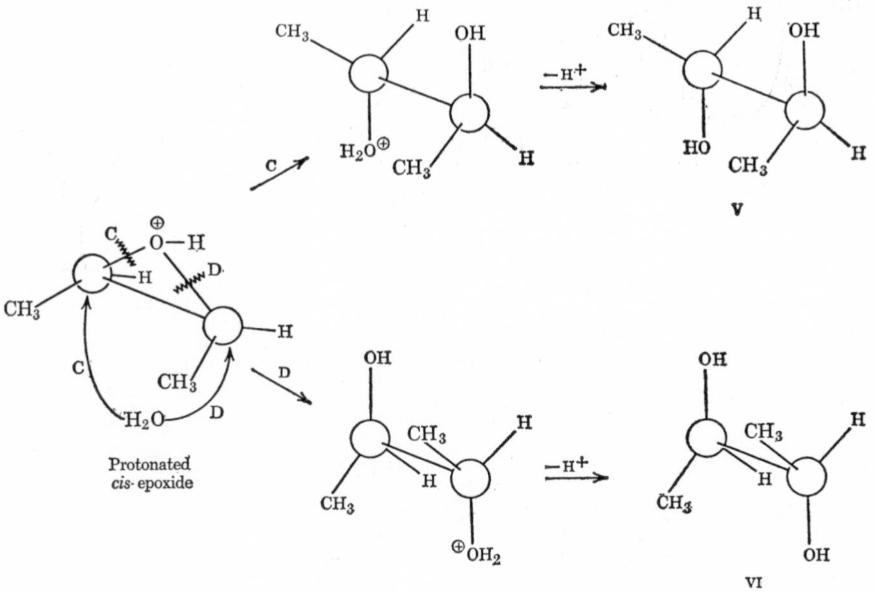

Protonated
cis·epoxide

v and vi are enantiomers

These predictions are borne out by experiment: hydrolysis of the epoxide from trans-2-butene yields a meso-glycol, whereas hydrolysis of the epoxide from cis-2-butene yields a racemic glycol.

Problem 24.8 Hydroxylation of cis-2-butene and of trans-2-butene by permanganate has been found to yield the products predicted by the mechanism of Sec. 15.18. What are these products?

Problem 24.9 (a) What is the relationship between the epoxides formed by attack on the upper and lower faces of trans-2-butene? In what proportions are they formed? (b) Answer the same questions for cis-2-butene. (c) For trans-2-pentene. (d) For cis-2-pentene.

Problem 24.10 (a) Predict the products from the peroxy acid hydroxylation of *trans*-2-pentene. Is attack by water by the two paths equally likely? Account for the fact that inactive material is actually obtained. (b) Do the same for *cis*-2-pentene.

Problem 24.11 Keeping in mind the stereochemistry of halogen addition (Sec. 15.19), predict the products of the addition of bromine to:

(a) *trans*-2-butene; (b) *cis*-2-butene; (c) *trans*-2-pentene; (d) *cis*-2-pentene.

24.8 Reactions

Glycols are alcohols, and most of the chemical properties of glycols are the chemical properties of alcohols; these have already been discussed in Chapter 12. In addition, glycols undergo certain reactions that are characteristic only of compounds containing two or more —OH groups. Of these reactions, we shall take up two: (a) a special kind of oxidation, *by periodic acid;* and (b) a special kind of dehydration, the *pinacol rearrangement.*

Problem 24.12 Predict the products of the reaction between:
(a) ethylene glycol and excess acetic acid in the presence of a little sulfuric acid
(b) trimethylene glycol and excess aqueous HBr and heat
(c) propylene glycol and excess PBr$_3$
(d) 1,3-butanediol and Al$_2$O$_3$ at 350°
(e) 2,3-butanediol and benzaldehyde in the presence of anhydrous hydrogen chloride $\longrightarrow$ C$_{11}$H$_{14}$O$_2$
(f) 1,2-diphenyl-1,2-ethanediol and KMnO$_4$
(g) ethylene glycol and ethylene oxide in the presence of acid
(h) ethylene glycol + H$_2$SO$_4$ + heat $\longrightarrow$ C$_4$H$_8$O$_2$

Problem 24.13 (a) *cis*-1,2-Cyclopentanediol reacts with acetone in the presence of dry HCl to yield compound X, C$_8$H$_{14}$O$_2$, which is resistant to boiling alkali, but which is readily converted into the starting materials by aqueous acids. What is the most likely structure for X? To what class of compounds does it belong?

(b) *trans*-1,2-Cyclopentanediol does not form an analogous compound. How do you account for this fact?

24.9 Oxidation by periodic acid

Upon treatment with periodic acid, HIO$_4$, compounds containing two or more —OH or =O groups attached to *adjacent* carbon atoms undergo oxidation with cleavage of carbon–carbon bonds. For example:

$$\begin{array}{c} R\text{—}CH\text{—}CH\text{—}R' + HIO_4 \longrightarrow RCHO + R'CHO \ \ (+ HIO_3) \\ \ \ \ \ | \ \ \ \ \ \ | \\ \ \ \ \ OH \ \ OH \end{array}$$

$$\begin{array}{c} R\text{—}C\text{—}C\text{—}R' + HIO_4 \longrightarrow RCOOH + R'COOH \\ \ \ \ \ || \ \ \ || \\ \ \ \ \ O \ \ \ O \end{array}$$

$$\begin{array}{c} R\text{—}CH\text{—}C\text{—}R' + HIO_4 \longrightarrow RCHO + R'COOH \\ \ \ \ \ \ | \ \ \ || \\ \ \ \ \ OH \ \ O \end{array}$$

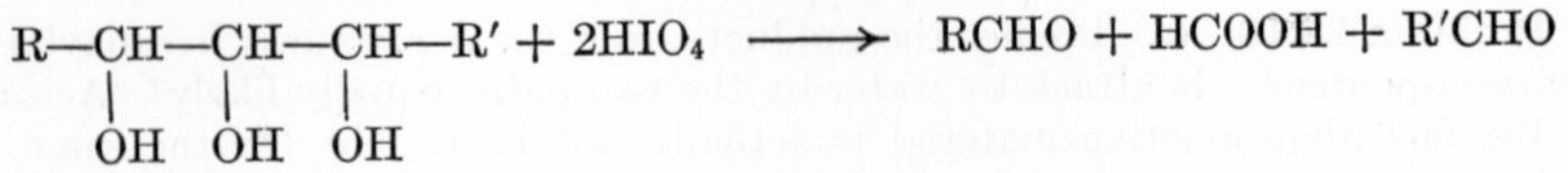

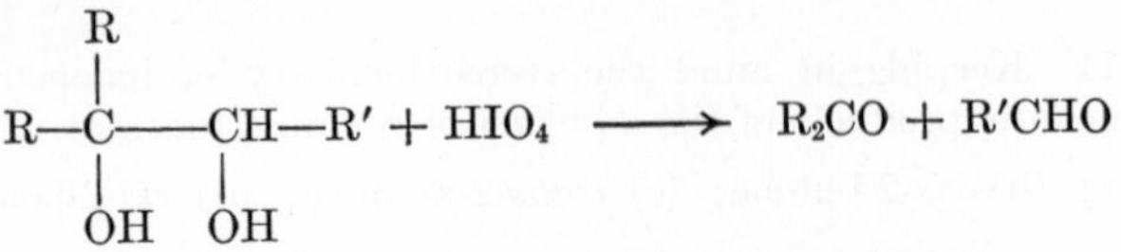

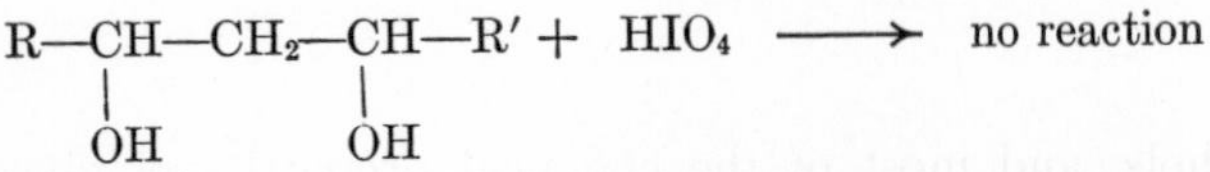

$$R-\underset{\underset{OH}{|}}{CH}-\underset{\underset{OH}{|}}{CH}-\underset{\underset{OH}{|}}{CH}-R' + 2HIO_4 \longrightarrow RCHO + HCOOH + R'CHO$$

$$R-\underset{\underset{OH}{|}}{\overset{\overset{R}{|}}{C}}-\underset{\underset{OH}{|}}{CH}-R' + HIO_4 \longrightarrow R_2CO + R'CHO$$

$$R-\underset{\underset{OH}{|}}{CH}-CH_2-\underset{\underset{OH}{|}}{CH}-R' + HIO_4 \longrightarrow \text{no reaction}$$

The oxidation is particularly useful in determination of structure. Qualitatively, oxidation by HIO_4 is indicated by formation of a white precipitate ($AgIO_3$) upon addition of silver nitrate. Since the reaction is usually quantitative, valuable information is given by the nature and amounts of the products, and by the quantity of periodic acid consumed.

Problem 24.14 When one mole of each of the following compounds is treated with HIO_4, what will the products be, and how many moles of HIO_4 would be consumed?

(a) $CH_3CHOHCH_2OH$
(b) $CH_3CHOHCHO$
(c) $CH_2OHCHOHCH_2OCH_3$
(d) $CH_2OHCH(OCH_3)CH_2OH$

(e) *cis*-1,2-cyclopentanediol
(f) $CH_2OH(CHOH)_3CHO$
(g) $CH_2OH(CHOH)_3CH_2OH$

Problem 24.15 Assign a structure to each of the following compounds:

A + one mole HIO_4 $\longrightarrow$ $CH_3COCH_3 + HCHO$
B + one mole HIO_4 $\longrightarrow$ $OHC(CH_2)_4CHO$
C + one mole HIO_4 $\longrightarrow$ $HOOC(CH_2)_4CHO$
D + one mole HIO_4 $\longrightarrow$ $2HOOC-CHO$
E + $3HIO_4$ $\longrightarrow$ $2HCOOH + 2HCHO$
F + $3HIO_4$ $\longrightarrow$ $2HCOOH + HCHO + CO_2$
G + $2HIO_4$ $\longrightarrow$ $2HCOOH + HCHO$
H + $5HIO_4$ $\longrightarrow$ $5HCOOH + HCHO$
I + $4HIO_4$ $\longrightarrow$ $3HCOOH + HCHO + OHCCOOH$

24.10 Pinacol rearrangement

Upon treatment with mineral acids, 2,3-dimethyl-2,3-butanediol (often called *pinacol*) is converted into methyl *tert*-butyl ketone (often called *pinacolone*).

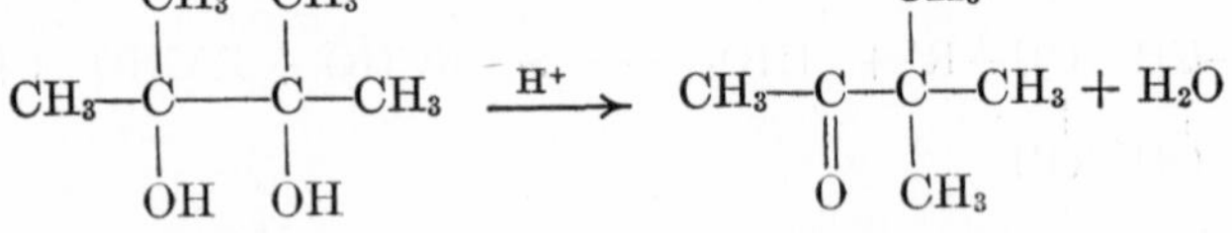

$$CH_3-\underset{\underset{OH}{|}}{\overset{\overset{CH_3}{|}}{C}}-\underset{\underset{OH}{|}}{\overset{\overset{CH_3}{|}}{C}}-CH_3 \xrightarrow{H^+} CH_3-\underset{\underset{O}{||}}{C}-\underset{\underset{CH_3}{|}}{\overset{\overset{CH_3}{|}}{C}}-CH_3 + H_2O$$

Pinacol
2,3-Dimethyl-2,3-butanediol

Pinacolone
Methyl *tert*-butyl ketone
3,3-Dimethyl-2-butanone

The glycol undergoes dehydration, and in such a way that rearrangement of the carbon skeleton occurs. Other glycols undergo analogous reactions, which are known collectively as **pinacol rearrangements.**

The pinacol rearrangement is believed to involve two important steps: (1) loss of water from the protonated glycol to form a carbonium ion; and (2) rearrangement of the carbonium ion by a 1,2-shift to yield the protonated ketone.

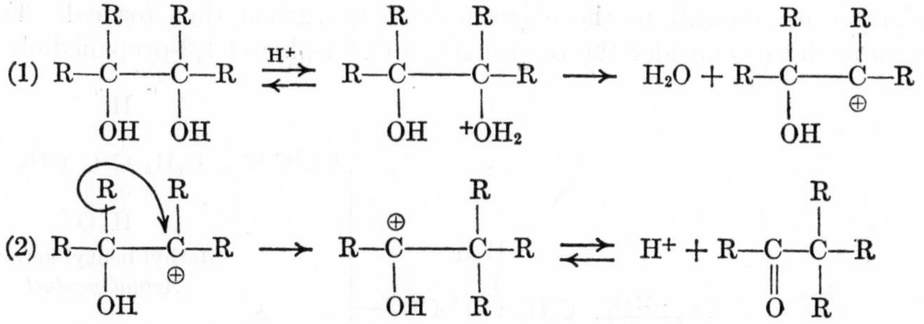

In some cases at least, it may be that the two steps occur simultaneously, attachment of the migrating group helping to expel the molecule of water.

Both steps in this reaction are already quite familiar to us: formation of a carbonium ion from an alcohol under the influence of acid, followed by a 1,2-shift to an electron-deficient atom.

As in most 1,2-shifts to electron-deficient atoms (Sec. 19.14), it is believed that the migrating group is at no time completely free; it does not break away from the carbon it is leaving until it has attached itself to electron-deficient carbon:

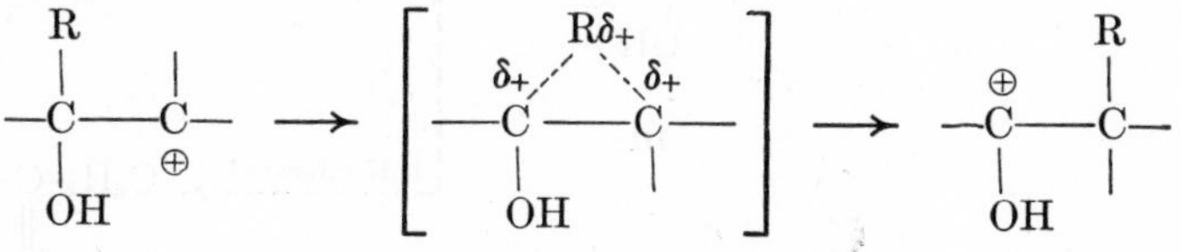

In the migration of an aryl group, the intermediate is believed to have structure I, and may be an actual compound. Again we notice the simi-

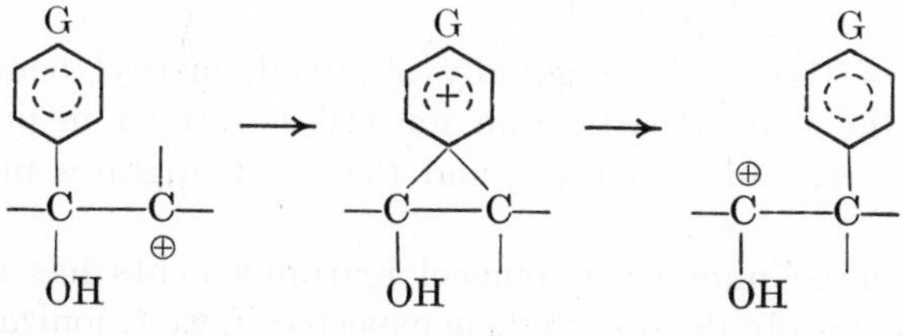

I

larity to the carbonium ion intermediate proposed for electrophilic aromatic substitution (Sec. 10.7). Migration of an aryl group can be viewed simply as a case of aromatic substitution, with the electron-deficient carbon as the electrophilic reagent.

Problem 24.16 How might you account for the fact that an aryl group has a greater migration tendency than an alkyl group?

Problem 24.17 Account for the products of the following reactions:

(a) 1,1,2-triphenyl-2-amino-1-propanol $\xrightarrow{\text{HONO}}$ 1,2,2-triphenyl-1-propanone (*Hint:* See Problem 20.11, page 563.)

(b) 2-phenyl-1-iodo-2-propanol + Ag$^+$ $\longrightarrow$ benzyl methyl ketone

When the groups attached to the carbon atoms bearing —OH differ from one another, the pinacol rearrangement can conceivably give rise to more than one compound. The product actually obtained is determined (a) by which —OH group is lost in step (1), and then (b) by which group migrates in step (2) to the electron-deficient carbon thus formed. For example, let us consider the rearrangement of 1-phenyl-1,2-propanediol:

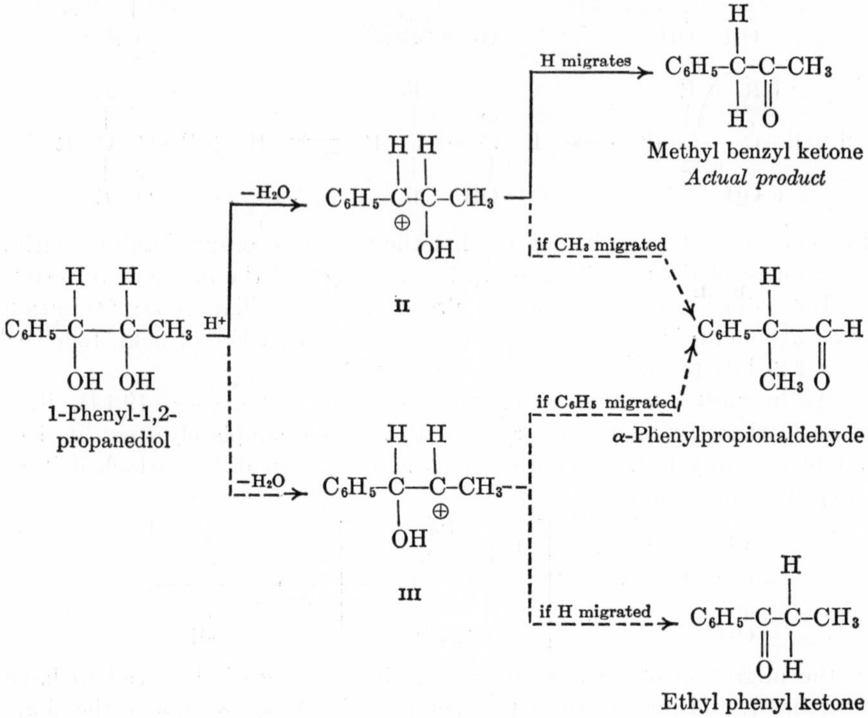

The structure of the product actually obtained, methyl benzyl ketone, indicates that the benzyl carbonium ion (II) is formed in preference to the secondary carbonium ion (III), and that —H migrates in preference to —CH$_3$.

Study of a large number of pinacol rearrangements has shown that usually the product obtained is the one expected if, first, ionization occurs to yield the more stable carbonium ion, and then, once the preferred ionization has taken place, migration takes place according to the sequence —Ar > —H > —R.

Problem 24.18 For the rearrangement of each of the following glycols show which carbonium ion you would expect to be the more stable, and then the rearrangement that this carbonium ion would most likely undergo.

(a) 1,2-propanediol
(b) 2-methyl-1,2-propanediol
(c) 1-phenyl-1,2-ethanediol
(d) 1,1-diphenyl-1,2-ethanediol
(e) 1-phenyl-1,2-propanediol

(f) 1,1-diphenyl-2,2-dimethyl-1,2-ethanediol
(g) 1,1,2-triphenyl-2-methyl-1,2-ethanediol
(h) 2-methyl-3-ethyl-2,3-pentanediol
(i) 1,1-bis(*p*-methoxyphenyl)-2,2-diphenyl-1,2-ethanediol

Problem 24.19   Do the products you predicted in the previous problem agree with the following products actually obtained?

(a) propionaldehyde
(b) isobutyraldehyde
(c) phenylacetaldehyde
(d) diphenylacetaldehyde
(e) benzyl methyl ketone
(f) 3,3-diphenyl-2-butanone

(g) 1,1,1-triphenyl-2-propanone
(h) a mixture of 4,4-dimethyl-3-hexanone and 3-methyl-3-ethyl-2-pentanone
(i) a mixture of p,p'-dimethoxytriphenylmethyl phenyl ketone (72%) and p-methoxytriphenylmethyl p-methoxyphenyl ketone (28%)

24.11   Stereochemistry of 1,2-shifts: the migration terminus

In our discussion of the stereochemistry of the Hofmann degradation of amides (Sec. 19.14), we saw that rearrangement takes place with complete retention of the configuration of the migrating group. Studies of other rearrangements have given similar results, and have led to the tentative conclusion: *in all 1,2-shifts there is complete retention of configuration in the migrating group,* indicating that the migrating group does not break away from the carbon it is leaving until it has attached itself to the electron-deficient atom to which it is going, and that the new bond takes the same relative position as that previously occupied by the old bond.

Let us turn to another aspect of the stereochemistry of 1,2-shifts. What happens at the migration terminus, that is, at the electron-deficient atom to which migration takes place?   Perhaps the best evidence has been furnished by a study of the closely related reaction in which a carbonium ion is generated by the action of nitrous acid on a primary aliphatic amino group.   When optically active 1,1-diphenyl-2-amino-1-propanol is treated with nitrous acid there is obtained 1,2-diphenyl-1-propanone of inverted configuration.   The migrating phenyl group attacks the back side of the electron-deficient carbon atom, that is, the side opposite to the one previously occupied by the —NH₂ group.

On the basis of this work and of other, similar studies, it has been tentatively concluded that *in all 1,2-shifts there is inversion of configuration at the migration terminus,* indicating that the migrating group attacks the back side of the electron-deficient atom.   This behavior is not surprising since, from one point of view, the rearrangement is simply a special case of nucleophilic substitution, in which the migrating group acts as a nucleophilic reagent.   Some rearrangements are of the S_N2 type in which the migrating group helps to push out the departing group; others are of the S_N1 type, in which a carbonium ion is actually formed before migration occurs.

The tendency for inversion to take place at the migration terminus is so great that it often determines the entire course of the reaction. Regardless of "intrinsic migration tendencies," the group that migrates is the one that can best get at the back side of the electron-deficient atom. Let us look at just one example of this effect, one that at the same time illustrates the importance of conformational analysis.

When *cis*-1,2-dimethyl-1,2-cyclohexanediol is treated with acid under the conditions of the pinacol rearrangement, it is converted into 2,2-dimethylcyclohexanone (I). Under the same conditions its stereoisomer *trans*-1,2-dimethyl-1,2-cyclohexanediol is converted into 1-aceto-1-methylcyclopentane (II).

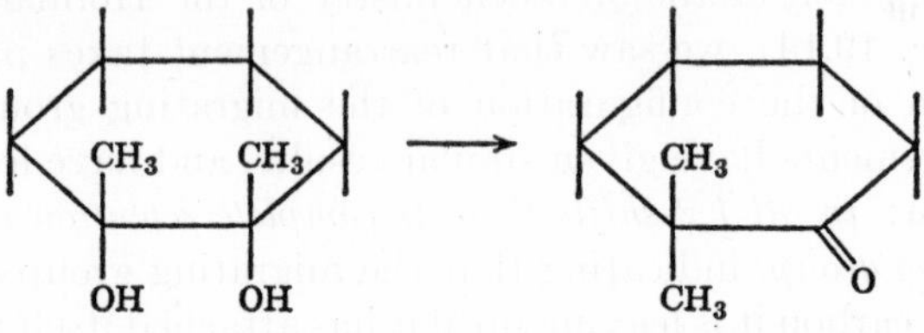

cis-1,2-Dimethyl-1,2-cyclohexanediol   2,2-Dimethylcyclohexanone

I

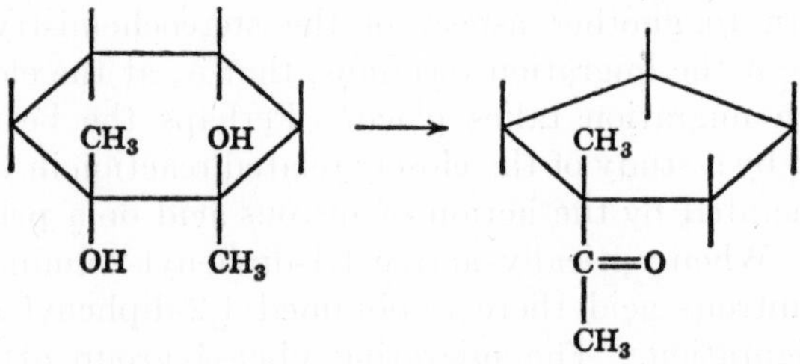

trans-1,2-Dimethyl-1,2-cyclohexanediol   1-Aceto-1-methylcyclopentane

II

Since the two glycols differ only in configuration, it is clear that the difference in product has a stereochemical cause.

Using models we find that the *cis*-glycol exists in two equivalent chair conformations (III and IV).

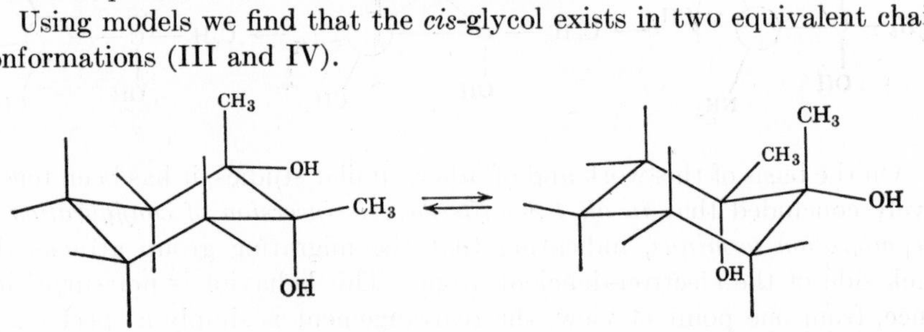

III   IV

cis-1,2-Dimethyl-1,2-cyclohexanediol

In each of these conformations one —OH group and the —CH₃ group attached to the adjacent carbon occupy axial positions. Upon loss of the axial —OH group (as a molecule of water), the axial —CH₃ group is perfectly situated to migrate to the back side of the electron-deficient carbon. The product formed is 2,2-dimethylcyclohexanone.

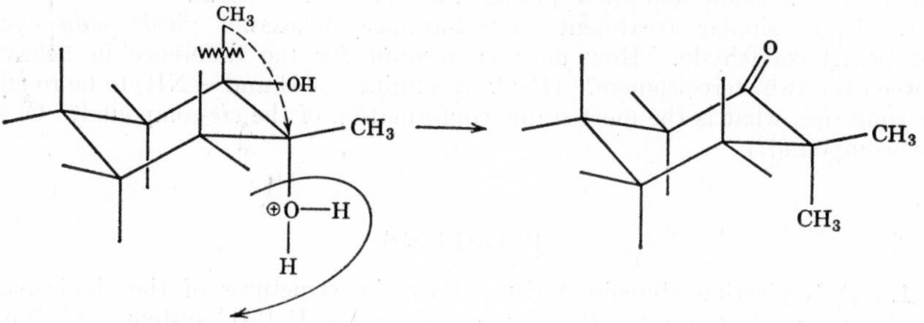

Protonated *cis*-glycol   2,2-Dimethylcyclohexanone

                                                    I

Any molecule of the *trans*-glycol can exist in two interconvertible conformations (V and VI, say, for one enantiomer). In V, both —OH

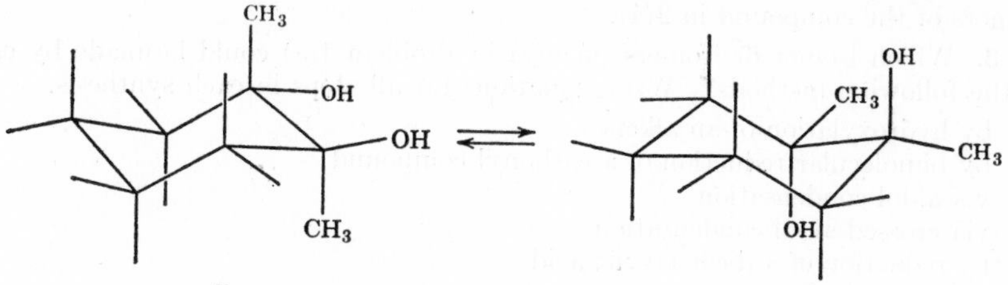

V   VI

trans-1,2-Dimethyl-1,2-cyclohexanediol

groups occupy equatorial positions and both —CH₃ groups occupy axial positions, and in VI the situation is exactly reversed. If an axial —OH group were lost from VI, only the second —OH group is in position for migration. If, however, an equatorial —OH group were lost from V, a carbon atom *of the ring* is perfectly located for attack on the back side of the electron-deficient carbon.

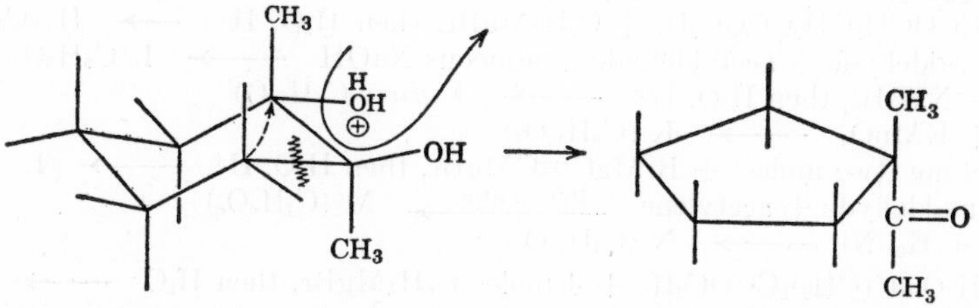

Protonated *trans*-glycol   1-Aceto-1-methylcyclopentane

                                                        II

This leads to a contraction of the ring and formation of the cyclopentane derivative (II).

Problem 24.20 Predict the products of the pinacol rearrangement of:

(a) *cis*-1-C¹⁴-1,2-dimethyl-1,2-cyclohexanediol
(b) *trans*-1-C¹⁴-1,2-dimethyl-1,2-cyclohexanediol

Problem 24.21 (a) Upon treatment with nitrous acid *cis*-2-aminocyclohexanol yields a mixture of cyclohexanone and cyclopentanecarboxaldehyde (cyclo-pentyl–CHO). Show how these products are probably formed.

(b) Upon similar treatment *trans*-2-aminocyclohexanol yields *only* cyclo-pentanecarboxaldehyde. How do you account for the difference in behavior between the two stereoisomers? (*Hint:* Assuming —OH and —NH₂ to be roughly the same size, what is the most stable conformation of the *cis*-compound? Of the *trans*-compound?)

PROBLEMS

1. (a) Neglecting stereoisomerism, draw the structures of the six isomeric glycols of formula $C_4H_{10}O_2$. (b) Name each by the IUPAC system. (c) Which is isobutylene glycol? Tetramethyleneglycol? (d) Draw structural formulas for all stereoisomers of each glycol in (a). (e) Which stereoisomers (when separated from all others) would be optically active, and which would be optically inactive?

2. (a) One of the isomers in Problem 1(d) is a *meso* compound. Which one is it? Suggest two ways to make it. (b) Suggest two ways to make the stereoisomers of the compound in 2(a).

3. Which isomer or isomers (if any) in Problem 1(a) could be made by each of the following methods? Write equations for all steps in each synthesis.
(a) by hydroxylation of an alkene
(b) by bimolecular reduction of a carbonyl compound
(c) via aldol condensation
(d) via crossed aldol condensation
(e) by reduction of a dicarboxylic acid

4. Which of the glycols (if any) in Problem 1(a) will react with periodic acid? Write a balanced equation for each reaction.

5. Give structures of compounds A through O:
(a) $HOOC(CH_2)_8COOH$ (sebacic acid) + $LiAlH_4$, then H_2O, H^+ ⟶ A
(b) $CH_3CO(CH_2)_2COCH_3$ (acetonylacetone) + $NaBH_4$, then H_2O, H^+ ⟶ B
(c) $C_2H_5OOC(CH_2)_4COOC_2H_5$ + H_2, $Cu_2Cr_2O_4$ ⟶ C
(d) $Br(CH_2)_5Br$ + CH_3COOK ⟶ D ($C_9H_{16}O_4$)
   D + H_2O, H^+, heat ⟶ E ($C_5H_{12}O_2$)
(e) coconut oil + NaOH, H_2O, heat ⟶ RCOONa + F
(f) $CH_3CH_2COCHOHCH_2CH_3$ + H_2, Ni ⟶ G ($C_6H_{14}O_2$)
(g) $CH_3COCH_2CH_2COOC_2H_5$ + C_2H_5MgBr, then H_2O, H^+ ⟶ H ($C_{11}H_{24}O_2$)
(h) benzaldehyde + acetaldehyde + aqueous NaOH ⟶ I (C_9H_8O)
   I + $NaBH_4$, then H_2O, H^+ ⟶ J (*trans*-$C_9H_{10}O$)
   J + $KMnO_4$ ⟶ K ($C_9H_{12}O_3$)
(i) acetone (two moles) + $BrMgC\equiv CMgBr$, then H_2O, H^+ ⟶ L
(j) formaldehyde + acetylene $\xrightarrow{100°, 5\ atm.}$ M ($C_4H_6O_2$)
   M + H_2, Ni ⟶ N ($C_4H_{10}O_2$)
(k) $C_2H_5OOC(CH_2)_2COOC_2H_5$ + 4 moles C_6H_5MgBr, then H_2O ⟶ O ($C_{28}H_{26}O_2$)

6. Outline all steps in a possible laboratory synthesis of each of the following from benzene, toluene, and alcohols of four carbons or less, using any needed inorganic reagents:

(a) $C_6H_5\overset{CH_3}{\underset{OH}{C}}-\overset{CH_3}{\underset{OH}{C}}-C_6H_5$

(b) $p\text{-}CH_3OC_6H_4\overset{C_6H_5}{\underset{OH}{C}}-\overset{C_6H_5}{\underset{OH}{C}}-p\text{-}C_6H_4OCH_3$

(c)
$$\underset{\underset{OH\quad OH}{\displaystyle|\quad\;\;|}}{\overset{\overset{CH_3\quad CH_3}{\displaystyle|\quad\;\;|}}{C_2H_5-C-\!\!\!-\!\!\!-C-C_2H_5}}$$

(d)
$$\underset{\underset{OH\quad OH}{\displaystyle|\quad\;\;|}}{\overset{\overset{CH_3\quad C_2H_5}{\displaystyle|\quad\;\;|}}{CH_3-C-\!\!\!-\!\!\!-C-C_2H_5}}$$

(*Hint:* via an alkene)

e)
$$\underset{\underset{OH\quad OH}{\displaystyle|\quad\;\;|}}{\overset{\overset{CH_3\quad C_2H_5}{\displaystyle|\quad\;\;|}}{C_6H_5-C-\!\!\!-\!\!\!-C-C_6H_5}}$$

(f)
$$\underset{\underset{OH\quad OH\quad OH}{\displaystyle|\quad\;\;|\quad\;\;|}}{CH_2-CH-CH_2}$$

(g)
$$\underset{\underset{OH\qquad\qquad OH}{\displaystyle|\qquad\qquad|}}{\overset{\overset{CH_3}{\displaystyle|}}{CH_2-CH-CH-CH_2-CH_3}}$$

(h)
$$\underset{\underset{OH\qquad OH}{\displaystyle|\qquad|}}{\overset{\overset{CH_3}{\displaystyle|}}{CH_3-C-CH_2-CH-CH_3}}$$

(i)
$$\underset{\underset{OH\quad OH}{\displaystyle|\quad\;\;|}}{C_6H_5-CH-CH-COOH}$$

(j)
$$\underset{\underset{OH\quad OH\quad OH}{\displaystyle|\quad\;\;|\quad\;\;|}}{CH_3-CH-CH-CH_2}$$

(k)
$$\underset{\underset{OH\quad OH\quad OH}{\displaystyle|\quad\;\;|\quad\;\;|}}{\overset{\overset{CH_3}{\displaystyle|}}{C_6H_5-C-\!\!\!-\!\!\!-CH-CH-C_6H_5}}$$

(l)
$$\underset{\underset{CH_2OH}{\displaystyle|}}{CH_3-CH_2-CH-CH_2OH}$$

(*Hint:* see Sec. 23.18.)

7. Describe simple chemical tests that would serve to distinguish among the possible products of rearrangement of 1-phenyl-1,2-propanediol shown on page 666. Tell exactly what you would do and see.

8. Describe chemical methods (simple tests where possible) that would serve to distinguish between:

(a) ethylene glycol and allyl alcohol
(b) glycerol and allyl alcohol
(c) ethylene glycol and ethylene bromohydrin
(d) ethylene glycol and glycerol
(e) propylene glycol and glycerol
(f) ethylene glycol and ethanolamine
(g) 1,3-propanediol and glycerol
(h) 1,2-propanediol and 1,3-propanediol
(i) 1,2-, 1,3-, 1,4-, and 2,3-butanediol
(j) 1,1-, 1,2-, and 1,3-dimethoxypropane
(k) $CH_3OCH_2CH_2OCH_3$, $C_2H_5OCH_2CH_2OH$, and

$$CH_3-\overset{\displaystyle\;\;H}{\underset{}{C}}\overset{\displaystyle O-CH_2}{\underset{\displaystyle O-CH_2}{\big\langle}} \;\Big|$$

Tell exactly what you would do and see.

9. On the basis of the following evidence assign structures to: (a) Compounds P to S, isomers of formula $C_3H_8O_2$; (b) compounds T to BB, isomers of formula $C_3H_6O_2$. (*Note:* α-hydroxy ketones, –CHOH–CO–, give positive tests with Tollens' reagent and Benedict's solution, but negative Schiff's tests.

		NaHCO₃	Acetic anhydride	Tollens'	Schiff's	HIO₄
(a)	P	—	$C_7H_{12}O_4$	—	—	—
	Q	—	$C_7H_{12}O_4$	—	—	+
	R	—	$C_5H_{10}O_3$	—	—	—
	S	—	—	—[1]	—[1]	—
(b)	T	—	$C_5H_8O_3$	+	+	+
	U	—	$C_5H_8O_3$	+	—	+
	V	—	$C_5H_8O_3$	+	+	—
	W	CO₂	—	—	—	—
	X	—[2]	—	+	—	—
	Y	—	—	—	—	—
	Z	—	$C_7H_{10}O_4$	—	—	+
	AA	—	—	—[1]	—[1]	—[1]
	BB	—	$C_5H_8O_3$	—	—	—[1]

[1] After treatment with dilute acid, solution gives positive test.
[2] After treatment with NaOH, solution gives positive iodoform test.

10. Give structures of compounds CC through KK:

(a) CC + HIO₄ ⟶ C_6H_5COOH + C_6H_5CHO

(b) DD + HIO₄ ⟶ $2C_6H_5COOH$

(c) EE + 6HIO₄ ⟶ 6HCOOH

(d) FF ($C_{18}H_{34}O_2$) + HCO₂OH ⟶ GG ($C_{18}H_{36}O_4$)
GG + HIO₄ ⟶ $CH_3(CH_2)_7CHO$ + $OHC(CH_2)_7COOH$

(e) HH + H₂O, OH⁻, heat, then H⁺ ⟶ C_6H_5COOH + II
II + 2HIO₄ ⟶ HCOOH + 2HCHO
HH + HIO₄ + Ag⁺ ⟶ AgIO₃ (white precipitate)

(f) JJ ($C_6H_{14}O_2$) + H⁺ ⟶ KK ($C_6H_{12}O$)
KK + NaOI ⟶ CHI₃ + (CH₃)₃CCOONa

11. Draw stereochemical formulas for all the possible stereoisomers of the following compounds. Indicate which are optically active, which are optically inactive, which are pairs of enantiomers, which are *meso* compounds.

(a) 3-bromo-2-butanol
(b) 2,3-dibromobutanoic acid
(c) 2,3-diphenylbutane
(d) 1,3-dichlorocyclobutane
(e) 2,4-dichloropentane
(f) 2,3,4-trihydroxypentanoic acid
(g) 1,3-cyclopentanedicarboxylic acid
(h) 1,2,3,4,5-pentahydroxypentane
(i) methylethyl-*n*-propyl-*sec*-butylammonium chloride

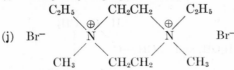

(j) Br⁻ ... Br⁻

(k) 1,2-diphenyl-1,2-bis(*p*-methoxyphenyl)-1,2-ethanediol
(l) 3-phenyl-2-butanol
(m) 4,5-dihydroxy-4,5-dimethyl-2,6-octadiene
(n) 3,6-dimethyl-4-octene

12. Give stereochemical formulas for fractions I through XI. Account for the optical activity or optical inactivity in each case. (*Hint:* see Problem 19.3, page 525.)

(a) (+)-*sec*-Butyl chloride (configuration same as bromide, page 512) was chlorinated at 300°, and the reaction mixture was fractionally distilled. Five fractions containing material of formula $C_4H_8Cl_2$ were obtained; three of these, I, II, and III, were found to be optically active, and two, IV and V, were found to be optically inactive.

(b) Under the same conditions (+)-1-chloro-2-methylbutane (see page 328 for its configuration) gave six fractions of formula $C_5H_{10}Cl_2$. Fractions VI, VII, VIII, and IX were optically active, and fractions X and XI were optically inactive.

13. Each of the following reactions is carried out, and the products are separated by careful fractional distillation or crystallization. For each reaction tell how many fractions will be collected. Draw stereochemical formulas of the compound or compounds making up each fraction. Tell whether each fraction, as collected, will show optical activity or inactivity.

(a) monochlorination of *n*-butane at 300°
(b) monochlorination of isopentane at 300°
(c) addition of bromine to propylene
(d) hydroxylation of a mixture of *cis*- and *trans*-2-pentene by $KMnO_4$
(e) addition of bromine to a mixture of *cis*- and *trans*-2-butene
(f) reduction of racemic benzoin, $C_6H_5COCHOHC_6H_5$
(g) reduction of 2,4-pentanedione to the diol
(h) reduction of the optically active 1,3,4-trihydroxy-2-butanone (XII)

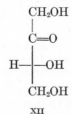

XII

(i) treatment of racemic 3,4-epoxy-1-butene with cold dilute $KMnO_4$, followed by treatment with dilute acid to give $C_4H_{10}O_4$.
(j) treatment of *cis*-2-butene with chlorine water, followed by treatment with base, and then with dilute acid to give $C_4H_{10}O_2$
(k) treatment of *trans*-2-butene as in (j)

14. There are nine stereoisomeric 1,2,3,4,5,6-hexahydroxycyclohexanes. (a) Draw their structures. (b) Tell which isomers, when separated from all others, will be optically active, and which will be optically inactive. (c) Which single isomer can exist in a chair conformation that has six equatorial –OH groups? Six axial –OH groups?

15. When hexestrol, 3,4-bis(*p*-hydroxyphenyl)hexane, is prepared by the method of Problem 13(e), page 607, the product obtained is a mixture of isomers, one a liquid and the other a solid. The solid isomer is the one with hormone activity. (a) How do you account for the existence of these isomers? (b) How would you go about establishing the structure of the biologically active compound?

16. (a) In Sec. 5.16 a mechanism was proposed for formation of a halohydrin by addition of halogen and water to an alkene. In view of Sec. 15.19, what product would you expect from addition of chlorine and water to oleic acid (*cis*-9-octadecenoic acid)? To elaidic acid (*trans*-9-octadecenoic acid)?

(b) Draw stereochemical structures of the epoxides expected from the action of a peroxy acid on oleic acid; on elaidic acid.

(c) On the basis of (a) and Sec. 15.13 account for the fact that addition of chlorine and water to oleic acid followed by treatment with base gives the same epoxide as does treatment of oleic acid with a peroxy acid.

17. Give the structures of compounds LL through OO:

(a) LL $(C_{10}H_{16})$ + O_3, then H_2O $\longrightarrow$ 1,6-cyclodecanedione

LL + HCO_2OH $\longrightarrow$ MM $(C_{10}H_{18}O_2)$

MM + H^+, warm $\longrightarrow$ NN $(C_{10}H_{16}O)$

(b) cyclopentanone + Mg, then H_2O, H^+ $\longrightarrow$ OO $(C_{10}H_{18}O_2)$

OO + H^+, warm $\longrightarrow$ NN $(C_{10}H_{16}O)$

18. (a) Upon treatment with acid XIII $(R = C_2H_5)$ yields XIV and XV. Show all steps in these transformations.

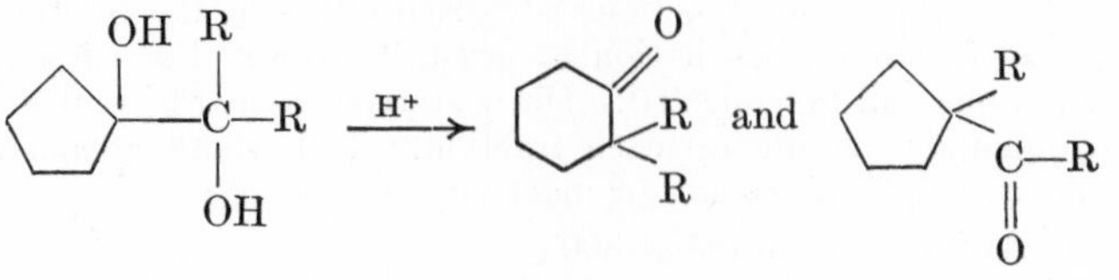

XIII   XIV   XV

(b) Account for the fact that when $R = C_6H_5$, XIII yields only XIV.

(c) Show the most likely steps in the following transformation:

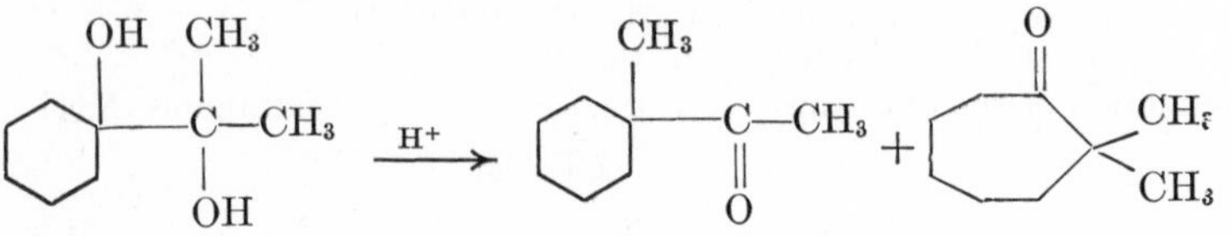

(d) Predict the products of the pinacol rearrangement of 2,3-diphenyl-2,3-butanediol; of 3-phenyl-1,2-propanediol. Describe a simple chemical test that would show whether your prediction was correct or incorrect.

19. $(-)$-*Erythrose*, $C_4H_8O_4$, gives positive tests with Tollens' reagent and Benedict's solution, and is oxidized by bromine water to an optically active acid, $C_4H_8O_5$. Treatment with acetic anhydride yields $C_{10}H_{14}O_7$. Erythrose consumes three moles of HIO_4 and yields three moles of formic acid and one mole of formaldehyde. Reduction of erythrose yields an *optically inactive* compound of formula $C_4H_{10}O_4$.

$(-)$-*Threose*, an isomer of erythrose, shows similar chemical behavior except that reduction yields an *optically active* compound of formula $C_4H_{10}O_4$.

On the basis of this evidence what structure or structures are possible for $(-)$-erythrose? For $(-)$-threose? (Check your answers in the index.)

20. (a) Draw formulas for all the stereoisomers of XVI.

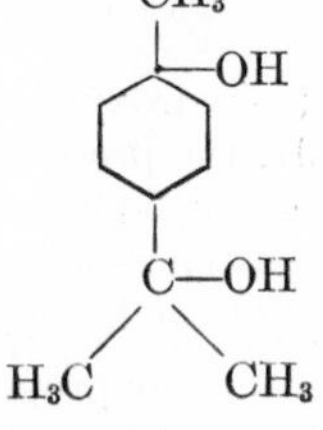

XVI

(b) Indicate which isomers, when separated from all others, will be optically active, and which will be optically inactive. (c) One of these stereoisomers is very readily converted into an ether, $C_{10}H_{18}O$. Which isomer is this, and what is the structure of the ether?

21. (a) Using models and then drawing formulas, show the possible chair conformations for *cis*-1,3-cyclohexanediol. (b) On the basis solely of 1,3-interaction, which would you expect to be the more stable conformation? (c) Infrared evidence indicates intramolecular hydrogen bonding in *cis*-1,3-cyclohexanediol. Which conformation in (a) is indicated by this evidence, and what is the source of its stability?

22. 2-Butyn-1,4-diol can be reduced to 2-buten-1,4-diol either catalytically with H_2/Pd or chemically with sodium and liquid NH_3. When the alkene obtained by catalytic reduction is hydroxylated by a peroxy acid, it yields a tetrahydroxy compound that is resolvable. When the alkene obtained by chemical reduction is hydroxylated by a peroxy acid, it yields a tetrahydroxy compound that is not resolvable.

(a) What is the configuration of each alkene? (b) What is the steric course of each reduction process? (c) The cinnamic acid obtained by the Perkin condensation is the more stable *trans*-isomer. Suggest a method of preparing *cis*-cinnamic acid.

Chapter twenty-five_____

DICARBOXYLIC ACIDS

25.1 Nomenclature

Aliphatic dicarboxylic acids have both common names and IUPAC names:

HOOC—COOH	HOOCCH$_2$COOH	HOOCCH$_2$CH$_2$COOH
Oxalic acid	Malonic acid	Succinic acid
Ethanedioic acid	Propanedioic acid	Butanedioic acid

HOOCCH$_2$CH$_2$CH$_2$COOH   HOOCCH$_2$CH$_2$CH$_2$CH$_2$COOH

Glutaric acid   Adipic acid

Pentanedioic acid   Hexanedioic acid

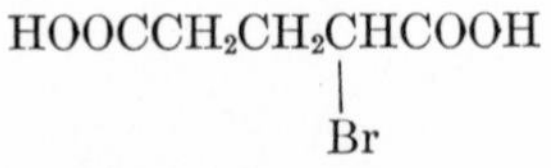

$$\underset{\substack{\\ \text{Br}}}{\text{HOOCCH}_2\text{CH}_2\text{CHCOOH}} \qquad \underset{\substack{\\ \text{CH}_3}}{\overset{\substack{\text{CH}_3 \\ }}{\text{HOOCCH}_2\text{CCH}_2\text{COOH}}} \qquad \underset{\substack{\\ \text{Cl} \quad \text{Cl}}}{\text{HOOCCHCH}_2\text{CHCOOH}}$$

α-Bromoglutaric acid   β,β-Dimethylglutaric acid   α,α'-Dichloroglutaric acid

2-Bromopentanedioic acid   3,3-Dimethylpentanedioic acid   2,4-Dichloro-
pentanedioic acid

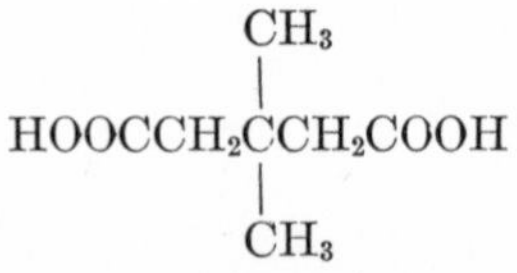

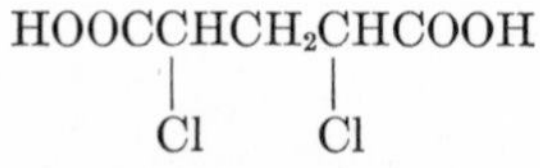

The student should know the common names of the first five acids (C$_2$–C$_6$).

The aromatic dicarboxylic acids are given the special names of **phthalic acids**:

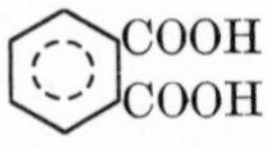

Phthalic acid	Isophthalic acid	Terephthalic acid
1,2-Benzenedicarboxylic	1,3-Benzenedicarboxylic	1,4-Benzenedicarboxylic
acid	acid	acid

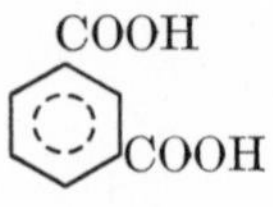

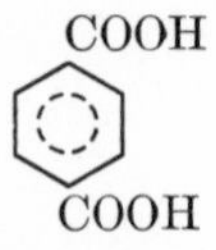

25.2 Physical properties

The dicarboxylic acids are all solids. The lower members are appreciably soluble in water, and only slightly soluble in organic solvents; borderline solubility in water is found at C$_6$–C$_7$. These properties are quite reasonable in view of the fact that polar carboxyl groups make up a high proportion of each molecule.

TABLE 25.1

DICARBOXYLIC ACIDS AND DERIVATIVES

Name	Formula	M.p., °C	Solub., g/100 g H_2O at 20°	K_1	K_2
Oxalic	HOOC—COOH	189	9	3500×10^{-5}	4.0×10^{-5}
Malonic	HOOCCH$_2$COOH	136	74	140	0.22
Succinic	HOOC(CH$_2$)$_2$COOH	185	6	6.4	.25
Glutaric	HOOC(CH$_2$)$_3$COOH	98	64	4.5	.38
Adipic	HOOC(CH$_2$)$_4$COOH	151	2	3.7	.24
Pimelic	HOOC(CH$_2$)$_5$COOH	105	5	3.4	.26
Suberic	HOOC(CH$_2$)$_6$COOH	144	0.2	2.6	.25
Azelaic	HOOC(CH$_2$)$_7$COOH	106	0.3	2.9	.28
Sebacic	HOOC(CH$_2$)$_8$COOH	134	0.1	2.6	.26
Maleic	cis-HOOCCH=CHCOOH	130.5	79	1200	.026
Fumaric	trans-HOOCCH=CHCOOH	302	0.7	93	2.9
Phthalic	1,2-C$_6$H$_4$(COOH)$_2$	231	0.7	120	0.3
Isophthalic	1,3-C$_6$H$_4$(COOH)$_2$	348.5	0.01	29	2.7
Terephthalic	1,4-C$_6$H$_4$(COOH)$_2$	300^{subl}	0.002	15	
Hemimellitic	1,2,3-C$_6$H$_3$(COOH)$_3$	190d	3	160	6.3
Trimellitic	1,2,4-C$_6$H$_3$(COOH)$_3$	238	sol.	300	14
Trimesic	1,3,5-C$_6$H$_3$(COOH)$_3$	380	2	76	13
Succinic anhydride		120			
Maleic anhydride		60			
Phthalic anhydride		131			
Succinimide		126	23	3×10^{-11}	
Phthalimide		238	0.6	5×10^{-9}	

25.3 Source

Outlined below are methods by which the more important dicarboxylic acids are made. Some of the methods are special ones applicable only to single acids (e.g., oxalic or succinic acid). Most, however, are simply adaptations of methods used for preparing monocarboxylic acids. For example: where hydrolysis of a nitrile yields a monocarboxylic acid, hydrolysis of a dinitrile yields a dicarboxylic acid; where oxidation of a methylbenzene yields a benzoic acid, oxidation of a dimethylbenzene yields a phthalic acid.

PREPARATION OF DICARBOXYLIC ACIDS

Oxalic acid

$$2\text{HCOO}^-\text{Na}^+ \xrightarrow{\text{NaOH, }360°} \text{H}_2 + \begin{array}{c}\text{COO}^-\text{Na}^+ \\ | \\ \text{COO}^-\text{Na}^+\end{array} \xrightarrow{\text{H}_2\text{SO}_4} \begin{array}{c}\text{COOH} \\ | \\ \text{COOH}\end{array}$$

Sodium formate   Sodium oxalate   Oxalic acid

Malonic acid

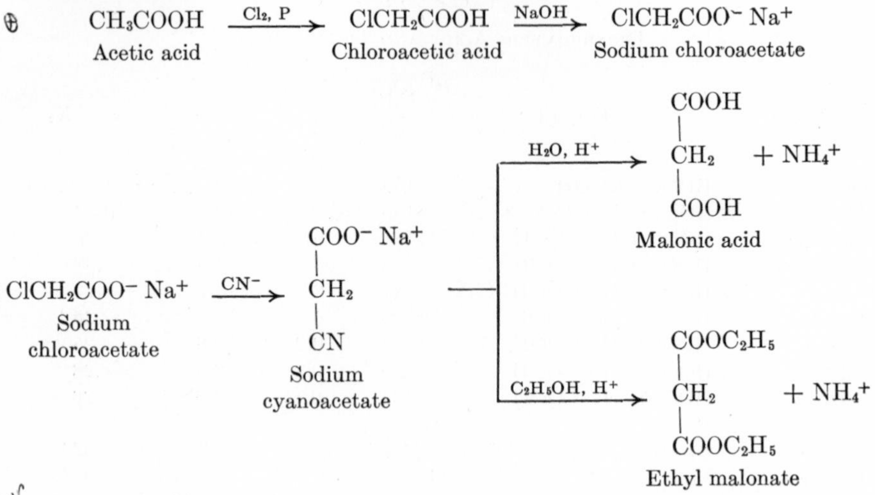

(a) CH_3COOH $\xrightarrow{\text{Cl}_2,\ P}$ $ClCH_2COOH$ $\xrightarrow{\text{NaOH}}$ $ClCH_2COO^-\ Na^+$
Acetic acid   Chloroacetic acid   Sodium chloroacetate

(b) $ClCH_2COO^-\ Na^+$ $\xrightarrow{\text{CN}^-}$
Sodium chloroacetate

$$\begin{array}{c} COO^-\ Na^+ \\ | \\ CH_2 \\ | \\ CN \end{array}$$
Sodium cyanoacetate

$\xrightarrow{\text{H}_2\text{O, H}^+}$
$$\begin{array}{c} COOH \\ | \\ CH_2 \\ | \\ COOH \end{array} + NH_4^+$$
Malonic acid

$\xrightarrow{\text{C}_2\text{H}_5\text{OH, H}^+}$
$$\begin{array}{c} COOC_2H_5 \\ | \\ CH_2 \\ | \\ COOC_2H_5 \end{array} + NH_4^+$$
Ethyl malonate

Succinic acid

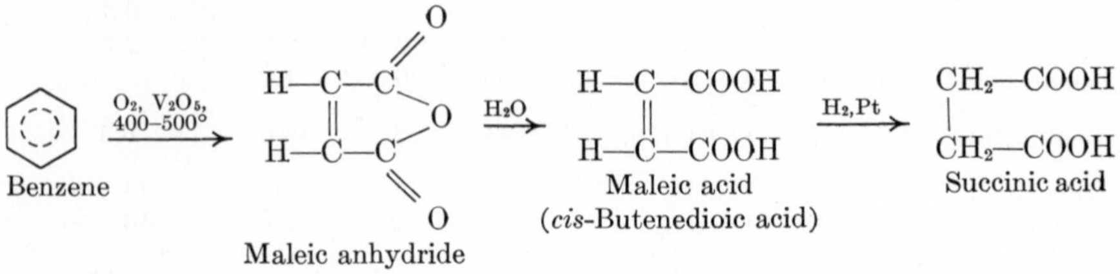

Benzene $\xrightarrow[\text{400–500}°]{\text{O}_2,\ \text{V}_2\text{O}_5,}$ Maleic anhydride $\xrightarrow{\text{H}_2\text{O}}$
$$\begin{array}{c} H-C-COOH \\ \| \\ H-C-COOH \end{array}$$
Maleic acid (*cis*-Butenedioic acid) $\xrightarrow{\text{H}_2,\text{Pt}}$
$$\begin{array}{c} CH_2-COOH \\ | \\ CH_2-COOH \end{array}$$
Succinic acid

Adipic acid

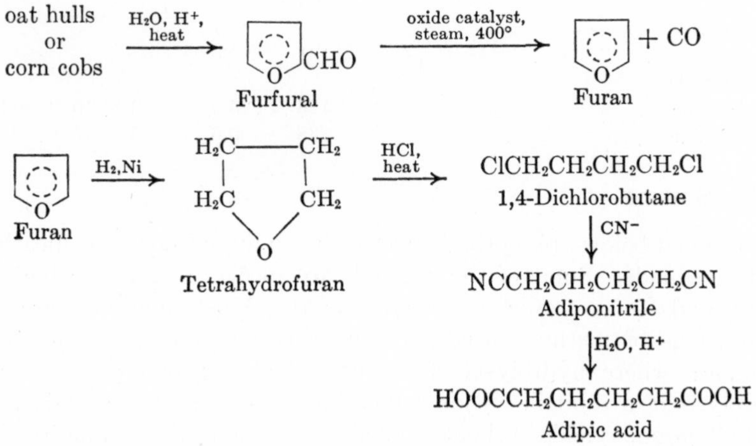

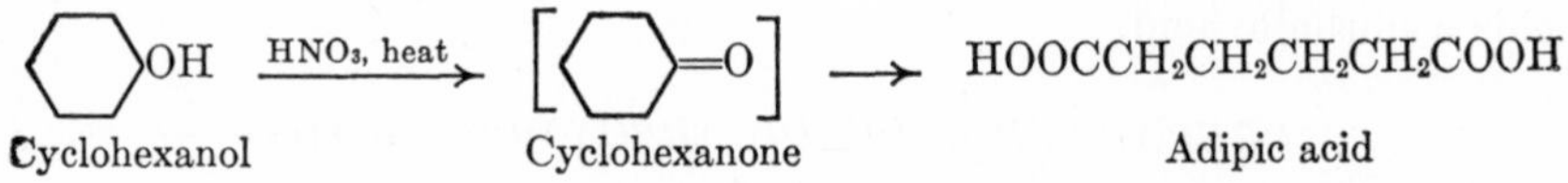

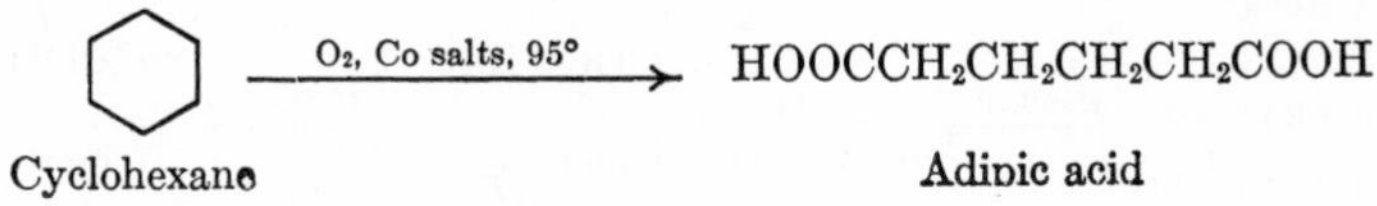

oat hulls or corn cobs $\xrightarrow[\text{heat}]{\text{H}_2\text{O, H}^+,}$ Furfural CHO $\xrightarrow[\text{steam, 400}°]{\text{oxide catalyst,}}$ Furan $+ CO$

Furan $\xrightarrow{\text{H}_2,\text{Ni}}$
$$\begin{array}{c} H_2C-CH_2 \\ |\qquad\ | \\ H_2C\quad CH_2 \\ \diagdown\ O\ \diagup \end{array}$$
Tetrahydrofuran $\xrightarrow[\text{heat}]{\text{HCl,}}$ $ClCH_2CH_2CH_2CH_2Cl$
1,4-Dichlorobutane

$\xrightarrow{\text{CN}^-}$ $NCCH_2CH_2CH_2CH_2CN$
Adiponitrile

$\xrightarrow{\text{H}_2\text{O, H}^+}$ $HOOCCH_2CH_2CH_2CH_2COOH$
Adipic acid

Cyclohexanol OH $\xrightarrow{\text{HNO}_3,\ \text{heat}}$ [Cyclohexanone =O] $\longrightarrow$ $HOOCCH_2CH_2CH_2CH_2COOH$
Adipic acid

Cyclohexane $\xrightarrow{\text{O}_2,\ \text{Co salts, 95}°}$ $HOOCCH_2CH_2CH_2CH_2COOH$
Adipic acid

Phthalic acid

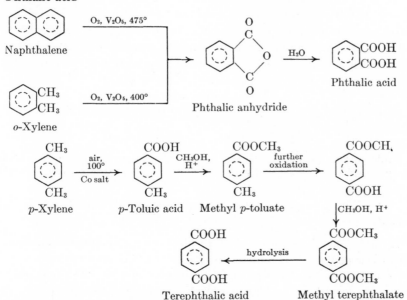

Naphthalene

o-Xylene

Phthalic anhydride

Phthalic acid

p-Xylene　　　　p-Toluic acid　　Methyl p-toluate

Terephthalic acid　　　　　Methyl terephthalate

Problem 25.1 Trimethylene glycol is available from a fermentation of glycerol. Outline a synthesis of glutaric acid from this glycol.

Problem 25.2 What is the ultimate source of each of the dicarboxylic acids synthesized above? Outline all steps in the preparation of each one from that source.

Problem 25.3 Why is chloroacetic acid converted into its salt before treatment with cyanide in the preparation of malonic acid or ethyl malonate?

Problem 25.4 One method listed for preparing adipic acid involves cleavage of a cyclic ketone by vigorous oxidation. Why is this method satisfactory here but not for the preparation of monocarboxylic acids from open-chain ketones?

25.4 Reactions

In general, dicarboxylic acids show the same chemical behavior as monocarboxylic acids. They can be converted into salts, acid chlorides, esters, amides, and anhydrides. The aliphatic acids undergo *alpha*-halogenation in the presence of phosphorus, and the aromatic acids undergo ring substitution. It is possible to prepare compounds in which only one of the carboxyl groups has been converted into a derivative; it is possible to prepare compounds in which the two carboxyl groups have been converted into different derivatives.

Problem 25.5 Predict the products of the following reactions:
(a) adipic acid (146 g) + 95% ethanol (146 g) + benzene + conc. H_2SO_4, 100°
(b) adipic acid (146 g) + 95% ethanol (50 g) + benzene + conc. H_2SO_4, 100°
(c) adipic acid (146 g) + ethyl adipate (101 g) + conc. H_2SO_4, 160°
(d) ethyl oxalate (1 mole) + $(C_2H_5)_2NH$ (0.5 mole)
(e) ethyl oxalate (1 mole) + $(C_2H_5)_2NH$ (1 mole)
(f) ethyl oxalate (1 mole) + o-phenylenediamine (1 mole)
(g) succinic anhydride (1 mole) + ethanol (1 mole), H^+

As with other acids containing more than one ionizable hydrogen (H_2SO_4, H_2CO_3, H_3PO_4, etc.), ionization of the second carboxyl group occurs less readily than ionization of the first (compare K_1's with K_2's in Table 25.1). More energy is required to separate a positive hydrogen ion from the doubly charged anion than from the singly charged anion.

$$\begin{matrix} COOH \\ \} \\ COOH \end{matrix} \xrightarrow[\leftarrow]{K_1} H^+ + \begin{matrix} COO^- \\ \} \\ COOH \end{matrix} \xrightarrow[\leftarrow]{K_2} H^+ + \begin{matrix} COO^- \\ \} \\ COO^- \end{matrix} \qquad K_1 > K_2$$

Problem 25.6 Compare the acidity (first ionization) of oxalic acid with that of formic acid; of malonic acid with that of acetic acid. How do you account for these differences?

Problem 25.7 Arrange oxalic, malonic, succinic, and glutaric acids in order of acidity (first ionization). How do you account for this order?

In addition to the reactions typical of any carboxylic acid, some of these dicarboxylic acids undergo reactions that are possible only because there are two carboxyl groups in each molecule, and because these carboxyl groups are located in a particular way with respect to each other. It is on these special reactions of dicarboxylic acids that we shall concentrate.

25.5 Condensation polymerization

As we know, carboxylic acids react with amines to yield amides, and with alcohols to form esters. When an acid that contains more than one —COOH group reacts with an amine that contains more than one —NH_2 group, or with an alcohol that contains more than one —OH group, then the products are *polyamides* and *polyesters*. For example:

$$HOOC(CH_2)_4COOH + H_2N(CH_2)_6NH_2 \longrightarrow \text{salt}$$

Adipic acid   Hexamethylenediamine   ↓ heat, —H_2O

$$\sim C(CH_2)_4 C - \overset{H}{\underset{\overset{|}{O}}{N}}(CH_2)_6 \overset{H}{\underset{|}{N}} - C(CH_2)_4 C - \overset{H}{\underset{\overset{|}{O}}{N}}(CH_2)_6 \overset{H}{\underset{|}{N}} \sim$$

Nylon
A polyamide

$$CH_3OOC\langle\bigcirc\rangle COOCH_3 + HOCH_2CH_2OH \xrightarrow[-CH_3OH]{\text{acid or base}}$$

Methyl terephthalate   Ethylene glycol

$$\sim \underset{\overset{\|}{O}}{C}-\langle\bigcirc\rangle-\underset{\overset{\|}{O}}{C}-OCH_2CH_2O-\underset{\overset{\|}{O}}{C}-\langle\bigcirc\rangle-\underset{\overset{\|}{O}}{C}-OCH_2CH_2O \sim$$

Dacron
A polyester

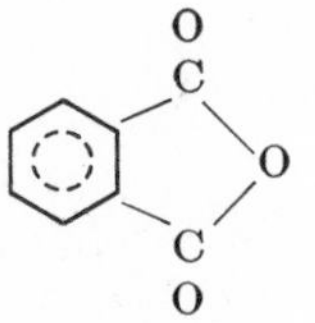

Phthalic anhydride + CH₂—CH—CH₂ (glycerol) $\xrightarrow{-H_2O}$ Glyptal (an alkyd resin), *A polyester*

These are examples of *condensation polymerization* (compare Sec. 6.20) since monomer molecules are combined with the loss of simple molecules, in these cases water or methanol.

Polymers like Nylon and Dacron are made up of long linear molecules that, stretched, can be made to lie roughly side by side, oriented along the axis of the fiber. The use of such polymers depends upon this ability to form fibers and hence threads.

A polymer like Glyptal, on the other hand, does not contain linear molecules, but has a highly cross-linked netlike structure. This structure does not permit formation of fibers, but makes these resins eminently suited for protective coatings (in lacquers, etc.).

Problem 25.8 Work out a possible structure for an alkyd resin formed from phthalic anhydride and glycerol, considering the following points: (a) In the first stage a linear polyester is formed. (Which hydroxyl groups are esterified more rapidly, primary or secondary?) (b) In the second stage these linear polymers are cross-linked to form a rather rigid network.

Problem 25.9 Compare the structure of Nylon with that of the naturally occurring polyamides known as proteins (Chapter 33). In both kinds of polyamide one long molecule can be held to another by hydrogen bonds. Show by structural formulas how this is possible.

Problem 25.10 Write an equation for the chemistry involved when a drop of hydrochloric acid makes a hole in a Nylon stocking.

Problem 25.11 Outline the synthesis from oat hulls or corn cobs of the hexamethylenediamine needed for making Nylon.

25.6 Effect of heat

The product formed when a dicarboxylic acid is heated depends upon the number of carbon atoms separating the carboxyl groups. For example:

Oxalic acid

$$\text{HOOC—COOH} \xrightarrow{150°} \text{HCOOH} + \text{CO}_2$$
Formic acid	Carbon dioxide

Malonic acid

$$\begin{array}{c} \text{COOH} \\ | \\ \text{CH}_2 \\ | \\ \text{COOH} \end{array} \xrightarrow{140°} \text{CH}_3\text{COOH} + \text{CO}_2$$
Acetic acid	Carbon dioxide

Succinic acid

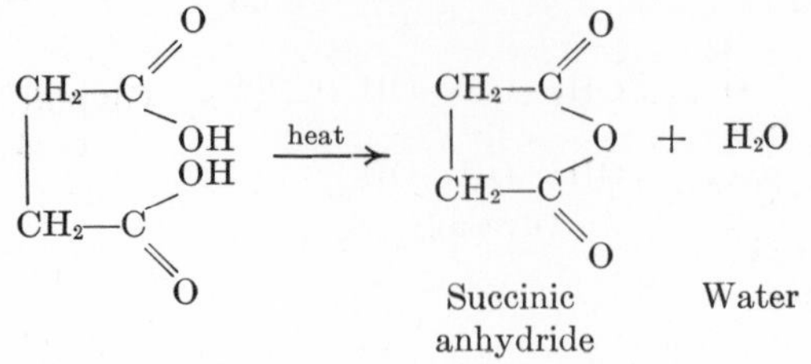

Succinic anhydride   Water

Phthalic acid

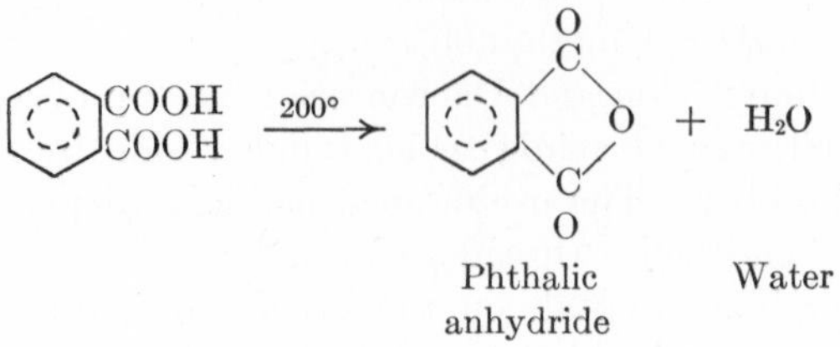

Phthalic anhydride   Water

Adipic acid

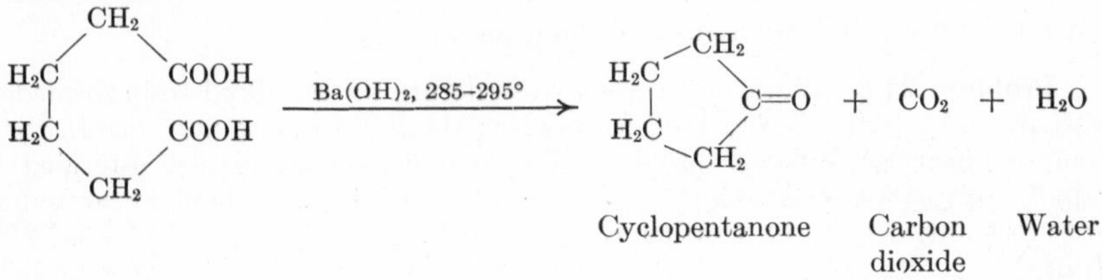

Cyclopentanone   Carbon dioxide   Water

Ring formation can have a decisive effect on the course of these reactions. Anhydrides are not usually formed when carboxylic acids are heated; yet anhydride formation that can produce a five- or six-membered ring readily takes place, as with succinic or phthalic acid.

With adipic acid, anhydride formation would give rise to a seven-membered ring, and does not take place. Instead, carbon dioxide is lost and cyclopentanone, a ketone with a five-membered ring, is formed. Although aliphatic monocarboxylic acids (RCOOH but not ArCOOH) can also be converted into ketones in a similar way,

$$2RCOOH \xrightarrow{\text{Ba(OH)}_2,\ \text{heat}} R-\underset{\underset{O}{\|}}{C}-R + CO_2 + H_2O$$

$$ArCOOH \xrightarrow{\text{base, heat}} ArH + CO_2$$

this reaction is of special importance when applied to dicarboxylic acids, since it gives rise to cyclic structures; the heating of adipic acid, for example, provides the best route to cyclopentane and its derivatives. For good yields of these cyclic ketones, it is necessary to heat the acids in the presence of a base, e.g., barium hydroxide, manganese carbonate, thorium oxide.

Problem 25.12   Write equations for the action of heat on glutaric acid and pimelic acid.

Problem 25.13   Draw the structural formula for the product formed when each of the following acids is heated (in the presence of barium hydroxide in (e) and (f)):

(a) methylmalonic acid
(b) dimethylmalonic acid
(c) benzylmalonic acid

(d) α,α'-diethylsuccinic acid
(e) γ-methylpimelic acid
(f) β,β'-diphenyladipic acid

Problem 25.14   Write equations for the action of heat on acetic acid, propionic acid, butyric acid, and stearic acid, in the presence of $Ba(OH)_2$.

Problem 25.15   Outline the preparation of the following compounds from cyclohexanol:

(a) cyclopentanone
(b) cyclopentanol
(c) cyclopentene
(d) cyclopentane
(e) cyclopentyl bromide
(f) cyclopentanecarboxylic acid

(g) cyclopentylamine (three different methods)
(h) cyclopentanone semicarbazone
(i) 1-methylcyclopentanol
(j) methylcyclopentane
(k) glutaric acid

Problem 25.16   Cyclic anhydrides can be formed from only the *cis*-1,2-cyclopentanedicarboxylic acid, but from both the *cis*- and *trans*-1,2-cyclohexanedicarboxylic acids. How do you account for this?

Problem 25.17   *Maleic acid* ($C_4H_4O_4$, m.p. 130°, highly soluble in water, heat of combustion 327 kcal) and *fumaric acid* ($C_4H_4O_4$, m.p. 302°, insoluble in water, heat of combustion 320 kcal) are both dicarboxylic acids; they both decolorize Br_2 in CCl_4 and aqueous $KMnO_4$; on hydrogenation both yield succinic acid. When heated (maleic acid at 100°, fumaric acid at 250–300°) both acids yield the same anhydride, which is converted by cold water into maleic acid. Interpret these facts.

25.7   Reactions of cyclic anhydrides

Anhydrides, as we know (Sec. 17.11), react with a variety of substances to form acyl compounds. For example, they react with alcohols to form esters, with ammonia or amines to form amides, and with aromatic rings (in the Friedel-Crafts reaction) to form ketones; in each case only one "half" of the anhydride appears in the acyl product, the other "half" forming a carboxylic acid:

$$(CH_3CO)_2O \xrightarrow{C_2H_5OH} CH_3COOC_2H_5 + CH_3COOH$$

Ethyl acetate

$$(CH_3CO)_2O \xrightarrow{2NH_3} CH_3CONH_2 + CH_3COONH_4$$

Acetamide

$$(CH_3CO)_2O \xrightarrow{C_6H_6,\ AlCl_3} C_6H_5-\underset{\underset{O}{\|}}{C}-CH_3 + CH_3COOH$$

Acetophenone

(CH₃CO)₂O — Acetic anhydride

A cyclic anhydride, like succinic anhydride or phthalic anhydride, undergoes exactly the same reactions as any other anhydride. However, since both "halves" of the anhydride are attached to each other by a carbon–carbon bond, the acyl compound and the carboxylic acid formed will have to be part of the same molecule. Cyclic anhydrides can thus be used to make compounds containing both the acyl group and the carboxyl group. For example:

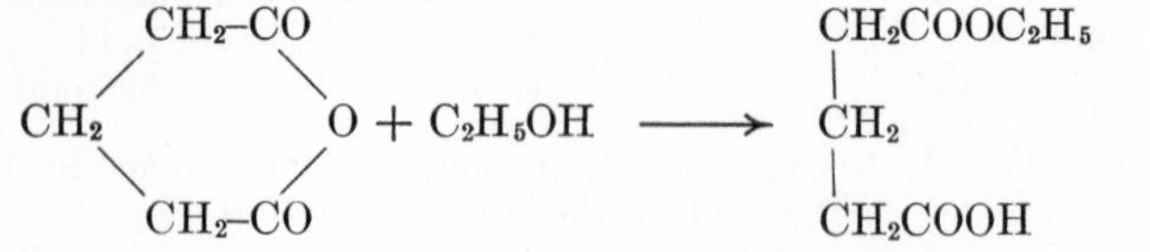

| Glutaric anhydride | Ethyl hydrogen glutarate |

| Succinic anhydride | Ammonium succinamate | Succinamic acid |

| Phthalic anhydride | o-Benzoylbenzoic acid |

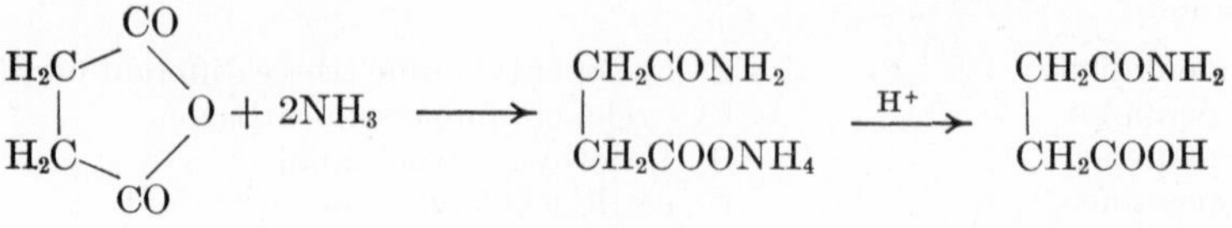

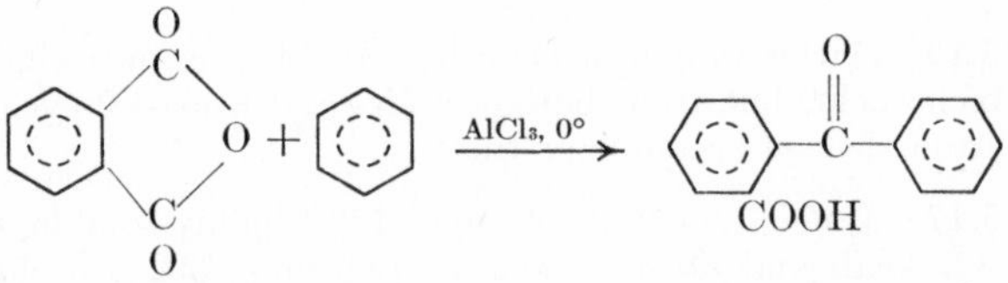

The reaction of phthalic anhydride with phenol takes a somewhat different course, and yields the familiar indicator *phenolphthalein*, one of a number of related compounds known as *phthaleins*:

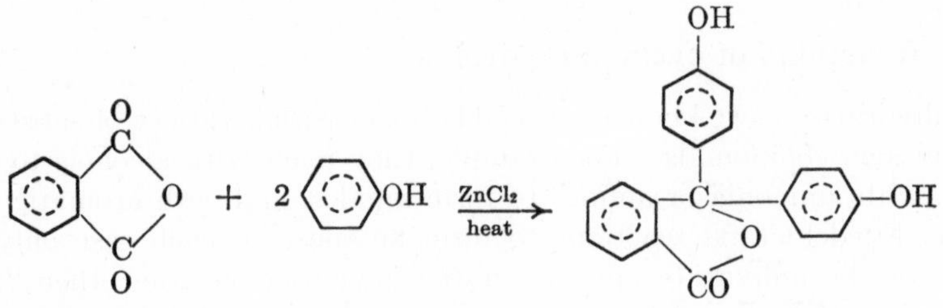

| Phthalic anhydride | Phenol | Phenolphthalein |

| *Colorless* | *Red*
Phenolphthalein | *Colorless* |

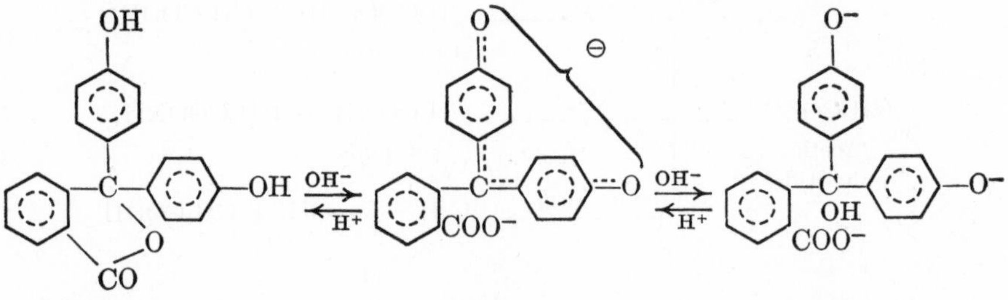

Problem 25.18 Give structural formulas for compounds A through G.

Benzene + succinic anhydride $\xrightarrow{\text{AlCl}_3}$ A ($C_{10}H_{10}O_3$)

A + Zn(Hg) $\xrightarrow{\text{HCl}}$ B ($C_{10}H_{12}O_2$)

$$B + SOCl_2 \longrightarrow C \ (C_{10}H_{11}OCl)$$
$$C \xrightarrow{\text{AlCl}_3} D \ (C_{10}H_{10}O)$$
$$D + H_2 \xrightarrow{\text{Pt}} E \ (C_{10}H_{12}O)$$
$$E + H_2SO_4 \xrightarrow{\text{heat}} F \ (C_{10}H_{10})$$
$$F \xrightarrow{\text{Pt, heat}} G \ (C_{10}H_8) + H_2$$

(Check your answers in Sec. 31.14.)

Problem 25.19   (a) What product will be obtained if D of the preceding problem is treated with C_6H_5MgBr and then water?   (b) What will you finally get if the product from (a) replaces E in the preceding problem?

Problem 25.20   When heated with acid (e.g., concentrated H_2SO_4), *o*-benzoylbenzoic acid yields a product of formula $C_{14}H_8O_2$. What is the structure of this product? What general type of reaction has taken place?   (Check your answer in Sec. 31.18.)

Problem 25.21   Predict the products of the following reactions:
(a) toluene + phthalic anhydride + $AlCl_3$
(b) the product from (a) + conc. H_2SO_4 + heat

25.8   Imides. Gabriel synthesis of pure primary amines

Like other anhydrides, cyclic anhydrides react with ammonia to yield amides; in this case the product contains both $-CONH_2$ and $-COOH$ groups. If this acid–amide is heated, a molecule of water is lost, a ring forms, and a product is obtained in which two acyl groups have become attached to nitrogen; compounds of this sort are called **imides.** Phthalic anhydride gives *phthalamic acid* and *phthalimide:*

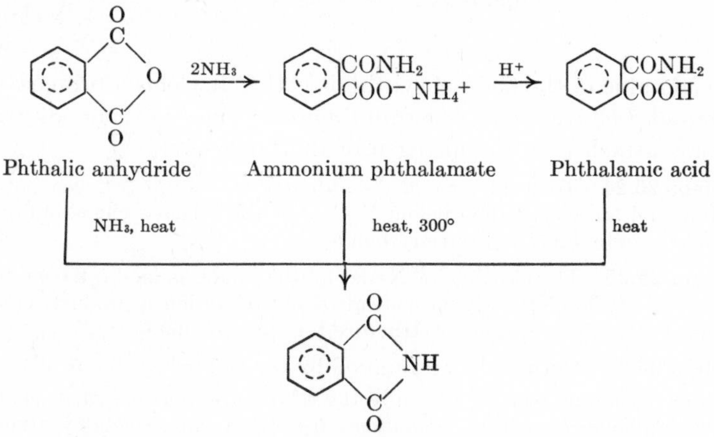

Phthalic anhydride   Ammonium phthalamate   Phthalamic acid

Phthalimide

Exactly analogous reactions occur with succinic anhydride to yield successively *succinamic acid* and *succinimide.*   (Write equations.)

Problem 25.22   Outline the synthesis of anthranilic acid (*o*-aminobenzoic acid) from phthalic anhydride. Of 3-aminopropanoic acid (*β-alanine*) from succinic anhydride.

Just as the presence of one acyl group makes amides more acidic than ammonia (Sec. 18.7), so the presence of two acyl groups makes imides more acidic than amides. Phthalimide ($K_a = 5 \times 10^{-9}$) and succinimide ($K_a = 3 \times 10^{-11}$) are acidic enough to dissolve in cold dilute aqueous sodium hydroxide.

Problem 25.23 On the basis of the relative stabilities of the acids and their anions, account for the following sequence of acidities:

$$K_a$$

Ammonia	10^{-33}
Benzamide	10^{-14} to 10^{-15}
Phthalimide	5×10^{-9}

(*Hint:* see, for example, Sec. 16.12.)

An important use of imides is based upon their acidity: the **Gabriel synthesis of pure primary amines.** An imide, often phthalimide, is converted into its potassium salt by the action of alcoholic KOH; treatment of this salt with an alkyl halide yields an N-substituted imide, from which a primary amine can be obtained by hydrolysis:

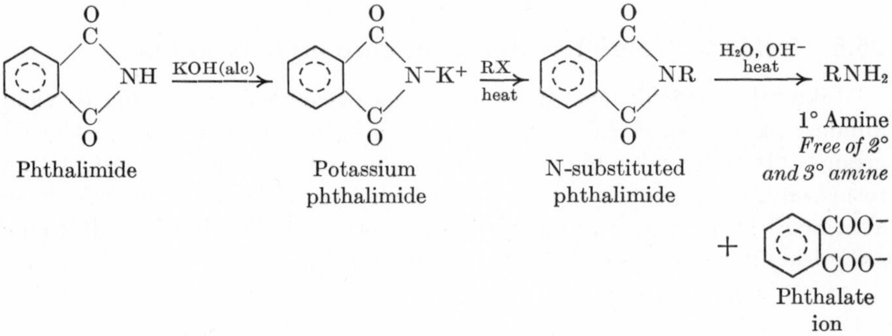

The special value of the Gabriel synthesis is that it yields a primary amine *uncontaminated by secondary or tertiary amines*, since only one alkyl group can become attached to the nitrogen of the imide.

Problem 25.24 To what general class does the reaction between potassium phthalimide and an alkyl halide belong? Predict the relative yields obtained by using primary, secondary, and tertiary halides.

Problem 25.25 The cleavage of N-alkylphthalimides is facilitated by heating with hydrazine, H_2N-NH_2, giving instead of phthalate ion a product which has the formula $C_8H_6O_2N_2$. Suggest a structure for this product.

Problem 25.26 Outline the preparation by the Gabriel synthesis of:
(a) β-bromoethylamine (specify carefully the relative proportions of reagents)
(b) *glycine* (aminoacetic acid). (*Caution:* use ethyl chloroacetate rather than chloroacetic acid. Why?)
(c) *alanine* (α-aminopropionic acid)
(d) *phenylalanine* ($C_6H_5CH_2CH(NH_2)COOH$)
(e) α-amino acids in general (Check your answer in Sec. 33.6.)

25.9 Malonic ester synthesis of carboxylic acids

One of the most valuable methods of preparing carboxylic acids makes use of ethyl malonate (*malonic ester*), and is called the **malonic ester synthesis.** This synthesis depends upon (a) the high acidity of the α-hydrogens of malonic ester, and (b) the extreme ease with which malonic acid and substituted malonic acids undergo decarboxylation.

We have already encountered reactions (Secs. 23.15, 23.18, and 23.20) that depend upon the acidity of hydrogens located *alpha* to the carbonyl group of aldehydes, ketones, anhydrides, and esters. We attributed this acidity to resonance stabilization of the carbanion by structures in which the carbonyl oxygen accommodates the negative charge. The α-hydrogens of malonic ester are located *alpha* to *two* carbonyl groups, and hence ionization yields a particularly stable carbanion in which two carbonyl oxygens help accommodate the charge:

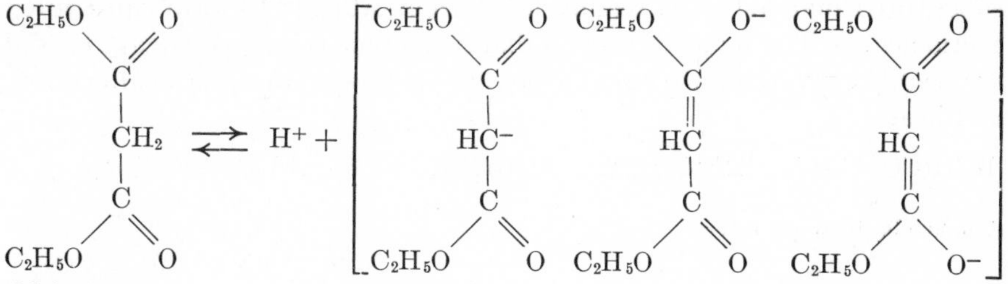

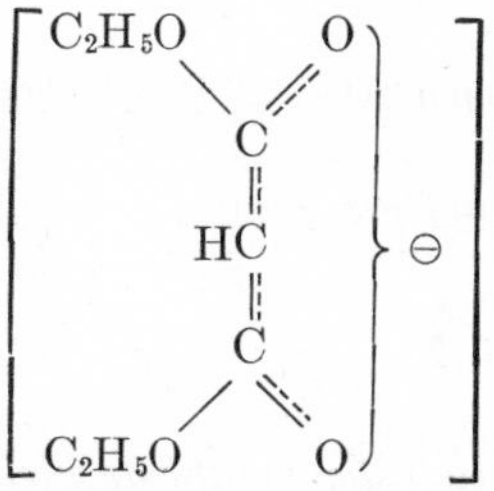

As a result, malonic ester is a much stronger acid than ordinary esters or other compounds containing a single carbonyl group; it is considerably stronger than ethyl alcohol.

When treated with sodium ethoxide in absolute alcohol, malonic ester is converted largely into its salt, *sodiomalonic ester*:

$$CH_2(COOC_2H_5)_2 + Na^+ {}^-OC_2H_5 \rightleftharpoons CH(COOC_2H_5)_2^-Na^+ + HOC_2H_5$$

Stronger acid   Sodiomalonic ester   Weaker acid

Reaction of this salt with an alkyl halide yields a substituted malonic ester, an *ethyl alkylmalonate*, often called an *alkylmalonic ester:*

$$CH(COOC_2H_5)_2^-Na^+ + RX \longrightarrow RCH(COOC_2H_5)_2 + Na^+ X^-$$

Ethyl alkylmalonate
Alkylmalonic ester

This reaction involves nucleophilic attack on the alkyl halide by the carbanion, $CH(COOC_2H_5)_2^-$, and, as we might expect, gives highest yields with primary alkyl halides, lower yields with secondary alkyl halides, and is worthless for tertiary alkyl halides and for aryl halides.

The alkylmalonic ester still contains one ionizable hydrogen, and on treatment with sodium ethoxide it, too, can be converted into its salt; this salt can react with an alkyl halide — which may be the same as, or different from, the first alkyl halide — to yield a dialkylmalonic ester:

$$RCH(COOC_2H_5)_2 + Na^+ {}^-OC_2H_5 \rightleftharpoons RC(COOC_2H_5)_2^- Na^+ + C_2H_5OH$$

$$\downarrow R'X$$

$$RR'C(COOC_2H_5)_2 + Na^+ X^-$$
Dialkylmalonic ester

The acidity of malonic ester thus permits the preparation of substituted malonic esters containing one or two alkyl groups. How can these substituted malonic esters be used to make carboxylic acids? We have seen (Sec. 25.6) that when heated above its melting point, malonic acid readily loses carbon dioxide to form acetic acid; in a similar way substituted malonic acids readily lose carbon dioxide to form substituted acetic acids. The monoalkyl- and dialkylmalonic esters we have prepared are readily converted into monocarboxylic acids by hydrolysis, acidification, and heat:

$$RCH(COOC_2H_5)_2 \xrightarrow{H_2O,\ OH^-,\ heat} RCH(COO^-)_2 \xrightarrow{H^+} RCH(COOH)_2$$

A monoalkylmalonic ester

$$\downarrow heat,\ 140°$$

$$RCH_2COOH + CO_2$$
A monosubstituted
acetic acid

$$RR'C(COOC_2H_5)_2 \xrightarrow{H_2O,\ OH^-,\ heat} RR'C(COO^-)_2 \xrightarrow{H^+} RR'C(COOH)_2$$

A dialkylmalonic ester

$$\downarrow heat,\ 140°$$

$$RR'CHCOOH + CO_2$$
A disubstituted
acetic acid

A malonic ester synthesis yields an acetic acid in which one or two hydrogens have been replaced by alkyl groups.

In planning a malonic ester synthesis, our problem is to select the proper alkyl halide or halides; to do this we have only to look at the structure of the acid we want. Isocaproic acid, for example, $(CH_3)_2CHCH_2CH_2COOH$, can be considered as acetic acid in which one hydrogen has been replaced by an isobutyl group. To prepare this acid by the malonic ester synthesis, we would have to use isobutyl bromide as the alkylating agent:

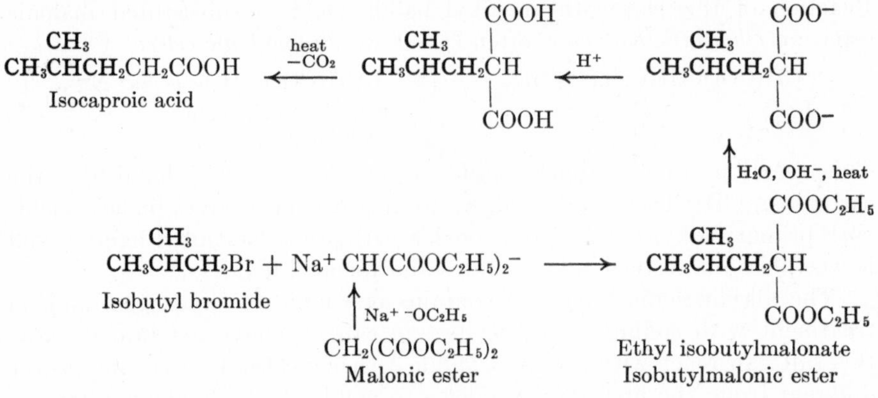

$$\underset{\text{Isocaproic acid}}{\underset{CH_3}{CH_3CHCH_2CH_2COOH}} \xleftarrow[-CO_2]{heat} \underset{\substack{CH_3 \\ CH_3CHCH_2CH \\ | \\ COOH}}{\overset{COOH}{|}} \xleftarrow{H^+} \underset{\substack{CH_3 \\ CH_3CHCH_2CH \\ | \\ COO^-}}{\overset{COO^-}{|}}$$

$$\uparrow H_2O,\ OH^-,\ heat$$

$$COOC_2H_5$$

$$\underset{\text{Isobutyl bromide}}{\underset{CH_3}{CH_3CHCH_2Br}} + Na^+ CH(COOC_2H_5)_2^- \longrightarrow \underset{\substack{CH_3 \\ CH_3CHCH_2CH \\ | \\ COOC_2H_5}}{\overset{CH_3}{|}}$$

$$\uparrow Na^+ {}^-OC_2H_5$$

$$\underset{\text{Malonic ester}}{CH_2(COOC_2H_5)_2}$$

Ethyl isobutylmalonate
Isobutylmalonic ester

An isomer of isocaproic acid, α-methylvaleric acid, $CH_3CH_2CH_2$-$CH(CH_3)COOH$, can be considered as acetic acid in which one hydrogen has been replaced by an n-propyl group and a second hydrogen has been replaced by a methyl group; we must therefore use two alkyl halides, n-propyl bromide and methyl bromide:

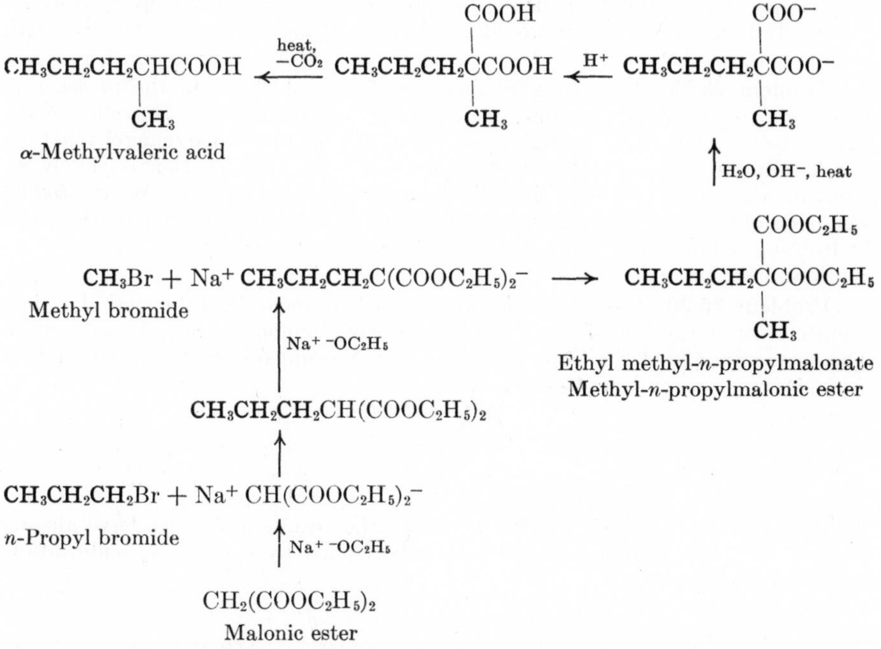

$$CH_3CH_2CH_2\underset{\underset{CH_3}{|}}{C}HCOOH \xleftarrow[-CO_2]{heat,} CH_3CH_2CH_2\underset{\underset{CH_3}{|}}{\overset{\overset{COOH}{|}}{C}}COOH \xleftarrow{H^+} CH_3CH_2CH_2\underset{\underset{CH_3}{|}}{\overset{\overset{COO^-}{|}}{C}}COO^-$$

α-Methylvaleric acid

$$\Big\uparrow H_2O,\ OH^-,\ heat$$

$$CH_3Br + Na^+\ CH_3CH_2CH_2C(COOC_2H_5)_2^- \longrightarrow CH_3CH_2CH_2\underset{\underset{CH_3}{|}}{\overset{\overset{COOC_2H_5}{|}}{C}}COOC_2H_5$$

Methyl bromide

Ethyl methyl-n-propylmalonate
Methyl-n-propylmalonic ester

$$\Big\uparrow Na^+\ ^-OC_2H_5$$

$$CH_3CH_2CH_2CH(COOC_2H_5)_2$$

$$\Big\uparrow$$

$$CH_3CH_2CH_2Br + Na^+\ CH(COOC_2H_5)_2^-$$

n-Propyl bromide

$$\Big\uparrow Na^+\ ^-OC_2H_5$$

$$CH_2(COOC_2H_5)_2$$
Malonic ester

In place of simple alkyl halides, certain other halogen-containing compounds may be used, in particular the readily available α-bromo esters (why can α-bromo*acids* not be used?), which yield substituted succinic acids by the malonic ester synthesis. For example:

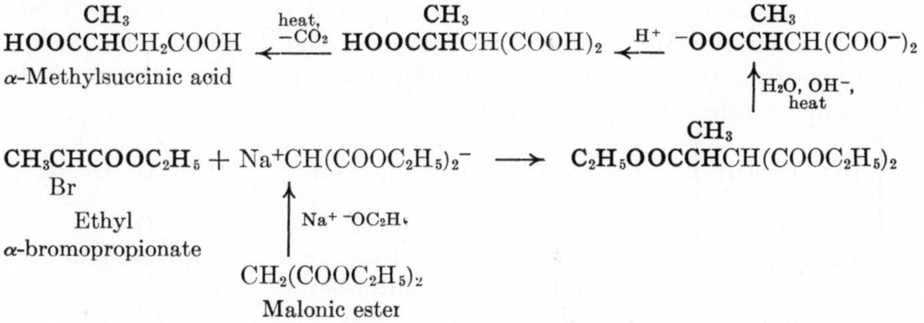

$$\underset{\alpha\text{-Methylsuccinic acid}}{HOOC\underset{\underset{CH_3}{|}}{C}HCH_2COOH} \xleftarrow[-CO_2]{heat,} HOOC\underset{\underset{CH_3}{|}}{C}HCH(COOH)_2 \xleftarrow{H^+} {}^-OOC\underset{\underset{CH_3}{|}}{C}HCH(COO^-)_2$$

$$\Big\uparrow \begin{matrix}H_2O,\ OH^-,\\ heat\end{matrix}$$

$$CH_3\underset{\underset{Br}{|}}{C}HCOOC_2H_5 + Na^+CH(COOC_2H_5)_2^- \longrightarrow C_2H_5OOC\underset{\underset{CH_3}{|}}{C}HCH(COOC_2H_5)_2$$

Ethyl
α-bromopropionate

$$\Big\uparrow Na^+\ ^-OC_2H_5$$

$$CH_2(COOC_2H_5)_2$$
Malonic ester

Problem 25.27 Outline the synthesis of the following compounds from malonic ester and alcohols of four carbons or less:

(a) the isomeric acids, n-valeric, isovaleric, and α-methylbutyric. (Why can the malonic ester synthesis not be used for the preparation of trimethylacetic acid?)

(b) *leucine* (α-aminoisocaproic acid)

(c) *isoleucine* (α-amino-β-methylvaleric acid)

Problem 25.28 *Adipic acid* is obtained from a malonic ester synthesis in which the first step is addition of one mole of ethylene bromide to a large excess of sodiomalonic ester in alcohol. *Cyclopropanecarboxylic acid* is the final product of a malonic ester synthesis in which the first step is addition of one mole of sodiomalonic ester to two moles of ethylene bromide followed by addition of one mole of sodium ethoxide.

(a) Account for the difference in the products obtained in the two syntheses.

(b) Tell exactly how you would go about synthesizing *cyclopentanecarboxylic acid.*

Problem 25.29 Malonic ester reacts with benzaldehyde in the presence of piperidine (a secondary amine, Sec. 32.12) to yield ethyl benzalmalonate, $C_6H_5CH\!=\!C(COOC_2H_5)_2$. This is an example of the **Knoevenagel reaction** (a) Account for the formation of this product. (b) This reaction is closely re lated to what other reaction that we have already studied? (c) What product would be obtained if this substituted malonic ester were subjected to the usual hydrolysis, acidification, and decarboxylation? (d) What is another way to synthesize the product of (c)?

Problem 25.30 Cyclohexanone reacts with cyanoacetic ester (ethyl cyanoacetate, $N\!\equiv\!CCH_2COOC_2H_5$) in the presence of ammonium acetate to yield I. This is an example of the **Cope reaction.** (a) Account for the formation of I.

$$\text{\Large \diagdown}=\text{C—COOC}_2\text{H}_5$$
$$|$$
$$\text{CN}$$

I

(b) This reaction is closely related to what other reaction that we have already studied? (c) What product would be formed from I by hydrolysis, acidification, and decarboxylation?

CARBONIC ACID AND RELATED COMPOUNDS

25.10 Functional derivatives of carbonic acid

Much of the chemistry of the functional derivatives of carbonic acid is already quite familiar to us through our study of carboxylic acids. The first step in dealing with one of these compounds is to recognize just how it is related to the parent acid. Since carbonic acid is bifunctional, each of its derivatives, too, contains two functional groups; these groups can be the same or different. For example:

$$\left[\begin{array}{c} \text{HO—C—OH} \\ \| \\ \text{O} \end{array}\right] \qquad \begin{array}{c} \text{Cl—C—Cl} \\ \| \\ \text{O} \end{array} \qquad \begin{array}{c} \text{H}_2\text{N—C—NH}_2 \\ \| \\ \text{O} \end{array} \qquad \begin{array}{c} \text{C}_2\text{H}_5\text{O—C—OC}_2\text{H}_5 \\ \| \\ \text{O} \end{array}$$

Carbonic acid	Phosgene (Carbonyl chloride)	Urea (Carbamide)	Ethyl carbonate
Acid	*Acid chloride*	*Amide*	*Ester*

$$\begin{array}{c} \text{C}_2\text{H}_5\text{O—C—Cl} \\ \| \\ \text{O} \end{array} \qquad\qquad \text{H}_2\text{N—C}\!\equiv\!\text{N} \qquad\qquad \begin{array}{c} \text{H}_2\text{N—C—OC}_2\text{H}_5 \\ \| \\ \text{O} \end{array}$$

Ethyl chlorocarbonate	Cyanamide	Urethane (Ethyl carbamate)
Acid chloride–ester	*Amide–nitrile*	*Ester–amide*

We use these functional relationships to carbonic acid simply for convenience. Many of these compounds could just as well be considered as derivatives of other acids, and, indeed, are often so named. For example:

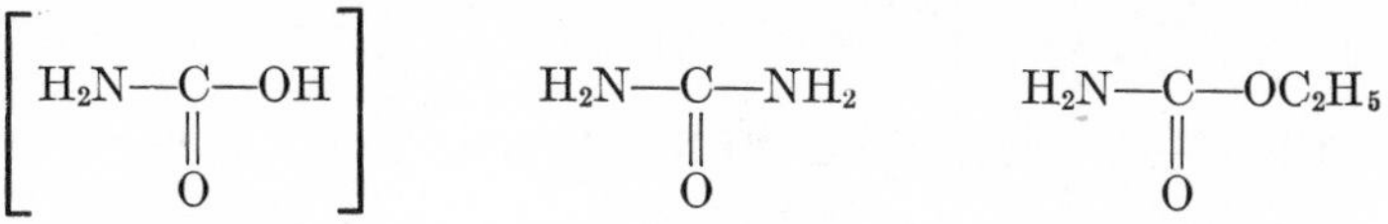

$$\left[\begin{array}{c} H_2N—C—OH \\ \| \\ O \end{array} \right] \qquad \begin{array}{c} H_2N—C—NH_2 \\ \| \\ O \end{array} \qquad \begin{array}{c} H_2N—C—OC_2H_5 \\ \| \\ O \end{array}$$

| Carbamic acid | Carbamide | Ethyl carbamate |
| *Acid* | *Amide* | *Ester* |

$$\left[HO—C≡N \right] \qquad H_2N—C≡N$$

| Cyanic acid | Cyanamide |
| *Acid* | *Amide* |

In general, a derivative of carbonic acid containing an –OH group is unstable, and decomposes to carbon dioxide. For example:

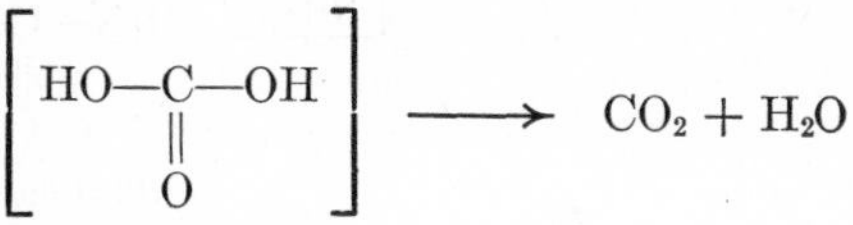

$$\left[\begin{array}{c} HO—C—OH \\ \| \\ O \end{array} \right] \longrightarrow CO_2 + H_2O$$

Carbonic acid

$$\left[\begin{array}{c} RO—C—OH \\ \| \\ O \end{array} \right] \longrightarrow CO_2 + ROH$$

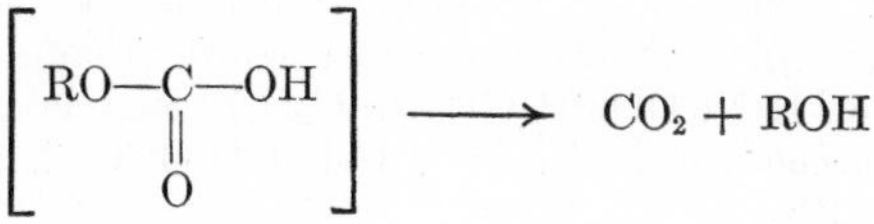

Alkyl hydrogen
carbonate

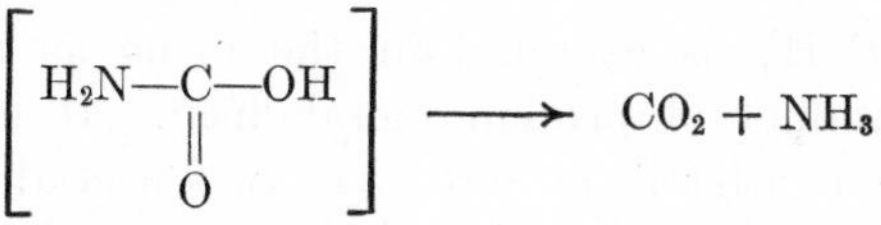

$$\left[\begin{array}{c} H_2N—C—OH \\ \| \\ O \end{array} \right] \longrightarrow CO_2 + NH_3$$

Carbamic acid

$$\left[\begin{array}{c} Cl—C—OH \\ \| \\ O \end{array} \right] \longrightarrow CO_2 + HCl$$

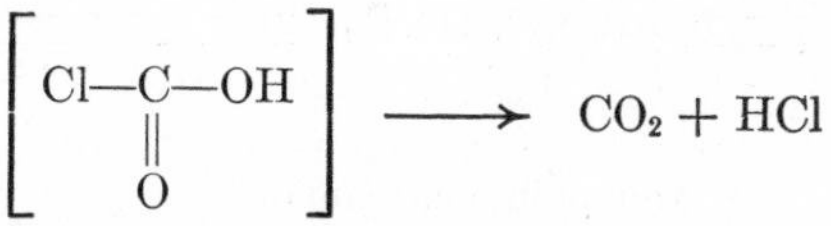

Chlorocarbonic
acid

Most derivatives of carbonic acid are made from one of three industrially available compounds: phosgene, urea, or cyanamide.

25.11 Phosgene

Phosgene, $COCl_2$, a highly poisonous gas, is manufactured by the reaction between carbon monoxide and chlorine.

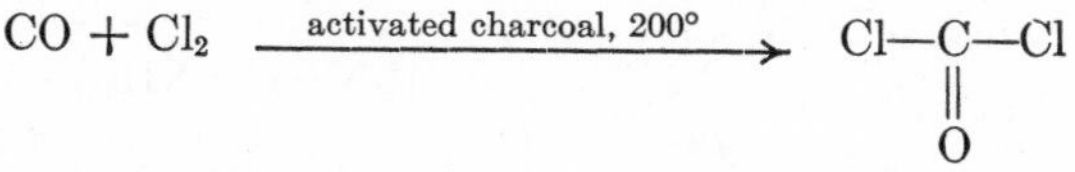

$$CO + Cl_2 \xrightarrow{\text{activated charcoal, 200°}} \begin{array}{c} Cl—C—Cl \\ \| \\ O \end{array}$$

Phosgene

It undergoes the usual reactions of an acid chloride.

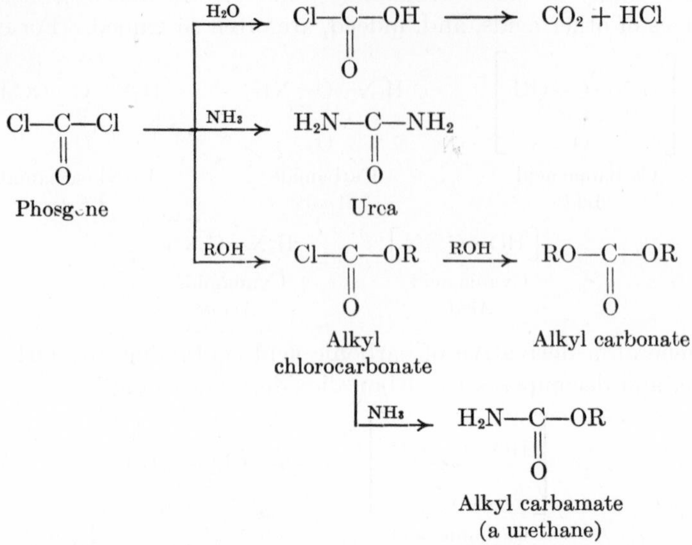

$$\text{H}_2\text{O} \longrightarrow \text{Cl—C—OH} \longrightarrow \text{CO}_2 + \text{HCl}$$
$$\overset{||}{\text{O}}$$

$$\text{Cl—C—Cl} \xrightarrow{\text{NH}_3} \text{H}_2\text{N—C—NH}_2$$
$$\overset{||}{\text{O}} \qquad\qquad \overset{||}{\text{O}}$$

Phosgene   Urea

$$\xrightarrow{\text{ROH}} \text{Cl—C—OR} \xrightarrow{\text{ROH}} \text{RO—C—OR}$$
$$\overset{||}{\text{O}} \qquad\qquad \overset{||}{\text{O}}$$

Alkyl   Alkyl carbonate
chlorocarbonate

$$\xrightarrow{\text{NH}_3} \text{H}_2\text{N—C—OR}$$
$$\overset{||}{\text{O}}$$

Alkyl carbamate
(a urethane)

Problem 25.31 Suggest a possible synthesis of (a) N,N′-dimethylurea, $CH_3NHCONHCH_3$; (b) N,N′-diphenylurea (*carbanilide*), $C_6H_5NHCONHC_6H_5$; (c) 2-pentylurethane, $H_2NCOOCH(CH_3)(n\text{-}C_3H_7)$, used as a hypnotic; (d) benzyl chlorocarbonate (*carbobenzoxy chloride*), $C_6H_5CH_2OCOCl$, used in the synthesis of peptides (Sec. 33.10).

25.12 Urea. Barbiturates

Urea, H_2NCONH_2, is excreted in the urine as the chief nitrogen-containing end-product of protein metabolism. It is synthesized on a large scale for use as a fertilizer and as a raw material in the manufacture of urea–formaldehyde plastics and of drugs.

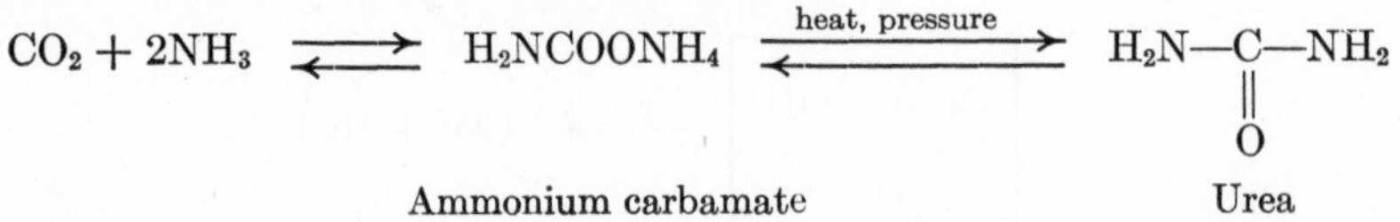

$$\text{CO}_2 + 2\text{NH}_3 \rightleftarrows \text{H}_2\text{NCOONH}_4 \underset{\text{heat, pressure}}{\rightleftarrows} \text{H}_2\text{N—C—NH}_2$$
$$\overset{||}{\text{O}}$$

Ammonium carbamate   Urea

Problem 25.32 The synthesis of urea is an example of what familiar method of amide preparation?

Urea is weakly basic, forming salts with strong acids. The fact that it is a stronger base than ordinary amides is attributed to resonance stabilization of the cation:

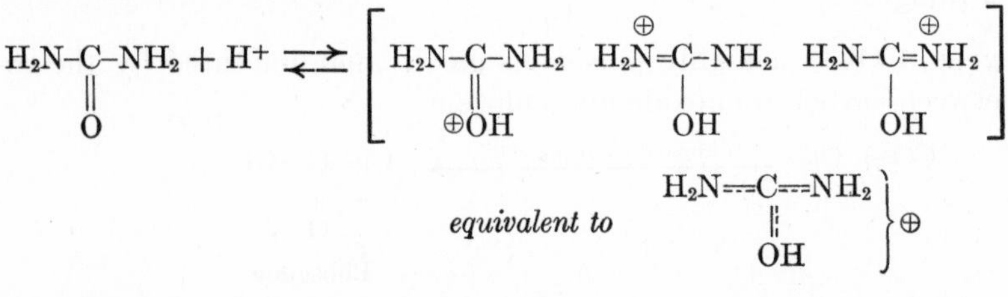

$$\text{H}_2\text{N-C-NH}_2 + \text{H}^+ \rightleftarrows \left[\text{H}_2\text{N-C-NH}_2 \quad \overset{\oplus}{\text{H}_2\text{N=C-NH}_2} \quad \overset{\oplus}{\text{H}_2\text{N-C=NH}_2} \right]$$
$$\overset{||}{\text{O}} \qquad\qquad\qquad \overset{|}{\oplus\text{OH}} \qquad\qquad \overset{|}{\text{OH}} \qquad\qquad \overset{|}{\text{OH}}$$

equivalent to $\left.\begin{array}{c} \text{H}_2\text{N}\text{=}\text{=}\text{C}\text{=}\text{=}\text{NH}_2 \\ \overset{|}{\text{OH}} \end{array}\right\}\oplus$

Problem 25.33   Account for the fact that *guanidine*, $(H_2N)_2C=NH$, is *strongly* basic.

Urea undergoes hydrolysis in the presence of acids, bases, or the enzyme *urease* (isolable from jack beans; generated by many bacteria, such as Micrococcus ureae).

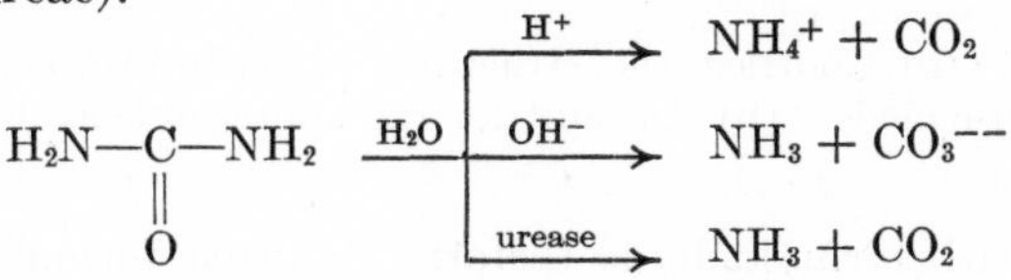

$$H_2N-\underset{\underset{O}{\|}}{C}-NH_2 \quad \xrightarrow{H_2O} \quad \begin{cases} \xrightarrow{H^+} & NH_4^+ + CO_2 \\ \xrightarrow{OH^-} & NH_3 + CO_3^{--} \\ \xrightarrow{urease} & NH_3 + CO_2 \end{cases}$$
Urea

Urea reacts with nitrous acid to yield carbon dioxide and nitrogen; this is a useful way to destroy excess nitrous acid in diazotizations.

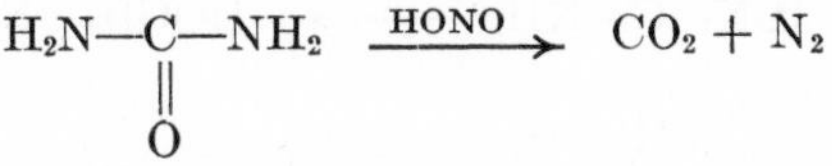

$$H_2N-\underset{\underset{O}{\|}}{C}-NH_2 \quad \xrightarrow{HONO} \quad CO_2 + N_2$$

Urea is converted by hypohalites into nitrogen and carbonate.

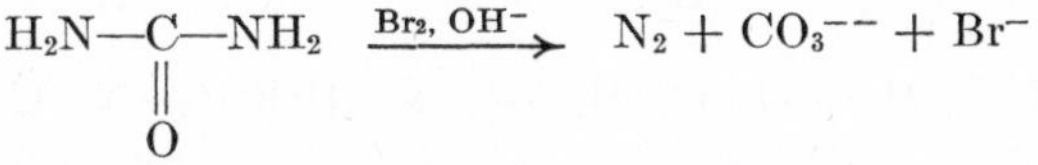

$$H_2N-\underset{\underset{O}{\|}}{C}-NH_2 \quad \xrightarrow{Br_2,\ OH^-} \quad N_2 + CO_3^{--} + Br^-$$

Problem 25.34   Given the fact that hydrazine, H_2N-NH_2, is oxidized to nitrogen by hypohalite, show that the above reaction of urea is simply an example of the Hofmann degradation of amides.

Treatment of urea with acid chlorides or anhydrides yields **ureides.**

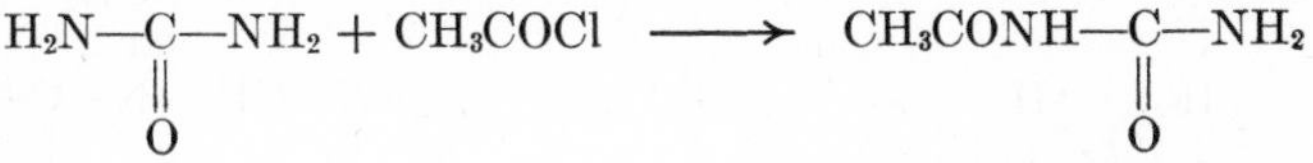

$$H_2N-\underset{\underset{O}{\|}}{C}-NH_2 + CH_3COCl \longrightarrow CH_3CONH-\underset{\underset{O}{\|}}{C}-NH_2$$
Acetylurea
A ureide

Of special importance are the cyclic ureides formed by reaction with malonic esters; these are known as **barbiturates** and are important hypnotics (sleep-producers). For example:

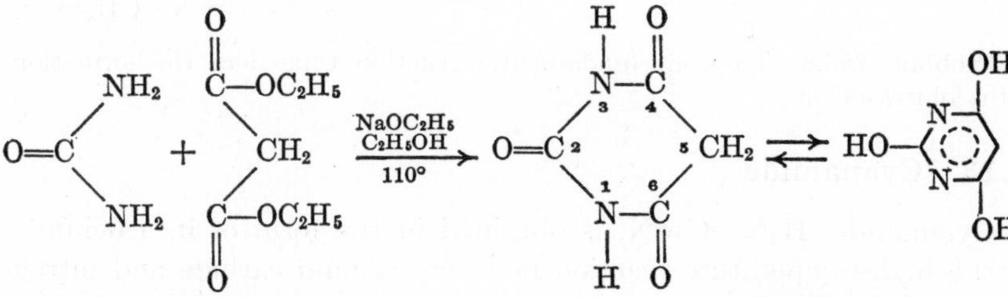

Urea   Ethyl malonate   I   Barbituric acid   II
                                               (Malonylurea)

Problem 25.35   Outline the synthesis from readily available compounds of the following hypnotics:
(a) α-bromoisovalerylurea (Bromural), $(CH_3)_2CHCHBrCONHCONH_2$
(b) 5,5-diethylbarbituric acid (Barbital, Veronal; long-acting)
(c) 5-allyl-5-(2-pentyl)barbituric acid (Seconal; short-acting)
(d) 5-ethyl-5-isopentylbarbituric acid (Amytal; intermediate length of action)

Problem 25.36 (a) Structure II for barbituric acid contains the aromatic *pyrimidine* ring. This is a resonance hybrid of what structures? (b) What is the relationship between I and II? (*Hint:* see Sec. 6.12.) (c) In what two ways could you account for the appreciable acidity ($K_a = 10^{-4}$) of barbituric acid? (d) Would you expect barbituric acid to dissolve in aqueous NaOH? In aqueous NaHCO₃?

Problem 25.37 (a) Contrast the structures of barbituric acid and Veronal (5,5-diethylbarbituric acid). (b) Account for the appreciable acidity ($K_a = 10^{-8}$) of Veronal.

Urea reacts with formaldehyde to form the urea–formaldehyde resins, highly important in molded plastics.

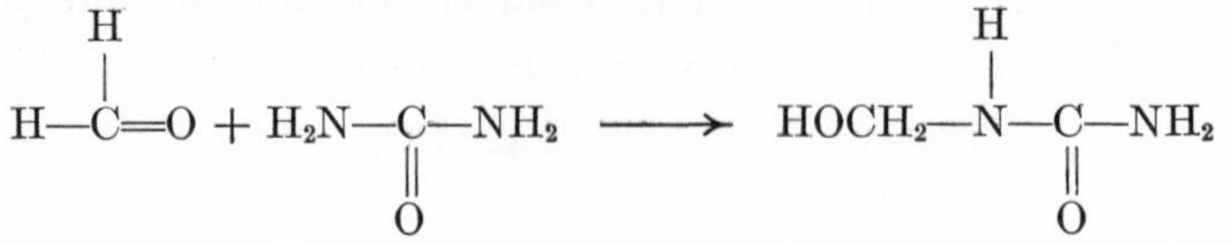

Formaldehyde   Urea   Methylolurea

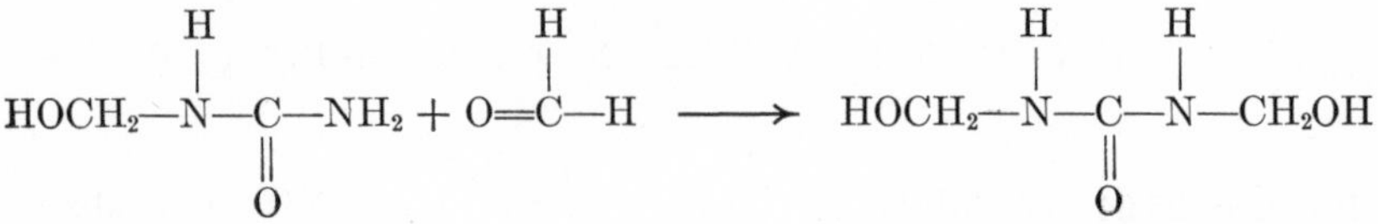

Dimethylolurea

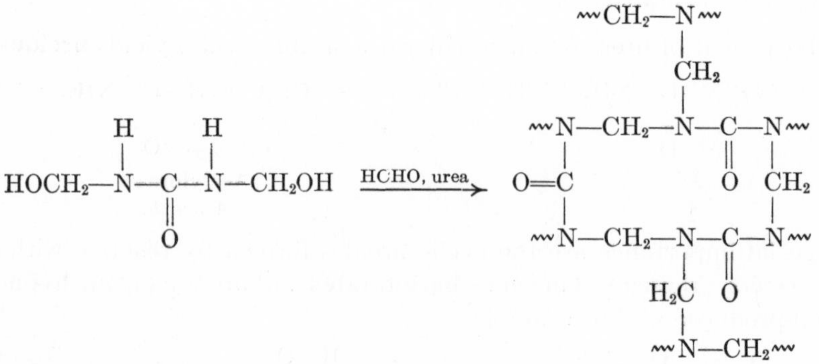

Problem 25.38 To what fundamental reaction type does the formation of methylolurea belong?

25.13 Cyanamide

Cyanamide, $H_2N—C{\equiv}N$, is obtained in the form of its calcium salt by the high-temperature reaction between calcium carbide and nitrogen.

$$CaC_2 + N_2 \xrightarrow{\;1000°\;} CaNCN + C$$

Calcium   Calcium
carbide   cyanamide

This reaction is important as a method of nitrogen fixation; calcium cyanamide is used as a fertilizer, releasing ammonia by the action of water.

Problem 25.39 Give the electronic structure of the cyanamide anion, $(NCN)^{--}$. Discuss its molecular shape, bond lengths, and location of charge.

Problem 25.40 Give equations for the individual steps probably involved in the conversion of calcium cyanamide into ammonia in the presence of water. What other product or products will be formed in this process? Label each step with the name of the fundamental reaction type to which it belongs.

Problem 25.41 Cyanamide reacts with water in the presence of acid or base to yield urea; with methanol in the presence of acid to yield methylisourea, $H_2NC(=NH)OCH_3$; with hydrogen sulfide to yield *thiourea*, $H_2NC(=S)NH_2$; and with ammonia to yield *guanidine*, $H_2CN(=NH)NH_2$. (a) What functional group of cyanamide is involved in each of these reactions? (b) To what general class of reaction do these belong? (c) Show the most probable mechanisms for these reactions, pointing out the function of acid or base wherever involved.

25.14 Isocyanates

Aryl isocyanates, $Ar-N=C=O$, are made by the action of phosgene on aryl amines. For example:

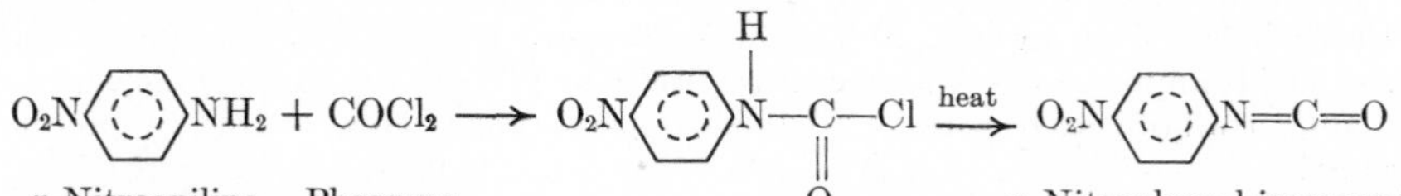

p-Nitroaniline   Phosgene   p-Nitrophenyl isocyanate

Problem 25.42 Phosgene must always be kept in excess in this synthesis. What product would be obtained if the amine were in excess?

The less stable, less useful alkyl isocyanates are important chiefly as intermediates in the synthesis of primary amines, as in the *Curtius reaction:*

$$RCOCl + NaN_3 \longrightarrow R-CON_3 \xrightarrow{heat} R-N=C=O + N_2$$

Sodium   An acyl   An alkyl
azide   azide   isocyanate

$$\downarrow H_2O$$

$$RNH_2 + CO_2$$

1° Amine

Problem 25.43 The conversion of azides into isocyanates is related to the Hofmann degradation of amides (Sec. 19.13) in both mechanism and synthetic application.

(a) Using the structure $R-\overset{\overset{\text{O}}{\|}}{C}-\overset{\ominus}{N}-\overset{\oplus}{N}\equiv N$ for the azide, and recognizing that N_2 is lost, suggest a mechanism for the Curtius reaction.

(b) Show how the Curtius reaction could be used in the conversion of α-phenylpro⁻ pionic acid into α-phenylethylamine.

(c) Give the configuration and sign of rotation of the amine obtained in (b) from (+)-α-phenylpropionic acid (the acid whose amide is given on page 537).

Isocyanates react with alcohols to give carbamates (urethanes) and with primary and secondary amines to give substituted ureas. For example:

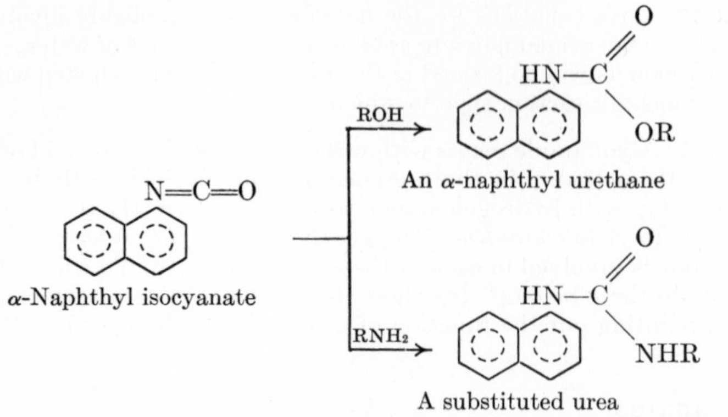

α-Naphthyl isocyanate

An α-naphthyl urethane

A substituted urea

These products are useful derivatives for the identification of alcohols and amines.

Problem 25.44 (a) Suggest a likely mechanism for the reaction of isocyanates with alcohols. With amines. (b) Show how a similar reaction of isocyanates with water yields amines. (c) An α-naphthyl urethane prepared from a *wet* alcohol will be badly contaminated with N,N'-di(α-naphthyl)urea. How is this by-product formed?

Problem 25.45 Predict the product of a Hofmann degradation of an amide carried out in methanol.

Problem 25.46 An alkyl halide can be identified by conversion into the Grignard reagent followed by treatment with an aryl isocyanate and then water. (a) What familiar class of compound is formed? (b) Give the structure and name of the product expected in the identification of *n*-butyl bromide by use of phenyl isocyanate.

Problem 25.47 Much synthetic foam rubber is made from polymers of this kind:

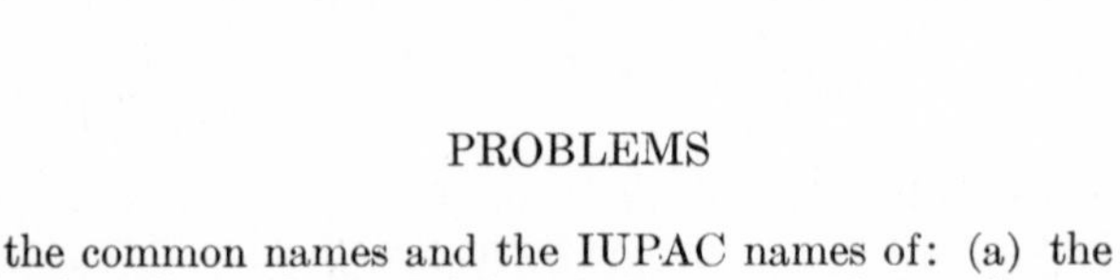

(a) Give a general family name to this kind of polymer.
(b) From what specific monomers could this particular polymer be made?

PROBLEMS

1. Give the common names and the IUPAC names of: (a) the straight-chain saturated dicarboxylic acids containing 2, 3, 4, 5, and 6 carbon atoms; (b) the isomeric phthalic acids.

2. (a) Draw the structures of all the isomeric dicarboxylic acids of formula $C_6H_{10}O_4$. (b) Give the common name and IUPAC name of each. (c) Show the stereoisomeric forms in which each can exist. Tell which stereoisomers, when separated from all others, would be optically active, and which would be optically inactive.

3. Give the structural formula of each of the following:

(a) α-methylglutaric acid
(b) α, α′-dibromosuccinic acid
(c) cis-1,3-cyclopentanedicarboxylic acid
(d) 3-nitrophthalic anhydride
(e) maleic acid
(f) fumaric acid
(g) 5-bromoisophthalic acid
(h) N-ethylphthalimide
(i) methyl succinate
(j) methyl hydrogen succinate

(k) N-bromosuccinimide
(l) ethyl malonate
(m) ethylmalonic acid
(n) ethyl ethylmalonate
(o) ethyl diethylmalonate
(p) ethyl cyanoacetate
(q) isopropyl carbamate
(r) benzyl chlorocarbonate
(s) N,N′-diethylurea

4. Write equations to show how succinic acid could be prepared from each of the following, using any other needed reagents:
(a) maleic acid; (b) ethylene bromide; (c) malonic ester; (d) 1,4-butynediol (from acetylene and formaldehyde, Problem 5(j), page 670).

5. Write equations to show how tetrahydrofuran could be converted into:
(a) succinic acid; (b) glutaric acid; (c) adipic acid.

6. Outline all steps in each of the following syntheses, using any needed reagents:
(a) azelaic acid (nonanedioic acid) from oleic acid (cis-9-octadecenoic acid)
(b) pimelic acid (heptanedioic acid) from ethyl glutarate
(c) cis-1,4-cyclohexanedicarboxylic acid from terephthalic acid
(d) adipic acid from scrap Nylon

7. Write equations to show the reaction (if any) of succinic acid with:
(a) aqueous NaOH
(b) aqueous NaHCO₃
(c) aqueous NH₃
(d) aqueous NH₃, then heat
(e) aqueous NH₃, then strong heat
(f) LiAlH₄
(g) excess SOCl₂
(h) 1 mole ethyl alcohol, H⁺, heat
(i) 2 moles ethyl alcohol, H⁺, heat
(j) 1 mole Br₂, P
(k) Br₂, Fe
(l) HNO₃, H₂SO₄
(m) fuming sulfuric acid
(n) CH₃Cl, AlCl₃
(o) strong heat

8. Answer Problem 7 for terephthalic acid.

9. Write equations to show the reaction (if any) of succinic anhydride with:
(a) hot aqueous NaOH
(b) aqueous ammonia
(c) aqueous ammonia, then cold dilute HCl
(d) aqueous ammonia, then strong heat
(e) benzyl alcohol
(f) toluene, AlCl₃, heat
(g) aniline, then strong heat

10. Write equations to show the reaction (if any) of phosgene with:
(a) water
(b) ammonia
(c) 1 mole n-butyl alcohol
(d) 2 moles n-butyl alcohol
(e) 1 mole n-butyl alcohol, followed by ammonia
(f) 1 mole n-butyl alcohol, followed by aniline
(g) 2 moles N-methylaniline
(h) excess benzene, AlCl₃, heat

11. Write equations to show the reaction (if any) of urea with:
(a) cold conc. HNO₃
(b) hot dilute HCl
(c) hot dilute NaOH
(d) NaNO₂ + HCl
(e) Br₂ + NaOH
(f) 1 mole C₆H₅COCl
(g) 2 moles C₆H₅COCl
(h) ethyl methylmalonate
(i) formaldehyde

12. Complete the following:
(a) p-C₆H₄(COCl)₂ + H₂ + Pd/BaSO₄ + catalyst moderator
(b) CH₃OOCCH₂CH₂COCl + (n-C₄H₉)₂Cd

(c) methyl adipate + excess CH_3MgI, then H_2O

(d) benzyl chlorocarbonate + glycine (aminoacetic acid)

(e) $C_6H_5NH—C—OC_2H_5$ + hot NaOH
$$\parallel$$
$$O$$

(f) oxalic acid + ethylene glycol $\longrightarrow$ $C_4H_4O_4$

(g) p-$C_6H_4(NCO)_2$ + ethylene glycol $\longrightarrow$ polymer

(h) phosgene + o-phenylenediamine

(i) adipoyl chloride + excess benzene, $AlCl_3$

(j) product (i) + Zn(Hg) + HCl

(k) ethyl chlorocarbonate + 2 moles NH_3

(l) ethyl chlorocarbonate + 3 moles NH_3

13. Write equations to show the action of heat upon each of the isomeric dicarboxylic acids of Problem 2(a).

14. Predict the products of the action of heat upon:

(a) o-$HOOCC_6H_4CH_2COOH$

(b) o-$C_6H_4(CH_2COOH)_2$

(c) o-$HOOCC_6H_4CH_2CH_2COOH$

(d) $C_6H_5CH(COOH)_2$

15. Outline the synthesis of each of the following from malonic ester and any other reagents:

(a) n-caproic acid

(b) isobutyric acid

(c) β-methylbutyric acid

(d) α,β-dimethylbutyric acid

(e) 2-ethylbutanoic acid

(f) dibenzylacetic acid

(g) α,β-dimethylsuccinic acid

(h) glutaric acid

(i) cyclobutanecarboxylic acid

16. Give structures of compounds A through J:

(a) 1,3-dibromopropane + 2 moles sodiomalonic ester $\longrightarrow$ A $(C_{17}H_{28}O_8)$

A + 2 moles sodium ethoxide, then CH_2I_2 $\longrightarrow$ B $(C_{18}H_{28}O_8)$

B + OH$^-$, heat; then H$^+$; then heat $\longrightarrow$ C $(C_8H_{12}O_4)$

(b) ethylene bromide + 2 moles sodiomalonic ester $\longrightarrow$ D $(C_{16}H_{26}O_8)$

D + 2 moles sodium ethoxide, then 1 mole ethylene bromide $\longrightarrow$ E $(C_{18}H_{28}O_8)$

E + OH$^-$, heat; then H$^+$; then heat $\longrightarrow$ F $(C_8H_{12}O_4)$

(c) 2 moles sodiomalonic ester + I_2 $\longrightarrow$ G $(C_{14}H_{22}O_8)$ + 2NaI

G + OH$^-$, heat; then H$^+$; then heat $\longrightarrow$ H $(C_4H_6O_4)$

(d) D + 2 moles sodium ethoxide, then I_2 $\longrightarrow$ I $(C_{16}H_{24}O_8)$

I + OH$^-$, heat; then H$^+$; then heat $\longrightarrow$ J $(C_6H_8O_4)$

(e) Suggest a possible synthesis for 1,3-cyclopentanedicarboxylic acid; for 1,2-cyclopentanedicarboxylic acid; for 1,1-cyclopentanedicarboxylic acid.

17. Give structures of compounds K through O:

allyl bromide + Mg $\longrightarrow$ K (C_6H_{10})

K + HBr $\longrightarrow$ L $(C_6H_{12}Br_2)$

sodiomalonic ester + excess L $\longrightarrow$ M $(C_{13}H_{23}O_4Br)$

M + sodium ethoxide $\longrightarrow$ N $(C_{13}H_{22}O_4)$

N + OH$^-$, heat; then H$^+$; then heat $\longrightarrow$ O $(C_8H_{14}O_2)$

18. Give structures of compounds P through S:

urea + cold conc. HNO_3 $\longrightarrow$ P, *urea nitrate*, $(CH_5ON_2)^+ NO_3^-$

P + cold conc. H_2SO_4 $\longrightarrow$ Q, *N-nitrourea*, $CH_3O_3N_3$

Q + Zn, H$^+$ $\longrightarrow$ R (CH_5ON_3)

R + acetone $\longrightarrow$ S $(C_4H_9ON_3)$

19. Draw stereochemical formulas of the products expected when maleic acid (*cis*-butenedioic acid) is treated with each of the following:

(a) Br_2/CCl_4

(b) cold dilute $KMnO_4$

(c) peroxyformic acid

(d) H_2, Ni

(e) HBr

(f) Br_2/CCl_4, followed by 1 mole C_2H_5OH, H$^+$

Tell which of the products as isolated by ordinary methods would be optically active, and which would be optically inactive. Tell which products could be resolved into optically active enantiomers, and which could not.

20. Answer Problem 19 for fumaric acid (*trans*-butenedioic acid).

21. Outline a possible synthesis of the tranquilizing drug Miltown from malonic ester, phosgene, alcohols of four carbons or less, using any needed inorganic reagents.

$$
\underset{\text{Miltown}}{
\begin{array}{c}
\hspace{3.2cm}\text{CH}_3 \\
\hspace{3.2cm}| \\
\text{H}_2\text{N}\!-\!\underset{\displaystyle\underset{\text{O}}{\|}}{\text{C}}\!-\!\text{OCH}_2\!-\!\underset{\displaystyle\underset{\displaystyle\underset{\text{C}_2\text{H}_5}{|}}{\underset{\text{CH}_2}{|}}}{\text{C}}\!-\!\text{CH}_2\text{O}\!-\!\underset{\displaystyle\underset{\text{O}}{\|}}{\text{C}}\!-\!\text{NH}_2
\end{array}}
$$

22. A compound is believed to be one of the following. Describe how you would go about finding out which of the possibilities the unknown actually is. Where possible, use simple chemical tests; where necessary, use more elaborate chemical methods.

succinic acid
methylmalonic acid
ethyl hydrogen oxalate

methyl hydrogen malonate
methyl oxalate

23. Compound T, $C_{12}H_{18}$, gives negative tests with dilute $KMnO_4$ and Br_2/CCl_4. Oxidation of T with hot $KMnO_4$ gives U, $C_{12}H_6O_{12}$, which is soluble in water, and gives a gas when treated with aqueous $NaHCO_3$. Dehydration of U gives V, $C_{12}O_9$. What are T, U, and V?

24. Two isomeric acids, *hemipinic acid* and *metahemipinic acid*, have the formula $C_{10}H_{10}O_6$. Each has a neutralization equivalent of 113 ± 2; each contains two methoxyl groups, as shown by Zeisel determinations. When heated, the two acids yield different products of formula $C_{10}H_8O_5$. When heated strongly with calcium oxide both acids yield veratrole (1,2-dimethoxybenzene).

Hemipinic acid reacts with ethyl alcohol to yield two products of formula $C_{12}H_{14}O_6$; metahemipinic acid reacts with ethyl alcohol to yield a single product of formula $C_{12}H_{14}O_6$.

What are the structures of hemipinic acid and metahemipinic acid?

25. 2,5-Dimethyl-1,1-cyclopentanedicarboxylic acid can be prepared as a mixture of two optically inactive substances of different physical properties, W and X. When each is heated and the reaction mixture worked up by fractional crystallization, W yields a single product, Y, of formula $C_8H_{14}O_2$, and X yields two products, Z and Z', both of formula $C_8H_{14}O_2$.

(a) Give stereochemical formulas for W, X, Y, Z, and Z'. (b) Describe another method by which you could assign configurations to W and X.

Chapter twenty-six

KETO ACIDS

26.1 Structure and properties

What can we expect of compounds that contain more than one kind of functional group?

First of all, we can expect to find more than one set of properties. A keto acid, for example, is a ketone and an acid, and in general behaves like *both* kinds of compound. At the carbonyl group it undergoes the reactions characteristic of any ketone: nucleophilic addition, hydrogenation, reductive amination. At the carboxyl group it undergoes the reactions characteristic of any acid: ionization, conversion into salts, amides, and esters.

Besides the properties of the individual functional groups, there may also be special properties that arise because the groups are located in a particular way with respect to each other. In this chapter we shall concentrate on the esters of *beta*-keto acids and on the special properties that make them the most important class of keto acid derivatives.

TABLE 26.1

KETO ACIDS AND RELATED COMPOUNDS

Name	Formula	M.p., °C	B.p., °C	K_a
Glyoxylic acid	OHC—COOH			47 $\times 10^{-5}$
Pyruvic acid	CH₃COCOOH	14	165d	320
Acetoacetic acid	CH₃COCH₂COOH		100d	15
Levulinic acid	CH₃COCH₂CH₂COOH	31	245	2.5
o-Benzoylbenzoic acid	o-C₆H₅COC₆H₄COOH	128		
β-Benzoylpropionic acid	C₆H₅COCH₂CH₂COOH	116		
Ethyl acetoacetate	CH₃COCH₂COOC₂H₅	− 39	41²	
Ethyl benzoylacetate	C₆H₅COCH₂COOC₂H₅		270d	
Glyoxal	OHC—CHO	15	50	
Biacetyl	CH₃COCOCH₃		88	
Acetylacetone	CH₃COCH₂COCH₃	− 23	139	5.8 $\times 10^{-9}$
Acetonylacetone	CH₃COCH₂CH₂COCH₃	− 9	193	

700

Problem 26.1　Predict the products of the following reactions:

(a)　acetoacetic acid (CH_3COCH_2COOH) + dil. aq. $NaHCO_3$
(b)　β-benzoylpropionic acid ($C_6H_5COCH_2CH_2COOH$) + C_2H_5OH + H_2SO_4
(c)　glyoxylic acid (OHC–COOH) + Tollens' reagent
(d)　levulinic acid ($CH_3COCH_2CH_2COOH$) + H_2 + Ni
(e)　ethyl acetoacetate + $NH_3OH^+Cl^-$ + CH_3COONa
(f)　pyruvic acid ($CH_3COCOOH$) + NH_3 + H_2 + Ni
(g)　glyoxylic acid + conc. aq. NaOH
(h)　ethyl acetoacetate + dil. aq. NaOH
(i)　β-benzoylpropionic acid + Zn(Hg) + conc. HCl
(j)　dichloroacetic acid + H_2O + heat

26.2　Preparation of β-keto esters.　Claisen condensation

When ethyl acetate is treated with sodium ethoxide, and the resulting mixture is acidified, there is obtained ethyl β-ketobutyrate (ethyl 3-oxo-butanoate) generally known as **ethyl acetoacetate** or **acetoacetic ester**:

$$2CH_3COOC_2H_5 + Na^+\ ^-OC_2H_5 \xrightarrow{C_2H_5OH} CH_3COCHCOOC_2H_5^-\ Na^+ + C_2H_5OH$$

Ethyl acetate　　　　Sodium　　　　　　　　Sodioacetoacetic ester
　2 moles　　　　　ethoxide

$$\downarrow H^+$$

$$\overset{\beta}{C}H_3\overset{\ }{C}O\overset{\alpha}{C}H_2COOC_2H_5$$

Ethyl acetoacetate
Acetoacetic ester
A β-keto ester

Ethyl acetoacetate is by far the most important of the β-keto acid derivatives; its preparation illustrates the reaction known as the **Claisen condensation**.

The generally accepted mechanism for the Claisen condensation (shown here for ethyl acetate) is:

(1)　$CH_3COOC_2H_5 + \ ^-OC_2H_5 \rightleftharpoons C_2H_5OH + \ ^-CH_2COOC_2H_5$
　　　　　　　　　　　　　　　　　　　　　　　　　　　　　　I

(2)
$$CH_3-\overset{O}{\overset{\|}{C}}\diagdown OC_2H_5 + \ ^-CH_2COOC_2H_5 \rightleftharpoons CH_3-\overset{O^-}{\underset{OC_2H_5}{\overset{|}{\underset{|}{C}}}}-CH_2COOC_2H_5$$
　　　　　　　　　　　　　　　　I

$$\updownarrow$$

$$CH_3\overset{O}{\overset{\|}{C}}CH_2COOC_2H_5 + \ ^-OC_2H_5$$

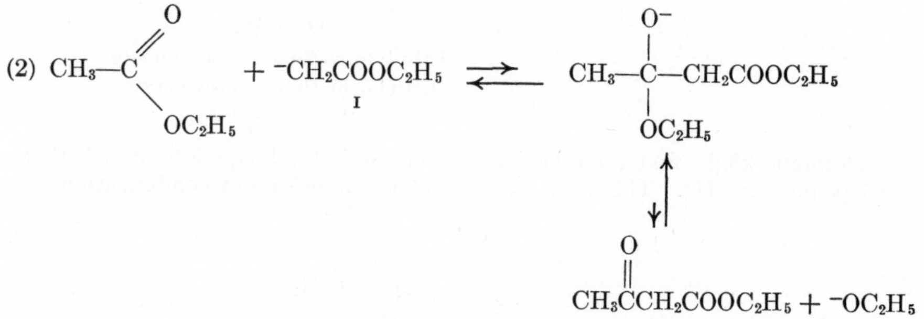

(3)　$CH_3\overset{O}{\overset{\|}{C}}CH_2COOC_2H_5 + \ ^-OC_2H_5 \rightleftharpoons CH_3COCHCOOC_2H_5^- + C_2H_5OH$
　　　　Stronger acid　　　　　　　　　　　　　　　　　　　　　　　　　**Weaker acid**

Ethoxide ion abstracts (step 1) a hydrogen ion from the α-carbon of the ester to form carbanion I. The powerfully nucleophilic carbanion I attacks (step 2) the carbonyl carbon of a second molecule of ester to displace ethoxide ion and yield the keto ester. Like malonic ester, and for exactly the same reason, acetoacetic ester is appreciably acidic. It is a stronger acid than ethyl alcohol, and hence it reacts (step 3) with ethoxide ion to form ethyl alcohol and the anion of sodioacetoacetic ester. Formation of the salt of acetoacetic ester is essential to the success of the reaction; of the various equilibria involved in the reaction, only (3) is favorable to the product we want.

Like the aldol condensation (Sec. 23.15) and related reactions, the Claisen condensation involves nucleophilic attack by a carbanion on an electron-deficient carbonyl carbon. In the aldol condensation, nucleophilic attack leads to addition, the typical reaction of aldehydes and ketones; in the Claisen condensation, nucleophilic attack leads to substitution, the typical reaction of acyl compounds (Sec. 17.4).

Problem 26.2 Account for the acidity of acetoacetic ester on the basis of the resonance theory.

Problem 26.3 Better yields are obtained if the Claisen condensation is carried out in ether with alcohol-free sodium ethoxide as catalyst instead of in ethyl alcohol solution. How do you account for this?

As we might expect, the Claisen condensation of more complicated esters yields the products resulting from ionization of an α-hydrogen of the ester; as a result it is always the α-carbon of one molecule that becomes attached to the carbonyl carbon of another. For example:

$$2CH_3CH_2COOC_2H_5 + {}^-OC_2H_5 \longrightarrow CH_3CH_2CO{-}CCOOC_2H_5{}^- + C_2H_5OH$$

Ethyl propionate
$$\overset{|}{CH_3}$$

$$\downarrow H^+$$

$$\overset{\beta\quad\alpha}{CH_3CH_2C{-}CHCOOC_2H_5}$$
$$\overset{||\quad\;|}{O\;\;\;CH_3}$$

Ethyl 3-oxo-2-methylpentanoate
Ethyl α-methyl-β-ketovalerate
A β-keto ester

Problem 26.4 Sodium ethoxide converts ethyl adipate into 2-carbethoxy-cyclopentanone (II). This is an example of the **Dieckmann condensation.**

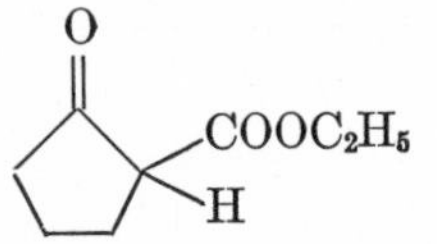

II

(a) How do you account for formation of II? (b) What product would you expect from the action of sodium ethoxide on ethyl pimelate? (c) Would you expect similar behavior from ethyl glutarate or ethyl succinate? (d) Actually, ethyl succinate reacts with sodium ethoxide to yield a compound of formula $C_{12}H_{16}O_6$ containing a six-membered ring. What is the likely structure for this last product?

26.3 Crossed Claisen condensation

Like a crossed aldol condensation (Sec. 23.18), a **crossed Claisen condensation** is generally feasible only when one of the reactants has no α-hydrogens and thus is incapable of undergoing self-condensation. For example:

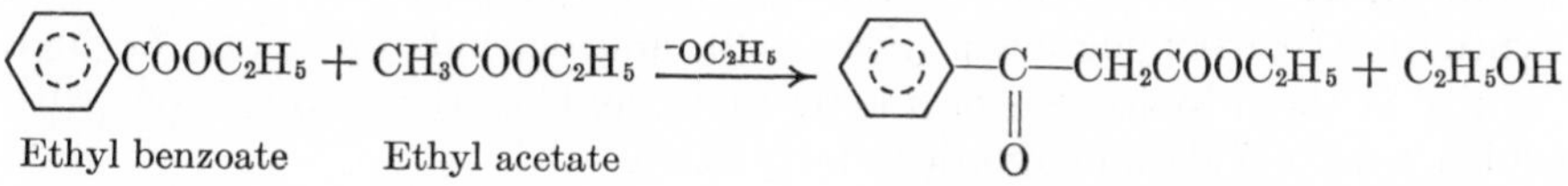

$$C_6H_5COOC_2H_5 + CH_3COOC_2H_5 \xrightarrow{\ ^-OC_2H_5\ } C_6H_5\overset{\|}{\underset{O}{C}}\!-\!CH_2COOC_2H_5 + C_2H_5OH$$

Ethyl benzoate   Ethyl acetate   Ethyl benzoylacetate

$$HCOOC_2H_5 + CH_3COOC_2H_5 \xrightarrow{\ ^-OC_2H_5\ } H\!-\!\overset{\|}{\underset{O}{C}}\!-\!CH_2COOC_2H_5 + C_2H_5OH$$

Ethyl formate   Ethyl acetate

Ethyl formylacetate
(known only as the Na salt)

$$\underset{\overset{|}{COOC_2H_5}}{\overset{COOC_2H_5}{|}} + CH_3COOC_2H_5 \xrightarrow{\ ^-OC_2H_5\ } C_2H_5OOC\!-\!\overset{\|}{\underset{O}{C}}\!-\!CH_2COOC_2H_5 + C_2H_5OH$$

Ethyl oxalate   Ethyl acetate

Ethyl oxaloacetate

$$C_2H_5O\!-\!\overset{\|}{\underset{O}{C}}\!-\!OC_2H_5 + C_6H_5CH_2COOC_2H_5 \xrightarrow{\ ^-OC_2H_5\ } C_2H_5O\!-\!\overset{\|}{\underset{O}{C}}\!-\!\underset{C_6H_5}{\overset{|}{CH}}COOC_2H_5 + C_2H_5OH$$

Ethyl carbonate   Ethyl phenylacetate

Ethyl phenylmalonate
Phenylmalonic ester

Problem 26.5 In what order should the reactants be mixed in each of the above crossed Claisen condensations? (*Hint:* see Sec. 23.18.)

Problem 26.6 As shown above, ethyl phenylmalonate can be made by a crossed Claisen condensation. Could it be made from bromobenzene and ethyl malonate?

Problem 26.7 Ketones (but not aldehydes) undergo a crossed Claisen condensation with esters. For example:

$$CH_3COOC_2H_5 + CH_3COCH_3 \xrightarrow{\ NaOC_2H_5\ } CH_3COCH_2COCH_3 + C_2H_5OH$$

Ethyl acetate   Acetone   Acetylacetone

(a) Outline all steps in the most likely mechanism for this reaction. (b) Predict the principal products expected from the reaction in the presence of sodium ethoxide of ethyl propionate and acetone; (c) of ethyl benzoate and acetophenone; (d) of ethyl oxalate and cyclohexanone.

Problem 26.8 Outline the synthesis from simple esters of:
(a) ethyl α-phenylbenzoylacetate, $C_6H_5COCH(C_6H_5)COOC_2H_5$
(b) ethyl 2,3-dioxo-1,4-cyclopentanedicarboxylate (I) (*Hint:* use ethyl oxalate as one ester)
(c) ethyl 1,3-dioxo-2-indanecarboxylate (II)

$$\text{I} \quad C_2H_5OOC \overset{H}{\diagup} \cdots \overset{O}{\diagdown} \cdots \overset{=O}{\underset{H}{\diagdown}} \overset{}{\underset{COOC_2H_5}{}}$$

$$\text{II} \quad \overset{O}{\underset{O}{\overset{\parallel}{C}}} \diagdown \text{CHCOOC}_2\text{H}_5$$

26.4 Acetoacetic ester synthesis of ketones

One of the most valuable methods of preparing ketones makes use of ethyl acetoacetate (acetoacetic ester) and is called the **acetoacetic ester synthesis of ketones.** This synthesis closely parallels the malonic ester synthesis of carboxylic acids (Sec. 25.9), and depends upon (a) the high acidity of the α-hydrogens of β-keto esters, and (b) the extreme ease with which β-keto acids undergo decarboxylation.

Acetoacetic ester is converted by sodium ethoxide into the sodioacetoacetic ester, which is then allowed to react with an alkyl halide to form an alkylacetoacetic ester (an ethyl alkylacetoacetate), $CH_3COCHRCOOC_2H_5$; if desired, the alkylation can be repeated to yield a dialkylacetoacetic ester, $CH_3COCRR'COOC_2H_5$. All alkylations are conducted in absolute alcohol.

When hydrolyzed by dilute aqueous alkali (or by acid) these monoalkyl- or dialkylacetoacetic esters yield the corresponding acids, $CH_3COCHRCOOH$ or $CH_3COCRR'COOH$, which undergo decarboxylation to form ketones, CH_3COCH_2R or $CH_3COCHRR'$. This loss of carbon dioxide occurs even more readily than from malonic acid, and may even take place before acidification of the hydrolysis mixture.

$CH_3COCH_2COOC_2H_5$
  Acetoacetic ester
      $\downarrow$ $^-OC_2H_5$
$CH_3COCHCOOC_2H_5{}^-$
      $\downarrow$ RX

$CH_3COCHCOOC_2H_5 \xrightarrow{\text{OH}^-} CH_3COCHCOO^- \xrightarrow[\text{or H}^+]{H_2O} CH_3COCHCOOH$
$\qquad | \qquad\qquad\qquad\qquad\qquad | \qquad\qquad\qquad\qquad\qquad |$
$\qquad R \qquad\qquad\qquad\qquad\qquad R \qquad\qquad\qquad\qquad\qquad R$
  Monoalkylacetoacetic ester $\downarrow$ $-CO_2$
      $\downarrow$ $^-OC_2H_5$ CH_3COCH_2R
$CH_3COCRCOOC_2H_5{}^-$ Monosubstituted
      $\downarrow$ R'X   acetone

$\qquad R' \qquad\qquad\qquad\qquad\qquad R' \qquad\qquad\qquad\qquad\qquad R'$
$\qquad | \qquad\qquad\qquad\qquad\qquad | \qquad\qquad\qquad\qquad\qquad |$
$CH_3COCCOOC_2H_5 \xrightarrow{\text{OH}^-} CH_3COCCOO^- \xrightarrow[\text{or H}^+]{H_2O} CH_3COCCOOH$
$\qquad | \qquad\qquad\qquad\qquad\qquad | \qquad\qquad\qquad\qquad\qquad |$
$\qquad R \qquad\qquad\qquad\qquad\qquad R \qquad\qquad\qquad\qquad\qquad R$
  Dialkylacetoacetic ester $\downarrow$ $-CO_2$

$\qquad\qquad\qquad\qquad\qquad\qquad\qquad\qquad\qquad\qquad CH_3COCHRR'$
$\qquad\qquad\qquad\qquad\qquad\qquad\qquad\qquad\qquad\qquad$ Disubstituted
$\qquad\qquad\qquad\qquad\qquad\qquad\qquad\qquad\qquad\qquad$ acetone

The acetoacetic ester synthesis of ketones yields an acetone molecule in which one or two hydrogens have been replaced by alkyl groups.

In planning an acetoacetic ester synthesis, as in planning a malonic ester synthesis, our problem is to select the proper alkyl halide or halides. To do this we have only to look at the structure of the ketone we want. For example, 5-methyl-2-hexanone can be considered as acetone in which one hydrogen has been replaced by an isobutyl group. In order to prepare this ketone by the acetoacetic ester synthesis we would have to use isobutyl bromide as the alkylating agent:

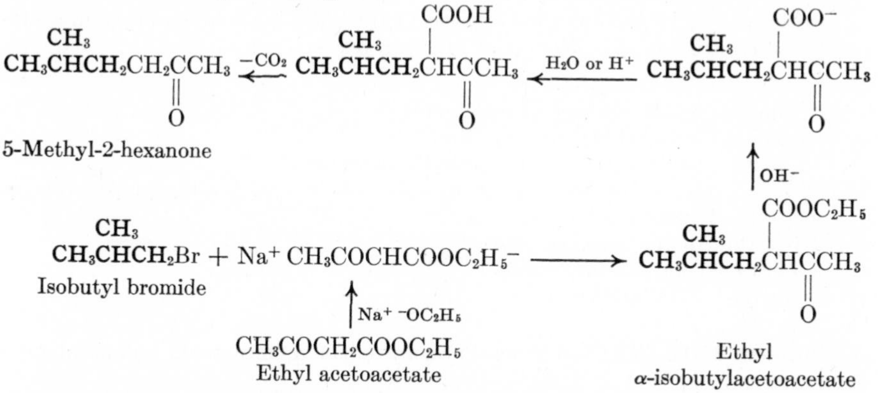

$$\underset{\text{5-Methyl-2-hexanone}}{CH_3CHCH_2CH_2CCH_3} \xleftarrow{-CO_2} \underset{}{CH_3CHCH_2CHCCH_3} \xleftarrow{H_2O \text{ or } H^+} CH_3CHCH_2CHCCH_3$$

with CH_3 groups, COOH, and COO⁻ substituents; O double bonds as shown.

$$\uparrow OH^-$$

$$\underset{\text{Isobutyl bromide}}{CH_3CHCH_2Br} + Na^+ CH_3COCHCOOC_2H_5{}^- \longrightarrow \underset{\text{Ethyl}\atop \alpha\text{-isobutylacetoacetate}}{CH_3CHCH_2CHCCH_3}$$

$$\uparrow Na^+ {}^-OC_2H_5$$

$$\underset{\text{Ethyl acetoacetate}}{CH_3COCH_2COOC_2H_5}$$

The isomeric ketone 3-methyl-2-hexanone can be considered as acetone in which one hydrogen has been replaced by an *n*-propyl group and a second hydrogen (on the same carbon) has been replaced by a methyl group; we must therefore use two alkyl halides, *n*-propyl bromide and methyl bromide:

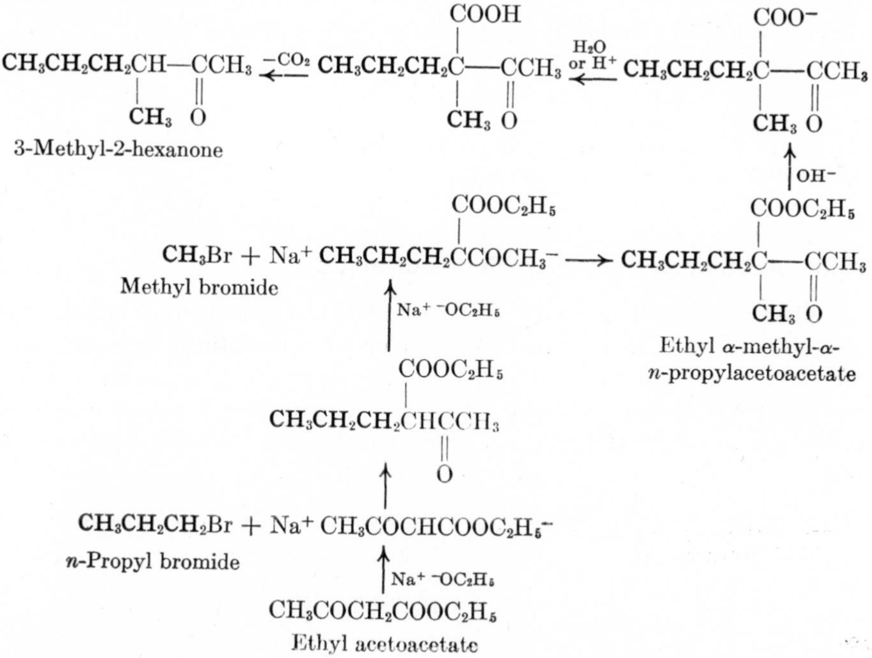

$$\underset{\text{3-Methyl-2-hexanone}}{CH_3CH_2CH_2CH—CCH_3} \xleftarrow{-CO_2} CH_3CH_2CH_2C—CCH_3 \xleftarrow[\text{or } H^+]{H_2O} CH_3CH_2CH_2C—CCH_3$$

with CH_3, O, COOH, COO⁻ substituents as shown.

$$\uparrow OH^-$$

$$\underset{\text{Methyl bromide}}{CH_3Br} + Na^+ CH_3CH_2CH_2CCOCH_3{}^- \longrightarrow \underset{\text{Ethyl }\alpha\text{-methyl-}\alpha\text{-}\atop n\text{-propylacetoacetate}}{CH_3CH_2CH_2C—CCH_3}$$

$$\uparrow Na^+ {}^-OC_2H_5$$

$$CH_3CH_2CH_2CHCCH_3$$

$$\uparrow$$

$$\underset{\textit{n}\text{-Propyl bromide}}{CH_3CH_2CH_2Br} + Na^+ CH_3COCHCOOC_2H_5{}^-$$

$$\uparrow Na^+ {}^-OC_2H_5$$

$$\underset{\text{Ethyl acetoacetate}}{CH_3COCH_2COOC_2H_5}$$

Problem 26.9 To what general class does the reaction between sodioaceto-acetic ester and an alkyl halide belong? Predict the relative yields using primary, secondary, and tertiary halides. Can aryl halides be used?

Problem 26.10 (a) Predict the product of the acetoacetic ester synthesis in which ethyl bromoacetate (why not bromoacetic *acid*?) is used as the alkyl halide. To what general class of compounds does this product belong? (b) Predict the product of the acetoacetic ester synthesis in which benzoyl chloride is used as the active halide; in which chloroacetone is used as the halide. To what general classes of compounds do these products belong?

Problem 26.11 Outline the synthesis of the following compounds from aceto-acetic ester, benzene, and alcohols of four carbons or less:

(a)–(c) the isomeric ketones:
       methyl *n*-butyl ketone (2-hexanone)
       methyl isobutyl ketone (4-methyl-2-pentanone)
       methyl *sec*-butyl ketone (3-methyl-2-pentanone)
(d) Why can the acetoacetic ester synthesis not be used for the preparation of methyl *tert*-butyl ketone?
(e) 2,4-pentanedione (*acetylacetone*)
(f) 2,5-hexanedione (*acetonylacetone*)
(g) 1-phenyl-1,4-pentanedione

Problem 26.12 The best general preparation of **α-keto acids** is illustrated by the sequence:

ethyl propionate + ethyl oxalate $\xrightarrow{\text{NaOC}_2\text{H}_5}$ A $(C_9H_{14}O_5)$

A + dil. H_2SO_4 $\xrightarrow{\text{boil}}$ CO_2 + $2C_2H_5OH$ + $CH_3CH_2\overset{\|}{\underset{O}{C}}COOH$ (α-ketobutyric acid)

What familiar reactions are involved? What is the structure of A?

Problem 26.13 Outline the synthesis from simple esters of:

(a) α-ketoisocaproic acid
(b) α-keto-β-phenylpropionic acid
(c) α-ketoglutaric acid
(d) *leucine* (α-aminoisocaproic acid). (*Hint:* see Sec. 19.11.)
(e) *glutamic acid* (α-aminoglutaric acid)

26.5 Acetoacetic ester synthesis of acids

When ethyl acetoacetate is treated with concentrated alkali, the Claisen condensation by which it was formed is essentially reversed, and the ester is cleaved to yield two moles of acetic acid (as a salt). Concentrated alkali has a similar effect on substituted acetoacetic esters, yielding a molecule of acetic acid and a molecule of a substituted acetic acid.

$$CH_3COCH_2COOC_2H_5 \xrightarrow{\text{conc. alkali}} CH_3COO^- + CH_3COO^- + C_2H_5OH$$

Ethyl acetoacetate

$$\downarrow H^+ \qquad \downarrow H^+$$

$$CH_3COOH \qquad CH_3COOH$$

Acetic acid

$$CH_3COCHRCOOC_2H_5 \xrightarrow{\text{conc. alkali}} CH_3COO^- + RCH_2COO^- + C_2H_5OH$$

Monosubstituted
acetoacetic ester

$$\downarrow H^+ \qquad \downarrow H^+$$

$$CH_3COOH \qquad RCH_2COOH$$

Acetic acid   Monosubstituted
acetic acid

$$CH_3COCRR'COOC_2H_5 \xrightarrow{\text{conc. alkali}} CH_3COO^- + RR'CHCOO^- + C_2H_5OH$$

Disubstituted
acetoacetic ester

$$\downarrow H^+ \qquad \downarrow H^+$$

$$CH_3COOH \qquad RR'CHCOOH$$

Acetic acid   Disubstituted
acetic acid

Before the development of the malonic ester synthesis, cleavage of substituted acetoacetic esters in this manner was an important method of synthesizing carboxylic acids; it is still used in certain cases. The reversed Claisen condensation occurs to an extent even during hydrolysis by dilute alkali, so that carboxylic acids are by-products in the synthesis of ketones.

Problem 26.14   Outline the steps in the synthesis of 2-hexanone via acetoacetic ester. What acids will be formed as by-products? Outline a procedure for purification of the desired ketone. (Remember that the alkylation is carried out in alcohol; that NaBr is formed; that aqueous base is used for hydrolysis; and that ethyl alcohol is a product of the hydrolysis.

26.6   Keto-enol tautomerism and ethyl acetoacetate

We have written the structural formula of ethyl acetoacetate as I, which contains a carbethoxy group, $-COOC_2H_5$, and a carbonyl group, $C=O$.

$$CH_3-C-CH_2-COOC_2H_5$$
$$\overset{||}{O}$$

I

In general, the properties of ethyl acetoacetate are consistent with this structure: as an ester it undergoes hydrolysis to a carboxylic acid; as a ketone it reacts with hydroxylamine, phenylhydrazine, or hydrogen cyanide to form an oxime, a phenylhydrazone, or a cyanohydrin.

But, besides these, ethyl acetoacetate has *another* set of properties: ones that esters and ketones do *not* usually have. It reacts with ferric chloride to give a red color similar to the one given by phenol (Sec. 22.22) and it instantly decolorizes bromine solutions. How are these unexpected properties to be accounted for?

For the answer to this question let us look at work reported in 1911 by Ludwig Knorr of the University of Jena. When Knorr cooled an ether–hexane solution of ordinary ethyl acetoacetate to $-78°$, a crystalline solid of m.p. $-39°$ separated. This compound did not decolorize bromine instantaneously, and did not give an immediate red color with ferric chloride. When Knorr passed dry hydrogen chloride into a suspension in petroleum ether of the sodium salt of ethyl acetoacetate, an oil separated. This substance *did* react instantaneously with bromine and with ferric chloride.

Each of these two substances retained its identity for long periods at $-78°$, and for weeks even at room temperature if acids and bases were carefully excluded. In the presence of an acid or base, however, both substances were rapidly converted into the same material, ordinary ethyl acetoacetate.

Ordinary ethyl acetoacetate has two sets of properties because it is a mixture of two compounds: a **keto** form and an **enol** form.

$$CH_3-\underset{\underset{O}{\|}}{C}-CH_2-\underset{\underset{O}{\|}}{C}-OC_2H_5 \;\underset{\longleftarrow}{\overset{\longrightarrow}{\;}}\; H^+ + CH_3-\underset{\underset{O}{\|}}{C}=CH=\underset{\underset{O}{\|}}{C}-OC_2H_5 \;\overset{\longrightarrow}{\underset{\longleftarrow}{\;}}$$

Keto form

Less soluble form:
crystallizes at $-78°$
Reacts with NH_2OH

                     $\overset{\ominus}{}$
                 Carbanion

$$CH_3-\underset{\underset{OH}{|}}{C}=CH-\underset{\underset{O}{\|}}{C}-OC_2H_5$$

Enol form

Formed more rapidly
by acidification of salt
Reacts with Br_2

These are tautomers and exist in equilibrium with each other (see Sec. 6.12). When hydroxylamine, for example, is added, the keto compound forms the oxime; the equilibrium shifts to provide more keto compound which also reacts, and so on, until the entire mixture is converted into the oxime. When bromine is added, the enol compound reacts, and the equilibrium shifts to replace the enol consumed. The mixture thus gives reactions of either component.

Knorr had actually isolated the components of a tautomeric mixture. When a solution of ordinary ethyl acetoacetate is cooled the less soluble component, the keto compound, separates; equilibrium shifts until essentially all the ester has crystallized. When the salt of ethyl acetoacetate is treated with acid, hydrogen ion attacks oxygen of the carbanion faster than it attacks carbon, yielding the enol compound.

26.7   Composition of keto-enol mixtures

What are the proportions of the keto and enol tautomers of ethyl acetoacetate in the equilibrium mixture? One way to answer this question was developed by Kurt Meyer of the University of Munich: bromine is added to a keto–enol mixture until it is no longer rapidly decolorized; the number of moles of bromine consumed is considered to be equal to the number of moles of enol originally present. The analysis depends upon the fact that bromine reacts much faster with an enol than with a keto compound, and that bromination is faster than formation of the enol from the keto compound. The Kurt Meyer method has been improved by modifications that tend to reduce the error due to shifting of the equilibrium during the titration.

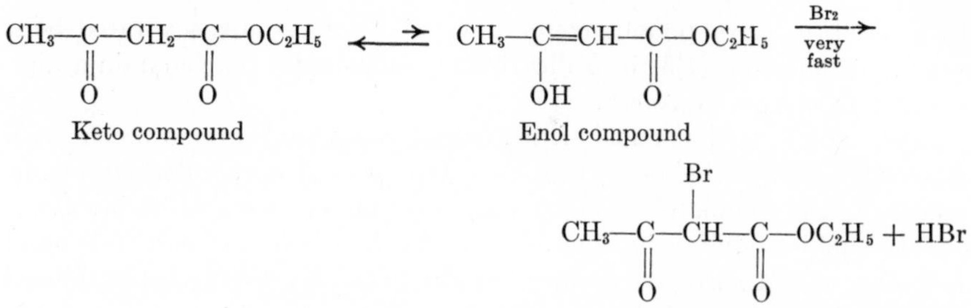

$$CH_3-\underset{\underset{O}{\|}}{C}-CH_2-\underset{\underset{O}{\|}}{C}-OC_2H_5 \; \rightleftharpoons \; CH_3-\underset{\underset{OH}{|}}{C}=CH-\underset{\underset{O}{\|}}{C}-OC_2H_5 \; \xrightarrow[\text{very fast}]{Br_2}$$

Keto compound   Enol compound

$$CH_3-\underset{\underset{O}{\|}}{C}-\underset{\overset{Br}{|}}{CH}-\underset{\underset{O}{\|}}{C}-OC_2H_5 + HBr$$

Bromoketone

The speed with which the enol undergoes bromination is readily under-standable: the electrophilic bromine rapidly attacks the carbon–carbon double bond to yield carbonium ion I, which is simply the protonated form of the bromoketone.

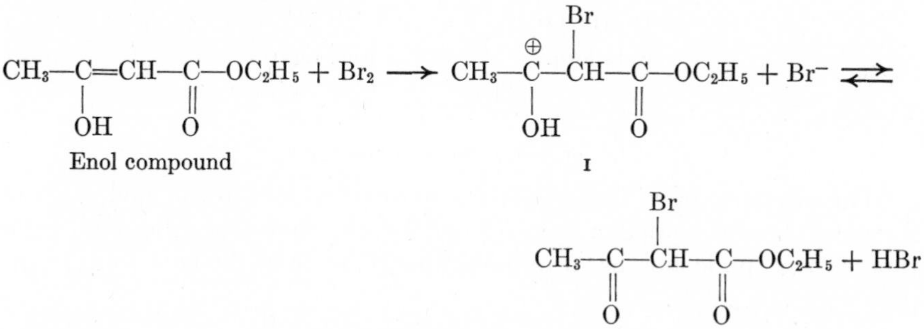

$$CH_3-\underset{\underset{OH}{|}}{C}=CH-\underset{\underset{O}{\|}}{C}-OC_2H_5 + Br_2 \longrightarrow CH_3-\underset{\underset{OH}{|}}{\overset{\oplus}{C}}-\underset{\overset{Br}{|}}{CH}-\underset{\underset{O}{\|}}{C}-OC_2H_5 + Br^- \rightleftharpoons$$

Enol compound   I

$$CH_3-\underset{\underset{O}{\|}}{C}-\underset{\overset{Br}{|}}{CH}-\underset{\underset{O}{\|}}{C}-OC_2H_5 + HBr$$

Liquid ethyl acetoacetate contains about 8% of the enol tautomer, in marked contrast to a simple ketone like acetone, which contains less than 0.001% of the enol. The enol contents of a number of other car-bonyl compounds are listed in Table 26.2.

TABLE 26.2

PER CENT ENOL IN CARBONYL COMPOUNDS

Name	Formula	% Enol in pure liquid
Acetoacetaldehyde	$CH_3\underset{\underset{O}{\|}}{C}CH_2\underset{\underset{O}{\|}}{C}H$	98
Acetylacetone	$CH_3\underset{\underset{O}{\|}}{C}CH_2\underset{\underset{O}{\|}}{C}CH_3$	80
Ethyl benzoylacetate	$C_6H_5\underset{\underset{O}{\|}}{C}CH_2\underset{\underset{O}{\|}}{C}OC_2H_5$	21
Ethyl acetoacetate	$CH_3\underset{\underset{O}{\|}}{C}CH_2\underset{\underset{O}{\|}}{C}OC_2H_5$	8
Acetone	$CH_3\underset{\underset{O}{\|}}{C}CH_3$	2.5×10^{-4}

In general, it is compounds containing two C=O groups separated by a single carbon atom (**1,3- or β-dicarbonyl compounds**) that contain a high percentage of enol tautomer.

Just why it is that enols of dicarbonyl compounds are so much more stable (relative to the keto form) than the enols of simple carbonyl compounds is not completely understood. Two factors seem to be involved: (a) the enol is stabilized by conjugation of the carbon–carbon double bond with the second carbonyl group; (b) the enol may be further stabilized by chelation, that is, by formation of an intramolecular hydrogen bond between the enolic hydroxyl and the second carbonyl group (see Sec. 22.2).

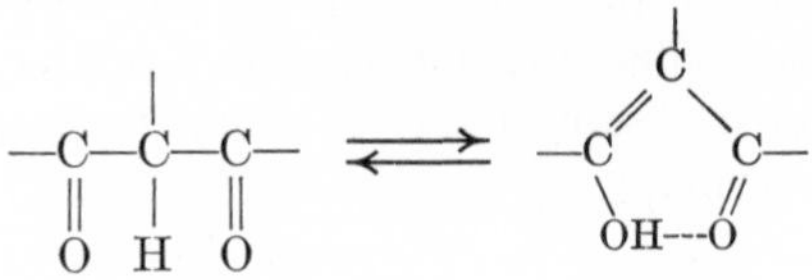

Keto form   Enol form

Conjugation
Chelation

1,3- or β-Dicarbonyl compounds

The existence of an intramolecular hydrogen bond in the enol of ethyl acetoacetate, for example, is indicated by the fact that the enol, even though it is an alcohol, has a lower boiling point than the keto form (compare with Sec. 22.2).

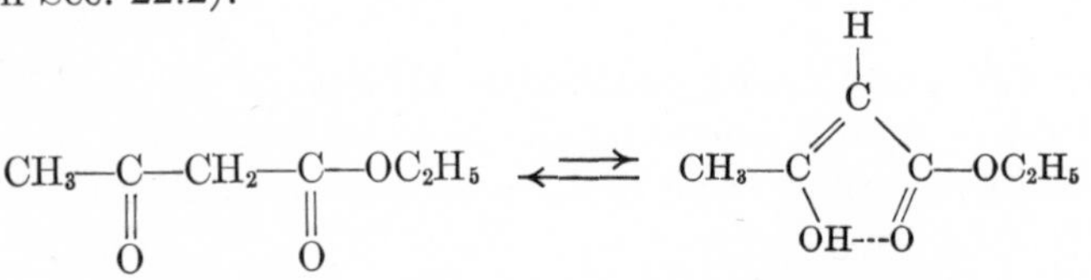

Keto form   Enol form
B.p. 40–41°/2mm   *B.p. 33°/2mm*

Ethyl acetoacetate

Problem 26.15 Why does allyl alcohol (b.p. 97°) have a higher boiling point than the carbonyl compound of the same molecular weight, acetone (b.p. 56°)?

Problem 26.16 The refractive index at 10° is 1.4217 for the pure keto form of ethyl acetoacetate, 1.4480 for the pure enol form, and 1.4235 for the equilibrium mixture. Assuming a linear relationship between composition and refractive index, calculate the per cent enol.

26.8 Acids and bases and keto-enol tautomerism

Acids and bases, we have seen, tremendously speed up interconversion of keto and enol forms. The following equations show that this effect is quite reasonable.

Base-catalyzed tautomerization

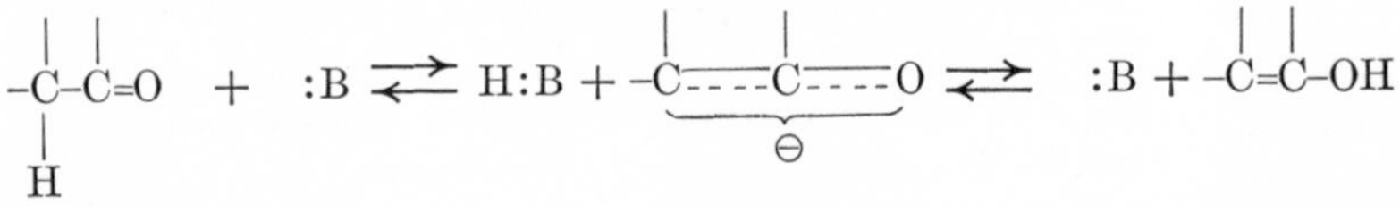

Keto form   Base   Hybrid anion   Base   Enol form

I

Acid-catalyzed tautomerization

$$
\underset{\substack{\text{Keto form} \quad \text{Acid}}}{\overset{\begin{array}{cc}|&|\\-\text{C}-\text{C}=\text{O}\\|\\\text{H}\end{array}}{} + \text{H:B}} \quad \rightleftarrows \quad
\underset{\substack{\text{Cation}\\\text{II}}}{\overset{\begin{array}{cc}|&|\\:\text{B} + -\text{C}-\text{C}-\text{OH}\\|&\oplus\\\text{H}\end{array}}{}} \quad \rightleftarrows \quad
\underset{\substack{\text{Acid}\quad\text{Enol form}}}{\overset{\begin{array}{cc}|&|\\\text{H:B} + -\text{C}=\text{C}-\text{OH}\end{array}}{}}
$$

A base abstracts hydrogen ion — from either keto or enol form — to yield the hybrid anion I. This anion can then recombine with hydrogen ion, at carbon to yield the keto form or at oxygen to yield the enol form.

An acid donates hydrogen ion — either to the carbon–oxygen bond of the keto form or to the carbon–carbon double bond of the enol form — to yield cation II. The cation can then lose hydrogen ion, from carbon to yield the enol form or from oxygen to yield the keto form.

In some cases at least, interconversion is caused by the concerted attack by an acid and a base on a single molecule. (*Problem:* show by suitable formulas how this would take place.)

These reactions of acids and bases with ketones are important to our understanding not only of keto-enol tautomerization but also of many other properties of ketones. For example, halogenation of ketones is catalyzed both by acids and by bases; the following mechanisms have been proposed.

(1) $\text{CH}_3\text{CCH}_3 + :\text{B} \quad \rightleftarrows \quad \text{H:B} + \text{CH}_3\text{C} = \text{CH}_2$
$\qquad\;\;\overset{\|}{\text{O}}\qquad\qquad\qquad\qquad\qquad\overset{\|}{\underset{\ominus}{\text{O}}}$

Base-catalyzed

(2) $\text{CH}_3\text{C} = \text{CH}_2 + \text{Br}_2 \longrightarrow \text{CH}_3\text{CCH}_2\text{Br} + \text{Br}^-$
$\qquad\;\overset{\|}{\underset{\ominus}{\text{O}}}\qquad\qquad\qquad\qquad\quad\overset{\|}{\text{O}}$

bromination

(1) $\text{CH}_3\text{CCH}_3 + \text{H:B} \quad \rightleftarrows \quad :\text{B} + \text{CH}_3\overset{\oplus}{\text{C}}\text{CH}_3$
$\qquad\;\;\overset{\|}{\text{O}}\qquad\qquad\qquad\qquad\qquad\overset{|}{\text{OH}}$

(2) $\text{CH}_3\overset{\oplus}{\text{C}}\text{CH}_3 + :\text{B} \quad \rightleftarrows \quad \text{H:B} + \text{CH}_3\text{C}=\text{CH}_2$
$\qquad\;\;\overset{|}{\text{OH}}\qquad\qquad\qquad\qquad\qquad\overset{|}{\text{OH}}$

Acid-catalyzed bromination

(3) $\text{CH}_3\text{C}=\text{CH}_2 + \text{Br}_2 \longrightarrow \text{CH}_3\overset{\oplus}{\text{C}}\text{CH}_2\text{Br} \xrightarrow{\;:\text{B}\;} \text{H:B} + \text{CH}_3\text{CCH}_2\text{Br}$
$\qquad\;\;\overset{|}{\text{OH}}\qquad\qquad\qquad\qquad\overset{|}{\text{OH}}\qquad\qquad\qquad\qquad\overset{\|}{\text{O}}$

Problem 26.17 Account for each of the following facts: (a) The rate of base-catalyzed bromination of acetone depends only upon [acetone] and [base], and is independent of [Br$_2$]. (*Hint:* see Sec. 13.12.) (b) At a given [acetone] and [base], base-catalyzed bromination and iodination of acetone proceed at identical rates. (Compare Problem 13.3, page 376.) (c) The rate of acid-catalyzed bromination of acetone depends only upon [acetone] and [acid], and is independent of [Br$_2$].

Problem 26.18 Optically active ketones like phenyl *sec*-butyl ketone are racemized in the presence of base. Suggest a mechanism for this racemization that would account for the fact that at the same [base], racemization and bromination of an optically active ketone proceed at identical rates. (*Hint:* see Problem 19.3, page 525.)

Problem 26.19   Optically active ketones like phenyl *sec*-butyl ketone are racemized by acids. Suggest a mechanism for this racemization that would account for the fact that under comparable conditions, the rate of racemization of an optically active ketone is the same as the rate of hydrogen–deuterium exchange:

$$
\underset{\substack{\| \ \ | \\ O \ \ H}}{C_6H_5\!-\!\overset{\overset{\displaystyle CH_3}{|}}{C}\!-\!C\!-\!CH_2CH_3} + D\!:\!B \ \rightleftarrows \ \underset{\substack{\| \ \ | \\ O \ \ D}}{C_6H_5\!-\!\overset{\overset{\displaystyle CH_3}{|}}{C}\!-\!C\!-\!CH_2CH_3} + H\!:\!B
$$

Problem 26.20   The haloform test (Sec. 12.11) depends upon the fact that three hydrogens on the same carbon atom are successively replaced by halogen. Using acetone as an example, show why the carbon that suffers the initial substitution should be the preferred site of further substitution. (*Hint:* see Sec. 16.14.)

Problem 26.21   (a) Suggest a mechanism for the base-catalyzed racemization of an optically active acid such as mandelic acid, $C_6H_5CHOHCOOH$. (b) Why is α-methylmandelic acid, $C_6H_5COH(CH_3)COOH$, not racemized by base?

PROBLEMS

1. Give the structures of the principal products expected from the reaction in the presence of sodium ethoxide of:

(a) ethyl *n*-butyrate
(b) ethyl phenylacetate
(c) ethyl isovalerate
(d) ethyl formate and ethyl propionate
(e) ethyl oxalate and ethyl succinate
(f) ethyl benzoate and ethyl phenylacetate
(g) ethyl propionate and cyclohexanone
(h) ethyl phenylacetate and acetophenone
(i) ethyl carbonate and acetophenone

2. What would each product in Problem 1, parts (a) through (f), yield (i) when hydrolyzed and decarboxylated? (ii) When cleaved with concentrated alkali?

3. Sodium ethoxide is added to a mixture of ethyl acetate and ethyl propionate. (a) Give the structures of the products expected. (b) Would this reaction be a good method of synthesizing any one of these?

4. Outline the synthesis of each of the following from acetoacetic ester and any other needed reagents:

(a) methyl ethyl ketone
(b) 3-ethyl-2-pentanone
(c) 3-ethyl-2-hexanone
(d) 5-methyl-2-heptanone
(e) 3,6-dimethyl-2-heptanone
(f) 4-oxo-2-methylpentanoic acid
(g) γ-hydroxy-*n*-valeric acid

(h) 3-methyl-2-hexanol
(i) 2,5-dimethylheptane
(j) β-methylcaproic acid
(k) β-methylbutyric acid
(l) methylsuccinic acid
(m) 2,5-hexanediol

5. Outline all steps in a possible synthesis of each of the following via the Claisen condensation, using any needed reagents:

(a) $C_6H_5COCH(CH_3)COOC_2H_5$
(b) $C_6H_5CH_2COCH(C_6H_5)COOC_2H_5$
(c) $C_2H_5OOCCOCH(CH_3)COOC_2H_5$
(d) $C_6H_5CH(CHO)COOC_2H_5$
(e) $(CH_3)_2CHCOCH_2COCH_3$
(f) $C_6H_5COCH_2COCH_3$

(g) 2-benzoylcyclohexanone

(h) $C_2H_5OOCCH(CHO)CH_2COOC_2H_5$

(i) 1,2-cyclopentanedione (*Hint:* see Problem 26.8, page 703.)

(j) $CH_3CH_2CH_2COCOOC_2H_5$ (*Hint:* see Problem 26.12, page 706.)

6. Draw stereochemical formulas of the products expected from each of the following reactions. Indicate which products as ordinarily isolated would be optically active, and which would be optically inactive.

(a) (+)-1-chloro-2-methylbutane (for its configuration see page 328) + sodio-acetoacetic ester, followed by hydrolysis and decarboxylation

(b) product of (a) + H_2, Ni

(c) product of (a) + C_2H_5MgBr, then H_2O

(d) product of (c) + PBr_3, then Zn, H^+ $\longrightarrow$ $C_{10}H_{22}$

(e) Answer part (a) for (+)-*sec*-butyl bromide (for its configuration see page 512).

7. What product would you expect from the hydrolysis by dilute alkali of 2-carbethoxycyclopentanone (see Problem 26.4, page 702)? Suggest a method of synthesis of 2-methylcyclopentanone.

8. (a) How could you synthesize 2,7-octanedione? (*Hint:* see Problem 25.28, page 690.) (b) Actually, the expected ketone reacts further to give

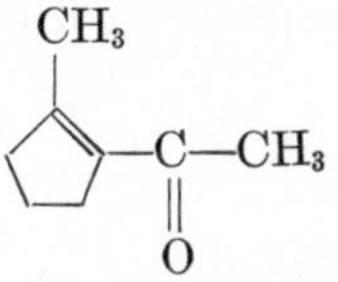

How does this last reaction occur? To what general type does it belong? (c) How could you synthesize 2,6-heptanedione? (d) What would happen to this ketone under the conditions of (b)?

9. Methyl ethyl ketone can be made to undergo the Claisen condensation to yield either of two products, depending upon experimental conditions. (a) What are these two products? (b) How could you tell quickly and simply which product you had obtained? (*Note:* use ethyl benzoate as the ester.)

10. The acetylenic ester $CH_3—C\equiv C—COOC_2H_5$ can be converted into ethyl acetoacetate. (a) How? (b) Outline a synthesis of the acetylenic ester from acetylene and any needed reagents.

11. The structure of *nerolidol*, $C_{15}H_{26}O$, a terpene found in oil of neroli, was established by the following synthesis:

geranyl chloride (RCl) + sodioacetoacetic ester $\longrightarrow$ A ($RC_6H_9O_3$)

A + $Ba(OH)_2$, then H^+, warm $\longrightarrow$ B (RC_3H_5O)

B + $NaC\equiv CH$, then H_2O $\longrightarrow$ C (RC_5H_7O)

C $\xrightarrow{\text{reduction}}$ D (RC_5H_9O), nerolidol

(a) Give the structure of nerolidol, using R for the geranyl group.

(b) Referring to Problem 18, page 360, what is the complete structure of nerolidol?

12. The structure of *menthone*, $C_{10}H_{18}O$, a terpene found in peppermint oil, was first established by synthesis in the following way:

ethyl β-methylpimelate + sodium ethoxide, then H_2O $\longrightarrow$ E ($C_{10}H_{16}O_3$)

E + sodium ethoxide, then isopropyl iodide $\longrightarrow$ F ($C_{13}H_{22}O_3$)

F + OH^-, heat; then H^+; then heat $\longrightarrow$ menthone

(a) What structures for menthone are consistent with this synthesis? (b) On the basis of the isoprene rule (Sec. 6.21) which structure is the more likely? (c) On vigorous reduction menthone yields *p-menthane*, 4-isopropyl-1-methylcyclohexane. On this basis what structure or structures are most likely for menthone?

HYDROXY ACIDS

27.1 Preparation

The method by which a hydroxy acid is prepared depends upon the relative positions of the —OH and —COOH groups. **α-Hydroxy acids** are most readily prepared via cyanohydrins:

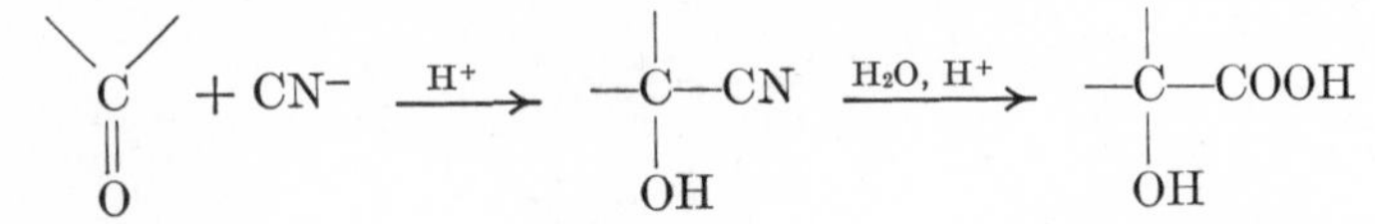

$$\underset{\substack{\text{Carbonyl} \\ \text{compound}}}{\overset{\displaystyle \underset{\|}{\underset{O}{C}}}{\diagdown \diagup}} + CN^{-} \xrightarrow{\ H^{+}\ } \underset{\substack{\text{Cyanohydrin}}}{-\underset{\underset{OH}{|}}{C}-CN} \xrightarrow{\ H_2O,\ H^{+}\ } \underset{\substack{\alpha\text{-Hydroxy acid}}}{-\underset{\underset{OH}{|}}{C}-COOH}$$

β-Hydroxy acids are generally prepared by the Reformatsky reaction, which is discussed in the next section. **β- and γ-Hydroxy acids** can be prepared from the corresponding β- and γ-keto esters by hydrogenation. For example:

$$\underset{\text{Ethyl acetoacetate}}{CH_3COCH_2COOC_2H_5} \xrightarrow{\ H_2,\ Ni,\ 125^\circ,\ 100\ atm.\ } \underset{\text{Ethyl }\beta\text{-hydroxybutyrate}}{CH_3CHOHCH_2COOC_2H_5}$$

$$\underset{\substack{\text{Ethyl }\gamma\text{-ketovalerate} \\ \text{(Ethyl levulinate)}}}{CH_3COCH_2CH_2COOC_2H_5} \xrightarrow{\ H_2,\ Ni,\ 100^\circ,\ 100\ atm.\ } \underset{\text{Ethyl }\gamma\text{-hydroxyvalerate}}{CH_3CHOHCH_2CH_2COOC_2H_5}$$

γ- and δ-Hydroxy acids are most frequently encountered as products derived from carbohydrates (Sec. 29.6).

In general, the methods of synthesis are adaptations of the familiar chemistry of alcohols and acids: where hydrolysis of a nitrile yields a carboxylic acid, hydrolysis of a hydroxy nitrile yields a hydroxy acid; where reduction of a ketone yields an alcohol, reduction of a keto acid yields a hydroxy acid.

Problem 27.1 Outline a possible synthesis of:
(a) glycolic acid (hydroxyacetic acid, $HOCH_2COOH$) from acetic acid
(b) lactic acid (α-hydroxypropionic acid, $CH_3CHOHCOOH$, the acid of sour milk) from acetylene
(c) α-hydroxyisobutyric acid, $(CH_3)_2COHCOOH$, from propylene
(d) mandelic acid (hydroxyphenylacetic acid, $C_6H_5CHOHCOOH$) from toluene
(e) γ-hydroxyvaleric acid, $CH_3CHOHCH_2CH_2COOH$, from ethyl acetate

(f) γ-hydroxy-α-methylvaleric acid, $CH_3CHOHCH_2CH(CH_3)COOH$, from simple esters (*Hint:* for (e) and (f) see Problem 26.10, page 706.)

TABLE 27.1

HYDROXY ACIDS

Name	Formula	M.p., °C	Solub., g/100 g H₂O at 25°	K_1
Glycolic	HOCH₂COOH	80	v.sol.	15×10^{-5}
(+)-Lactic	CH₃CHOHCOOH	53	v.sol.	
(±)-Lactic	CH₃CHOHCOOH	17	∞	15
(±)-α-Hydroxybutyric	CH₃CH₂CHOHCOOH	43		
(±)-Mandelic	C₆H₅CHOHCOOH	120	22	43
(−)-Glyceric	HOCH₂CHOHCOOH		∞	
(−)-Malic	HOOCCH₂CHOHCOOH	101	v.sol.	39
(±)-Malic	HOOCCH₂CHOHCOOH	130	138	40
(+)-Tartaric	HOOCCHOHCHOHCOOH	170	147	90
(−)-Tartaric	HOOCCHOHCHOHCOOH	170	147	90
(±)-Tartaric	HOOCCHOHCHOHCOOH	205	21	117
Mesotartaric	HOOCCHOHCHOHCOOH	140	167	77
Citric	HOOCCH₂C(OH)(COOH)CH₂COOH	135	240	88
β-Propiolactone		− 33		
γ-Butyrolactone		liq.	∞	
γ-Valerolactone		− 31		

27.2 Preparation of β-hydroxy acids. Reformatsky reaction

Aldehydes and ketones react with α-bromo esters and metallic zinc to yield β-hydroxy esters. This reaction, known as the **Reformatsky reaction,** is the most important method of preparing β-hydroxy acids and their derivatives. For example:

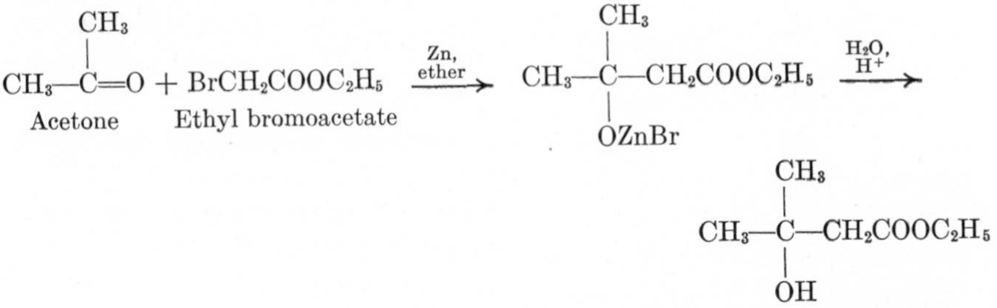

Ethyl β-hydroxyisovalerate
Ethyl 3-hydroxy-3-methylbutanoate

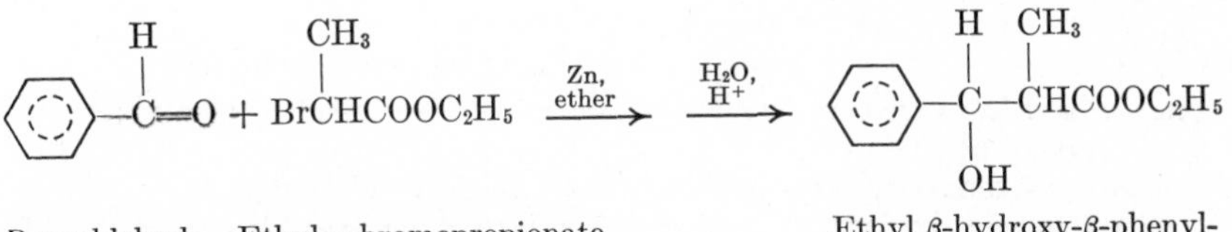

Benzaldehyde   Ethyl α-bromopropionate

Ethyl β-hydroxy-β-phenyl-
α-methylpropionate

The α-bromo ester and zinc react in absolute ether to yield an intermediate organozinc compound, which then adds to the carbonyl group of the aldehyde or ketone. The formation and subsequent reaction of the organozinc compound is similar to the formation and reaction of a Grignard reagent. Zinc is used in place of magnesium simply because the organozinc compounds are less reactive than Grignard reagents; they do not react with the ester function but only with the aldehyde or ketone.

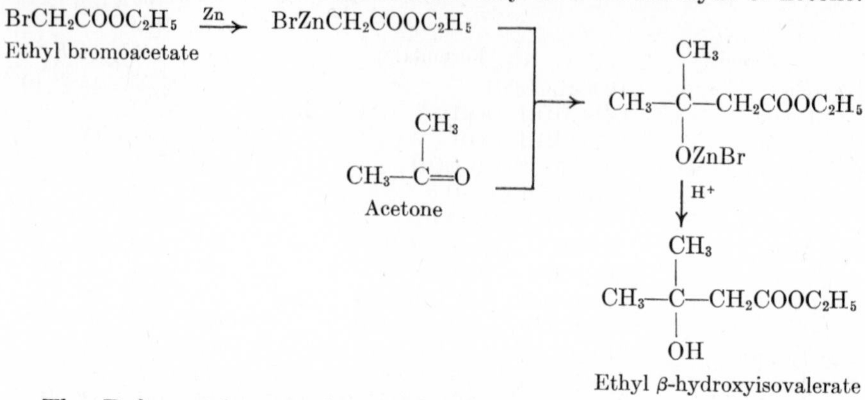

$$BrCH_2COOC_2H_5 \xrightarrow{Zn} BrZnCH_2COOC_2H_5$$

Ethyl bromoacetate

$$
\begin{array}{c}
CH_3 \\
| \\
CH_3-C=O \\
\text{Acetone}
\end{array}
$$

$$
\begin{array}{c}
CH_3 \\
| \\
CH_3-C-CH_2COOC_2H_5 \\
| \\
OZnBr
\end{array}
\downarrow H^+
$$

$$
\begin{array}{c}
CH_3 \\
| \\
CH_3-C-CH_2COOC_2H_5 \\
| \\
OH
\end{array}
$$

Ethyl β-hydroxyisovalerate

The Reformatsky reaction takes place only with esters containing bromine in the *alpha* position, and hence necessarily yields *beta*-hydroxy esters. By the proper selection of ester and carbonyl compound, a wide variety of rather complicated β-hydroxy carboxylic acids can be prepared.

Like β-hydroxyaldehydes and -ketones (Sec. 23.16), β-hydroxyesters and -acids are readily dehydrated. The unsaturated compounds thus obtained (chiefly α,β-unsaturated) can be hydrogenated to saturated carboxylic acids. Extended in this way the Reformatsky reaction is a useful general method for preparing carboxylic acids, competing with such methods as the malonic ester synthesis (Sec. 25.9) and the Perkin condensation (Sec. 23.20). In general:

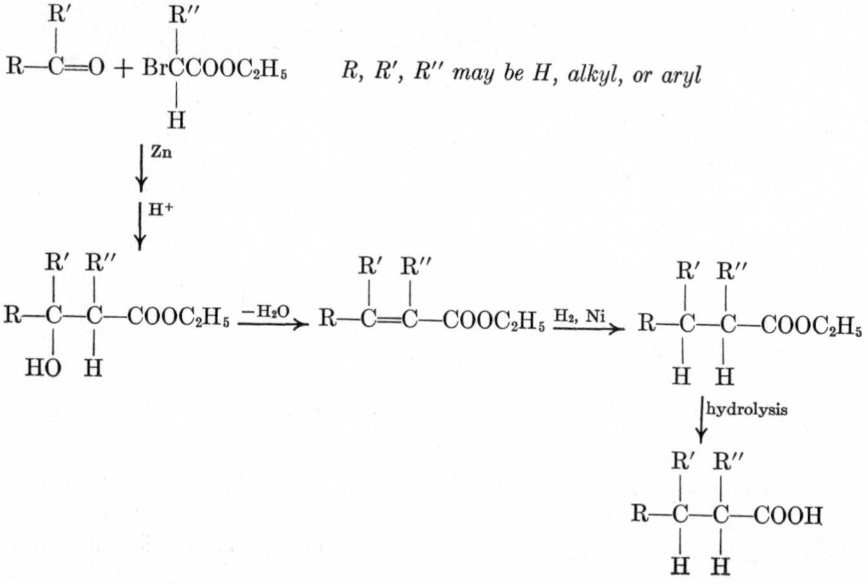

$$
\begin{array}{cc}
R' & R'' \\
| & | \\
R-C=O & + BrCCOOC_2H_5 \\
& | \\
& H
\end{array}
\qquad R, R', R'' \text{ may be } H, \text{ alkyl, or aryl}
$$

$$\downarrow Zn$$

$$\downarrow H^+$$

$$
\begin{array}{c}
R' \; R'' \\
| \;\; | \\
R-C-C-COOC_2H_5 \\
| \;\; | \\
HO \; H
\end{array}
\xrightarrow{-H_2O}
\begin{array}{c}
R' \; R'' \\
| \;\; | \\
R-C=C-COOC_2H_5
\end{array}
\xrightarrow{H_2, Ni}
\begin{array}{c}
R' \; R'' \\
| \;\; | \\
R-C-C-COOC_2H_5 \\
| \;\; | \\
H \; H
\end{array}
$$

$$\downarrow \text{hydrolysis}$$

$$
\begin{array}{c}
R' \; R'' \\
| \;\; | \\
R-C-C-COOH \\
| \;\; | \\
H \; H
\end{array}
$$

In planning the synthesis of a carboxylic acid by the Reformatsky reaction, our problem is to select the proper starting materials; to do this we have only to look at the structure of the product we want. For example:

Acid wanted:	Requires:	Starting materials:

$$CH_3—\underset{\underset{CH_3}{|}}{CH}—\underset{\underset{H}{|}}{CH}—COOH \qquad \begin{cases} R = CH_3- \\ R' = CH_3- \\ R'' = H- \end{cases} \qquad CH_3—\underset{\underset{CH_3}{|}}{C}{=}O + Br\underset{\underset{H}{|}}{C}HCOOC_2H_5$$

$$C_6H_5—\underset{\underset{H}{|}}{\overset{\overset{H}{|}}{C}}—\underset{\underset{H}{|}}{\overset{\overset{CH_3}{|}}{C}}—COOH \qquad \begin{cases} R = C_6H_5- \\ R' = H- \\ R'' = CH_3- \end{cases} \qquad C_6H_5—\underset{\underset{H}{|}}{C}{=}O + Br\underset{\underset{CH_3}{|}}{C}HCOOC_2H_5$$

Problem 27.2 Outline the syntheses of the following acids by the indicated methods:

(a) *n*-valeric acid: Reformatsky, malonic ester
(b) α,γ-dimethylvaleric acid: Reformatsky, malonic ester
(c) cinnamic acid: Reformatsky, Perkin, Knoevenagel (see Problem 25.29, page 690)

Problem 27.3 When an ester like ethyl α-bromoisobutyrate is used in a Reformatsky reaction, the resulting β-hydroxy ester cannot yield an α,β-unsaturated ester upon dehydration. What will it give? Will this make any difference if the ultimate goal is a saturated acid?

Problem 27.4 Outline the synthesis of the following, starting from benzaldehyde and ethyl bromoacetate:

(a) $C_6H_5CH_2CH_2COOH$ (b) $C_6H_5CH_2CH_2CHO$ (c) $C_6H_5CH_2CH_2CH_2CH_2COOH$

27.3 Dehydration. Lactone formation

The different kinds of hydroxy acid undergo dehydration in different ways: the product obtained from a particular hydroxy acid depends upon the location of the —OH group with respect to the —COOH group.

We have seen that a β-hydroxyacid or -ester, (like a β-hydroxyaldehyde or -ketone, Sec. 23.16) loses water extremely easily to form unsaturated compounds. Dehydration can be brought about by heating with acid, although many hydroxy compounds lose water spontaneously during distillation.

$$R—\underset{\underset{HO}{|}}{\overset{\overset{H}{|}}{C}}—\underset{\underset{H}{|}}{\overset{\overset{R'}{|}}{C}}—COOH \xrightarrow{acid,\ heat} R—\underset{}{\overset{\overset{H}{|}}{C}}{=}\underset{}{\overset{\overset{R'}{|}}{C}}—COOH + H_2O$$

$$\underset{\text{β-Hydroxy acid}}{} \qquad\qquad\qquad \underset{\substack{\text{α,β-Unsaturated acid}\\ \textit{Major product}}}{}$$

Although the major product is usually the α,β-unsaturated compound, considerable β,γ-unsaturated product is also obtained. (Does this make any difference in the synthesis of saturated carboxylic acids?) A pure

α,β-unsaturated acid is better prepared by dehydrohalogenation of an α-haloacid.

When an α-hydroxy acid is heated, it loses water by the process of esterification, which takes place in such a way as to form a six-membered ring. The product is called a *lactide* (named after the important α-hydroxy acid, lactic acid, $CH_3CHOHCOOH$).

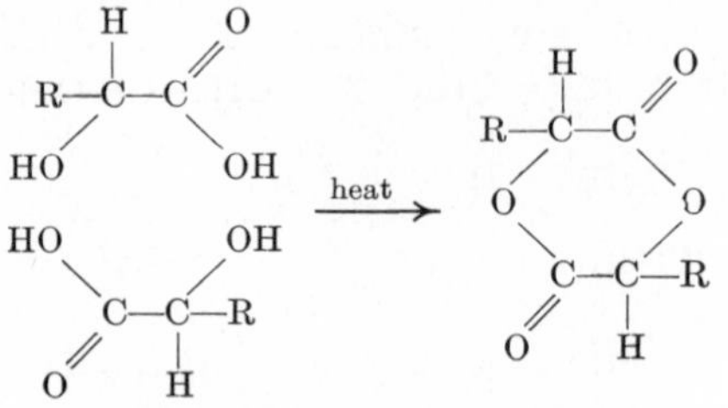

An α-hydroxy acid   A lactide
2 moles   *A cyclic ester: six-membered ring*

A γ- or δ-hydroxy acid also loses water by esterification, but this time the reaction occurs within a single molecule to yield a cyclic ester known as a **lactone.** Here again the course of reaction is determined by the tendency to form a five- or six-membered ring. Lactonization occurs spontaneously to give an equilibrium mixture that is chiefly lactone; treatment with base (actually saponification of an ester) rapidly opens the lactone ring to give the open-chain salt.

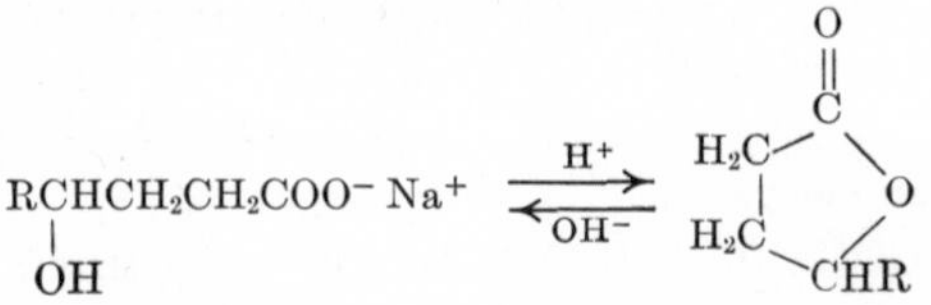

$$RCHCH_2CH_2COO^- Na^+ \quad \underset{OH^-}{\overset{H^+}{\rightleftarrows}}$$
$$|$$
$$OH$$

Salt of a   A γ-lactone
γ-hydroxy acid   *A cyclic ester: five-membered ring*

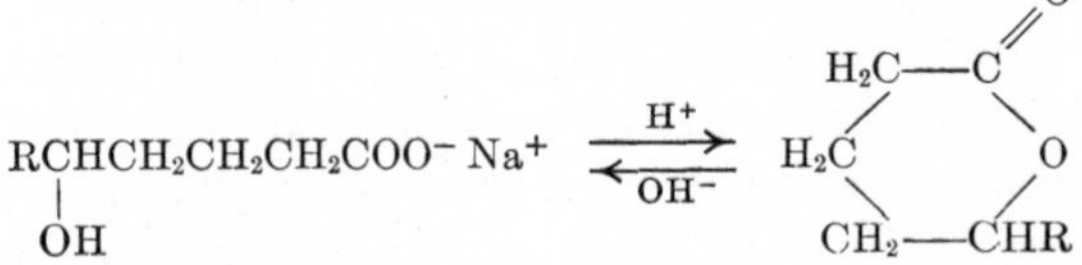

$$RCHCH_2CH_2CH_2COO^- Na^+ \quad \underset{OH^-}{\overset{H^+}{\rightleftarrows}}$$
$$|$$
$$OH$$

Salt of a   A δ-lactone
δ-hydroxy acid   *A cyclic ester: six-membered ring*

We shall encounter lactones again in our study of carbohydrates (Sec. 29.8).

Problem 27.5 When 10-hydroxydecanoic acid is heated there is obtained a material of high molecular weight (1000–9000). Suggest a structure for this product.

Problem 27.6 Predict the product of the reaction of γ-butyrolactone with (a) ammonia, (b) $LiAlH_4$, (c) $C_2H_5OH + H_2SO_4$.

Problem 27.7 Using the behavior of hydroxy acids as a pattern, predict structures for the products obtained when the following amino acids are heated:

(a) an α-amino acid, glycine, $H_2NCH_2COOH \longrightarrow C_4H_6N_2O_2$ (*diketopiperazine*)

(b) a β-amino acid, $CH_3CHNH_2CH_2COOH \longrightarrow C_4H_6O_2$
(c) a γ-amino acid, $CH_3CHNH_2CH_2CH_2COOH \longrightarrow C_5H_9NO$ (a *lactam*)
(d) a δ-amino acid, $H_2NCH_2CH_2CH_2CH_2COOH \longrightarrow C_5H_9NO$ (a *lactam*)

27.4   Stereochemistry of hydroxy acids

Hydroxy acids have played a key role in the development of stereo-chemistry. Many of them are available in optically active form from biological sources. They have been of special interest to the chemist because of their relationship to the carbohydrates.

In 1848 Louis Pasteur, using a hand lens and a pair of tweezers, la-boriously separated a quantity of the sodium ammonium salt of racemic tartaric acid, HOOCCHOHCHOHCOOH, into two piles, one of left-handed crystals and the other of right-handed crystals, and in this way accomplished the first resolution of an optically inactive racemate into its optically active components (enantiomers). Almost exactly 100 years later, in 1949, Bijvoet, using x-ray diffraction — and also laboriously — determined the actual arrangement in space of the atoms of the sodium rubidium salt of (+)-tartaric acid, and thus made the first determination of the absolute configuration of an optically active substance.

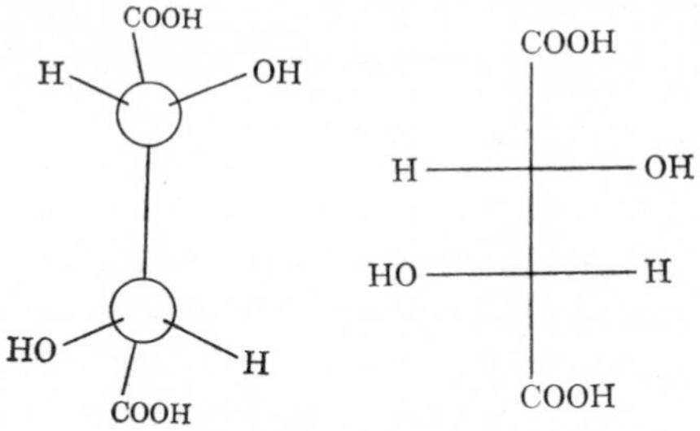

(+)-Tartaric acid

The first inversion of configuration discovered, by Walden in 1895, involved the formation of malic acid, $HOOCCH_2CHOHCOOH$.

In the following sections, we shall learn a little more of the principles of stereochemistry, using hydroxy acids as examples.

27.5   Optical families. Glyceraldehyde

Most applications of stereochemistry, as we have already seen, are based upon the *relative* configurations of different compounds, not upon their absolute configurations. We are chiefly interested in whether the configurations of a reactant and its product are the same or different, not with what either configuration actually is.

In the days before any absolute configurations had been determined, there was the problem not only of determining the relative configurations of various optically active compounds, but also of indicating these re-lationships once they had been established. This was a particularly pressing problem with the carbohydrates, an extremely important family of polyhydroxy aldehydes and ketones (Chapter 29).

The compound **glyceraldehyde**, $CH_2OHCHOHCHO$, was selected as a standard of reference, because it is the simplest polyhydroxy carbonyl compound capable of optical isomerism. Its configuration could be related to those of the carbohydrates, and because of its highly reactive functional groups, it could be converted into, and thus related to, many other kinds of organic compounds. (+)-Glyceraldehyde was arbitrarily assigned configuration I, and was designated D-glyceraldehyde; (−)-glyceraldehyde was assigned configuration II and was designated L-glyceraldehyde.

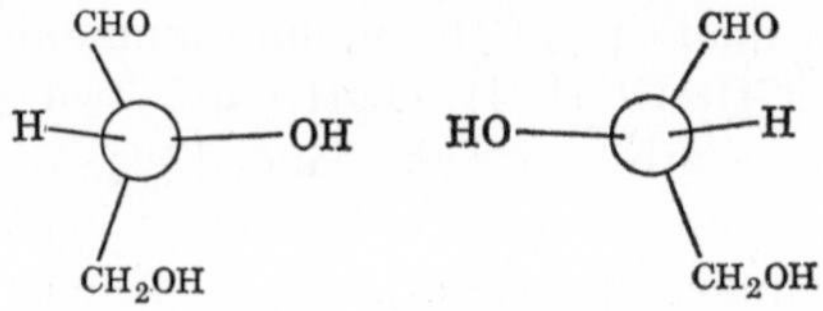

D-Glyceraldehyde   L-Glyceraldehyde
        I   II

Configurations were assigned to the glyceraldehydes purely for convenience; the particular assignment had a 50:50 chance of being correct, and, as it has turned out, the configuration chosen actually is the correct absolute configuration.

Other compounds could be related configurationally to one or the other of the glyceraldehydes by means of reactions that did not involve breaking bonds to an asymmetric carbon (Sec. 15.8). On the basis of the *assumed* configuration of the glyceraldehyde these related compounds could be assigned configurations, too. As it has turned out, these configurations are the correct absolute ones; in any case, for many years they served as a convenient way of indicating structural relationships. For example:

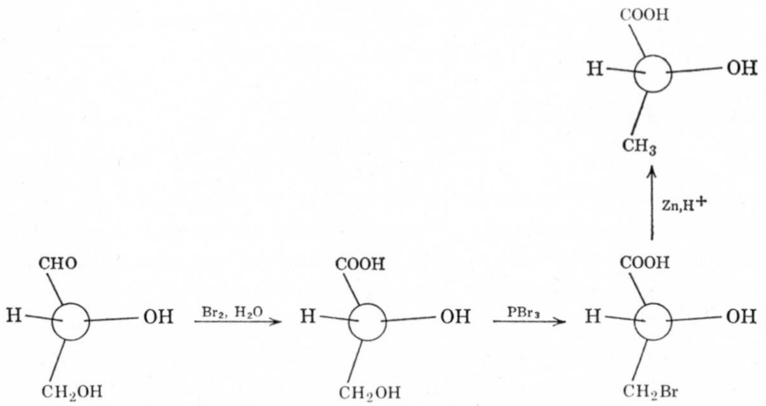

D-(+)-Glyceraldehyde   D-(−)-Glyceric acid   D-(−)-3-Bromo-
                                                            2-hydroxypropanoic
                                                                  acid

| D-(+)-ester | D-(−)-Lactic acid | D-(+)-ether |

To indicate the relationship thus established, compounds related to D-glyceraldehyde are given the designation D, compounds related to L-glyceraldehyde are given the designation L. The symbols D and L (pronounced "dee" and "ell") thus refer to configuration, not to sign of rotation, so that we have, for example, D-(−)-glyceric acid and L-(+)-lactic acid. (One frequently encounters the prefixes d and l, pronounced "dextro" and "levo," but their meaning is not always clear. Today they usually refer to direction of rotation; in some of the older literature they refer to optical family.   It was because of this confusion that D and L were introduced.)

Unfortunately, the use of the designations D and L is not unambiguous.   In relating glyceraldehyde to lactic acid, for example, we might envision carrying out a sequence of steps in which the —CH₂OH rather than the —CHO group is converted into the —COOH group:

| (+)-Glyceraldehyde | (+)-1,2-Propanediol | (+)-Lactic acid |

By this series of reactions, (+)-glyceraldehyde would yield (+)-lactic acid; by the previous sequence (+)-glyceraldehyde yields (−)-lactic acid. It would appear that, depending upon the particular sequence used, we could designate either of the lactic acids as D-lactic acid; the first sequence is the more direct, and by convention is the accepted one. We should notice that, whatever the ambiguity associated with the use of D and L, there is no ambiguity about the configurational relationship; we arrive at the proper configurations for (+)- and (−)-lactic acids whichever route we use. The designations D and L tell us nothing of the configuration of the compound unless we know the route by which the configurational relationship has been established; however, there are certain conventions about this, particularly in the case of the carbohydrates (Chapter 29), which make these designations extremely useful.

Problem 27.8   The transformation of L-(+)-lactic acid into (+)-2-butanol was accomplished by the following sequence of reactions.

L-(+)-lactic acid $\xrightarrow{\text{C}_2\text{H}_5\text{OH, H}_2\text{SO}_4}$ A $\xrightarrow{\text{Na, C}_2\text{H}_5\text{OH}}$ B $\xrightarrow{\text{HBr}}$ C

C $\xrightarrow{\text{KCN}}$ D $\xrightarrow{\text{H}_2\text{O, HCl, heat}}$ E $\xrightarrow{\text{CH}_3\text{OH, HCl}}$ F $\xrightarrow{\text{Na, CH}_3\text{COOH}}$ G

G $\xrightarrow{\text{HI}}$ H $\xrightarrow{\text{H}_2, \text{Pd}}$ (+)-2-butanol

What is the absolute configuration of (+)-2-butanol?

27.6   Tartaric acid.   Generation of a second asymmetric carbon

Next, let us see how the **tartaric acids,** HOOCCHOHCHOHCOOH, have been related configurationally to the glyceraldehydes. From this example we can learn something of what happens when a new asymmetric carbon is generated in a compound that is already optically active. The particular case that we have chosen is important in its own right; when the absolute configuration of tartaric acid was determined in 1949, knowledge of its relationship to glyceraldehyde permitted assignment of absolute configurations to a host of optically active compounds.

Tartaric acid can be prepared from glyceraldehyde by the method usually applied to the preparation of α-hydroxy acids (formation and hydrolysis of a cyanohydrin) followed by oxidation with nitric acid.

$$
\begin{array}{ccccccc}
 & & \text{CN} & & \text{COO}^- & & \text{COOH} \\
 & & | & & | & & | \\
\text{CHO} & & \text{CHOH} & & \text{CHOH} & & \text{CHOH} \\
| & & | & & | & & | \\
\text{CHOH} & \xrightarrow{\text{CN}^-,\,\text{H}^+} & \text{CHOH} & \xrightarrow{\text{Ba(OH)}_2} & \text{CHOH} & \xrightarrow{\text{HNO}_3} & \text{CHOH} \\
| & & | & & | & & | \\
\text{CH}_2\text{OH} & & \text{CH}_2\text{OH} & & \text{CH}_2\text{OH} & & \text{COOH}
\end{array}
$$

Glyceraldehyde   Tartaric acid

When hydrogen cyanide adds to the carbonyl group of D-glyceraldehyde a new asymmetric carbon is generated. There are two possible configurations about this new asymmetric carbon atom, leading to I and II (on the opposite page). We see that the configuration about the *original* asymmetric carbon is retained in both products; I and II differ only in the configuration about the *new* asymmetric carbon atom. I and II are not superimposable, and they are not mirror images; they must therefore be diastereomers.

Using models of (+)-glyceraldehyde, we can see that the particular configuration obtained depends upon which face of the carbonyl group is attacked by cyanide ion. Both I and II are actually formed, indicating that cyanide ion attacks both faces; I and II are not formed in equal amounts, however, but in a ratio of about 1:3, indicating that attack on the two faces is not equally likely. This is reasonable; because there is an asymmetric carbon already present in the molecule, the environment through which a cyanide ion passes is not the same for the two directions of attack.

Generation of the first asymmetric carbon atom in a compound yields equal amounts of enantiomers (Sec. 11.23), that is, yields an optically inactive racemate. Now we see that generation of a new asymmetric carbon atom in a compound that is *already* optically active yields an optically active product containing unequal amounts of diastereomers.

Completion of the synthetic sequence, by hydrolysis of the diastereomeric cyanohydrins (I and II) to diastereomeric hydroxy acids and oxidation of these by nitric acid, should lead to diastereomeric tartaric acids (III and IV). Being diastereomers, they should have different

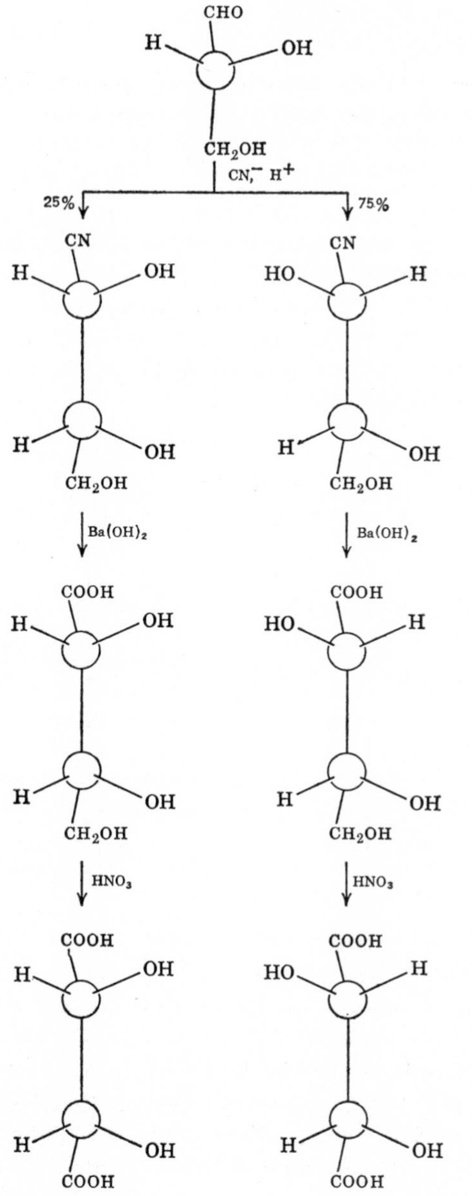

Mesotartaric acid　　　　　　　D-(−)-Tartaric acid

physical properties and should be separable by ordinary methods of purification: in this case, fractional crystallization of their salts. We recognize
III as a *meso* structure; hence one of the tartaric acids produced should
be inactive. We find that IV is not superimposable on its mirror image;
hence the other tartaric acid produced should show optical activity.

When these reactions were actually carried out (in 1917), starting
from D-glyceraldehyde, two products were obtained, one inactive and
one which rotated the plane of polarized light to the left. The active

(−)-tartaric acid thus obtained must have configuration IV; since it is related to D-glyceraldehyde we designate it as D-(−)-tartaric acid.

Problem 27.9 (a) Outline the same sequence starting from L-(−)-glyceraldehyde. What would be the relative proportions of the diastereomeric cyanohydrins? What can you say about the activity or inactivity of the cyanohydrins, monocarboxylic acids, and tartaric acids produced?

(b) Outline the same sequence starting from racemic (±)-glyceraldehyde. How do you account for the fact that only inactive materials are obtained in spite of the unequal amounts of diastereomeric cyanohydrins formed from each of the enantiomeric glyceraldehydes?

On the basis of the assumed configuration of D-(+)-glyceraldehyde, then, L-(+)-tartaric acid, the enantiomer of D-(−)-tartaric acid, would have configuration V, the mirror image of IV.

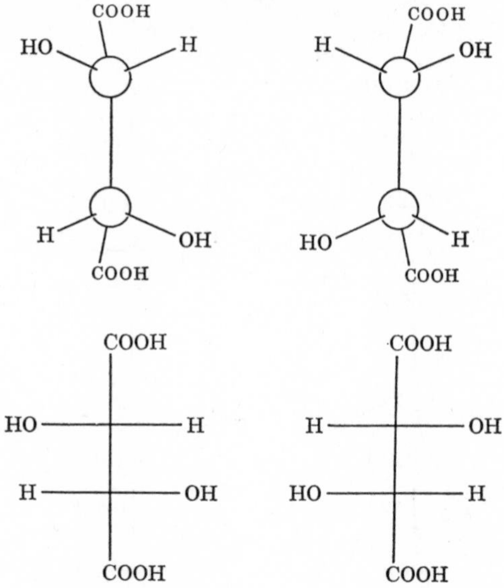

IV   V

D-(−)-Tartaric acid   L-(+)-Tartaric acid

When Bijvoet determined the absolute configuration of (+)-tartaric acid he found that it actually has the configuration that had been previously assumed. The assumed configurations of the glyceraldehydes, and hence the assumed configurations of all compounds related to them, were indeed the correct ones.

Problem 27.10 In Chapter 24 we discussed the isomeric 2,3-butanediols. They are D-(−)-, L-(+)-, and *meso*-2,3-butanediol. Draw the structures and assign the proper names to them.

Problem 27.11 How many stereoisomers of formula $CH_2OHCHOHCHOH-CH_2OH$ can exist? Which are D-family compounds, which L-family, and which have no family designation? Which tartaric acid will each give upon oxidation?

Problem 27.12 How many stereoisomers of formula $CH_2OHCHOHCHOH-CHO$ can exist? Which are D-family compounds, which L-family, and which have no family designation? Which tartaric acid will each give upon oxidation?

PROBLEMS

1. Write equations to show how lactic acid can be prepared from each of the following:

(a) acetaldehyde
(b) propionic acid
(c) pyruvic acid (α-ketopropionic acid)
(d) propylene glycol

2. Write equations to show how β-hydroxybutyric acid can be prepared from each of the following, using a different synthetic route in each case:

(a) ethyl acetate
(b) acetaldehyde
(c) ethyl acetate and acetaldehyde
(d) propylene
(e) *n*-butyric acid   (*Hint:* see Sec. 28.5.)

3. Outline all steps in the synthesis of α-methyl-β-phenylpropionic acid via:

(a) a Reformatsky reaction
(b) a Perkin reaction
(c) a malonic ester synthesis
(d) a crossed aldol condensation

4. Predict the products of the action of heat upon:

(a) α-hydroxyisobutyric acid
(b) β-methyl-γ-hydroxyvaleric acid
(c) 3-hydroxyhexanoic acid
(d) δ-hydroxyvaleric acid
(e) glycolic acid
(f) β-hydroxy-β-phenylpropionic acid
(g) o-HOOCC$_6$H$_4$CH$_2$OH
(h) lactic acid
(i) malic acid   ($\longrightarrow$ C$_4$H$_2$O$_3$)
(j) β-hydroxyglutaric acid ($\longrightarrow$ C$_5$H$_4$O$_3$)

5. Give structures of compounds A through Q:

(a) ethyl oxalate + ethyl acetate + sodium ethoxide $\longrightarrow$ A (C$_8$H$_{12}$O$_5$)
A + ethyl bromoacetate + Zn, then H$_2$O $\longrightarrow$ B (C$_{12}$H$_{20}$O$_7$)
B + OH$^-$ + heat, then H$^+$ $\longrightarrow$ C (C$_6$H$_8$O$_7$)

(b) adipic acid + ethyl alcohol + H$^+$ $\longrightarrow$ D (C$_8$H$_{14}$O$_4$)
D + Na + C$_2$H$_5$OH $\longrightarrow$ E (C$_6$H$_{12}$O$_3$)

(c) glycerol + HCl $\longrightarrow$ F (C$_3$H$_6$OCl$_2$)
F + NaOCl $\longrightarrow$ CHCl$_3$
F + Na$_2$Cr$_2$O$_7$ + H$_2$SO$_4$ $\longrightarrow$ G (C$_3$H$_4$OCl$_2$)
G + CN$^-$, H$^+$ $\longrightarrow$ H (C$_4$H$_5$ONCl$_2$)
H + KCN $\longrightarrow$ I (C$_6$H$_5$ON$_3$)
I + H$_2$O, warm $\longrightarrow$ J (C$_6$H$_8$O$_7$)

(d) salicylaldehyde + acetic anhydride + sodium acetate + heat, then H$^+$
$\longrightarrow$ K (C$_{11}$H$_{10}$O$_4$)
K + H$_2$O, H$^+$, warm $\longrightarrow$ [L (C$_9$H$_8$O$_3$)] $\longrightarrow$ M (C$_9$H$_6$O$_2$), *coumarin*, an artificial flavor

(e) heptanal (heptaldehyde) + ethyl bromoacetate + Zn, then H$_2$O
$\longrightarrow$ N (C$_{11}$H$_{22}$O$_3$)
N + CrO$_3$ in glacial acetic acid $\longrightarrow$ O (C$_{11}$H$_{20}$O$_3$)
O + sodium ethoxide, then benzyl chloride $\longrightarrow$ P (C$_{18}$H$_{26}$O$_3$)
P + OH$^-$, heat; then H$^+$, warm $\longrightarrow$ Q (C$_{15}$H$_{22}$O)

6. How do you account for the formation of γ-methylparaconic acid (page 726) from the reaction of acetaldehyde with succinic acid?

7. Outline all steps in a possible laboratory synthesis of each of the following from benzene, toluene, alcohols of four carbons or less, and available straight-chain monocarboxylic acids, using any needed inorganic reagents.

(a) 2,3-dimethyl-2-pentenoic acid
(b) 3-hydroxy-4-phenylbutanoic acid
(c) racemic *erythro*-2,3-dihydroxy-3-phenylpropanoic acid (R and its enantiomer)
(*Hint:* aldol condensations and variations generally give *trans*-isomers.)
(d) α,α-dimethylcaproic acid
(e) *m*-hydroxybenzoic acid
(f) 2-keto-3-hydroxydihydrobenzofuran

$$\begin{array}{c} COOH \\ H{-}\!|{-}OH \\ H{-}\!|{-}OH \\ C_6H_5 \end{array}$$

R

2-Keto-3-hydroxydihydrobenzofuran

γ-Methylparaconic acid

8. Give stereochemical formulas of products S through KK. Each letter may refer to a mixture of stereoisomers. Label all meso compounds and racemates. Tell how many fractions could be obtained by ordinary methods of separation from each reaction mixture.

(a) ethylene glycol + Cu, air, heat $\longrightarrow$ S ($C_2H_2O_2$)
   S + CN$^-$ + H$^+$ $\longrightarrow$ T ($C_4H_4O_2N_2$)
   T + H$_2$O, H$^+$ $\longrightarrow$ U ($C_4H_6O_6$)
(b) racemic β-bromobutyric acid + one mole Br$_2$, P $\longrightarrow$ V ($C_4H_6O_2Br_2$)
(c) benzaldehyde + acetophenone + base $\longrightarrow$ W (*trans*-$C_{15}H_{12}O$)
   W + NaBH$_4$, then H$_2$O $\longrightarrow$ X (*trans*-$C_{15}H_{14}O$)
   X + cold dilute KMnO$_4$ $\longrightarrow$ Y ($C_{15}H_{16}O_3$)
(d) mesotartaric acid + one mole ethyl alcohol, H$^+$ $\longrightarrow$ Z ($C_6H_{10}O_6$)
(e) L-tartaric acid + one mole acetic anhydride $\longrightarrow$ AA ($C_6H_8O_7$)
(f) fumaric acid + peroxyformic acid $\longrightarrow$ BB ($C_4H_6O_6$)
(g) methyl hydrogen fumarate + peroxyformic acid $\longrightarrow$ CC ($C_5H_8O_6$)
(h) (−)-DD + CN$^-$, H$^+$; then Ba(OH)$_2$; then H$^+$ $\longrightarrow$ EE ($C_5H_{10}O_6$)
   EE + HNO$_3$ $\longrightarrow$ FF ($C_5H_8O_7$)

$$\begin{array}{c} CHO \\ H{-}\!|{-}OH \\ H{-}\!|{-}OH \\ CH_2OH \end{array}$$

(−)-DD

$$\begin{array}{c} CHO \\ HO{-}\!|{-}H \\ H{-}\!|{-}OH \\ CH_2OH \end{array}$$

(−)-GG

(i) (−)-GG + CN$^-$, H$^+$; then Ba(OH)$_2$; then H$^+$ $\longrightarrow$ HH ($C_5H_{10}O_6$)
   HH + HNO$_3$ $\longrightarrow$ II ($C_5H_8O_7$)
(j) benzidine + 2 moles (−)-*sec*-butyl chloride, then OH$^-$ $\xrightarrow{S_N2}$ JJ ($C_{20}H_{28}N_2$)
(k) *cis*-1,2-cyclohexanedicarboxylic acid + 2 moles ($\pm$)-*sec*-butyl alcohol + H$^+$
   $\longrightarrow$ KK ($C_{16}H_{28}O_4$)

9. In Problem 19, page 674, you arrived at certain possible structures for (−)-threose and for (−)-erythrose. On the basis of the following additional evidence, assign a single structure to each.

Upon oxidation by nitric acid, (−)-threose is converted into (−)-tartaric acid and (−)-erythrose into mesotartaric acid.

When D-glyceraldehyde is treated with cyanide and the resulting product LL is hydrolyzed, two monocarboxylic acids are formed (see Sec. 27.6). These acids are identical with the acids obtained by oxidation with bromine water of (−)-threose and (−)-erythrose.

10. Each of the following syntheses leads to 2,3-dihydroxybutanoic acid. In each the final reaction products are separated by careful fractional distillation or crystallization. For each synthesis tell how many fractions will be collected. Draw stereochemical formulas of the compound or compounds making up each fraction. Tell whether each fraction, as collected, will show optical activity or inactivity.

(a) racemic $CH_3CHOHCHO + CN^-$, H^+; then H_2O, H^+

(b) L-$CH_3CHOHCHO + CN^-$, H^+; then H_2O, H^+

(c) *trans*-$CH_3CH{=}CHCOOH$ + peroxyformic acid

(d) a mixture of *cis*- and *trans*-$CH_3CH{=}CHCOOH$ + cold dilute $KMnO_4$

11. (a) Draw the structures of all the stereoisomeric chloromalic acids, $HOOCCHOHCHClCOOH$.

(b) Draw the structures of the stereoisomeric tartaric acid (or acids) obtained from *each* of these by the following sequence of reactions (*Hint:* see Sec. 15.13):

$$HOOCCHOHCHClCOOH \xrightarrow{OH^-} HOOCCHCHCOOH \xrightarrow{H_2O} \text{tartaric acid}$$
$$\underset{O}{\diagdown\diagup}$$

(c) Answer part (b) for the reaction:

$$HOOCCHOHCHClCOOH \xrightarrow{H_2O} HOOCCHOHCHOHCOOH$$

12. Treatment of 2,4-pentanedione with KCN and acetic acid, followed by hydrolysis, gives two products, MM and NN. Both MM and NN are dicarboxylic acids of formula $C_7H_{12}O_6$. MM melts at 98°. When heated, NN gives first a lactonic acid ($C_7H_{10}O_5$, m.p. 90°) and finally a dilactone ($C_7H_8O_4$, m.p. 105°). (a) What structure must NN have that permits ready formation of both a monolactone and a dilactone? (b) What is the structure of MM? (*Hint:* use models.)

13. The structure of *camphoronic acid* (a degradation product of the terpene camphor) was established by the following synthesis:

sodioacetoacetic ester + $CH_3I \longrightarrow OO \xrightarrow{NaOC_2H_5} \xrightarrow{CH_3I} PP\ (C_8H_{14}O_3)$

PP + ethyl bromoacetate + Zn, then $H_2O \longrightarrow QQ\ (C_{12}H_{22}O_5)$

$QQ + PCl_5$, then KCN $\longrightarrow RR\ (C_{13}H_{21}O_4N)$

$RR + H_2O$, H^+, heat $\longrightarrow$ camphoronic acid ($C_9H_{14}O_6$)

What is the structure of camphoronic acid?

14. *Pantothenic acid*, $C_9H_{17}O_5N$, is a growth factor for yeast and bacteria; its significance in human nutrition is still undetermined. It reacts with dilute NaOH to give $C_9H_{16}O_5NNa$, with ethyl alcohol to give $C_{11}H_{21}O_5N$, and with hot NaOH to give compound WW (see below) and β-aminopropionic acid. Its nitrogen is non-basic. Pantothenic acid has been synthesized as follows:

isobutyraldehyde + formaldehyde + $K_2CO_3 \longrightarrow SS\ (C_5H_{10}O_2)$

$SS + NaHSO_3$, then KCN $\longrightarrow TT\ (C_6H_{11}O_2N)$

$TT + H_2O$, H^+, heat $\longrightarrow [UU\ (C_6H_{12}O_4)] \longrightarrow VV\ (C_6H_{10}O_3)$

$VV + NaOH(aq)$, warm $\longrightarrow WW\ (C_6H_{11}O_4Na)$

VV + sodium β-aminopropionate, then $H^+ \longrightarrow$ pantothenic acid ($C_9H_{17}O_5N$)

(a) What is the structure of pantothenic acid? (b) Suggest a way of synthesizing β-aminopropionic acid (β-alanine) from succinic anhydride. (*Hint:* see Sec. 25.8.)

15. Two of the oxidation products of the terpene α-terpineol are *terebic acid* and *terpenylic acid*. Their structures were first established by the following syntheses:

ethyl chloroacetate + sodioacetoacetic ester $\longrightarrow XX\ (C_{10}H_{16}O_5)$

XX + one mole CH_3MgI, then $H_2O \longrightarrow YY\ (C_{11}H_{20}O_5)$

$YY + OH^-$, H_2O, heat, then $H^+ \longrightarrow [ZZ\ (C_7H_{12}O_5)] \longrightarrow$ terebic acid ($C_7H_{10}O_4$)

XX + sodium ethoxide, then ethyl chloroacetate $\longrightarrow AAA\ (C_{14}H_{22}O_7)$

$AAA + OH^-$, then H^+, warm $\longrightarrow BBB\ (C_7H_{10}O_5)$

BBB + ethyl alcohol, $H^+ \longrightarrow CCC\ (C_{11}H_{18}O_5)$

CCC + one mole CH_3MgI, then $H_2O \longrightarrow DDD\ (C_{12}H_{22}O_5)$

$DDD + OH^-$, H_2O, heat, then $H^+ \longrightarrow [EEE\ (C_8H_{14}O_5)] \longrightarrow$ terpenylic acid ($C_8H_{12}O_4$)

What is the structure of terebic acid? Of terpenylic acid?

α, β - U N S A T U R A T E D
C A R B O N Y L
C O M P O U N D S

28.1 Structure and properties

In general, a compound that contains both a carbon–carbon double bond and a carbon–oxygen double bond has properties that are characteristic of both functional groups. At the carbon–carbon double bond an unsaturated ester or unsaturated ketone undergoes electrophilic addition of acids and halogens, hydrogenation, hydroxylation, and cleavage; at the carbonyl group it undergoes the nucleophilic substitution typical of an ester or the nucleophilic addition typical of a ketone.

Problem 28.1 What will be the products of the following reactions:

(a) $CH_3CH=CHCOOH + H_2 + Pt$
(b) $CH_3CH=CHCOOC_2H_5 + OH^- + H_2O + heat$
(c) $C_6H_5CH=CHCOCH_3 + Br_2/CCl_4$
(d) $C_6H_5CH=CHCOCH_3 + I_2 + OH^-$
(e) $CH_3CH=CHCHO + C_6H_5NHNH_2 + acid catalyst$
(f) $CH_3CH=CHCHO + Ag(NH_3)_2{}^+$
(g) $C_6H_5CH=CHCOC_6H_5 + O_3$, followed by $Zn + H_2O$
(h) $CH_3CH=CHCHO + excess H_2 + Ni$, heat, pressure

Problem 28.2 What are A, B, and C, given the following facts?

(a) Cinnamaldehyde $(C_6H_5CH=CHCHO) + H_2 + Ni$, at low temperatures and pressures $\longrightarrow$ A
(b) Cinnamaldehyde $+ H_2 + Ni$, at high temperatures and pressures $\longrightarrow$ B
(c) Cinnamaldehyde $+ NaBH_4$, followed by H^+ $\longrightarrow$ C

	A	B	C
$KMnO_4$ test	positive	negative	positive
Br_2/CCl_4 test	negative	negative	positive
Tollens' test	positive	negative	negative
$NaHSO_3$ test	positive	negative	negative

In the α,β-unsaturated carbonyl compounds, the carbon–carbon double bond and the carbon–oxygen double bond are separated by just one carbon–carbon single bond, that is, the double bonds are *conjugated*.

$$\overset{\beta}{\underset{|}{C}}=\overset{\alpha}{\underset{|}{C}}-\underset{|}{C}=O$$

α,β-**Unsaturated
carbonyl compound:**
conjugated system

Because of this conjugation, such compounds possess not only the properties of the individual functional groups, but certain other properties besides. In this chapter we shall concentrate on the α,β-unsaturated compounds, and on the special reactions characteristic of the conjugated system.

TABLE 28.1

α,β-UNSATURATED CARBONYL COMPOUNDS

Name	Formula	M.p., °C	B.p., °C
Acrolein	$CH_2=CHCHO$	-88	52
Crotonaldehyde	$CH_3CH=CHCHO$	-69	104
Cinnamaldehyde	$C_6H_5CH=CHCHO$	-7	254
Mesityl oxide	$(CH_3)_2C=CHCOCH_3$	42	131
Benzalacetone	$C_6H_5CH=CHCOCH_3$	42	261
Dibenzalacetone	$C_6H_5CH=CHCOCH=CHC_6H_5$	113	
Benzalacetophenone (Chalcone)	$C_6H_5CH=CHCOC_6H_5$	62	348
Dypnone	$C_6H_5C(CH_3)=CHCOC_6H_5$		150–5[1]
Acrylic acid	$CH_2=CHCOOH$	12	142
Crotonic acid	$trans\text{-}CH_3CH=CHCOOH$	72	189
Isocrotonic acid	$cis\text{-}CH_3CH=CHCOOH$	16	172d
Methacrylic acid	$CH_2=C(CH_3)COOH$	16	162
Sorbic acid	$CH_3CH=CHCH=CHCOOH$	134	
Cinnamic acid	$trans\text{-}C_6H_5CH=CHCOOH$	137	300
Maleic acid	$cis\text{-}HOOCCH=CHCOOH$	130.5	
Fumaric acid	$trans\text{-}HOOCCH=CHCOOH$	302	
Maleic anhydride		60	202
Methyl acrylate	$CH_2=CHCOOCH_3$		80
Methyl methacrylate	$CH_2=C(CH_3)COOCH_3$		101
Ethyl cinnamate	$C_6H_5CH=CHCOOC_2H_5$	12	271
Acrylonitrile	$CH_2=CH-C\equiv N$	-82	79

28.2   Nomenclature

Many of the most important unsaturated carbonyl compounds have common names with which the student should become familiar. For example:

$$CH_2=CH-CHO \qquad CH_2=CH-COOH \qquad CH_2=CH-C\equiv N \qquad \underset{\underset{\text{Methacrylic acid}}{}}{\overset{\overset{CH_3}{\underset{|}{}}}{CH_2=C-COOH}}$$

Acrolein	Acrylic acid	Acrylonitrile	Methacrylic acid
Propenal	Propenoic acid	Propenenitrile	2-Methylpropenoic acid

$$CH_3CH{=}CHCHO \quad C_6H_5CH{=}CHCHO \quad C_6H_5CH{=}CHCCH_3 \quad CH_3\overset{\displaystyle CH_3}{\underset{}{C}}{=}CHCCH_3$$

		Benzalacetone	
Crotonaldehyde	Cinnamaldehyde	4-Phenyl-3-	Mesityl oxide
2-Butenal	3-Phenylpropenal	buten-2-one	4-Methyl-3-
			penten-2-one

Fumaric acid	Maleic acid	Maleic anhydride
trans-Butenedioic	*cis*-Butenedioic	*cis*-Butenedioic
acid	acid	anhydride

28.3   Preparation

There are several general ways to make compounds of this kind: the **aldol condensation,** to make unsaturated aldehydes and ketones; **dehydrohalogenation of α-halo acids** and the **Perkin condensation,** to make unsaturated acids.   Besides these, there are certain methods useful only for making single compounds.

All these methods make use of chemistry with which we are already familiar: the fundamental chemistry of alkenes and carbonyl compounds.

Problem 28.3   Outline a possible synthesis of:
(a) crotonaldehyde from acetylene
(b) cinnamaldehyde from compounds of lower carbon number
(c) cinnamic acid from compounds of lower carbon number
(d) 4-methyl-2-pentenoic acid via a malonic ester synthesis

Problem 28.4   The following compounds are of great industrial importance for the manufacture of polymers: acrylonitrile (for Orlon), methyl acrylate (for Acryloid), methyl methacrylate (for Lucite and Plexiglas).   Outline a possible industrial synthesis of (a) acrylonitrile from ethylene, (b) methyl acrylate from ethylene, (c) methyl methacrylate from acetone and methanol.

(d) Polymerization of these compounds is similar to that of ethylene, vinyl chloride, etc. (Sec. 6.20).   Draw a structural formula for each of the polymers.

Problem 28.5   Acrolein, $CH_2{=}CHCHO$, is prepared by heating glycerol with sodium hydrogen sulfate, $NaHSO_4$.   (a) Outline the likely steps in this synthesis, which involves acid-catalyzed dehydration and keto-enol tautomerization.   (*Hint:* which —OH is easier to eliminate, a primary or a secondary?)   (b) How could acrolein be converted into acrylic acid?

Problem 28.6   Dilute aqueous potassium permanganate converts maleic acid into mesotartaric acid, and converts fumaric acid into racemic tartaric acid. (a) How do you account for these results? (b)   Predict the product formed by the action of hydrogen peroxide and acetic acid on maleic acid.   On fumaric acid. (c) Predict the product from the addition of bromine to maleic acid.   To fumaric acid.

28.4   Interaction of functional groups

We have seen (Sec. 5.11) that, with regard to electrophilic addition, a carbon–carbon double bond is activated by an electron-releasing substituent and deactivated by an electron-withdrawing substituent. The carbon–carbon double bond serves as a source of electrons for the electrophilic reagent; the availability of its electrons is determined by the groups attached to it. More specifically, an electron-releasing substituent stabilizes the transition state leading to the initial carbonium ion by dispersing the developing positive charge; an electron-withdrawing substituent destabilizes the transition state by intensifying the positive charge.

Electrophilic Addition

$$-\overset{|}{C}=\overset{|}{C}-G + Y^+ \longrightarrow \left[-\overset{|}{\underset{\underset{Y\ \delta_+}{|}}{C}----\overset{|}{\underset{\delta_+}{C}}-G \right] \longrightarrow -\overset{|}{\underset{Y}{C}}-\overset{|}{\underset{\oplus}{C}}-G$$

G releases electrons: *Activates*
G withdraws electrons: *Deactivates*

The C=O, —COOH, —COOR, and —CN groups are powerful electron-withdrawing groups, and therefore would be expected to deactivate a carbon–carbon double bond toward electrophilic addition. This is found to be true: α,β-unsaturated ketones, acids, esters, and nitriles are in general less reactive than simple alkenes toward reagents like bromine and the hydrogen halides.

But this powerful electron withdrawal, which deactivates a carbon–carbon double bond toward reagents seeking electrons, at the same time *activates* toward reagents that are electron-rich. As a result, the carbon–carbon double bond of an α,β-unsaturated ketone, acid, ester, or nitrile is susceptible to nucleophilic attack, and undergoes a set of reactions, **nucleophilic addition,** that is uncommon for the simple alkenes.

28.5   Electrophilic addition

The presence of the carbonyl group not only lowers the **reactivity** of the carbon–carbon double bond toward electrophilic addition, but also controls the **orientation** of the addition.

In general, it is observed that addition of an unsymmetrical reagent to an α,β-unsaturated carbonyl compound takes place in such a way that hydrogen becomes attached to the α-carbon and the negative group becomes attached to the β-carbon. For example:

$$CH_2=CH-CHO + HCl\,(g) \xrightarrow{\;-10°\;} \underset{\underset{Cl\quad H}{|\qquad|}}{CH_2-CH-CHO}$$

Acrolein β-Chloropropionaldehyde

$$CH_2=CH-COOH + H_2O \xrightarrow{\;H_2SO_4,\ 100°\;} \underset{\underset{OH\quad H}{|\qquad|}}{CH_2-CH-COOH}$$

Acrylic acid β-Hydroxypropionic acid

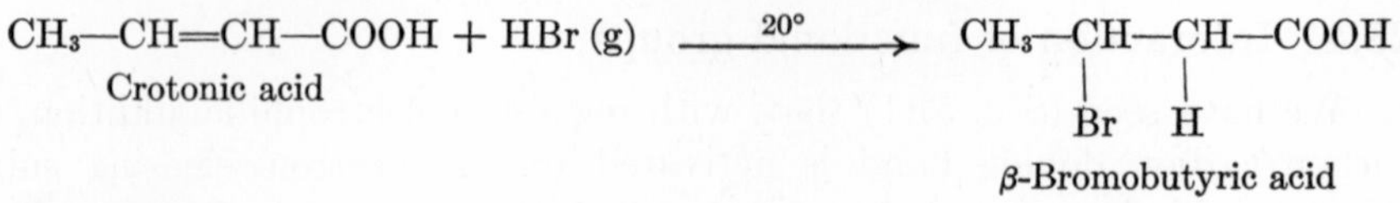

$$CH_3-CH=CH-COOH + HBr\ (g) \xrightarrow{20°} CH_3-\underset{\underset{Br}{|}}{CH}-\underset{\underset{H}{|}}{CH}-COOH$$

Crotonic acid   β-Bromobutyric acid

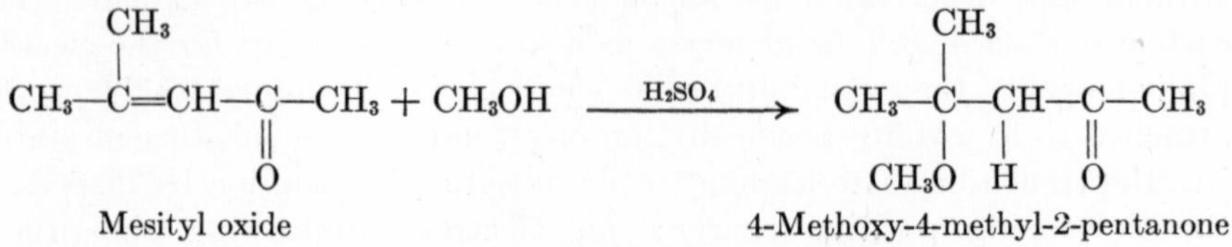

$$CH_3-\overset{\overset{CH_3}{|}}{C}=CH-\underset{\underset{O}{\|}}{C}-CH_3 + CH_3OH \xrightarrow{H_2SO_4} CH_3-\overset{\overset{CH_3}{|}}{\underset{\underset{CH_3O}{|}}{C}}-\underset{\underset{H}{|}}{CH}-\underset{\underset{O}{\|}}{C}-CH_3$$

Mesityl oxide   4-Methoxy-4-methyl-2-pentanone

Electrophilic addition to simple alkenes takes place in such a way as to form the most stable intermediate carbonium ion. Addition to α,β-unsaturated carbonyl compounds, too, is consistent with this principle; to see that this is so, however, we must look at the conjugated system as a whole. As in the case of conjugated dienes (Sec. 6.16), addition to an *end* of the conjugated system is preferred, since this yields (step 1) a resonance-stabilized carbonium ion. Addition to the carbonyl oxygen end would yield carbonium ion I; addition to the β-carbon end would yield carbonium ion II.

(1) 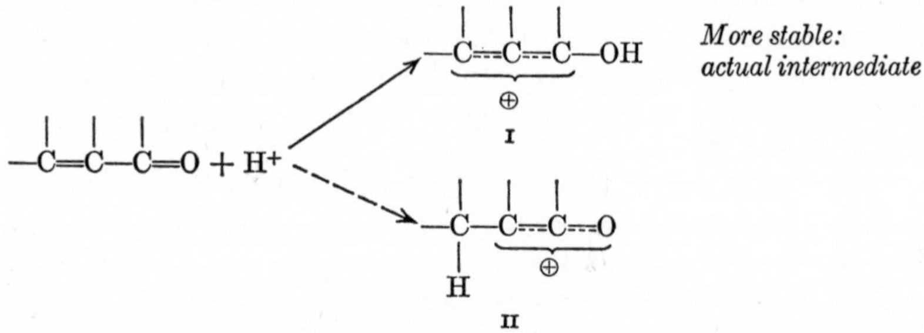 $-\overset{|}{C}=\overset{|}{C}-\overset{|}{C}=O + H^+$

I: $-\underbrace{\overset{|}{C}\text{=}\overset{|}{C}\text{=}\overset{|}{C}}_{\oplus}-OH$ *More stable: actual intermediate*

II: $-\underset{\underset{H}{|}}{\overset{|}{C}}-\underbrace{\overset{|}{C}\text{=}\overset{|}{C}\text{=}O}_{\oplus}$

Of the two, I is the more stable, since the positive charge is carried by carbon atoms alone, rather than partly by the highly electronegative oxygen atom.

In the second step of addition, a negative ion or basic molecule attaches itself either to the carbonyl carbon or to the β-carbon of the hybrid ion I.

(2) 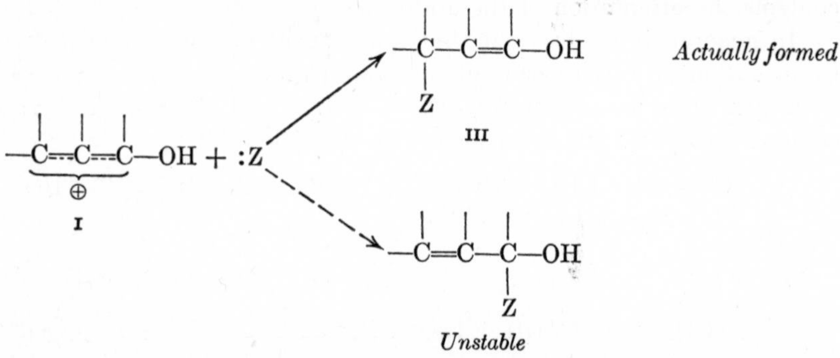 $\underbrace{-\overset{|}{C}\text{=}\overset{|}{C}\text{=}\overset{|}{C}}_{\oplus}-OH + :Z$

I

III: $-\underset{\underset{Z}{|}}{\overset{|}{C}}-\overset{|}{C}=\overset{|}{C}-OH$ *Actually formed*

$-\overset{|}{C}=\overset{|}{C}-\underset{\underset{Z}{|}}{\overset{|}{C}}-OH$

Unstable

Of the two possibilities only addition to the β-carbon yields a stable product (III), which is simply the enol form of the saturated carbonyl compound.

The enol form then undergoes tautomerization to the keto form to give the observed product (IV).

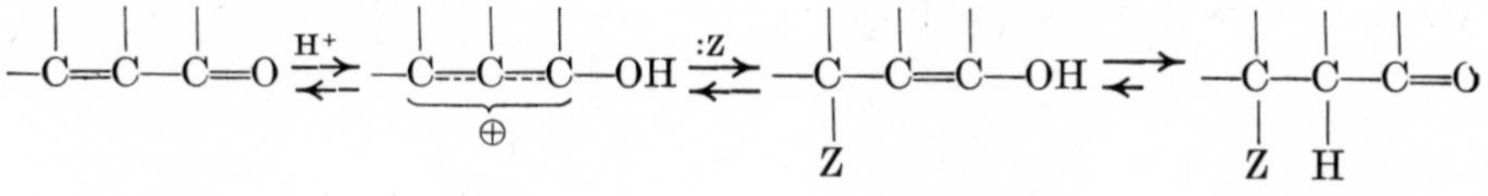

$$-\overset{|}{C}=\overset{|}{C}-\overset{|}{C}=O \underset{\longleftarrow}{\overset{H^+}{\longrightarrow}} \underset{\oplus}{-\overset{|}{C}\cdots\overset{|}{C}\cdots\overset{|}{C}}-OH \underset{\longleftarrow}{\overset{:Z}{\longrightarrow}} -\overset{|}{\underset{Z}{C}}-\overset{|}{C}=\overset{|}{C}-OH \rightleftarrows -\overset{|}{\underset{Z}{C}}-\overset{|}{\underset{H}{C}}-\overset{|}{C}=O$$

| α,β-Unsaturated compound | I Carbonium ion | III Enol form | IV Keto form |

28.6 Nucleophilic addition

Aqueous sodium cyanide converts α,β-unsaturated carbonyl compounds into β-cyano carbonyl compounds. The reaction amounts to addition of the elements of HCN to the carbon–carbon double bond. For example:

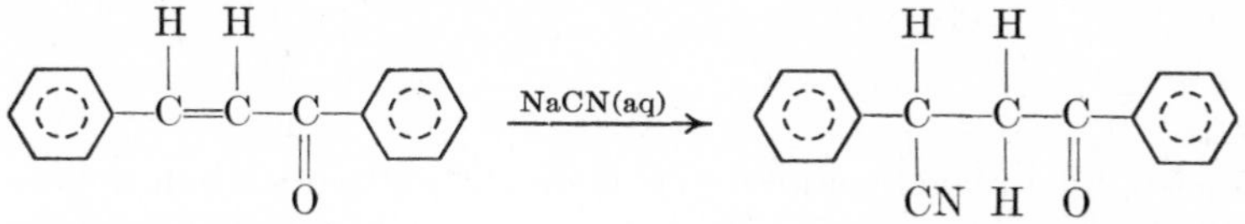

Benzalacetophenone $\xrightarrow{\text{NaCN(aq)}}$ 3-Cyano-1,3-diphenyl-1-propanone

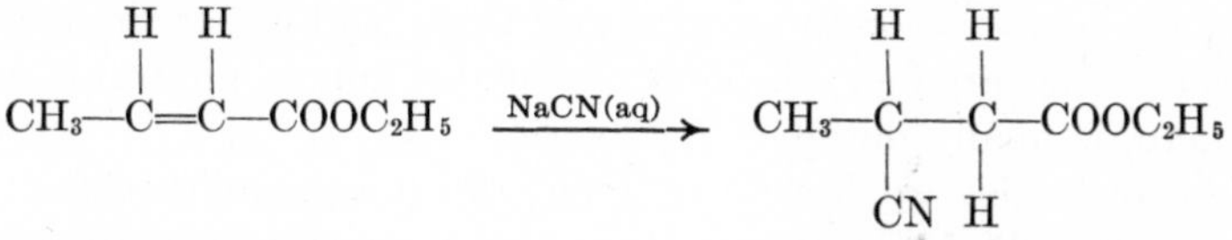

$$CH_3-\overset{H}{\underset{}{C}}=\overset{H}{\underset{}{C}}-COOC_2H_5 \xrightarrow{\text{NaCN(aq)}} CH_3-\overset{H}{\underset{CN}{C}}-\overset{H}{\underset{}{C}}-COOC_2H_5$$

Ethyl crotonate　　　　　　　Ethyl β-cyanobutyrate

Ammonia or certain derivatives of ammonia (amines, hydroxylamine, phenylhydrazine, etc.) add to α,β-unsaturated carbonyl compounds to yield β-amino carbonyl compounds. For example:

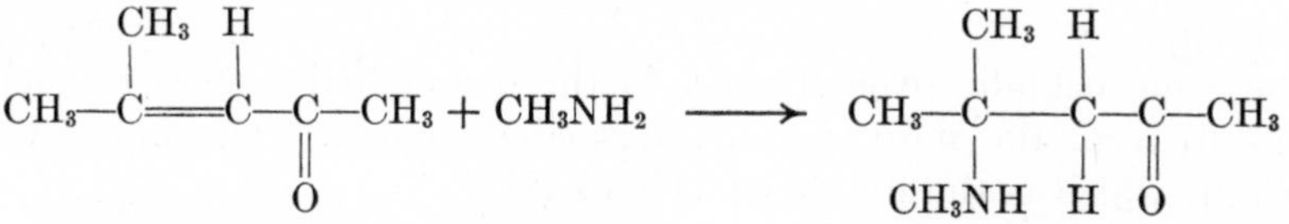

$$CH_3-\overset{CH_3}{\underset{}{C}}=\overset{H}{\underset{}{C}}-\overset{}{\underset{O}{C}}-CH_3 + CH_3NH_2 \longrightarrow CH_3-\overset{CH_3}{\underset{CH_3NH}{C}}-\overset{H}{\underset{H}{C}}-\overset{}{\underset{O}{C}}-CH_3$$

Mesityl oxide　　　　Methylamine　　　4-(N-Methylamino)-4-methyl-2-pentanone

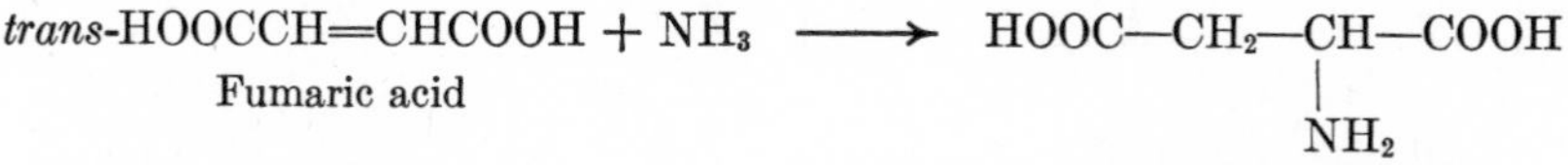

$$trans\text{-}HOOCCH=CHCOOH + NH_3 \longrightarrow HOOC-CH_2-\underset{NH_2}{CH}-COOH$$

Fumaric acid　　　　　　　　　　　Aminosuccinic acid (Aspartic acid)

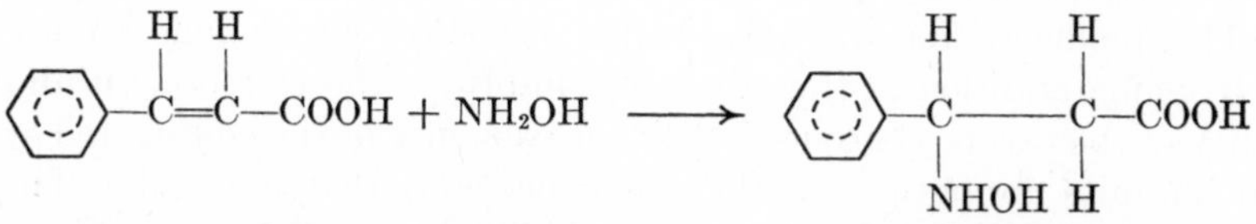

Cinnamic acid + NH₂OH ⟶ 3-(N-Hydroxylamino)-3-phenylpropanoic acid

Cinnamic acid　　　　Hydroxylamine　　　3-(N-Hydroxylamino)-3-phenylpropanoic acid

These reactions are believed to take place by the following mechanism:

(1)

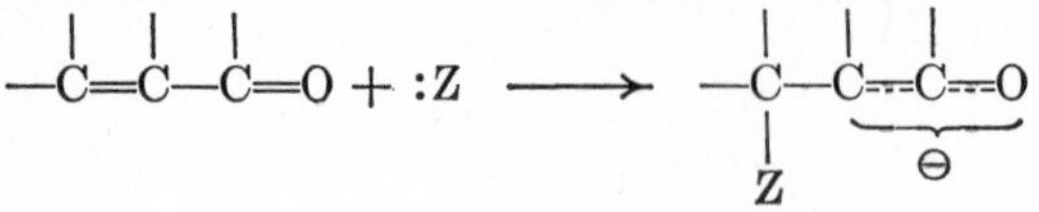

(2)

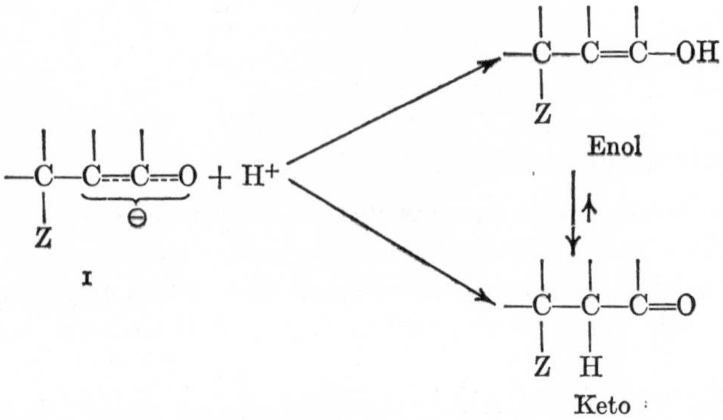

The nucleophilic reagent adds (step 1) to the carbon–carbon double bond to yield the hybrid anion I, which then accepts (step 2) a hydrogen ion from the solvent to yield the final product. This hydrogen ion can add either to the α-carbon or to oxygen, and thus yield either the keto or the enol form of the product; in either case the same equilibrium mixture, chiefly keto, is finally obtained.

In the examples we have just seen, the nucleophilic reagent, :Z, is either the strongly basic anion, $:CN^-$, or a neutral base like ammonia and its derivatives, $:NH_2—G$. These are the same reagents which, we have seen, add to the carbonyl group of simple aldehydes and ketones. (Indeed, nucleophilic reagents rarely add to the carbon–carbon double bond of α,β-unsaturated *aldehydes*, but rather to the highly reactive carbonyl group.)

These nucleophilic reagents add to the conjugated system in such a way as to form the most stable intermediate anion. The most stable anion is I, which is the hybrid of II and III.

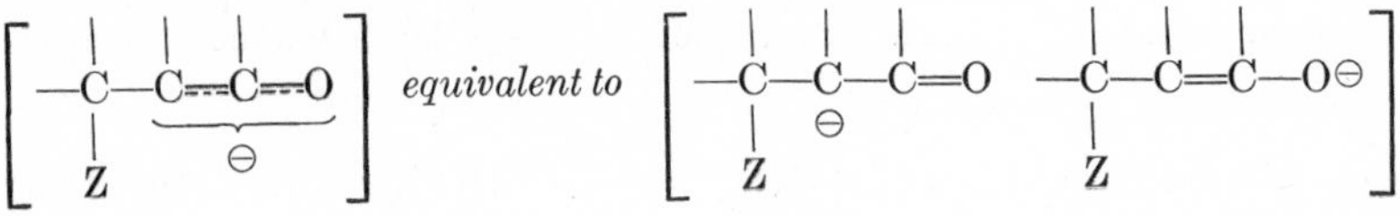

As usual, initial addition occurs at an *end* of the conjugated system, and in this case to the particular end (β-carbon) that enables the electronegative element oxygen to accommodate the negative charge.

The tendency for α,β-unsaturated carbonyl compounds to undergo nucleophilic addition is thus due not simply to the electron-withdrawing ability of the carbonyl group, but to the existence of the conjugated system that permits formation of the resonance-stabilized anion I. The importance in synthesis of α,β-unsaturated aldehydes, ketones, acids, esters, and nitriles is due to the fact that they provide such a conjugated system.

Problem 28.7 Draw structures of the anion expected from nucleophilic addition to each of the other positions in the conjugated system, and compare its stability with that of I.

Problem 28.8 Treatment of crotonic acid, $CH_3CH{=}CHCOOH$, with phenylhydrazine yields compound IV.

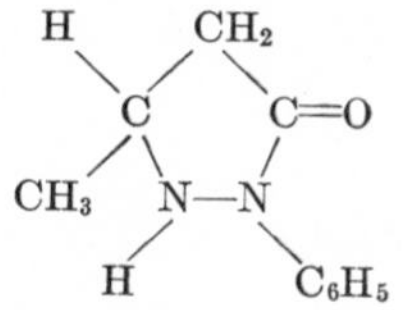

IV

To what simple class of compounds does IV belong? How can you account for its formation? (*Hint:* see Sec. 17.12.)

Problem 28.9 Treatment of acrylonitrile, $CH_2{=}CHCN$, with ammonia yields a mixture of β-aminopropionitrile, $H_2NCH_2CH_2CN$, and di(β-cyanoethyl)-amine, $NCCH_2CH_2NHCH_2CH_2CN$. How do you account for their formation?

Problem 28.10 Treatment of ethyl acrylate, $CH_2{=}CHCOOC_2H_5$, with methylamine yields $CH_3N(CH_2CH_2COOC_2H_5)_2$. How do you account for its formation?

Problem 28.11 Benzalacetone, $C_6H_5CH{=}CHCOCH_3$, reacts with ethylmagnesium bromide to yield not only the alcohol V but also the saturated ketone VI. How do you account for the formation of VI?

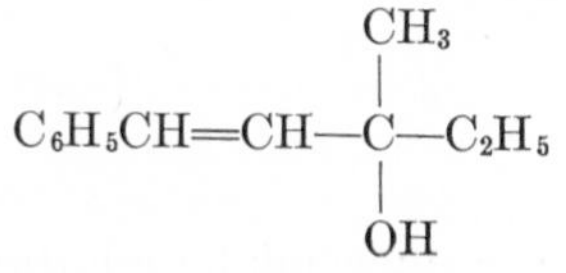

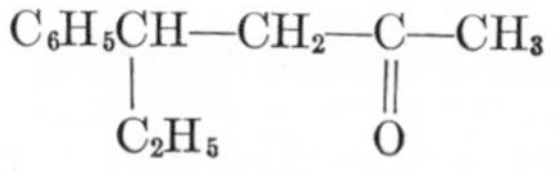

28.7 Comparison of nucleophilic and electrophilic addition

We can see that nucleophilic addition is closely analogous to electrophilic addition: (a) addition proceeds in two steps; (b) the first and controlling step is the formation of an intermediate ion; (c) both orientation of addition and reactivity are determined by the stability of the intermediate ion, or, more exactly, by the stability of the transition state leading to its formation; (d) this stability depends upon dispersal of the charge.

The difference between nucleophilic and electrophilic addition is, of course, that the intermediate ions have opposite charges: negative in nucleophilic addition, positive in electrophilic addition. As a result, the effects of substituents are exactly opposite. Where an electron-withdrawing group deactivates a carbon–carbon double bond toward electrophilic addition, it activates toward nucleophilic addition. An electron-withdrawing group stabilizes the transition state leading to the formation of an intermediate anion in nucleophilic addition by helping to disperse the developing negative charge:

Nucleophilic addition

$$-\overset{|}{C}=\overset{|}{C}-G + :Z \longrightarrow \left[\begin{array}{c} -\overset{|}{C}=\overset{|}{C}-G \\ \underset{\delta-}{} \\ \overset{..}{\underset{..}{Z}} \end{array}\right] \longrightarrow -\overset{|}{C}-\overset{|}{C}-G$$

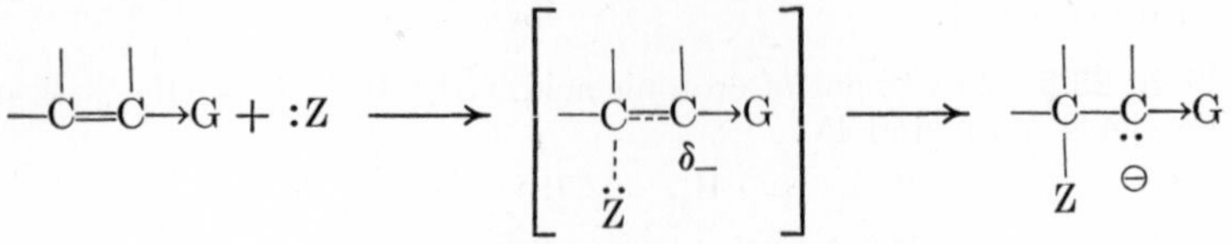

G withdraws electrons: *Activates*

Addition to an α,β-unsaturated carbonyl compound can be understood best in terms of an attack on the entire conjugated system. To yield the most stable intermediate ion, this attack must occur at an end of the conjugated system. A nucleophilic reagent attacks at the β-carbon to form an ion in which the negative charge is partly accommodated by the electronegative atom oxygen; an electrophilic reagent attacks oxygen to form a carbonium ion in which the positive charge is accommodated by carbon.

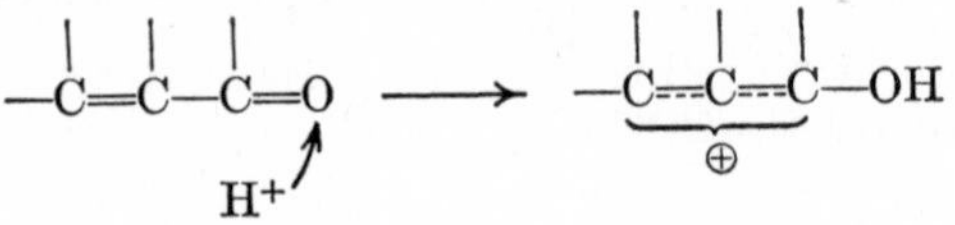

$$-\overset{|}{C}=\overset{|}{C}-\overset{|}{C}=O \longrightarrow -\overset{|}{C}\underset{\oplus}{=\!=}\overset{|}{C}\underset{}{=\!=}\overset{|}{C}-OH \qquad \textit{Electrophilic attack}$$

H+

$$-\overset{|}{C}=\overset{|}{C}-\overset{|}{C}=O \longrightarrow -\overset{|}{\underset{Z}{C}}-\overset{|}{C}\underset{\ominus}{=\!=}\overset{|}{C}\underset{}{=\!=}O \qquad \textit{Nucleophilic attack}$$

:Z

28.8 The Michael reaction

Of special importance in synthesis is the nucleophilic addition of carbanions to α,β-unsaturated carbonyl compounds known as the **Michael reaction.** For example:

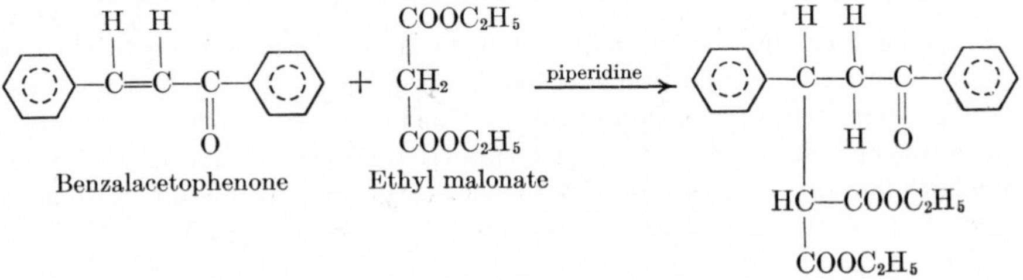

Benzalacetophenone   Ethyl malonate

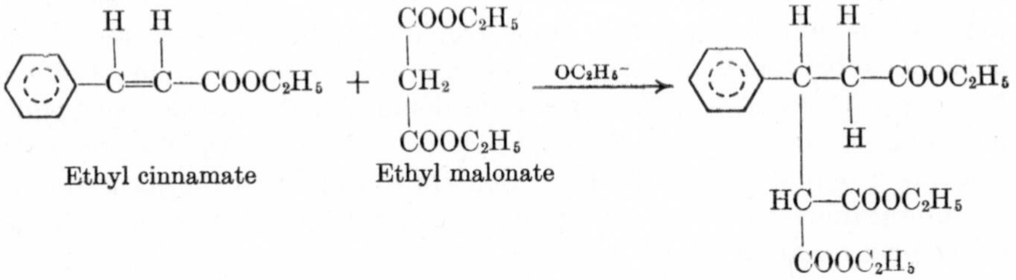

Ethyl cinnamate   Ethyl malonate

$$
\underset{\text{Ethyl crotonate}}{CH_3-\overset{\overset{\displaystyle H}{|}}{C}=\overset{\overset{\displaystyle H}{|}}{C}-COOC_2H_5} + \underset{\underset{\displaystyle COOC_2H_5}{|}}{\overset{\overset{\displaystyle COOC_2H_5}{|}}{HC}-CH_3} \xrightarrow{\text{OC}_2\text{H}_5{}^-} \underset{\underset{\underset{\displaystyle COOC_2H_5}{|}}{\overset{\displaystyle CH_3-\overset{|}{C}-COOC_2H_5}{}}}{CH_3-\overset{\overset{\displaystyle H}{|}}{\underset{\underset{\displaystyle H}{|}}{C}}-\overset{\overset{\displaystyle H}{|}}{C}-COOC_2H_5}
$$

Ethyl crotonate　　Ethyl methylmalonate

$$
\underset{\text{Ethyl }\alpha\text{-methylacrylate}}{H-\overset{\overset{\displaystyle H}{|}}{C}=\overset{\overset{\displaystyle CH_3}{|}}{C}-COOC_2H_5} + \underset{\text{Ethyl cyanoacetate}}{\underset{\underset{\displaystyle CN}{|}}{\overset{\overset{\displaystyle COOC_2H_5}{|}}{CH_2}}} \xrightarrow{\text{OC}_2\text{H}_5{}^-} \underset{\underset{\underset{\displaystyle CN}{|}}{\overset{\displaystyle HC-COOC_2H_5}{}}}{H-\overset{\overset{\displaystyle H}{|}}{\underset{\underset{\displaystyle H}{|}}{C}}-\overset{\overset{\displaystyle CH_3}{|}}{C}-COOC_2H_5}
$$

Ethyl α-methylacrylate　Ethyl cyanoacetate

The Michael reaction is believed to proceed by the following mechanism (shown for malonic ester):

(1) $\qquad CH_2(COOC_2H_5)_2 + :Base \longrightarrow H:Base^+ + CH(COOC_2H_5)_2{}^-$

(2) $\underset{\substack{\textit{Nucleophilic}\\ \textit{reagent}}}{-\overset{|}{C}=\overset{|}{C}-\overset{|}{C}=O} + CH(COOC_2H_5)_2{}^- \longrightarrow \underset{\underset{\underset{\displaystyle COOC_2H_5}{|}}{\overset{\displaystyle HC-COOC_2H_5}{}}}{-\overset{|}{C}-\underset{\ominus}{\underbrace{\overset{|}{C}=C=O}}}$

(3) $\underset{\underset{\underset{\displaystyle COOC_2H_5}{|}}{\overset{\displaystyle HC-COOC_2H_5}{}}}{-\overset{|}{C}-\underset{\ominus}{\underbrace{\overset{|}{C}=C=O}}} + H:Base^+ \longrightarrow \underset{\underset{\underset{\displaystyle COOC_2H_5}{|}}{\overset{\displaystyle HC-COOC_2H_5}{}}}{-\overset{|}{C}-\overset{\overset{\displaystyle H}{|}}{\underset{\underset{\displaystyle H}{|}}{C}}-C=O} + :Base$

The function of the base is to abstract (step 1) a hydrogen ion from malonic ester and thus generate a carbanion which, acting as a nucleophilic reagent, then attacks (step 2) the conjugated system in the usual manner.

In general, the compound from which the carbanion is generated must be a fairly acidic substance, so that an appreciable concentration of the carbanion can be obtained. Such a compound is usually one that contains a —CH$_2$— or —CH— group flanked by two electron-withdrawing groups which can help accommodate the negative charge of the anion. In place of ethyl malonate, compounds like ethyl cyanoacetate and ethyl aceto-acetate can be used.

$$\begin{array}{c}\text{C}_2\text{H}_5\text{O} \diagdown \quad \text{O} \\ \text{C} \\ | \\ \text{HCH} \quad +\ :\text{Base} \\ | \\ \text{C} \\ \diagup \diagdown \\ \text{C}_2\text{H}_5\text{O} \quad \text{O} \end{array} \ \rightleftarrows\ \text{H:Base}^+ + \begin{array}{c}\text{C}_2\text{H}_5\text{O} \diagdown \quad \text{O} \\ \text{C} \\ \| \\ \text{HC} \\ \| \\ \text{C} \\ \diagup \diagdown \\ \text{C}_2\text{H}_5\text{O} \quad \text{O} \end{array} \Bigg\} \ominus$$

Ethyl malonate

$$\begin{array}{c}\text{C}_2\text{H}_5\text{O} \diagdown \quad \text{O} \\ \text{C} \\ | \\ \text{HCH} \quad +\ :\text{Base} \\ | \\ \text{C} \\ \| \| \\ \text{N} \end{array} \ \rightleftarrows\ \text{H:Base}^+ + \begin{array}{c}\text{C}_2\text{H}_5\text{O} \diagdown \quad \text{O} \\ \text{C} \\ \| \\ \text{HC} \\ \| \\ \text{C} \\ \| \| \\ \text{N} \end{array} \Bigg\} \ominus$$

Ethyl cyanoacetate

$$\begin{array}{c}\text{C}_2\text{H}_5\text{O} \diagdown \quad \text{O} \\ \text{C} \\ | \\ \text{HCH} \quad +\ :\text{Base} \\ | \\ \text{C} \\ \diagup \diagdown \\ \text{CH}_3 \quad \text{O} \end{array} \ \rightleftarrows\ \text{H:Base}^+ + \begin{array}{c}\text{C}_2\text{H}_5\text{O} \diagdown \quad \text{O} \\ \text{C} \\ \| \\ \text{HC} \\ \| \\ \text{C} \\ \diagup \diagdown \\ \text{CH}_3 \quad \text{O} \end{array} \Bigg\} \ominus$$

Ethyl acetoacetate

Problem 28.12 Predict the products of the following Michael reactions:

(a) ethyl crotonate + malonic ester $\longrightarrow$ A $\xrightarrow{\text{OH}^-}$ $\xrightarrow{\text{H}^+}$ $\xrightarrow{\text{heat}}$ B

(b) ethyl acrylate + ethyl acetoacetate $\longrightarrow$ C $\xrightarrow{\text{H}_2\text{O, H}^+}$ D

(c) methyl vinyl ketone + malonic ester $\longrightarrow$ E

(d) benzalacetophenone + acetophenone $\longrightarrow$ F

(e) acrylonitrile + allyl cyanide $\longrightarrow$ G $\xrightarrow{\text{H}_2\text{O, H}^+}$ H + 2NH$_4$$^+$

(f) C$_2$H$_5$OOC—C≡C—COOC$_2$H$_5$ (1 mole) + ethyl acetoacetate (1 mole) $\longrightarrow$ I

(g) I $\xrightarrow{\text{strong OH}^-,\ \text{H}_2\text{O}}$ $\xrightarrow{\text{H}^+}$ J + CH$_3$COOH

Problem 28.13 Formaldehyde and malonic ester react in the presence of ethoxide ion to give K, C$_8$H$_{12}$O$_4$. (a) What is the structure of K? (*Hint:* see Problem 25.29, page 690.) (b) How can K be converted into L, (C$_2$H$_5$OOC)$_2$-CHCH$_2$CH(COOC$_2$H$_5$)$_2$? (c) What would you get if L were subjected to hydrolysis, acidification, and heat?

Problem 28.14 Show how a Michael reaction followed by an aldol condensation can transform a mixture of methyl vinyl ketone and cyclohexanone into Δ^{1,9}-octalone.

Δ^{1,9}–Octalone

Problem 28.15 When mesityl oxide, $(CH_3)_2C{=}CHCOCH_3$, is treated with ethyl malonate in the presence of sodium ethoxide, compound M is obtained. (a) Outline the steps in its formation. (b) How could M be turned into 5,5-dimethyl-1,3-cyclohexanedione?

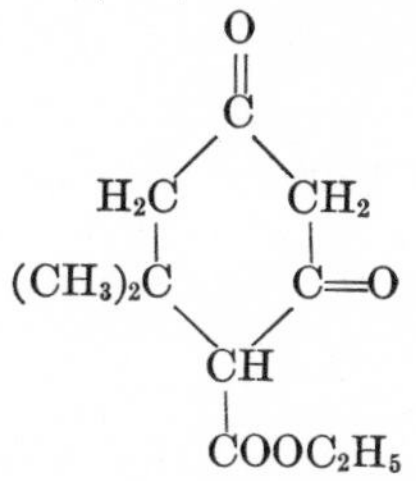

M

Problem 28.16 In the presence of piperidine (a secondary amine, Sec. 32.12), 1,3-cyclopentadiene and benzal-*p*-bromoacetophenone yield N. Outline the steps in its formation.

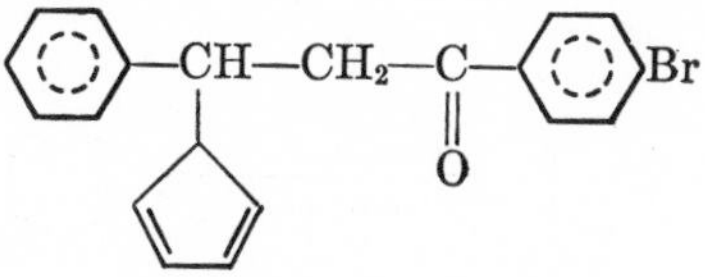

N

28.9 The Diels–Alder reaction

α,β-Unsaturated carbonyl compounds undergo an exceedingly important reaction with conjugated dienes, known as the **Diels–Alder reaction.** This is an addition reaction in which C–1 and C–4 of the conjugated diene system become attached to the doubly-bonded carbons of the unsaturated carbonyl compound. The result is invariably formation of a six-membered ring.

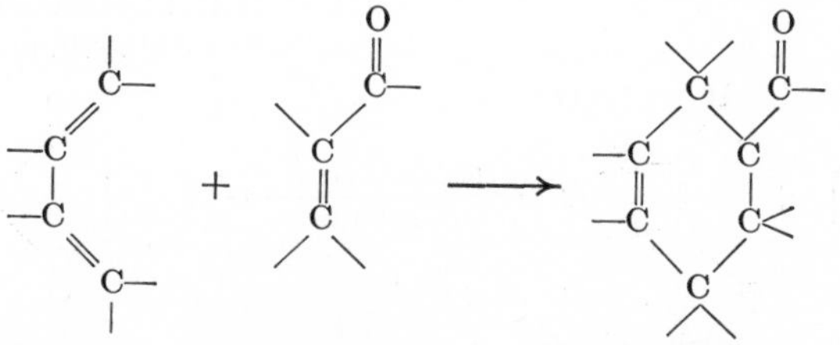

| Diene | Dienophile (from the Greek, diene-loving) | Adduct *Six-membered ring* |

Although the mechanism is not well understood, the Diels-Alder reaction seems to be favored by the presence of electron-releasing groups in the diene, and of electron-withdrawing groups in the dienophile. The reaction has been extended to dienophiles of a wide variety of structures, including even simple alkenes.

The Diels-Alder reaction often takes place with the evolution of heat when the reactants are simply mixed together. A few examples of the Diels-Alder reaction are shown on the next page.

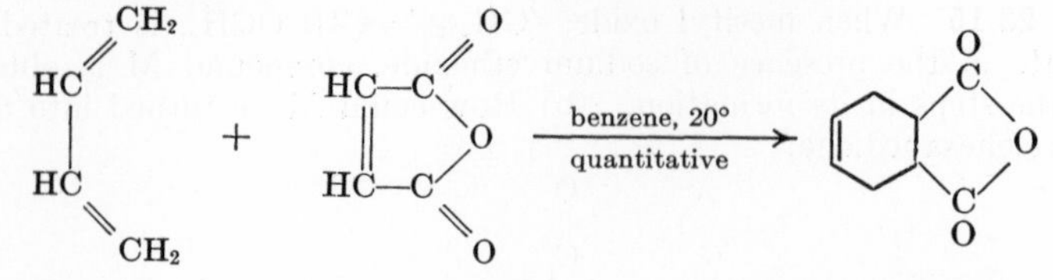

1,3-Butadiene   Maleic anhydride   *cis*-1,2,3,6-Tetrahydrophthalic anhydride

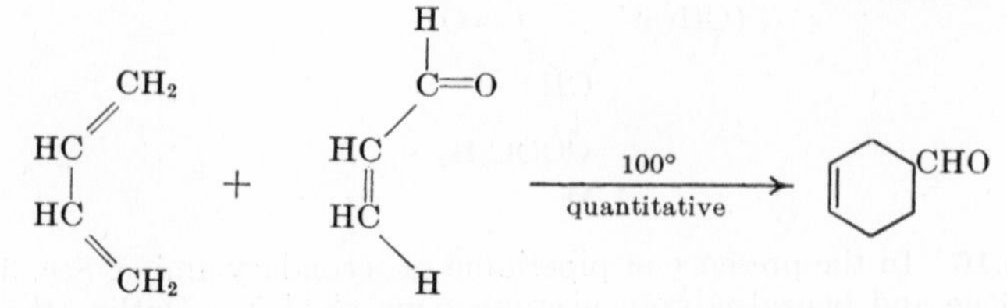

1,3-Butadiene   Acrolein   1,2,3,6-Tetrahydrobenzaldehyde

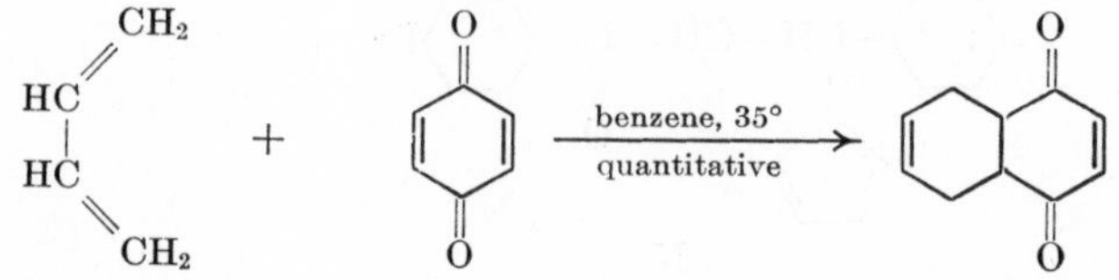

1,3-Butadiene   *p*-Benzoquinone   5,8,9,10-Tetrahydro-1,4-naphthoquinone

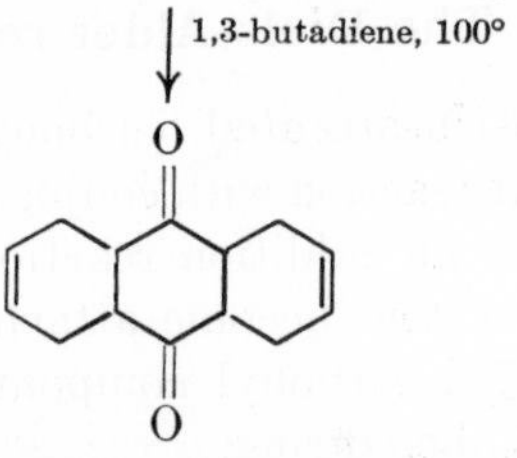

1,3-butadiene, 100°

1,4,5,8,11,12,13,14-Octahydro-9,10-anthraquinone

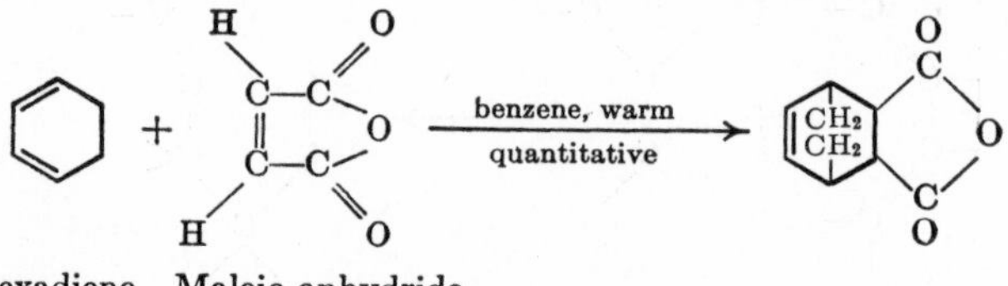

1,3-Cyclohexadiene   Maleic anhydride

Problem 28.17   From what reactants could the following compounds be synthesized?

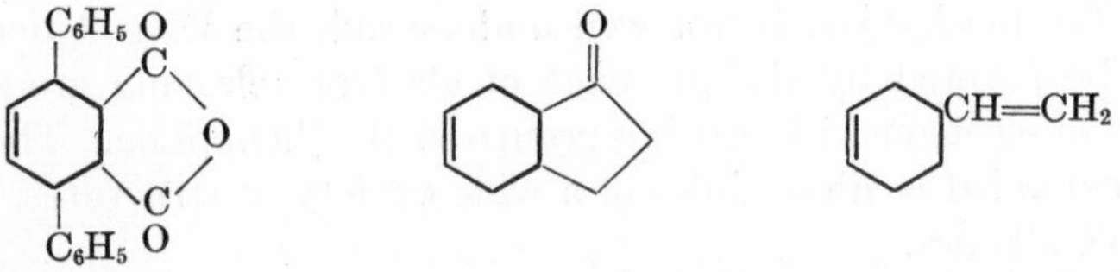

Problem 28.18   (a) In one synthesis of the hormone *cortisone* (by Lewis Sarett of Merck, Sharp and Dohme) the initial step was the formation of I by a Diels-Alder reaction. What were the starting materials?

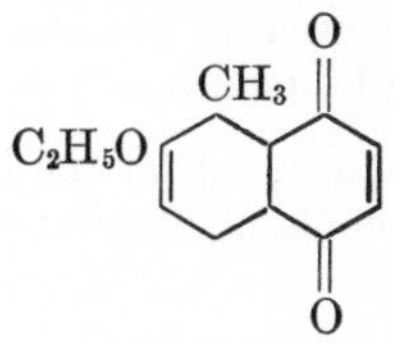

I

(b) In another synthesis of cortisone (by Robert Woodward of Harvard University) the initial step was the formation of II by a Diels-Alder reaction. What were the starting materials?

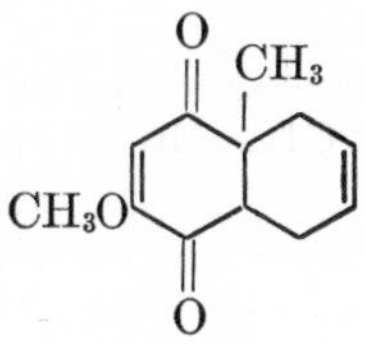

II

28.10 Quinones

α,β-Unsaturated ketones of a rather special kind are given the name of **quinones**: these are cyclic diketones of such a structure that they are converted by reduction into hydroquinones, phenols containing two —OH groups. For example:

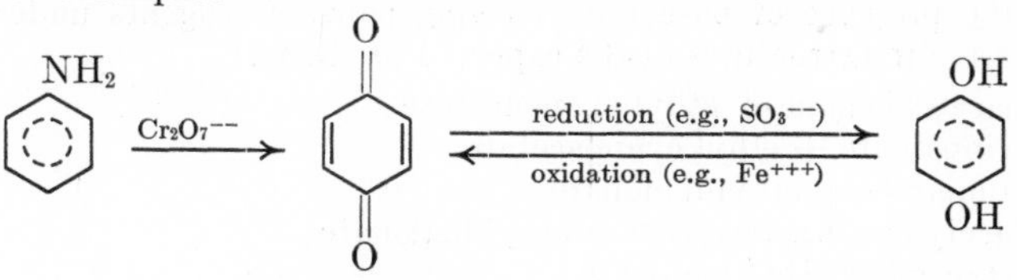

p-Benzoquinone
(Quinone)
Yellow

Hydroquinone

Because they are highly conjugated, quinones are colored; p-benzoquinone, for example, is yellow.

Also because they are highly conjugated, quinones are rather closely balanced, energetically, against the corresponding hydroquinones. The ready interconversion provides a convenient oxidation–reduction system that has been studied intensively. Many properties of quinones result from the tendency to form the aromatic hydroquinone system.

Quinones — some related to more complicated aromatic systems (Chapter 31) — have been isolated from biological sources (molds, fungi, higher plants). In many cases they seem to take part in oxidation–reduction cycles essential to the living organism.

Problem 28.19 When p-benzoquinone is treated with HCl, there is obtained 2-chlorohydroquinone. It has been suggested that this product arises via an initial 1,4-addition. Show how this might be so.

Problem 28.20 (a) Hydroquinone is used in photographic developers to aid in the conversion of silver ion into free silver. What property of hydroquinone is being taken advantage of here?

(b) *p*-Benzoquinone can be used to convert iodide ion into iodine. What property of the quinone is being taken advantage of here?

Problem 28.21   How do you account for the fact that the treatment of phenol with nitrous acid yields the mono-oxime of *p*-benzoquinone?

PROBLEMS

1. Outline all steps in a possible laboratory synthesis of each of the unsaturated carbonyl compounds in Table 28.1, page 729, using any readily available monofunctional compounds: simple alcohols, aldehydes, ketones, acids, esters, and hydrocarbons.

2. Give the structures of the organic products expected from the reaction of benzalacetone, C_6H_5CH=$CHCOCH_3$, with each of the following:

(a) H_2, Ni
(b) $NaBH_4$
(c) NaOI
(d) O_3, then Zn, H_2O
(e) Br_2
(f) HCl
(g) HBr
(h) H_2O, H^+
(i) CH_3OH, H^+
(j) NaCN (aq)
(k) CH_3NH_2
(l) aniline
(m) NH_3
(n) NH_2OH
(o) benzaldehyde, base
(p) ethyl malonate, base
(q) ethyl cyanoacetate, base
(r) ethyl methylmalonate, base
(s) ethyl acetoacetate, base
(t) 1,3-butadiene
(u) 1,3-cyclohexadiene
(v) 1,3-cyclopentadiene

3. In the presence of base the following pairs of reagents undergo Michael addition. Give the structures of the expected products.

(a) benzalacetophenone + ethyl cyanoacetate
(b) ethyl cinnamate + ethyl cyanoacetate
(c) ethyl fumarate + ethyl malonate
(d) ethyl acetylenedicarboxylate + ethyl malonate
(e) mesityl oxide + ethyl malonate
(f) mesityl oxide + ethyl acetoacetate
(g) ethyl crotonate + ethyl methylmalonate
(h) formaldehyde + 2 moles ethyl malonate
(i) acetaldehyde + 2 moles ethyl acetoacetate
(j) methyl acrylate + nitromethane
(k) 2 moles ethyl crotonate + nitromethane
(l) 3 moles acrylonitrile + nitromethane
(m) 1 mole acrylonitrile + $CHCl_3$

4. Give the structures of the compounds expected from the hydrolysis and decarboxylation of the products obtained in Problem 3, parts (a) through (i).

5. Depending upon reaction conditions, dibenzalacetone and ethyl malonate can be made to yield any of three products by Michael addition.

dibenzalacetone + 2 moles ethyl malonate $\longrightarrow$ A (no unsaturation)
dibenzalacetone + 1 mole ethyl malonate $\longrightarrow$ B (one carbon–carbon double bond)
dibenzalacetone + 1 mole ethyl malonate $\longrightarrow$ C (no unsaturation)
    What are A, B, and C?

6. Give the structure of the product of the Diels-Alder reaction between:
(a) maleic anhydride and isoprene
(b) maleic anhydride and 1,1'-bicyclohexenyl (I)
(c) maleic anhydride and 1-vinyl-1-cyclohexene
(d) 1,3-butadiene and methyl vinyl ketone
(e) 1,3-butadiene and crotonaldehyde

(f)   2 moles 1,3-butadiene and dibenzalacetone
(g)   1,3-butadiene and β-nitrostyrene ($C_6H_5CH{=}CHNO_2$)
(h)   1,3-butadiene and 1,4-naphthoquinone (II)
(i)   p-benzoquinone and 1,3-cyclohexadiene
(j)   p-benzoquinone and 1,1'-bicyclohexenyl (I)
(k)   p-benzoquinone and 2 moles 1,3-cyclohexadiene
(l)   p-benzoquinone and 2 moles 1,1'-bicyclohexenyl (I)
(m)   1,3-cyclopentadiene and acrylonitrile
(n)   1,3-cyclohexadiene and acrolein

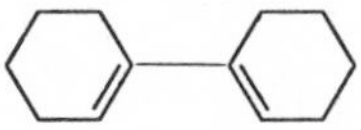

I

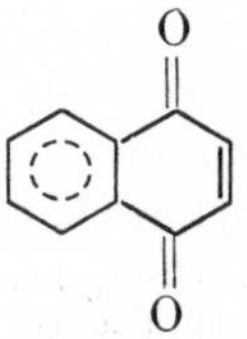

II

7. From what reactants could the following be synthesized by the Diels-Alder reaction?

(a)

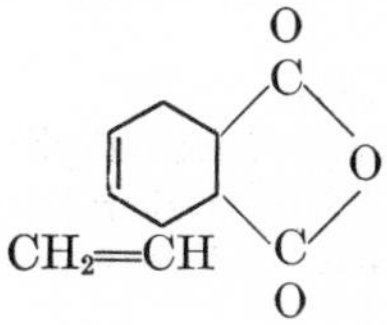

(b)

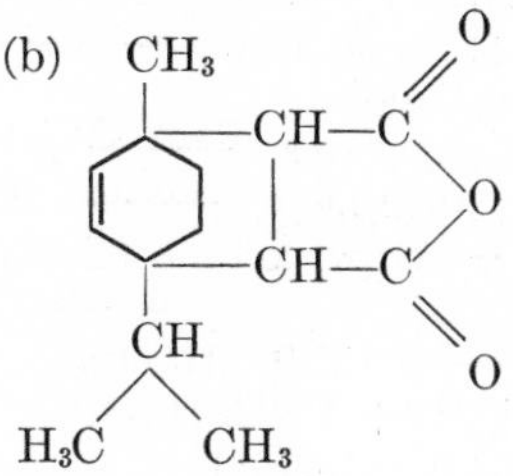

(c)

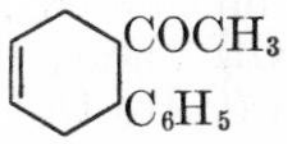

(d)

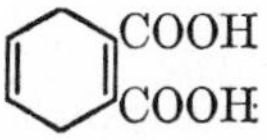

(e)

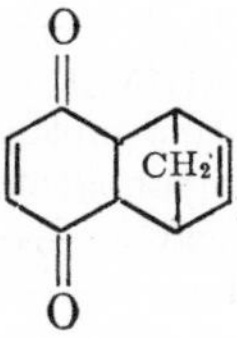

(f)

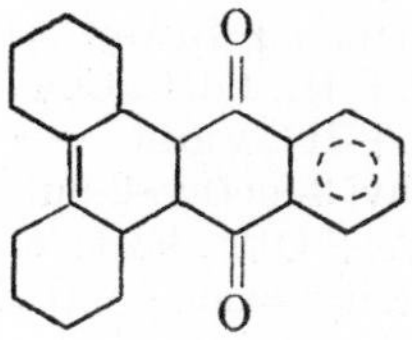

(g)

(h)

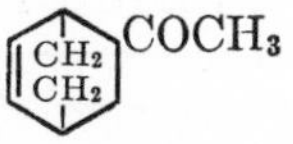

8. The following observations illustrate the stereochemistry of the Diels-Alder reaction:

maleic anhydride + 1,3-butadiene $\longrightarrow$ D ($C_8H_8O_3$)
D + H_2O, heat $\longrightarrow$ E ($C_8H_{10}O_4$)
E + H_2, Ni $\longrightarrow$ F ($C_8H_{12}O_4$), m.p. 192°
fumaryl chloride (trans-ClOCCH=CHCOCl) + 1,3-butadiene $\longrightarrow$ G ($C_8H_8O_2Cl_2$)
G + H_2O, heat $\longrightarrow$ H ($C_8H_{10}O_4$)
H + H_2, Ni $\longrightarrow$ I ($C_8H_{12}O_4$), m.p. 215°
I can be resolved; F cannot be resolved.

Does the Diels-Alder reaction involve a cis-addition or a trans-addition?

9. On the basis of your answer to Problem 8, give the stereochemical formulas of the products expected from each of the following reactions. Label meso compounds and racemates.

(a) crotonaldehyde (*trans*-2-butenal) + 1,3-butadiene
(b) *p*-benzoquinone + 1,3-butadiene
(c) maleic anhydride + 1,3-butadiene, followed by cold dilute $KMnO_4$
(d) maleic anhydride + 1,3-butadiene, followed by hot $KMnO_4$ $\longrightarrow$ $C_8H_{10}O_8$

10. Account for the following observations:

(a) Dehydration of 3-hydroxy-2,2-dimethylpropanoic acid yields 2-methyl-2-butenoic acid.

(b)
$$\left.\begin{array}{c} C_2H_5OOC—COOC_2H_5 \\ \text{Ethyl oxalate} \\ + \\ CH_3CH{=}CHCOOC_2H_5 \\ \text{Ethyl crotonate} \end{array}\right] \xrightarrow{OC_2H_5^-} C_2H_5OOC—\underset{\underset{O}{\|}}{C}—CH_2CH{=}CHCOOC_2H_5$$

11. Give structures of compounds J through JJ:

(a) glycerol + $NaHSO_4$, heat $\longrightarrow$ J (C_3H_4O)
    J + ethyl alcohol + HCl $\longrightarrow$ K $(C_7H_{15}O_2Cl)$
    K + NaOH, heat $\longrightarrow$ L $(C_7H_{14}O_2)$
    L + cold neutral $KMnO_4$ $\longrightarrow$ M $(C_7H_{16}O_4)$
    M + dilute H_2SO_4 $\longrightarrow$ N $(C_3H_6O_3)$ + ethyl alcohol

(b) $C_2H_5OOC—C{\equiv}C—COOC_2H_5$ + sodiomalonic ester $\longrightarrow$ O $(C_{15}H_{22}O_8)$
    O + OH^-, heat; then H^+; then heat $\longrightarrow$ P $(C_6H_6O_6)$, *aconitic acid*, found in sugar cane and beet root

(c) ethyl fumarate + sodiomalonic ester $\longrightarrow$ Q $(C_{15}H_{24}O_8)$
    Q + OH^-, heat; then H^+; then heat $\longrightarrow$ R $(C_6H_8O_6)$, *tricarballylic acid*

(d) benzil $(C_6H_5COCOC_6H_5)$ + benzyl ketone $(C_6H_5CH_2COCH_2C_6H_5)$ + base $\longrightarrow$ S $(C_{29}H_{20}O)$, "tetracyclone"
    S + maleic anhydride $\longrightarrow$ T $(C_{33}H_{22}O_4)$
    T + heat $\longrightarrow$ CO + H_2 + U $(C_{32}H_{20}O_3)$

(e) S + $C_6H_5C{\equiv}CH$ $\longrightarrow$ V $(C_{37}H_{26}O)$
    V + heat $\longrightarrow$ CO + W $(C_{36}H_{26})$

(f) acetone + $BrMgC{\equiv}COC_2H_5$, then H_2O $\longrightarrow$ X $(C_7H_{12}O_2)$
    X + H_2, $Pd/CaCO_3$ $\longrightarrow$ Y $(C_7H_{14}O_2)$
    Y + H^+, warm $\longrightarrow$ Z (C_5H_8O), β-methylcrotonaldehyde

(g) ethyl 3-methyl-2-butenoate + ethyl cyanoacetate + base $\longrightarrow$ AA $(C_{12}H_{19}O_4N)$
    AA + OH^-, heat; then H^+; then heat $\longrightarrow$ BB $(C_7H_{12}O_4)$

(h) mesityl oxide + ethyl malonate + base $\longrightarrow$ CC $(C_{13}H_{22}O_5)$
    CC + NaOBr, OH^-, heat; then H^+ $\longrightarrow$ $CHBr_3$ + BB $(C_7H_{12}O_4)$

(i) $CH_3C{\equiv}CNa$ + acetaldehyde $\longrightarrow$ DD (C_5H_8O)
    DD + $K_2Cr_2O_7$, H_2SO_4 $\longrightarrow$ EE (C_5H_6O)

(j) 3-pentyn-2-one + H_2O, Hg^{++}, H^+ $\longrightarrow$ FF $(C_5H_8O_2)$

(k) mesityl oxide + NaOCl, then H^+ $\longrightarrow$ GG $(C_5H_8O_2)$

(l) methallyl chloride (3-chloro-2-methylpropene) + HOCl $\longrightarrow$ HH $(C_4H_8OCl_2)$
    HH + KCN $\longrightarrow$ II $(C_6H_8ON_2)$
    II + H_2SO_4, H_2O, heat $\longrightarrow$ JJ $(C_6H_8O_4)$

12. *Spermine*, $H_2NCH_2CH_2CH_2NHCH_2CH_2CH_2CH_2NHCH_2CH_2CH_2NH_2$, found in seminal fluid, has been synthesized from acrylonitrile and 1,4-diamino-butane (putrescine). Show how this was probably done.

13. Outline all steps in each of the following syntheses:

(a) $HOOC—CH{=}CH—CH{=}CH—COOH$ from adipic acid
(b) $HC{\equiv}C—CHO$ from acrolein (*Hint:* see Problem 11(a) above.)
(c) $CH_3COCH{=}CH_2$ from acetone and formaldehyde
(d) $CH_3COCH{=}CH_2$ from vinylacetylene
(e) β-phenylglutaric acid from benzaldehyde and aliphatic reagents
(f) phenylsuccinic acid from benzaldehyde and aliphatic reagents
(g) 4-phenyl-2,6-heptanedione from benzaldehyde and aliphatic reagents (*Hint:* see Problem 3(f), page 742.)

CARBOHYDRATES I.
MONOSACCHARIDES

29.1 Introduction

In the leaf of a plant, the simple compounds carbon dioxide and water are combined to form the sugar **(+)-glucose.** This process, known as *photosynthesis*, requires catalysis by the green coloring matter *chlorophyll*, and requires energy in the form of light. Thousands of (+)-glucose molecules can then be combined to form the much larger molecules of **cellulose,** which constitutes the supporting framework of the plant. (+)-Glucose molecules can also be combined, in a somewhat different way, to form the large molecules of **starch,** which is then stored in the seeds to serve as food for a new, growing plant.

When eaten by an animal, the starch — and in the case of certain animals also the cellulose — is broken down into the original (+)-glucose units. These can be carried by the blood stream to the liver to be recombined into **glycogen,** or animal starch; when the need arises the glycogen can be broken down once more into (+)-glucose. (+)-Glucose is carried by the blood stream to the tissues, where it is oxidized, ultimately to carbon dioxide and water, with the release of the energy originally supplied as sunlight. Some of the (+)-glucose is converted into fats; some reacts with nitrogen-containing compounds to form amino acids, which in turn are combined to form the proteins that make up a large part of the animal body.

(+)-Glucose, cellulose, starch, and glycogen all belong to the class of organic compounds known as **carbohydrates.** Carbohydrates are the ultimate source of most of our food: we eat starch-containing grain, or feed it to animals to be converted into meat and fat which we then eat. We clothe ourselves with cellulose in the form of cotton and linen, rayon and cellulose acetate. We build houses and furniture from cellulose in the form of wood. Thus carbohydrates quite literally provide us with the necessities of life: food, clothing, and shelter.

Basic necessities aside, our present civilization depends to a surprising degree upon cellulose, particularly as *paper:* the books and newspapers we read, the letters we write, the bills we pay and the money and checks with which we pay them; marriage licenses, drivers' licenses, birth certificates, mortgages; paper in the form of bags and boxes, sheets and rolls.

The study of carbohydrates is one of the most exciting fields of organic chemistry. It extends from the tremendously complicated problem of understanding the process of photosynthesis to the equally difficult problem of unraveling the tangled steps in the enzyme-catalyzed reconversion of (+)-glucose into carbon dioxide and water. Between these two biochemical problems there lie the more traditional problems of the organic chemist: determination of the structure and properties of the carbohydrates, and the study of their conversion into other organic compounds.

In this book we shall learn something of the fundamental chemical properties of the carbohydrates, knowledge that is basic to any further study of these compounds.

29.2   Definition and classification

Carbohydrates are polyhydroxy aldehydes, polyhydroxy ketones, or compounds that can be hydrolyzed to them. A carbohydrate that cannot be hydrolyzed to simpler compounds is called a **monosaccharide.** A carbohydrate that can be hydrolyzed to two monosaccharide molecules is called a **disaccharide.** A carbohydrate that can be hydrolyzed to many monosaccharide molecules is called a **polysaccharide.**

A monosaccharide may be further classified. If it contains an aldehyde group it is known as an **aldose;** if it contains a keto group it is known as a **ketose.** Depending upon the number of carbon atoms it contains, a monosaccharide is known as a **triose, tetrose, pentose, hexose,** and so on. An **aldohexose,** for example, is a six-carbon monosaccharide containing an aldehyde group; a **ketopentose** is a five-carbon monosaccharide containing a keto group. Most naturally occurring monosaccharides are pentoses or hexoses.

Carbohydrates that reduce Fehling's (or Benedict's) or Tollens' reagent are known as **reducing sugars.** All monosaccharides, whether aldose or ketose, are reducing sugars. Most disaccharides are reducing sugars; sucrose (common table sugar) is a notable exception, for it is a non-reducing sugar.

29.3   (+)-Glucose: an aldohexose

Because it is the unit of which starch, cellulose, and glycogen are made up, and because of its special role in biological processes, (+)-glucose is by far the most abundant monosaccharide — there are probably more (+)-glucose units in nature than any other organic group — and by far the most important monosaccharide.

Most of what we need to know about monosaccharides we can learn from the study of just this one compound, and indeed from the study of just one aspect: its structure, and how that structure was arrived at. In learning about the structure of (+)-glucose we shall at the same time learn about its properties, since it is on these properties that the structure has been based. (+)-Glucose is a typical monosaccharide, so that in learning about its structure and properties, we shall be learning about the structure and properties of the other members of this family.

(+)-Glucose has the molecular formula $C_6H_{12}O_6$, as shown by elemental analysis and molecular weight determination. Among the properties that give evidence for its structure are:

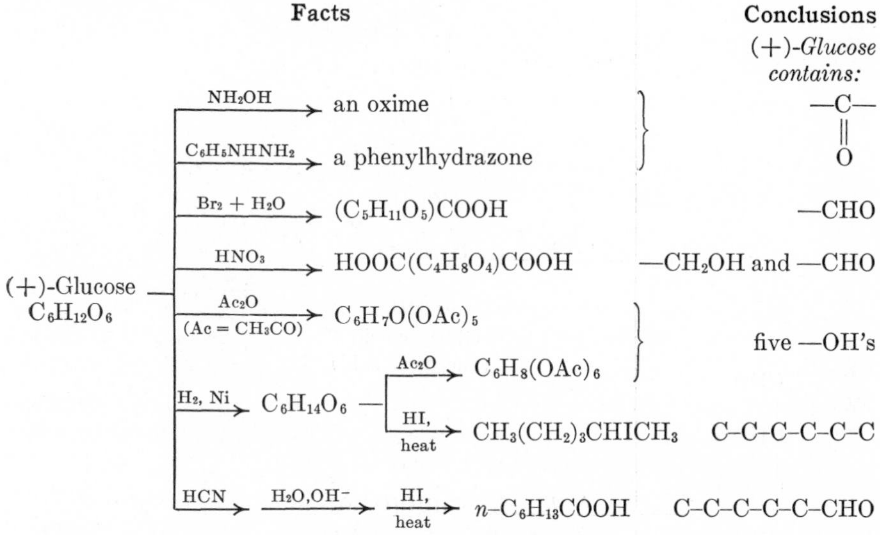

Facts	Conclusions
	(+)-*Glucose contains:*

Figure 29.1 (next page) shows that this evidence is consistent with the idea that (+)-glucose is a six-carbon, straight-chain, pentahydroxy aldehyde, that is, (+)-glucose is an aldohexose. (However, as we shall see in Sec. 29.14, there is additional evidence that will require us to modify this structure in one important way.)

29.4 (−)-Fructose: a 2-ketohexose

The most important ketose is **(−)-fructose,** which occurs widely in fruits and, combined with glucose, in the disaccharide *sucrose* (common table sugar).

The following sequence shows that (−)-fructose is a ketone rather than an aldehyde, and gives the position of the keto group in the chain:

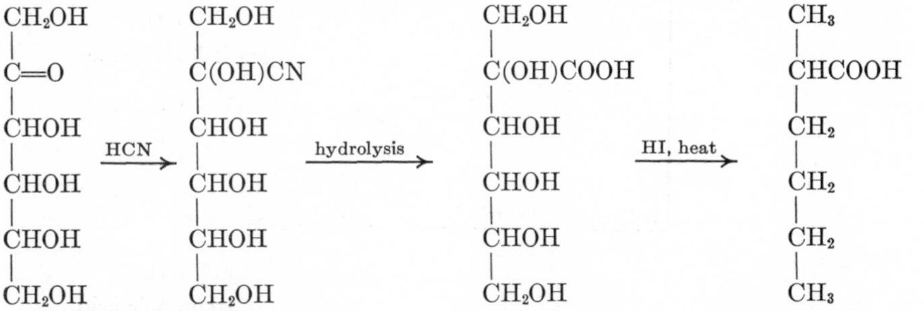

Fructose is thus a 2-ketohexose.

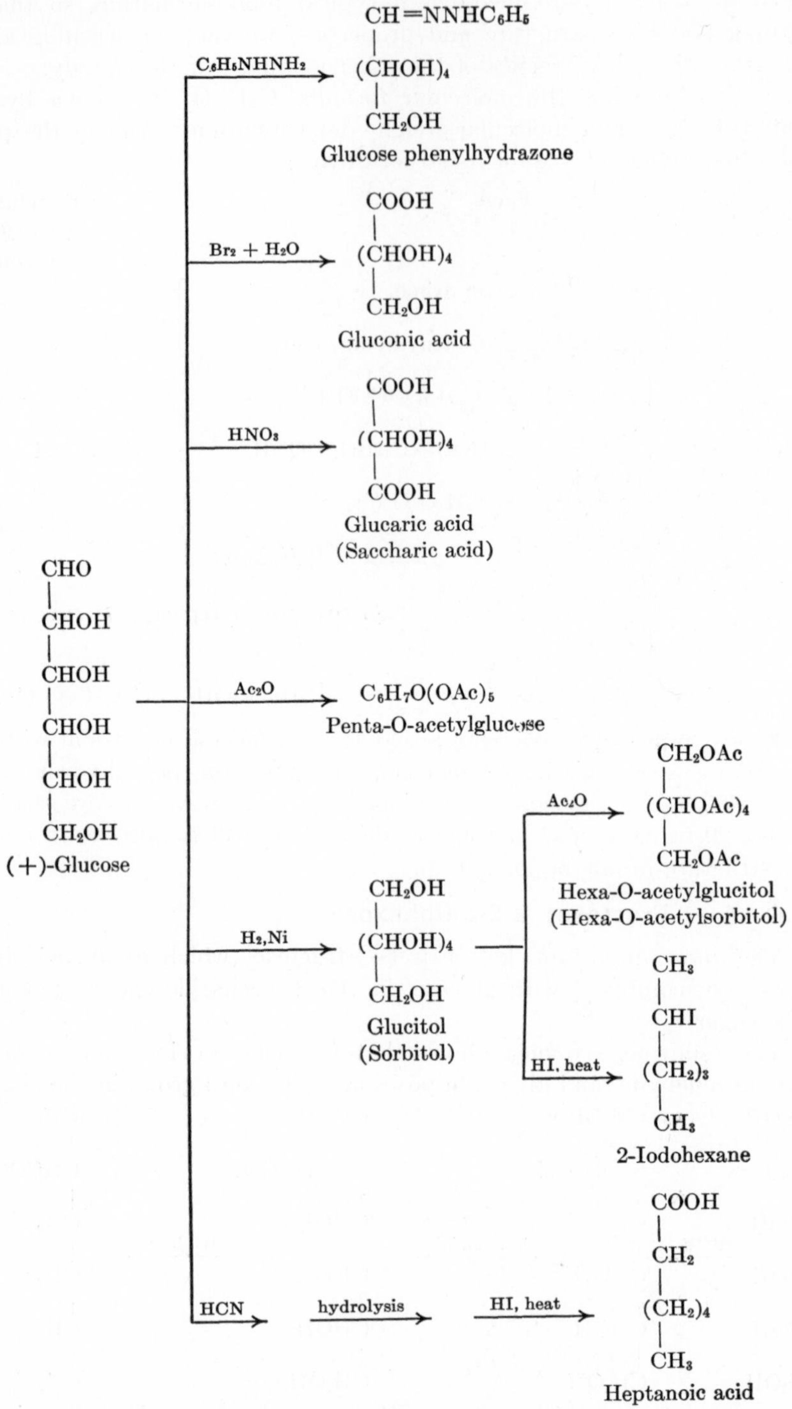

FIGURE 29.1. (+)-Glucose as an aldohexose.

29.5 Stereoisomers of (+)-glucose. Nomenclature of aldose derivatives

If we examine the structural formula we have drawn for glucose, we see that it contains four asymmetric carbon atoms (marked by asterisks):

$$
\begin{array}{ll}
1 & \text{CHO} \\
2 & *\,\text{CHOH} \\
3 & *\,\text{CHOH} \\
4 & *\,\text{CHOH} \\
5 & *\,\text{CHOH} \\
6 & \text{CH}_2\text{OH}
\end{array}
$$

Each of the possible stereoisomers is commonly represented by a "cross" formula, as, for example, in I.

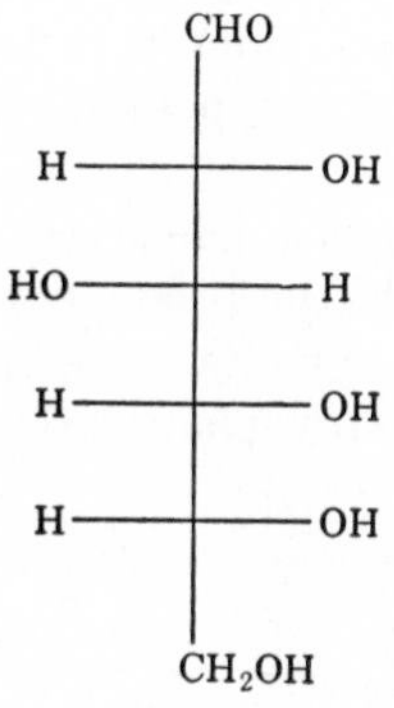

stands for

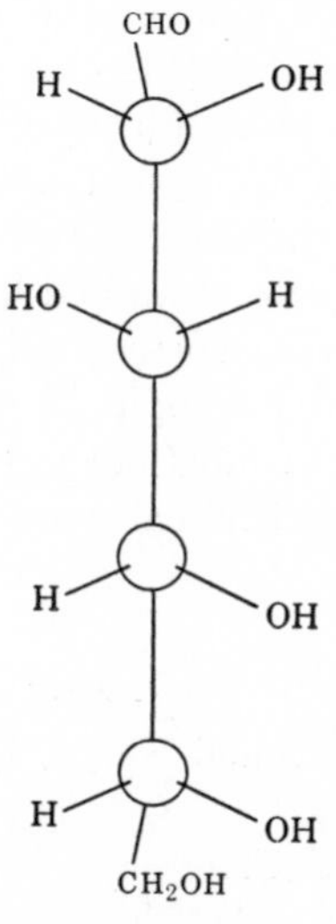

As always in formulas of this kind, it is understood that *horizontal* lines represent bonds coming *toward us* out of the plane of the paper, and *vertical* lines represent bonds going *away from us* behind the plane of the paper.

Only molecular models can show us what is really meant by formulas like I. A correct model of one of these stereoisomers is difficult to build unless we follow certain rules first clearly stated by the great carbohydrate chemist Emil Fischer:

(1) Construct a chain of carbon atoms with a —CHO group at one end and a —CH₂OH group at the other. (2) Hold the —CHO group in one hand and let the rest of the chain hang down. (3) Take the —CH₂OH group at the bottom end in the other hand and bring it up *behind* the chain until it touches the —CHO group. (4) Now one hand can hold both groups firmly and the rest of the chain will form a rather rigid ring projecting *toward you*. (This is the object of the whole operation up to this point: to impart rigidity to an otherwise flexible chain.) By this procedure you have —CHO above —CH₂OH as in formula I, and both these

groups directed *away from you.* (5) Finally, still holding the ring as described above, look in turn at each carbon atom, and attach the —OH or —H to the right or to the left just as it appears in the "cross" formula. In each case, these groups will be directed *toward you.*

The dissimilarity of the two ends of an aldohexose molecule prevents the existence of *meso* compounds (Sec. 24.5), and hence we expect that there should be 2^4 or 16 stereoisomers — eight pairs of enantiomers. All 16 of these possible stereoisomers are now known, through either synthesis in the laboratory or isolation from natural sources; only three — (+)-glucose, (+)-mannose, (+)-galactose — are found in abundance.

Problem 29.1 Draw a "cross" formula of one enantiomer of each of these eight pairs, placing —CHO at the top, —CH$_2$OH at the bottom, and —OH on the right on the lowest asymmetric carbon (C–5).

Of these 16 isomers only one is the (+)-glucose that we have described as the most abundant monosaccharide. A second isomer is (−)-glucose, the enantiomer of the naturally occurring compound. The other 14 isomers are all diastereomers of (+)-glucose, and are given names of their own, e.g., *mannose, galactose, gulose*, etc. As we might expect, these other aldohexoses undergo the same set of reactions that we have described for glucose. Although as diastereomers they undergo these reactions at different rates and yield different individual compounds, the chemistry is essentially the same.

The products obtained from these other aldohexoses are generally given names that correspond to the names of the products obtained from glucose. This principle is illustrated in Table 29.1 for the aldohexose (+)-mannose, which occurs naturally in many plants (the name is derived from the Biblical word *manna*).

TABLE 29.1

NAMES OF ALDOSE DERIVATIVES

Type of Compound	Type Name	Examples of Specific Names	
Monosaccharide HOCH$_2$(CHOH)$_n$CHO ↓ Br_2/H_2O	Glycose	*Glucose*	*Mannose*
Monocarboxylic acid HOCH$_2$(CHOH)$_n$COOH ↓ HNO_3	Glyconic acid	*Gluconic acid*	*Mannonic acid*
Dicarboxylic acid HOOC(CHOH)$_n$COOH	Glycaric acid	*Glucaric acid* (*Saccharic acid*)	*Mannaric acid* (*Mannosaccharic acid*)
Polyhydroxy alcohol HOCH$_2$(CHOH)$_n$CH$_2$OH	Glykitol	*Glucitol* (*Sorbitol*)	*Mannitol*
Aldehydo acid HOOC(CHOH)$_n$CHO	Glycuronic acid	*Glucuronic acid*	*Mannuronic acid*

The structural formula we have drawn to represent (+)-glucose so far could actually represent any of the 16 aldohexoses. Only when we have specified the configuration about each of the asymmetric carbons will we have the structural formula that applies only to (+)-glucose itself. Before we can discuss the brilliant way in which the configuration of (+)-glucose was worked out, we must first learn a little more about the chemistry of monosaccharides.

Problem 29.2   (a) How many asymmetric carbon atoms are there in (−)-fructose? (b) How many stereoisomeric 2-ketohexoses should there be? (c) Draw a "cross" formula of one enantiomer of each pair, placing C=O near the top, and —OH on the right on the lowest asymmetric carbon (C–5).

29.6 Oxidation. Effect of alkali

Aldoses can be oxidized in four important ways: (a) by Fehling's or Tollens' reagent; (b) by bromine water; (c) by nitric acid; and (d) by periodic acid, HIO_4.

Aldoses reduce **Fehling's** and **Tollens' reagents;** as aldehydes they would be expected to do this (Sec. 23.8). This reaction is less useful, however, than we might at first have expected.

In the first place, it cannot be used to differentiate aldoses from ketoses. Ketoses, too, reduce Fehling's and Tollens' reagents; this behavior is characteristic of α-hydroxy ketones.

In the second place, oxidation by Fehling's or Tollens' reagent cannot be used for the preparation of glyconic acids (monocarboxylic acids) from aldoses. Both Fehling's and Tollens' reagents are alkaline reagents, and the treatment of sugars with alkali can cause extensive isomerization and even decomposition of the chain. Alkali exerts this effect, in part at least, by establishing an equilibrium between the monosaccharide and an enediol structure.

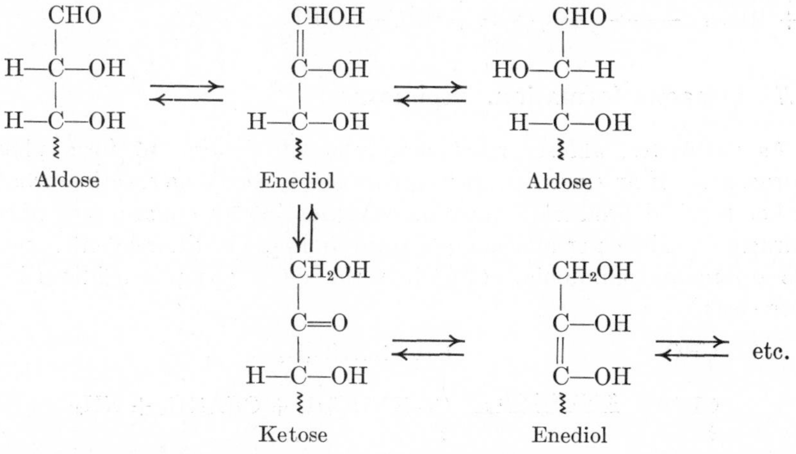

Bromine water oxidizes aldoses, but not ketoses; as an acidic reagent it does not cause isomerization of the molecule. It can therefore be used to differentiate an aldose from a ketose, and is the reagent chosen to synthesize the *glyconic acid* (monocarboxylic acid) from an aldose.

Treatment of an aldose with the more vigorous oxidizing agent **nitric acid** brings about oxidation not only of the —CHO group but also of the

—CH_2OH group, and leads to the formation of the *glycaric acid* (dicarboxylic acid).

$$
\begin{array}{c}
\text{CHO} \\
| \\
\text{(CHOH)}_n \\
| \\
\text{CH}_2\text{OH} \\
\text{Aldose}
\end{array}
\quad
\xrightarrow[\quad\text{HNO}_3\quad]{\quad\text{Br}_2 + \text{H}_2\text{O}\quad}
$$

$$
\begin{array}{c}
\text{COOH} \\
| \\
\text{(CHOH)}_n \\
| \\
\text{CH}_2\text{OH} \\
\text{Glyconic acid} \\
\\
\text{COOH} \\
| \\
\text{(CHOH)}_n \\
| \\
\text{COOH} \\
\text{Glycaric acid}
\end{array}
$$

Like other compounds that contain two or more —OH or =O groups on *adjacent* carbon atoms, carbohydrates undergo oxidative cleavage by **periodic acid,** HIO_4 (Sec. 24.9). This reaction, introduced in 1928 by Malaprade (University of Nancy, France) is one of the most useful tools in modern research on carbohydrate structure.

Problem 29.3 Treatment of (+)-glucose with HIO_4 gives results that confirm its aldohexose structure. What products should be formed, and how much HIO_4 should be consumed?

Problem 29.4 Identify each of the following glucose derivatives:

A + $4HIO_4$ ⟶ 3HCOOH + HCHO + OHC—COOH
B + $5HIO_4$ ⟶ 4HCOOH + 2HCHO
C + $3HIO_4$ ⟶ 2HCOOH + 2OHC—COOH
D + $4HIO_4$ ⟶ 4HCOOH + OHC—COOH

29.7 Osazone formation. Epimers

As aldehydes, aldoses react with phenylhydrazine to form phenylhydrazones. If an excess of phenylhydrazine is used, the reaction proceeds further to yield products known as **osazones,** which contain two phenylhydrazine residues per molecule; a third molecule of the reagent is turned into aniline and ammonia. (Just how the —OH group is oxidized is not quite clear.)

$$
\begin{array}{c}
\text{CHO} \\
| \\
\text{CHOH} \\
\wr
\end{array}
\quad
\xrightarrow{\quad 3C_6H_5NHNH_2\quad}
\quad
\begin{array}{c}
\text{CH}{=}\text{NNHC}_6\text{H}_5 \\
| \\
\text{C}{=}\text{NNHC}_6\text{H}_5 + C_6H_5NH_2 + NH_3 \\
\wr
\end{array}
$$

Aldose   Osazone

Osazone formation is not limited to carbohydrates, but is typical of α-hydroxy aldehydes and α-hydroxy ketones in general (e.g., *benzoin,* $C_6H_5CHOHCOC_6H_5$).

Removal of the phenylhydrazine groups yields dicarbonyl compounds known as **osones.** For example:

CH=NNHC$_6$H$_5$　　　　　　　　　　CHO
|　　　　　　　　　　　　　　　　　　　|
C=NNHC$_6$H$_5$　$\xrightarrow{\text{C}_6\text{H}_5\text{CHO, H}^+}$　C=O　+　2C$_6$H$_5$CH=NNHC$_6$H$_5$
⌇　　　　　　　　　　　　　　　　　⌇

Osazone　　　　　　　　　　Osone　　Benzaldehyde phenylhydrazone

Problem 29.5　Aldehydes are more easily reduced than ketones.　On this basis what product would you expect from the reduction of glucosone by zinc and acetic acid?　Outline a sequence of reactions by which an aldose can be turned into a 2-ketose.

In 1858 Peter Griess (in time taken from his duties in an English brewery) discovered diazonium salts (Chapter 21).　In 1875 Emil Fischer (at the University of Munich) found that reduction of benzenediazonium chloride by sulfur dioxide yields phenylhydrazine.　Nine years later, in 1884, Fischer reported that the phenylhydrazine he had discovered could be used as a powerful tool in the study of carbohydrates.

One of the difficulties of working with carbohydrates is their tendency to form sirups, rather than solids that can be readily handled and purified. Treatment with phenylhydrazine converts carbohydrates into easily isolable osazones that can be identified by their characteristic crystalline forms.

Fischer found osazone formation to be useful not only in identifying carbohydrates, but also — and this was much more important — in determining their configurations.　For example, the two diastereomeric aldohexoses (+)-glucose and (+)-mannose yield the same osazone. Osazone formation destroys the configuration about C–2 of an aldose, but does not affect the configuration of the rest of the molecule.

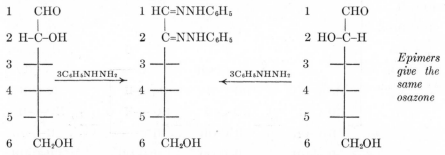

It therefore follows that (+)-glucose and (+)-mannose differ only in configuration about C–2, and have the same configuration about C–3, C–4, and C–5.　We can see that whenever the configuration of either of these compounds is established, the configuration of the other is immediately known through this osazone relationship.　*A pair of diastereomeric aldoses that differ only in configuration about C–2 are called* **epimers.** One way in which a pair of aldoses can be identified as epimers is through the formation of the same osazone.

Problem 29.6　When the ketohexose (−)-fructose is treated with phenylhydrazine, it yields an osazone that is identical with the one prepared from either (+)-glucose or (+)-mannose.　How is the configuration of (−)-fructose related to those of (+)-glucose and (+)-mannose?

29.8 Lengthening the carbon chain of aldoses. The Kiliani-Fischer synthesis

In the next few sections we shall examine some of the ways in which an aldose can be converted into a different aldose. These conversions can be used not only to synthesize new carbohydrates but also, as we shall see, to help determine their configurations.

First, let us look at a method for converting an aldose into another aldose containing one more carbon atom, that is, at a method for lengthening the carbon chain. In 1886, Heinrich Kiliani (at the Technische Hochschule in Munich) showed that an aldose can be converted into two glyconic acids of the next higher carbon number by addition of HCN and hydrolysis of the resulting cyanohydrins. In 1890, Fischer reported that reduction of a glyconic acid (in the form of its lactone, Sec. 27.3) can be controlled to yield the corresponding aldose. The entire **Kiliani-Fischer synthesis** is illustrated for the conversion of an aldopentose into two aldohexoses.

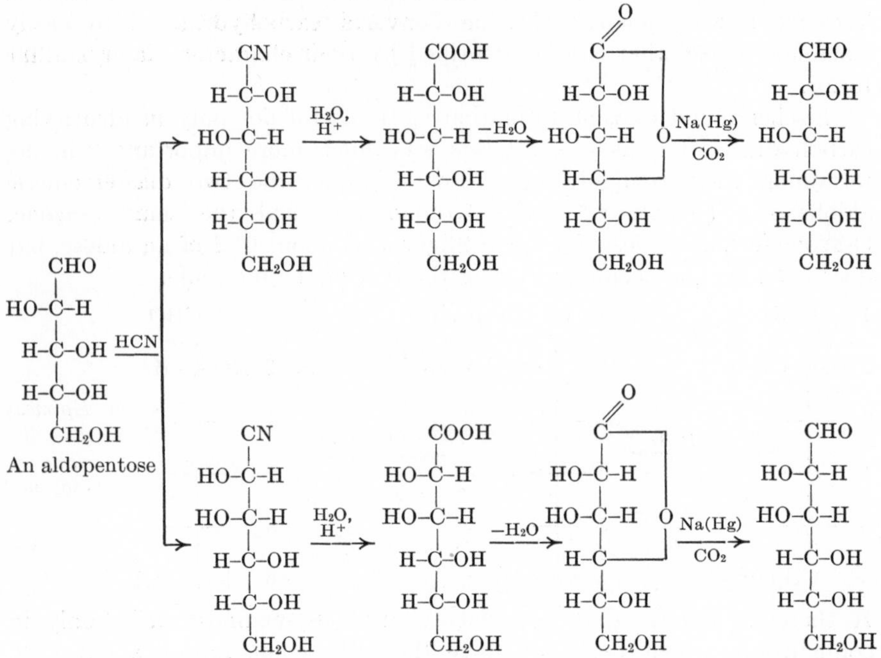

Diastereomeric cyanohydrins — Diastereomeric glyconic acids — Diastereomeric glyconolactones — Diastereomeric aldohexoses

Mixture usually separated at this point

Epimers

Addition of cyanide to the aldopentose generates a new asymmetric carbon, about which there are two possible configurations (see Sec. 27.6). As a result, two diastereomeric cyanohydrins are obtained, which yield diastereomeric carboxylic acids (glyconic acids) and finally diastereomeric aldoses.

Since a six-carbon glyconic acid contains —OH groups in the γ- and δ-positions, we would expect it to form a lactone under acidic conditions (Sec. 27.3). This occurs, the γ-lactone generally being the more stable product. It is the lactone that is actually reduced to an aldose in the last step of a Kiliani-Fischer synthesis.

The pair of aldoses obtained from the sequence differ only in configuration about C–2, and hence are epimers. A pair of aldoses can be recognized as epimers not only by their conversion into the same osazone (Sec. 29.7), but also by their formation in the same Kiliani-Fischer synthesis.

Like other diastereomers, these epimers differ in physical properties and therefore are separable. However, since carbohydrates are difficult to purify, it is usually more convenient to separate the diastereomeric products at the acid stage, where crystalline salts are easily formed, so that a single pure lactone can be reduced to a single pure aldose.

Problem 29.7 (a) Using cross formulas to show configuration, outline all steps in a Kiliani-Fischer synthesis, starting with the aldotriose D-(+)-glyceraldehyde (Sec. 27.5). How many aldotetroses would be expected?

(b) Give configurations of the aldopentoses expected from each of these aldotetroses by a Kiliani-Fischer synthesis; of the aldohexoses expected from each of these aldopentoses.

(c) Make a "family tree" showing configurations of these aldoses hypothetically descended from D-(+)-glyceraldehyde. What family designation (D or L) should be given to all these aldoses? If the —CHO is placed at the top in each case, what configurational feature is the same in all these formulas? Why?

(d) What designation (D or L) would be given to all the aldoses hypothetically descended from L-(−)-glyceraldehyde? What common configurational feature would their formulas have? Why?

(e) What was the status before 1949 of the configurations given above? After 1949?

Problem 29.8 Give the configuration and name of the dicarboxylic acid (glycaric acid) that would be obtained by nitric acid oxidation of each of the tetroses derived from D-(+)-glyceraldehyde. Derived from L-(−)-glyceraldehyde. Which are optically active, which optically inactive? Which are members of the D-family? Of the L-family? Of neither family?

29.9 Shortening the carbon chain of aldoses. The Ruff degradation

An aldohexose   A glyconic acid   A calcium glyconate   An aldopentose

There are a number of ways in which an aldose can be converted into another aldose of one less carbon atom. One of these methods for shortening the carbon chain is the **Ruff degradation.** An aldose is oxidized by bromine water to the glyconic acid; oxidation of the calcium salt of this acid by hydrogen peroxide in the presence of ferric salts yields carbonate ion and an aldose of one less carbon atom.

29.10   Conversion of an aldose into its epimer

In the presence of a tertiary amine, in particular pyridine (Sec. 32.6), an equilibrium is established between a glyconic acid and its epimer. This reaction is the basis of the best method for converting an aldose into its epimer, since the only configuration affected is that at C–2. The aldose is oxidized by bromine water to the glyconic acid, which is then treated with pyridine. From the equilibrium mixture thus formed, the epimeric glyconic acid is separated, and reduced (in the form of its lactone) to the epimeric aldose. For example:

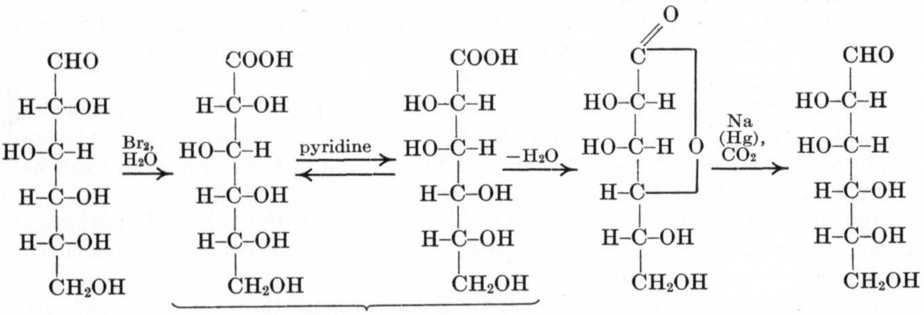

An aldohexose   Epimeric glyconic acids   A glyconolactone   Epimeric aldohexose

29.11   Configuration of (+)-glucose.   The Fischer proof

Let us turn back to the year 1888. Only a few monosaccharides were known, among them (+)-glucose, (−)-fructose, (+)-arabinose. (+)–Mannose had just been synthesized. It was known that (+)-glucose was an aldohexose and that (+)-arabinose was an aldopentose. Emil Fischer had discovered (1884) that phenylhydrazine could convert carbohydrates into osazones. The Kiliani cyanohydrin method for lengthening the chain was just two years old.

It was known that aldoses could be reduced to glykitols, and could be oxidized to the monocarboxylic glyconic acids and to the dicarboxylic glycaric acids. A theory of optical isomerism had been proposed (1874) by van't Hoff and Le Bel. Methods for separating optical isomers were known and optical activity could be measured. The concepts of racemates, *meso* compounds, and epimers were well established.

(+)-Glucose was known to be an aldohexose; but as an aldohexose it could have any one of 16 possible configurations. The question was: *which* configuration did it have? In 1888, Emil Fischer (at the University of Würzburg) set out to find the answer to that question, and in 1891 announced the completion of a most remarkable piece of chemical research, for which he received the Nobel Prize in 1902. Let us follow Fischer's steps to the configuration of (+)-glucose. Although somewhat modified, the following arguments are essentially those of Fischer.

The 16 possible configurations consist of eight pairs of enantiomers. Since methods of determining absolute configuration were not then available, Fischer realized that he could at best limit the configuration of (+)-glucose to a pair of enantiomeric configurations; he would not be able to tell which one of the pair was the correct absolute configuration.

To simplify the problem, Fischer therefore rejected eight of the possible configurations, arbitrarily retaining only those (I–VIII) in which C–5 carried the —OH on the right (with the understanding that —H and —OH project toward the observer). He realized that any argument that led to the selection of one of these formulas applied with equal force to the mirror image of that formula. (As it turned out, his arbitrary choice of an —OH on the right of C–5 in (+)-glucose was the correct one.)

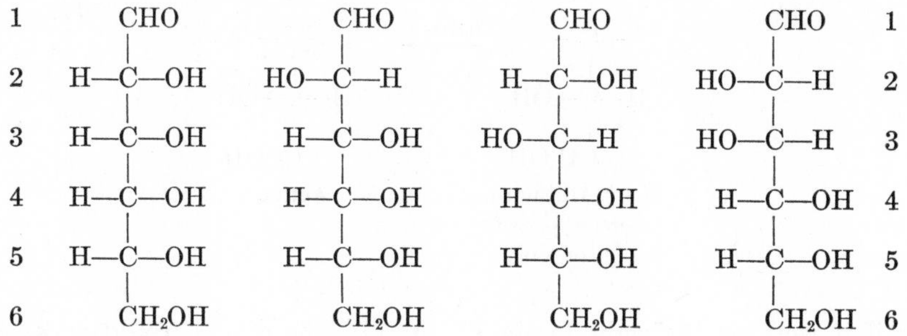

	I	II	III	IV	
1	CHO	CHO	CHO	CHO	1
2	H—C—OH	HO—C—H	H—C—OH	HO—C—H	2
3	H—C—OH	H—C—OH	HO—C—H	HO—C—H	3
4	H—C—OH	H—C—OH	H—C—OH	H—C—OH	4
5	H—C—OH	H—C—OH	H—C—OH	H—C—OH	5
6	CH₂OH	CH₂OH	CH₂OH	CH₂OH	6

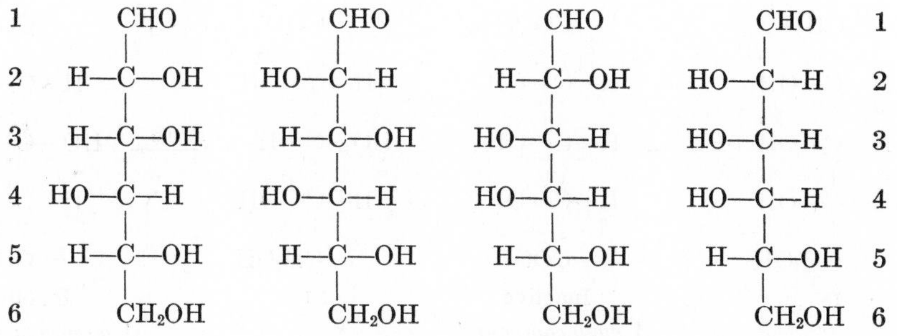

	V	VI	VII	VIII	
1	CHO	CHO	CHO	CHO	1
2	H—C—OH	HO—C—H	H—C—OH	HO—C—H	2
3	H—C—OH	H—C—OH	HO—C—H	HO—C—H	3
4	HO—C—H	HO—C—H	HO—C—H	HO—C—H	4
5	H—C—OH	H—C—OH	H—C—OH	H—C—OH	5
6	CH₂OH	CH₂OH	CH₂OH	CH₂OH	6

Since his proof depended in part on the relationship between (+)-glucose and the aldopentose (−)-arabinose, Fischer also had to consider the configurations of the five-carbon aldoses. Of the eight possible configurations, he retained only four, IX–XII, again those in which the bottom asymmetric carbon atom carried the —OH on the right.

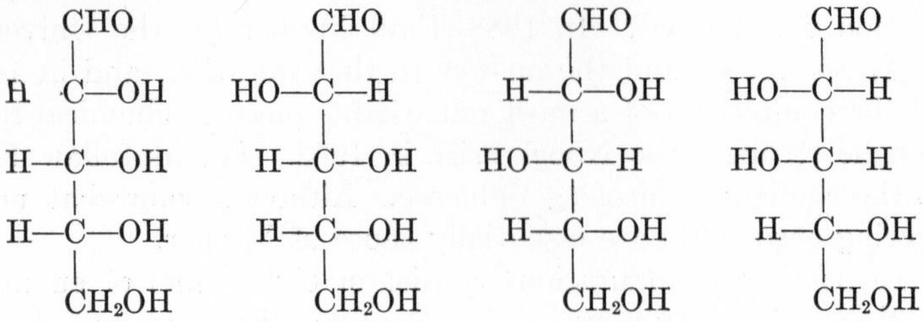

```
      CHO              CHO              CHO              CHO
       |                |                |                |
  H—C—OH          HO—C—H           H—C—OH           HO—C—H
       |                |                |                |
  H—C—OH           H—C—OH           HO—C—H           HO—C—H
       |                |                |                |
  H—C—OH           H—C—OH           H—C—OH           H—C—OH
       |                |                |                |
    CH₂OH            CH₂OH            CH₂OH            CH₂OH
      IX                X               XI               XII
```

The line of argument is as follows:

(1) Upon oxidation by nitric acid, (−)-arabinose yields an optically active dicarboxylic acid. Since the —OH on the lowest asymmetric carbon atom is arbitrarily placed on the right, this fact means that the —OH on the uppermost asymmetric carbon atom is on the left (as in X or XII),

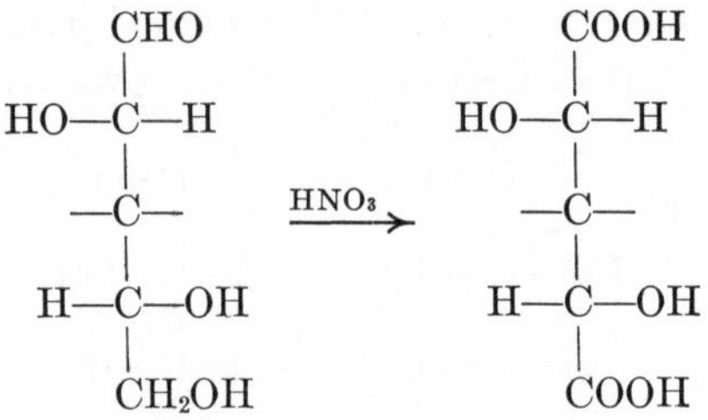

```
      CHO                         COOH
       |                            |
  HO—C—H                      HO—C—H
       |          HNO₃             |
    —C—          ———→          —C—
       |                            |
  H—C—OH                       H—C—OH
       |                            |
    CH₂OH                        COOH
  (−)-Arabinose                 Active
  Partial formula
  X or XII
```

for if it were on the right (as in IX or XI), the diacid would necessarily be an inactive *meso* acid.

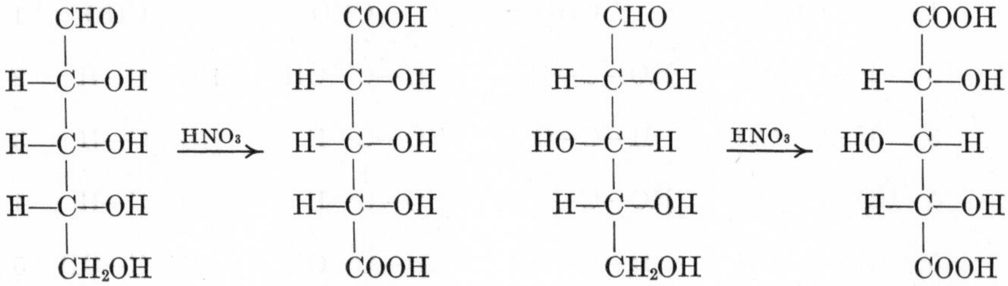

```
      CHO              COOH             CHO              COOH
       |                |                |                |
  H—C—OH          H—C—OH           H—C—OH           H—C—OH
       |    HNO₃       |                |    HNO₃       |
  H—C—OH   ——→    H—C—OH           HO—C—H   ——→    HO—C—H
       |                |                |                |
  H—C—OH          H—C—OH           H—C—OH           H—C—OH
       |                |                |                |
    CH₂OH            COOH             CH₂OH            COOH
      IX            Inactive            XI            Inactive
              A meso compound                    A meso compound
```

(2) (−)-Arabinose is converted by the Kiliani-Fischer synthesis into (+)-glucose and (+)-mannose. (+)-Glucose and (+)-mannose therefore are epimers, differing only in configuration about C–2, and have the same configuration about C–3, C–4, and C–5 as does (−)-arabinose. (+)-Glucose and (+)-mannose must be III and IV, or VII and VIII.

$$
\begin{array}{cccc}
 & 1 & \text{CHO} & \text{CHO} \quad 1 \\
 & & | & | \\
\text{CHO} & 2 & \text{H—C—OH} & \text{HO—C—H} \quad 2 \\
| & & | & | \\
\text{HO—C—H} & 3 & \text{HO—C—H} & \text{HO—C—H} \quad 3 \\
| & & & \text{and} \\
\text{—C—} \longrightarrow & 4 & \text{—C—} & \text{—C—} \quad 4 \\
| & & | & | \\
\text{H—C—OH} & 5 & \text{H—C—OH} & \text{H—C—OH} \quad 5 \\
| & & | & | \\
\text{CH}_2\text{OH} & 6 & \text{CH}_2\text{OH} & \text{CH}_2\text{OH} \quad 6 \\
\end{array}
$$

(−)-Arabinose
Partial formula
x or xii

(+)-Glucose and (+)-Mannose: epimers
Partial formulas
iii and iv, or vii and viii

(3) Upon oxidation by nitric acid, both (+)-glucose and (+)-mannose yield dicarboxylic acids that are optically active. This means that the —OH on C–4 is on the right, as in III and IV,

$$
\begin{array}{cccc}
1 \quad \text{CHO} & \text{COOH} & 1 \quad \text{CHO} & \text{COOH} \\
| & | & | & | \\
2 \quad \text{H—C—OH} & \text{H—C—OH} & 2 \; \text{HO—C—H} & \text{HO—C—H} \\
| & | & | & | \\
3 \; \text{HO—C—H} & \text{HO—C—H} & 3 \; \text{HO—C—H} & \text{HO—C—H} \\
| \quad \xrightarrow{\text{HNO}_3} & | & | \quad \xrightarrow{\text{HNO}_3} & | \\
4 \quad \text{H—C—OH} & \text{H—C—OH} & 4 \quad \text{H—C—OH} & \text{H—C—OH} \\
| & | & | & | \\
5 \quad \text{H—C—OH} & \text{H—C—OH} & 5 \quad \text{H—C—OH} & \text{H—C—OH} \\
| & | & | & | \\
6 \quad \text{CH}_2\text{OH} & \text{COOH} & 6 \quad \text{CH}_2\text{OH} & \text{COOH} \\
\text{iii} & \textbf{Active} & \text{iv} & \textbf{Active} \\
\end{array}
$$

for if it were on the left, as in VII and VIII, *one* of the glycaric acids would necessarily be an inactive *meso* acid.

$$
\begin{array}{cccc}
\text{CHO} & \text{COOH} & \text{CHO} & \text{COOH} \\
| & | & | & | \\
\text{H—C—OH} & \text{H—C—OH} & \text{HO—C—H} & \text{HO—C—H} \\
| & | & | & | \\
\text{HO—C—H} & \text{HO—C—H} & \text{HO—C—H} & \text{HO—C—H} \\
| \quad \xrightarrow{\text{HNO}_3} & | & | \quad \xrightarrow{\text{HNO}_3} & | \\
\text{HO—C—H} & \text{HO—C—H} & \text{HO—C—H} & \text{HO—C—H} \\
| & | & | & | \\
\text{H—C—OH} & \text{H—C—OH} & \text{H—C—OH} & \text{H—C—OH} \\
| & | & | & | \\
\text{CH}_2\text{OH} & \text{COOH} & \text{CH}_2\text{OH} & \text{COOH} \\
\text{vii} & \textbf{Inactive} & \text{viii} & \textbf{Active} \\
 & \textit{A meso compound} & & \\
\end{array}
$$

(−)-Arabinose must also have that same —OH on the right, and hence has configuration X (next page).

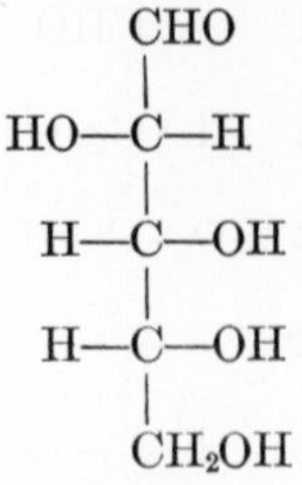

$$
\begin{array}{c}
\text{CHO} \\
| \\
\text{HO—C—H} \\
| \\
\text{H—C—OH} \\
| \\
\text{H—C—OH} \\
| \\
\text{CH}_2\text{OH}
\end{array}
$$

x
(±)-Arabinose

(+)-Glucose and (+)-mannose have configurations III and IV, but one question remains: which compound has which configuration? One more step is needed.

(4) Oxidation of another hexose, (−)-gulose, yields the same dicarboxylic acid, (+)-glucaric acid, as does oxidation of (+)-glucose. (The gulose was synthesized for this purpose by Fischer.) If we examine the two possible configurations for (+)-glucaric acid, IIIa and IVa, we see that only IIIa can be derived from two different hexoses: from III and the enantiomer of V.

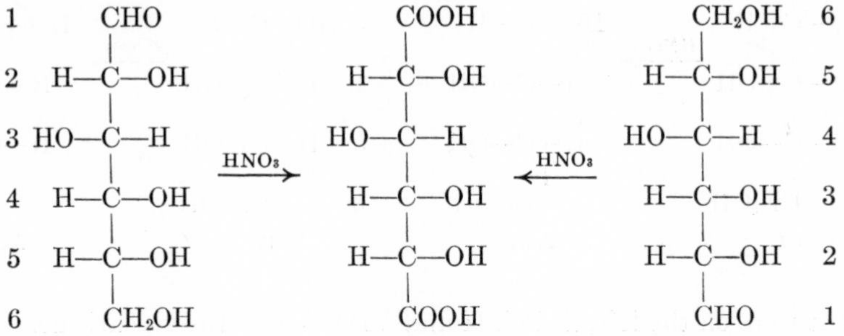

$$
\begin{array}{llll}
1 & \text{CHO} & \text{COOH} & \text{CH}_2\text{OH} \quad 6 \\
2 & \text{H—C—OH} & \text{H—C—OH} & \text{H—C—OH} \quad 5 \\
3 & \text{HO—C—H} & \text{HO—C—H} & \text{HO—C—H} \quad 4 \\
  & \xrightarrow{\text{HNO}_3} & \xleftarrow{\text{HNO}_3} & \\
4 & \text{H—C—OH} & \text{H—C—OH} & \text{H—C—OH} \quad 3 \\
5 & \text{H—C—OH} & \text{H—C—OH} & \text{H—C—OH} \quad 2 \\
6 & \text{CH}_2\text{OH} & \text{COOH} & \text{CHO} \quad 1 \\
  & \text{III} & \text{IIIa} & \text{Enantiomer of V}
\end{array}
$$

The acid IVa can be derived from just one hexose: from IV.

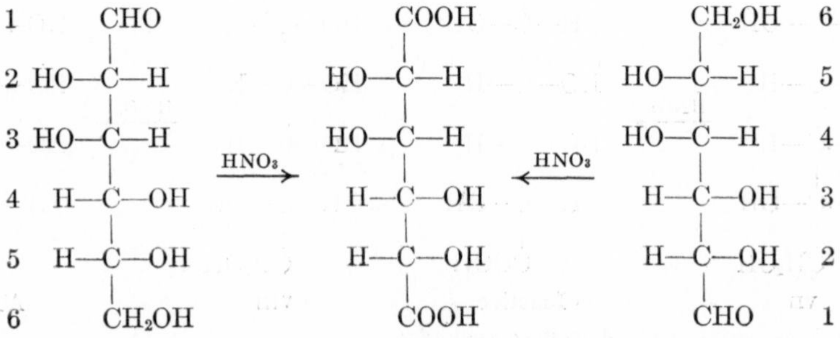

$$
\begin{array}{llll}
1 & \text{CHO} & \text{COOH} & \text{CH}_2\text{OH} \quad 6 \\
2 & \text{HO—C—H} & \text{HO—C—H} & \text{HO—C—H} \quad 5 \\
3 & \text{HO—C—H} & \text{HO—C—H} & \text{HO—C—H} \quad 4 \\
  & \xrightarrow{\text{HNO}_3} & \xleftarrow{\text{HNO}_3} & \\
4 & \text{H—C—OH} & \text{H—C—OH} & \text{H—C—OH} \quad 3 \\
5 & \text{H—C—OH} & \text{H—C—OH} & \text{H—C—OH} \quad 2 \\
6 & \text{CH}_2\text{OH} & \text{COOH} & \text{CHO} \quad 1 \\
  & \text{IV} & \text{IVa} & \text{IV (rotated 180°)}
\end{array}
$$

It follows that (+)-glucaric acid has configuration IIIa, and therefore that (+)-glucose has configuration III.

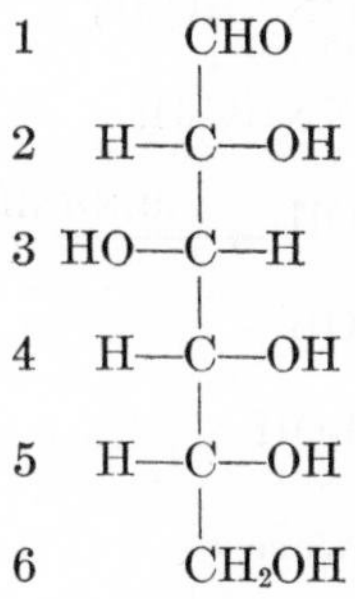

```
        1        CHO
                  |
        2    H—C—OH
                  |
        3   HO—C—H
                  |
        4    H—C—OH
                  |
        5    H—C—OH
                  |
        6        CH₂OH
```
III
(+)-Glucose

(+)-Mannose, of course, has configuration IV, and (+)-gulose (the enantiomer of the one used by Fischer) has configuration V.

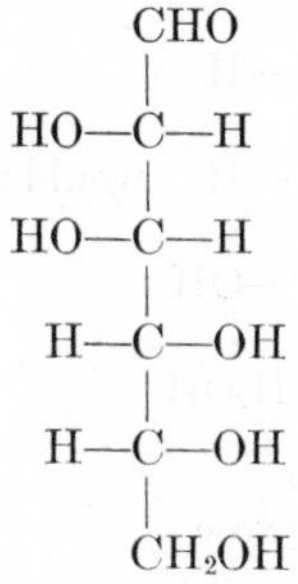

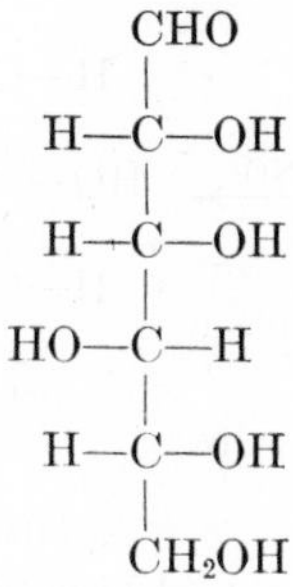

```
        CHO                        CHO
         |                          |
    HO—C—H                     H—C—OH
         |                          |
    HO—C—H                     H—C—OH
         |                          |
     H—C—OH                    HO—C—H
         |                          |
     H—C—OH                     H—C—OH
         |                          |
        CH₂OH                      CH₂OH
```
IV   V
(+)-Mannose   (+)-Gulose

29.12 Configurations of aldoses

Today all possible aldoses (and ketoses) of six carbons or less, and many of more than six carbons, are known; most of these do not occur naturally and have been synthesized. The configurations of all these have been determined by application of the same principles that Fischer used to establish the configuration of (+)-glucose; indeed, twelve of the sixteen aldohexoses were worked out by Fischer and his students.

So far in our discussion, we have seen how configurations III, IV, V, and X of the previous section were assigned to (+)-glucose, (+)-mannose, (+)-gulose, and (−)-arabinose, respectively. Let us see how configurations have been assigned to some other monosaccharides.

The aldopentose **(−)-ribose** forms the same osazone as (−)-arabinose. Since (−)-arabinose was shown to have configuration X, (−)-ribose must have configuration IX. This configuration is confirmed by the reduction of (−)-ribose to the optically inactive (*meso*) pentahydroxy compound *ribitol* (next page).

$$
\begin{array}{ccccc}
\text{CHO} & \text{CH=NNHC}_6\text{H}_5 & \text{CHO} & \text{CH}_2\text{OH} \\
| & | & | & | \\
\text{HO–C–H} & \text{C=NNHC}_6\text{H}_5 & \text{H–C–OH} & \text{H–C–OH} \\
| & | & | & | \\
\text{H–C–OH} \xrightarrow{\text{C}_6\text{H}_5\text{NHNH}_2} & \text{H–C–OH} \xleftarrow{\text{C}_6\text{H}_5\text{NHNH}_2} & \text{H–C–OH} \xrightarrow{\text{H}_2,\ \text{Ni}} & \text{H–C–OH} \\
| & | & | & | \\
\text{H–C–OH} & \text{H–C–OH} & \text{H–C–OH} & \text{H–C–OH} \\
| & | & | & | \\
\text{CH}_2\text{OH} & \text{CH}_2\text{OH} & \text{CH}_2\text{OH} & \text{CH}_2\text{OH}
\end{array}
$$

X		IX	Ribitol
(−)-Arabinose	Osazone	(−)-Ribose	*A meso compound*
			Inactive

The two remaining aldopentoses, **(+)-xylose** and **(−)-lyxose,** must have the configurations XI and XII. Oxidation by nitric acid converts (+)-xylose into an optically inactive *(meso)* glyceric acid. (+)-Xylose must therefore be XI and (−)–lyxose must be XII.

$$
\begin{array}{cccc}
\text{CHO} & \text{COOH} & \text{CHO} & \text{COOH} \\
| & | & | & | \\
\text{H–C–OH} & \text{H–C–OH} & \text{HO–C–H} & \text{HO–C–H} \\
| & | & | & | \\
\text{HO–C–H} \xrightarrow{\text{HNO}_3} & \text{HO–C–H} & \text{HO–C–H} \ \text{would give} & \text{HO–C–H} \\
| & | & | & | \\
\text{H–C–OH} & \text{H–C–OH} & \text{H–C–OH} & \text{H–C–OH} \\
| & | & | & | \\
\text{CH}_2\text{OH} & \text{COOH} & \text{CH}_2\text{OH} & \text{COOH}
\end{array}
$$

XI	Xylaric acid	XII	
(+)-Xylose	*A meso compound*	(−)-Lyxose	**Active**
	Inactive		

Degradation of (−)-arabinose yields the tetrose **(−)-erythrose,** which therefore has configuration XIII. In agreement with this configuration, (−)-erythrose is found to yield *meso*tartaric acid upon oxidation by nitric acid.

$$
\begin{array}{ccc}
\text{CHO} & \text{CHO} & \text{COOH} \\
| & | & | \\
\text{HO–C–H} & \text{H–C–OH} & \text{H–C–OH} \\
| & | & | \\
\text{H–C–OH} \xrightarrow{\text{Ruff degradation}} & \text{H–C–OH} \xrightarrow{\text{HNO}_3} & \text{H–C–OH} \\
| & | & | \\
\text{H–C–OH} & \text{H–C–OH} & \text{COOH} \\
| & | & \\
\text{CH}_2\text{OH} & \text{CH}_2\text{OH} & \\
\end{array}
$$

(−)-Arabinose	XIII	Mesotartaric acid
	(−)-Erythrose	**Inactive**

Degradation of (+)-xylose by the Ruff method yields the tetrose (∼)-threose, which must therefore have configuration XIV. This is confirmed by oxidation of (−)-threose to optically active (−)-tartaric acid.

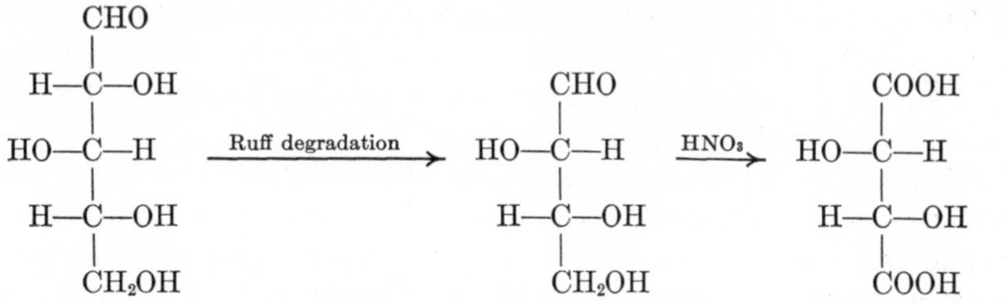
CHO
H—C—OH
HO—C—H
H—C—OH
CH₂OH
Ruff degradation
CHO
HO—C—H
H—C—OH
CH₂OH
HNO₃
COOH
HO—C—H
H—C—OH
COOH

XIV

(+)-Xylose (−)-Threose (−)-Tartaric acid
Active

Problem 29.9 Assign a name to I, II, VI, VII, and VIII (page 757) on the basis of the following evidence and the configurations already assigned:

(a) The aldohexoses **(+)-galactose** and **(+)-talose** yield the same osazone. Degradation of (+)-galactose yields (−)-lyxose. Oxidation of (+)-galactose by nitric acid yields an inactive *meso* acid, *galactaric acid* (also called *mucic acid*).

(b) (−)-Ribose is converted by the Kiliani-Fischer synthesis into the two aldohexoses **(+)-allose** and **(+)-altrose.** Oxidation of (+)-altrose yields optically active (+)-*altraric acid.* Reduction of (+)-allose to a hexahydroxy alcohol yields optically inactive *allitol.*

(c) The aldohexose **(−)-idose** yields the same osazone as (+)-gulose.

Problem 29.10 Go back to the "family tree" you constructed in Problem 29.7, page 755, and assign names to all structures.

Problem 29.11 What is the configuration of the 2-ketohexose **(−)-fructose?** (See Problem 29.6, page 753.)

Problem 29.12 Give the configurations of (−)-glucose, (−)-mannose, and (+)-fructose.

29.13 Families of aldoses. Absolute configuration

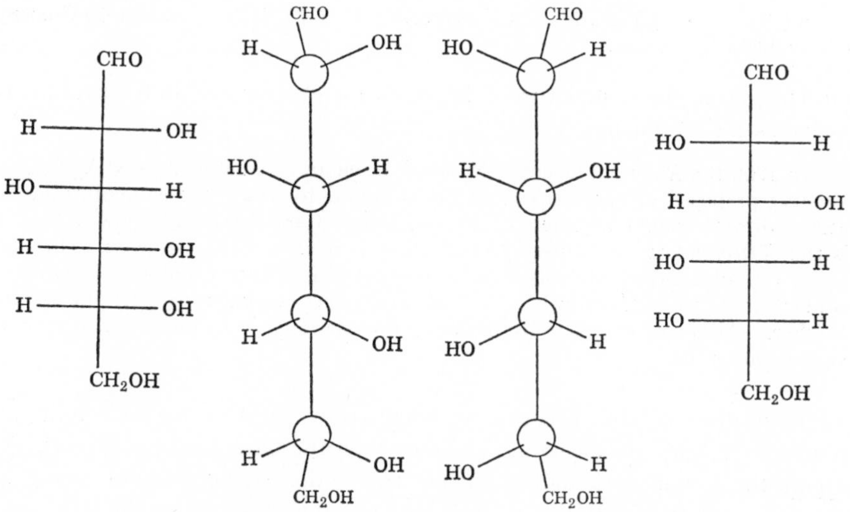
CHO
H OH
HO H
H OH
H OH
CH₂OH
CHO
H OH
HO H
H OH
H OH
CH₂OH
CHO
HO H
H OH
HO H
HO H
CH₂OH
CHO
HO H
H OH
HO H
HO H
CH₂OH

I D-(+)-Glucose

II L-(−)-Glucose

The evidence on which Fischer assigned a configuration to (+)-glucose leads to either of the enantiomeric structures I and II. Fischer, we have seen, arbitrarily selected I, in which the lowest asymmetric carbon atom carries —OH on the right.

We recognize I as the enantiomer that would hypothetically be derived from D-(+)-glyceraldehyde by a series of Kiliani-Fischer syntheses, the asymmetric carbon atom of (+)-glyceraldehyde being retained as the *lowest* asymmetric carbon atom of the aldoses derived from it. (See Problem 29.7, page 755.) That (+)-glucose is related to D-(+)-glyceraldehyde has been established by a number of reaction sequences, one of which is:

$$
\begin{array}{ccc}
\text{CHO} & \text{COOH} & \text{CH}_2\text{OH} \\
\text{H--C--OH} & \text{H--C--OH} & \text{H--C--OH} \\
\text{HO--C--H} & \text{HO--C--H} & \text{HO--C--H} \\
\text{H--C--OH} \xrightarrow{\text{HNO}_3} & \text{H--C--OH} \xleftarrow{\text{HNO}_3} & \text{H--C--OH} \\
\text{H--C--OH} & \text{H--C--OH} & \text{H--C--OH} \\
\text{CH}_2\text{OH} & \text{COOH} & \text{CHO} \\
\text{D-(+)-Glucose} & \text{(+)-Glucaric acid} & \text{(--)-Gulose}
\end{array}
$$

$$
\begin{array}{cccccc}
& & & & & \text{CHO} \\
& & & \text{CHO} & & \text{H--C--OH} \\
& \text{COOH} & \text{CHO} & \text{H--C--OH} & & \text{H--C--OH} \\
\text{CHO} & \text{HO--C--H} & \text{HO--C--H} & \text{HO--C--H} & & \text{HO--C--H} \\
\text{H--C--OH} \xrightarrow[27.6]{\text{Sec.}} & \text{H--C--OH} \xleftarrow{\text{HNO}_3} & \text{H--C--OH} \xleftarrow[\substack{\text{degra-}\\ \text{dation}}]{\text{Ruff}} & \text{H--C--OH} \xleftarrow[\substack{\text{degra-}\\ \text{dation}}]{\text{Ruff}} & & \text{H--C--OH} \\
\text{CH}_2\text{OH} & \text{COOH} & \text{CH}_2\text{OH} & \text{CH}_2\text{OH} & & \text{CH}_2\text{OH} \\
\text{D-(+)-} & \text{(--)-Tartaric} & \text{(--)-Threose} & \text{(+)-Xylose} & & \text{(+)-Gulose} \\
\text{Glyceraldehyde} & \text{acid} & & & &
\end{array}
$$

On this basis, then, structure I becomes D-(+)-glucose, and structure II becomes L-(−)-glucose.

In 1906 the American chemist Rosanoff (then an instructor at New York University) proposed glyceraldehyde as the standard to which the configurations of carbohydrates should be related. Eleven years later experiment showed that it is the *dextrorotatory* (+)-glyceraldehyde that is related to (+)-glucose. On that basis, (+)-glyceraldehyde was then given the designation D and was assigned a configuration to conform with the one arbitrarily assigned to (+)-glucose by Fischer. Although rejected by Fischer, the Rosanoff convention became universally accepted.

Regardless of the direction in which they rotate polarized light, all monosaccharides are designated as D or L on the basis of the configuration about the lowest asymmetric carbon atom, the carbonyl group being at the top: D if the —OH is on the right, L if the —OH is on the left. (As always, it is understood that —H and —OH project toward us from the plane of the paper.) (+)-Mannose and (−)-arabinose, for example, are both assigned to the D-family on the basis of their relationship to D-(+)-glu-cose, and, through it, to D-(+)-glyceraldehyde.

Until 1949, these configurations were accepted on a purely empirical basis; they were a convenient way to show configurational relationships among the various carbohydrates, and between them and other organic compounds. But so far as anyone knew the configurations of these com-pounds might actually have been the mirror images of those assigned; the lowest asymmetric carbon atom in the D-series of monosaccharides might have carried —OH on the left. However, when Bijvoet determined the absolute configuration of (+)-tartaric acid by x-ray analysis in 1949 (Secs. 11.22 and 27.6), he found that it actually has the configuration that had been up to then merely assumed. The arbitrary choice that Emil Fischer made in 1891 was the correct one; the configuration he assigned to (+)-glucose — and, through it, to every carbohydrate — is the correct absolute configuration.

Problem 29.13 The (−)-gulose that played such an important part in the proof of configuration of D-(+)-glucose was synthesized by Fischer via the following sequence:

D-(+)-glucose $\xrightarrow{\text{HNO}_3}$ (+)-glucaric acid $\xrightarrow{\text{−H}_2\text{O}}$ A and B (lactones, separated)

A $\xrightarrow{\text{Na(Hg)}}$ C (glyconic acid) $\xrightarrow{\text{−H}_2\text{O}}$ D (lactone) $\xrightarrow[\text{acid}]{\text{Na(Hg),}}$ D-(+)-glucose

B $\xrightarrow{\text{Na(Hg)}}$ E (glyconic acid) $\xrightarrow{\text{−H}_2\text{O}}$ F (lactone) $\xrightarrow[\text{acid}]{\text{Na(Hg),}}$ (−)-gulose

Give the structures of A through F. What is the configuration of (−)-gulose? Is it a member of the D-family or of the L-family? Why?

29.14 Cyclic structure of D-(+)-glucose. Formation of glucosides

We have seen evidence indicating that D-(+)-glucose is a pentahydroxy aldehyde. We have seen how its configuration has been established. It might seem, therefore, that D-(+)-glucose had been definitely proved to have structure I.

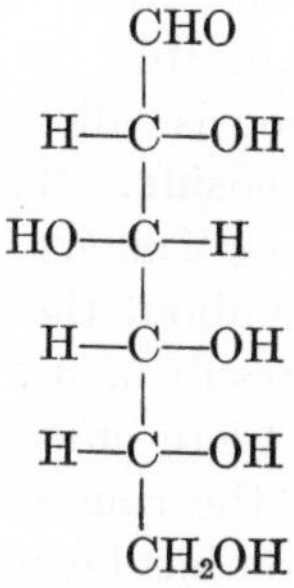

$$\text{CHO}$$
$$|$$
$$\text{H—C—OH}$$
$$|$$
$$\text{HO—C—H}$$
$$|$$
$$\text{H—C—OH}$$
$$|$$
$$\text{H—C—OH}$$
$$|$$
$$\text{CH}_2\text{OH}$$

I

D-(+)-Glucose

But during the time that much of the work we have just described was going on, certain facts were accumulating that were inconsistent with this structure of D-(+)-glucose. By 1895 it had become clear that the picture of D-(+)-glucose as a pentahydroxy aldehyde had to be modified.

Among the facts that had still to be accounted for were the following:

(a) D-(+)-Glucose fails to undergo certain reactions typical of aldehydes. Although it is readily oxidized, it gives a negative Schiff test and does not form a bisulfite addition product.

(b) D-(+)-Glucose exists in two isomeric forms which undergo mutarotation. When crystals of ordinary D-(+)-glucose of m.p. 146° are dissolved in water the specific rotation gradually drops from an initial +112° to +52.7°. On the other hand, when crystals of D-(+)-glucose of m.p. 150° (obtained by crystallization at temperatures above 98°) are dissolved in water the specific rotation gradually rises from an initial +19° to +52.7°. The form with the higher positive rotation is called α-D-(+)-glucose and that with lower rotation β-D-(+)-glucose. The change in rotation of each of these to the equilibrium value is called **muta-rotation.**

(c) D-(+)-Glucose forms two isomeric methyl D-glucosides. Aldehydes, we remember, react with alcohols in the presence of anhydrous HCl to form acetals (Sec. 23.14). If the alcohol is, say, methanol, the acetal contains two methyl groups:

$$\begin{array}{ccccc}
\text{H} & & \text{H} & & \text{H} \\
| & \xrightarrow{\text{CH}_3\text{OH, H}^+} & | & \xrightarrow{\text{CH}_3\text{OH, H}^+} & | \\
-\text{C}=\text{O} & \xleftarrow{} & -\text{C}-\text{OCH}_3 & \xleftarrow{} & -\text{C}-\text{OCH}_3 \\
& & | & & | \\
& & \text{OH} & & \text{OCH}_3 \\
\text{Aldehyde} & & \text{Hemiacetal} & & \text{Acetal}
\end{array}$$

When D-(+)-glucose is treated with methanol and HCl, the product, **methyl D-glucoside,** contains only one —CH₃ group; yet it has properties resembling those of a full acetal. It does not spontaneously revert to aldehyde and alcohol on contact with water, but requires hydrolysis by aqueous acids.

Furthermore, not just one but two of these monomethyl derivatives of D-(+)-glucose are known, one with m.p. 165° and specific rotation +158°, and the other with m.p. 107° and specific rotation −33°. The isomer of higher positive rotation is called **methyl α-D-glucoside,** and the other is called **methyl β-D-glucoside.** These glucosides do not undergo mutarotation, and do not reduce Tollens' or Fehling's reagent.

To fit facts like these, ideas about the structure of D-(+)-glucose had to be changed. In 1895, as a result of work by many chemists, including Tollens, Fischer, and Tanret, there emerged a picture of D-(+)-glucose as a *cyclic* structure. In 1926 the ring size was corrected, and in recent years the preferred conformation has been elucidated.

D-(+)-Glucose has the cyclic structure represented crudely by IIa and IIIa, more accurately by IIb and IIIb, and best of all by IIc and IIIc.

D-(+)-Glucose is the hemiacetal corresponding to reaction between the aldehyde group and the C–5 hydroxyl group of the open-chain structure (I). It has a cyclic structure simply because aldehyde and alcohol are part of the same molecule.

Glucose anomers: Hemiacetals

Reducing sugars
Mutarotate

1	H—C—OH
2	H—C—OH
3	HO—C—H
4	H—C—OH
5	H—C
6	CH₂OH

IIa   IIb   IIc

α-D-(+)-Glucose (m.p. 146°, [α] = +112°)

1	HO—C—H
2	H—C—OH
3	HO—C—H
4	H—C—OH
5	H—C
6	CH₂OH

IIIa   IIIb   IIIc

β-D-(+)-Glucose (m.p. 150°, [α] = +19°)

Mutarotation

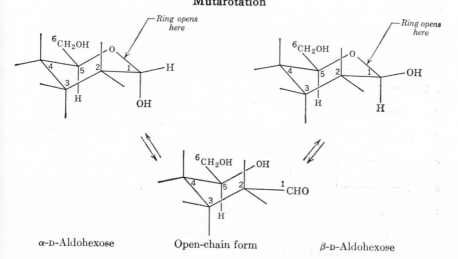

α-D-Aldohexose   Open-chain form   β-D-Aldohexose

There are two isomeric forms of D-(+)-glucose because this cyclic structure has one more asymmetric carbon atom than Fischer's original open-chain structure (I). α-D-(+)-Glucose and β-D-(+)-glucose are diastereomers, differing in configuration about C–1. Such a pair of diastereomers are called **anomers**.

As hemiacetals, α- and β-D-(+)-glucose are readily hydrolyzed by water. In aqueous solution either anomer is converted — via the open-chain form — into an equilibrium mixture containing both cyclic isomers. Thus mutarotation results from the ready opening and closing of the hemiacetal ring.

The typical aldehyde reactions of D-(+)-glucose — osazone formation, and perhaps reduction of Tollens' and Fehling's reagents — are presumably due to a small amount of open-chain compound, which is replenished as fast as it is consumed. The concentration of this open-chain structure is, however, too low (less than 0.5%) for certain easily reversible aldehyde reactions like bisulfite addition and the Schiff test.

The isomeric forms of methyl D-glucoside are anomers and have the cyclic structures IV and V:

Glucoside anomers: Acetals

Non-reducing sugars
Do not mutarotate

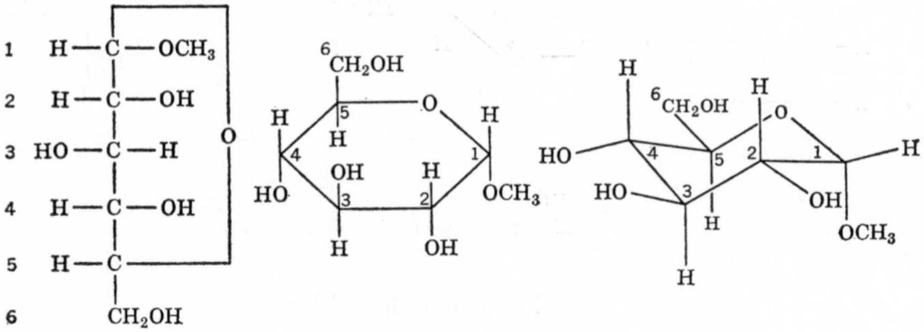

IVa IVb IVc
Methyl α-D-glucoside (m.p. 165°, [α] = +158°)

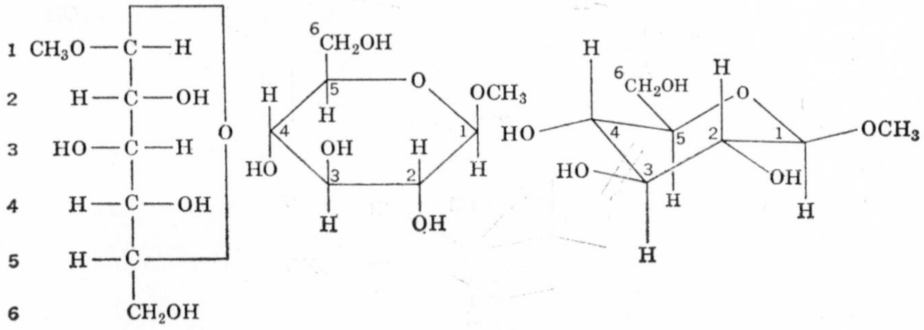

va vb vc
Methyl β-D-glucoside (m.p. 107°, [α] = −33°)

Although formed from only one mole of methanol, they are nevertheless full acetals, the other mole of alcohol being D-(+)-glucose itself through the C–5 hydroxyl group. The glucosides do not undergo mutarotation since, being acetals, they are fairly stable in aqueous solution. On being heated with aqueous acids they undergo hydrolysis to yield the original hemiacetals (II and III). Toward bases glucosides, like acetals generally, are stable. Since they are not readily hydrolyzed to the open-chain aldehyde by the alkali in Tollens' or Fehling's reagent, glucosides are non-reducing sugars.

Like D-(+)-glucose, other monosaccharides exist in anomeric forms capable of mutarotation, and react with alcohols to yield anomeric **glycosides.**

We have represented the cyclic structures of D-glucose and methyl D-glucoside in several different ways: β-D-glucose, for example, by IIIa, IIIb, and IIIc. At this point we should convince ourselves that all three representations correspond to the same structure, and that the configurations about C–2, C–3, C–4, and C–5 are the same as in the open-chain structure worked out by Fischer. These relationships are best seen by use of models.

We can convert the open-chain model of D-glucose into a cyclic model by joining oxygen of the C–5 —OH to the aldehyde carbon C–1. Whether we end up with the α- or β-structure depends upon which face of the flat carbonyl group we join the C–5 oxygen to. IIb and IIIb represent this ring lying on its side, so that groups that were on the right in the vertical model are directed downward, and groups that were on the left in the vertical model are directed upward. (Note particularly that the —CH₂OH group points *upward.*) In the more accurate representations IIc and IIIc, the disposition of these groups is modified by puckering of the six-membered ring, which will be discussed further in Sec. 29.18.

Problem 29.14   (a) From the values for the specific rotations of aqueous solutions of pure α- and β-D-(+)-glucose, and for the solution after mutarotation, calculate the relative amounts of α- and of β-forms at equilibrium (assuming a negligible amount of open-chain form).

(b) From examination of structures IIc and IIIc, suggest a reason for the greater proportion of one isomer. (*Hint:* see Sec. 7.13.)

Problem 29.15   Knowing the mechanism of acid-catalyzed carbonyl addition (Sec. 23.7), suggest a mechanism for the acid-catalyzed mutarotation of D-(+)-glucose.

Problem 29.16   (+)-Glucose reacts with acetic anhydride to give two isomeric pentaacetyl derivatives neither of which reduces Fehling's or Tollens' reagent. Account for these facts.

29.15   Configuration about C–1

Knowledge that aldoses and their glycosides have cyclic structures immediately raises the question: what is the configuration about C–1 in each of these anomeric structures?

In 1909 C. S. Hudson (of the U. S. Public Health Service) made the following proposal. *In the D-series the more dextrorotatory member of an α,β-pair of anomers is to be named α-D-, the other being named β-D. In the L-series the more levorotatory member of such a pair is given the name α-L and the other β-L.* Thus the enantiomer of α-D-(+)-glucose is α-L-(−)-glucose.

Furthermore, *the —OH or —OCH₃ group on C–1 is on the right in an α-D-anomer and on the left in a β-D-anomer.* Thus for aldohexoses:

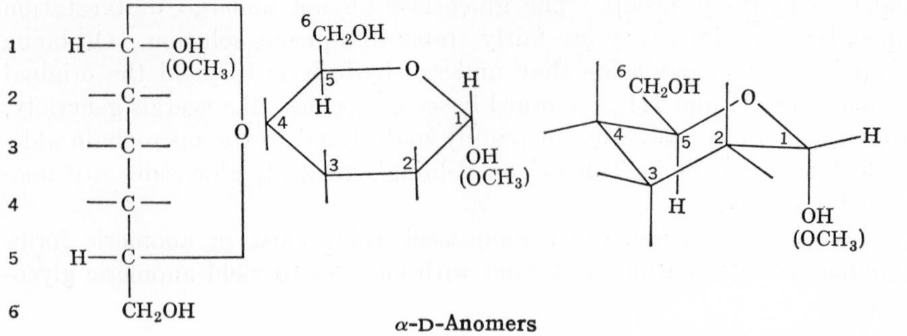

α-D-**Anomers**

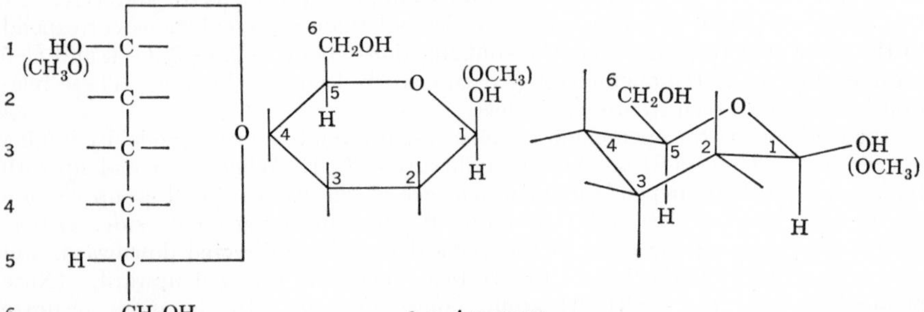

β-D-**Anomers**

(Notice that "on the right" means "down" in the cyclic structure.)

Hudson's proposals have been adopted generally. Although they were originally based upon certain apparent but unproved relationships between configuration and optical rotation, all the evidence indicates that the assigned configurations are the correct ones. For example:

α-D-Glucose and methyl α-D-glucoside have the same configuration, as do β-D-glucose and methyl β-D-glucoside. *Evidence:* enzymatic hydrolysis of methyl α-D-glucoside liberates initially the more highly rotating α-D-glucose, and hydrolysis of methyl β-D-glucoside liberates initially β-D-glucose.

The configuration about C–1 is the same in the methyl α-glycosides of all the D-aldohexoses. *Evidence:* they all yield the same compound upon oxidation by HIO_4.

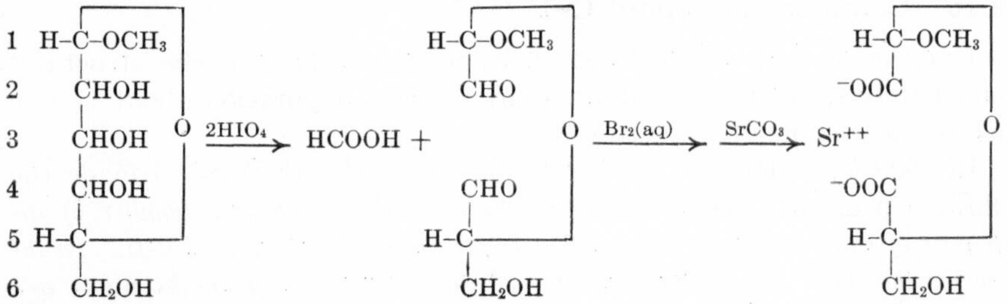

Methyl α-glycoside
of any D-aldohexose

Same Sr salt

Oxidation destroys the asymmetric centers at C–2, C–3, and C–4, but configuration is preserved about C–1 and C–5. Configuration about C–5 is the same for all members of the D-family. The same products can be obtained from all these glycosides *only* if they also have the same configuration about C–1.

The C–1 —OH is on the right in the α-D-series and on the left in the β-D-series. *Evidence:* results of x-ray analysis.

Problem 29.17 (a) What products would be formed from the strontium salts shown above by treatment with dilute HCl?

(b) An oxidation of this sort was used to confirm the configurational relationship between (+)-glucose and (+)-glyceraldehyde. How was this done?

29.16 Methylation

Before we can go on to the next aspect of the structure of D-(+)-glucose, determination of ring size, we must first learn a little more about the methylation of carbohydrates.

As we know, treatment of D-(+)-glucose with methanol and dry hydrogen chloride yields the methyl D-glucosides:

Acetal formation

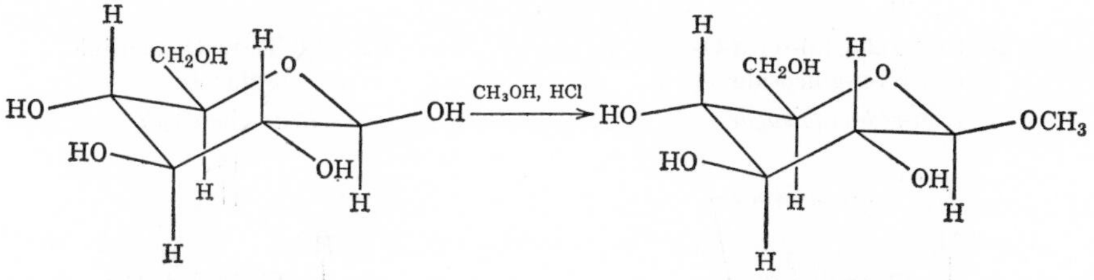

+ α-anomer

β-D-(+)-Glucose
Reducing sugar

+ α-anomer

Methyl β-D-glucoside
Non-reducing sugar

In this reaction, an aldehyde (or more exactly, its hemiacetal) is converted into an acetal in the usual manner.

Treatment of a methyl D-glucoside with methyl sulfate and sodium hydroxide brings about methylation of the four remaining —OH groups, and yields a methyl tetra-O-methyl-D-glucoside:

Ether formation

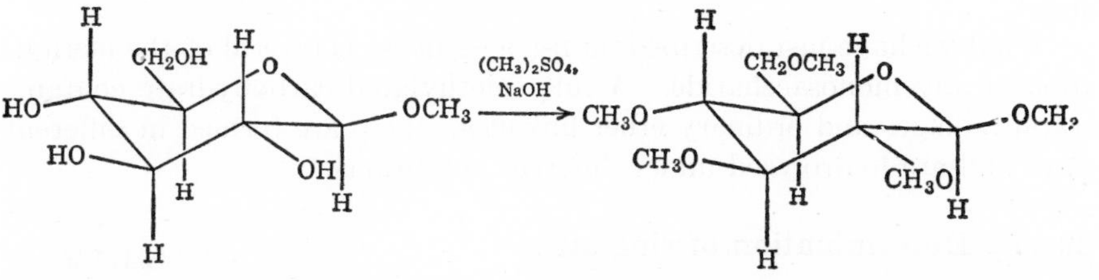

Methyl β-D-glucoside
Non-reducing sugar

Methyl β-2,3,4,6-tetra-O-methyl-D-glucoside
Non-reducing sugar

In this reaction, ether linkages are formed by a modification of the William-son synthesis that is possible here because of the comparatively high acidity of these —OH groups. (Why are these —OH groups more acidic than those of an ordinary alcohol?)

There is now an —OCH₃ group attached to every carbon in the carbohydrate except the one joined to C–1 through the acetal linkage; if the six-membered ring structure is correct there is an —OCH₃ group on every carbon except C–5.

Treatment of the methyl tetra-O-methyl-D-glucoside with dilute hydrochloric acid removes only one of these —OCH₃ groups, and yields a tetra-O-methyl-D-glucose:

Hydrolysis of an acetal

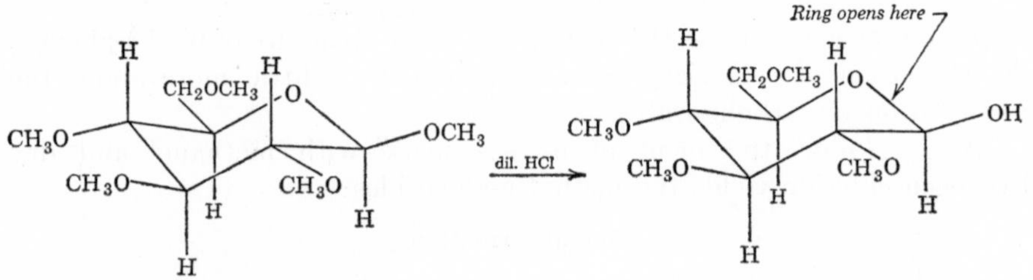

Methyl β-2,3,4,6-tetra-O-
methyl-D-glucoside
Non-reducing sugar

β-2,3,4,6-Tetra-O- methyl-
D-glucose
Reducing sugar

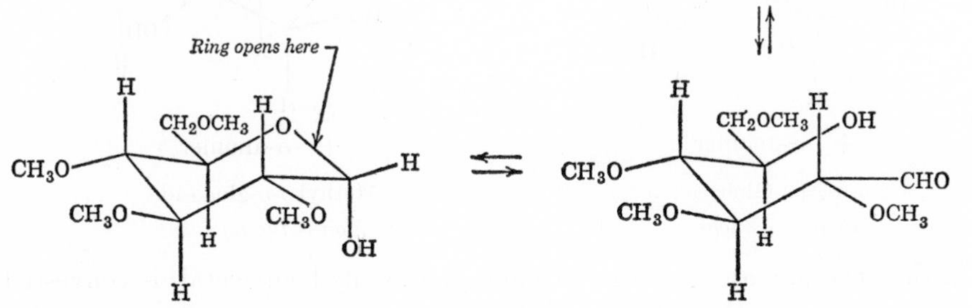

α-2,3,4,6-Tetra-O-methyl-
D-glucose
Reducing sugar

Only the reactive acetal linkage is hydrolyzed under these mild conditions; the other four —OCH₃ groups, held by ordinary ether linkages, remain intact.

What we have just described for D-(+)-glucose is typical of the methylation of any monosaccharide. A fully methylated carbohydrate contains acetal linkages and ordinary ether linkages; these are formed in different ways and are hydrolyzed under different conditions.

29.17 Determination of ring size

In the cyclic structures that we have used so far for α- and β-D-(+)-glucose and the glucosides, oxygen has been shown as joining together C–1 and C–5; that is, these compounds are represented as containing a six-membered ring. But other ring sizes are possible, in particular, a five-membered ring, one in which C–1 is joined to C–4. What is the evidence that these compounds actually contain a six-membered ring?

When methyl β-D-glucoside is treated with methyl sulfate and sodium hydroxide, and the product is hydrolyzed by dilute hydrochloric acid, there is obtained a tetra-O-methyl-D-glucose. This compound is a cyclic hemiacetal which, in solution, presumably exists in equilibrium with a little of the open-chain form.

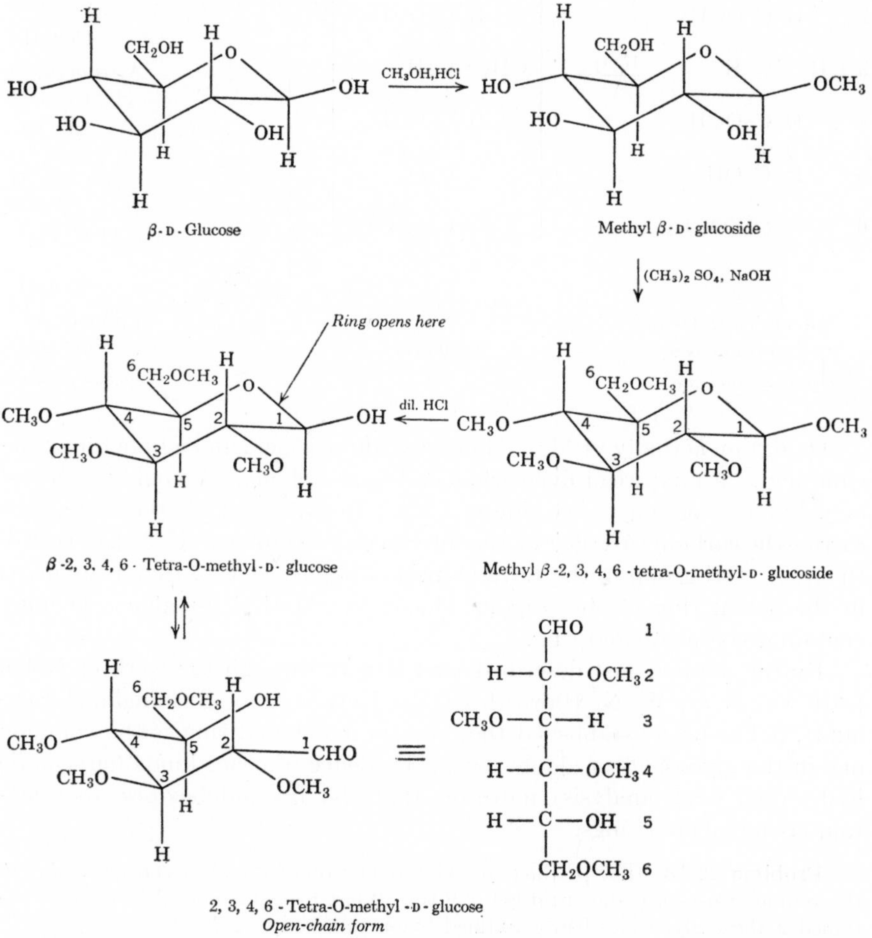

β-D-Glucose

Methyl β-D-glucoside

$(CH_3)_2 SO_4$, NaOH

Ring opens here

β-2, 3, 4, 6-Tetra-O-methyl-D-glucose

Methyl β-2, 3, 4, 6-tetra-O-methyl-D-glucoside

2, 3, 4, 6-Tetra-O-methyl-D-glucose
Open-chain form

This open-chain tetra-O-methyl-D-glucose contains an aldehyde group and four —OCH₃ groups. It also contains a free, unmethylated —OH group at whichever carbon was originally involved in the acetal ring — on C–5, if the six-membered ring is correct. *Determination of ring size becomes a matter of finding out which carbon carries the free —OH group.*

What would we expect to happen if the tetra-O-methyl-D-glucose were vigorously oxidized by nitric acid? The —CHO and the free —OH group should be oxidized to yield a keto acid. But, from what we know about ketones (Sec. 23.8) we would not expect oxidation to stop here: the keto acid should be cleaved on one side or the other of the carbonyl group.

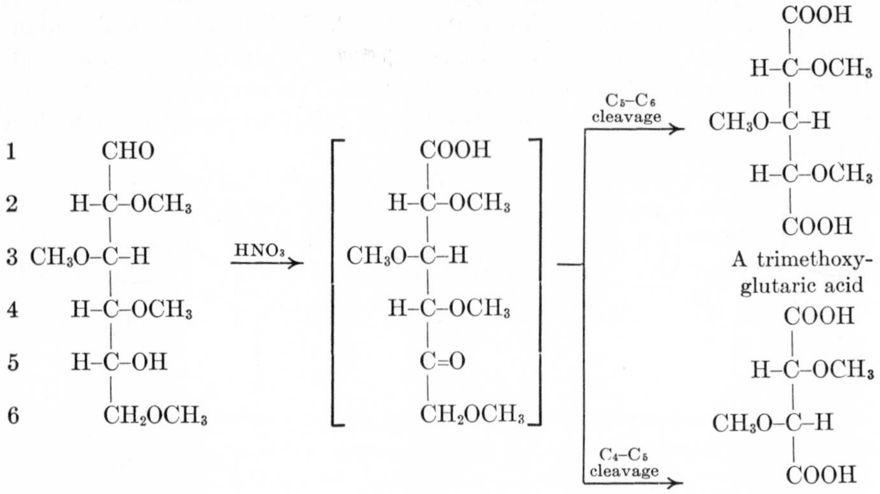

C$_5$–C$_6$ cleavage → A trimethoxyglutaric acid

C$_4$–C$_5$ cleavage → A dimethoxysuccinic acid

2,3,4,6-Tetra-O-methyl-D-glucose

Hydroxyaldehyde

Keto acid

Cleavage products

Oxidation actually yields a trimethoxyglutaric acid and a dimethoxysuccinic acid. A mixture of five-carbon and four-carbon acids could be formed only by cleavage on either side of C–5. It must be C–5, therefore, that carries the carbonyl oxygen of the intermediate keto acid, C–5 that carries the free —OH group in the tetra-O-methyl-D-glucose, C–5 that is involved in the acetal ring of the original glucoside. Methyl β-D-glucoside must contain a six-membered ring.

By the method just described, and largely through the work of Nobel prize winner Sir W. N. Haworth (of the University of Birmingham, England), it has been established that the six-membered ring is the common one in the glycosides of aldohexoses. Evidence of other kinds (enzymatic hydrolysis, x-ray analysis) indicates that the *free* aldohexoses, too, contain six-membered rings.

Problem 29.18   The products of HIO_4 oxidation of the methyl α-glycosides of the D-aldohexoses are shown in Sec. 29.15. What products would have been obtained if these glycosides had contained five-membered rings?

Problem 29.19   When either methyl α-L-arabinoside or methyl β-D-xyloside is methylated, hydrolyzed, and then oxidized by nitric acid, there is obtained a trimethoxyglutaric acid. (a) What ring size is indicated for these aldopentosides? (b) Predict the products of HIO_4 oxidation of each of these aldopentosides.

Problem 29.20   When crystalline methyl α-D-fructoside is methylated, hydrolyzed, oxidized by $KMnO_4$ and then nitric acid, there is obtained a trimethoxyglutaric acid. (a) What ring size is indicated for this 2-ketohexoside? (b) How does this acid compare with the one obtained from methyl α-L-arabinoside?

Problem 29.21 The crystalline methyl α- and β-D-glycosides we have discussed are usually prepared using methanolic HCl at 120°. When D-(+)-glucose is methylated *at room temperature* there is obtained a liquid methyl D-glucoside. When this so-called "γ"-glucoside is methylated, hydrolyzed, and oxidized by nitric acid, there is obtained a dimethoxysuccinic acid. (a) What ring size is indicated for this "γ"-glucoside? (b) Should the dimethoxysuccinic acid be optically active or inactive? What is its absolute configuration? (c) When the liquid "γ"-glycoside obtained from D-(−)-fructose is methylated, hydrolyzed, and oxidized by nitric acid, there is also obtained a dimethoxysuccinic acid. How does this acid compare with the one in (b)?

If the name of a carbohydrate is exactly to define a particular structure, it must indicate ring size. Following a suggestion made by Haworth, carbohydrates are named to show their relationship to one of the heterocycles *pyran* or *furan*.

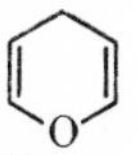

Pyran 　　　　　　　　　　Furan

A glycose containing a six-membered ring is thus a **pyranose** and its glycosides are **pyranosides.** A glycose containing a five-membered ring is a **furanose** and its glycosides are **furanosides.** For example:

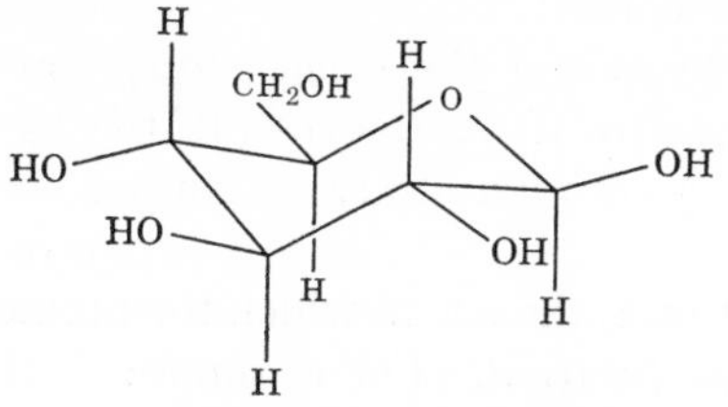

β-D-Glucopyranose 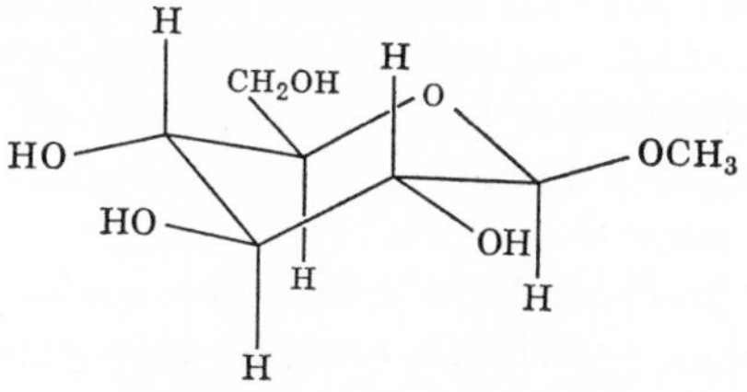　　　　　　Methyl β-D-glucopyranoside

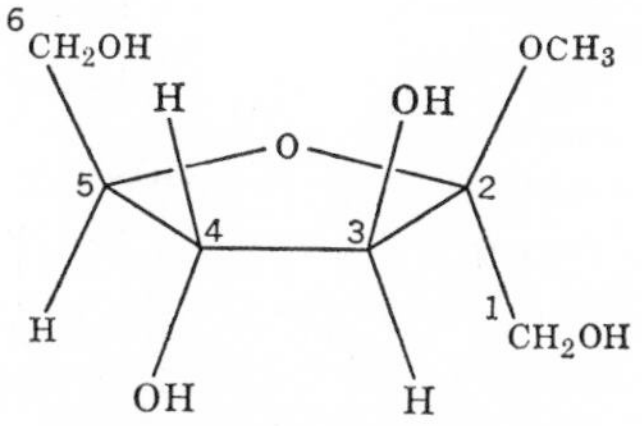

Methyl β-D-fructofuranoside

29.18　Conformation

We have followed the unraveling of the structure of D-(+)-glucose, and with it structures of the other monosaccharides, to the final working out of the ring size in 1926. Left to be discussed is one aspect whose importance has only been realized since about 1950: **conformation.**

D-(+)-Glucose contains the six-membered, pyranose ring. Since the C—O—C bond angle (111°) is very nearly equal to the tetrahedral angle (109.5°), the pyranose ring should be quite similar to the cyclohexane ring (Sec. 7.11). It should be puckered and, to minimize interaction of substituents, should exist in chair conformations in preference to boat conformations. X-ray analysis shows this reasoning to be correct.

But there are *two* chair conformations possible for a D-(+)-gluco-pyranose anomer: I and II for β-D-(+)-glucopyranose, for example.

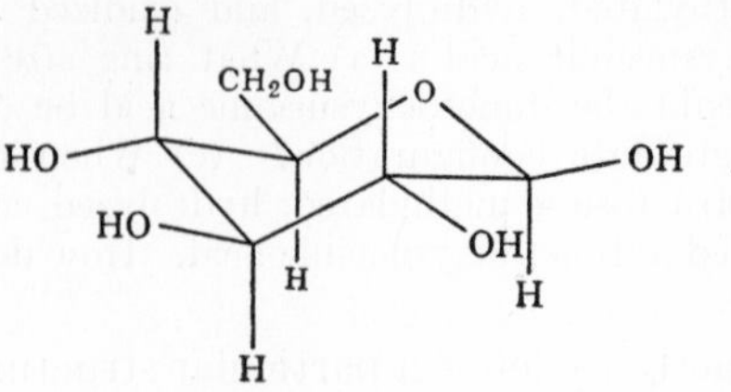

I

More stable:
all bulky groups equatorial

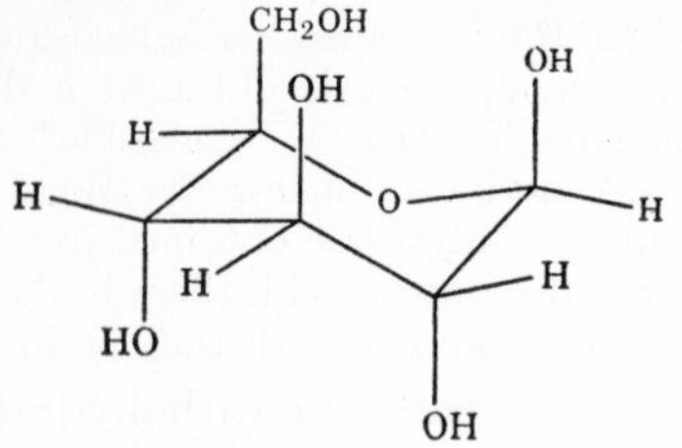

II

Less stable:
all bulky groups axial

β-D-(+)-Glucopyranose

Which of these is the more stable one, the one in which the molecules spend most of the time? For β-D-(+)-glucopyranose, the answer seems clear: I, in which all bulky substituents (—CH₂OH and —OH) occupy roomy equatorial positions, should certainly be much more stable than II, in which all bulky groups are crowded into axial positions. Again, x-ray analysis shows this reasoning to be correct.

What can we say about α-D-(+)-glucose and the other aldohexoses? This problem has been largely worked out by R. E. Reeves (at the U. S. Southern Regional Research Laboratory) through study of copper complexes.

In general, the more stable conformation is the one in which the bulkiest group, —CH₂OH, occupies an equatorial position. For example:

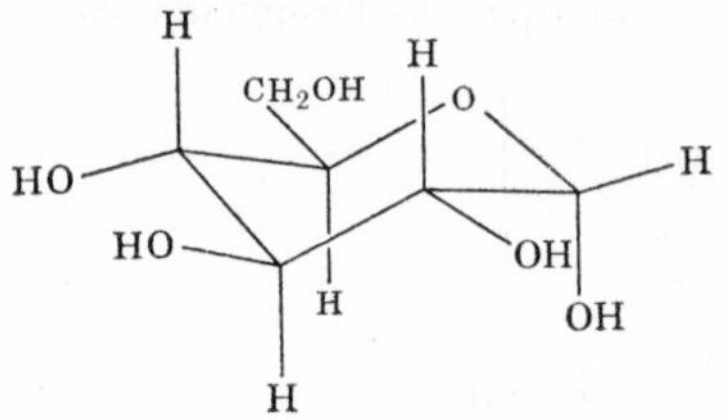

III

α-D-Glucopyranose
Stable conformation

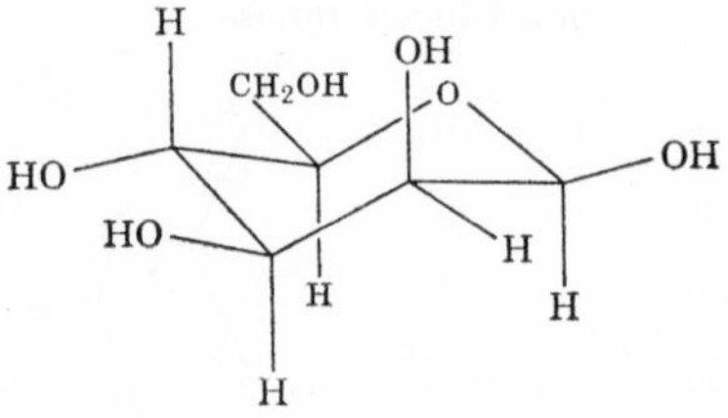

IV

β-D-Mannopyranose
Stable conformation

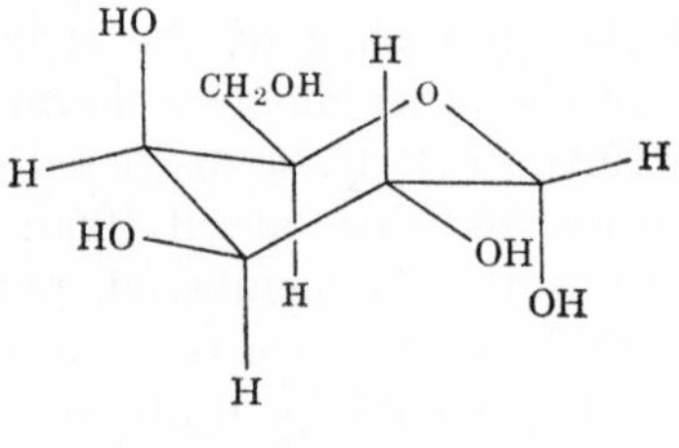

V

α-D-Galactopyranose
Stable conformation

In an extreme case, to permit many —OH groups to take up equatorial positions, the —CH₂OH group may be forced into an axial position. For example:

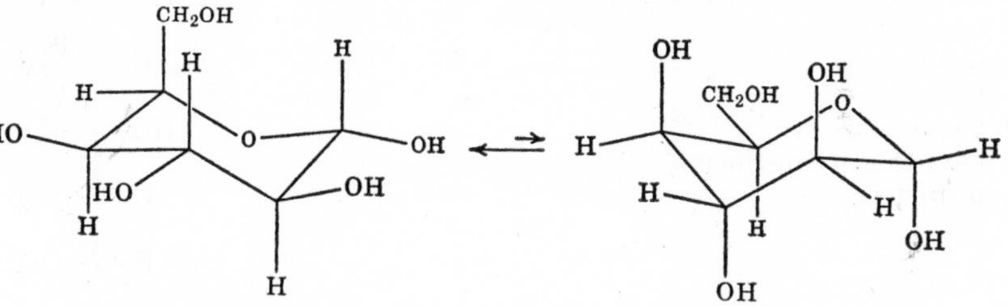

More stable:
4 equatorial OH's,
1 axial –CH₂OH

Less stable:
4 axial OH's,
1 equatorial –CH₂OH

α-D-Idopyranose

We notice that of all D-aldohexoses it is β-D-(+)-glucose that can assume a conformation in which every bulky group occupies an equatorial position. It is probably not just coincidence that β-D-(+)-glucose is the most widely occurring organic group in nature.

In drawing structural formulas or making models for the aldohexoses, a convenient point of reference is β-D-(+)-glucose. We draw the ring as shown in I — C-1 down, C-4 up, and oxygen at the right-hand back corner — and place all —OH groups and the —CH₂OH group in equatorial positions. We draw the structures of other D-family aldohexoses merely by taking into account their differences from I. Thus α-D-(+)-glucose (III) differs in configuration at C-1; β-D-mannose (IV) differs in configuration at C-2; α-D-galactose (V) differs at C-1 and C-4. L-Family compounds are of course mirror images of these.

Problem 29.22 Draw the conformation you predict to be the most stable for:

(a) β-D-allopyranose
(b) β-D-gulopyranose
(c) β-D-xylopyranose
(d) α-D-arabinopyranose
(e) β-L-(−)-glucopyranose
(f) β-D-(−)-fructopyranose

PROBLEMS

1. Give structures and, where possible, names of the principal products of the reaction (if any) of D-(+)-galactose with:

(a) hydroxylamine
(b) phenylhydrazine
(c) bromine water
(d) HNO_3
(e) HIO_4
(f) acetic anhydride
(g) benzoyl chloride, pyridine
(h) CH_3OH, HCl
(i) CH_3OH, HCl; then $(CH_3)_2SO_4$, NaOH
(j) reagents of (i), then dilute HCl
(k) reagents of (i) and (j), then vigorous oxidation
(l) H_2, Ni
(m) $NaBH_4$
(n) CN^-, H^+; then hydrolysis; then Na(Hg), CO_2
(o) H_2, Ni; then oxidation to monocarboxylic acid
(p) Br_2(aq); then pyridine; then H^+; then Na(Hg), CO_2
(q) phenylhydrazine; then benzaldehyde, H^+
(r) reagents of (q), then reduction to monocarbonyl compound
(s) Br_2(aq); then $CaCO_3$; then H_2O_2, Fe^{+++}
(t) reagents of (i), then NaOH
(u) CH_3OH, HCl; then HIO_4
(v) reagents of (u); then Br_2(aq); then dilute HCl

2. Write equations to show how D-(+)-glucose could be converted into:

(a) methyl β-D-glucoside
(b) methyl β-2,3,4,6-tetra-O-methyl-D-glucoside
(c) 2,3,4,6-tetra-O-methyl-D-glucose
(d) D-mannose
(e) L-gulose
(f) D-arabinose
(g) mesotartaric acid
(h) hexa-O-acetyl-D-glucitol
(i) D-fructose

(j)

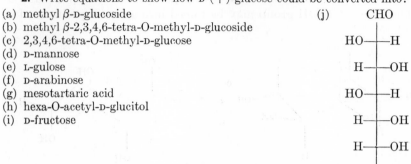

3. Besides D-fructose, there are three D-2-ketohexoses: D-*psicose*, D-*sorbose*, and D-*tagatose*. (a) Draw the possible configurations for these three ketoses. (b) Given the configurations of all aldohexoses, tell how you could assign definite configurations to the ketoses.

4. Reduction of a carbon-carbon triple bond by hydrogen over a palladium–calcium carbonate catalyst partly deactivated by lead acetate (Lindlar's catalyst) gives a *cis*-alkene; whereas reduction by sodium or lithium in liquid ammonia gives a *trans*-alkene. Using this information, and the knowledge you already have about *cis*- and *trans*-hydroxylation, draw stereochemical formulas for products A through O, and tell what aldoses E, E', F, H, I, I', N, and O are related to.

(a) $ClCH_2CHO + BrMgC{\equiv}CMgBr + OHCCH_2Cl \longrightarrow$ A ($C_6H_8O_2Cl_2$), mainly
meso

$meso\text{-A} + KOH \longrightarrow$ B ($C_6H_6O_2$), a diepoxide
$B + H_2O, OH^- \longrightarrow$ C ($C_6H_{10}O_4$)
$C + H_2, Pd/CaCO_3 \longrightarrow$ D ($C_6H_{12}O_4$)
$D +$ cold dilute $KMnO_4 \dashrightarrow$ E and E' (both $C_6H_{14}O_6$)
$D +$ peroxyformic acid $\longrightarrow$ F ($C_6H_{14}O_6$)
$C + Na, NH_3 \longrightarrow$ G ($C_6H_{12}O_4$)
$G +$ cold dilute $KMnO_4 \longrightarrow$ H ($C_6H_{14}O_6$)
$G +$ peroxyformic acid $\dashrightarrow$ I and I' (both $C_6H_{14}O_6$)

(b) *trans*-2-penten-4-yn-1-ol $+ HCO_2OH \longrightarrow$ J ($C_5H_8O_3$), 4-pentyn-1,2,3-triol
$J +$ acetic anhydride, then $Pd/CaCO_3 + H_2 \longrightarrow$ K ($C_{11}H_{16}O_6$)
$K + HOBr \longrightarrow$ L and M (both $C_{11}H_{17}O_7Br$)
$L +$ hydrolysis $\longrightarrow$ N ($C_5H_{12}O_5$)
$M +$ hydrolysis $\longrightarrow$ O ($C_5H_{12}O_5$), a racemate

(c) Starting with 2-butyn-1,4-diol (made from acetylene and formaldehyde, Problem 5(j), page 670) outline a synthesis of erythritol; of DL-threitol.

5. When borneol (ROH) is fed to a dog, this toxic substance is excreted as compound P, $C_6H_9O_6$—OR, where R stands for the bornyl group. Compound P does not reduce Benedict's solution. It reacts with aqueous $NaHCO_3$ with the liberation of a gas. Treatment of P with aqueous acid yields borneol (ROH) and D-glucuronic acid (Table 29.1), which is oxidized by bromine water to D-glucaric acid.

(a) What is the structure of P?

(b) Hydrolysis of the polysaccharide *pectin* (from fruits and berries) gives chiefly D-galacturonic acid; hydrolysis of the polysaccharide *algin* (from seaweed) yields D-mannuronic acid. Give the structures of these glycuronic acids.

(c) There are two uronic acids related to D-fructose. Draw their structures. Give the name and family of the glyconic acids formed from each "fructuronic acid" by reduction of the carbonyl group.

(d) What compound would you expect from the treatment of D-glucosone with bromine water?

6. Upon oxidation by HIO_4 the methyl glycoside Q yields the same product (shown on page 770) as that obtained from methyl α-glycosides of the D-aldohexoses; however, it consumes only one mole of HIO_4 and yields *no* formic acid.

(a) How many carbon atoms are there in Q, and what is the ring size? (b) For which carbon atoms do you know the configuration? (c) When Q is methylated, hydrolyzed, and then vigorously oxidized, the dicarboxylic acid obtained is the di-O-methyl ether of (−)-tartaric acid. What is the complete structure and configuration of Q?

7. *Salicin*, $C_{13}H_{18}O_7$, found in willow (*Salix*, whence the name *salicylic*), is hydrolyzed by emulsin to D-glucose and saligenin, $C_7H_8O_2$. Salicin does not reduce Tollens' reagent. Oxidation of salicin by nitric acid yields a compound that can be hydrolyzed to D-glucose and salicylaldehyde.

Methylation of salicin gives pentamethylsalicin, which on hydrolysis gives 2,3,4,6-tetra-O-methyl-D-glucose.

What is the structure of salicin?

8. *Indican*, $C_{14}H_{17}O_6N$, found in indigo plants, is hydrolyzed by emulsin to D-glucose and indoxyl, C_8H_7ON.

Indoxyl

It does not reduce Tollens' reagent.

Methylation of indican gives tetramethylindican, which on treatment with methanol and hydrochloric acid gives indoxyl and methyl 2,3,4,6-tetra-O-methyl-D-glucoside.

What is the most likely structure of indican?

9. The optically inactive carbohydrate *bio-inonose*, $C_6H_{10}O_6$, reduces Benedict's solution, but does not react with bromine water. It is reduced to R and S, of formula $C_6H_{12}O_6$. Compounds R and S are oxidized by HIO_4 to six moles of $HCOOH$, and react with acetic anhydride to yield products of formula $C_{18}H_{24}O_{12}$. Vigorous oxidation of bio-inonose yields DL-idaric acid (the dicarboxylic acid from idose) as the only six-carbon fragment.

What is the structure of bio-inonose? Of R and S?

10. Much of what is known about photosynthesis has been learned by determining the fate of radioactive carbon dioxide, $C^{14}O_2$. The C^{14} was found in many products, including glucose, fructose, and sucrose. To measure the radioactivity of each carbon atom in a particular molecule, degradations to one-carbon fragments were carried out.

Tell which position or positions in the molecule each of the following one-carbon products came from.

Show how the activity of the carbon atom in every position could be figured out.

(a) glucose $\xrightarrow{\text{Ruff degradation}}$ CO_2 + arabinose $\xrightarrow{\text{Ruff degradation}}$ CO_2

glucose + HIO_4 $\longrightarrow$ HCHO
glucose + CH_3OH, HCl; then HIO_4 $\longrightarrow$ HCOOH
glucose $\xrightarrow{\text{Lactobacillus casei}}$ 2 lactic acid (carboxyls are C–3 and C–4)

$$\Big\downarrow \text{KMnO}_4$$

CO_2 + CH_3CHO $\xrightarrow{\text{NaOI}}$ CHI_3 + $HCOOH$

(b) ribulose (a 2-ketopentose) + $HIO_4 \longrightarrow HOCH_2COOH + 2HCOOH + HCHO$

ribulose + H_2, Pt; then $HIO_4 \longrightarrow$ 2HCHO + 3HCOOH

ribulose + $C_6H_5NHNH_2 \longrightarrow$ ribosazone

$$\text{ribosazone} + HIO_4 \longrightarrow HCHO + HCOOH + \begin{array}{c} HC = NNHC_6H_5 \\ | \\ C = NNHC_6H_5 \\ | \\ CHO \end{array}$$

11. *Nucleic acids*, the hereditary materials of the genes, are polymers composed of nucleotide units. The structures of nucleotides have been determined in the following way, as illustrated for *adenylic acid*, a nucleotide isolated from yeast cells.

Hydrolysis of adenylic acid yields one molecule each of a heterocyclic base, a sugar T, and phosphoric acid. The base is called *adenine*, and will be represented as R_2NH. Adenylic acid has the formula $R_2N-C_5H_8O_3-OPO_3H_2$.

The sugar T is levorotatory and has the formula $C_5H_{10}O_5$; it reduces Tollens' reagent and Benedict's solution. T is oxidized by bromine water to optically active $C_5H_{10}O_6$, and by nitric acid to optically inactive $C_5H_8O_7$. T forms an osazone that is identical with the osazone obtained from another pentose, $(-)$-U. Degradation of $(-)$-U, followed by oxidation by nitric acid, yields optically inactive $C_4H_6O_6$.

(a) What is T?

Careful acidic hydrolysis of adenylic acid yields adenine and a phosphate of T, $C_5H_9O_4-OPO_3H_2$. Reduction of the phosphate with H_2/Pt yields optically inactive V, $C_5H_{11}O_4-OPO_3H_2$. Hydrolysis of V yields optically inactive W, $C_5H_{12}O_5$, which reacts with acetic anhydride to yield optically inactive X, $C_{15}H_{22}O_{10}$.

(b) What is the structure of the phosphate of T?

Adenylic acid does not reduce Tollens' reagent or Benedict's solution. When hydrolyzed by aqueous ammonia, adenylic acid yields phosphoric acid and the nucleoside *adenosine*. Treatment of adenosine with methyl sulfate and NaOH, followed by acidic hydrolysis, yields Y, a methylation product of T. Compound Y has the formula $C_8H_{16}O_5$. Vigorous oxidation of Y yields 2,3-di-O-methylmeso-tartaric acid and no larger fragments.

Synthesis of adenosine shows that a nitrogen atom of adenine is joined to a carbon atom in T; synthesis also shows that T has the β-configuration.

(c) Give the structure of adenylic acid, using R_2NH for the adenine unit.

(Check your answers in Figure 33.6, page 885.)

Chapter thirty

CARBOHYDRATES II.
DISACCHARIDES AND
POLYSACCHARIDES

30.1 Disaccharides

Disaccharides are carbohydrates that are made up of two monosaccharide units. On hydrolysis a molecule of disaccharide yields two molecules of monosaccharide.

We shall study four disaccharides: **(+)-maltose** (malt sugar), **(+)-cellobiose, (+)-lactose** (milk sugar), and **(+)-sucrose** (cane or beet sugar). As with the monosaccharides, we shall focus our attention on the structure of these molecules: on which monosaccharides make up the disaccharide, and how they are attached to each other. In doing this, we shall also learn something about the properties of these disaccharides.

30.2 (+)-Maltose

(+)-Maltose can be obtained, among other products, by partial hydrolysis of starch in aqueous acid. (+)-Maltose is also formed in one stage of the fermentation of starch to ethyl alcohol; here hydrolysis is catalyzed by the enzyme *diastase*, which is present in malt (sprouted barley).

Let us look at some of the facts from which the structure of (+)-maltose has been deduced.

(+)–Maltose has the molecular formula $C_{12}H_{22}O_{11}$. It reduces Tollens' and Fehling's reagents and hence is a reducing sugar. It reacts with phenylhydrazine to yield an osazone, $C_{12}H_{20}O_9(=NNHC_6H_5)_2$. It is oxidized by bromine water to a monocarboxylic acid, $(C_{11}H_{21}O_{10})COOH$, *maltobionic acid*. (+)-Maltose exists in *alpha* ($[\alpha] = +168°$) and *beta* ($[\alpha] = +112°$) forms which undergo mutarotation in solution (equilibrium $[\alpha] = +136°$).

All these facts indicate the same thing: (+)-maltose contains a carbonyl group that exists in the reactive hemiacetal form as in the monosaccharides we have studied. It contains only one such "free" carbonyl group, however, since (a) the osazone contains only two phenylhydrazine residues, and (b) oxidation by bromine water yields only a *mono*carboxylic acid.

When hydrolyzed in aqueous acid, or when treated with the enzyme *maltase* (from yeast), (+)-maltose is completely converted into D-(+)-glucose. This indicates that (+)-maltose ($C_{12}H_{22}O_{11}$) is made up of two D-(+)-glucose units joined together in some manner with the loss of one molecule of water ($2C_6H_{12}O_6 - H_2O = C_{12}H_{22}O_{11}$).

Hydrolysis by acid to give a new reducing group (two reducing D-(+)-glucose molecules in place of one (+)-maltose molecule) is characteristic of glycosides; hydrolysis by the enzyme maltase is characteristic of *alpha*-glucosides. A glycoside is an acetal formed by interaction of an alcohol with a carbonyl group of a carbohydrate (Sec. 29.14); in this case the alcohol concerned can only be a second molecule of D-(+)-glucose. We conclude that (+)-maltose contains two D-(+)-glucose units, joined by an *alpha*-glucoside linkage between the carbonyl group of one D-(+)-glucose unit and an —OH group of the other.

Two questions remain: which —OH group is involved, and what are the sizes of the rings in the two D-(+)-glucose units? Answers to both these questions are given by a sequence of oxidation, methylation, and hydrolysis.

Oxidation by bromine water converts (+)-maltose into the monocarboxylic acid D-maltobionic acid. Treatment of this acid with methyl sulfate and sodium hydroxide yields octa-O-methyl-D-maltobionic acid. Upon hydrolysis in acidic solution, the methylated acid yields two products, 2,3,5,6-tetra-O-methyl-D-gluconic acid and 2,3,4,6-tetra-O-methyl-D-glucose.

These facts indicate that (+)-maltose has structure I, which is given the name 4-O-(α-D-glucopyranosyl)-D-glucopyranose. It is the —OH group on C–4 that serves as the alcohol in the glucoside formation; both halves of the molecule contain the six-membered, pyranose ring.

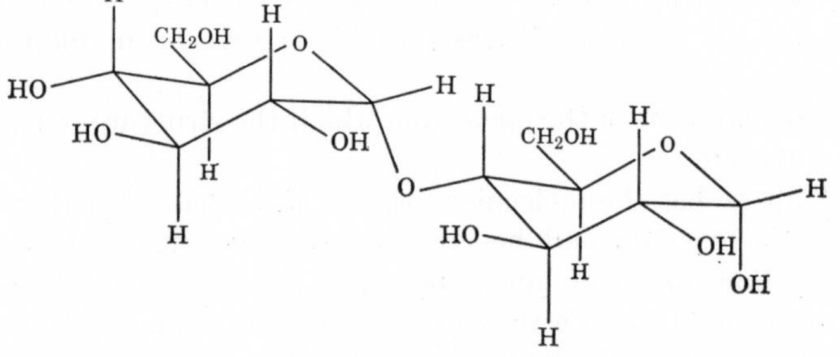

(+)-Maltose (α-anomer)
4-O-(α-D-Glucopyranosyl)-D-glucopyranose

I

Let us see how we arrive at structure I from the experimental facts.

First of all, the initial oxidation labels (with a —COOH group) the D-glucose unit that contains the "free" aldehyde group.

Oxidation

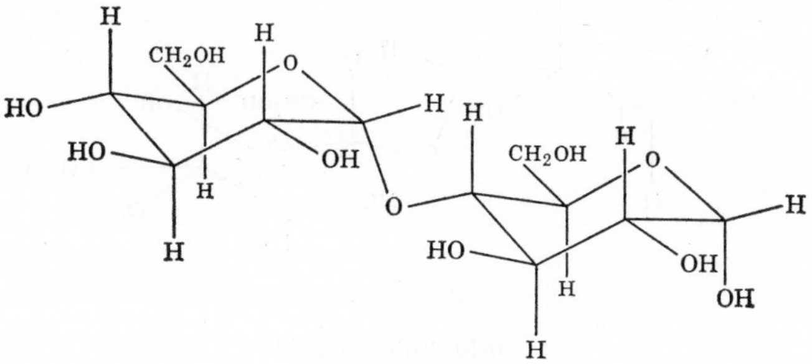

(+)-Maltose
(α-anomer)

Br₂, H₂O

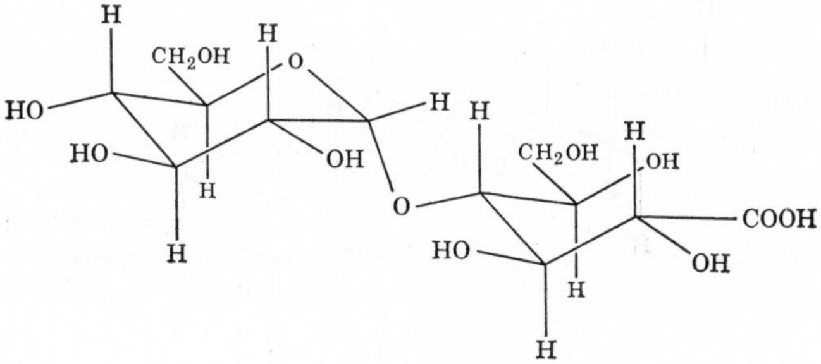

D-Maltobionic acid
(probably as a lactone)

Next, methylation labels (as —OCH₃) every free —OH group.

Methylation

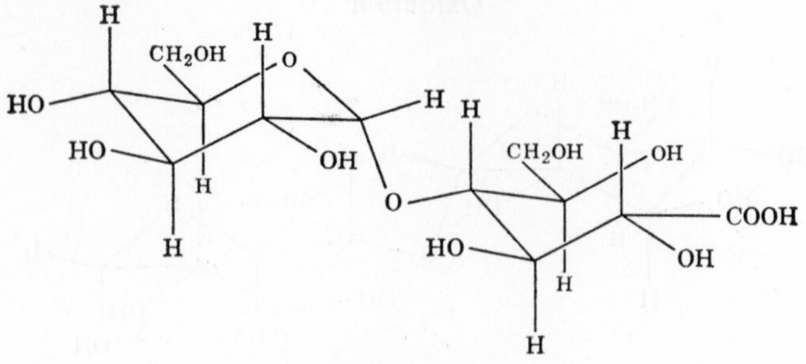

D-Maltobionic acid
(probably as a lactone)

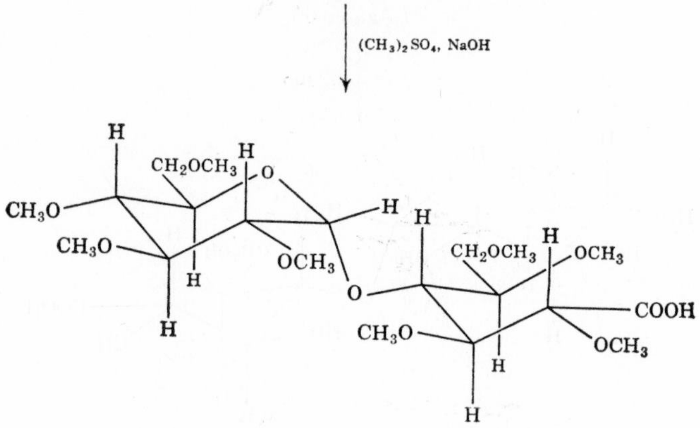

$(CH_3)_2SO_4$, NaOH

Octa-O-methyl-D-maltobionic acid

Finally, upon hydrolysis, the absence of a methoxyl group shows which —OH groups were *not* free.

Hydrolysis

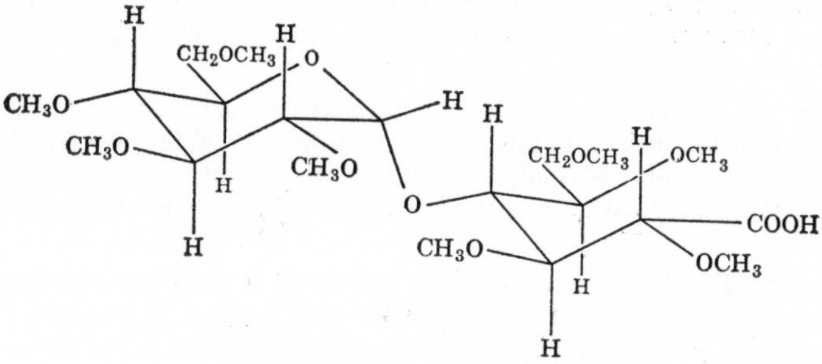

CH$_2$OCH$_3$ H O
CH$_3$O—
CH$_3$O—
H
CH$_3$O
H
H
—H H
CH$_2$OCH$_3$ OCH$_3$
O—
CH$_3$O—
—COOH
OCH$_3$
H
H

Octa-O-methyl-D-maltobionic acid

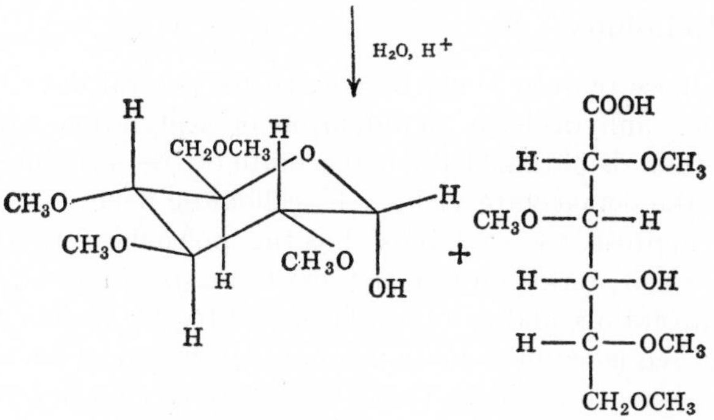

$\downarrow$ H$_2$O, H$^+$

CH$_2$OCH$_3$ H O
CH$_3$O—
CH$_3$O—
H
CH$_3$O
H
H
—H
OH

+

COOH
H—C—OCH$_3$
CH$_3$O—C—H
H—C—OH
H—C—OCH$_3$
CH$_2$OCH$_3$

2,3,4,6-Tetra-O-methyl-
D-glucopyranose
(α-anomer)

2,3,5,6-Tetra-O-methyl-
D-gluconic acid
(probably as a lactone)

The oxidized product, 2,3,5,6-tetra-O-methyl-D-gluconic acid, must have arisen from the reducing (oxidizable) D-glucose unit. The presence of a free —OH group at C–4 shows that this position was not available for methylation at the maltobionic acid stage; hence it is the —OH on C–4 that is tied up in the glucoside linkage of maltobionic acid and of (+)-maltose itself. This leaves only the —OH group on C–5 to be involved in the ring of the reducing (oxidizable) unit in the original disaccharide. On the basis of these facts, therefore, we designate one D-(+)-glucose unit as a 4-O-substituted-D-glucopyranose.

The unoxidized product, 2,3,4,6-tetra-O-methyl-D-glucose, must have arisen from the non-reducing (non-oxidizable) D-glucose unit. The presence of the free —OH group at C–5 indicates that this position escaped methylation at the maltobionic acid stage; hence it is the —OH on C–5 that is tied up as a ring in maltobionic acid and in (+)-maltose itself. On the basis of these facts, therefore, we designate the second D-(+)-glucose unit as an α-D-glucopyranosyl group.

Problem 30.1   Formula I shows the structure of only the α-form of (+)-maltose. What is the structure of the β-(+)-maltose that in solution is in equilibrium with I?

Problem 30.2   The position of the free —OH group in 2,3,4,6-tetra-O-methyl-D-glucose was shown by the products of oxidative cleavage, as described in Sec. 29.17. What products would be expected from oxidative cleavage of 2,3,5,6-tetra-O-methyl-D-gluconic acid?

Problem 30.3   What products would have been obtained if (+)-maltose itself were subjected to methylation and hydrolysis? What would this tell us about the structure of (+)-maltose? What uncertainty would remain in the (+)-maltose structure? Why was it necessary to oxidize (+)-maltose first before methylation?

Problem 30.4   When (+)-maltose is subjected to two successive one-carbon degradations, there is obtained a disaccharide that reduces Tollens' and Fehling's reagents but that does not form an osazone. What products would be expected from the acidic hydrolysis of this disaccharide? What would these facts indicate about the structure of (+)-maltose?

30.3   (+)-Cellobiose

When cellulose (cotton fibers) is treated for several days with sulfuric acid and acetic anhydride, a combination of acetylation and hydrolysis takes place; there is obtained the octaacetate of (+)-cellobiose. Alkaline hydrolysis of the octaacetate yields (+)-cellobiose itself.

Like (+)-maltose, (+)-cellobiose has the molecular formula $C_{12}H_{22}O_{11}$, is a reducing sugar, forms an osazone, exists in *alpha* and *beta* forms that undergo mutarotation, and can be hydrolyzed to two molecules of D-(+)-glucose. The sequence of oxidation, methylation, and hydrolysis (as described for (+)-maltose) shows that (+)-cellobiose contains two pyranose rings and a glucoside linkage to an —OH group on C–4.

(+)-Cellobiose differs from (+)-maltose in one respect: it is hydrolyzed by the enzyme *emulsin* (from bitter almonds), not by maltase. Since emulsin is known to hydrolyze only β-glycoside linkages, we can conclude that the structure of (+)-cellobiose differs from that of (+)-maltose in only one respect: the D-glucose units are joined by a *beta* linkage rather than by an *alpha* linkage. (+)-Cellobiose is therefore 4-O-(β-D-glucopyranosyl)-D-glucopyranose.

(+)-Cellobiose (β-anomer)
4-O-(β-D-Glucopyranosyl)-D-glucopyranose

Although the D-glucose unit on the right in the formula of (+)-cellobiose may look different from the D-glucose unit on the left, this is only because it has been turned over to permit a reasonable bond angle at the glycosidic oxygen atom.

Problem 30.5 Why is *alkaline* hydrolysis of cellobiose octaacetate (better named octa-O-acetylcellobiose) to (+)-cellobiose preferred over acidic hydrolysis?

Problem 30.6 Write equations for the sequence of oxidation, methylation, and hydrolysis as applied to (+)-cellobiose.

30.4   (+)-Lactose

(+)-Lactose makes up about 5% of human milk and of cow's milk. It is obtained commercially as a by-product of cheese manufacture, being found in the *whey*, the aqueous solution that remains after the milk proteins have been coagulated. Milk *sours* when lactose is converted into lactic acid (sour, like all acids) by bacterial action (e.g., by Lactobacillus bulgaricus).

(+)-Lactose has the molecular formula $C_{12}H_{22}O_{11}$, is a reducing sugar, forms an osazone, and exists in *alpha* and *beta* forms which undergo mutarotation. Acidic hydrolysis or treatment with emulsin (which splits β-linkages only) converts (+)-lactose into equal amounts of D-(+)-glucose and D-(+)-galactose. (+)-Lactose is evidently a β-glycoside formed by the union of a molecule of D-(+)-glucose and a molecule of D-(+)-galactose.

The question next arises: which is the reducing monosaccharide unit and which the non-reducing unit? Is (+)-lactose a glucoside or a galactoside? Hydrolysis of lactosazone yields D-(+)-galactose and D-glucosone; hydrolysis of *lactobionic acid* (monocarboxylic acid) yields D-gluconic acid and D-(+)-galactose (see Figure 30.1, next page). Clearly it is the D-(+)-glucose unit that contains the "free" aldehyde group and undergoes osazone formation and oxidation to the acid. (+)-Lactose is thus a substituted D-glucose in which a D-galactosyl unit is attached to one of the oxygens; it is a galactoside, not a glucoside.

The sequence of oxidation, methylation, and hydrolysis gives results analogous to those obtained with (+)-maltose and (+)-cellobiose: the glycoside linkage involves an —OH group on C-4, and both units exist in the six-membered, pyranose form. (+)-Lactose is therefore 4-O-(β-D-galactopyranosyl)-D-glucopyranose.

Problem 30.7 (a) Write equations for the sequence of oxidation, methylation, and hydrolysis as applied to (+)-lactose.
(b) What compounds would be expected from oxidative cleavage of the final products of (a)?

Problem 30.8 What products would be expected if (+)-lactose were subjected to two successive one-carbon degradations followed by acidic hydrolysis?

30.5   (+)-Sucrose

(+)-Sucrose is our common table sugar, obtained from sugar cane and sugar beets. Of organic chemicals, it is the one produced in the largest amount in pure form.

(+)-Sucrose has the molecular formula $C_{12}H_{22}O_{11}$. It does not reduce Tollens' or Fehling's reagent. It is a non-reducing sugar, and in this respect it differs from the other disaccharides we have studied. Moreover,

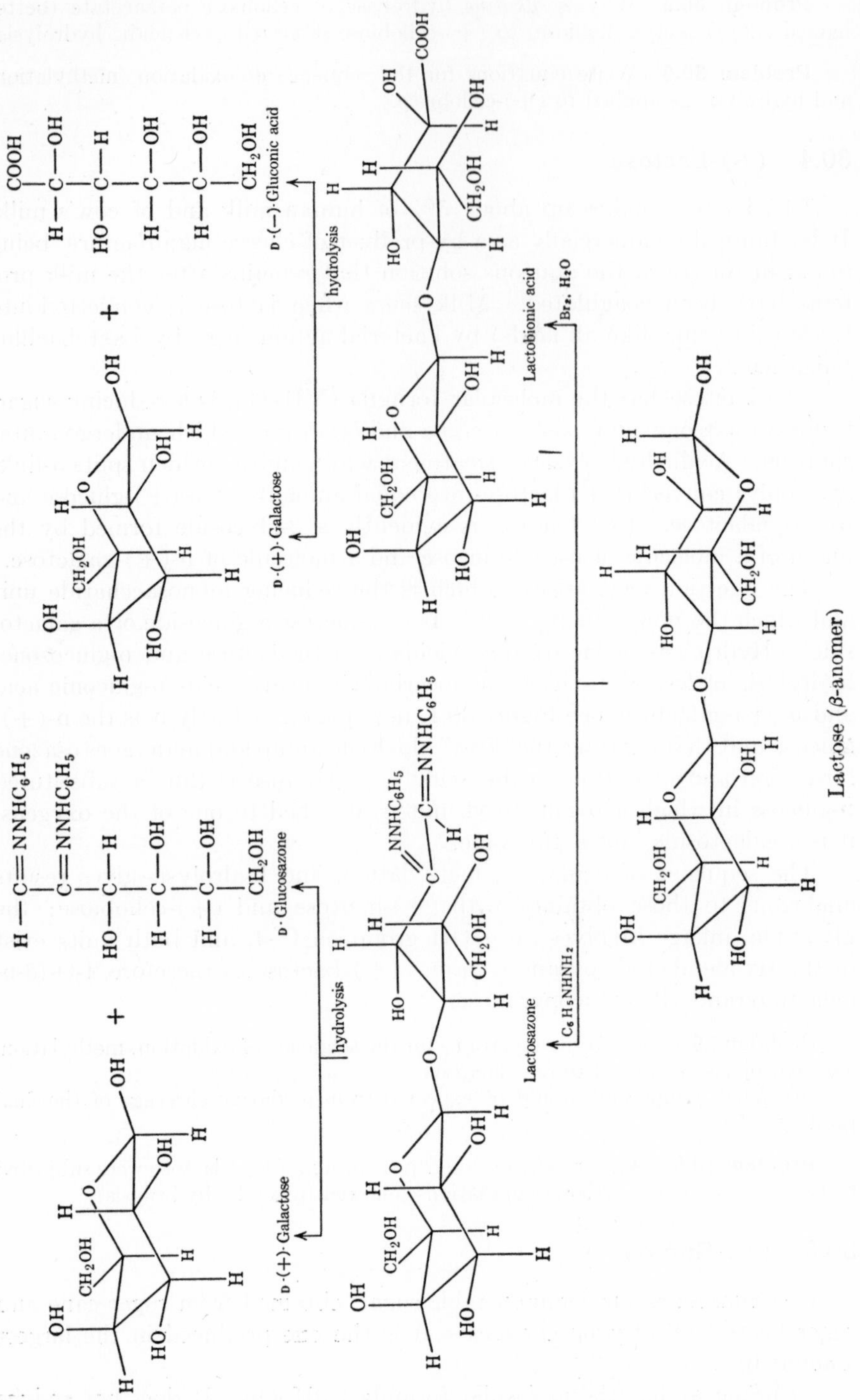

FIGURE 30.1. Hydrolysis of (+)-lactose derivatives. Shows that glucose is the reducing unit. (+)-Lactose is 4-O-(β-D-Galactopyranosyl)-D-glucopyranose.

(+)-sucrose does not form an osazone, it does not exist in anomeric forms, and does not show mutarotation in solution. All these facts indicate that (+)-sucrose does not contain a "free" aldehyde or ketone group.

When (+)-sucrose is hydrolyzed by dilute aqueous acid, or by the action of the enzyme *invertase* (from yeast), it yields equal amounts of D-(+)-glucose and D-(−)-fructose. This hydrolysis is accompanied by a change in the sign of rotation from positive to negative; it is therefore often called the *inversion* of (+)-sucrose, and the levorotatory mixture of D-(+)-glucose and D-(−)-fructose obtained has been called *invert sugar*. (Honey is mostly invert sugar; the bees supply the invertase.) While (+)-sucrose has a specific rotation of +66.5° and D-(+)-glucose has a specific rotation of +52.7°, D-(−)-fructose has a large negative specific rotation of −92.4°, giving a net negative value for the specific rotation of the mixture. (Because of their opposite rotations and their importance as components of (+)-sucrose, D-(+)-glucose and D-(−)-fructose are commonly called **dextrose** and **levulose**.)

Problem 30.9 How do you account for the experimentally observed $[\alpha] = -19.9°$ for invert sugar?

(+)-Sucrose is made up of a D-glucose unit and a D-fructose unit; since there is no "free" carbonyl group, it must be both a D-glucoside and a D-fructoside. The two hexose units are evidently joined by a glycoside linkage between C–1 of glucose and C–2 of fructose, for only in this way can the single link between the two units effectively block *both* carbonyl functions.

Problem 30.10 What would be the molecular formula of (+)-sucrose if C–1 of glucose were attached to, say, C–4 of fructose, and C–2 of fructose were joined to C–4 of glucose? Would this be a reducing or non-reducing sugar?

Determination of the stereochemistry of the D-glucoside and D-fructoside linkages is complicated by the fact that both linkages are hydrolyzed at the same time. The weight of evidence, including the results of x-ray studies and finally the synthesis of (+)-sucrose (1953), leads to the conclusion that (+)-sucrose is a *beta* D-fructoside and an *alpha* D-glucoside. (The synthesis of sucrose, by R. U. Lemieux of the Prairie Regional Laboratory, Saskatoon, Saskatchewan, has been described as "the Mount Everest of organic chemistry.")

(+)-Sucrose

α-D-Glucopyranosyl β-D-fructofuranoside

β-D-Fructofuranosyl α-D-glucopyranoside

(no anomers; *non-mutarotating*)

Problem 30.11   When (+)-sucrose is hydrolyzed enzymatically, the D-glucose initially obtained mutarotates *downward* to +52.7°. What does this fact indicate about the structure of (+)-sucrose?

Methylation and hydrolysis show that (+)-sucrose contains a D-gluco-pyranose unit and a D-fructofuranose unit. (The unexpected occurrence of the relatively rare five-membered, furanose ring caused no end of dif-ficulties in both structure proof and synthesis of (+)-sucrose.) (+)-Su-crose is named equally well as either α-D-glucopyranosyl β-D-fructofurano-side or β-D-fructofuranosyl α-D-glucopyranoside.

Problem 30.12   (a) Write equations for the sequence of methylation and hydrolysis as applied to (+)-sucrose.
(b) What compounds would be expected from oxidative cleavage of the final products of (a)?

30.6   Polysaccharides

Polysaccharides are compounds made up of many — hundreds or even thousands — monosaccharide units per molecule. As in disaccharides, these units are held together by glycoside linkages, which can be broken by hydrolysis.

Polysaccharides are naturally occurring polymers, which can be con-sidered as derived from aldoses or ketoses by condensation polymerization. A polysaccharide derived from hexoses, for example, has the general formula $(C_6H_{10}O_5)_n$. This formula, of course, tells us very little about the structure of the polysaccharide. We need to know what the monosaccharide units are and how many there are in each molecule; how they are joined to each other; and whether the huge molecules thus formed are straight-chained or branched, looped or coiled.

By far the most important polysaccharides are **cellulose** and **starch.** Both are produced in plants from carbon dioxide and water by the process of photosynthesis, and both, as it happens, are made up of D-(+)-glucose units. Cellulose is the chief structural material of plants, giving the plants rigidity and form. It is probably the most widespread organic material known. Starch makes up the reserve food supply of plants and occurs chiefly in seeds. It is more water-soluble than cellulose, is more easily hydrolyzed, and hence more readily digested.

Both cellulose and starch are, of course, enormously important to us. Generally speaking, we use them in very much the same way as the plant does. We use cellulose for its structural properties: as wood for houses, as cotton or rayon for clothing, as paper for communication and packaging. We use starch as a food: potatoes, corn, wheat, rice, cassava, etc.

30.7   Starch

Starch occurs as granules whose size and shape are characteristic of the plant from which the starch is obtained. When intact, starch granules are insoluble in cold water; if the outer membrane has been broken by grinding, the granules swell in cold water and form a gel. When the intact granule is treated with warm water a soluble portion of the starch diffuses through the granule wall; in hot water the granules swell to such an extent that they burst.

In general, starch contains about 20% of a water-soluble fraction called **amylose**, and 80% of a water-insoluble fraction called **amylopectin**. These two fractions appear to correspond to different carbohydrates of high molecular weight and formula $(C_6H_{10}O_5)_n$. Upon treatment with acid or under the influence of enzymes, the components of starch are hydrolyzed progressively to dextrin (a mixture of low molecular weight polysaccharides), (+)-maltose, and finally D-(+)-glucose. (A mixture of all these is found in corn sirup, for example.) Both amylose and amylopectin are made up of D-(+)-glucose units, but differ in molecular size and shape.

30.8 Structure of amylose. End group analysis

(+)-Maltose is the only disaccharide that is obtained by hydrolysis of amylose, and D-(+)-glucose is the only monosaccharide. To account for this, it has been proposed that amylose is made up of chains of many D-(+)-glucose units, each unit joined by an *alpha* glycoside linkage to C-4 of the next one.

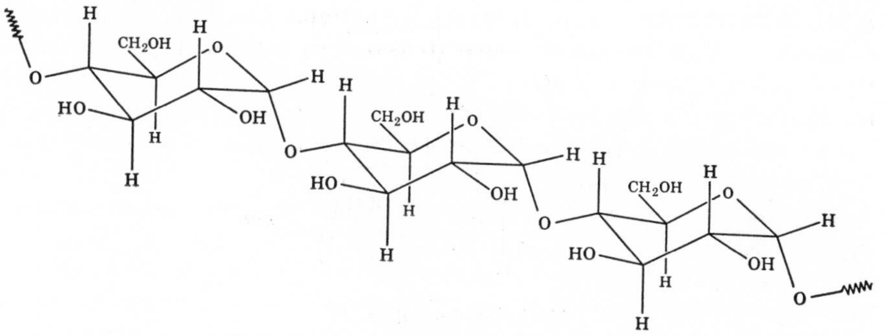

Amylose
(chair conformations assumed)

We could conceive of a structure for amylose in which α- and β-linkages regularly alternate. However, a compound of such a structure would be expected to yield (+)-cellobiose as well as (+)-maltose unless hydrolysis of the β-linkages occurred much faster than hydrolysis of the α-linkages. Since hydrolysis of the β-linkage in (+)-cellobiose is actually slower than hydrolysis of the α-linkage in (+)-maltose, such a structure seems unlikely.

How many of these α-D-(+)-glucose units are there per molecule of amylose, and what are the shapes of these large molecules? These are difficult questions, and attempts to find the answers have made use of chemical and enzymatic methods, and of physical methods like x-ray analysis, electron microscopy, osmotic pressure and viscosity measurements, and behavior in an ultracentrifuge.

Valuable information about molecular size and shape has been obtained by the combination of methylation and hydrolysis that was so effective in studying the structures of disaccharides. D-(+)-Glucose, a mono-saccharide, contains five free —OH groups and forms a pentamethyl derivative, methyl tetra-O-methyl-D-glucopyranoside. When two D-(+)-glucose units are joined together, as in (+)-maltose, each unit contains four free —OH groups; an octamethyl derivative is formed. If each D-(+)-glucose unit in amylose is joined to two others, it contains only three free —OH groups; methylation of amylose should therefore yield a compound containing only three —OCH$_3$ groups per glucose unit. What are the facts?

When amylose is methylated and hydrolyzed there is obtained, as expected, 2,3,6-tri-O-methyl-D-glucose.

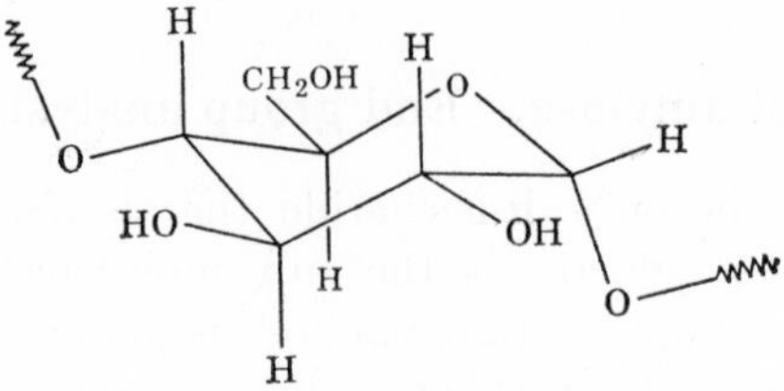

Amylose

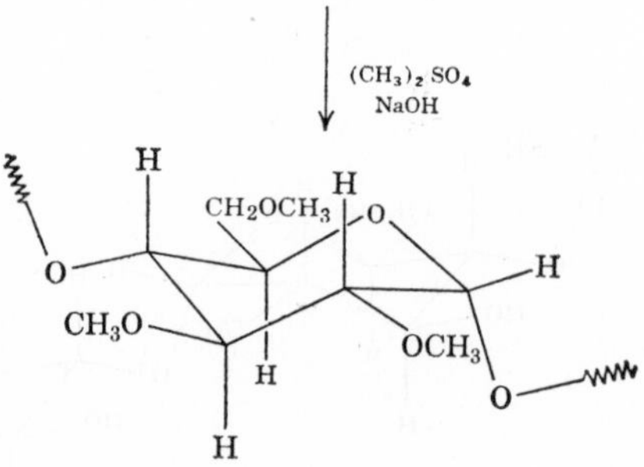

$(CH_3)_2 SO_4$
NaOH

Methylated amylose

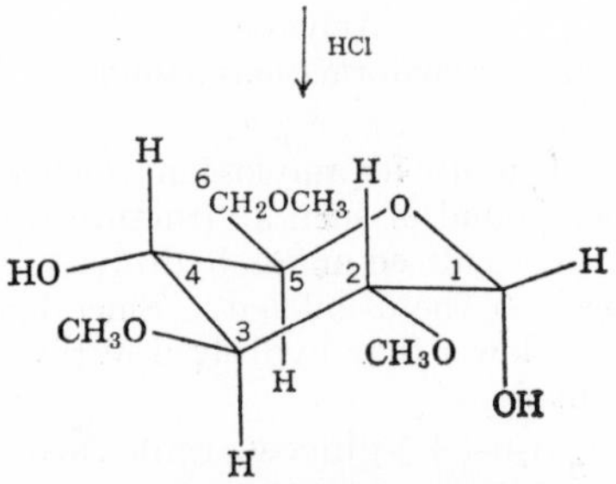

HCl

2,3,6-Tri-O-methyl-D-glucose
(α-anomer)

But there is also obtained a little bit of 2,3,4,6-tetra-O-methyl-D-glucose, amounting to about 0.3–0.5% of the total product. Consideration of the

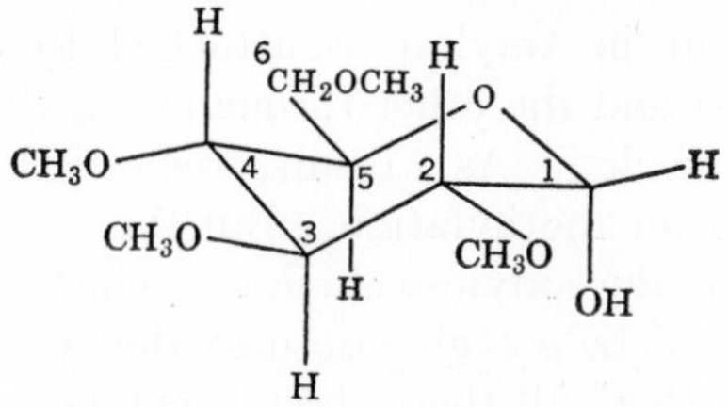

2,3,4,6-Tetra-O-methyl-D-glucose
(α-anomer)

structure of amylose shows that this, too, is to be expected, and an important principle emerges: that of **end group analysis.**

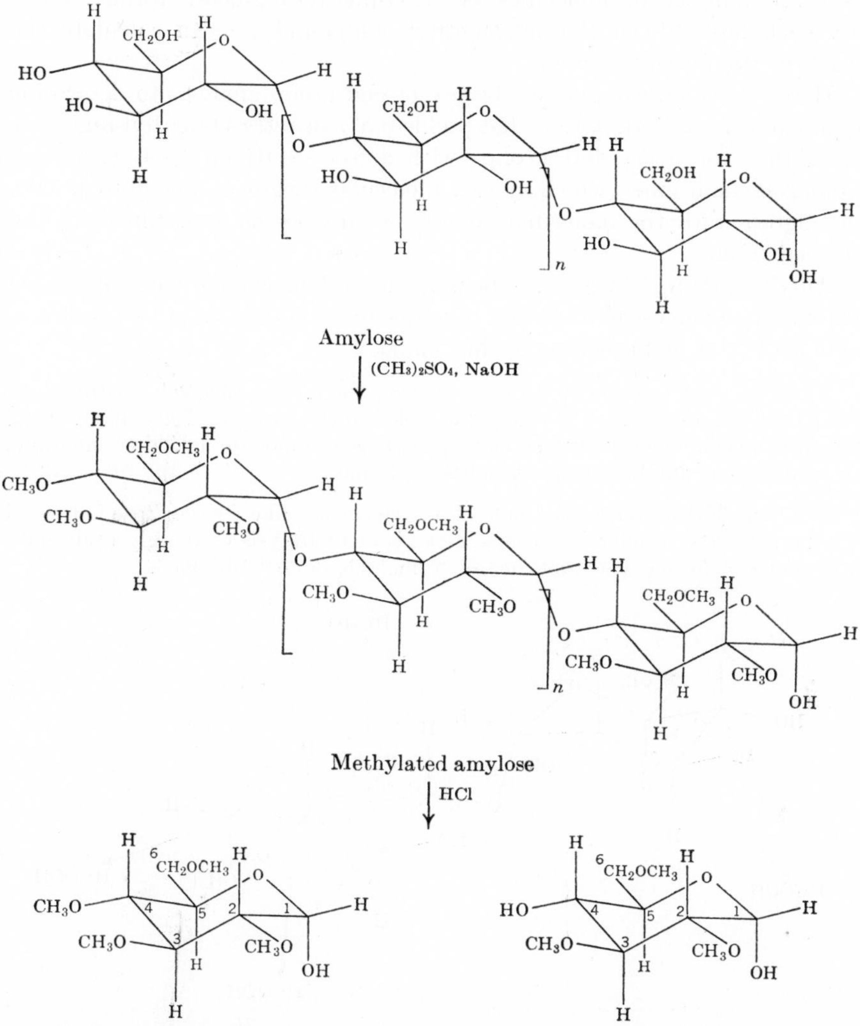

Amylose

$(CH_3)_2SO_4$, NaOH

Methylated amylose

HCl

2,3,4,6-Tetra-O-methyl-D-glucose
0.5% yield

and

(n + 1) 2,3,6-Tri-O-
methyl-D-glucose

Each D-glucose unit in amylose is attached to two other D-glucose units, one through C–1 and the other through C–4, with C–5 in every unit tied up in the pyranose ring. As a result, free —OH groups at C–2, C–3, and C–6 are available for methylation. But this is not the case for *every* D-glucose unit. Unless the amylose chain is cyclic it must have two ends. At one end there should be a D-glucose unit that contains a "free" aldehyde group. At the other end there should be a D-glucose unit that has a free —OH on C–4. This last D-glucose unit should undergo methylation at *four* —OH groups, and on hydrolysis should give a molecule of 2,3,4,6-tetra-O-methyl-D-glucose. (See preceding page.)

Thus each molecule of completely methylated amylose that is hydrolyzed should yield one molecule of 2,3,4,6-tetra-O-methyl-D-glucose; from the number of molecules of tri-O-methyl-D-glucose formed *along with* each molecule of the tetramethyl compound we can calculate the length of the amylose chain.

Here we see an example of the use of end group analysis to determine chain length. A methylation that yields 0.5% of tetra-O-methyl-D-glucose shows that for every end group (with a free —OH on C–4) there are about 200 chain units, which gives a molecular weight of 30,000 to 40,000. This agrees with the molecular weight of amylose as determined by the ultracentrifuge.

Amylose, then, is believed to be made up of long chains, each containing 200 or more D-glucose units joined together by α-linkages as in (+)-maltose; there is little or no branching of the chain.

Amylose is the fraction of starch that gives the intense blue color with iodine. It has been suggested that the chains are coiled in the form of a helix (like a spiral staircase), inside which is just enough space to accommodate an iodine molecule; the blue color is due to entrapped iodine molecules.

Problem 30.13 When one mole of a disaccharide like (+)-maltose is treated with periodic acid (under conditions that avoid hydrolysis of the glycoside link) three moles of formic acid (and one of formaldehyde) are obtained.

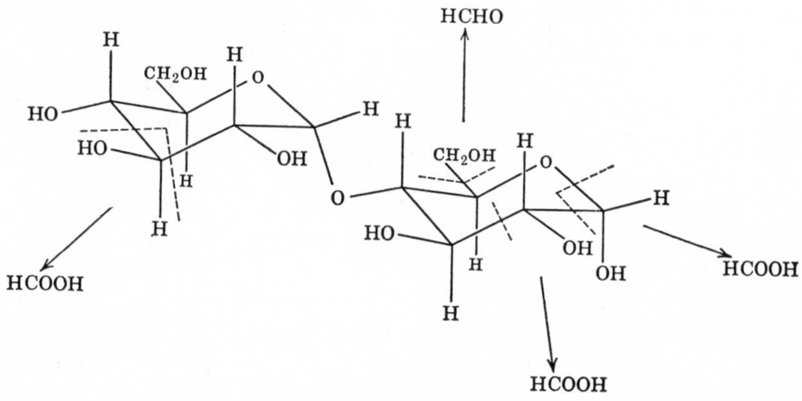

(a) Show what would happen to amylose (see formula on page 793) when treated with HIO_4. (b) How could this reaction be used to determine chain length?

(c) Oxidation by HIO_4 of 261 mg of amylose (from the sago plant) yielded 0.0102 millimoles of HCOOH. What is the chain length of this amylose?

Problem 30.14 On the basis of certain evidence it has been suggested that the rings of amylose have a boat conformation, rather than the usual chair conformation. (a) What feature would tend to make any chair conformation unstable? (b) Suggest a boat conformation that would avoid this difficulty. (*Hint:* what are the largest groups attached to a ring in amylose?)

30.9 Structure of amylopectin

Amylopectin is hydrolyzed to the single disaccharide (+)-maltose; the sequence of methylation and hydrolysis yields chiefly 2,3,6-tri-O-methyl-D-glucose. Like amylose, amylopectin is made up of chains of D-glucose units, each unit joined by an *alpha* glycoside linkage to C–4 of the next one. However, its structure is more complex than that of amylose.

Molecular weights determined by physical methods show that there are at least 1000 D-glucose units per molecule. Yet hydrolysis of methylated amylopectin gives as high as 5% of 2,3,4,6-tetra-O-methyl-D-glucose, indicating only 20 units per chain. How can these facts be reconciled by the same structure?

The answer is found in the following fact: along with the trimethyl and tetramethyl compounds, hydrolysis yields 2,3-di-O-methyl-D-glucose and in an amount nearly equal to that of the tetramethyl derivative.

Methylated amylopectin

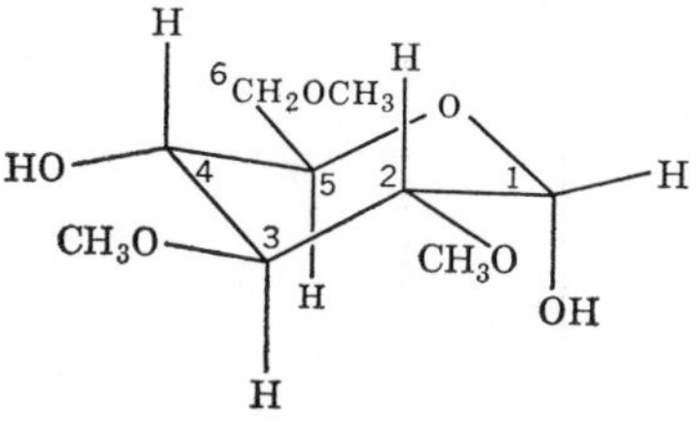

2,3,6-Tri-O-methyl-D-glucose   2,3,4,6-Tetra-O-methyl-D-glucose
~ 90%   ~ 5%

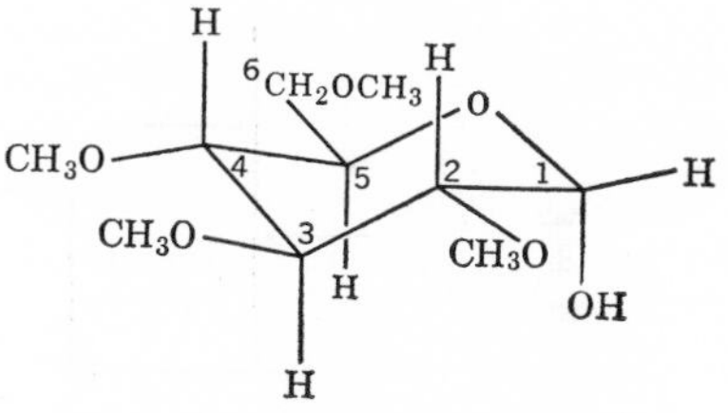

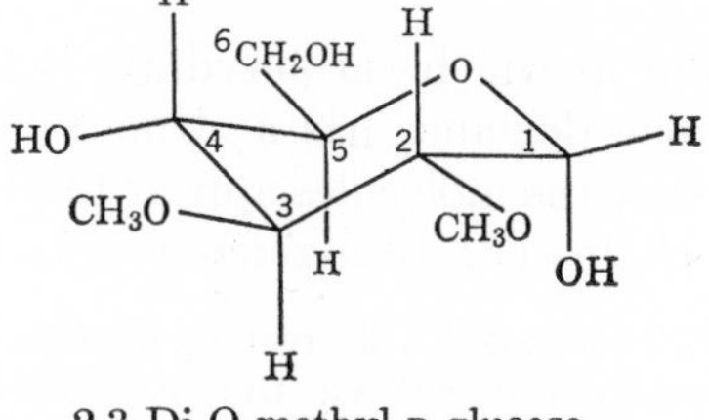

2,3-Di-O-methyl-D-glucose
~ 5%

Amylopectin has a highly branched structure consisting of several hundred short chains of about 20–25 D-glucose units each. One end of each of these chains is joined through C–1 to a C–6 on the next chain (following page).

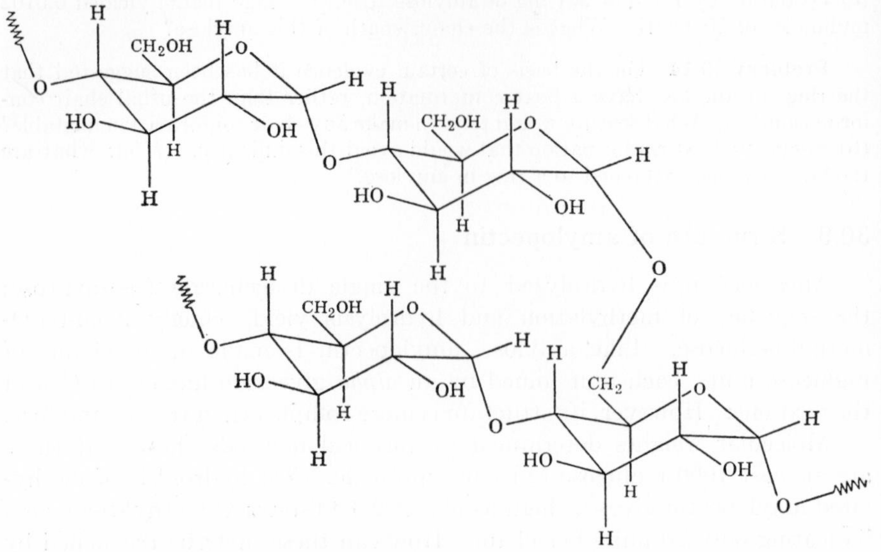

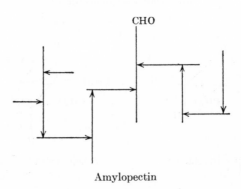

Amylopectin
(chair conformations assumed)

Schematically the amylopectin molecule is believed to be something like this:

CHO

Amylopectin

Glycogen, the form in which carbohydrate is stored in animals to be released upon metabolic demand, has a structure very similar to that of amylopectin, except that the molecules appear to be more highly branched, and to have shorter chains (12–18 D-glucose units each).

Problem 30.15 Polysaccharides known as *dextrans* have been used as substitutes for blood plasma in transfusions; they are made by the action of certain bacteria on (+)-sucrose. Interpret the following properties of a dextran: Complete hydrolysis by acid yields only D-(+)-glucose. Partial hydrolysis yields only one disaccharide and only one trisaccharide, which contain only α-glycoside linkages. Upon methylation and hydrolysis there is obtained chiefly 2,3,4-tri-O-methyl-D-glucose, together with smaller amounts of 2,4-di-O-methyl-D-glucose and 2,3,4,6-tetra-O-methyl-D-glucose.

Problem 30.16   Polysaccharides called *xylans* are found along with cellulose in wood and straw.   Interpret the following properties of a sample of xylan: Its large negative rotation suggests β-linkages.   Complete hydrolysis by acids yields only D-(+)-xylose.   Upon methylation and hydrolysis there is obtained chiefly 2,3-di-O-methyl-D-xylose, together with smaller amounts of 2,3,4-tri-O-methyl-D-xylose and 2-O-methyl-D-xylose.

30.10   Structure of cellulose

Cellulose is the chief component of wood and plant fibers; cotton, for instance, is nearly pure cellulose.   It is insoluble in water and tasteless; it is a non-reducing carbohydrate.   These properties, in part at least, are due to its extremely high molecular weight.

Cellulose has the formula $(C_6H_{10}O_5)_n$.   Complete hydrolysis by acid yields D-(+)-glucose as the only monosaccharide.   Hydrolysis of completely methylated cellulose gives a high yield of 2,3,6-tri-O-methyl-D-glucose.   Like starch, therefore, cellulose is made up of chains of D-glucose units, each unit joined by a glycoside linkage to C–4 of the next.

Cellulose differs from starch, however, in the configuration of the glycoside linkage.   Upon treatment with acetic anhydride and sulfuric acid, cellulose yields octa-O-acetylcellobiose; there is evidence that all glycoside linkages in cellulose, like the one in (+)-cellobiose, are *beta* linkages.

Cellulose

Physical methods give molecular weights for cellulose ranging from 250,000 to 1,000,000 or more; it seems likely that there are at least 1500 glucose units per molecule.   End group analysis by both methylation and periodic acid oxidation gives a chain length of 1000 glucose units or more.   X-ray analysis and electron microscopy indicate that these long chains lie side by side in bundles, undoubtedly held together by hydrogen bonds between the numerous neighboring —OH groups.   These bundles are twisted together to form rope-like structures, which themselves are grouped to form the fibers we can see.   In wood these cellulose "ropes" are embedded in lignin to give a structure that has been likened to reinforced concrete.

30.11   Reactions of cellulose

We have seen that the glycoside linkages of cellulose are broken by the action of acid, each cellulose molecule yielding many molecules of D-(+)-glucose.   Now let us look briefly at reactions of cellulose in which the chain remains essentially intact.   Each glucose unit in cellulose contains three free —OH groups; these are the positions at which reaction occurs.

These reactions of cellulose, carried out to modify the properties of a cheap, available, ready-made polymer, are of tremendous industrial importance.

30.12   Cellulose nitrate

Like any alcohol, cellulose forms esters. Treatment with a mixture of nitric and sulfuric acids converts cellulose into *cellulose nitrate*. The properties and uses of the product depend upon the extent of nitration.

Guncotton, which is used in making smokeless powder, is very nearly completely nitrated cellulose, and is often called *cellulose trinitrate* (three nitrate groups per glucose unit).

Pyroxylin is less highly nitrated material containing between two and three nitrate groups per glucose unit. It is used in the manufacture of plastics like celluloid and collodion, in photographic film, and in lacquers. It has the disadvantage of being flammable, and forms highly toxic nitrogen oxides upon burning.

30.13   Cellulose acetate

In the presence of acetic anhydride, acetic acid, and a little sulfuric acid, cellulose is converted into the triacetate. Partial hydrolysis removes some of the acetate groups, degrades the chains to smaller fragments (of 200–300 units each), and yields the vastly important commercial *cellulose acetate* (roughly a *di*acetate).

Cellulose acetate is less flammable than cellulose nitrate and has replaced the nitrate in many of its applications, in safety-type photographic film, for example. When a solution of cellulose acetate in acetone is forced through the fine holes of a spinnerette, the solvent evaporates and leaves solid filaments. Threads from these filaments make up the material known as *acetate rayon*.

30.14   Rayon.   Cellophane

When an alcohol is treated with carbon disulfide and aqueous sodium hydroxide, there is obtained a compound called a *xanthate*.

$$RONa + S{=}C{=}S \longrightarrow RO{-}\underset{\underset{S}{\|}}{C}{-}SNa \xrightarrow{\;H^+\;} ROH + CS_2$$

A xanthate

Cellulose undergoes an analogous reaction to form *cellulose xanthate*, which dissolves in the alkali to form a viscous colloidal dispersion called *viscose*.

When viscose is forced through a spinnerette into an acid bath, cellulose is regenerated in the form of fine filaments which yield threads of the material known as *rayon*. There are other processes for making rayon, but the viscose process is still the principal one used in the United States.

If viscose is forced through a narrow slit, cellulose is regenerated as thin sheets which, when softened by glycerol, are used for protective films (Cellophane).

Although rayon and Cellophane are often spoken of as "regenerated cellulose," they are made up of much shorter chains than the original cellulose because of degradation by the alkali treatment.

30.15 Cellulose ethers

Industrially, cellulose is alkylated by the action of alkyl chlorides (cheaper than sulfates) in the presence of alkali. Considerable degradation of the long chains is unavoidable in these reactions.

Methyl, ethyl, and benzyl ethers of cellulose are important in the production of textiles, films, and various plastic objects.

PROBLEMS

1. (+)-*Gentiobiose*, $C_{12}H_{22}O_{11}$, is found in the roots of gentians. It is a reducing sugar, forms an osazone, undergoes mutarotation, and is hydrolyzed by aqueous acid or by emulsin to D-glucose. Methylation of (+)-gentiobiose, followed by hydrolysis, gives 2,3,4,6-tetra-O-methyl-D-glucose and 2,3,4-tri-O-methyl-D-glucose. What is the structure and systematic name of (+)-gentiobiose?

2. (a) (+)-*Trehalose*, $C_{12}H_{22}O_{11}$, a non-reducing sugar found in young mushrooms, gives only D-glucose when hydrolyzed by aqueous acid or by maltase. Methylation gives an octa-O-methyl derivative that, upon hydrolysis, yields only 2,3,4,6-tetra-O-methyl-D-glucose. What is the structure and systematic name for (+)-trehalose?

(b) (−)-*Isotrehalose* and (+)-*neotrehalose* resemble trehalose in most respects. However, isotrehalose is hydrolyzed by either emulsin or maltase, and neotrehalose is hydrolyzed only by emulsin. What are the structures and systematic names for these two carbohydrates?

3. *Ruberythric acid*, $C_{25}H_{26}O_{13}$, a non-reducing glycoside, is obtained from madder root. Complete hydrolysis gives *alizarin* ($C_{14}H_8O_4$), D-glucose, and D-xylose;

Alizarin

graded hydrolysis gives alizarin and *primeverose*, $C_{11}H_{20}O_{10}$. Oxidation of primeverose with bromine water, followed by hydrolysis, gives D-gluconic acid and D-xylose. Methylation of primeverose, followed by hydrolysis, gives 2,3,4-tri-O-methyl-D-xylose and 2,3,4-tri-O-methyl-D-glucose.

What structure or structures are possible for ruberythric acid? How can any uncertainties be cleared up?

4. (+)-*Raffinose*, a non-reducing sugar found in beet molasses, has the formula $C_{18}H_{32}O_{16}$. Hydrolysis by acid gives D-fructose, D-galactose, and D-glucose; hydrolysis by the enzyme α-galactosidase gives D-galactose and sucrose; hydrolysis by invertase (a sucrose-splitting enzyme) gives D-fructose and the disaccharide *melibiose*.

Methylation of raffinose, followed by hydrolysis, gives 1,3,4,6-tetra-O-methyl-D-fructose, 2,3,4,6-tetra-O-methyl-D-galactose, and 2,3,4-tri-O-methyl-D-glucose. What is the structure of raffinose? Of melibiose?

5. (+)-*Melezitose*, a non-reducing sugar found in honey, has the formula $C_{18}H_{32}O_{16}$. Hydrolysis by acid gives D-fructose and two moles of D-glucose; partial hydrolysis gives D-glucose and the disaccharide *turanose*. Hydrolysis by maltase gives D-glucose and D-fructose; hydrolysis by another enzyme gives sucrose.

Methylation of melezitose, followed by hydrolysis, gives 1,4,6-tri-O-methyl-D-fructose and two moles of 2,3,4,6-tetra-O-methyl-D-glucose.

(a) What structure of melezitose is consistent with these facts? What is the structure of turanose?

Melezitose reacts with four moles of HIO_4 to give two moles of formic acid but no formaldehyde.

(b) Show that the absence of formaldehyde means either a furanose or pyranose structure for the fructose unit, and either a pyranose or septanose (7-membered ring) structure for the glucose units.

(c) How many moles of HIO_4 would be consumed and how many moles of formic acid would be produced if the two glucose units had septanose rings? (d) Answer (c) for one septanose ring and one pyranose ring. (e) Answer (c) for two pyranose rings. (f) What can you say about the size of the rings in the glucose units?

(g) Answer (c) for a pyranose ring in the fructose unit; for a furanose ring. (h) What can you say about the size of the ring in the fructose unit?

(i) Are the oxidation data consistent with the structure of melezitose you gave in (a)?

6. Cellulose can be oxidized by N_2O_4 to $[(C_5H_7O_4)COOH]_n$. (a) What is the structure of this product? (b) What will it give on hydrolysis of the chain? What is the name of this hydrolysis product?

(c) The oxidation product in (a) is readily decarboxylated to $(C_5H_8O_4)_n$. What will this give on hydrolysis of the chain? What is the name of this hydrolysis product? Is it a D or L compound?

7. Suggest structural formulas for the following polysaccharides, neglecting the stereochemistry of the glycoside linkages:

(a) An *araban* from peanut hulls yields only L-arabinose on hydrolysis. Methylation, followed by hydrolysis, yields equimolar amounts of 2,3,5-tri-O-methyl-L-arabinose, 2,3-di-O-methyl-L-arabinose, and 3-O-methyl-L-arabinose.

(b) A *mannan* from yeast yields only D-mannose on hydrolysis. Methylation, followed by hydrolysis, yields 2,3,4,6-tetra-O-methyl-D-mannose, 2,4,6-tri-O-methyl-D-mannose, 3,4,6-tri-O-methyl-D-mannose, and 3,4-di-O-methyl-D-mannose in a molecular ratio of 2: 1: 1: 2, together with small amounts of 2,3,4-tri-O-methyl-D-mannose.

8. When a *xylan* (see Problem 30.16, page 797) is boiled with dilute hydrochloric acid, a pleasant-smelling liquid, *furfural*, $C_5H_4O_2$, steam-distills. Furfural gives positive tests with Tollens' and Schiff's reagents; it forms an oxime and a phenylhydrazone but not an osazone. Furfural can be oxidized by $KMnO_4$ to A, $C_5H_4O_3$, which is soluble in aqueous $NaHCO_3$.

Compound A can be readily decarboxylated to B, C_4H_4O, which can be hydrogenated to C, C_4H_8O. C gives no tests for functional groups except solubility in cold concentrated H_2SO_4; it gives negative tests for unsaturation with dilute $KMnO_4$ or Br_2/CCl_4.

Prolonged treatment of C with HCl gives D, $C_4H_8Cl_2$, which on treatment with KCN gives E, $C_6H_8N_2$. E can be hydrolyzed to F, $C_6H_{10}O_4$, identifiable as adipic acid.

What is the structure of furfural? Of compounds A through E?

9. Give a likely structure for each of the following polysaccharides:

(a) *Alginic acid,* from sea weed, is used as a thickening agent in ice cream and other foods. Hydrolysis yields only D-mannuronic acid. Methylation, followed by hydrolysis, yields 2,3-di-O-methyl-D-mannuronic acid. (Mannuronic acid is HOOC(CHOH)$_4$CHO.) The glycoside linkages in alginic acid are thought to be *beta.*

(b) *Pectic acid* is the main constituent of the *pectin* responsible for the formation of jellies from fruits and berries. Methylation of pectic acid, followed by hydrolysis, gives only 2,3,di-O-methyl-D-galacturonic acid. The glycoside linkages in pectic acid are thought to be *alpha.*

(c) *Agar,* from sea weed, is used in the growing of microorganisms. Hydrolysis yields a 9:1:1 molar ratio of D-galactose, L-galactose, and sulfuric acid. Methylation, followed by hydrolysis, yields 2,4,6-tri-O-methyl-D-galactose, 2,3-di-O-methyl-L-galactose, and sulfuric acid in the same 9:1:1 ratio. What uncertainties are there in your proposed structure?

10. The main constituent of the capsule surrounding the Type III pneumonococcus, and the substance responsible for the specificity of its antigen–antibody reactions, is a polysaccharide (mol. wt. about 150,000). Hydrolysis yields equimolar amounts of D-glucose and D-glucuronic acid, HOOC(CHOH)$_4$CHO; careful hydrolysis gives cellobiuronic acid (the uronic acid related to cellobiose). Methylation, followed by hydrolysis, gives equimolar amounts of 2,3,6-tri-O-methyl-D-glucose and 2,4-di-O-methyl-D-glucuronic acid.

What is a likely structure for the polysaccharide?

11. Draw structures of compounds G through J:

amylose + HIO$_4$ ⟶ G + a little HCOOH and HCHO
G + bromine water ⟶ H
H + H$_2$O, H$^+$ ⟶ I (C$_4$H$_8$O$_5$) + J (C$_2$H$_2$O$_3$)

12. (a) Show what would happen to cellulose when treated with HIO$_4$. (b) How could this reaction be used to determine chain length? (c) If oxidation by HIO$_4$ of 203 mg of a sample of cellulose yields 0.0027 millimoles of HCOOH, what is the chain length of the cellulose?

Chapter thirty-one_____

POLYNUCLEAR
AROMATIC COMPOUNDS

31.1 Fused ring aromatic compounds

Two aromatic rings that share a pair of carbon atoms are said to be *fused*. In this chapter we shall study the chemistry of the simplest and most important of the fused ring hydrocarbons, **naphthalene**, $C_{10}H_8$, and look briefly at two others of formula $C_{14}H_{10}$, **anthracene** and **phenanthrene**.

Naphthalene   Anthracene   Phenanthrene

All three of these hydrocarbons are obtained from coal tar, naphthalene being the most abundant (5%) of all constituents of coal tar.

TABLE 31.1

POLYNUCLEAR AROMATIC COMPOUNDS

Name	M.p., °C	B.p., °C	Name	M.p., °C	B.p., °C
Naphthalene	80	218	1-Naphthalenesulfonic acid	90	
1,4-Dihydronaphthalene	25	212	2-Naphthalenesulfonic acid	91	
Tetralin	− 30	208	1-Naphthol	96	280
cis-Decalin	− 43	194	2-Naphthol	122	286
trans-Decalin	− 31	185	1,4-Naphthoquinone	125	
1-Methylnaphthalene	− 22	241	Anthracene	217	354
2-Methylnaphthalene	38	240	9,10-Anthraquinone	286	380
1-Bromonaphthalene	6	281	Phenanthrene	101	340
2-Bromonaphthalene	59	281	9,10-Phenanthrenequinone	207	
1-Chloronaphthalene		263	Chrysene	255	
2-Chloronaphthalene	46	265	Pyrene	150	
1-Nitronaphthalene	62	304	1,2-Benzanthracene	160	
2-Nitronaphthalene	79		1,2,5,6-Dibenzanthracene	262	
1-Naphthylamine	50	301	Methylcholanthrene	180	
2-Naphthylamine	113	294			

The ultimate in fused ring aromatic systems is *graphite*, one of the allotropic forms of elemental carbon. X-ray analysis shows that the carbon atoms are arranged in layers. Each layer is a continuous network of planar, hexagonal rings;

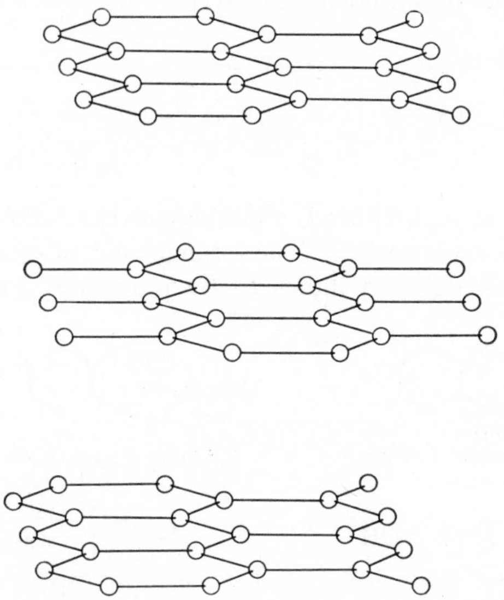

the carbon atoms within a layer are held together by strong, covalent bonds 1.42 A long (only slightly longer than those in benzene, 1.39 A). The different layers, 3.4 A apart, are held to each other by comparatively weak forces. The lubricating properties of graphite (its "greasy" feel) may be due to slipping of layers (with adsorbed gas molecules between) over one another.

If graphite is the ultimate fused ring aromatic system, then the other allotropic form of carbon, *diamond*, might be considered the ultimate branched-chain aliphatic system. In diamond each carbon atom is attached to four others by tetrahedral bonds of the usual single bond length, 1.54 A. (Note the cyclohexane chairs.)

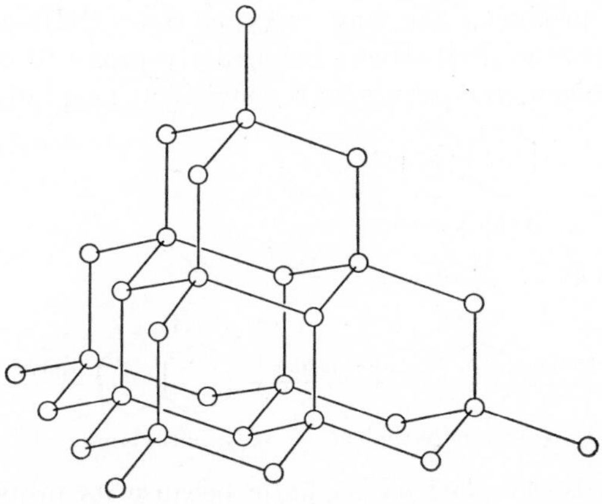

NAPHTHALENE

31.2   Nomenclature of naphthalene derivatives

Positions in the naphthalene ring system are designated as in I.

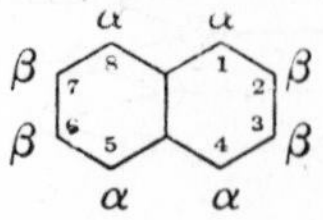

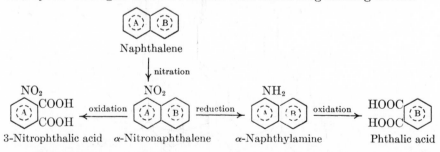

Two isomeric monosubstituted naphthalenes are differentiated by the prefixes 1- and 2-, or α- and β-. The arrangement of groups in more highly substituted naphthalenes is indicated by numbers.   For example:

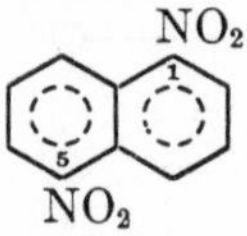

1,5-Dinitronaphthalene 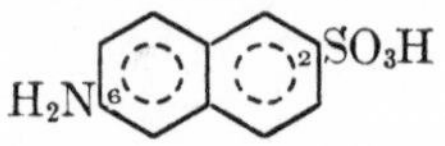   6-Amino-2-naphthalenesulfonic acid

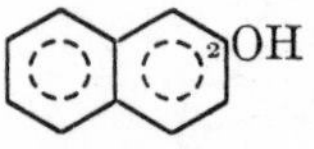

2-Naphthol
β-Naphthol   2,4-Dinitro-1-naphthylamine

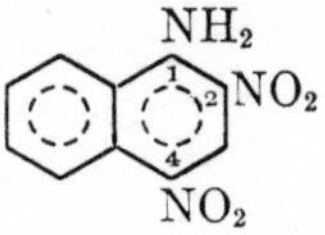

Problem 31.1   How many different mononitronaphthalenes are possible? Dinitronaphthalenes?   Nitronaphthylamines?

31.3   Structure of naphthalene

Evidence that naphthalene contains two equivalent benzene rings fused together was discovered as early as 1868.   It was found, for example, that α-nitronaphthalene can be oxidized directly to a nitrophthalic acid, or indirectly (via the amine) to phthalic acid containing no nitrogen at all.   The ring carrying the —NO₂ group is resistant to oxidation and is retained in the product; the ring carrying the —NH₂ group is (as we have seen for benzene derivatives) particularly prone to oxidation and is destroyed.   Nitrogen thus serves as a convenient ring-labeling device.

Naphthalene

nitration

3-Nitrophthalic acid α-Nitronaphthalene α-Naphthylamine   Phthalic acid

Naphthalene is classified as aromatic because its properties resemble those of benzene (see Sec. 8.13, Aromatic character).   Its molecular formula, $C_{10}H_8$, might lead one to expect a high degree of unsaturation; yet naphthalene is resistant (although less so than benzene) to the addition reactions characteristic of unsaturated compounds. Instead, the typical reactions of naphthalene are electrophilic substitution reactions, in which hydrogen is displaced as hydrogen ion and the naphthalene ring system is preserved. Like benzene, naphthalene is unusually stable: its heat of combustion is 61 kcal lower than that calculated on the assumption that it is aliphatic (see Problem 8.2, page 223).

From the experimental standpoint, then, naphthalene is classified as aromatic on the basis of its properties. From a theoretical standpoint, naphthalene has the structure required of an aromatic compound: it contains flat six-membered rings, and consideration of atomic orbitals shows that the structure can provide π clouds containing six electrons — the *aromatic sextet* (Figure 31.1).

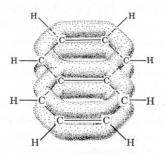

FIGURE 31.1. Naphthalene molecule. π clouds above and below plane of rings.

Ten carbons lie at the corners of two fused hexagons. Each carbon is attached to three other atoms by σ bonds; since these σ bonds result from the overlapping of trigonal sp^2 orbitals, all carbon and hydrogen atoms lie in a single plane. Above and below this plane there is a cloud of π electrons formed by the overlapping of p orbitals and shaped like a figure 8. We can consider this cloud as two partially overlapping sextets that have a pair of π electrons in common.

In terms of valence bonds, naphthalene is considered to be a resonance hybrid of the three structures I, II, and III. Its resonance energy, as shown by the heat of combustion, is 61 kcal/mole.

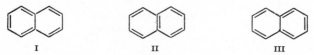

I   II   III

X-ray analysis shows that, in contrast to benzene, all carbon–carbon bonds in naphthalene are not the same; in particular, the C_1—C_2 bond is considerably shorter (1.365 A) than the C_2—C_3 bond (1.404 A). Examination of structures I, II, and III shows us that this difference in bond lengths is to be expected. The C_1—C_2 bond is double in two structures and single in only one; the C_2—C_3 bond is single in two structures and double in only one. We would therefore expect the C_1—C_2 bond to be more double than single, and the C_2—C_3 bond to be more single than double.

For convenience we shall represent naphthalene as the single structure IV,

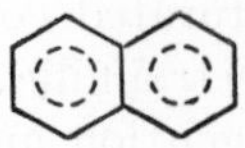

IV

in which the broken circles stand for partially overlapping aromatic sextets.

Although representation IV suggests a greater symmetry for naphthalene than exists, it has the advantage of emphasizing the aromatic nature of the system.

31.4 Reactions of naphthalene

Like benzene, naphthalene typically undergoes electrophilic substitution; this is one of the properties that entitle it to the designation of "aromatic." An electrophilic reagent finds the π cloud a source of available electrons, and attaches itself to the ring to form an intermediate carbonium ion; to restore the stable aromatic system, the carbonium ion then gives up a proton.

Naphthalene undergoes oxidation or reduction more readily than benzene, but only to the stage where a substituted benzene is formed; further oxidation or reduction requires more vigorous conditions. Naphthalene is stabilized by resonance to the extent of 61 kcal/mole; benzene is stabilized to the extent of 36 kcal/mole. When the aromatic character of one ring of naphthalene is destroyed, only 25 kcal of resonance energy is sacrificed; in the next stage, 36 kcal has to be sacrificed.

REACTIONS OF NAPHTHALENE

1. Oxidation

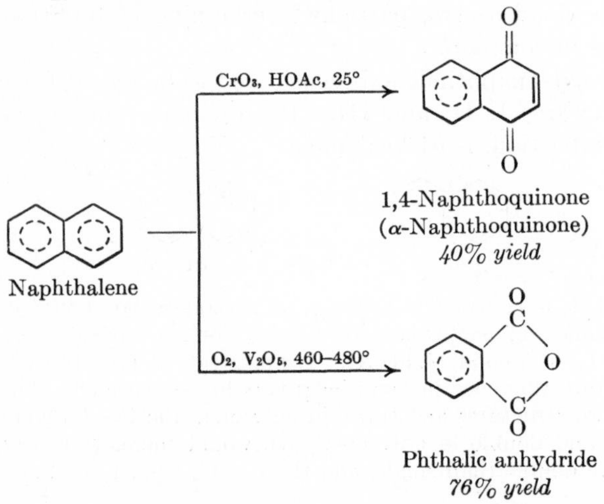

CrO₃, HOAc, 25°

1,4-Naphthoquinone
(α-Naphthoquinone)
40% yield

Naphthalene

O₂, V₂O₅, 460–480°

Phthalic anhydride
76% yield

2. Reduction

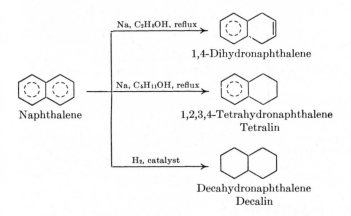

Naphthalene

Na, C₂H₅OH, reflux → 1,4-Dihydronaphthalene

Na, C₅H₁₁OH, reflux → 1,2,3,4-Tetrahydronaphthalene
Tetralin

H₂, catalyst → Decahydronaphthalene
Decalin

3. Electrophilic substitution

(a) Nitration

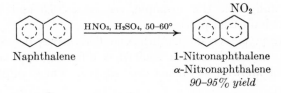

Naphthalene $\xrightarrow{\text{HNO}_3,\ \text{H}_2\text{SO}_4,\ 50-60°}$ 1-Nitronaphthalene
α-Nitronaphthalene
90–95% yield

(b) Halogenation

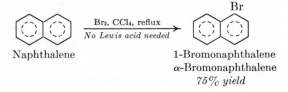

Naphthalene $\xrightarrow[\textit{No Lewis acid needed}]{\text{Br}_2,\ \text{CCl}_4,\ \text{reflux}}$ 1-Bromonaphthalene
α-Bromonaphthalene
75% yield

(c) Sulfonation

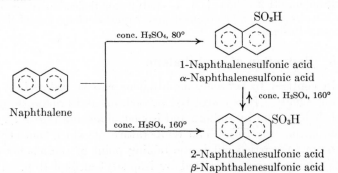

Naphthalene

conc. H₂SO₄, 80° → 1-Naphthalenesulfonic acid
α-Naphthalenesulfonic acid

conc. H₂SO₄, 160°

conc. H₂SO₄, 160° → 2-Naphthalenesulfonic acid
β-Naphthalenesulfonic acid

(d) Friedel-Crafts acylation

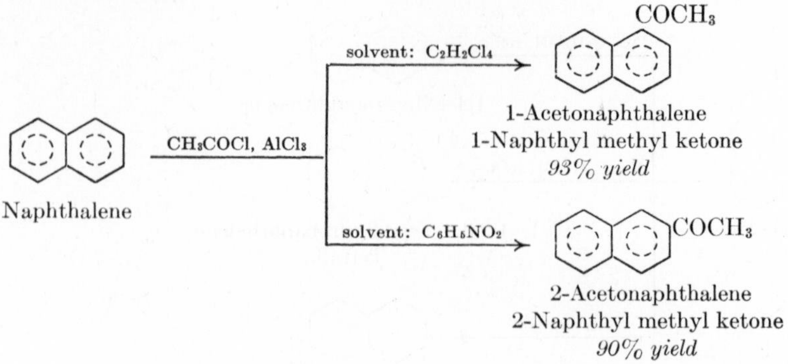

Naphthalene

$CH_3COCl, AlCl_3$

solvent: $C_2H_2Cl_4$

COCH₃

1-Acetonaphthalene
1-Naphthyl methyl ketone
93% yield

solvent: $C_6H_5NO_2$

COCH₃

2-Acetonaphthalene
2-Naphthyl methyl ketone
90% yield

31.5   Oxidation of naphthalene

Oxidation of naphthalene by oxygen in the presence of vanadium pentoxide destroys one ring and yields phthalic anhydride. Because of the availability of naphthalene from coal tar, and the large demand for phthalic anhydride (for example, see Secs. 25.5 and 31.18), this is an important industrial process.

Oxidation of certain naphthalene derivatives destroys the aromatic character of one ring in a somewhat different way, and yields diketo compounds known as *quinones* (Sec. 28.10). For example:

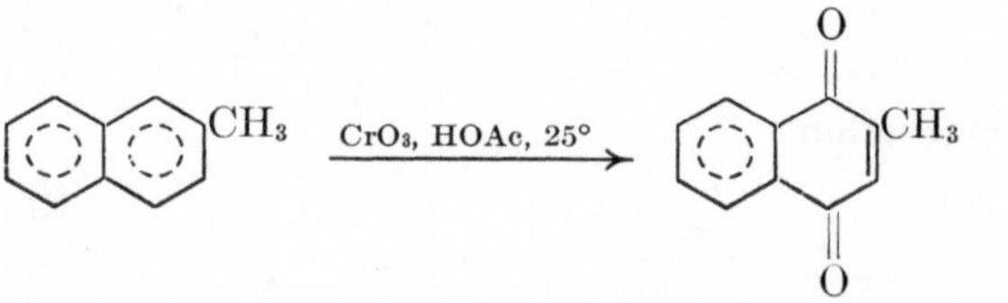

2-Methylnaphthalene

CrO_3, HOAc, 25°

2-Methyl-1,4-naphthoquinone
70% yield

Because of this tendency to form quinones, it is not feasible to prepare naphthalenecarboxylic acids as we do benzoic acids, by oxidation of methyl side chains.

Problem 31.2 Show how 1- and 2-naphthalenecarboxylic acids (α- and *β-naphthoic acids*) can be obtained from naphthalene by way of the corresponding acetonaphthalenes.

31.6   Reduction of naphthalene

In contrast to benzene, naphthalene can be reduced by chemical reducing agents. It is converted by sodium and ethanol into 1,4-dihydronaphthalene, and by sodium and isopentyl alcohol into 1,2,3,4-tetrahydronaphthalene (*tetralin*). The temperature at which one of these sodium reductions is carried out is the boiling point of the alcohol used; at the higher temperature permitted by isopentyl alcohol (b.p. 132°) reduction proceeds further than with the lower boiling ethyl alcohol (b.p. 78°).

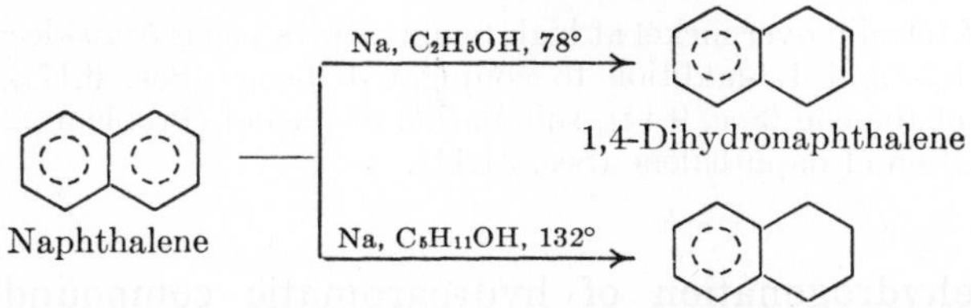

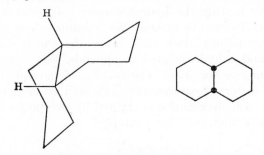

Na, C₂H₅OH, 78°

1,4-Dihydronaphthalene

Naphthalene

Na, C₅H₁₁OH, 132°

1,2,3,4-Tetrahydronaphthalene
Tetralin

The tetrahydronaphthalene is simply a dialkyl derivative of benzene. As with other benzene derivatives, the aromatic ring that remains is reduced only by vigorous catalytic hydrogenation.

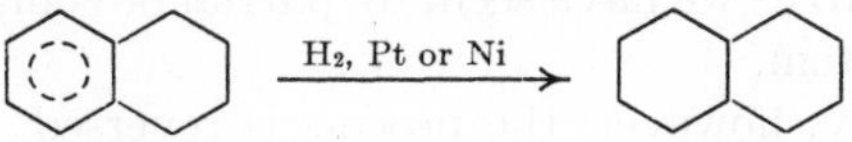

Tetralin $\xrightarrow{\text{H}_2,\ \text{Pt or Ni}}$ Decalin

Problem 31.3 *Decalin* exists in two stereoisomeric forms, *cis*-decalin (b.p. 194°) and *trans*-decalin (b.p. 185°).

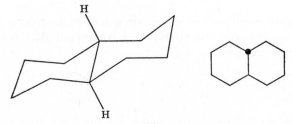

cis-Decalin

trans-Decalin

(a) Build models of these compounds and see that they differ from one another. Locate in the models the pair of hydrogen atoms on the fused carbons that are *cis* or *trans* to each other.

(b) In *trans*-decalin is one ring attached to the other by two equatorial bonds, by two axial bonds, or by one axial bond and one equatorial bond? In *cis*-decalin? Remembering (Sec. 7.12) that an equatorial position gives more room than an axial position for a bulky group, predict which should be the more stable isomer, *cis*- or *trans*-decalin.

(c) Account for the following facts: rapid hydrogenation of tetralin over a platinum black catalyst at low temperatures yields *cis*-decalin, while slow hydrogenation of tetralin over nickel at high temperatures yields *trans*-decalin. Compare this with 1,2- and 1,4-addition to conjugated dienes (Sec. 6.17), Friedel-Crafts alkylation of toluene (Sec. 9.14), sulfonation of phenol (Problem 22.13, page 601), and sulfonation of naphthalene (Sec. 31.11).

31.7 Dehydrogenation of hydroaromatic compounds. Aromatization

Compounds like 1,4-dihydronaphthalene, tetralin, and decalin, which contain the carbon skeleton of an aromatic system but too many hydrogen atoms for aromaticity, are called *hydroaromatic compounds*. They are sometimes prepared, as we have seen, by partial or complete hydrogenation of an aromatic system.

More commonly, however, the process is reversed, and hydroaromatic compounds are converted into aromatic compounds. Such a process is called **aromatization.**

One of the best methods of aromatization is **catalytic dehydrogenation,** accomplished by heating the hydroaromatic compound with a catalyst like platinum, palladium, or nickel. We recognize these as the catalysts used for hydrogenation; since they lower the energy barrier between hydrogenated and dehydrogenated compounds, they speed up reaction in *both* directions (see Sec. 5.3). The position of the equilibrium is determined by other factors: hydrogenation is favored by an excess of hydrogen under pressure; dehydrogenation is favored by sweeping away the hydrogen in a stream of inert gas. For example:

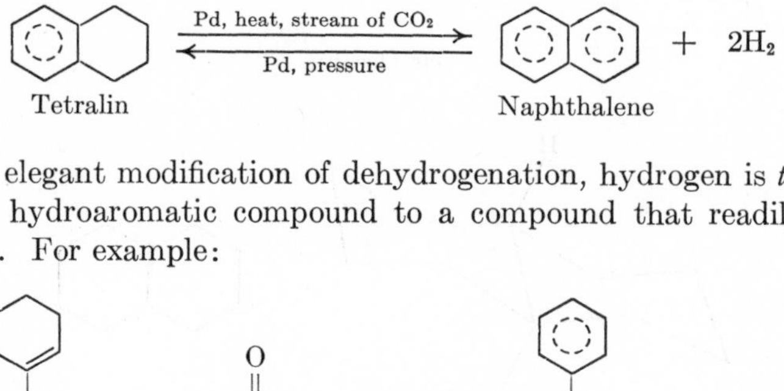

$$\text{Tetralin} \xrightleftharpoons[\text{Pd, pressure}]{\text{Pd, heat, stream of } CO_2} \text{Naphthalene} + 2H_2$$

In an elegant modification of dehydrogenation, hydrogen is *transferred* from the hydroaromatic compound to a compound that readily accepts hydrogen. For example:

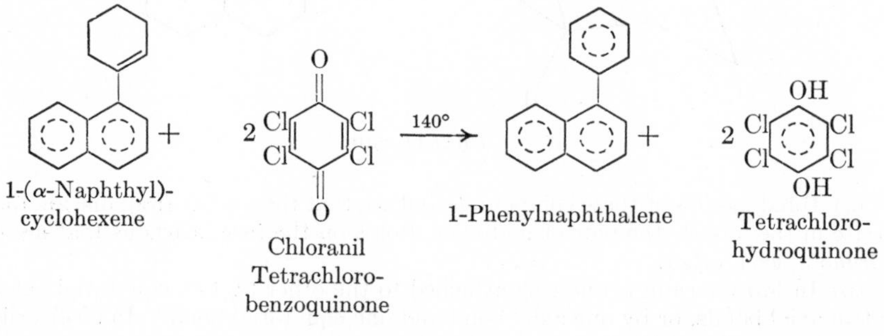

1-(α-Naphthyl)-cyclohexene

Chloranil
Tetrachloro-benzoquinone

1-Phenylnaphthalene

Tetrachloro-hydroquinone

The tendency to form the stable aromatic system is so strong that, when necessary, groups can be eliminated: for example, a methyl group located at the point of fusion between two rings, a so-called *angular methyl group.*

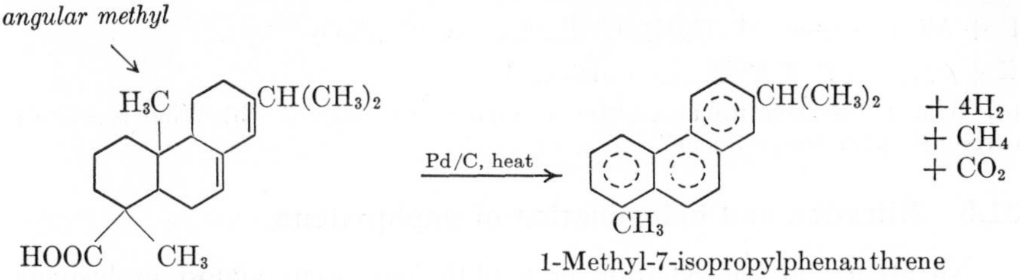

angular methyl

H_3C ... $CH(CH_3)_2$

$\xrightarrow{\text{Pd/C, heat}}$

$CH(CH_3)_2$ $+ 4H_2$
$+ CH_4$
$+ CO_2$

CH_3

HOOC CH_3
Abietic acid
(in rosin)

1-Methyl-7-isopropylphenanthrene

Aromatization has also been accomplished by heating hydroaromatic compounds with selenium, sulfur, or organic disulfides, RSSR. Here hydrogen is eliminated as H_2Se, H_2S, or RSH.

Problem 31.4 In a convenient laboratory preparation of dry hydrogen bromide, Br_2 is dripped into boiling tetralin; the vapors react to form naphthalene and four moles of hydrogen bromide. Account, step by step, for the formation of these products. What familiar reactions are involved in this aromatization?

Aromatization is important in both *synthesis* and *analysis*. Many polynuclear aromatic compounds are made from open-chain compounds by ring closure; the last step in such a synthesis is aromatization (see, for example, Secs. 31.14, 31.19, and 32.13). Many naturally occurring substances are hydroaromatic; conversion into identifiable aromatic compounds gives important information about their structures. For example:

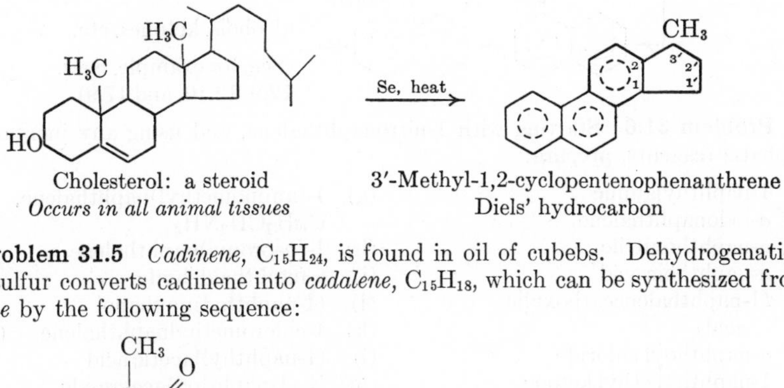

H_3C H_3C ... HO ...

$\xrightarrow{\text{Se, heat}}$

CH_3 ... $3'$ $2'$ $1'$ ... 1 2

Cholesterol: a steroid
Occurs in all animal tissues

3'-Methyl-1,2-cyclopentenophenanthrene
Diels' hydrocarbon

Problem 31.5 *Cadinene*, $C_{15}H_{24}$, is found in oil of cubebs. Dehydrogenation with sulfur converts cadinene into *cadalene*, $C_{15}H_{18}$, which can be synthesized from *carvone* by the following sequence:

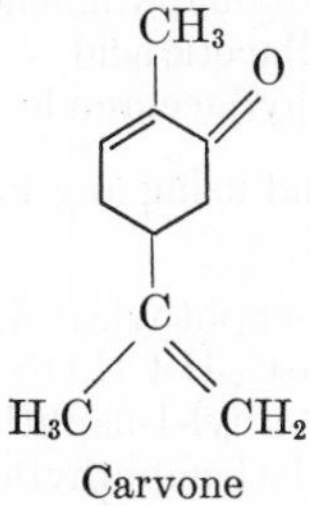

CH_3 O ... C ... H_3C CH_2
Carvone

$+ BrCH_2COOC_2H_5 + Zn \longrightarrow A\ (C_{14}H_{22}O_3)$

A + acid $\xrightarrow{\text{heat}}$ [B] $\xrightarrow{\text{isomerization}}$ C ($C_{12}H_{16}O_2$), *a benzene derivative*

C + C_2H_5OH + H_2SO_4 $\longrightarrow$ D ($C_{14}H_{20}O_2$)

D + Na + alcohol $\longrightarrow$ E ($C_{12}H_{18}O$) $\xrightarrow{\text{HBr}}$ F ($C_{12}H_{17}Br$)

F + $CH_3C(COOC_2H_5)_2^-Na^+$ $\longrightarrow$ G ($C_{20}H_{30}O_4$)

G + H_2SO_4 $\xrightarrow{\text{heat}}$ H ($C_{15}H_{22}O_2$) $\xrightarrow{\text{SOCl}_2}$ I ($C_{15}H_{21}OCl$)

$I + AlCl_3 \longrightarrow J (C_{15}H_{20}O) \xrightarrow{H_2, Ni} K (C_{15}H_{22}O)$

$K + sulfur \xrightarrow{strong\ heating} cadalene$

(a) What is the structure and systematic name of cadalene? (b) What is a likely carbon skeleton for cadinene?

31.8 Nitration and halogenation of naphthalene

Nitration and halogenation of naphthalene occur almost exclusively in the 1-position. Chlorination or bromination takes place so readily that a Lewis acid is not required for catalysis.

As we would expect, introduction of these groups opens the way to the preparation of a series of *alpha*-substituted naphthalenes: from 1-nitro-naphthalene via the amine and diazonium salts, and from 1-bromonaphtha-lene via the Grignard reagent.

Synthesis of α-substituted naphthalenes

halides, nitrile, azo compounds, etc.

(See Chapter 21)

alcohols, ketones, etc.

(See, for example, Secs. 12.9, 12.10, and 17.9)

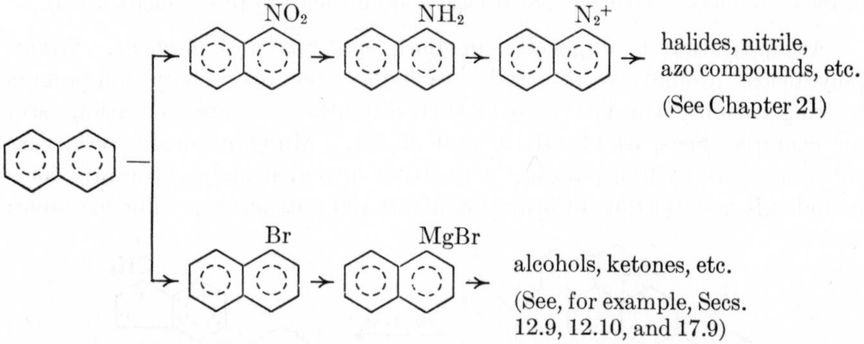

Problem 31.6 Starting with 1-nitronaphthalene, and using any inorganic or aliphatic reagents, prepare:

(a) 1-naphthylamine
(b) α-iodonaphthalene
(c) α-naphthonitrile
(d) α-naphthoic acid
   (1-naphthalenecarboxylic acid)
(e) α-naphthoyl chloride
(f) 1-naphthyl ethyl ketone

(g) 1-(aminomethyl)naphthalene, $C_{10}H_7CH_2NH_2$
(h) 1-(n-propyl)naphthalene
(i) α-naphthaldehyde
(j) (1-naphthyl)methanol
(k) 1-chloromethylnaphthalene
(l) (1-naphthyl)acetic acid
(m) N-(1-naphthyl)acetamide

Problem 31.7 Starting with 1-bromonaphthalene, and using any inorganic or aliphatic reagents, prepare:

(a) 1-naphthylmagnesium bromide
(b) α-naphthoic acid
   (1-naphthalenecarboxylic acid)
(c) 2-(1-naphthyl)-2-propanol
   (dimethyl-1-naphthylcarbinol)
(d) 1-isopropylnaphthalene

(e) 1-naphthylcarbinol
   (1-$C_{10}H_7CH_2OH$)
(f) methyl-1-naphthylcarbinol
   (1-(1-naphthyl)ethanol)
(g) 2-(1-naphthyl)ethanol

31.9 Orientation of electrophilic substitution in naphthalene

Nitration and halogenation of naphthalene take place almost ex-clusively in the α-position. Is this orientation of substitution reasonable?

In our study of electrophilic substitution in the benzene ring (Chapter 10), we found that we could account for the observed orientation on the following basis: (a) the controlling step is the attachment of an electrophilic reagent to the aromatic ring to form an intermediate carbonium ion; and (b) this attachment takes place in such a way as to yield the most stable intermediate carbonium ion. Let us see if this approach can be applied to the nitration of naphthalene.

Attack by nitronium ion at the α-position of naphthalene yields an intermediate carbonium ion that is a hybrid of structures I and II in which the positive charge is accommodated by the ring under attack, and several structures like III in which the charge is accommodated by the other ring.

Alpha-attack

I	II	III
More stable:	*More stable:*	*Less stable:*
Aromatic sextet	Aromatic sextet	Aromatic sextet
preserved	preserved	disrupted

Attack at the β-position yields an intermediate carbonium ion that is a hybrid of IV and V in which the positive charge is accommodated by the ring under attack, and several structures like VI in which the positive charge is accommodated by the other ring.

Beta-attack

IV	V	VI
More stable:	*Less stable:*	*Less stable:*
Aromatic sextet	Aromatic sextet	Aromatic sextet
preserved	disrupted	disrupted

In structures I, II, and IV, the aromatic sextet is preserved in the ring that is not under attack; these structures thus retain the full resonance stabilization of one benzene ring (36 kcal/mole). In structures like III, V, and VI, on the other hand, the aromatic sextet is disrupted in both rings, with a large sacrifice of resonance stabilization. Clearly structures like I, II, and IV are much the more stable.

But there are two of these stable contributing structures (I and II) for attack at the α-position and only one (IV) for attack at the β-position. On this basis we would expect the carbonium ion resulting from attack at the α-position (and also the transition state leading to that ion) to be much more stable than the carbonium ion (and the corresponding transition state) resulting from attack at the β-position, and that nitration would therefore occur much more rapidly at the α-position.

Throughout our study of polynuclear hydrocarbons, we shall find that the matter of orientation is generally understandable on the basis of this principle: of the large number of structures contributing to the intermediate carbonium ion, the important ones are those that require the smallest sacrifice of resonance stabilization. Indeed, we shall find that this principle accounts for orientation not only in electrophilic substitution but also in oxidation, reduction, and addition.

31.10 Friedel–Crafts acylation of naphthalene

Naphthalene can be acetylated by acetyl chloride in the presence of aluminum chloride. The orientation of substitution is determined by the particular solvent used: predominantly *alpha* in carbon disulfide or solvents like tetrachloroethane, predominantly *beta* in nitrobenzene. (The effect of nitrobenzene has been attributed to its forming a complex with the acid chloride and aluminum chloride which, because of its bulkiness, attacks the roomier *beta* position.)

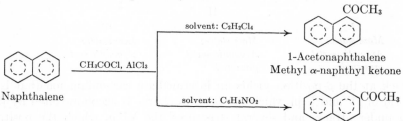

Thus acetylation (as well as sulfonation, following section) affords access to the *beta* series of naphthalene derivatives. Treatment of 2-aceto-naphthalene with hypohalite, for example, provides the best route to β-naphthoic acid.

Acylation of naphthalene by succinic anhydride yields a mixture of *alpha* and *beta* products. These are separable, however, and both are of importance in the synthesis of higher ring systems (see Sec. 31.19).

Friedel-Crafts alkylation of naphthalene is of little use, probably for a combination of reasons: the high reactivity of naphthalene which causes side reactions and polyalkylations, and the availability of alkylnaphthalenes via acylation or ring closure (Sec. 31.14).

Problem 31.8 The position of the —COOH in β-naphthoic acid was shown by vigorous oxidation and identification of the product. What was this product? What product would have been obtained from α-naphthoic acid?

Problem 31.9 Outline the synthesis of the following compounds via an initial acylation:

(a) 2-ethylnaphthalene
(b) methylethyl-2-naphthylcarbinol (2-(2-naphthyl)-2-butanol)
(c) 2-(sec-butyl)naphthalene
(d) 1-(2-naphthyl)ethanol
(e) γ-(2-naphthyl)butyric acid

(f) 4-(2-naphthyl)-1-butanol
(g) 5-(2-naphthyl)-2-methyl-2-pentanol
(h) 2-isohexylnaphthalene
(i) 1-amino-1-(2-naphthyl)ethane
(j) β-vinylnaphthalene

31.11 Sulfonation of naphthalene

Sulfonation of naphthalene at 80° yields chiefly 1-naphthalenesulfonic acid; sulfonation at 160° or higher yields chiefly 2-naphthalenesulfonic acid. When 1-naphthalenesulfonic acid is heated in sulfuric acid at 160° it is largely converted into the 2-isomer.

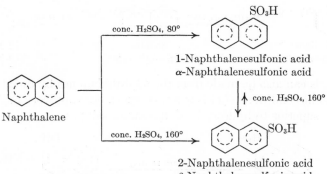

conc. H₂SO₄, 80°

SO_3H

1-Naphthalenesulfonic acid
α-Naphthalenesulfonic acid

conc. H₂SO₄, 160°

Naphthalene

conc. H₂SO₄, 160°

SO_3H

2-Naphthalenesulfonic acid
β-Naphthalenesulfonic acid

These facts become understandable when we recall that sulfonation is readily reversible (Sec. 18.5).

Sulfonation, like nitration and halogenation, occurs more rapidly at the α-position, since this involves the more stable intermediate carbonium ion. But, for the same reason, attack by hydrogen ion, with subsequent desulfonation, also occurs more readily at the α-position. Sulfonation at the β-position occurs more slowly but, once formed, the β-sulfonic acid tends to resist desulfonation. At low temperatures desulfonation is slow and we isolate the product that is formed faster, the *alpha* naphthalenesulfonic acid. At higher temperatures, desulfonation becomes important, equilibrium is more readily established, and we isolate the product that is more stable, the *beta* naphthalenesulfonic acid.

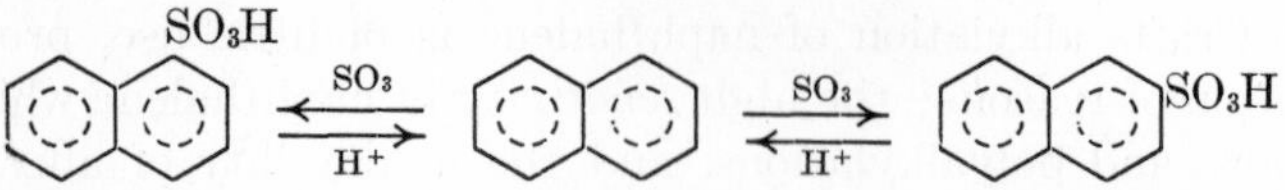

α-Isomer
Formed rapidly
Desulfonated rapidly

β-Isomer
Formed slowly
Desulfonated slowly

We see here a situation exactly analogous to one we have encountered several times before: in 1,2- and 1,4-addition to conjugated dienes (Sec. 6.17), in Friedel-Crafts alkylation of toluene (Sec. 9.14), and in sulfonation of phenols (Sec. 22.14). At low temperatures the controlling factor is *rate of reaction*, at high temperatures, *position of equilibrium*.

Sulfonation is of special importance in the chemistry of naphthalene because it gives access to the *beta* substituted naphthalenes, as shown in the next section.

Problem 31.10 (a) Show all steps in the sulfonation and desulfonation of naphthalene. (b) Draw a potential energy curve for the reactions involved. (Compare your answer with Figure 6.6, page 181.)

31.12 Naphthols

Like the phenols we have already studied, naphthols can be prepared from the corresponding sulfonic acids by fusion with alkali.

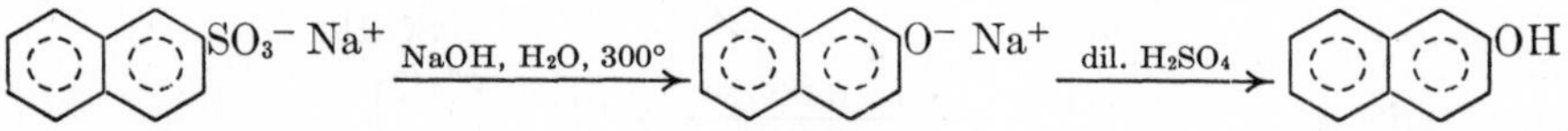

Sodium
2-naphthalenesulfonate

Sodium
2-naphthoxide

2-Naphthol
β-Naphthol

Naphthols can also be made from the naphthylamines by direct hydrolysis under acidic conditions. (This reaction, which does not work in the benzene series, is superior to hydrolysis of diazonium salts.)

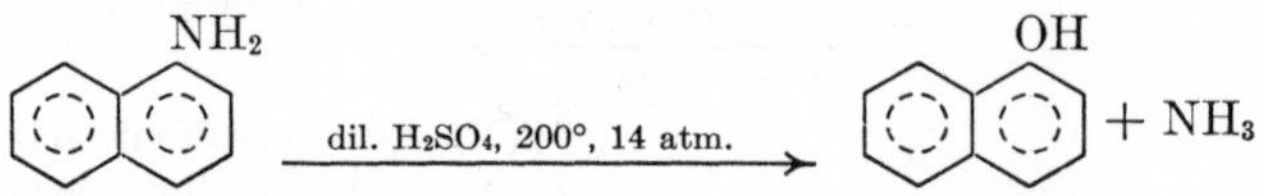

1-Naphthylamine

1-Naphthol
α-Naphthol
95% yield

The α-substituted naphthalenes, like substituted benzenes, are most commonly prepared by a sequence of reactions that ultimately goes back to a nitro compound (Sec. 31.8). Preparation of β-substituted naphthalenes, on the other hand, cannot start with the nitro compound, since nitration does not take place in the β-position. The route to β-naphthylamine, and through it to the versatile diazonium salts, lies through β-naphthol. β-Naphthol is made from the β-sulfonic acid; it is converted into β-naphthylamine when heated under pressure with ammonia and ammonium sulfite (the **Bucherer reaction,** not useful in the benzene series except in rare cases).

Synthesis of β-substituted naphthalenes

Naphtha-   2-Naphthalene-   2-Naphthol   2-Naphthylamine
lene   sulfonic acid

NH₃, (NH₄)₂SO₃, heat, pressure

Halides,
nitriles, azo
compounds, etc.
(See Chapter 21)

2-Naphthalenediazonium
salt

Naphthols undergo the usual reactions of phenols. Coupling with diazonium salts is particularly important in dye manufacture (see Sec. 21.10); the orientation of this substitution is discussed in the following section.

Problem 31.11 Starting from naphthalene, and using any readily available reagents, prepare the following compounds:

(a) 2-bromonaphthalene   (d) β-naphthoic acid
(b) 2-fluoronaphthalene   (e) β-naphthaldehyde
(c) β-naphthonitrile   (f) 3-(2-naphthyl)propenoic acid

Problem 31.12 Diazonium salts can be converted into nitro compounds by treatment with sodium nitrite, usually in the presence of a catalyst. Suggest a method for preparing 2-nitronaphthalene.

31.13 Orientation of electrophilic substitution in naphthalene derivatives

We have seen that naphthalene undergoes nitration and halogenation chiefly at the α-position, and sulfonation and Friedel-Crafts acylation at either the α- or β-position depending upon conditions. Now, to what position will a *second* substituent attach itself, and how is the orientation influenced by the group already present?

Orientation of substitution in the naphthalene series is more complicated than in the benzene series. An entering group may attach itself either to the ring that already carries the first substituent, or to the other ring; there are seven different positions open to attack, in contrast to only three positions in a monosubstituted benzene.

The major products of further substitution in a monosubstituted naphthalene can usually be predicted by the following rules. As we shall see, these rules are reasonable ones in light of structural theory and our understanding of electrophilic aromatic substitution.

(a) An activating group (electron-releasing group) tends to direct further substitution into the same ring. An activating group in position 1 directs further substitution to position 4 (and, to a lesser extent, to position 2). An activating group in position 2 directs further substitution to position 1.

(b) A deactivating group (electron-withdrawing group) tends to direct further substitution into the other ring: at an α-position in nitration or halogenation, or at an α- or β-position (depending upon temperature) in sulfonation.

For example:

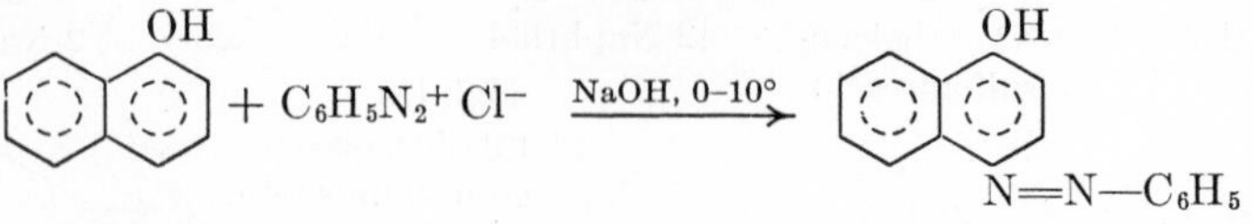

OH
1-Naphthol $+ C_6H_5N_2^+ Cl^-$ $\xrightarrow{\text{NaOH, 0-10°}}$ OH, N=N—C$_6$H$_5$
4-Phenylazo-1-naphthol

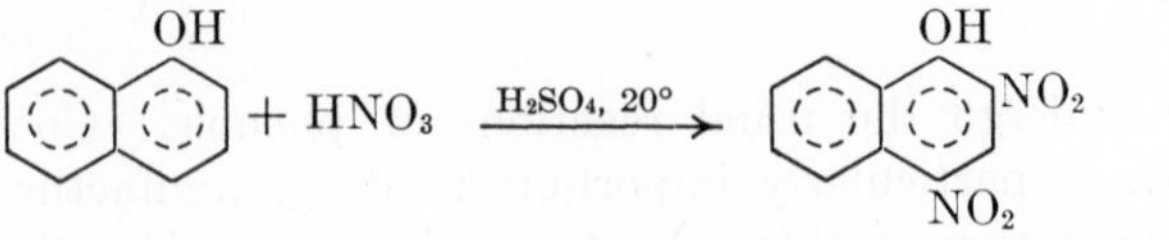

OH
1-Naphthol $+ HNO_3$ $\xrightarrow{\text{H}_2\text{SO}_4, 20°}$ OH, NO$_2$, NO$_2$
2,4-Dinitro-1-naphthol

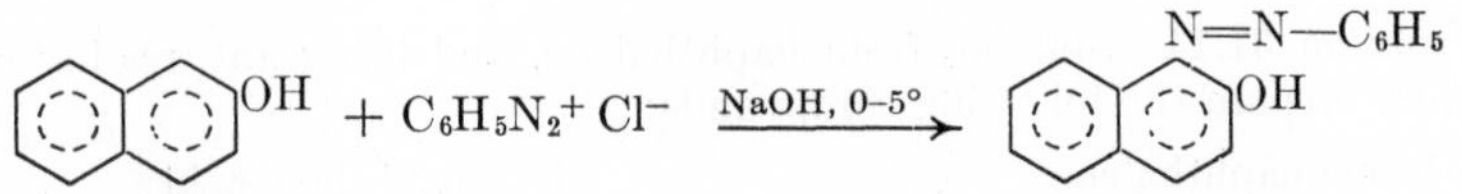

OH
2-Naphthol $+ C_6H_5N_2^+ Cl^-$ $\xrightarrow{\text{NaOH, 0-5°}}$ N=N—C$_6$H$_5$, OH
1-Phenylazo-2-naphthol

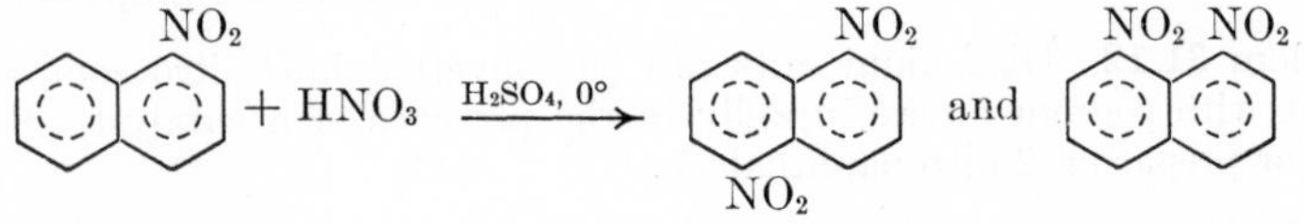

NO$_2$
1-Nitronaphthalene $+ HNO_3$ $\xrightarrow{\text{H}_2\text{SO}_4, 0°}$ NO$_2$, NO$_2$ (1,5-Dinitronaphthalene) and NO$_2$ NO$_2$ (1,8-Dinitronaphthalene)
Chief product

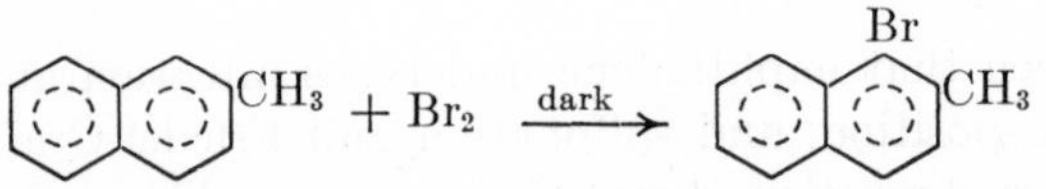

CH$_3$
2-Methylnaphthalene $+ Br_2$ $\xrightarrow{\text{dark}}$ Br, CH$_3$
1-Bromo-2-methylnaphthalene

These rules do not always hold in sulfonation, because the reaction is reversible and at high temperatures tends to take place in a β-position. However, the observed products can usually be accounted for if this feature of sulfonation is kept in mind.

Problem 31.13 Predict the orientation in each of the following reactions, giving structural formulas and names for the predicted products:

(a) 1-methylnaphthalene $+ Br_2$
(b) 1-methylnaphthalene $+ HNO_3 + H_2SO_4$
(c) 1-methylnaphthalene $+ CH_3COCl + AlCl_3$
(d) the same as (a), (b), and (c) for 2-methylnaphthalene
(e) 2-nitronaphthalene $+ Br_2$
(f) 2-methoxynaphthalene $+ Br_2$

Problem 31.14 How do you account for the following observed orientations?

(a) 2-methoxynaphthalene $+ CH_3COCl + AlCl_3 + CS_2$ $\longrightarrow$ 1-aceto compound
(b) 2-methoxynaphthalene $+ CH_3COCl + AlCl_3 + C_6H_5NO_2$ $\longrightarrow$ 6-aceto compound
(c) 2-methylnaphthalene $+ H_2SO_4$ above 100° $\longrightarrow$ 6-sulfonic acid
(d) 2,6-dimethylnaphthalene $+ H_2SO_4$ at 40° $\longrightarrow$ 8-sulfonic acid

(e) 2,6-dimethylnaphthalene + H_2SO_4 + 140° $\longrightarrow$ 3-sulfonic acid

(f) 2-naphthalenesulfonic acid + HNO_3 + H_2SO_4 $\longrightarrow$ 5-nitro and 8-nitro
compounds

Problem 31.15   Give the steps for the synthesis of each of the following from
naphthalene and any needed reagents:

(a) 4-nitro-1-naphthylamine

(b) 1,4-dinitronaphthalene
    (*Hint:* see Problem 31.12, page 817.)

(c) 2,4-dinitro-1-naphthylamine

(d) 1,3-dinitronaphthalene

(e) 1,2-dinitronaphthalene

(f) 4-amino-1-naphthalenesulfonic acid
    (*naphthionic acid*)

(g) 8-amino-1-naphthalenesulfonic acid

(h) 5-amino-2-naphthalenesulfonic acid

(i) 8-amino-2-naphthalenesulfonic acid

We have seen (Sec. 31.9) that orientation in naphthalene can be accounted for on the same basis as orientation in substituted benzenes:
formation of the more stable intermediate carbonium ion. In judging the
relative stabilities of these naphthalene carbonium ions, we have considered
that those in which an aromatic sextet is preserved are by far the more
stable and hence the more important. Let us see if we can account for
orientation in substituted naphthalenes in the same way.

The structures preserving an aromatic sextet are those in which the
positive charge is carried by the ring under attack; it is in this ring, therefore, that the charge chiefly develops. Consequently, attack occurs most
readily on whichever ring can best accommodate the positive charge:
the ring that carries an electron-releasing (activating) group or the ring
that does *not* carry an electron-withdrawing (deactivating) group. (We
have arrived at the quite reasonable conclusion that a substituent exerts
its greatest effect — activating or deactivating — on the ring to which
it is attached.)

G *is electron-releasing:*
Activating
Attack in same ring

G *is electron-withdrawing:*
Deactivating
Attack in other ring

An electron-releasing group located at position 1 can best help accommodate the positive charge if attack occurs at position 4 (or position 2),
through the contribution of structures like I and II.

I   II

G *is electron-releasing:*
when on position 1
it directs attack to
positions 4 or 2

This is true whether the group releases electrons by an inductive effect **or**
by a resonance effect. For example:

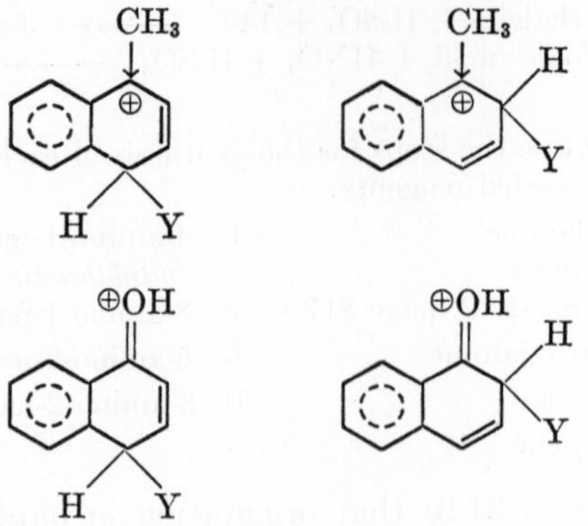

An electron-releasing group located at position 2 could help accommodate the positive charge if attack occurred at position 1 (through structures like III), or if attack occurred at position 3 (through structures like IV).

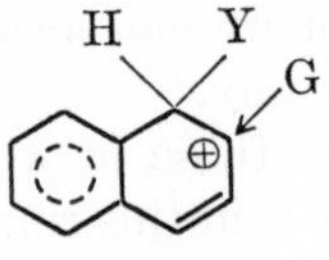

G *is electron-releasing:*
when on position 2
it directs attack to
position 1

III
More stable:
Aromatic sextet
preserved

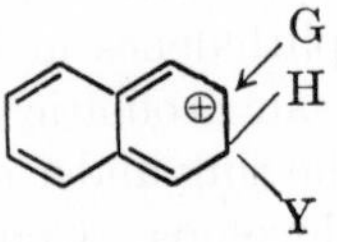

IV
Less stable:
Aromatic sextet
disrupted

However, we can see that only the structures like III preserve an aromatic sextet; these are much more stable than the structures like IV, and are the important ones. It is not surprising, therefore, that substitution occurs almost entirely at position 1.

31.14 Synthesis of naphthalene derivatives by ring closure. The Haworth synthesis

Derivatives of benzene, we have seen, are almost always prepared from a compound that already contains the benzene ring: benzene itself or some simple substituted benzene. One seldom generates the benzene ring in the course of a synthesis.

While compounds containing other aromatic ring systems, too, are often prepared from the parent hydrocarbon, there are important exceptions: syntheses in which the ring system, or part of it, is actually generated. Such syntheses usually involve two stages: **ring closure** (or **cyclization**) and **aromatization.**

As an example, let us look at just one method used to make certain naphthalene derivatives: the **Haworth synthesis** (developed by R. D. Haworth at the University of Durham, England). Chart 31.1 shows the basic scheme, which would yield naphthalene itself (not, of course, actually prepared in this way).

Chart 31.1

Haworth Synthesis of Naphthalene Derivatives

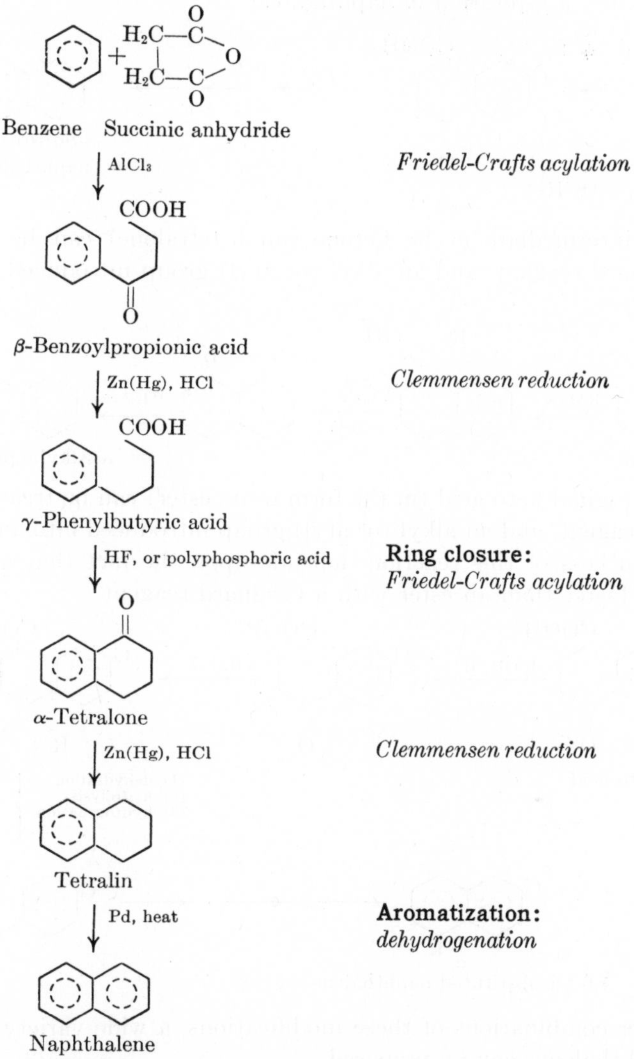

Benzene   Succinic anhydride

| AlCl₃   *Friedel-Crafts acylation*

β-Benzoylpropionic acid

| Zn(Hg), HCl   *Clemmensen reduction*

γ-Phenylbutyric acid

| HF, or polyphosphoric acid   **Ring closure:**
Friedel-Crafts acylation

α-Tetralone

| Zn(Hg), HCl   *Clemmensen reduction*

Tetralin

| Pd, heat   **Aromatization:**
dehydrogenation

Naphthalene

All the steps are familiar ones. The reaction in which the second ring is formed is simply Friedel-Crafts acylation that happens to involve two parts of the same molecule. Like most methods of ring closure, this one does not involve a new reaction, but merely an adaptation of an old one.

Problem 31.16 Why is ring closure possible after the first Clemmensen reduction but not before?

To obtain substituted naphthalenes the basic scheme can be modified in any or all the following ways:

(a) A substituted benzene can be used in place of benzene and a β-substituted naphthalene obtained. Toluene or anisole or bromobenzene, for example, undergoes the initial Friedel-Crafts reaction chiefly at the *para* position; when the ring is closed the substituent originally on the benzene ring must occupy a β-position in naphthalene.

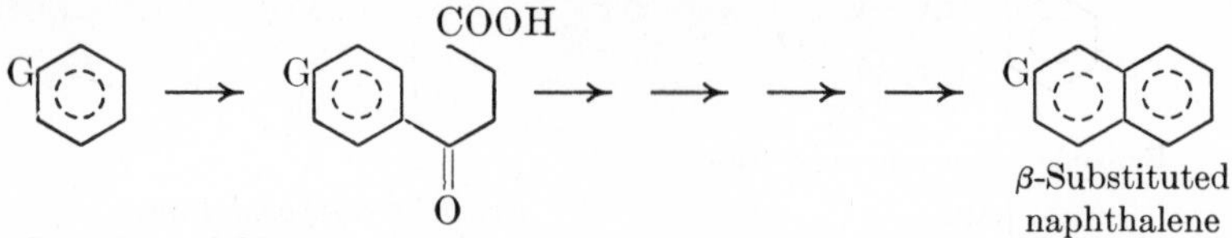

β-Substituted naphthalene

G = —R, —X, —OCH_3

(b) The intermediate cyclic ketone (an α-tetralone) can be treated with a Grignard reagent, and an alkyl (or aryl) group introduced into an α-position.

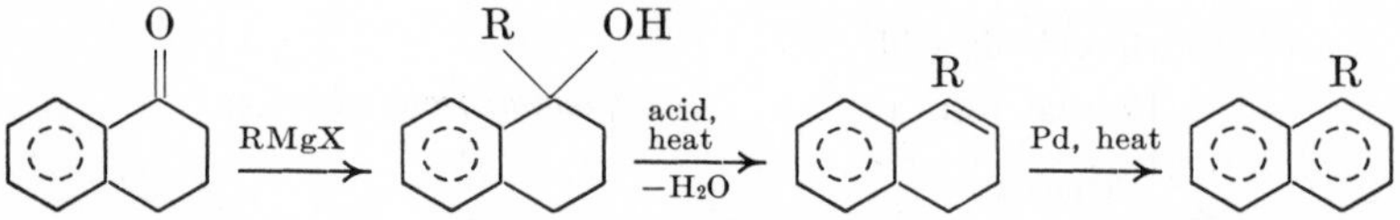

α-Tetralone α-Alkylnaphthalene

(c) The original keto acid (in the form of its ester) can be treated with a Grignard reagent, and an alkyl (or aryl) group introduced into an α-position. The success of this reaction depends upon the fact that a ketone reacts much faster than an ester with a Grignard reagent.

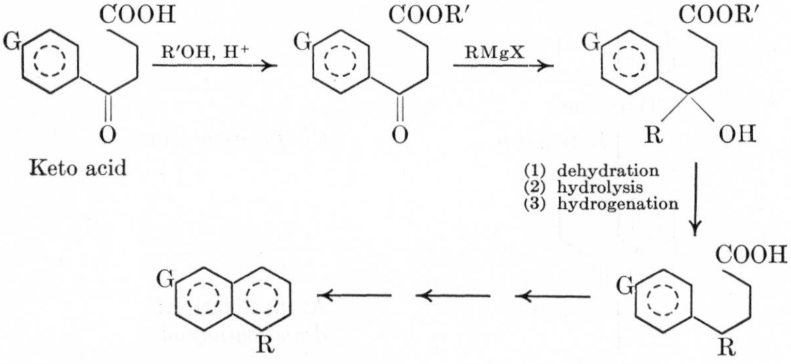

1,6-Disubstituted naphthalene

By proper combinations of these modifications, a wide variety of substituted naphthalenes can be prepared.

Problem 31.17 Outline all steps in the synthesis of the following compounds, starting from benzene and using any necessary aliphatic and inorganic reagents:

(a) 2-methylnaphthalene
(b) 1-methylnaphthalene
(c) 1,4-dimethylnaphthalene
(d) 1,7-dimethylnaphthalene
(e) 1,6-dimethylnaphthalene
(f) 1,4,7-trimethylnaphthalene
(g) 1-ethyl-4-methylnaphthalene
(h) 7-bromo-1-ethylnaphthalene
(i) 1-phenylnaphthalene

Problem 31.18 Outline the Haworth sequence of reactions starting with naphthalene and succinic anhydride. What is the final hydrocarbon or hydrocarbons? (Remember the orientation rules for naphthalene.) Check your answer in Sec. 31.19.

ANTHRACENE AND PHENANTHRENE

31.15   Nomenclature of anthracene and phenanthrene derivatives

The positions in anthracene and phenanthrene are designated by numbers as shown:

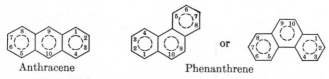

Anthracene   Phenanthrene

Examples are found in the various reactions that follow.

31.16   Structure of anthracene and phenanthrene

Like naphthalene, anthracene and phenanthrene are classified as aromatic on the basis of their properties. Consideration of atomic orbitals follows the same pattern as for naphthalene, and leads to the same kind of picture: a flat structure with partially overlapping π clouds lying above and below the plane of the molecule.

In terms of valence bonds, anthracene is considered to be a hybrid of structures I–IV,

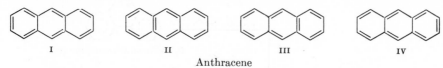

I   II   III   IV

Anthracene

and phenanthrene, a hybrid of structures V–IX.

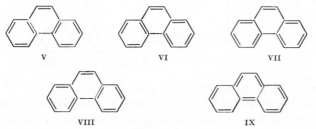

V   VI   VII

VIII   IX

Phenanthrene

Heats of combustion indicate that anthracene has a resonance energy of 84 kcal/mole, and that phenanthrene has a resonance energy of 92 kcal/mole.

For convenience we shall represent anthracene as the single structure X, and phenanthrene as XI, in which the broken circles can be thought of as representing partially overlapping aromatic sextets.

Anthracene   Phenanthrene
X   XI

31.17   Reactions of anthracene and phenanthrene

Anthracene and phenanthrene are even less resistant toward oxidation or reduction than naphthalene.   Both hydrocarbons are oxidized to the 9,10-quinones and reduced to the 9,10-dihydro compounds.

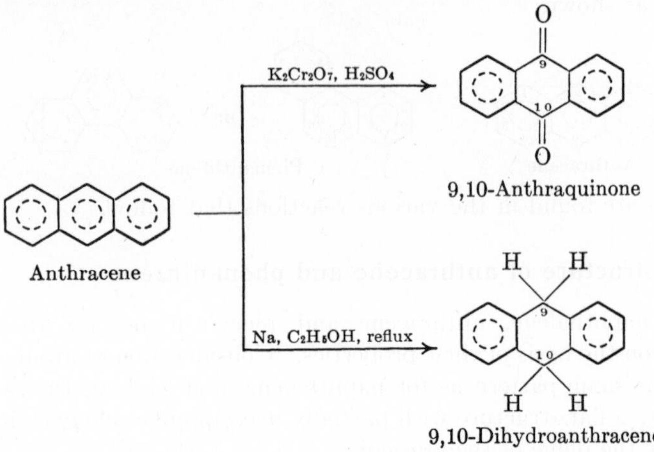

9,10-Anthraquinone

9,10-Dihydroanthracene

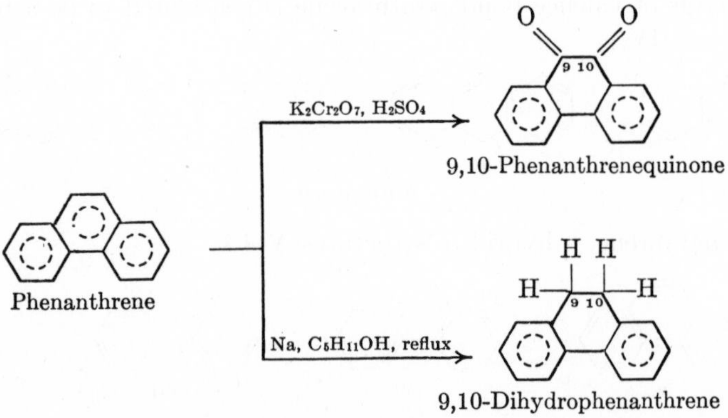

9,10-Phenanthrenequinone

9,10-Dihydrophenanthrene

Both the orientation of these reactions and the comparative ease with which they take place are understandable on the basis of the structures involved.   Attack at the 9- and 10-positions leaves two benzene rings intact; thus there is a sacrifice of only 12 kcal of resonance energy (84 − 2 × 36) for anthracene, and 20 kcal (92 − 2 × 36) for phenanthrene.

Problem 31.19   How much resonance energy would be sacrificed by oxidation or reduction of one of the outer rings of anthracene?   Of phenanthrene?

Both anthracene and phenanthrene undergo electrophilic substitution. With a few exceptions, however, these reactions are of little value in synthesis because of the formation of mixtures and polysubstitution products.   Derivatives of these two hydrocarbons are usually obtained in other ways: by electrophilic substitution in 9,10-anthraquinone or 9,10-dihydrophenanthrene, for example, or by ring closure methods (Secs. 31.18 and 31.19).

Bromination of anthracene or phenanthrene takes place at the 9-position. (9-Bromophenanthrene is a useful intermediate for the preparation of certain 9-substituted phenanthrenes.) In both cases, especially for anthracene, there is a tendency for addition to take place with the formation of the 9,10-dibromo-9,10-dihydro derivatives.

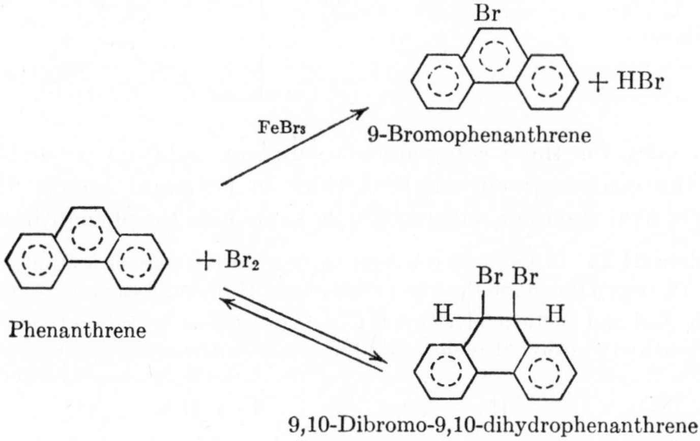

9-Bromophenanthrene

Phenanthrene + Br$_2$

9,10-Dibromo-9,10-dihydrophenanthrene

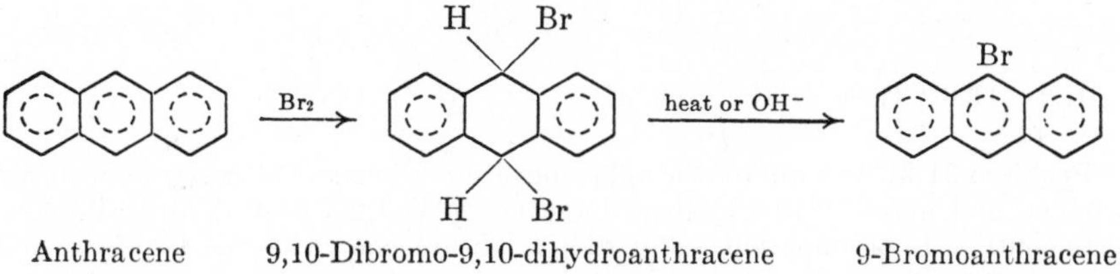

Anthracene   9,10-Dibromo-9,10-dihydroanthracene   9-Bromoanthracene

This reactivity of the 9- and 10-positions toward electrophilic attack is understandable, whether reaction eventually leads to substitution or addition. The carbonium ion initially formed is the most stable one, I or II, in which aromatic sextets are preserved in two of the three rings. This carbonium ion can then either (a) give up a proton to yield the substitution product, or (b) accept a base to yield the addition product.

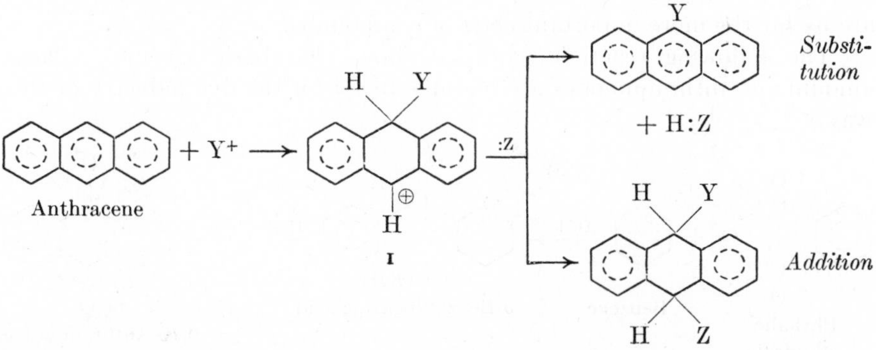

Anthracene + Y$^+$ →

Substitution

+ H:Z

Addition

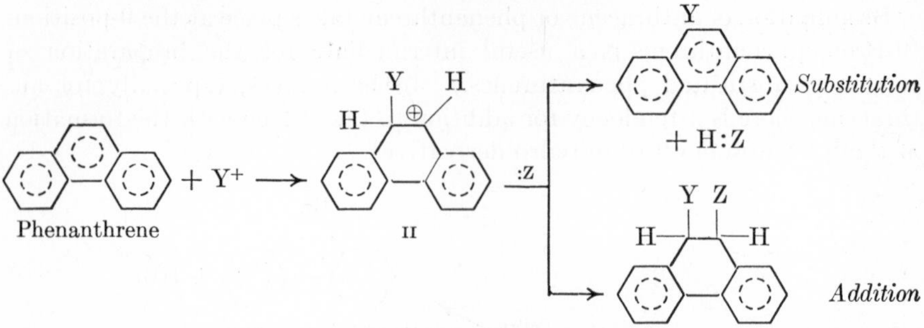

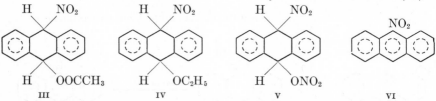

The tendency for these compounds to undergo addition is undoubtedly due to the comparatively small sacrifice in resonance energy that this entails (12 kcal/mole for anthracene, 20 kcal/mole for phenanthrene).

Problem 31.20 Nitric acid converts anthracene into any of a number of products, III–VI, depending upon the exact conditions. How could each be accounted for?
(a) Nitric acid and acetic acid yields III
(b) Nitric acid and ethyl alcohol yields IV
(c) Excess nitric acid yields V
(d) Nitric acid and acetic anhydride yields 9-nitroanthracene (VI)

III	IV	V	VI
H NO$_2$ ... H OOCCH$_3$	H NO$_2$ ... H OC$_2$H$_5$	H NO$_2$ ... H ONO$_2$	NO$_2$

Problem 31.21 Account for the following observations: (a) Upon treatment with hydrogen and nickel, 9,10-dihydroanthracene yields 1,2,3,4-tetrahydroanthracene. (b) In contrast to bromination, sulfonation of anthracene yields the 1-sulfonic acid.

31.18 Preparation of anthracene derivatives by ring closure. Anthraquinones

Derivatives of anthracene are seldom prepared from anthracene itself, but rather by ring-closure methods. As in the case of naphthalene, the most important method of ring closure involves adaptation of Friedel-Crafts acylation. The products initially obtained are **anthraquinones,** which can be converted into corresponding anthracenes by reduction with zinc and alkali. This last step is seldom carried out, since the quinones are by far the more important class of compounds.

The following reaction sequence shows the basic scheme. (Large amounts of anthraquinones are manufactured for the dye industry in this way.)

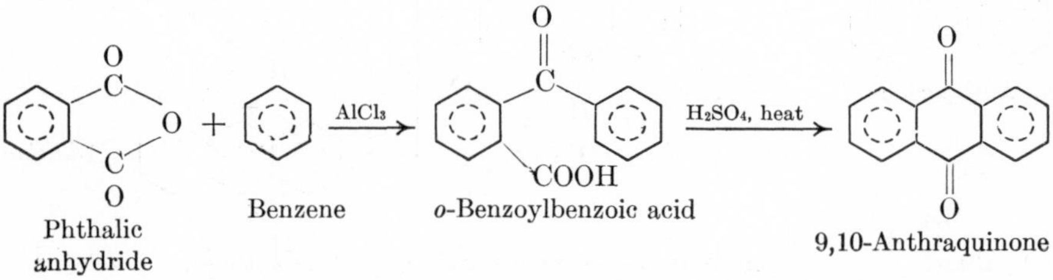

Phthalic anhydride + Benzene $\xrightarrow{AlCl_3}$ o-Benzoylbenzoic acid (COOH) $\xrightarrow{H_2SO_4,\ heat}$ 9,10-Anthraquinone

The basic scheme can be modified in a number of ways.

(a) A monosubstituted benzene can be used in place of benzene, and a 2-substituted anthraquinone obtained. (The initial acylation goes chiefly *para*. If the *para* position is blocked, *ortho* acylation is possible.) For example:

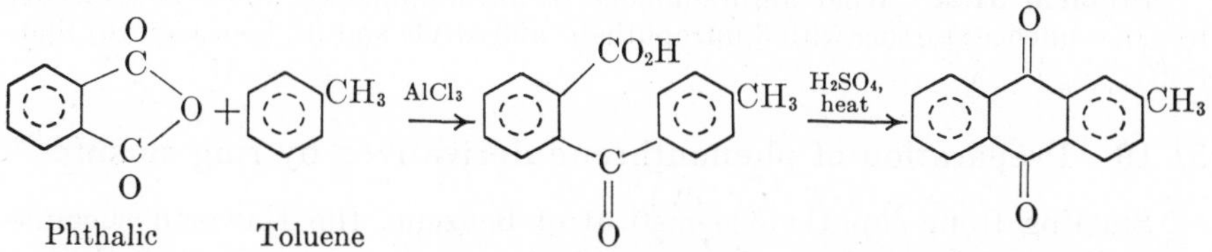

Phthalic anhydride   Toluene   *o*-(*p*-Toluyl)benzoic acid   2-Methyl-9,10-anthraquinone

(b) A polynuclear compound can be used in place of benzene, and a product having more than three rings obtained. For example:

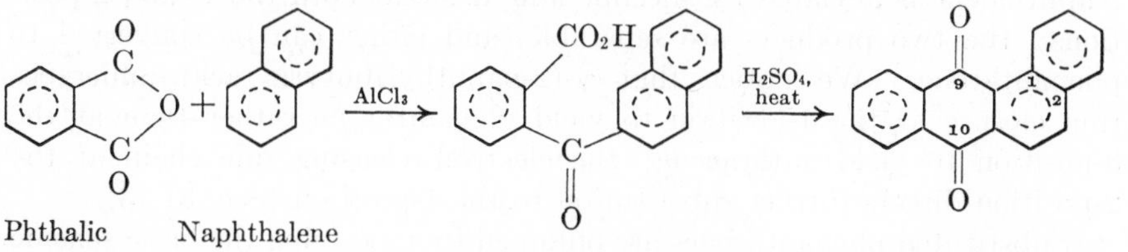

Phthalic anhydride   Naphthalene   *o*-(2-Naphthoyl)benzoic acid   1,2-Benz-9,10-anthraquinone

(c) The intermediate *o*-aroylbenzoic acid can be reduced before ring closure, and 9-substituted anthracenes obtained via Grignard reactions.

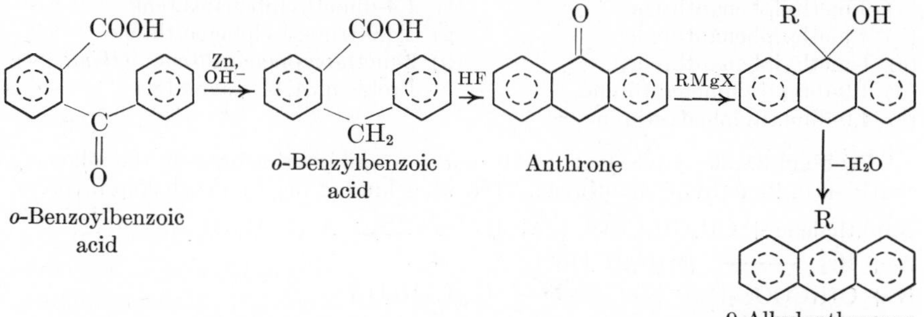

o-Benzoylbenzoic acid   *o*-Benzylbenzoic acid   Anthrone   9-Alkylanthracene

Anthraquinoid dyes are of enormous technological importance, and much work has done in devising syntheses of large ring systems embodying the quinone structure. Several examples of anthraquinoid dyes are:

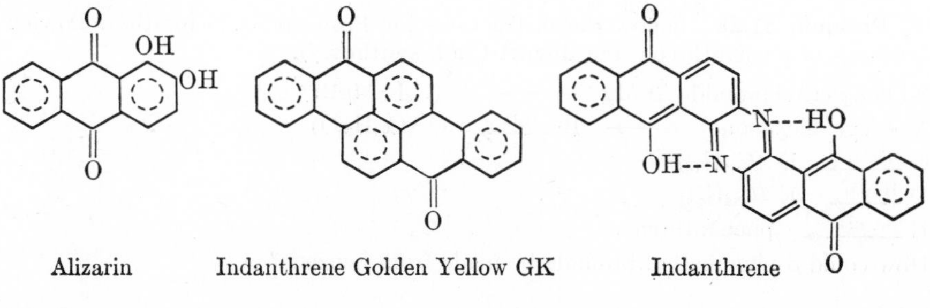

Alizarin   Indanthrene Golden Yellow GK   Indanthrene

Problem 31.22 Outline the synthesis of the following, starting from compounds having fewer rings:

(a) 1,4-dimethylanthraquinone
(b) 1,2-dimethylanthraquinone
(c) 1,3-dimethylanthraquinone

(d) 2,9-dimethylanthracene
(e) 9-methyl-1,2-benzanthracene (a potent cancer-producing hydrocarbon)

Problem 31.23 What anthraquinone or anthraquinones would be expected from a sequence starting with 3-nitrophthalic anhydride and (a) benzene; (b) toluene?

31.19 Preparation of phenanthrene derivatives by ring closure

Starting from naphthalene instead of benzene, the Haworth succinic anhydride synthesis (Sec. 31.14) provides an excellent route to substituted phenanthrenes.

The basic scheme is outlined in Chart 31.2, shown on the opposite page. Naphthalene is acylated by succinic anhydride at both the 1- and 2-positions; the two products are separable, and either can be converted to phenanthrene. We notice that γ-(2-naphthyl)butyric acid undergoes ring closure at the 1-position to yield phenanthrene rather than at the 3-position to yield anthracene; the electron-releasing side chain at the 2-position directs further substitution to the 1-position (Sec. 31.13).

Substituted phenanthrenes are obtained by modifying the basic scheme in the ways already described for the Haworth method (Sec. 31.14).

Problem 31.24 Apply the Haworth method to the synthesis of the following, starting from naphthalene or a monosubstituted naphthalene:

(a) 9-methylphenanthrene
(b) 4-methylphenanthrene
(c) 1-methylphenanthrene
(d) 1,9-dimethylphenanthrene
(e) 4,9-dimethylphenanthrene

(f) 1,4-dimethylphenanthrene
(g) 1,4,9-trimethylphenanthrene
(h) 2-methoxyphenanthrene (*Hint:* See Problem 31.14, page 818.)

Problem 31.25 Give structural formulas for all intermediates in the following synthesis of 2-methylphenanthrene. Tell what kind of reaction each step involves.

Naphthalene + CH_3CH_2COCl + $AlCl_3$ $\xrightarrow{C_6H_5NO_2}$ A ($C_{13}H_{12}O$)

A + Br_2 $\longrightarrow$ B ($C_{13}H_{11}OBr$)

B + $CH(COOC_2H_5)_2^-$ Na^+ $\longrightarrow$ C ($C_{20}H_{22}O_5$)

C $\xrightarrow{aq. KOH, heat}$ D $\xrightarrow{HCl}$ E $\xrightarrow{heat}$ F ($C_{15}H_{14}O_3$) + CO_2

F + Zn(Hg) + HCl $\longrightarrow$ G ($C_{15}H_{16}O_2$)

G $\xrightarrow{polyphosphoric acid}$ H ($C_{15}H_{14}O$)

H + Zn(Hg) + HCl $\longrightarrow$ I ($C_{15}H_{16}$)

I $\xrightarrow{Pd, heat}$ 2-methylphenanthrene

Problem 31.26 Follow the instructions for Problem 31.25 for the following synthesis of phenanthrene (the **Bogert-Cook synthesis**).

β-Phenylethyl bromide + Mg $\longrightarrow$ A (C_8H_9MgBr)

A + cyclohexanone $\longrightarrow$ B $\xrightarrow{H_2O}$ C ($C_{14}H_{20}O$)

C $\xrightarrow{H_2SO_4}$ D ($C_{14}H_{18}$)

D $\xrightarrow{H_2SO_4}$ E ($C_{14}H_{18}$)

E $\xrightarrow{Se, heat}$ phenanthrene

How could β-phenylethyl bromide be made from benzene?

CHART 31.2

HAWORTH SYNTHESIS OF PHENANTHRENE DERIVATIVES

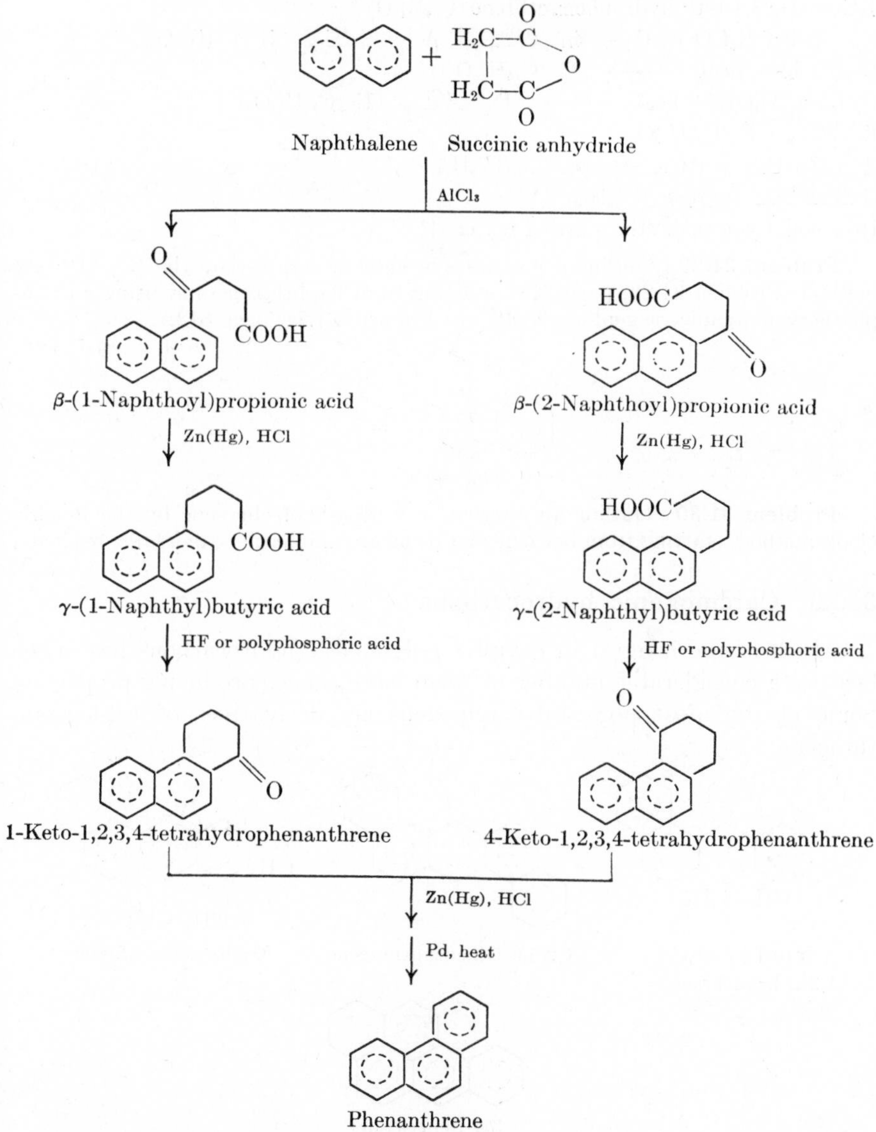

Naphthalene   Succinic anhydride

AlCl₃

β-(1-Naphthoyl)propionic acid

Zn(Hg), HCl

β-(2-Naphthoyl)propionic acid

Zn(Hg), HCl

γ-(1-Naphthyl)butyric acid

HF or polyphosphoric acid

γ-(2-Naphthyl)butyric acid

HF or polyphosphoric acid

1-Keto-1,2,3,4-tetrahydrophenanthrene

4-Keto-1,2,3,4-tetrahydrophenanthrene

Zn(Hg), HCl

Pd, heat

Phenanthrene

Problem 31.27 Follow the instruction for Problem 31.25 for the following synthesis of phenanthrene (the **Bardhan-Sengupta synthesis**).

Potassium + ethyl 2-keto-1-cyclohexanecarboxylate $\longrightarrow$ A (C₉H₁₃O₃K)

A + β-phenylethyl bromide $\longrightarrow$ B (C₁₇H₂₂O₃)

B $\xrightarrow{\text{aq. KOH, heat}}$ C $\xrightarrow{\text{HCl}}$ D (C₁₄H₁₈O)

D + Na + moist ether $\longrightarrow$ E (C₁₄H₂₀O)

E $\xrightarrow{\text{P}_2\text{O}_5}$ [F (C₁₄H₁₈)] $\xrightarrow{\text{P}_2\text{O}_5}$ G (C₁₄H₁₈)

G $\xrightarrow{\text{Se, heat}}$ phenanthrene

Problem 31.28   Follow the instructions for Problem 31.25 for the following synthesis of *pyrene*.

4-Keto-1,2,3,4-tetrahydrophenanthrene ($C_{14}H_{12}O$)

$+ BrCH_2COOC_2H_5 + Zn \xrightarrow{\text{ether}} A \xrightarrow{H_2O,\ H^+} B\ (C_{18}H_{20}O_3)$

$B + \text{acid} + \text{heat} \longrightarrow C\ (C_{18}H_{18}O_2)$

$C + \text{aq. NaOH} + \text{heat} \longrightarrow D \xrightarrow{HCl} E\ (C_{16}H_{14}O_2)$

$E \xrightarrow{HF} F\ (C_{16}H_{12}O)$

$F + Zn(Hg) + HCl \longrightarrow G\ (C_{16}H_{14})$

$G \xrightarrow{\text{Pd, heat}} \text{pyrene}\ (C_{16}H_{10})$

How could you make the starting material?

Problem 31.29   Outline a possible synthesis of *chrysene* by the Bogert-Cook method (Problem 31.26, page 828), starting from naphthalene and using any aliphatic or inorganic reagents. (*Hint:* see Problem 31.7g, page 812.)

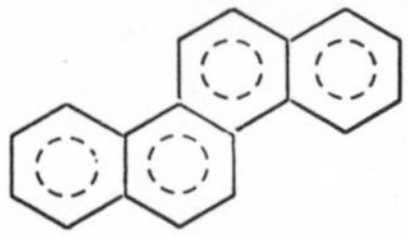

Chrysene

Problem 31.30   Outline an alternative synthesis of chrysene by the Bogert-Cook method, starting from benzene and using any aliphatic or inorganic reagents.

31.20 Carcinogenic hydrocarbons

Much of the interest in complex polynuclear hydrocarbons has arisen because a considerable number of them have cancer-producing properties. Some of the most powerful carcinogens are derivatives of 1,2-benzanthracene:

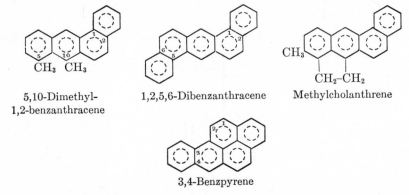

5,10-Dimethyl-   1,2,5,6-Dibenzanthracene   Methylcholanthrene
1,2-benzanthracene

3,4-Benzpyrene

The relationship between carcinogenic activity and chemical properties is far from clear, but the possibility of uncovering this relationship has inspired a tremendous amount of research in the fields of synthesis and of structure and reactivity.

PROBLEMS

1. Give the structures and names of the principal products of the reaction (if any) of naphthalene with:

(a) CrO_3, CH_3COOH
(b) O_2, V_2O_5
(c) Na, C_2H_5OH
(d) Na, $C_5H_{11}OH$
(e) H_2, Ni
(f) HNO_3, H_2SO_4

(g) Br_2
(h) conc. H_2SO_4, 80°
(i) conc. H_2SO_4, 160°
(j) CH_3COCl, $AlCl_3$, CS_2
(k) CH_3COCl, $AlCl_3$, $C_6H_5NO_2$
(l) succinic anhydride, $AlCl_3$, $C_6H_5NO_2$

2. Give the structures and names of the principal products of the reaction of HNO_3/H_2SO_4 with:

(a) 1-methylnaphthalene
(b) 2-methylnaphthalene
(c) 1-nitronaphthalene
(d) 2-nitronaphthalene
(e) 1-naphthalenesulfonic acid
(f) 2-naphthalenesulfonic acid

(g) N-(1-naphthyl)acetamide
(h) N-(2-naphthyl)acetamide
(i) α-naphthol
(j) β-naphthol
(k) anthracene

3. When 2-methylnaphthalene is nitrated, three isomeric mononitro derivatives are obtained. Upon vigorous oxidation one of these yields 3-nitro-1,2,4-benzene-tricarboxylic acid, and the other two both yield 3-nitrophthalic acid. Give the names and structures of the original three isomeric nitro compounds.

4. Outline all steps in a possible synthesis of each of the following from naphthalene, using any needed organic and inorganic reagents:

(a) α-naphthol
(b) β-naphthol
(c) α-naphthylamine
(d) β-naphthylamine
(e) 1-iodonaphthalene
(f) 2-iodonaphthalene
(g) 1-nitronaphthalene
(h) 2-nitronaphthalene
(i) α-naphthoic acid
(j) β-naphthoic acid
(k) 4-(1-naphthyl)butanoic acid
(l) α-naphthaldehyde
(m) β-naphthaldehyde
(n) 1-phenylazo-2-naphthol

(o) 1-amino-2-naphthol (*Hint:* use product of (n).)
(p) 4-amino-1-naphthol
(q) 1-bromo-2-methoxynaphthalene
(r) 1,5-diaminonaphthalene
(s) 4,8-dibromo-1,5-diiodonaphthalene
(t) 5-nitro-2-naphthalenesulfonic acid
(u) 1,2-diaminonaphthalene
(v) 1,3-diaminonaphthalene
(w) o-aminobenzoic acid
(x) phenanthrene
(y) 9,10-anthraquinone
(z) anthracene

5. Suggest a synthesis of each of the following azo dyes from coal tar hydrocarbons and any other needed reagents.

(a) Congo red (see page 583)

(b) the orange dye

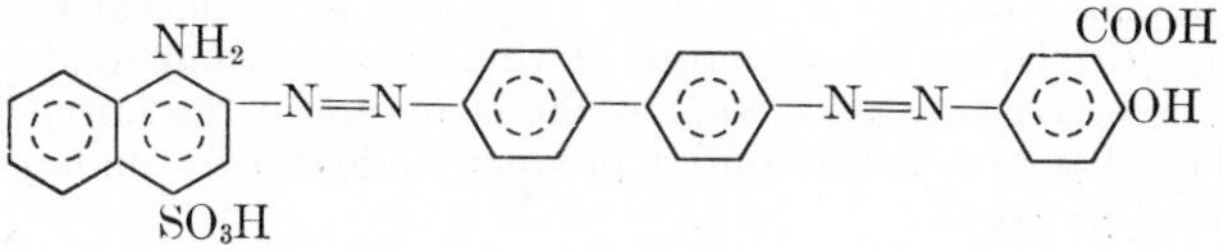

(c) the red dye

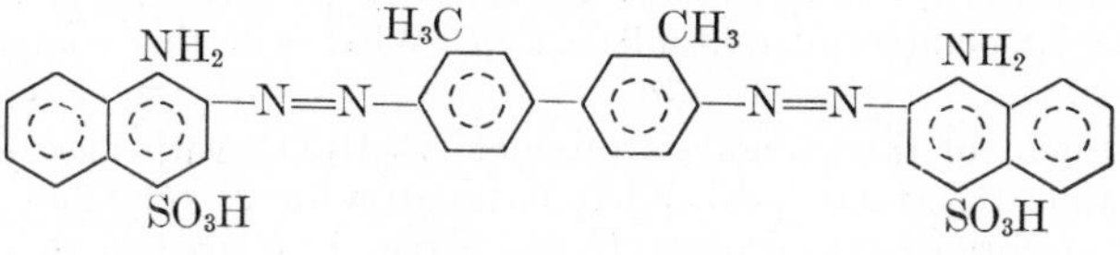

(d) the scarlet dye

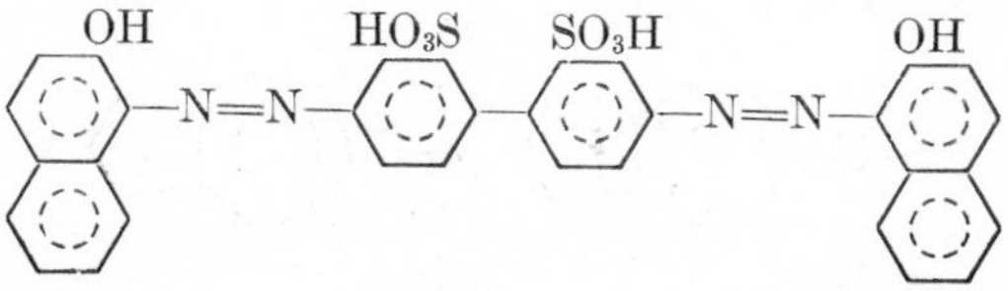

6. Naphthalene was transformed into another hydrocarbon by the following sequence of reactions:

naphthalene + Na, $C_5H_{11}OH$ $\longrightarrow$ A ($C_{10}H_{12}$)

A + succinic anhydride, $AlCl_3$ $\longrightarrow$ B ($C_{14}H_{16}O_3$)

B + Zn(Hg) + HCl $\longrightarrow$ C ($C_{14}H_{18}O_2$)

C + anhydrous HF $\longrightarrow$ D ($C_{14}H_{16}O$)

D + Zn(Hg) + HCl $\longrightarrow$ E ($C_{14}H_{18}$)

E + Pd/C + heat $\longrightarrow$ F ($C_{14}H_{10}$, m.p. 100–101°) + $4H_2$

What was F?

7. Outline all steps in a possible synthesis of each of the following from hydrocarbons containing fewer rings:

(a) 6-methoxy-4-phenyl-1-methylnaphthalene

(b) 1,2-benzanthracene

(c) 9-phenylanthracene

(d) 1-phenylphenanthrene

(e) 1,9-diphenylphenanthrene

8. Acylation of phenanthrene by succinic anhydride takes place at the 2- and 3-positions. The sequence of reduction, ring closure, and aromatization converts the 2-isomer into G and H, and converts the 3-isomer into G.

What is the structure and name of G? Of H?

9. When 4-phenyl-3-butenoic acid is refluxed there is formed a product, $C_{10}H_8O$, which is soluble in aqueous NaOH but not in aqueous $NaHCO_3$, and which reacts with benzenediazonium chloride to yield a red-orange solid. What is the product, and by what series of steps is it probably formed?

10. Anthracene reacts readily with maleic anhydride to give I, $C_{18}H_{12}O_2$, which can be hydrolyzed to J, a dicarboxylic acid of formula $C_{18}H_{14}O_4$. (a) What reaction do you think is involved in the formation of I? (b) What is the most probable structure of I? Of J?

Anthracene reacts with methyl fumarate to give a product that on hydrolysis yields K, a dicarboxylic acid of formula $C_{18}H_{14}O_4$. (c) Compare the structures of J and K. (*Hint:* see Problem 8, page 743.)

Anthracene reacts with p-benzoquinone to yield L, $C_{20}H_{14}O_2$. In acid, L undergoes rearrangement to a hydroquinone M, $C_{20}H_{14}O_2$. Oxidation of M gives a new quinone N, $C_{20}H_{12}O_2$. Reductive amination of N gives a diamine O, $C_{20}H_{16}N_2$. Deamination of O by the usual method gives the hydrocarbon *triptycene*, $C_{20}H_{14}$. (d) What is a likely structure for triptycene?

11. Reduction of aromatic rings by the action of Li metal in ammonia generally gives 1,4-addition and yields a dihydro compound. Thus from naphthalene, $C_{10}H_8$, one can obtain $C_{10}H_{10}$. (a) Draw the structure of this dihydro compound.

Similar reduction is possible for 2-methoxynaphthalene (methyl 2-naphthyl ether. (b) Draw the structure of this dihydro compound. (c) If this dihydro ether is cleaved by acid, what is the structure of the initial product? (d) What further change will this initial product undoubtedly undergo, and what will be the final product?

12. Reduction of naphthalene by Li metal in $C_2H_5NH_2$ gives a 52% yield of 1,2,3,4,5,6,7,8-octahydronaphthalene. (a) What will this compound yield upon ozonolysis?

Treatment of the ozonolysis product ($C_{10}H_{16}O_2$) with base yields an unsaturated ketone ($C_{10}H_{14}O$). (b) What is its structure? (c) Show how this ketone can be transformed into *azulene*, $C_{10}H_8$, a blue hydrocarbon that is isomeric with naphthalene.

or

Azulene

(d) How do you account for the aromatic properties of azulene?

13. The structure of *eudalene*, $C_{14}H_{16}$, a degradation product of eudesmol (a terpene found in eucalyptus oil), was first established by the following synthesis:

p-isopropylbenzaldehyde + ethyl bromoacetate, Zn; then $H_2O \longrightarrow$ P $(C_{14}H_{20}O_3)$

P + acid, heat $\longrightarrow$ Q $(C_{14}H_{18}O_2)$

Q + Na, ethyl alcohol $\longrightarrow$ R $(C_{12}H_{18}O)$

R $\xrightarrow{\text{HBr}}$ $\xrightarrow{\text{KCN}}$ $\xrightarrow{\text{H}_2\text{O, H}^+}$ $\xrightarrow{\text{SOCl}_2}$ S $(C_{13}H_{17}OCl)$

S + AlCl$_3$, warm $\longrightarrow$ T $(C_{13}H_{16}O)$

T + CH$_3$MgBr, then H$_2$O $\longrightarrow$ U $(C_{14}H_{20}O)$

U + acid, heat $\longrightarrow$ V $(C_{14}H_{18})$

V + sulfur, heat $\longrightarrow$ eudalene $(C_{14}H_{16})$

What is the structure and systematic name of eudalene?

14. Many polynuclear aromatic compounds do not contain fused ring systems, e.g., biphenyl and triphenylmethane. Give structures and names of compounds W through II, formed in the following syntheses of such polynuclear compounds.

(a) o-nitrotoluene + Zn + NaOH $\longrightarrow$ W $(C_{14}H_{16}N_2)$

    W + acid + heat $\longrightarrow$ X $(C_{14}H_{16}N_2)$

    X + NaNO$_2$ + HCl; then H$_3$PO$_2$ $\longrightarrow$ Y $(C_{14}H_{14})$

(b) m-bromotoluene + Mg, ether $\longrightarrow$ Z (C_7H_7MgBr)

    Z + 4-methylcyclohexanone, then H$_2$O $\longrightarrow$ AA $(C_{14}H_{20}O)$

    AA + H$^+$, heat $\longrightarrow$ BB $(C_{14}H_{18})$

    BB + Pd/C, heat $\longrightarrow$ CC $(C_{14}H_{14})$

(c) ethyl benzoate + C$_6$H$_5$MgBr, then H$_2$O $\longrightarrow$ DD $(C_{19}H_{16}O)$

    DD + conc. HBr $\longrightarrow$ EE $(C_{19}H_{15}Br)$

    EE + Ag $\longrightarrow$ FF $(C_{38}H_{30})$

(d) $(C_6H_5)_3COH + C_6H_5NH_2$ + acid $\longrightarrow$ GG $(C_{25}H_{21}N)$

    GG + NaNO$_2$ + HCl; then H$_3$PO$_2$ $\longrightarrow$ HH $(C_{25}H_{20})$

(e) $C_6H_5COCH_3$ + acid + heat $\longrightarrow$ II $(C_{24}H_{18})$ (*Hint:* acids catalyze aldol condensations.)

Chapter thirty-two_____

HETEROCYCLIC
COMPOUNDS

32.1 Heterocyclic systems

A **heterocyclic compound** is one that contains a ring made up of more than one kind of atom.

In most of the cyclic compounds that we have studied so far — benzene, naphthalene, cyclohexanol, cyclopentadiene — the rings are made up only of carbon atoms; such compounds are called *homocyclic* or *alicyclic* compounds. But there are also rings containing, in addition to carbon, other kinds of atoms, most commonly nitrogen, oxygen, or sulfur. For example:

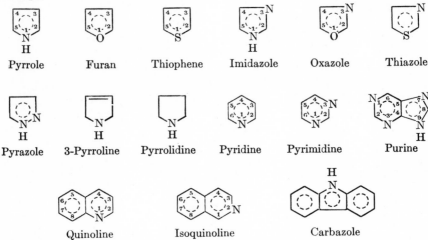

Pyrrole   Furan   Thiophene   Imidazole   Oxazole   Thiazole

Pyrazole   3-Pyrroline   Pyrrolidine   Pyridine   Pyrimidine   Purine

Quinoline   Isoquinoline   Carbazole

We notice that, in the numbering of ring positions, hetero atoms are generally given the lowest possible numbers.

In this chapter we can take up only a very few of the many different heterocyclic systems, and look only briefly at them. Perhaps the most important and most interesting heterocycles are the ones that possess aromatic properties; we shall focus our attention on a few of these, and in particular upon their aromatic properties.

Some idea of the importance — as well as complexity — of heterocyclic systems can be gotten from the following examples. Some others are *hemin* (page 876), *diphosphopyridine nucleotide* (page 877), and *oxytocin* (page 867).

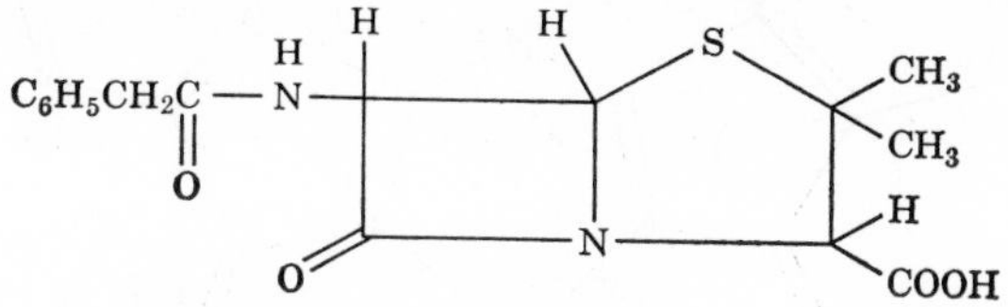

Penicillin G
Anti-biotic

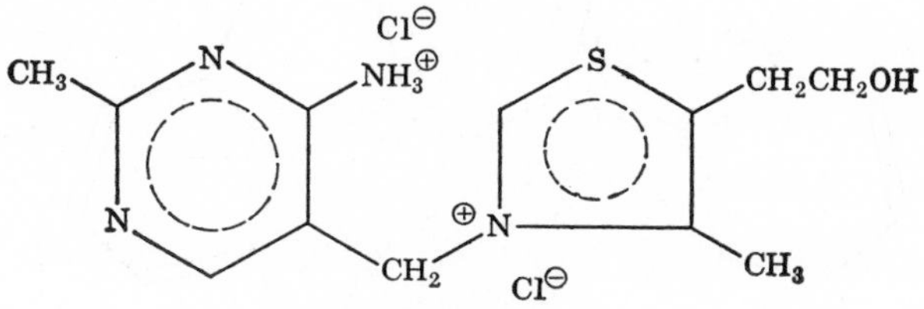

Thiamine
Vitamin B$_1$
Anti-beriberi factor

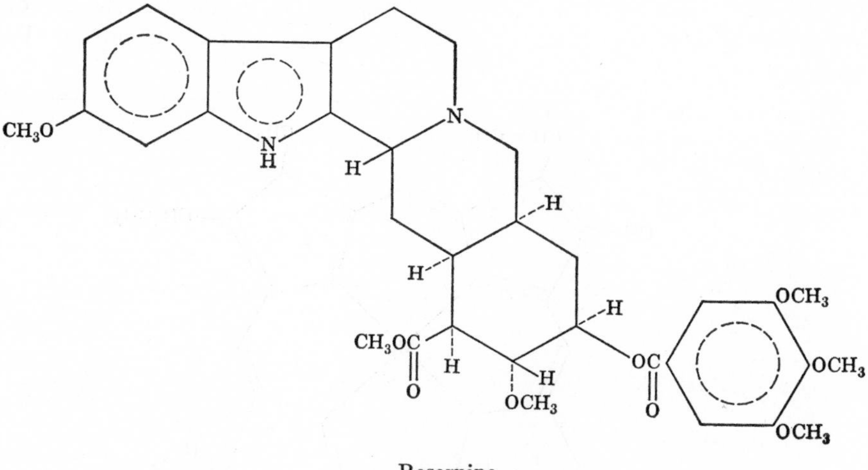

Reserpine
A tranquilizing drug

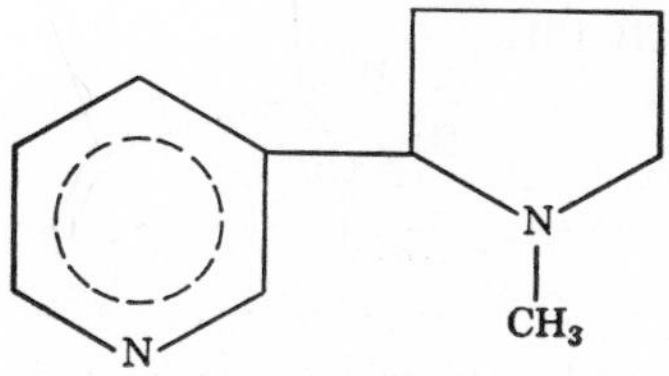

Nicotine
A tobacco alkaloid

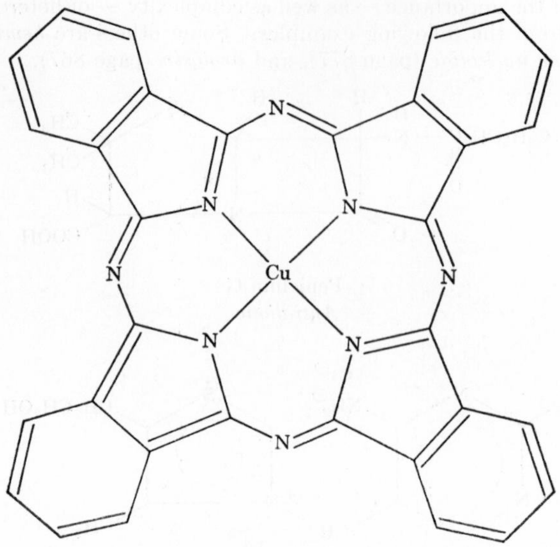

Copper phthalocyanine
A blue pigment

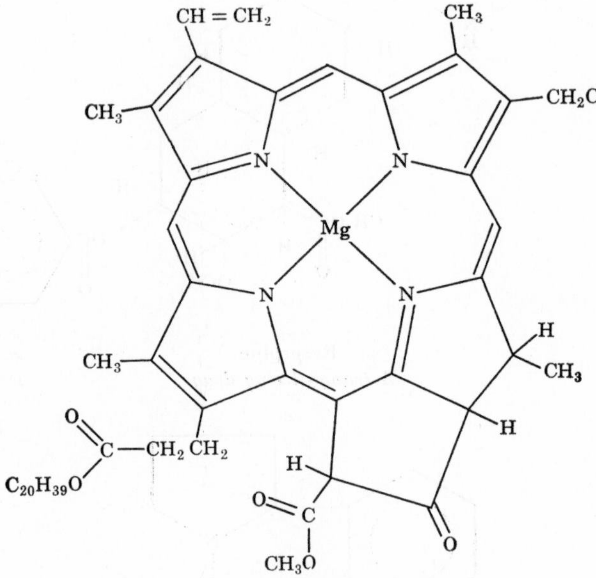

Chlorophyll a
Green plant pigment:
catalyst for photosynthesis

TABLE 32.1

HETEROCYCLIC COMPOUNDS

Name	M.p., °C	B.p., °C	Name	M.p., °C	B.p., °C
Furan	−30	32	Pyridine	−42	115
Tetrahydrofuran	−108	66	α-Picoline	−64	128
Furfuryl alcohol		171	β-Picoline		143
Furfural	−36	162	γ-Picoline		144
Furoic acid	134		Piperidine	−9	106
Pyrrole		130	Picolinic acid	137	
Pyrrolidine		88	Nicotinic acid	237	
Thiophene	−40	87	Isonicotinic acid	317	
			Indole	53	254
			Quinoline	−19	238
			Isoquinoline	23	243

FIVE–MEMBERED RINGS

32.2 Structure of pyrrole, furan, and thiophene

The simplest of the five-membered heterocyclic compounds are **pyrrole, furan,** and **thiophene,** each of which contains a single hetero atom.

Judging from the commonly used structures I, II, and III, we might expect each of these compounds to have the properties of a conjugated

Pyrrole   Furan   Thiophene

I   II   III

diene and of an amine, an ether, or a sulfide (thioether). Except for a certain tendency to undergo addition reactions, however, these heterocycles do not have the expected properties: thiophene does not undergo the oxidation typical of a sulfide, for example; pyrrole does not possess the basic properties typical of amines.

Instead, these heterocycles and their derivatives most commonly undergo electrophilic substitution: nitration, sulfonation, halogenation, Friedel-Crafts acylation, even the Reimer-Tiemann reaction and coupling with diazonium salts. Heats of combustion indicate resonance stabilization to the extent of 22–28 kcal/mole: somewhat less than the resonance energy of benzene (36 kcal/mole), but much greater than that of most conjugated dienes (about 3 kcal/mole). On the basis of these properties pyrrole, furan, and thiophene must be considered *aromatic.* Clearly, formulas I, II, and III do not adequately represent the structures of these compounds.

Let us look at the orbital picture of one of these molecules, pyrrole. Each atom of the ring, whether carbon or nitrogen, is held by a σ bond to three other atoms. In forming these bonds the atom uses three sp^2 orbitals, which lie in a plane and are 120° apart. After contributing one electron to each σ bond, each carbon atom of the ring has left *one* electron and the nitrogen atom has left *two* electrons; these electrons occupy p orbitals. Overlap of the p orbitals gives rise to π clouds, one above and one below the plane of the ring; the π clouds contain a total of six electrons, the *aromatic sextet* (Figure 32.1).

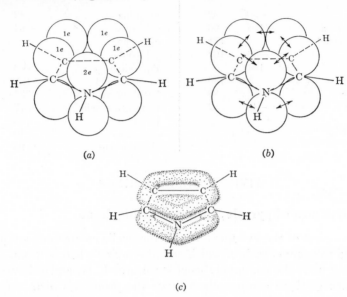

(a)   (b)

(c)

FIGURE 32.1. Pyrrole molecule. (a) Two electrons in p orbital of nitrogen; one electron in p orbital of each carbon. (b) Overlap of p orbitals to form π bonds. (c) π clouds above and below plane of ring; total of six π electrons, the aromatic sextet.

Delocalization of the π electrons stabilizes the ring. As a result, pyrrole has an abnormally low heat of combustion; it tends to undergo reactions in which the stabilized ring is retained, that is, to undergo substitution.

Nitrogen's extra pair of electrons, which is responsible for the usual basicity of nitrogen compounds, is involved in the π cloud, and is not available for sharing with acids. In contrast to most amines, therefore, pyrrole is an extremely weak base ($K_b \sim 2.5 \times 10^{-14}$). By the same token there is a high electron density in the ring, which causes pyrrole to be extremely reactive toward electrophilic substitution: it undergoes reactions like nitrosation and coupling with diazonium salts which are characteristic of only the most reactive benzene derivatives, phenols and amines.

It thus appears that pyrrole is better represented by IV,

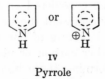

IV

Pyrrole

in which the broken circle represents the aromatic sextet.

What does IV mean in terms of conventional valence bond structures? Pyrrole can be considered a hybrid of structures V–IX. Donation of electrons to the ring

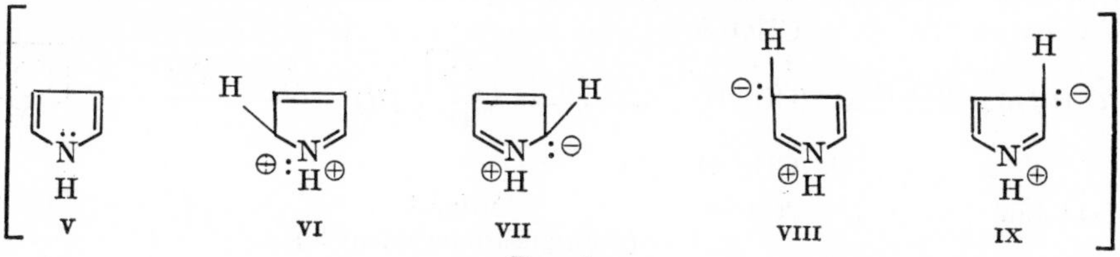

Pyrrole

by nitrogen is indicated by the ionic structures in which nitrogen bears a positive charge and the carbon atoms of the ring bear a negative charge.

Furan and thiophene have structures that are analogous to the structure of pyrrole. Where nitrogen in pyrrole carries a hydrogen atom, the oxygen or sulfur carries an unshared pair of electrons in an sp^2 orbital.

Furan   Thiophene

Like nitrogen, the oxygen or sulfur atom provides two electrons for the π cloud; as a result these compounds, too, behave like extremely reactive benzene derivatives.

32.3 Source of pyrrole, furan, and thiophene

Pyrrole and thiophene are found in small amounts in coal tar. During the fractional distillation of coal tar, thiophene (b.p. 87°) is collected along with the benzene (b.p. 80°); as a result ordinary benzene contains about 0.5% of thiophene, and must be specially treated if *thiophene-free benzene* is desired.

Thiophene can be synthesized on an industrial scale by the high-temperature reaction between *n*-butane and sulfur.

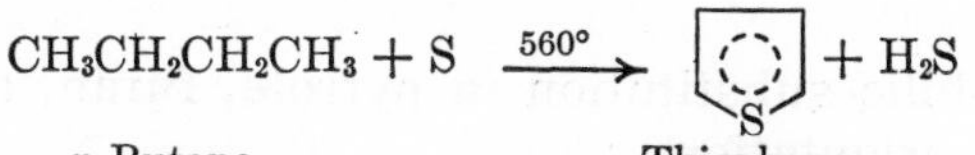

$$CH_3CH_2CH_2CH_3 + S \xrightarrow{560°} \left[\text{Thiophene}\right] + H_2S$$

n-Butane   Thiophene

Pyrrole can be synthesized in a number of ways. For example:

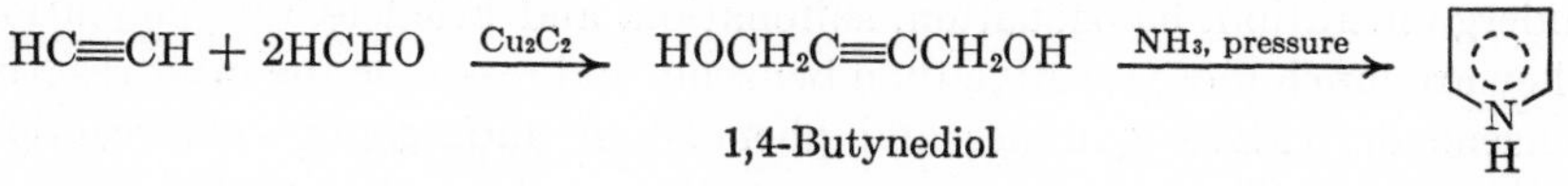

$$HC\equiv CH + 2HCHO \xrightarrow{Cu_2C_2} HOCH_2C\equiv CCH_2OH \xrightarrow{NH_3, \text{ pressure}} \left[\text{Pyrrole}\right]$$

1,4-Butynediol   Pyrrole

The pyrrole ring is the basic unit of the *porphyrin* system, which occurs, for example, in chlorophyll (page 836) and in hemoglobin (page 876).

Furan is most readily prepared by decarbonylation (elimination of carbon monoxide) of **furfural** (furfuraldehyde), which in turn is made by the treatment of oat hulls, corncobs, or rice hulls with hot hydrochloric acid. In the latter reaction pentosans (polypentosides) are hydrolyzed to pentoses, which then undergo dehydration and cyclization to form furfural.

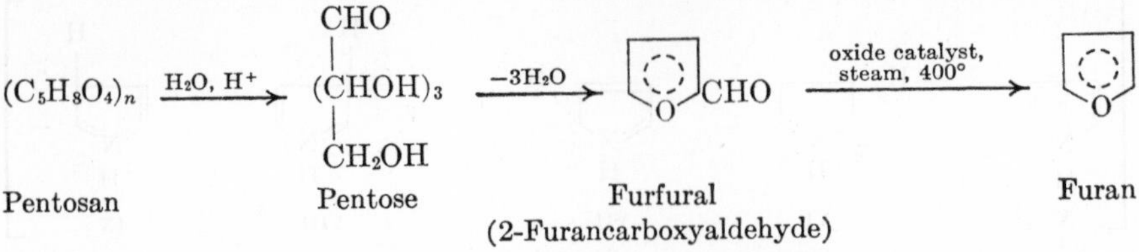

$$(C_5H_8O_4)_n \xrightarrow{H_2O,\ H^+} \underset{\underset{\text{Pentose}}{}}{\overset{\text{CHO}}{\underset{\text{CH}_2\text{OH}}{(\text{CHOH})_3}}} \xrightarrow{-3H_2O} \underset{\underset{\text{(2-Furancarboxyaldehyde)}}{\text{Furfural}}}{\square\text{CHO}} \xrightarrow[\text{steam, 400°}]{\text{oxide catalyst,}} \underset{\text{Furan}}{\square}$$

Pentosan

Certain substituted pyrroles, furans, and thiophenes can be prepared from the parent heterocycles by substitution (see Sec. 32.4); most, however, are prepared from open-chain compounds by ring closure. For example:

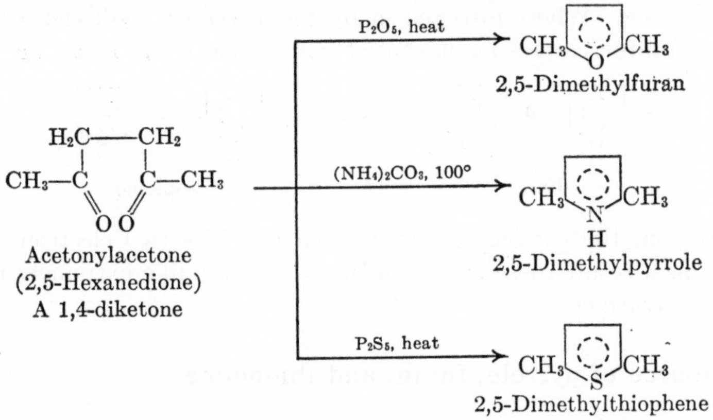

$$\text{CH}_3\text{--}\underset{\underset{\text{O}}{\parallel}}{C}\underset{}{\overset{\text{H}_2\text{C}\text{---}\text{CH}_2}{\diagup}}\underset{\underset{\text{O}}{\parallel}}{C}\text{--}\text{CH}_3$$

Acetonylacetone
(2,5-Hexanedione)
A 1,4-diketone

$\xrightarrow{\text{P}_2\text{O}_5,\ \text{heat}}$ CH₃⬠CH₃ 2,5-Dimethylfuran

$\xrightarrow{(\text{NH}_4)_2\text{CO}_3,\ 100°}$ CH₃⬠CH₃ (N–H) 2,5-Dimethylpyrrole

$\xrightarrow{\text{P}_2\text{S}_5,\ \text{heat}}$ CH₃⬠CH₃ 2,5-Dimethylthiophene

Problem 32.1 Give structural formulas for all intermediates in the following synthesis of acetonylacetone (2,5-hexanedione).

Ethyl acetoacetate + NaOC₂H₅ $\longrightarrow$ A $(C_6H_9O_3Na)$
A + I₂ $\longrightarrow$ B $(C_{12}H_{18}O_6)$ + NaI
B + dilute acid + heat $\longrightarrow$ acetonylacetone + carbon dioxide + ethanol

Problem 32.2 Outline a synthesis of 2,5-diphenylfuran, starting from ethyl benzoate and ethyl acetate.

32.4 Electrophilic substitution in pyrrole, furan, and thiophene. Reactivity and orientation

Like other aromatic compounds, these five-membered heterocycles undergo nitration, halogenation, sulfonation, and Friedel-Crafts acylation. They are much more reactive than benzene, and resemble the most reactive benzene derivatives (amines and phenols) in undergoing such reactions as the Reimer-Tiemann reaction, nitrosation, and coupling with diazonium salts.

Reaction takes place predominantly at the 2-position. For example:

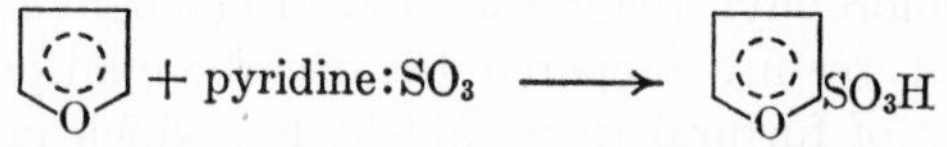

$$\underset{\text{Furan}}{\square} + \text{pyridine:SO}_3 \longrightarrow \underset{\text{2-Furansulfonic acid}}{\square\text{SO}_3\text{H}}$$

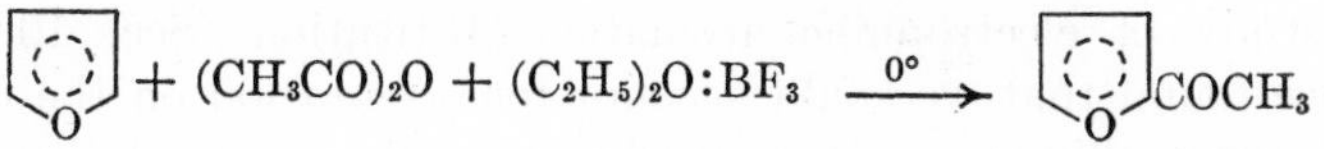

Furan　　　　　　Boron trifluoride　　　　2-Acetylfuran
　　　　　　　　　　　etherate

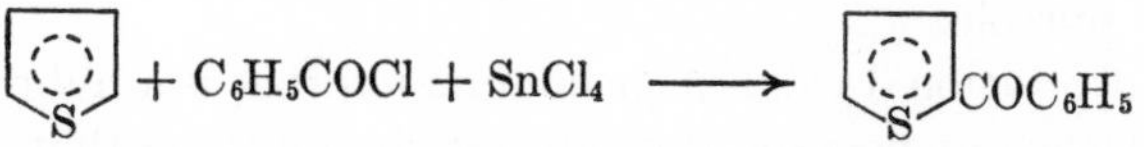

Thiophene　　　　　　　　　　　2-Benzoylthiophene

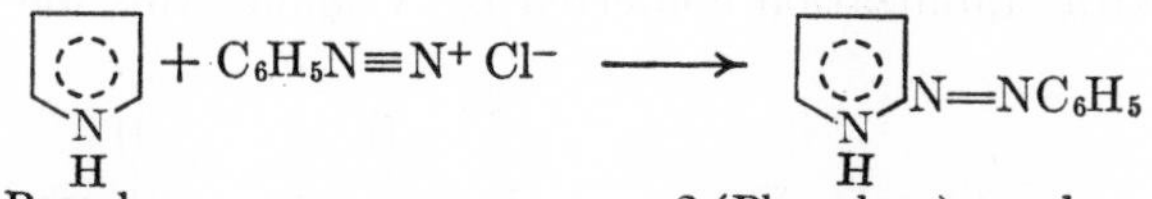

Pyrrole　　　　　　　　　2-(Phenylazo)pyrrole

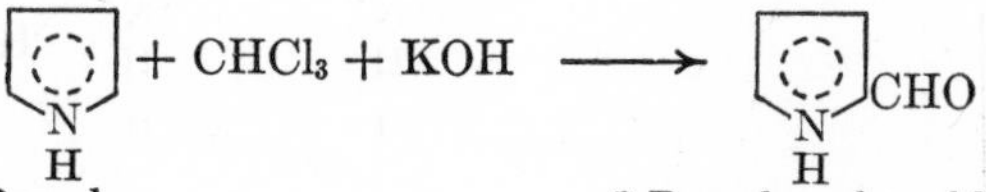

Pyrrole　　　　　　　　　2-Pyrrolecarboxaldehyde
　　　　　　　　　　　　　　　Low yield

In some of the examples we notice modifications in the usual electrophilic reagents. The high reactivity of these rings makes it possible to use milder reagents in many cases, as, for example, the weak Lewis acid stannic chloride in the Friedel-Crafts acylation of thiophene. The sensitivity to protic acids of furan (which undergoes ring opening) and pyrrole (which undergoes polymerization) makes it necessary to modify the usual sulfonating agent.

Problem 32.3 Furan undergoes ring opening upon treatment with sulfuric acid; it reacts almost explosively with halogens. Account for the fact that 2-furoic acid, however, can be sulfonated (in the 5-position) by treatment with fuming sulfuric acid, and brominated (in the 5-position) by treatment with bromine at 100°.

2-Furoic acid

Problem 32.4 Upon treatment with formaldehyde and acid, ethyl 2,4-dimethyl-3-pyrrolecarboxylate is converted to a compound of formula $C_{19}H_{26}O_4N_2$. What is the most likely structure for this product? How is it formed?

Problem 32.5 Predict the products from the treatment of furfural (2-furancarboxaldehyde) with concentrated aqueous NaOH.

Problem 32.6 Sulfur trioxide dissolves in the tertiary amine pyridine to form a salt:

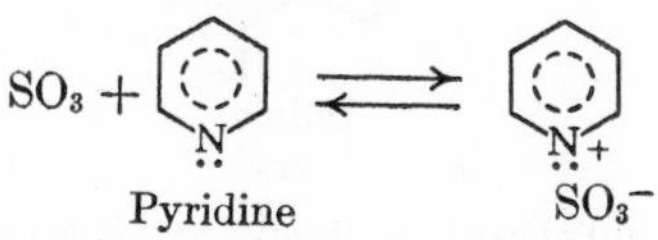

Pyridine

Show all steps in the most likely mechanism for the sulfonation of an aromatic compound by this reagent.

In our study of electrophilic aromatic substitution (Sec. 10.9 and Sec. 31.9), we found that we could account for orientation on the following basis: the controlling step is the attachment of the electrophilic reagent to the aromatic ring, which takes place in such a way as to yield the most stable intermediate carbonium ion. Let us apply this approach to the reactions of pyrrole.

Attack at position 3 yields a carbonium ion that is a hybrid of structures I and II. Attack at position 2 yields a carbonium ion that is a hybrid not only of structures III and IV (equivalent to I and II) but also of structure V; the extra stabilization conferred by V makes this ion the more stable one.

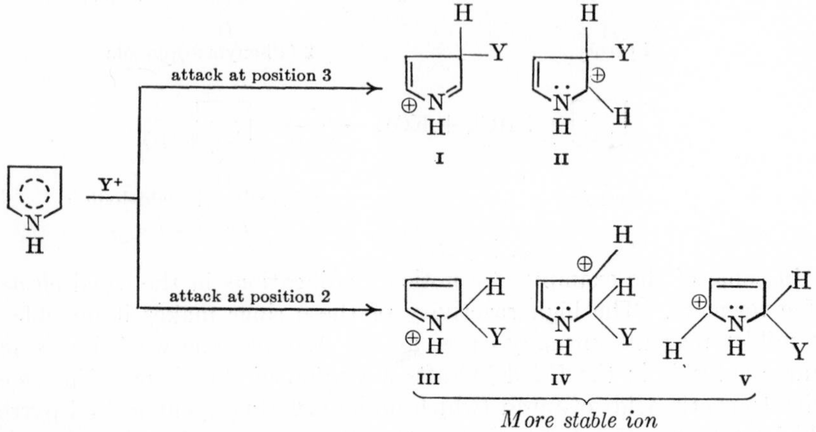

More stable ion

Viewed differently, attack at position 2 is faster because the developing positive charge is accommodated by *three* atoms of the ring instead of by only two.

Pyrrole is highly reactive, compared with benzene, because of contribution from the relatively stable structure III. In III *every atom has an octet of electrons;* nitrogen accommodates the positive charge simply by *sharing* four pairs of electrons. It is no accident that pyrrole resembles aniline in reactivity: both owe their high reactivity to the ability of nitrogen to share four pairs of electrons.

Orientation of substitution in furan and thiophene, as well as their high reactivity, can be accounted for in a similar way.

Problem 32.7 The heterocycle *indole*, commonly represented as formula VI, is found in coal tar and in orange blossoms.

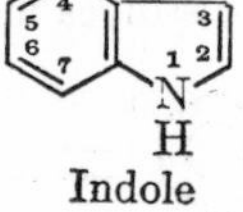

Indole

VI

It undergoes electrophilic substitution, chiefly at position 3. Account (a) for the aromatic properties of indole, and (b) for the orientation in electrophilic substitution. (*Hint:* see Sec. 31.9.)

32.5 Saturated five-membered heterocycles

Catalytic hydrogenation converts pyrrole and furan into the corresponding saturated heterocycles, *pyrrolidine* and *tetrahydrofuran*. Since thiophene poisons most catalysts, *tetrahydrothiophene* is synthesized instead from open-chain compounds.

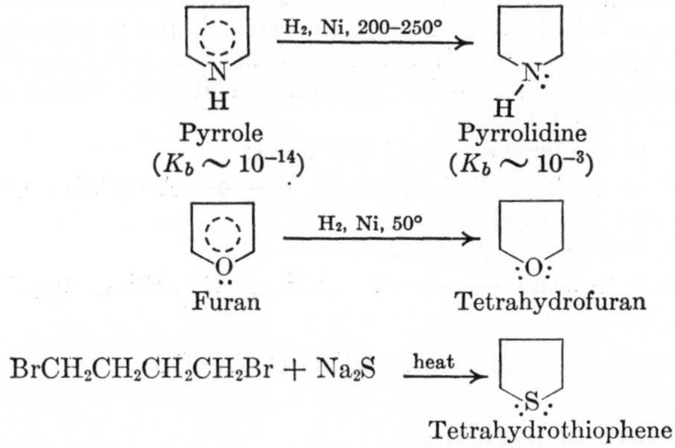

Pyrrole
$(K_b \sim 10^{-14})$

H2, Ni, 200–250°

Pyrrolidine
$(K_b \sim 10^{-3})$

Furan

H2, Ni, 50°

Tetrahydrofuran

$$BrCH_2CH_2CH_2CH_2Br + Na_2S \xrightarrow{heat}$$

Tetrahydrothiophene

Saturation of these rings destroys the aromatic structure and, with it, the aromatic properties. Each of the saturated heterocycles has the properties we would expect of it: the properties of a secondary aliphatic amine, an aliphatic ether, or an aliphatic sulfide. With nitrogen's extra pair of electrons now available for sharing with acids, pyrrolidine $(K_b \sim 10^{-3})$ has the normal basicity of an amine. Hydrogenation of pyrrole increases the base strength by a factor of 10^{11} (100 billion); clearly a fundamental change in structure has taken place.

Tetrahydrofuran is converted by hydrochloric acid into 1,4-dichlorobutane; we have already encountered this reaction (Sec. 25.3) as an important step in the industrial synthesis of adipic acid and Nylon. We should notice that the conversion is simply (1) the cleavage of an ether by acid, and (2) the conversion of a primary alcohol into a halide. Tetrahydrofuran is an important solvent, used, for example, in reductions with lithium aluminum hydride, and in the preparation of arylmagnesium chlorides (Sec. 14.6).

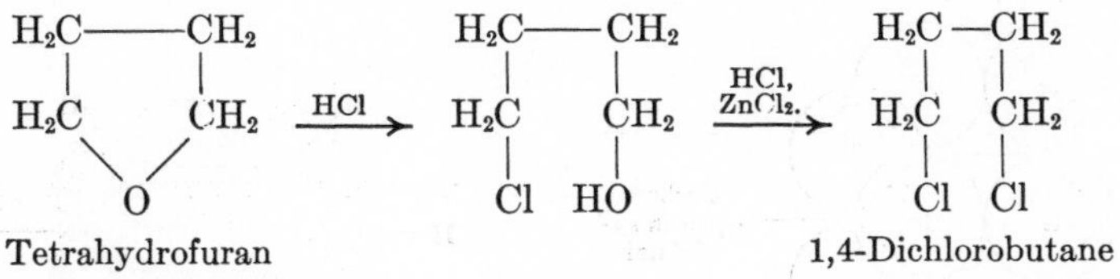

Tetrahydrofuran

1,4-Dichlorobutane

The pyrrolidine ring occurs naturally in a number of alkaloids (Sec. 20.5), providing the basicity that gives these compounds their name (*alkali-like*).

Problem 32.8 Predict the products of the treatment of pyrrolidine with:
(a) aqueous HCl
(b) aqueous NaOH
(c) acetic anhydride

(d) benzenesulfonyl chloride + aqueous NaOH

(e) methyl iodide, followed by aqueous NaOH

(f) repeated treatment with methyl iodide, followed by Ag_2O and then strong heating

Problem 32.9 The alkaloid *hygrine* is found in the coca plant. Suggest a structure for it on the basis of the following evidence:

Hygrine ($C_8H_{15}ON$) is insoluble in aqueous NaOH but soluble in aqueous HCl. It does not react with benzenesulfonyl chloride. It reacts with phenylhydrazine to yield a phenylhydrazone. It reacts with NaOI to yield a yellow precipitate and a carboxylic acid ($C_7H_{13}O_2N$). Vigorous oxidation by CrO_3 converts hygrine into *hygrinic acid* ($C_6H_{11}O_2N$).

Hygrinic acid can be synthesized as follows:

$BrCH_2CH_2CH_2Br + CH(COOC_2H_5)_2{}^-Na^+ \longrightarrow$ A ($C_{10}H_{17}O_4Br$)

$A + Br_2 \longrightarrow$ B ($C_{10}H_{16}O_4Br_2$)

$B + CH_3NH_2 \longrightarrow$ C ($C_{11}H_{19}O_4N$)

$C + aq.\ Ba(OH)_2 + heat \longrightarrow$ D $\xrightarrow{HCl}$ E $\xrightarrow{heat}$ hygrinic acid + CO_2

SIX–MEMBERED RINGS

32.6 Structure of pyridine

Of the six-membered aromatic heterocycles, we shall take up only one, **pyridine.**

Pyridine is classified as aromatic on the basis of its properties: it resists addition and undergoes electrophilic substitution. Its heat of combustion indicates a resonance energy of 23 kcal/mole.

Pyridine can be considered a hybrid of the Kekulé structures I and II. We shall represent it as structure III, in which the broken circle represents the aromatic sextet.

In electronic configuration, the nitrogen of pyridine is considerably different from the nitrogen of pyrrole. In pyridine the nitrogen atom, like each of the carbon atoms, is bonded to other members of the ring by the use of sp^2 orbitals, and provides one electron for the π cloud. The

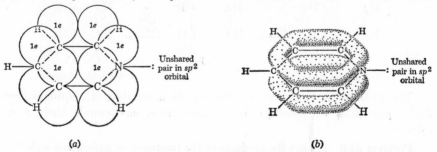

(a) *(b)*

FIGURE 32.2. Pyridine molecule. (*a*) One electron in each *p* orbital; two electrons in sp^2 orbital of nitrogen. (*b*) The *p* orbitals overlap to form π clouds above and below plane of ring; two unshared electrons still in sp^2 orbital of nitrogen.

third sp^2 orbital of each carbon atom is used to form a bond to hydrogen; the third sp^2 orbital of nitrogen simply contains a pair of electrons, which are available for sharing with acids (Figure 32.2). Because of this electronic configuration, the nitrogen atom makes pyridine a much stronger base than pyrrole, and affects the reactivity of the ring in a quite different way.

32.7   Source of pyridine compounds

Pyridine is found in coal tar. Along with it are found a number of methylpyridines, the most important of which are the monomethyl compounds, known as *picolines*.

Oxidation of the picolines yields the pyridinecarboxylic acids.

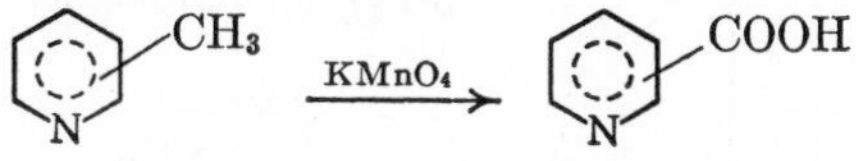

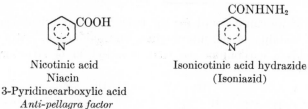

Picoline	Pyridinecarboxylic acid
(2-, 3-, or 4-)	(2-, 3-, or 4-)

The 3-isomer (*nicotinic acid* or *niacin*) is a vitamin. The 4-isomer (*isonicotinic acid*) has been used, in the form of its hydrazide, in the treatment of tuberculosis.

Nicotinic acid
Niacin
3-Pyridinecarboxylic acid
Anti-pellagra factor

Isonicotinic acid hydrazide
(Isoniazid)

The increasing demand for certain pyridine derivatives has led to the development of syntheses involving ring closure. For example:

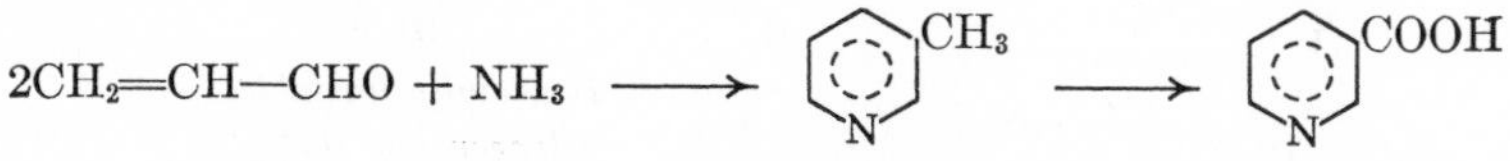

$$2CH_2=CH-CHO + NH_3 \longrightarrow$$

Acrolein

3-Methylpyridine
β-Picoline

Nicotinic acid

32.8   Reactions of pyridine

The chemical properties of pyridine are those we would expect on the basis of its structure. The ring undergoes the substitution, both electrophilic and nucleophilic, typical of aromatic rings; our interest will lie chiefly in the way the nitrogen atom affects these reactions.

There is another set of reactions in which pyridine acts as a base or nucleophile; these reactions involve nitrogen directly and are due to its unshared pair of electrons.

32.9   Electrophilic substitution in pyridine

Toward electrophilic substitution pyridine resembles a highly deactivated benzene derivative. It undergoes nitration, sulfonation, and halogenation only under very vigorous conditions, and does not undergo the Friedel-Crafts reaction at all.

Substitution occurs chiefly at the 3- (or β-) position.

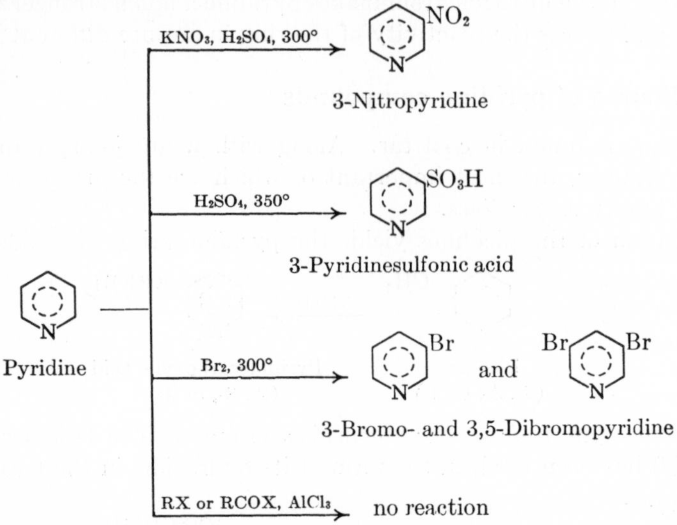

Let us see if we can account for the reactivity and orientation on our usual basis of stability of the intermediate carbonium ion. Attack at the 4-position yields a carbonium ion that is a hybrid of structures I, II, and III;

I II III

Especially unstable: nitrogen has sextet

Electrophilic attack at 4-position

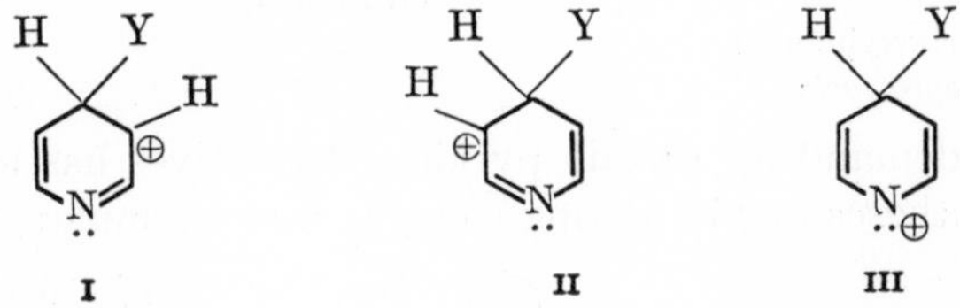

attack at the 3-position yields an ion that is a hybrid of structures IV, V and VI.

IV V VI

Electrophilic attack at 3-position

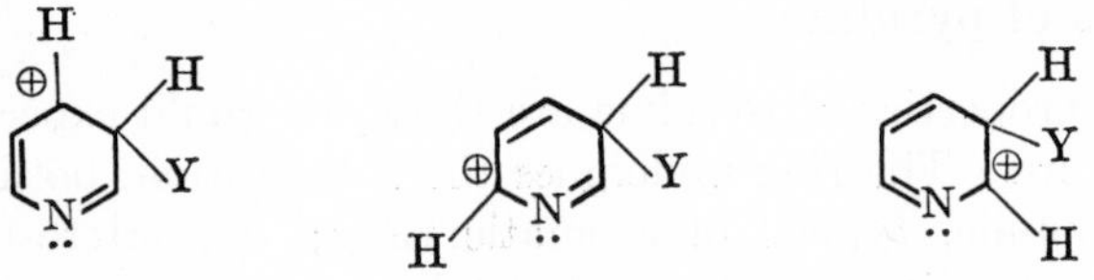

(Attack at the 2-position resembles attack at the 4-position just as *ortho* attack resembles *para* attack in the benzene series.)

All these structures are less stable than the corresponding ones for attack on benzene, because of electron withdrawal by the nitrogen atom. As a result, pyridine undergoes substitution more slowly than benzene.

Of these structures, III is *especially* unstable, since in it the electronegative nitrogen atom has only a sextet of electrons. As a result, attack at the 4-position (or 2-position) is especially slow, and substitution occurs predominantly at the 3-position.

It is important to see the difference between substitution in pyridine and substitution in pyrrole. In the case of pyrrole a structure in which nitrogen bears a positive charge (see Sec. 32.4) is especially stable since every atom has an octet of electrons; nitrogen accommodates the positive charge simply by sharing four pairs of electrons. In the case of pyridine a structure in which nitrogen bears a positive charge (III) is especially unstable since nitrogen has only a sextet of electrons; nitrogen *shares* electrons readily, but as an electronegative atom it resists the *removal* of electrons.

Problem 32.10 2-Aminopyridine can be nitrated or sulfonated under much milder conditions than pyridine itself; substitution occurs chiefly at the 5-position. Account for these facts.

Problem 32.11 Because of the difficulty of nitrating pyridine, 3-aminopyridine is most conveniently made via nicotinic acid. Outline the synthesis of 3-amino-pyridine from β-picoline.

32.10 Nucleophilic substitution in pyridine

Here, as in electrophilic substitution, the pyridine ring resembles a benzene ring that contains strongly electron-withdrawing groups. Nucleophilic substitution takes place readily, particularly at the 2- and 4-positions. For example:

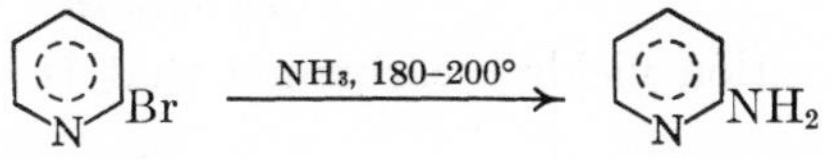

2-Bromopyridine   2-Aminopyridine

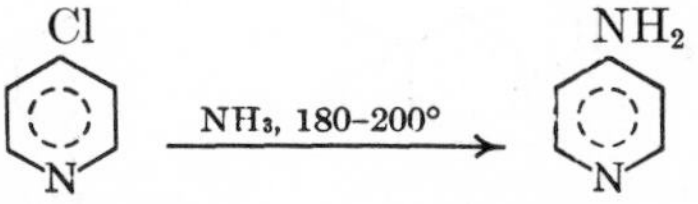

4-Chloropyridine   4-Aminopyridine

The reactivity of pyridine toward nucleophilic substitution is so great that even the powerfully basic hydride ion, $:H^-$, can be displaced. Two important examples of this reaction are amination by sodium amide (**Chichibabin reaction**), and alkylation or arylation by organolithium compounds.

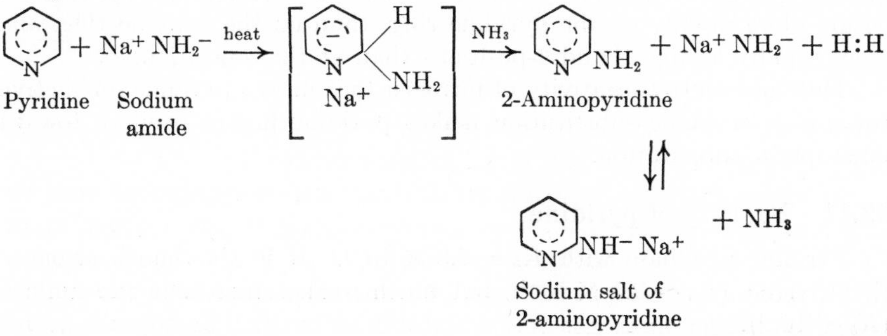

Pyridine   Sodium   2-Aminopyridine
           amide

Sodium salt of
2-aminopyridine

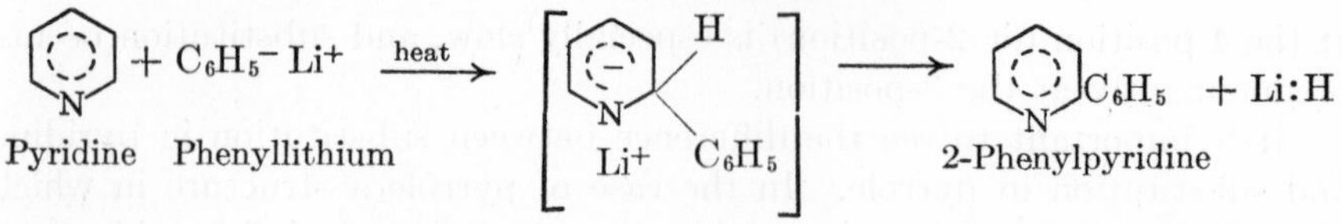

Pyridine   Phenyllithium   2-Phenylpyridine

As we have seen (Sec. 14.11), nucleophilic aromatic substitution is believed to take place by a mechanism that is quite analogous to the mechanism for electrophilic substitution. Reaction proceeds by two steps; the rate of the first step, formation of a charged particle, determines the rate of the over-all reaction. In electrophilic substitution, the intermediate is positively charged; in nucleophilic substitution, the intermediate is negatively charged. The ability of the ring to accommodate the charge determines the stability of the intermediate and of the transition state leading to it, and hence determines the rate of the reaction.

Nucleophilic attack at the 4-position yields a carbanion that is a hybrid of structures I, II, and III;

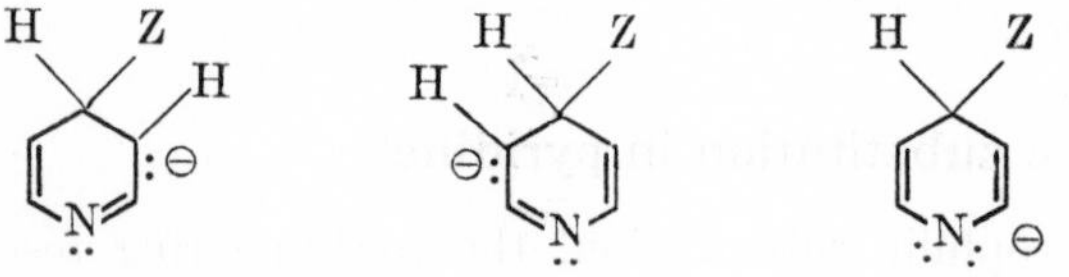

Nucleophilic attack at 4-position

*Especially stable:
negative charge
on nitrogen*

attack at the 3-position yields a carbanion that is a hybrid of structures IV, V, and VI.

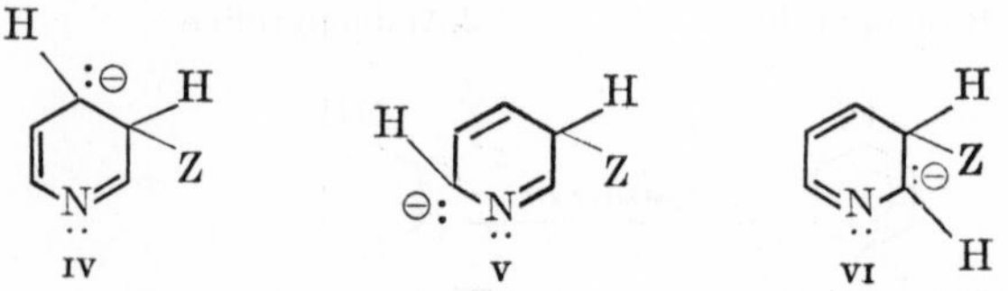

Nucleophilic attack at 3-position

(As before, attack at the 2-position resembles attack at the 4-position.)

All these structures are more stable than the corresponding ones for attack on a benzene derivative, because of electron withdrawal by the nitrogen atom. Structure III is *especially* stable, since the negative charge is located on the atom that can best accommodate it, the electronegative nitrogen atom. It is reasonable, therefore, that nucleophilic substitution occurs more rapidly on the pyridine ring than on the benzene ring, and more rapidly at the 2- and 4-positions than at the 3-position.

The same electronegativity of nitrogen that makes pyridine unreactive toward electrophilic substitution makes pyridine highly reactive toward nucleophilic substitution.

32.11 Basicity of pyridine

Pyridine is a base with $K_b = 2.3 \times 10^{-9}$. It is thus much stronger than pyrrole ($K_b \sim 2.5 \times 10^{-14}$) but much weaker than aliphatic amines ($K_b \sim 10^{-4}$).

Pyridine has a pair of electrons (in an sp^2 orbital) that is available for sharing with acids; pyrrole has not, and can accept an acid only at the expense of the aromatic character of the ring.

The fact that pyridine is a weaker base than aliphatic amines is more difficult to account for, but at least it fits into a pattern. Let us turn for a moment to the basicity of the carbon analogs of amines, the carbanions, and use the approach of Sec. 6.9.

Benzene is a stronger acid than an alkane, as shown by its ability to displace an alkane from its salts; this of course means that the phenyl anion, $C_6H_5^-$, is a weaker base than an alkyl anion, R^-.

$$R:^- Na^+ + C_6H_5:H \quad \rightleftharpoons \quad R:H + C_6H_5:^- Na^+$$

| Stronger base | Stronger acid | | Weaker acid | Weaker base |

In the same way, acetylene is a stronger acid than benzene, and the acetylide ion is a weaker base than the phenyl anion.

$$C_6H_5:^- Na^+ + HC\equiv C:H \quad \rightleftharpoons \quad C_6H_5:H + HC\equiv C:^- Na^+$$

| Stronger base | Stronger acid | | Weaker acid | Weaker base |

Thus we have the following sequences of acidity of hydrocarbons and basicity of their anions:

Relative acidity: $HC\equiv C:H > C_6H_5:H > R:H$

Relative basicity: $HC\equiv C:^- < C_6H_5:^- < R:^-$

A possible explanation for these sequences can be found in the electronic configuration of the carbanions. In the alkyl, phenyl, and acetylide anions the unshared pair of electrons occupies respectively an sp^3, an sp^2, and an sp orbital. The availability of this pair for sharing with acids determines the basicity of the particular anion. As we proceed along the series sp^3, sp^2, sp, the p character of the orbital decreases and the s character increases. Now, an electron in a p orbital is at some distance from the nucleus and is held relatively loosely; an electron in an s orbital, on the other hand, is close to the nucleus and is held more tightly. Of the three anions, the alkyl ion is the strongest base since its pair of electrons is held most loosely, in an sp^3 orbital. The acetylide ion is the weakest base since its pair of electrons is held most tightly, in an sp orbital.

Pyridine bears the same relationship to an aliphatic amine as the phenyl anion bears to an alkyl anion. The pair of electrons that gives pyridine its basicity occupies an sp^2 orbital; it is held more tightly and is less available for sharing with acids than the pair of electrons of an aliphatic amine, which occupies an sp^3 orbital.

Problem 32.12 Predict the relative basicities of amines (RCH_2NH_2), imines ($RCH\!\!=\!\!NH$), and nitriles ($RC\equiv N$).

Pyridine is widely used in organic chemistry as a water-soluble base, as, for example, in the Schotten-Baumann acylation procedure (Sec. 17.7).

Problem 32.13 Ethyl bromosuccinate is converted into the unsaturated ester ethyl fumarate by the action of pyridine. What is the function of the pyridine? What advantage does it have here over the usual alcoholic KOH?

Like other amines, pyridine has nucleophilic properties, and reacts with alkyl halides to form quaternary ammonium salts.

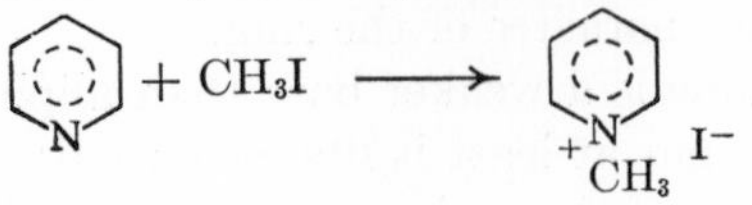

Pyridine   N-Methylpyridinium iodide
                 (Pyridine methiodide)

Problem 32.14   Like any other tertiary amine pyridine can be converted (by peroxybenzoic acid) into its N-oxide.

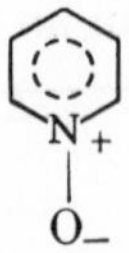

Pyridine N-oxide

In contrast to pyridine itself, pyridine N-oxide readily undergoes nitration chiefly in the 4-position. How do you account for this reactivity and orientation?

Problem 32.15   Pyridine N-oxides not only are reactive toward electrophilic substitution, but also seem to be reactive toward nucleophilic substitution, particularly at the 2- and 4-positions. For example, treatment of 4-nitropyridine N-oxide with hydrobromic acid gives 4-bromopyridine N-oxide. How do you account for this reactivity and orientation?

Problem 32.16   The oxygen of pyridine N-oxide is readily removed by treatment with PCl_3. Suggest a practical route to 4-nitropyridine. To 4-bromopyridine.

32.12   Reduction of pyridine

Catalytic hydrogenation of pyridine yields the aliphatic heterocyclic compound **piperidine**, $C_5H_{11}N$.

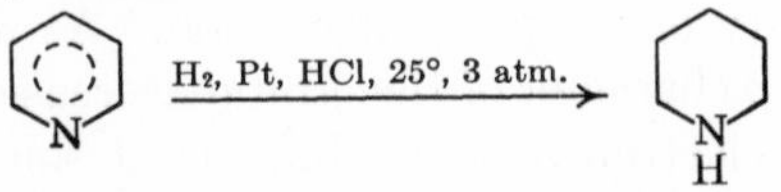

$$\xrightarrow{\text{H}_2,\ \text{Pt, HCl, 25}^\circ,\ 3\ \text{atm.}}$$

Pyridine   Piperidine
$(K_b = 2.3 \times 10^{-9})$ $(K_b = 2 \times 10^{-3})$

Piperidine $(K_b = 2 \times 10^{-3})$ has the usual basicity of a secondary amine. Like pyridine it is often used as a basic catalyst in such reactions as the Knoevenagel (Problem 25.29, page 690) or Michael reaction (Sec. 28.8).

Like the pyrrolidine ring, the piperidine and pyridine rings are found in a number of alkaloids, including *nicotine, strychnine, cocaine,* and *reserpine* (see page 835).

Problem 32.17   Why can piperidine not be used in place of pyridine in the Schotten-Baumann procedure?

FUSED RINGS

32.13   Quinoline. The Skraup synthesis

Quinoline, C_9H_7N, contains a benzene ring and a pyridine ring fused as shown in I.

Quinoline

$(K_b = 3 \times 10^{-10})$

I

In general, its properties are the ones we would expect from what we have learned about pyridine and naphthalene.

Problem 32.18 Account for the following properties of quinoline:

(a) Treatment with nitric and sulfuric acids gives 5- and 8-nitroquinolines; treatment with fuming sulfuric acid gives 5- and 8-quinolinesulfonic acids.

(b) Oxidation by $KMnO_4$ gives 2,3-pyridinedicarboxylic acid (*quinolinic acid*).

(c) Treatment with sodamide gives 2-aminoquinoline; treatment with alkyllithium compounds gives 2-alkylquinolines.

Problem 32.19 *8-Hydroxyquinoline* (8-quinolinol) is an important reagent in inorganic analysis. Suggest a method of synthesizing it.

Quinoline is found in coal tar. Although certain derivatives of quinoline can be made from quinoline itself by substitution, most are prepared from benzene derivatives by ring closure.

Perhaps the most generally useful method for preparing substituted quinolines is the **Skraup synthesis.** In the simplest example, quinoline itself is obtained from the reaction of aniline with glycerol, concentrated sulfuric acid, nitrobenzene, and ferrous sulfate.

$$
\underset{\text{Aniline}}{\text{C}_6\text{H}_5\text{NH}_2} + \underset{\text{Glycerol}}{\begin{array}{c}\text{CH}_2\text{OH}\\|\\\text{CHOH}\\|\\\text{CH}_2\text{OH}\end{array}} + \underset{\text{Nitrobenzene}}{\text{C}_6\text{H}_5\text{NO}_2} \xrightarrow[\text{heat}]{\text{H}_2\text{SO}_4,\ \text{FeSO}_4,} \underset{\text{Quinoline}}{\text{ }} + \text{C}_6\text{H}_5\text{NH}_2 + \text{H}_2\text{O}
$$

The following steps seem to be involved:

(1) Dehydration of glycerol by hot sulfuric acid to yield the unsaturated aldehyde acrolein:

$$
\underset{\text{Glycerol}}{\begin{array}{c}\text{CH}_2-\text{CH}-\text{CH}_2\\|\quad\ \ |\quad\ \ |\\\text{OH}\ \ \text{OH}\ \ \text{OH}\end{array}} \xrightarrow{\text{H}_2\text{SO}_4,\ \text{heat}} \underset{\text{Acrolein}}{\text{CH}_2\text{=}\text{CH}-\text{CHO}} + 2\text{H}_2\text{O}
$$

(2) Nucleophilic addition of aniline to acrolein to yield β-(phenylamino)-propionaldehyde:

$$
\underset{\text{Aniline}}{\text{C}_6\text{H}_5\text{NH}_2} + \underset{\text{Acrolein}}{\begin{array}{c}\text{H}\quad\ \ \text{O}\\\diagdown\quad\diagup\ \\\text{C}\\\diagdown\ \\\text{CH}\\||\\\text{CH}_2\end{array}} \longrightarrow \underset{\beta\text{-(Phenylamino)propionaldehyde}}{\begin{array}{c}\text{H}\quad\ \ \text{O}\\\diagdown\quad\diagup\ \\\text{C}\\\diagdown\ \\\text{CH}_2\\|\\\text{CH}_2\\\diagup\\\text{N}\\|\\\text{H}\end{array}}
$$

(3) Electrophilic attack on the aromatic ring by the electron-deficient carbonyl carbon of the protonated aldehyde (this is the actual ring-closing step):

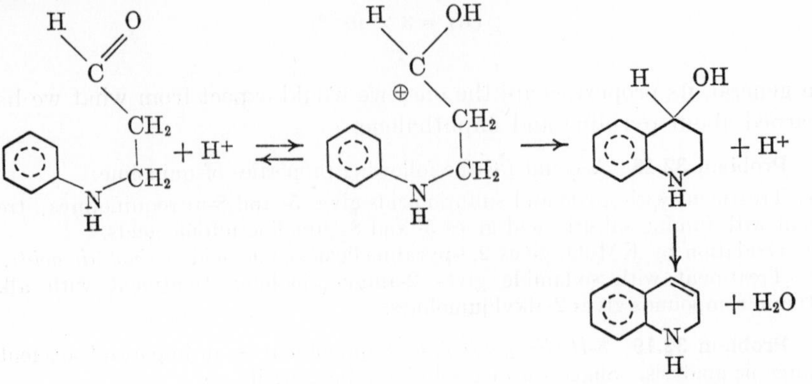

1,2-Dihydroquinoline

(4) Oxidation by nitrobenzene resulting in the aromatization of the newly formed ring:

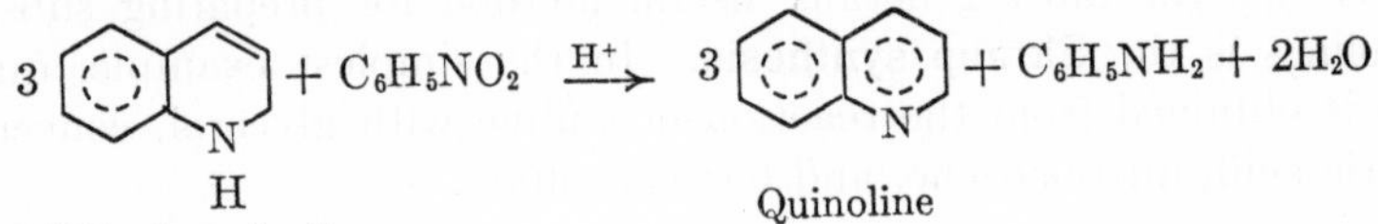

1,2-Dihydroquinoline   Quinoline

Ferrous sulfate in some way moderates the otherwise very vigorous reaction.

Thus we see that what at first appears to be a complicated reaction is actually a sequence of simple steps involving familiar, fundamental types of reaction: acid-catalyzed dehydration, nucleophilic addition to an α,β-unsaturated carbonyl compound, electrophilic aromatic substitution, and oxidation.

The components of the basic synthesis can be modified to yield a wide variety of quinoline derivatives. For example:

aniline + crotonaldehyde ⟶ 2-methylquinoline (quinaldine)

3-nitro-4-aminoanisole + glycerol ⟶ 6-methoxy-8-nitroquinoline

2-aminonaphthalene + glycerol ⟶

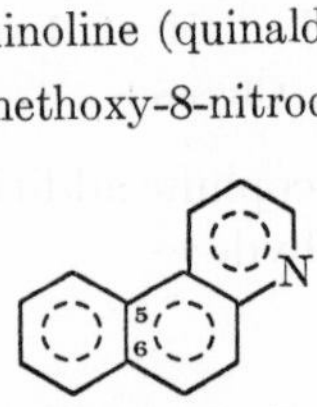

5,6-Benzoquinoline
(1-Azaphenanthrene)

Nitrobenzene is often replaced as oxidizing agent by arsenic acid, H_3AsO_4, which usually gives a less violent reaction; vanadium pentoxide is sometimes added as a catalyst. Sulfuric acid can be replaced by phosphoric acid or other acids.

Problem 32.20 Show all steps in the Skraup syntheses mentioned above.

Problem 32.21 The dehydration of glycerol to yield acrolein involves acid-catalyzed dehydration and keto-enol tautomerization. Outline the possible steps in the dehydration. (*Hint:* which —OH is easier to eliminate, a primary or a secondary?)

Problem 32.22 What is the product of the application of the Skraup synthesis to *o*-nitroaniline, *o*-aminophenol, *o*-phenylenediamine, *m*-phenylenediamine, *p*-toluidine.

Problem 32.23 Outline the synthesis of 6-bromoquinoline. Of 8-methyl-quinoline.

Problem 32.24 In the **Doebner-von Miller** modification of the Skraup synthesis, aldehydes, ketones, or mixtures of aldehydes and ketones replace the glycerol. If acetaldehyde is used, for example, the product from aniline is 2-methylquinoline (*quinaldine*). (a) Account for its formation. (b) Predict the product if methyl vinyl ketone were used. (c) If a mixture of benzaldehyde and pyruvic acid, $CH_3COCOOH$, were used.

Problem 32.25 Account for the formation of 2,4-dimethylquinoline from aniline and acetylacetone (2,4-pentanedione) by the Doebner-von Miller synthesis. (*Hint:* see Sec. 26.7.)

32.14 Isoquinoline. The Bischler-Napieralski synthesis

Isoquinoline, C_9H_7N, contains a benzene ring and a pyridine ring fused as shown in I:

Isoquinoline
$(K_b = 1.1 \times 10^{-9})$

I

Isoquinoline, like quinoline, has the properties we would expect from what we know about pyridine and naphthalene.

Problem 32.26 Account for the following properties of isoquinoline. (*Hint:* review orientation in β-substituted naphthalenes, Sec. 31.13.)

(a) Nitration gives 5-nitroisoquinoline.

(b) Treatment with potassium amide, KNH_2, gives 1-aminoisoquinoline, and treatment with alkyllithium compounds gives 1-alkylisoquinolines; the 3-substituted products are not obtained.

(c) 1-Methylisoquinoline reacts with benzaldehyde to yield compound II, whereas 3-methylisoquinoline undergoes no reaction. (*Hint:* see Problem 23.27(c), page 642.

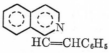

HC=CHC₆H₅

II

An important method for making derivatives of isoquinoline is the **Bischler-Napieralski synthesis.** Acyl derivatives of β-phenylethylamine are cyclized by treatment with acids (often P_2O_5) to yield dihydroisoquinolines, which can then be aromatized, as shown on the next page.

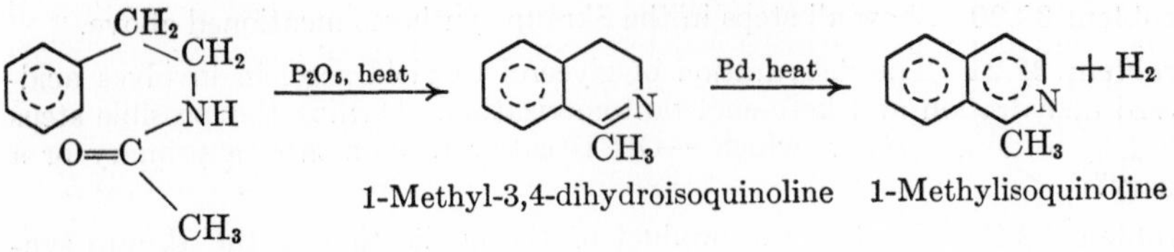

1-Methyl-3,4-dihydroisoquinoline　　1-Methylisoquinoline

N-(2-phenylethyl)acetamide

Problem 32.27　To what general class of reactions does the ring closure belong? What is the function of the acid? (Check your answers in Sec. 22.21.)

Problem 32.28　Outline the synthesis of N-(2-phenylethyl)acetamide from toluene and aliphatic and inorganic reagents.

PROBLEMS

1. Give structures and names of the principal products from the reaction (if any) of pyridine with:

(a) Br_2, 300°

(b) H_2SO_4, 350°

(c) acetyl chloride, $AlCl_3$

(d) KNO_3, H_2SO_4, 300°

(e) $NaNH_2$, heat

(f) C_6H_5Li

(g) dilute HCl

(h) dilute NaOH

(i) acetic anhydride

(j) benzenesulfonyl chloride

(k) ethyl bromide

(l) benzyl chloride

(m) peroxybenzoic acid

(n) peroxybenzoic acid, then HNO_3, H_2SO_4

(o) H_2, Pt

2. Give structures and names of the principal products from each of the following reactions:

(a) thiophene + conc. H_2SO_4

(b) thiophene + acetic anhydride, $ZnCl_2$

(c) thiophene + acetyl chloride, $TiCl_4$

(d) thiophene + fuming nitric acid in acetic anhydride

(e) product of (d) + Sn, HCl

(f) thiophene + one mole Br_2

(g) product of (f) + Mg; then CO_2; then H^+

(h) pyrrole + pyridine:SO_3

(i) pyrrole + diazotized sulfanilic acid

(j) product of (i) + $SnCl_2$

(k) pyrrole + H_2, Ni ⟶ C_4H_9N

(l) furfural + acetone + base

(m) quinoline + HNO_3/H_2SO_4

(n) quinoline N-oxide + HNO_3/H_2SO_4

(o) isoquinoline + n-butyllithium

3. Pyrrole can be reduced by zinc and acetic acid to a *pyrroline*, C_4H_7N. (a) What structures are possible for this pyrroline?

(b) On the basis of the following evidence which structure must the pyrroline have?

pyrroline + O_3; then H_2O; then H_2O_2 ⟶ A $(C_4H_7O_4N)$

chloroacetic acid + NH_3 ⟶ B $(C_2H_5O_2N)$

B + chloroacetic acid ⟶ A

4. Furan and its derivatives are sensitive to protic acids. The following reactions illustrate what happens.

2,5-dimethylfuran + dilute H_2SO_4 ⟶ C $(C_6H_{10}O_2)$

C + NaOI ⟶ succinic acid

(a) What is C? (b) Outline a likely series of steps for its formation from 2,5-dimethylfuran.

5. Pyrrole reacts with formaldehyde in hot pyridine to yield a mixture of products from which there can be isolated a small amount of a compound of formula $(C_5H_5N)_4$. Suggest a possible structure for this compound. (*Hint:* see Sec. 22.21 and page 836.)

6. There are three isomeric pyridinecarboxylic acids, $(C_5H_4N)COOH$: D, m.p. 137°; E, m.p. 234–7°; and F, m.p. 317°. Their structures were proved as follows:

quinoline + KMnO$_4$, OH⁻ $\longrightarrow$ a diacid $(C_7H_5O_4N)$ $\xrightarrow{\text{heat}}$ E, m.p. 234–7°
isoquinoline + KMnO$_4$, OH⁻ $\longrightarrow$ a diacid $(C_7H_5O_4N)$ $\xrightarrow{\text{heat}}$ E, m.p. 234–7° and F, m.p. 317°

What structures should be assigned to D, E, and F?

7. (a) What structures are possible for G?
m-toluidine + glycerol $\xrightarrow{\text{Skraup}}$ G $(C_{10}H_9N)$

(b) On the basis of the following evidence which structure must G actually have?
2,3-diaminotoluene + glycerol $\xrightarrow{\text{Skraup}}$ H $(C_{10}H_{10}N_2)$
H + NaNO$_2$, HCl; then H$_3$PO$_2$ $\longrightarrow$ G

8. Outline all steps in a possible synthesis of each of the following from benzene, toluene, and any needed aliphatic and inorganic reagents:

(a) 1-phenylisoquinoline
(b) 1-benzylisoquinoline
(c) 1,5-dimethylisoquinoline
(d) 6-nitroquinoline

(e) 2-methyl-6-quinolinecarboxylic acid
(f) 1,8-diazaphenanthrene (*Hint:* use the Skraup synthesis twice.)

1,8-Diazaphenanthrene

9. Outline all steps in each of the following syntheses, using any other needed reagents:

(a) β-cyanopyridine from β-picoline
(b) 2-methylpiperidine from pyridine
(c) 5-aminoquinoline from quinoline
(d) ethyl 5-nitro-2-furoate from furfural

(e) furylacrylic acid, —CH=CHCOOH, from furfural

(f) 1,2,5-trichloropentane from furfural
(g) 3-indolecarboxaldehyde from indole

10. Give the structures of compounds I through GG formed in the following syntheses of heterocyclic systems.

(a) ethyl malonate + urea, base, heat $\longrightarrow$ I $(C_4H_4O_3N_2)$, a *pyrimidine* (1,3-diazine)
(b) acetonylacetone + H$_2$N—NH$_2$ $\longrightarrow$ J $(C_6H_{10}N_2)$
    J + air $\longrightarrow$ K $(C_6H_8N_2)$, a *pyridazine* (1,2-diazine)
(c) acetylacetone + H$_2$N—NH$_2$ $\longrightarrow$ L $(C_5H_8N_2)$, a *pyrazole*
(d) 2,3-butanedione + *o*-C$_6$H$_4$(NH$_2$)$_2$ $\longrightarrow$ M $(C_{10}H_{10}N_2)$, a *quinoxaline*
(e) ethylene glycol + phosgene $\longrightarrow$ N $(C_3H_4O_3)$, a *1,3-dioxolanone*
(f) anthranilic acid + chloroacetic acid $\longrightarrow$ O $(C_9H_9O_4N)$
    O + base, strong heat $\longrightarrow$ P (C_8H_7ON), *indoxyl*, an intermediate in the synthesis of indigo
(g) aminoacetone $\longrightarrow$ Q $(C_6H_{10}N_2)$
    Q + air $\longrightarrow$ R $(C_6H_8N_2)$, a *pyrazine* (1,4-diazine)

(h) ethylenediamine + ethyl carbonate   ⟶   S ($C_3H_6ON_2$), an *imidazolidone*

(i) o-$C_6H_4(NH_2)_2$ + acetic acid, strong heat   ⟶   T ($C_8H_8N_2$), a *benzimidazole*

(j) ethyl o-aminobenzoate + malonic ester   ⟶   U ($C_{14}H_{17}O_5N$), insoluble in dilute acid

U $\xrightarrow{\text{NaOC}_2\text{H}_5}$ V ($C_{12}H_{11}O_4N$)

V + acid, warm   ⟶   W ($C_9H_7O_2N$), a *quinoline*

(k) repeat (j) starting with ethyl 3-amino-2-pyridinecarboxylate   ⟶   a *1,5-diazanaphthalene*

(l) benzalacetophenone + KCN + acetic acid   ⟶   X ($C_{16}H_{13}ON$)

X + CH_3OH, H^+, H_2O ⟶   Y ($C_{17}H_{16}O_3$) + NH_4^+

Y + phenylhydrazine   ⟶   Z ($C_{22}H_{18}ON_2$), a *dihydro-1,2-diazine*

(m) acrylic acid + H_2N—NH_2 ⟶   AA ($C_3H_8O_2N_2$)   ⟶   BB ($C_3H_6ON_2$), a *pyrazolidone*

(n) o-$C_6H_4(NH_2)_2$ + glycerol $\xrightarrow{\text{Skraup}}$ CC ($C_{12}H_8N_2$), a *4,5-diazaphenanthrene*

(o) di(o-nitrophenyl)acetylene + Br_2 ⟶   DD ($C_{14}H_8O_4N_2Br_2$)

DD + Sn, HCl   ⟶   EE ($C_{14}H_{12}N_2Br_2$)

EE $\xrightarrow{\text{warm}}$ [FF ($C_{14}H_{11}N_2Br$)]   ⟶   GG ($C_{14}H_{10}N_2$), which contains four fused aromatic rings

11. The structure of *papaverine*, $C_{20}H_{21}O_4N$, one of the opium alkaloids, has been established by the following synthesis:

3,4-dimethoxybenzyl chloride + KCN   ⟶   HH ($C_{10}H_{11}O_2N$)

HH + hydrogen, Ni   ⟶   II ($C_{10}H_{15}O_2N$)

HH + aqueous acid, heat   ⟶   JJ $\xrightarrow{\text{PCl}_5}$ KK ($C_{10}H_{11}O_3Cl$)

II + KK   ⟶   LL ($C_{20}H_{25}O_5N$)

LL + P_2O_5, heat   ⟶   MM ($C_{20}H_{23}O_4N$)

MM + Pd, 200°   ⟶   papaverine

12. *Plasmochin* (also called *Pamaquine*), a drug effective against malaria, has been synthesized as follows:

ethylene oxide + diethylamine   ⟶   NN ($C_6H_{15}ON$)

NN + $SOCl_2$ ⟶   OO ($C_6H_{14}NCl$)

OO + sodioacetoacetic ester   ⟶   PP ($C_{12}H_{23}O_3N$)

PP + dilute H_2SO_4, warm   ⟶   QQ ($C_9H_{19}ON$) + CO_2 + C_2H_5OH

QQ + H_2, Ni   ⟶   RR ($C_9H_{21}ON$)

RR + conc. HBr   ⟶   SS ($C_9H_{20}NBr$)

4-amino-3-nitroanisole + glycerol $\xrightarrow{\text{Skraup}}$ TT ($C_{10}H_8O_3N_2$)

TT + Sn + HCl   ⟶   UU ($C_{10}H_{10}ON_2$)

SS + UU   ⟶   Plasmochin ($C_{19}H_{29}ON_3$)

What is the most likely structure of Plasmochin?

13. (−)-*Nicotine*, the alkaloid in tobacco, can be synthesized in the following way:

nicotinic acid + $SOCl_2$, heat   ⟶   nicotinoyl chloride (C_6H_4ONCl)

nicotinoyl chloride + $C_2H_5OCH_2CH_2CH_2CdCl$ ⟶   VV ($C_{11}H_{15}O_2N$)

VV + NH_3, H_2, catalyst   ⟶   WW ($C_{11}H_{18}ON_2$)

WW + HBr + strong heat   ⟶   XX ($C_9H_{12}N_2$) + ethyl bromide

XX + CH_3I, NaOH   ⟶   (±)-nicotine ($C_{10}H_{14}N_2$)

(±)-nicotine + (+)-tartaric acid   ⟶   YY and ZZ (both $C_{14}H_{20}O_6N_2$)

YY + NaOH   ⟶   (−)-nicotine + sodium tartrate

What is the structure of (±)-nicotine? Write equations for all the above reactions.

14. The red and blue colors of many flowers and fruits are due to the *antho-cyanins*, glycosides of pyrylium salts. The parent structure of the pyrylium salts is *flavylium chloride*, which can be synthesized as follows:

salicylaldehyde + acetophenone $\xrightarrow{\text{aldol}}$ AAA ($C_{15}H_{12}O_2$)

AAA + HCl   ⟶   flavylium chloride, a salt containing **three aromatic rings**

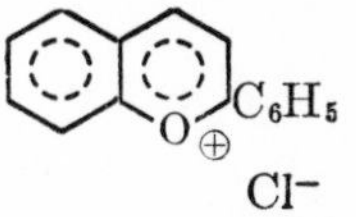

Flavylium chloride

(a) What is the structure of AAA? (b) Outline a likely series of steps leading from AAA to flavylium chloride. (c) Account for the aromatic character of the fused ring system.

15. *Tropinic acid*, $C_8H_{13}O_4N$, is a degradation product of atropine, an alkaloid of the deadly nightshade, *Atropa belladonna*. It has a neutralization equivalent of 94 ± 1. It does not react with benzenesulfonyl chloride, cold dilute $KMnO_4$, or Br_2/CCl_4. Exhaustive methylation gives the following results:

tropinic acid + CH_3I $\longrightarrow$ BBB ($C_9H_{16}O_4NI$)
BBB + Ag_2O, then strong heat $\longrightarrow$ CCC ($C_9H_{15}O_4N$)
CCC + CH_3I $\longrightarrow$ DDD ($C_{10}H_{18}O_4NI$)
DDD + Ag_2O, then strong heat $\longrightarrow$ EEE ($C_7H_8O_4$) + $(CH_3)_3N$ + H_2O
EEE + H_2, Ni $\longrightarrow$ heptanedioic acid (pimelic acid)

(a) What structures are likely for tropinic acid?
(b) Tropinic acid is formed by oxidation with CrO_3 of *tropinone*, whose structur has been shown by synthesis to be

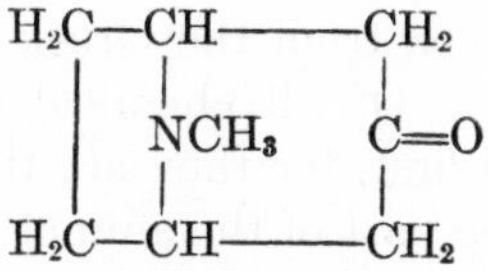

$$
\begin{array}{ccc}
H_2C\text{—}CH & \text{———} & CH_2 \\
| & & | \\
& NCH_3 & C{=}O \\
| & & | \\
H_2C\text{—}CH & \text{———} & CH_2
\end{array}
$$

Tropinone

Now what is the most likely structure for tropinic acid?

16. *Tropilidene*, 1,3,5-cycloheptatriene, has been made from tropinone (see Problem 15). Show how this might have been done. (*Hint:* see Problem 19, page 568.)

17. *Arecaidine*, $C_7H_{11}O_2N$, an alkaloid of betel nut, has been synthesized in the following way:

ethyl acrylate + NH_3 $\xrightarrow{\text{Michael}}$ FFF ($C_5H_{11}O_2N$)
FFF + ethyl acrylate $\xrightarrow{\text{Michael}}$ GGG ($C_{10}H_{19}O_4N$)
GGG + sodium ethoxide $\xrightarrow{\text{Dieckmann}}$ HHH ($C_8H_{13}O_3N$)
HHH + benzoyl chloride $\longrightarrow$ III ($C_{15}H_{17}O_4N$)
III + H_2, Ni $\longrightarrow$ JJJ ($C_{15}H_{19}O_4N$)
JJJ + acid, heat $\longrightarrow$ KKK ($C_6H_9O_2N$), *guvacine*, another betel nut alkaloid + C_6H_5COOH + C_2H_5OH
KKK + CH_3I $\longrightarrow$ arecaidine ($C_7H_{11}O_2N$)

(a) What is the most likely structure of arecaidine? Of guvacine?
(b) What will guvacine give upon dehydrogenation?

18. (a) Account for the aromatic properties of the imidazole ring.

(b) Arrange the nitrogen atoms of *histamine* (the substance responsible for many allergenic reactions) in order of their expected basicity, and account for your answer.

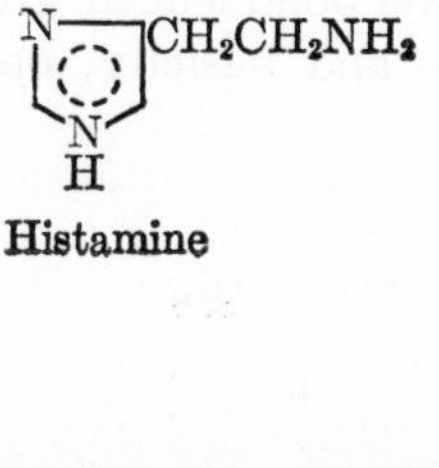

Histamine

Chapter thirty-three _____

AMINO ACIDS AND
PROTEINS

33.1 Introduction

The name **protein** is taken from the Greek *proteios*, which means *first*. This name is well chosen. Of all chemical compounds, proteins must almost certainly be ranked first, for they are the substance of life.

Proteins make up a large part of the animal body, they hold it together, and they run it. They are found in all living cells. They are the principal material of skin, muscle, tendons, nerves, and blood; of enzymes, antibodies, and many hormones.

(Only the nucleic acids, which control heredity, can challenge the position of proteins; and the nucleic acids are important because they direct the synthesis of proteins.)

Chemically, proteins are high polymers. They are polyamides, and the monomers from which they are derived are the α-amino carboxylic acids. A single protein molecule contains hundreds or even thousands of amino acid units; these units can be of twenty-six or more different kinds. The number of different combinations, that is, the number of different protein molecules that are possible, is almost infinite. It is likely that tens of thousands of different proteins are required to make up and run an animal body; and this set of proteins is not identical with the set required by an animal of a different kind.

In this chapter we shall look first at the chemistry of the amino acids, and then briefly at the proteins that they make up. Our chief purpose will be to see the ways in which the structures of these enormously complicated molecules are being worked out, and how, in the last analysis, all this work rests on the basic principles of organic structural theory: on the concepts of bond angle and bond length, group size and shape, hydrogen bonding, resonance, acidity and basicity, optical activity, configuration and conformation.

33.2 Structure of amino acids

Table 33.1 gives the structures and names of twenty-six amino acids that have been found in proteins. Certain of these (marked *e*) are the *essential* amino acids, which must be fed to young animals if proper growth is to take place; these particular amino acids evidently cannot be synthesized by the animal from the other materials in its diet.

We see that all are *alpha*-amino carboxylic acids; in two cases (proline and hydroxyproline) the amino group forms part of a pyrrolidine ring. This common feature gives the amino acids a common set of chemical properties, one of which is the ability to form the long polyamide chains that make up proteins. It is on these common chemical properties that we shall concentrate.

In other respects the structures of these compounds vary rather widely. In addition to the carboxyl group and the amino group *alpha* to it, some amino acids contain a second carboxyl group (e.g., aspartic acid or glutamic acid), or a potential carboxyl group in the form of a carboxamide (e.g., asparagine); these are called *acidic amino acids*. Some contain a second basic group, which may be an amino group (e.g., lysine), a guanidino group (arginine), or the imidazole ring (histidine); these are called *basic amino acids*. Some of the amino acids contain benzene or heterocyclic ring

TABLE 33.1

NATURAL AMINO ACIDS

Name	Abbreviation	Formula
(+)-Alanine	Ala	CH_3CHCOO^- $^+NH_3$
(+)-Arginine[e]	Arg	$H_2NCNHCH_2CH_2CH_2CHCOO^-$ $\parallel \qquad\qquad\qquad\quad NH_2$ $^+NH_2$
(−)-Asparagine	Asp(NH₂)	$H_2NCOCH_2CHCOO^-$ $^+NH_3$
(+)-Aspartic acid	Asp	$HOOCCH_2CHCOO^-$ $^+NH_3$
(−)-Cysteine	CySH	$HSCH_2CHCOO^-$ $^+NH_3$
(−)-Cystine	CyS–SCy	$^-OOCCHCH_2S-SCH_2CHCOO^-$ $^+NH_3 \qquad\qquad\qquad ^+NH_3$
(+)-3,5-Dibromotyrosine		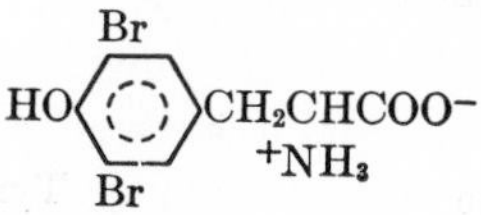 $\overset{Br}{\underset{Br}{HO\langle \bigcirc \rangle}}CH_2CHCOO^-$ $^+NH_3$
(+)-3,5-Diiodotyrosine		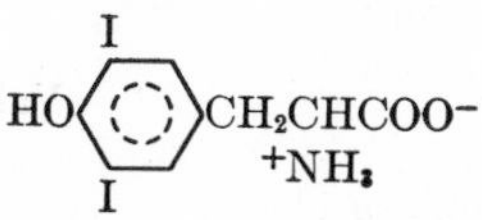 $\overset{I}{\underset{I}{HO\langle \bigcirc \rangle}}CH_2CHCOO^-$ $^+NH_3$

(+)-Glutamic acid	Glu	$HOOCCH_2CH_2CHCOO^-$ $\quad\quad\quad\quad\quad\;\; ^+NH_3$
(+)-Glutamine	Glu(NH₂)	$H_2NCOCH_2CH_2CHCOO^-$ $\quad\quad\quad\quad\quad\quad\;\; ^+NH_3$
Glycine	Gly	CH_2COO^- $^+NH_3$
(−)-Histidine[e]	His	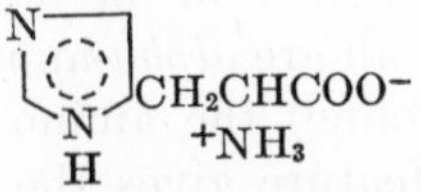 CH_2CHCOO^- $\quad\quad\quad\quad\; ^+NH_3$
(−)-Hydroxylysine	Hylys	$^+H_3NCH_2CHCH_2CH_2CHCOO^-$ $\quad\quad\quad\quad OH \quad\quad\quad NH_2$
(−)-Hydroxyproline	Hypro	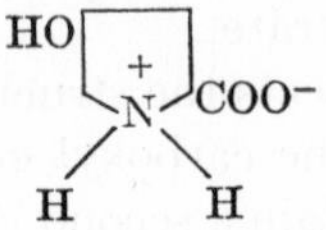
(+)-Isoleucine[e]	Ileu	$CH_3CH_2CH(CH_3)CHCOO^-$ $\quad\quad\quad\quad\quad\quad\quad ^+NH_3$
(−)-Leucine[e]	Leu	$(CH_3)_2CHCH_2CHCOO^-$ $\quad\quad\quad\quad\quad\quad ^+NH_3$
(+)-Lysine[e]	Lys	$^+H_3NCH_2CH_2CH_2CH_2CHCOO^-$ $\quad\quad\quad\quad\quad\quad\quad\quad NH_2$
(−)-Methionine[e]	Met	$CH_3SCH_2CH_2CHCOO^-$ $\quad\quad\quad\quad\quad ^+NH_3$
(−)-Phenylalanine[e]	Phe	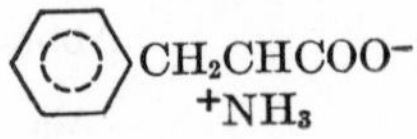 CH_2CHCOO^- $\quad\quad\quad\quad\; ^+NH_3$
(−)-Proline	Pro	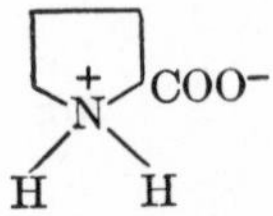
(−)-Serine	Ser	$HOCH_2CHCOO^-$ $\quad\quad\quad\; ^+NH_3$
(−)-Threonine[e],	Thr	$CH_3CHOHCHCOO^-$ $\quad\quad\quad\quad\; ^+NH_3$
(+)-Thyroxine		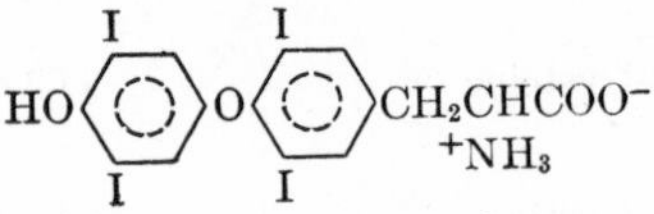
(−)-Tryptohane[e]	Try	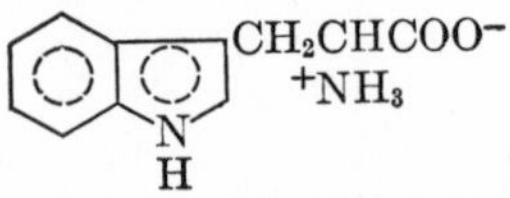
(−)-Tyrosine	Tyr	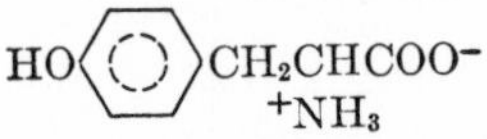 CH_2CHCOO^- $\quad\quad\quad\quad\; ^+NH_3$
(+)-Valine[e]	Val	$(CH_3)_2CHCHCOO^-$ $\quad\quad\quad\quad\; ^+NH_3$

[e]Essential amino acid

systems, phenolic or alcoholic hydroxyl groups, halogen or sulfur atoms. Each of these ring systems or functional groups undergoes its own typical set of reactions.

33.3 Amino acids as dipolar ions

Although the amino acids are commonly shown as containing an amino group and a carboxyl group, $H_2NCHRCOOH$, certain properties, both physical and chemical, are not consistent with this structure:

(a) In contrast to amines and carboxylic acids, the amino acids are non-volatile crystalline solids which melt with decomposition at fairly high temperatures.

(b) They are insoluble in non-polar solvents like petroleum ether, benzene, or ether, and are appreciably soluble in water.

(c) Their aqueous solutions behave like solutions of substances of high dipole moment.

(d) Acidity and basicity constants are ridiculously low for —COOH and —NH_2 groups. Glycine, for example, has $K_a = 1.6 \times 10^{-10}$ and $K_b = 2.5 \times 10^{-12}$, whereas most carboxylic acids have K_a's of about 10^{-5} and most aliphatic amines have K_b's of about 10^{-4}.

All these properties are quite consistent with a dipolar ion structure for the amino acids (I).

$$^+H_3N\text{—}CHR\text{—}COO^-$$

I

Amino acids: dipolar ions

The physical properties — melting point, solubility, high dipole moment — are just what would be expected of such a salt. The acid-base properties also become reasonable when it is realized that the measured K_a actually refers to the acidity of an ammonium ion, RNH_3^+,

$$^+H_3NCHRCOO^- + H_2O \;\rightleftharpoons\; H_3O^+ + H_2NCHRCOO^-$$
Acid

$$K_a = \frac{[H_3O^+][H_2NCHRCOO^-]}{[^+H_3NCHRCOO^-]}$$

and K_b actually refers to the basicity of a carboxylate ion, $RCOO^-$.

$$H_3NCHRCOO^- + H_2O \;\rightleftharpoons\; H_3NCHRCOOH + OH^-$$
Base

$$K_b = \frac{[^+H_3NCHRCOOH][OH^-]}{[^+H_3NCH_2COO^-]}$$

In aqueous solution, the acidity and basicity of an acid and its conjugate base (CH_3COOH and CH_3COO^-, or $CH_3NH_3^+$ and CH_3NH_2, for example) are related by the expression $K_a \times K_b = 10^{-14}$. From this it can be calculated that a K_a of 1.6×10^{-10} for the —NH_3^+ of glycine means $K_b = 6.3 \times 10^{-5}$ for —NH_2: a quite reasonable value for an aliphatic amine. In the same way, a K_b of 2.5×10^{-12} for the —COO^- of glycine means $K_a = 4 \times 10^{-3}$ for —COOH: a quite reasonable value for a carboxylic acid containing the strongly electron-withdrawing (acid-strengthening) —NH_3^+ group.

When the solution of an amino acid is made alkaline, the dipolar ion I is converted into the anion II; the stronger base, hydroxide ion, removes a proton from the ammonium ion and displaces the weaker base, the amine.

$$^+H_3NCHRCOO^- + OH^- \rightleftarrows H_2NCHRCOO^- + H_2O$$

I		II	
Stronger	Stronger	Weaker	Weaker
acid	base	base	acid

When the solution of an amino acid is made acidic, the dipolar ion I is converted into the cation III; the stronger acid, H_3O^+, gives up a proton to the carboxylate ion, and displaces the weaker carboxylic acid.

$$^+H_3NCHRCOO^- + H_3O^+ \rightleftarrows {}^+H_3NCHRCOOH + H_2O$$

I		III	
Stronger	Stronger	Weaker	Weaker
base	acid	acid	base

In summary, the acidic group of a simple amino acid like glycine is —NH_3^+ not —COOH, and the basic group is —COO^- not —NH_2.

Problem 33.1 In quite alkaline solution, an amino acid contains two basic groups, —NH_2 and —COO^-. Which is the more basic? To which group will a proton preferentially go as acid is added to the solution? What will the product be?

Problem 33.2 In quite acidic solution, an amino acid contains two acidic groups, —NH_3^+ and —COOH. Which is the more acidic? Which group will more readily give up a proton as base is added to the solution? What will the product be?

Problem 33.3 Account for the fact that p-aminobenzoic acid or o-amino-benzoic acid (*anthranilic acid*) does not exist appreciably as the dipolar ion, but p-aminobenzenesulfonic acid (*sulfanilic acid*) does. (*Hint:* what is K_b for most aromatic amines?)

We must keep in mind that ions II and III, which contain a free —NH_2 or —COOH group, are in equilibrium with dipolar ion I; consequently amino acids undergo reactions characteristic of amines and carboxylic acids. As ion II is removed, by reaction with benzoyl chloride for example, the equilibrium shifts to supply more of ion II so that eventually the amino acid is completely benzoylated.

$$H_2NCHRCOO^- \underset{OH^-}{\overset{H^+}{\rightleftarrows}} {}^+H_3NCHRCOO^- \underset{OH^-}{\overset{H^+}{\rightleftarrows}} {}^+H_3NCHRCOOH$$

II	I	III

Where feasible we can speed up a desired reaction by adjusting the acidity or basicity of the solution in such a way as to increase the concentration of the reactive species.

Problem 33.4 Suggest a way to speed up esterification of an amino acid; acylation of an amino acid.

33.4 Isoelectric point of amino acids

What happens when a solution of an amino acid is placed in an electric field depends upon the acidity or basicity of the solution.

$$H_2NCHRCOO^- \underset{OH^-}{\overset{H^+}{\rightleftarrows}} {}^+H_3NCHRCOO^- \underset{OH^-}{\overset{H^+}{\rightleftarrows}} {}^+H_3NCHRCOOH$$

II	I	III

In quite alkaline solution, anions II exceed cations III, and there is a net migration of amino acid toward the anode. In quite acidic solution, cations III are in excess, and there is a net migration of amino acid toward the cathode. If II and III are exactly balanced there is no net migration; under such conditions any one molecule exists as a positive ion and as a negative ion for exactly the same amount of time, and any small movement in the direction of one electrode is subsequently canceled by an equal movement back toward the other electrode. The hydrogen ion concentration of the solution in which a particular amino acid does not migrate under the influence of an electric field is called the **isoelectric point** of that amino acid.

A monoamino monocarboxylic acid, $^+H_3NCHRCOO^-$, is somewhat more acidic than basic (for example, glycine: $K_a = 1.6 \times 10^{-10}$ and $K_b = 2.5 \times 10^{-12}$). If crystals of such an amino acid are added to water, the resulting solution contains more of the anion II, $H_2NCHRCOO^-$, than of the cation III, $^+H_3NCHRCOOH$. This "excess" ionization of ammonium ion to amine (I $\rightleftarrows$ II + H$^+$) must be repressed, by addition of acid, to reach the isoelectric point, which therefore lies somewhat on the acid side of neutrality (pH 7). For glycine, for example, the isoelectric point is at pH 6.1.

Problem 33.5 (a) Will the isoelectric point be on the acid or alkaline side of pH 7 (neutrality) for a monoamino dicarboxylic acid? (b) For a diamino monocarboxylic acid? (c) Compare each of these isoelectric points with that for glycine.

An amino acid usually shows its lowest solubility in a solution at the isoelectric point, since here there is the highest concentration of the dipolar ion. As the solution is made more alkaline or more acidic the concentration of one of the more soluble ions, II or III, increases.

Problem 33.6 Account for the fact that sulfanilic acid dissolves in alkalies but not in acids.

Problem 33.7 Suggest a way to separate a mixture of amino acids into three fractions: monoamino monocarboxylic acids, monoamino dicarboxylic acids (the acidic amino acids), and diamino monocarboxylic acids (the basic amino acids).

33.5 Configuration of natural amino acids

From the structures in Table 33.1 we can see that every amino acid except glycine contains at least one asymmetric carbon atom. As obtained by acidic or enzymatic hydrolysis of proteins, every amino acid except glycine has been found optically active. Stereochemical studies of these naturally occurring amino acids have shown that all have the same configuration about the carbon atom carrying the *alpha* amino group, and that this configuration is the same as that in L-(−)-glyceraldehyde.

L-Amino acid   L-Glyceraldehyde

Problem 33.8 Draw all possible stereoisomeric formulas for the amino acid threonine. Naturally occurring threonine gets its name from its relationship to the tetrose *threose;* on this basis which is the correct configuration for natural threonine?

Problem 33.9 Besides threonine there are four amino acids in Table 33.1 that can exist in more than two stereoisomeric forms. (a) What are they? (b) How many isomers are possible in each case? Indicate enantiomers, diastereomers, any *meso* compounds.

33.6 Preparation of amino acids

Of the many methods that have been developed for synthesizing amino acids, we shall take up only one: **amination of α-halo acids.** Considered in its various modifications, this method is probably the most generally useful, although, like any of the methods, it cannot be applied to the synthesis of all the amino acids.

Sometimes an α-chloro or α-bromo acid is subjected to **direct ammonolysis** with a large excess (Why?) of concentrated aqueous ammonia. For example:

$$CH_3CH_2COOH \xrightarrow{Br_2, P} \underset{\substack{| \\ Br}}{CH_3CHCOOH} \xrightarrow{NH_3 \text{ (excess)}} \underset{\substack{| \\ NH_3^+}}{CH_3CHCOO^-}$$

Propionic acid   α-Bromopropionic acid   Alanine
70% yield

The necessary α-halo acids or esters can be prepared by the Hell-Volhard-Zelinsky halogenation of the unsubstituted acids (Sec. 16.21), or by a modification of the **malonic ester synthesis,** the usual route to the unsubstituted acids. For example:

$$Na^+ \begin{Bmatrix} COOC_2H_5 \\ | \\ CH \\ | \\ COOC_2H_5 \end{Bmatrix}^- \xrightarrow{C_6H_5CH_2Cl} \underset{\substack{| \\ COOC_2H_5}}{HC-CH_2C_6H_5} \xrightarrow[\text{heat}]{KOH} \xrightarrow{HCl} \underset{\substack{| \\ COOH}}{H-C-CH_2C_6H_5}$$

Sodiomalonic ester   Ethyl benzylmalonate   Benzylmalonic acid

$$\underset{\substack{| \\ NH_3^+}}{C_6H_5CH_2CHCOO^-} \xleftarrow{NH_3 \text{ (excess)}} \underset{\substack{| \\ Br}}{C_6H_5CH_2CHCOOH} \xleftarrow{heat} \underset{\substack{| \\ COOH}}{Br-C-CH_2C_6H_5} \quad \downarrow \substack{Br_2, \text{ ether,} \\ \text{reflux}}$$

Phenylalanine
35% overall yield

Better yields are generally obtained by the **Gabriel phthalimide synthesis** (Sec. 25.8); the α-halo esters are used instead of α-halo acids (Why?). A further modification, the **phthalimidomalonic ester method,** is a combined malonic ester–Gabriel synthesis.

These synthetic amino acids are, of course, optically inactive, and must be resolved if the active materials are desired for comparison with the naturally occurring acids or for synthesis of peptides (Sec. 33.10).

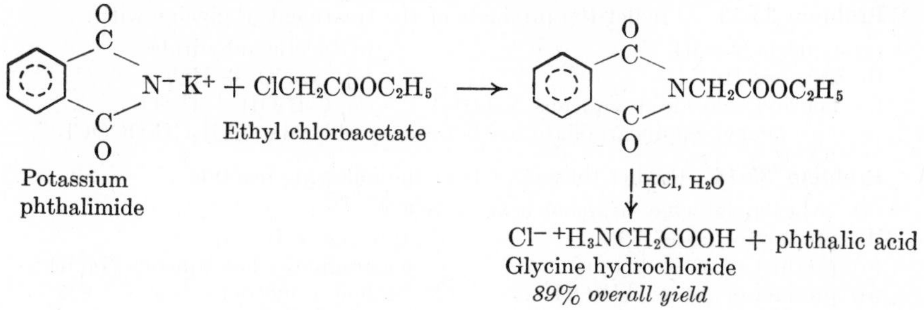

Potassium phthalimide $N^- K^+$ + $ClCH_2COOC_2H_5$ (Ethyl chloroacetate) $\longrightarrow$ phthalimido-$NCH_2COOC_2H_5$

$\downarrow$ HCl, H₂O

$Cl^- {}^+H_3NCH_2COOH$ + phthalic acid
Glycine hydrochloride
89% overall yield

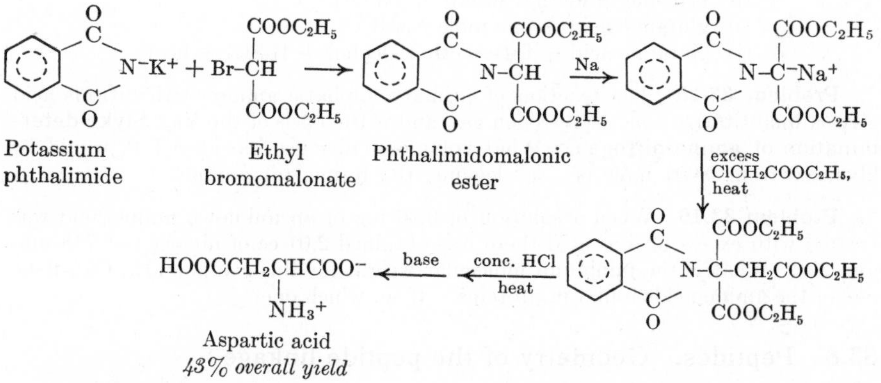

Potassium phthalimide $N^- K^+$ + $Br-CH\begin{smallmatrix}COOC_2H_5\\COOC_2H_5\end{smallmatrix}$ (Ethyl bromomalonate) $\longrightarrow$ $N-CH\begin{smallmatrix}COOC_2H_5\\COOC_2H_5\end{smallmatrix}$ (Phthalimidomalonic ester) $\xrightarrow{Na}$ $N-C^-Na^+\begin{smallmatrix}COOC_2H_5\\COOC_2H_5\end{smallmatrix}$

$\downarrow$ excess $ClCH_2COOC_2H_5$, heat

$N-C-CH_2COOC_2H_5$ with $COOC_2H_5$ and $COOC_2H_5$

$\xrightarrow[\text{heat}]{\text{conc. HCl}}$ $\xrightarrow{\text{base}}$ $HOOCCH_2CHCOO^-$ with NH_3^+
Aspartic acid
43% overall yield

Problem 33.10 Various amino acids have been made in the following ways:

Direct ammonolysis: glycine, alanine, valine, leucine, aspartic acid
Gabriel synthesis: glycine, leucine
Malonic ester synthesis: valine, isoleucine
Phthalimidomalonic ester method: serine, glutamic acid, aspartic acid.

List the necessary starting materials in each case, and outline the entire sequence for one example from each group.

Problem 33.11 Acetaldehyde reacts with a mixture of KCN and NH₄Cl **(Strecker synthesis)** to give a product, $C_3H_6N_2$ (What is its structure?), which upon hydrolysis yields alanine. Show how the Strecker synthesis can be applied to the synthesis of glycine, leucine, isoleucine, valine, and serine (start with $C_2H_5OCH_2CH_2OH$). Make all required carbonyl compounds from readily available materials.

Problem 33.12 (a) Synthesis of amino acids by **reductive amination** (Sec. 19.11) is illustrated by the following synthesis of leucine:

ethyl isovalerate + ethyl oxalate $\xrightarrow{NaOC_2H_5}$ A $(C_{11}H_{18}O_5)$
A + 10% H₂SO₄ $\xrightarrow{boil}$ B $(C_6H_{10}O_3)$ + CO₂ + C₂H₅OH
B + NH₃ + H₂ $\xrightarrow{Pd, \text{ heat}}$ leucine

(b) Outline the synthesis by this method of alanine. Of glutamic acid.

33.7 Reactions of amino acids

The reactions of amino acids are in general the ones we would expect of compounds containing amino and carboxyl groups. In addition, any other groups that may be present undergo their own characteristic reactions.

Problem 33.13 Predict the products of the treatment of glycine with:

(a) aqueous NaOH

(b) aqueous HCl

(c) benzoyl chloride + aqueous NaOH

(d) acetic anhydride

(e) $NaNO_2$ + HCl

(f) C_2H_5OH + H_2SO_4

(g) benzyl chlorocarbonate (carbobenzoxy chloride), $C_6H_5CH_2OCOCl$

Problem 33.14 Predict the products of the following reactions:

(a) N-benzoylglycine (*hippuric acid*) + $SOCl_2$

(b) product of (a) + NH_3

(c) product of (a) + alanine

(d) product of (a) + C_2H_5OH

(e) tyrosine + Br_2(aq)

(f) asparagine + hot aqueous NaOH

(g) proline + methyl iodide

(h) tyrosine + methyl sulfate + NaOH

(i) glutamic acid + one mole $NaHCO_3$

(j) glutamic acid + excess ethyl alcohol + H_2SO_4 + heat

Problem 33.15 The reaction of primary aliphatic amines with nitrous acid gives a quantitative yield of nitrogen gas, and is the basis of the **Van Slyke determination of amino nitrogen.** What volume of nitrogen gas at S.T.P. would be liberated from 0.001 mole of: (a) leucine, (b) lysine, (c) proline?

Problem 33.16 When a solution of 9.36 mg of an unknown amino acid was treated with excess nitrous acid there was obtained 2.01 cc of nitrogen at 748 mm and 20°. What is the minimum molecular weight for this compound? Can it be one of the amino acids found in proteins? If so, which one?

33.8   Peptides.   Geometry of the peptide linkage

Peptides are amides formed by interaction between amino groups and carboxyl groups of amino acids. The amide group, —NHCO—, in such compounds is often referred to as the *peptide linkage.*

Depending upon the number of amino acid residues per molecule they are known as *dipeptides, tripeptides,* and so on, and finally *polypeptides.* (By convention, peptides of molecular weight up to 10,000 are known as polypeptides and above that as proteins.)   For example:

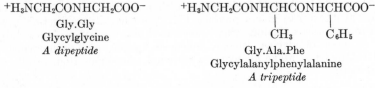

$^+H_3NCH_2CONHCH_2COO^-$

Gly.Gly
Glycylglycine
A dipeptide

$^+H_3NCH_2CONHCHCONHCHCOO^-$

CH$_3$ C$_6$H$_5$

Gly.Ala.Phe
Glycylalanylphenylalanine
A tripeptide

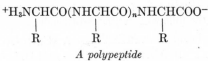

$^+H_3NCHCO(NHCHCO)_nNHCHCOO^-$

R   R   R

A polypeptide

A convenient way of representing peptide structures by use of standard abbreviations (see Table 33.1) is illustrated here. According to convention, the **N-terminal amino acid residue** (having the free amino group) is written at the left end, and the **C-terminal amino acid residue** (having the free carboxyl group) at the right end.

X-ray studies of amino acids and dipeptides indicate that the entire amide group is flat: carbonyl carbon, nitrogen, and the four atoms attached to them all lie in a plane. The short carbon–nitrogen distance (1.32 A as compared with 1.47 A for the usual carbon–nitrogen single bond) indicates that the carbon–nitrogen bond has considerable double bond character (about 50%); as a result the angles of the bonds to nitrogen are similar to the angles about the trigonal carbon atom (Figure 33.1).

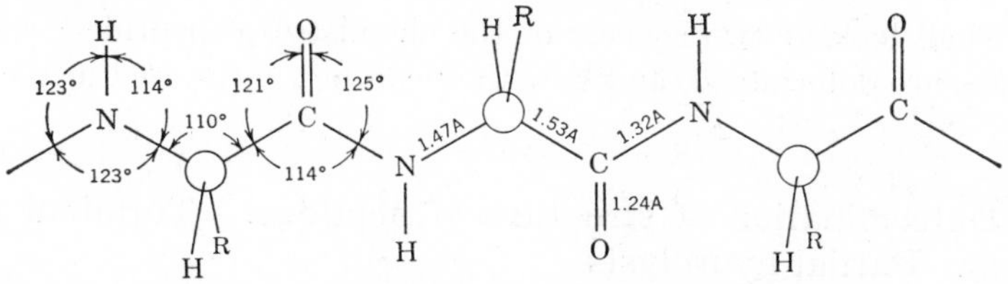

FIGURE 33.1.   Geometry of the peptide link.   Carbon–nitrogen bond has much double bond character.   Carbonyl carbon, nitrogen, and atoms attached to them lie in a plane.

Problem 33.17   (a) What contributing structure(s) would account for the double bond character of the carbon–nitrogen bond?   (b) What does this resonance mean in terms of orbitals?

Peptides have been studied chiefly as a step toward the understanding of the much more complicated substances, the proteins.   However, peptides are extremely important compounds in their own right: the tripeptide *glutathione*, for example, is found in most living cells; the nonapeptide *oxytocin* is a posterior pituitary hormone concerned with contraction of the uterus; *α-corticotropin*, made up of 39 amino acid residues, is one component of the adrenocorticotropic hormone ACTH.

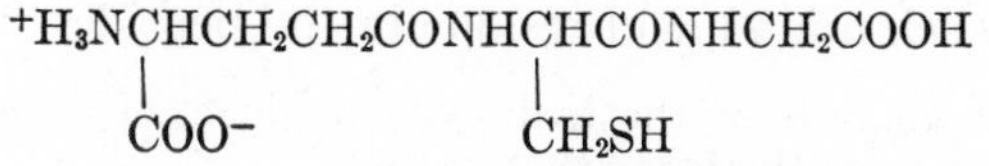

$$+H_3NCHCH_2CH_2CONHCHCONHCH_2COOH \quad or \quad Glu.CySH.Gly$$

COO⁻ 　　　　　　　　 CH₂SH

Glutathione
(Glutamylcysteinylglycine)

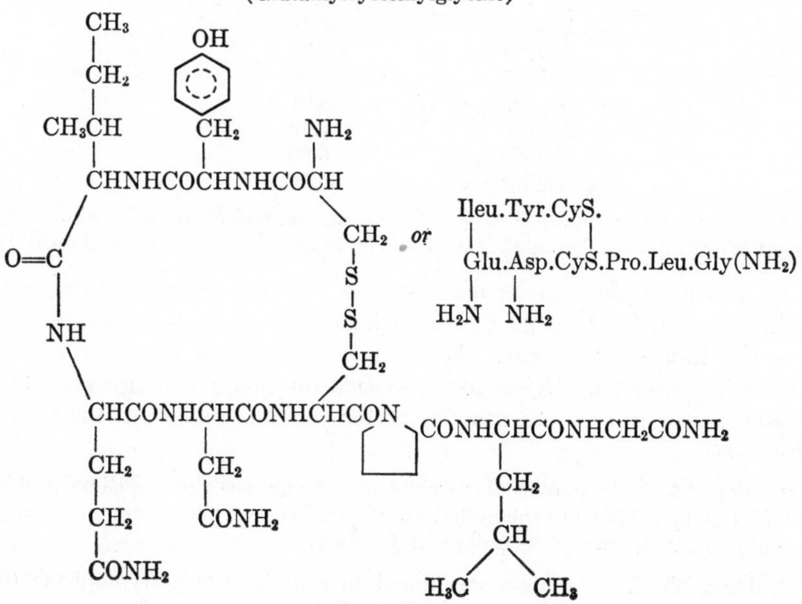

Oxytocin

Ser.Tyr.Ser.Met.Glu.His.Phe.Arg.Try.Gly.Lys.Pro.Val.⌐
└Gly.Lys.Lys.Arg.Arg.Pro.Val.Lys.Val.Tyr.Pro.Ala.Gly.⌐
└Glu.Asp.Asp.Glu.Ala.Ser.Glu.Ala.Phe.Pro.Leu.Glu.Phe

α-Corticotropin (sheep)

We shall look at two aspects of the chemistry of peptides: how their structures are determined, and how they can be synthesized in the laboratory.

33.9   Determination of structure of peptides.   Terminal residue analysis.   Partial hydrolysis

To assign a structure to a particular peptide, one must know (a) what amino acid residues make up the molecule and how many of each there are, and (b) the sequence in which they follow one another along the chain.

To determine the composition of a peptide, one hydrolyzes the peptide (in acidic solution since alkali causes racemization) and determines the amount of each amino acid thus formed.   One of the best ways of analyzing a mixture of amino acids is to separate the mixture into its components by chromatography.

From the weight of each amino acid obtained, one can calculate the number of moles of each amino acid, and in this way know the relative numbers of the various amino acid residues in the peptide.   At this stage one knows what might be called the "empirical formula" of the peptide: the relative abundance of each amino acid residue in the peptide.

Problem 33.18   A recent analysis of the hydrolysis products of *salmine*, a polypeptide from salmon sperm, gave the following results:

	g/100 g salmine
Isoleucine	1.28
Alanine	0.89
Valine	3.68
Glycine	3.01
Serine	7.29
Proline	6.90
Arginine	86.40

What are the relative numbers of the various amino acid residues in salmine, that is, what is its empirical formula?   (Why do the weights add up to more than 100 g?)

To calculate the "molecular formula" of the peptide — the actual number of each kind of residue in each peptide molecule — one needs to know the molecular weight.   Molecular weights can be determined by chemical methods and by various physical methods: osmotic pressure or light-scattering measurements, behavior in an ultracentrifuge, x-ray diffraction.

Problem 33.19   The molecular weight of salmine (see the preceding problem) is about 10,000.   What are the actual numbers of the various amino acid residues in salmine, that is, what is its molecular formula?

Problem 33.20   A protein was found to contain 0.29% tryptophane (mol. wt. 204).   What is the minimum molecular weight of the protein?

Problem 33.21 (a) Horse hemoglobin contains 0.335% Fe. What is the minimum molecular weight of the protein? (b) Osmotic pressure measurements give a molecular weight of about 67,000. How many iron atoms are there per molecule?

There remains the most difficult job of all: to determine the sequence in which these amino acid residues are arranged along the peptide chain, that is, the structural formula of the peptide. This is accomplished by a combination of terminal residue analysis and partial hydrolysis.

Terminal residue analysis is the identifying of the amino acid residues at the ends of the peptide chain. The procedures used depend upon the fact that the residues at the two ends are different from all the other residues and from each other: one, the *N-terminal residue*, contains a free *alpha* amino group and the other, the *C-terminal residue*, contains a free carboxyl group *alpha* to a peptide linkage.

A very successful method of identifying the N-terminal residue (introduced in 1945 by Frederick Sanger of Cambridge University) makes use of 2,4-dinitrofluorobenzene (DNFB), which undergoes nucleophilic substitution by the free amino group to give an N-dinitrophenyl (DNP) derivative.

$$O_2N\langle\bigcirc\rangle F + H_2NCHCONHCHCO\text{\small$\sim$} \xrightarrow[\text{medium}]{\text{alkaline}} O_2N\langle\bigcirc\rangle NHCHCONHCHCO\text{\small$\sim$}$$

$$\underset{NO_2}{\quad} \quad \underset{R}{|} \quad \underset{R'}{|} \qquad\qquad\qquad \underset{NO_2}{\quad} \quad \underset{R}{|} \quad \underset{R'}{|}$$

Peptide   Labeled peptide

2,4-Dinitrofluorobenzene
(DNFB)

$\downarrow$ aq. HCl, heat

$$O_2N\langle\bigcirc\rangle NHCHCOOH + {}^+H_3NCHCOOH, \text{etc.}$$

$$\underset{NO_2}{\quad}\;\underset{R}{|} \qquad\qquad\qquad \underset{R'}{|}$$

Unlabeled amino acids

N-(2,4-Dinitrophenyl)amino acid
(DNP.AA)

The substituted peptide is hydrolyzed to the component amino acids, and the N-terminal residue, labeled by the 2,4-dinitrophenyl group, is separated and identified.

Another method of N-terminal residue analysis (introduced in 1950 by Pehr Edman of the University of Lund, Sweden) is based upon the reaction between an amino group and phenyl isothiocyanate to form a substituted thiourea (compare Sec. 25.14). Mild hydrolysis with hydrochloric acid selectively removes the N-terminal residue as the phenylthiohydantoin, which is then identified. (See equations on the following page.) The great advantage of this method is that it leaves the rest of the peptide chain intact, so that the analysis can be repeated and the *new* terminal group of the shortened peptide identified. Ideally this method could be repeated over and over again until the entire sequence had been determined, amino acid by amino acid; in actual practice this is not feasible.

$$C_6H_5NCS + H_2NCHCONHCHCO\text{\textasciitilde} \xrightarrow[\text{medium}]{\text{alkaline}} C_6H_5N-\overset{\text{H}}{\underset{\text{S}}{C}}-NHCHCONHCHCO\text{\textasciitilde}$$

Phenyl isothiocyanate   R   R′   S   R   R′

Peptide   Labeled peptide

↓ H₂O, HCl

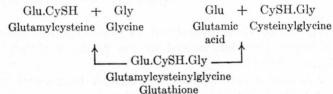

$$C_6H_5N \overset{\overset{S}{\|}}{\underset{\underset{O}{\|}}{\underset{C-CHR}{C}}} NH + H_2NCHCO\text{\textasciitilde}$$
                                                        R′

A phenylthiohydantoin   Degraded peptide (one less residue)

The most successful method of determining the C-terminal residue has been enzymatic rather than chemical. The C-terminal residue is removed selectively by the enzyme *carboxypeptidase* (obtained from the pancreas) which cleaves only peptide linkages adjacent to *free alpha-carboxyl* groups in polypeptide chains. The analysis can be repeated on the shortened peptide and the *new* C-terminal residue identified, and so on.

In practice it is not feasible to determine the sequence of all the residues in a long peptide chain by the stepwise removal of terminal residues. Instead, the chain is subjected to partial hydrolysis (acidic or enzymatic), and the fragments formed — dipeptides, tripeptides, and so on — are identified, with the aid of terminal residue analysis. When enough of these small fragments have been identified, it is possible to work out the sequence of residues in the entire chain.

To take an extremely simple example, there are six possible ways in which the three amino acids making up glutathione could be arranged; partial hydrolysis to the dipeptides glutamylcysteine (Glu.CySH) and cysteinylglycine (CySH.Gly) makes it clear that the cysteine is in the middle and that the sequence Glu.CySH.Gly is the correct one.

Glu.CySH + Gly   Glu + CySH.Gly
Glutamylcysteine Glycine   Glutamic   Cysteinylglycine
                            acid

↑_____ Glu.CySH.Gly _____↑

Glutamylcysteinylglycine
Glutathione

It was by the use of the approach just outlined that structures of such peptides as oxytocin and α-corticotropin (see pages 867–8) were worked out. One of the most notable of these achievements was the determination of the entire amino acid sequence in the insulin molecule by a Cambridge University group headed by Frederick Sanger, who received the Nobel prize in 1958 for this work. (See Problem 12, page 888.)

As usual, final confirmation of the structure assigned to a peptide lies in its synthesis by a method that must unambiguously give a compound of the assigned structure. This problem is discussed in the following section.

Problem 33.22 Work out the sequence of amino acid residues in the following peptides:

(a) Asp,Glu,His,Phe,Val (commas indicate unknown sequence) *gives* Val.Asp + Glu.His + Phe.Val + Asp.Glu.

(b) CySH,Gly,His$_2$,Leu$_2$,Ser *gives* CySH.Gly.Ser + His.Leu.CySH + Ser.His.Leu.

(c) Arg,CySH,Glu,Gly$_2$,Leu,Phe$_2$,Tyr,Val *gives* Val.CySH.Gly + Gly.Phe.Phe + Glu.Arg.Gly + Tyr.Leu.Val + Gly.Glu.Arg.

33.10 Synthesis of peptides

Methods have been developed by which a single amino acid (or sometimes a di- or tripeptide) can be polymerized to yield polypeptides of high molecular weight. These products have been extremely useful as model compounds: to show, for example, what kind of x-ray pattern or infrared spectrum is given by a peptide of known, comparatively simple structure.

Most work on peptide synthesis, however, has had as its aim the preparation of compounds identical with naturally occurring ones. For this purpose a method must permit the joining together of optically active amino acids to form chains of predetermined length and with a predetermined sequence of residues. Syntheses of this sort not only have confirmed some of the particular structures assigned to natural peptides, but also — and this is more fundamental — have proved that peptides and proteins are indeed polyamides.

It was Emil Fischer who first prepared peptides (ultimately one containing 18 amino acid residues) and thus offered support for his proposal that proteins contain the amide link. It is evidence of his extraordinary genius that Fischer played the same role in laying the foundations of peptide and protein chemistry as he did in carbohydrate chemistry.

The basic problem of peptide synthesis is one of *protecting the amino group*. In bringing about interaction between the carboxyl group of one amino acid and the amino group of a different amino acid, one must prevent interaction between the carboxyl group and the amino group of the same amino acid. In preparing glycylalanine, for example, one must prevent the simultaneous formation of glycylglycine. Reaction can be forced to take place in the desired way by attaching to one amino acid a group that renders the —NH$_2$ unreactive. There are many such protecting groups; the problem is to find one that can be removed later without destruction of any peptide linkages that may have been built up.

$$^+\text{H}_3\text{NCHCOO}^- \longrightarrow \text{Q–NHCHCOOH} \longrightarrow \text{Q–NHCHCOCl}$$

Protection of amino group

(with R below each)

$$\text{Q–NHCHCOCl} + {}^+\text{H}_3\text{NCHCOO}^- \longrightarrow \text{Q–NHCHC–NHCHCOOH}$$

Formation of peptide linkage

(R, R′, R O R′)

$$\text{Q–NHCHC–NHCHCOOH} \longrightarrow {}^+\text{H}_3\text{NCHC–NHCHCOO}^-$$

Removal of the protecting group

(R O R′)

Peptide

We could, for example, benzoylate glycine (Q = C_6H_5CO), convert this into the acid chloride, allow the acid chloride to react with alanine, and thus obtain benzoylglycylalanine. But if we attempted to remove the benzoyl group by hydrolysis, we would simultaneously hydrolyze the other amide linkage (the peptide linkage) and thus destroy the peptide we were trying to make.

Of the numerous methods developed to protect an amino group, we shall look at just one: **acylation by benzyl chlorocarbonate,** also called **carbobenzoxy chloride.** (This method was introduced in 1932 by Max Bergmann of the University of Berlin, later of the Rockefeller Institute.) The reagent, $C_6H_5CH_2OCOCl$, is both an ester and an acid chloride of carbonic acid, $HOCOOH$; it is readily made by reaction between benzyl alcohol and phosgene (carbonyl chloride), $COCl_2$. (In what order should the alcohol and phosgene be mixed?)

$$CO + Cl_2 \xrightarrow{\text{active carbon, 200°}} Cl-\underset{\underset{O}{\|}}{C}-Cl \xrightarrow{C_6H_5CH_2OH} C_6H_5CH_2O-\underset{\underset{O}{\|}}{C}-Cl$$

Phosgene   Carbobenzoxy chloride
(Carbonyl chloride)   (Benzyl chlorocarbonate)

Like any acid chloride the reagent can convert an amine into an amide:

$$C_6H_5CH_2O-\underset{\underset{O}{\|}}{C}-Cl + H_2NR \longrightarrow C_6H_5CH_2O-\underset{\underset{O}{\|}}{C}-NHR$$

Amine   An amide

Such amides, $C_6H_5CH_2OCONHR$, differ from most amides, however, in one feature that is significant for peptide synthesis. The carbobenzoxy group can be cleaved by reagents that do not disturb peptide linkages: catalytic hydrogenation or hydrolysis with hydrogen bromide in cold acetic acid.

$$C_6H_5CH_2O-\underset{\underset{O}{\|}}{C}-NHR \begin{cases} \xrightarrow{H_2,\ Pd} C_6H_5CH_3 + \left[HO-\underset{\underset{O}{\|}}{C}-NHR \right] \longrightarrow CO_2 + RNH_2 \\[2em] \xrightarrow[\substack{\text{cold} \\ \text{HOAc}}]{\text{HBr,}} C_6H_5CH_2Br + \left[HO-\underset{\underset{O}{\|}}{C}-NHR \right] \longrightarrow CO_2 + RNH_2 \end{cases}$$

A carbamic acid
Unstable

The carbobenzoxy method is illustrated by the synthesis of glycylalanine (Gly.Ala):

$$C_6H_5CH_2OCOCl + {}^+H_3NCH_2COO^- \longrightarrow C_6H_5CH_2OCONHCH_2COOH$$

Carbobenzoxy   Glycine   Carbobenzoxyglycine
chloride | $SOCl_2$
                                   ↓
$C_6H_5CH_2OCONHCH_2COCl$
Acid chloride of carbobenzoxyglycine

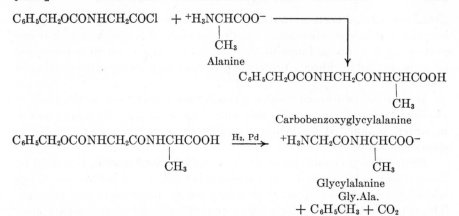

$$C_6H_5CH_2OCONHCH_2COCl \;+\; {}^+H_3NCHCOO^- $$

with CH₃ below (Alanine)

$$C_6H_5CH_2OCONHCH_2CONHCHCOOH$$
with CH₃ below

Carbobenzoxyglycylalanine

$$C_6H_5CH_2OCONHCH_2CONHCHCOOH \xrightarrow{\text{H}_2,\ \text{Pd}} {}^+H_3NCH_2CONHCHCOO^-$$
with CH₃ below each

Glycylalanine
Gly.Ala.
$$+\; C_6H_5CH_3 + CO_2$$

Problem 33.23 (a) How could the preceding synthesis be extended to the tripeptide glycylalanylphenylalanine (Gly.Ala.Phe)?

(b) How could the carbobenzoxy method be used to prepare alanylglycine (Ala.Gly)?

An outstanding peptide synthesis has been that of the hormone oxytocin (page 867) by Vincent du Vigneaud of Cornell Medical College, who received the Nobel Prize for this and other work.

Stop

33.11 Proteins. Classification and function. Denaturation

Proteins are divided into two broad classes: **fibrous proteins,** which are insoluble in water, and **globular proteins,** which are soluble in water or aqueous solutions of acids, bases, or salts. (Because of the large size of protein molecules, these solutions are colloidal.) The difference in solubility between the two classes is a result of a difference in molecular shape, which is indicated in a rough way by their names.

Molecules of fibrous proteins are long and threadlike, and tend to lie side by side to form fibers; in some cases they are held together at many points by hydrogen bonds. As a result, the intermolecular forces that must be overcome by a solvent are very strong.

Molecules of globular proteins are folded into compact units that often approach spheroidal shapes. Hydrogen bonds are internal, and areas of contact between molecules are small. Intermolecular forces here are comparatively weak.

Molecular and intermolecular structure determines not only the solubility of a protein but also the general kind of function it performs.

Fibrous proteins serve as the chief structural materials of animal tissues, a function to which their insolubility and fiber-forming tendency suit them. They make up: *keratin*, in skin, hair, nails, wool, horn, and feathers; *collagen*, in tendons; *myosin*, in muscle; *fibroin*, in silk.

Globular proteins serve a variety of functions related to the maintenance and regulation of the life process, functions that require mobility and hence solubility. They make up: all enzymes; many hormones, as, for example, *insulin* (from the pancreas), *thyroglobulin* (from the thyroid gland), *ACTH* (from the adrenal cortex); antibodies, responsible for allergies and for defense against foreign organisms; *albumin* in eggs; *hemoglobin,* which transports oxygen from the lungs to the tissues; *fibrinogen,* which is converted into the insoluble, fibrous protein *fibrin,* and thus causes the clotting of blood.

Within the two broad classes, proteins are subdivided on the basis of physical properties, especially solubility: for example, albumins (soluble in water, coagulated by heat), globulins (insoluble in water, soluble in dilute salt solutions), etc.

Irreversible precipitation of proteins, called **denaturation,** is caused by heat, strong acids or bases, or various other agents. Coagulation of egg white by heat, for example, is denaturation of the protein egg albumin. The extreme ease with which many proteins are denatured makes their study difficult. Denaturation causes a fundamental change in a protein, in particular destroying any physiological activity. (Denaturation appears to involve changes in the secondary structure of proteins, Sec. 33.16.)

Only one other class of compounds, the *nucleic acids* (Sec. 33.17), shows the phenomenon of denaturation. Although closely related to the proteins, polypeptides do not undergo denaturation, presumably because their molecules are smaller and less complex.

33.12 Structure of proteins

We can look at the structure of proteins on a number of levels. At the lowest level, there is the *primary* structure: the way in which the atoms of protein molecules are joined to one another by covalent bonds to form chains. Next, there is the *secondary* structure: the way in which these chains are arranged in space to form coils, sheets, or compact spheroids, with hydrogen bonds holding together different chains or different parts of the same chain. Even higher levels of structure are gradually becoming understood: the weaving together of coiled chains to form ropes, for example, or the clumping together of individual molecules to form larger aggregates. Let us look first at the primary structure of proteins.

33.13 Peptide chain

Proteins are made up of peptide chains, that is, of amino acid residues joined by amide linkages.

$$\text{\textasciitilde\textasciitilde N--C--C--N--C--C--N--C--C\textasciitilde\textasciitilde}$$

They differ from polypeptides in having higher molecular weights (by convention over 10,000) and more complex structures.

The peptide structure of proteins is indicated by many lines of evidence: hydrolysis of proteins by acids, bases, or enzymes yields peptides and finally amino acids; there are bands in their infrared spectra characteristic of the amide group; secondary structures based on the peptide linkage can be devised that exactly fit x-ray data.

33.14 Side chains. Isoelectric point. Electrophoresis

To every third atom of the peptide chain is attached a side chain. Its structure depends upon the particular amino acid residue involved: —H for glycine, —CH_3 for alanine, —$CH(CH_3)_2$ for valine, —$CH_2C_6H_5$ for phenylalanine, etc.

$$\begin{array}{ccccccc}
& H & & H & & H & \\
& | & & | & & | & \\
\text{\tiny www}N{-}CH{-}C{-}N{-}CH{-}C{-}N{-}CH{-}C\text{\tiny www} \\
& | \;\; \| & & | \;\; \| & & | \;\; \| \\
& R \;\; O & & R' \;\; O & & R'' \;\; O
\end{array}$$

Some of these side chains contain basic groups: —NH_2 in lysine, or the imidazole ring in histidine. Some side chains contain acidic groups: —COOH in aspartic acid or glutamic acid. Because of these acidic and basic side chains, there are positively and negatively charged groups along the peptide chain. The behavior of a protein in an electric field is deter-

$$\begin{array}{cccc}
H & O & H & O \\
| & \| & | & \| \\
\text{\tiny wwwww}N{-}CH{-}C\text{\tiny wwwwww} & N{-}CH{-}C\text{\tiny wwww} \\
| & & | \\
CH_2 & & (CH_2)_4 \\
| & & | \\
COO^- & & {}^+NH_3
\end{array}$$

mined by the relative numbers of these positive and negative charges, which in turn are affected by the acidity of the solution. At the isoelectric point, the positive and negative charges are exactly balanced and the protein shows no net migration; as with amino acids, solubility is usually at a minimum here. On the acid side of the isoelectric point, positive charges exceed negative charges and the protein moves to the cathode; on the basic side of the isoelectric point, negative charges exceed positive charges and the protein moves to the anode.

While all proteins contain the peptide backbone, each protein has its own characteristic sequence of side chains, which gives it its characteristic properties. Different proteins have different proportions of acidic and basic side chains, and hence have different isoelectric points. In a solution of a particular hydrogen ion concentration, some proteins move toward a cathode and others toward an anode; depending upon the size of the charge as well as upon molecular size and shape, different proteins move at different speeds. This difference in behavior in an electric field is the basis of one method of separation and analysis of protein mixtures: **electrophoresis.**

Side chains affect the properties of proteins not only by their acidity or basicity, but also by their other chemical properties and even by their sizes and shapes. It seems likely that the "permanent" waving of hair depends upon changes in disulfide (—S—S—) cross-linkages provided by cysteine side chains; that much of the difference between silk and wool is related to the small side chains, —H and —CH₃, that predominate in silk fibroin; that the toughness of tendon is due to the flatness of the pyrrolidine ring and the ability of the —OH group of hydroxyproline to form hydrogen bonds. Replacement of *one* glutamic acid side chain in the hemoglobin molecule (300 side chains in all) by a valine unit seems to be the cause of the fatal sickle cell anemia.

33.15 Conjugated proteins. Prosthetic groups

Some protein molecules contain a non-peptide portion called a **prosthetic group**; such proteins are called *conjugated proteins*. The prosthetic group is intimately concerned with the specific biological action of the protein.

The prosthetic group of hemoglobin, for example, is *hemin*.

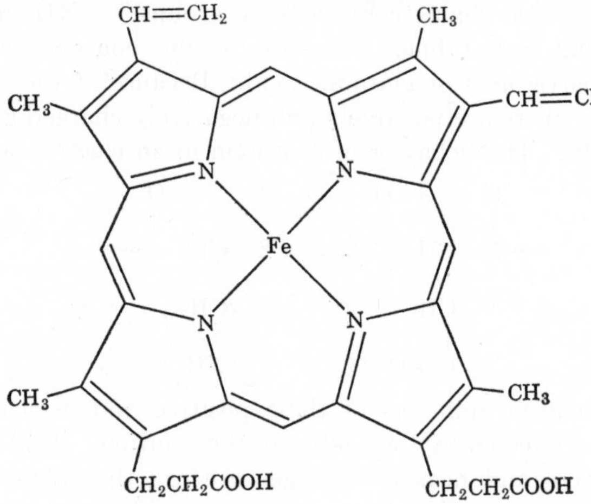

Hemin

As we see, hemin contains iron bound to the pyrrole system known as *porphin* (compare with the structure of chlorophyll, page 836). It is the formation of a reversible oxygen–hemin complex that enables hemoglobin to carry oxygen from the lungs to the tissues. Carbon monoxide forms a similar, but more stable, complex; it thus ties up hemoglobin, prevents oxygen transport, and causes death. Hemin is separated from the peptide portion (*globin*) of the protein by mild hydrolysis; the two units are presumably held together by an amide linkage between a carboxyl group of hemin and an amino group of the polypeptide.

Many enzymes contain prosthetic groups. *Coenzyme I* (a dehydrogenation enzyme found in yeast), for example, contains the prosthetic group *diphosphopyridinenucleotide* (DPN). This prosthetic group, we see, is made up of two molecules of D-ribose linked as phosphate esters, the fused heterocyclic system known as *adenine*, and nicotinamide in the form of a quaternary ammonium salt. The characteristic biological function of this enzyme involves the conversion of the nicotinamide portion into the dihydro structure.

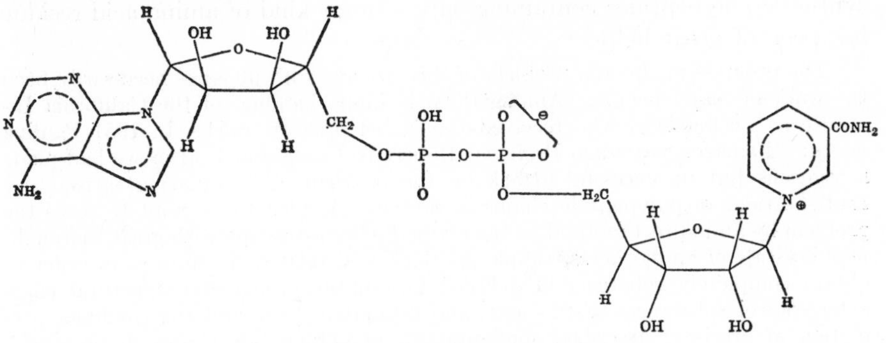

Diphosphopyridinenucleotide
(DPN)

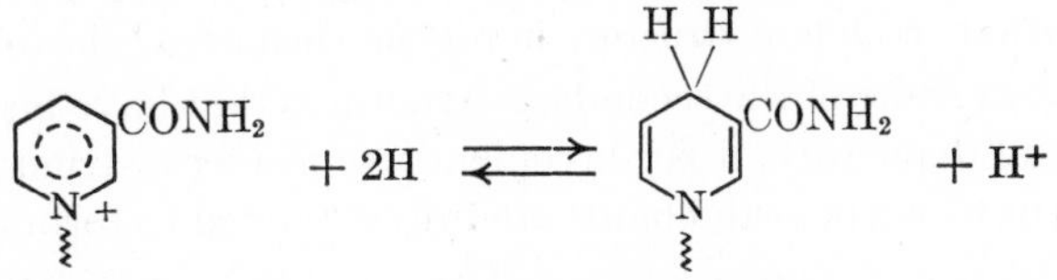

$$\text{DPN} + 2H \rightleftharpoons \text{Reduced DPN} + H^+$$

DPN   Reduced DPN

Like nicotinamide, many molecules making up the prosthetic groups of enzymes are **vitamins,** that is, substances that must be supplied in the diet to permit proper growth or maintenance of structure; undoubtedly the need for these substances is due to their function as prosthetic groups.

33.16 Secondary structure of proteins

It seems clear that proteins are made up of polypeptide chains. How are these chains arranged in space and in relationship to each other? Are they stretched out side by side, looped and coiled about one another, or folded into independent spheroids?

Much of our understanding of the secondary structure of proteins is the result of x-ray analysis. For many proteins the x-ray diffraction pattern indicates a regular repetition of certain structural units. For example, there are *repeat distances* of 7.0 A in silk fibroin, and of 1.5 A and 5.1 A in α-keratin of unstretched wool.

The problem is to devise structures that account for the characteristic x-ray diffraction patterns, and are at the same time consistent with what is known about the primary structure: bond lengths and bond angles, planarity of the amide group, similarity of configuration about asymmetric carbon atoms (all L-family), size and sequence of side chains. Of key importance in this problem has been recognition of the stabilizing effect of hydrogen bonds (5–10 kcal per mole per hydrogen bond), and the principle that the most stable structure is one that permits formation of the maximum number of hydrogen bonds. On the basis of the study of simpler compounds, it has been further assumed that the N—H - - - - O bond is very nearly linear, hydrogen lying on, or within 20° of, the line between nitrogen and oxygen. In all this work the simultaneous study of simpler, synthetic polypeptides containing only a single kind of amino acid residue has been of great help.

The progress made on a problem of this size and difficulty has necessarily been the work of many people. Among them is Linus Pauling, of the California Institute of Technology, who received the Nobel prize in 1954. In 1951 Pauling wrote: "Fourteen years ago Professor Robert B. Corey and I, after we had made a vigorous but unsuccessful attack on the problem of formulating satisfactory configurations of polypeptide chains in proteins, decided to attempt to solve the problem by an indirect method — the method of investigating with great thoroughness crystals of amino acids, simple peptides, and related substances, in order to obtain completely reliable and detailed information about the structural characteristics of substances of this sort, and ultimately to permit the confident prediction of precisely described configurations of polypeptide chains in proteins." (Record Chem. Prog., *12*, 156–7 (1951).) This work on simple substances, carried on for more than fourteen years, gave information about the geometry of the amide group that eventually led Pauling and his co-workers to propose what may well be the most important secondary structure in protein chemistry: the α-helix.

Let us look at some of the secondary structures that have been proposed.

As a point of departure, it is convenient to consider a structure (perhaps hypothetical) in which peptide chains are fully extended to form flat zig-zags:

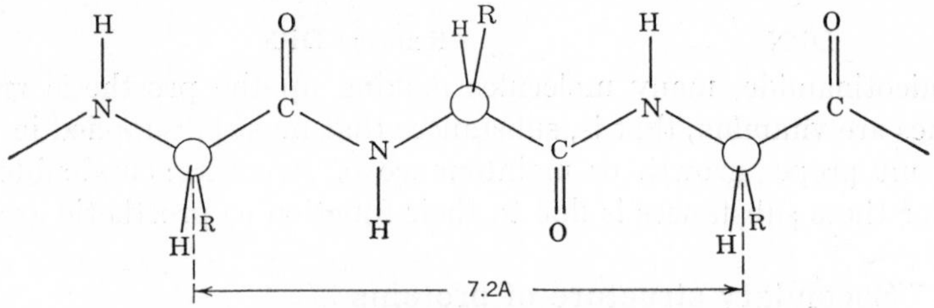

Extended peptide chain

These chains lie side by side to form a *flat sheet*. Each chain is held by hydrogen bonds to the two neighboring chains (Figure 33.2):

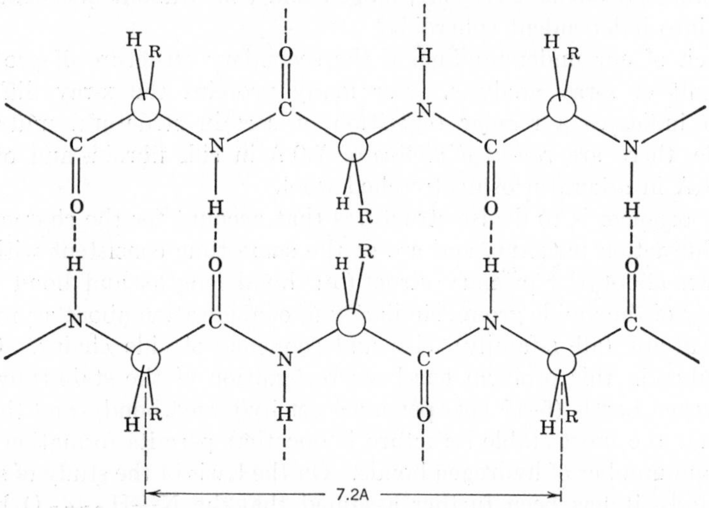

FIGURE 33.2. Hypothetical flat sheet structure for a protein. Chains fully extended; adjacent chains head in opposite directions; hydrogen bonding between adjacent chains. Side chains (R) are crowded.

This structure has a repeat distance of 7.2 A, the distance between *alternate* amino acid residues. (Notice that alternate side chains lie on the same side of the sheet.) However, crowding between side chains makes this idealized flat structure impossible, except perhaps for synthetic polyglycine.

Room can be made for small or medium-sized side chains by a slight contraction of the peptide chains:

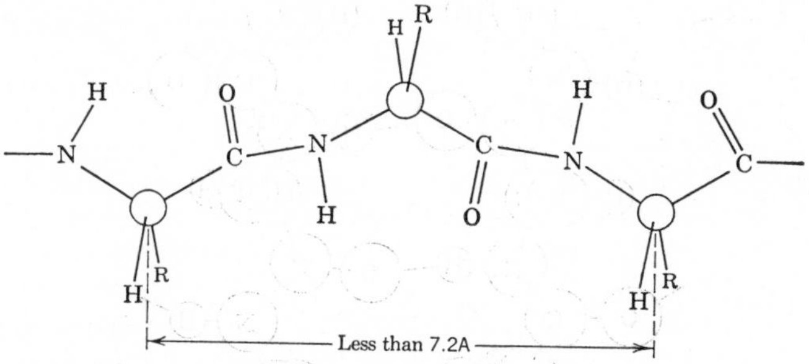

Contracted peptide chain

The chains still lie side by side, held to each other by hydrogen bonds. The contraction results in a *pleated sheet*, with a somewhat shorter distance between alternate amino acid residues (see Figure 33.3, next page). Such a structure, called the **beta** arrangement, has been proposed for silk fibroin, which has a repeat distance of 7.0 A and most closely approaches the fully extended, flat sheet structure. It is significant that, although fifteen kinds of amino acid residue are found in silk fibroin, 46% of the residues are glycine, which has no side chain, and another 38% are alanine and serine with the small side chains —CH_3 and —CH_2OH.

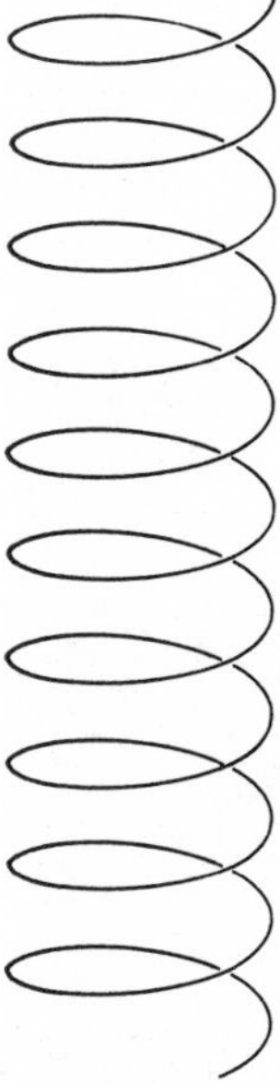

When the side chains are quite large, they are best accommodated by a quite different kind of structure. Each chain is coiled to form a *helix* (like a spiral staircase). Hydrogen bonding occurs between different parts of the *same* chain, and holds the helix together. For α-keratin (unstretched wool, hair, horn, nails) Pauling has proposed a helix in which there are 3.6 amino acid residues per turn (Figure 33.4, page 881). Models show that this 3.6-helix provides room for the side chains and allows all possible hydrogen bonds to form. It accounts for the repeat distance of 1.5 A, which is the distance between amino acid residues measured along the axis of the helix. Just as all amino acid residues in proteins are of the same configuration (L-family) so all helixes are *right-handed*, as shown. It is becoming increasingly clear that the **alpha helix,** as it is called, is of fundamental importance in the chemistry of proteins.

A helix
(right-handed)

(To account for the second repeat distance of 5.1 A for α-keratin, we must go to what is properly the *tertiary structure*. Pauling has suggested

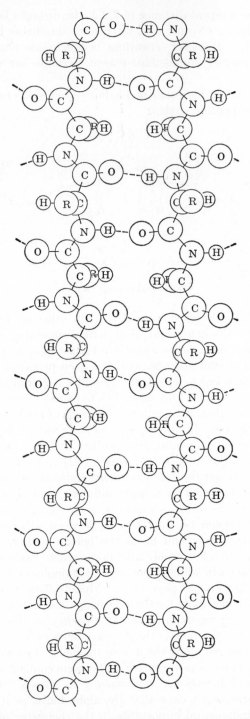

FIGURE 33.3. Pleated sheet structure (*beta arrangement*) proposed by Pauling for silk fibroin. Chains contracted to make room for small side chains. Adjacent chains head in opposite directions; hydrogen bonding between adjacent chains.

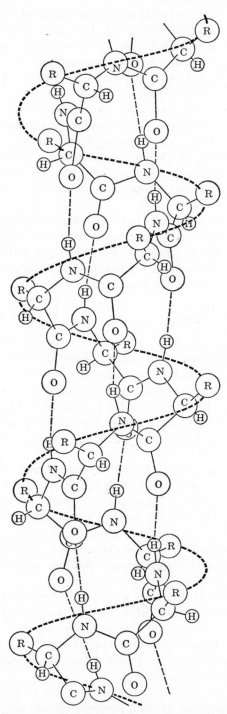

FIGURE 33.4. Alpha helix structure proposed by Pauling for α-keratin. Makes room for large side chains. Right-handed helix with 3.6 residues per turn; hydrogen bonding within a chain.

that each helix can itself be coiled into a superhelix which has one turn for every 35 turns of the *alpha* helix. Six of these superhelixes are woven about a seventh, straight helix to form a seven-strand cable.)

When wool is stretched, α-keratin is converted into β-keratin, with a change in the x-ray diffraction pattern. It is believed that the helixes are uncoiled and the chains stretched side by side to give a sheet structure of the *beta* type. The hydrogen bonds within the helical chain are broken, and are replaced by hydrogen bonds between adjacent chains. Because of the larger side chains, the peptide chains are less extended (repeat distance 6.4 A) than in silk fibroin (repeat distance 7.0 A).

Myosin, the fibrous protein of muscle, has the *alpha* helix structure. It has been suggested that contraction of muscle involves a reversible *alpha–beta* change.

Besides the x-ray diffraction patterns characteristic of the *alpha-* and *beta*-type proteins, there is a third kind: that of *collagen*, the protein of tendon and skin. On the primary level, collagen is characterized by a high proportion of proline and hydroxyproline residues, and by frequent repetitions of the sequence Gly.Pro.Hypro.

Proline residue   Hydroxyproline residue

The pyrrolidine ring of proline and hydroxyproline can affect the secondary structure in several ways. The amido nitrogen carries no hydrogen for hydrogen bonding. The flatness of the five-membered ring, in conjunction with the flatness of the amide group, prevents extension of the peptide chain as in the *beta* arrangement, and interferes with the compact coiling of the *alpha* helix.

A structure currently being considered for collagen combines the helical nature of the *alpha*-type proteins with the inter-chain hydrogen bonding of the *beta*-type proteins. Three peptide chains are twisted about one another to form a three-strand helix. A small glycine residue at every third position of each chain makes room for the bulky pyrrolidine rings on the other two chains. The three chains are held strongly to each other by hydrogen bonding between glycine residues and between the —OH groups of hydroxyproline.

When collagen is boiled with water, it is converted into the familiar water-soluble protein *gelatin;* when cooled, the solution does not revert to collagen but sets to a gel. Gelatin has a molecular weight one-third that of collagen. Evidently the treatment separates the strands of the helix, breaking inter-chain hydrogen bonds and replacing them with hydrogen bonds to water molecules.

Turning from the insoluble, fibrous proteins to the soluble, globular proteins (e.g., hemoglobin, insulin, *gamma*-globulin, egg albumin), we find that the matter of secondary structure is even more speculative. Evidence is accumulating that here, too, the *alpha* helix plays a key role. These long peptide chains are not uniform: certain segments are coiled into helixes and are comparatively rigid; other segments are looped and coiled randomly and are flexible. When a protein is denatured, it has been found, the helical sections are uncoiled, and the entire chain takes on a random arrangement.

In their physiological functions proteins are highly specific. We have encountered, for example, an enzyme that will cleave α-glucosides but not β-glucosides, and an enzyme that will cleave only C-terminal amino acid residues in polypeptides. It seems clear that the biological activity of a protein depends not only upon its prosthetic group (if any) and its particular amino acid sequence, but also upon its molecular shape. As Emil Fischer said in 1894: ". . . enzyme and glucoside must fit together like a lock and key. . . ."

It seems reasonable that the rigid, helical segments of a globular protein chain are required to maintain the shape of the molecule. Denaturation uncoils the helixes, destroys the characteristic shape, and with it the characteristic biological activity.

We have looked, very briefly, at the structure of proteins at the secondary and higher levels. We must realize that none of these structures has been proved, although certain of them are more firmly established than others; in most cases, alternative structures have been proposed and are still being considered. Whatever the structures of these proteins should ultimately turn out to be, it has been worthwhile for us to see the kinds of structure that are being considered, and how the basic concepts of the structural theory are applied.

33.17 Nucleoproteins and nucleic acids. Chemistry and heredity

In every living cell there are found **nucleoproteins**: substances made up of proteins combined with natural polymers of another kind, the **nucleic acids.** Of all fields of chemistry, the study of the nucleic acids is perhaps the most exciting, for these compounds are the substance of heredity.

Nucleic acids, it seems almost certain, control heredity on the molecular level. They are believed to do this through two properties: (a) nucleic acids can duplicate themselves, that is, can bring about the synthesis of other nucleic acid molecules identical with the originals; and (b) nucleic acids can control the synthesis, in an exact and specific way, of the proteins that are characteristic of each kind of organism. Let us look very briefly at the structure of nucleic acids, and see just how this structure may be related to these two literally vital properties.

The structure of nucleic acids has been studied in essentially the same way as the structure of proteins: by hydrolytic degradation and x-ray analysis. Although chemically quite different, nucleic acids resemble proteins in a fundamental way: there is a long chain — a backbone — that is the same (except for length) in all nucleic acid molecules; and attached to this backbone are various groups, which by their nature and sequence characterize each individual nucleic acid.

Where the backbone of the protein molecule is a polyamide chain (a polypeptide chain), the backbone of the nucleic acid molecule is a polyester chain (called a *polynucleotide* chain). The ester is derived from phosphoric acid (the acid portion) and a sugar (the alcohol portion).

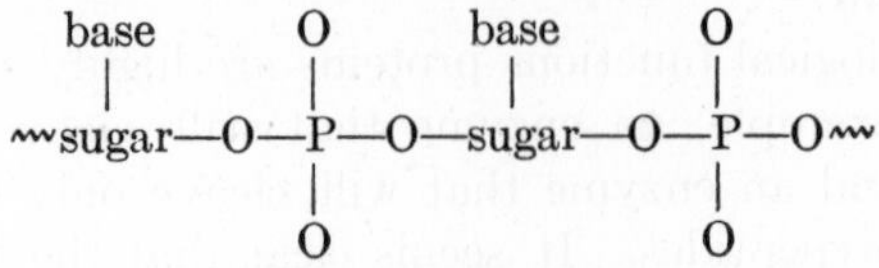

$$
\begin{array}{ccccc}
\text{base} & & \text{O} & \text{base} & \text{O} \\
| & & \| & | & \| \\
\text{\small www}\text{sugar}\!-\!\text{O}\!-\!\text{P}\!-\!\text{O}\!-\!\text{sugar}\!-\!\text{O}\!-\!\text{P}\!-\!\text{O}\text{\small www} \\
& & | & & | \\
& & \text{O} & & \text{O}
\end{array}
$$

Polynucleotide chain

The sugar is D-ribose (page 761) in the group of nucleic acids known as ribonucleic acids (RNA), and D-2-deoxyribose in the group known as deoxyribonucleic acids (DNA). (The prefix *2-deoxy* simply indicates the lack of an –OH group at the 2-position.) The sugar units are in the furanose form, and are joined to phosphate through the C–3 and C–5 hydroxyl groups (Figure 33.5):

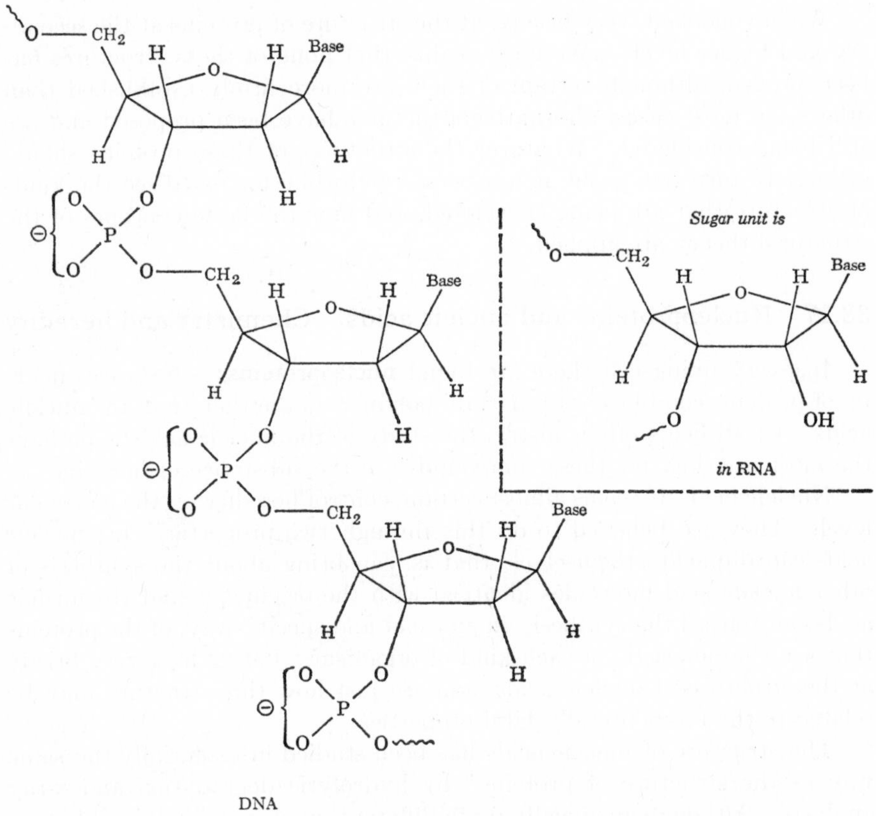

FIGURE 33.5. Deoxyribonucleic acid (DNA) and ribonucleic acid (RNA).

Attached to C–1 of each sugar, through a β-linkage, is one of a number of heterocyclic bases. A base–sugar unit is called a *nucleoside;* a base–

sugar–phosphoric acid unit is called a *nucleotide*. An example of a nucleotide is shown in Figure 33.6:

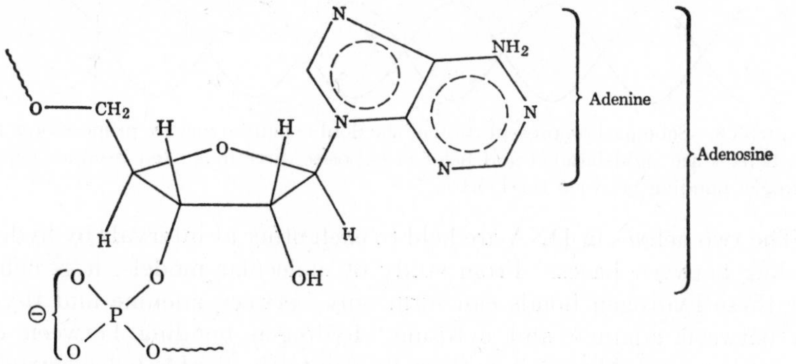

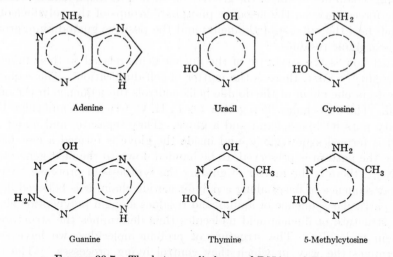

FIGURE 33.6. A nucleotide: an adenylic acid unit of RNA. Here, the nucleoside is
adenosine, and the heterocyclic base is adenine.

The bases found in DNA are *adenine* and *guanine,* which contain the
purine ring system, and *cytosine, thymine,* and *5-methylcytosine,* which
contain the pyrimidine ring system. RNA contains adenine, guanine,
cytosine, and *uracil.*

Adenine   Uracil   Cytosine

Guanine   Thymine   5-Methylcytosine

FIGURE 33.7. The heterocyclic bases of DNA and RNA.

The proportions of these bases and the sequence in which they follow
each other along the polynucleotide chain differ from one kind of nucleic
acid to another. A particular sequence of bases, it is believed, is responsible
for a particular set of hereditary characteristics.

What can we say about the secondary structure of nucleic acids? The
following picture of DNA fits both chemical and x-ray evidence. Two
polynucleotide chains, identical but heading in opposite directions, are
wound about each other to form a double helix 18 A in diameter (shown

schematically in Figure 33.8). Both helixes are right-handed and have ten nucleotide residues per turn.

FIGURE 33.8. Schematic representation of the double helix structure proposed for DNA. Both helixes are right-handed and head in opposite directions; ten residues per turn. Hydrogen bonding between the helixes.

The two helixes in DNA are held to each other at intervals by hydrogen bonding between bases. From study of molecular models, it is believed that these hydrogen bonds can form only between adenine and thymine and between guanine and cytosine; hydrogen bonding between other pairs of bases would not allow them to fit into the double helical structure. In agreement with this idea, the adenine: thymine and guanine: cytosine ratios are found to be 1: 1.

(Much less is known about the structure of RNA, although helical structures have been proposed here, too.)

So far we have discussed only the nucleic acid portion of nucleoproteins. There is evidence that in one nucleoprotein (found in fish sperm), a poly-arginine chain lies in one of the grooves of the double helix, held by electro-static forces between the negative phosphate groups of the polynucleotide (which face the outside of the helix) and the positive guanidinium groups of the arginine residues.

Just how is the structure of the nucleic acids related to their function in heredity? First, there is the matter of self-duplication. The sequence of bases in one chain of the double helix controls the sequence in the other chain. The two chains fit together (as F. H. C. Crick of Cambridge University puts it) like a hand and a glove. They separate, and about the hand is formed a new glove, and inside the glove is formed a new hand. Thus, the pattern is preserved, to be handed down to the next generation.

Next, there is the matter of guiding the synthesis of proteins. A particular sequence of bases along a polynucleotide chain, it is believed, leads to a particular sequence of amino acid residues along a polypeptide chain. The structure of nucleic acid molecules thus determines the structure of protein molecules. The structure of protein molecules, we have seen, determines the way in which they control living processes. (The tiny defect in the hemoglobin molecule that results in sickle cell anemia has been traced to a single gene.) Biology is becoming more and more a matter of shapes and sizes of molecules.

At the beginning of this book, we said that the structural theory is the basis of the science of organic chemistry. It is much more than that: the structural theory is the basis of our understanding of life.

PROBLEMS

1. Outline all steps in the synthesis of phenylalanine from toluene and any needed aliphatic and inorganic reagents by each of the following methods:

(a) direct ammonolysis
(b) Gabriel synthesis
(c) malonic ester synthesis

(d) phthalimidomalonic ester method
(e) Strecker synthesis
(f) reductive amination

2. (a) Give structures of all intermediates in the following synthesis of proline:

potassium phthalimide + bromomalonic ester $\longrightarrow$ A

A + $Br(CH_2)_3Br$ $\xrightarrow{NaOC_2H_5}$ B $(C_{18}H_{20}O_6NBr)$

B + potassium acetate $\longrightarrow$ C $(C_{20}H_{23}O_8N)$

C + NaOH, heat; then H^+, heat $\longrightarrow$ D $(C_5H_{11}O_3N)$

D + HCl $\longrightarrow$ [E $(C_5H_{10}O_2NCl)$] $\longrightarrow$ proline

(b) Outline a possible synthesis of lysine by the phthalimidomalonic ester method.

3. Give structures of all intermediates in the following syntheses of amino acids:

(a) ethyl acetamidomalonate $[CH_3CONHCH(COOC_2H_5)_2]$ + acrolein $\xrightarrow{Michael}$ F $(C_{12}H_{19}O_6N)$

F + KCN + acetic acid $\longrightarrow$ G $(C_{13}H_{20}O_6N_2)$

G + acid + heat $\longrightarrow$ H $(C_{13}H_{18}O_5N_2)$

H + H_2, catalyst, in acetic anhydride $\longrightarrow$ [I $(C_{13}H_{24}O_5N_2)$]

I $\xrightarrow{acetic\ anhydride}$ J $(C_{15}H_{26}O_6N_2)$

J + OH^-, heat; then H^+; then heat $\longrightarrow$ ($\pm$)-lysine

(b) acrylonitrile + ethyl malonate $\xrightarrow{Michael}$ K $(C_{10}H_{15}O_4N)$

K + H_2, catalyst $\longrightarrow$ [L $(C_{10}H_{19}O_4N)$] $\longrightarrow$ M $(C_8H_{13}O_3N)$

M + SO_2Cl_2 in $CHCl_3$ $\longrightarrow$ N $(C_8H_{12}O_3NCl)$

N + HCl, heat $\longrightarrow$ O $(C_5H_{10}O_2NCl)$

O $\xrightarrow{base}$ ($\pm$)-proline

(c) Glutamic acid has been made from acrolein via a Strecker synthesis. Show how this might have been done. (*Hint:* see Sec. 28.6.)

4. Using the behavior of hydroxy acids (Chapter 27) as a pattern, predict structures for the products obtained when the following amino acids are heated:

(a) the α-amino acid, glycine $\longrightarrow$ $C_4H_6O_2N_2$ (*diketopiperazine*)
(b) the β-amino acid, $CH_3CH(NH_2)CH_2COOH$ $\longrightarrow$ $C_4H_6O_2$
(c) the γ-amino acid, $CH_3CH(NH_2)CH_2CH_2COOH$ $\longrightarrow$ C_5H_9ON (a *lactam*)
(d) the δ-amino acid, $H_2NCH_2CH_2CH_2CH_2COOH$ $\longrightarrow$ C_5H_9ON (a *lactam*)

5. (a) Show how the particular dipolar structure given for histidine in Table 33.1 is related to the answer to Problem 18(b), page 857.

(b) Draw the two possible dipolar structures for lysine. Justify the choice of structure given in Table 33.1. (c) Answer (b) for aspartic acid. (d) Answer (b) for arginine. (*Hint:* see Problem 25.33, page 693.) (e) Answer (b) for tyrosine.

6. (a) *Betaine*, $C_5H_{11}O_2N$, occurs in beet sugar molasses. It is a water-soluble solid that melts with decomposition at 300°. It is unaffected by base but reacts with hydrochloric acid to form a crystalline product, $C_5H_{12}O_2NCl$. It can be made in either of two ways: treatment of glycine with methyl iodide, or treatment of chloroacetic acid with trimethylamine.

Draw a structure for betaine that accounts for its properties.

(b) *Trigonelline*, $C_7H_7O_2N$, is an alkaloid found in coffee beans; it is also excreted from the body as a metabolic product of nicotinic acid. It is insoluble in benzene or ether, and dissolves in water to give a neutral solution. It is unaffected by boiling aqueous acid or base. It has been synthesized as follows:

nicotinic acid + CH_3I + KOH $\longrightarrow$ P $(C_8H_{10}O_2NI)$

P + Ag_2O + H_2O, warm $\longrightarrow$ trigonelline + AgI + CH_3OH

What structure for trigonelline is consistent with these properties?

7. Three of the bases found in nucleic acids are *uracil*, *thymine*, and *cytosine*. (See page 885 for their structures.) They have been synthesized as follows:

(a) urea + ethyl acrylate $\xrightarrow{\text{Michael}}$ [Q $(C_6H_{12}O_3N_2)$] $\longrightarrow$ R $(C_4H_6O_2N_2)$ + C_2H_5OH

R + Br_2 in acetic acid $\longrightarrow$ S $(C_4H_5O_2N_2Br)$

S + boiling pyridine $\longrightarrow$ uracil $(C_4H_4O_2N_2)$

Give structures of Q, R, and S.

(b) Thymine $(C_5H_6O_2N_2)$ has been made in the same way, except that ethyl methacrylate, $CH_2=C(CH_3)COOC_2H_5$, is used instead of ethyl acrylate. Write equations for all the steps.

(c) uracil + $POCl_3$, heat $\longrightarrow$ T $(C_4H_2N_2Cl_2)$, chlorine atoms on different carbon atoms

T + NH_3(alc), 100° $\longrightarrow$ U $(C_4H_4N_3Cl)$ and V $(C_4H_4N_3Cl)$

U + $NaOCH_3$ $\longrightarrow$ W $(C_5H_7ON_3)$

W + HCl(aq) $\longrightarrow$ cytosine $(C_4H_5ON_3)$

Give structures of T through W.

(d) Six tautomeric structures for uracil have been considered. What are they? Which would show aromatic properties?

8. An amino group can be protected by acylation with phthalic anhydride to form an N-substituted phthalimide. The protecting group can be removed by treatment with hydrazine, $H_2N—NH_2$ (see Problem 25.25, page 686) without disturbing any peptide linkages. Write equations to show how this procedure (exploited by John C. Sheehan of the Massachusetts Institute of Technology) could be applied to the synthesis of glycylalanine (Gly.Ala) and alanylglycine (Ala.Gly).

9. An elemental analysis of *Cytochrome c*, an enzyme involved in oxidation-reduction processes, gave 0.43% Fe and 1.48% S. What is the minimum molecular weight of the enzyme? What is the minimum number of iron atoms per molecule? Of sulfur atoms?

10. A protein, *β-lactoglobulin*, from cheese whey, has a molecular weight of 42020 ± 105. When a 100-mg sample was hydrolyzed by acid and the mixture was made alkaline, 1.31 mg of ammonia was evolved. (a) Where did the ammonia come from, and approximately how many such groups are there in the protein?

Complete hydrolysis of a 100-mg sample of the protein used up approximately 17 mg of water. (b) How many amide linkages per molecule were cleaved?

(c) Combining the results of (a) and (b), and adding the fact that there are four N-terminal groups (four peptide chains in the molecule), how many amino acid residues are there in the protein?

11. The complete structure of *Gramicidin S*, a polypeptide with antibiotic properties, has been worked out as follows:

(a) Analysis of the hydrolysis products gave an empirical formula of Leu,Orn,Phe,Pro,Val. (*Ornithine*, Orn, is a rare amino acid of formula $\overset{+}{H_3}NCH_2CH_2CH_2CH(NH_2)COO^-$.) It is interesting that the phenylalanine has the unusual D-configuration.

Measurement of the molecular weight gave an approximate value of 1300. On this basis, what is the molecular formula of Gramicidin S?

(b) Analysis for the C-terminal residue was negative; analysis for the N-terminal residue using DNFB yielded only $DNP—NHCH_2CH_2CH_2CH(\overset{+}{N}H_3)COO^-$. What structural feature must the peptide chain possess?

(c) Partial hydrolysis of Gramicidin S gave the following di- and tripeptides:

Leu.Phe	Phe.Pro	Phe.Pro.Val	Val.Orn.Leu
Orn.Leu	Val.Orn	Pro.Val.Orn	

What is the structure of Gramicidin S?

12. The structure of beef insulin was determined by Sanger (see Sec. 33.9) on the basis of the following information. Work out for yourself the sequence of amino acid residues in the protein.

Beef insulin appears to have a molecular weight of about 6000 and to consist of two polypeptide chains linked by disulfide bridges of cystine residues. The chains can be separated by oxidation, which changes any CyS—SCy or CySH residues to sulfonic acids (CySO$_3$H).

One chain, A, of 21 amino acid residues, is acidic and has the empirical formula

GlyAlaVal$_2$Leu$_2$Ileu(CySH)$_4$Asp$_2$Glu$_4$Ser$_2$Tyr$_2$

The other chain, B, of 30 amino acid residues, is basic and has the empirical formula

Gly$_3$Ala$_2$Val$_3$Leu$_4$ProPhe$_3$(CySH)$_2$ArgHis$_2$LysAspGlu$_3$SerThrTyr$_2$

(Chain A has four simple side-chain amide groups, and chain B has two, but these will be ignored for the time being.)

Treatment of chain B with 2,4-dinitrofluorobenzene (DNFB) followed by hydrolysis gave DNP.Phe and DNP.Phe.Val; chain B lost alanine (Ala) when treated with carboxypeptidase.

Acidic hydrolysis of chain B gave the following tripeptides:

Glu.His.Leu	Leu.Val.CySH	Tyr.Leu.Val
Gly.Glu.Arg	Leu.Val.Glu	Val.Asp.Glu
His.Leu.CySH	Phe.Val.Asp	Val.CySH.Gly
Leu.CySH.Gly	Pro.Lys.Ala	Val.Glu.Ala
	Ser.His.Leu	

Many dipeptides were isolated and identified; two important ones were Arg.Gly and Thr.Pro.

(a) At this point construct as much of the B chain as the data will allow.

Among the numerous tetrapeptides and pentapeptides from chain B were found:

His.Leu.Val.Glu   Tyr.Leu.Val.CySH
Ser.His.Leu.Val   Phe.Val.Asp.Glu.His

(b) How much more of the chain can you reconstruct now? What amino acid residues are still missing?

Enzymatic hydrolysis of chain B gave the necessary final pieces:

Val.Glu.Ala.Leu   His.Leu.CySH.Gly.Ser.His.Leu
Tyr.Thr.Pro.Lys.Ala   Tyr.Leu.Val.CySH.Gly.Glu.Arg.Gly.Phe.Phe

(c) What is the complete sequence in the B chain of beef insulin?

Treatment of chain A with DNFB followed by hydrolysis gave DNP.Gly; the C-terminal group was shown to be aspartic acid (Asp).

Acidic hydrolysis of chain A gave the following tripeptides:

CySH.CySH.Ala   Glu.Leu.Glu
Glu.Asp.Tyr   Leu.Tyr.Glu
Glu.CySH.CySH   Ser.Leu.Tyr
Glu.Glu.CySH   Ser.Val.CySH

Among other peptides isolated from acidic hydrolysis of chain A were:

CySH.Asp   Tyr.CySH   Gly.Ileu.Val.Glu.Glu

(d) Construct as much of chain A as the data will allow. Are there any amino acid residues missing?

Up to this point it is possible to arrive at the sequences of four parts of chain A, but it is still uncertain which of the two center fragments, Ser Val.CySH or Ser.Leu.Tyr. etc., comes first. This was settled by digestion of chain A with pepsin, which gave a peptide that contained no aspartic acid (Asp) or tyrosine (Tyr). Hydrolysis of this peptide gave Ser.Val.CySH and Ser.Leu.

(e) Now what is the complete structure of chain A of beef insulin?

In insulin the cysteine units (CySH) are involved in cystine disulfide links (CyS—SCy). Residue 7 of chain A (numbering from the N-terminal residue) is linked to residue 7 of chain B, residue 20 of chain A to residue 19 of chain B, and there is a link between residues 6 and 11 of chain A.

There are amide groups on residues 5, 15, 18, and 21 of chain A, and on residues 3 and 4 of chain B.

(f) Draw a structure of the complete insulin molecule. (*Note:* the disulfide loop in chain A is a 20-atom, pentapeptide ring, of the same size as the one in oxytocin.)

In the analysis for the N-terminal group in chain B of insulin, equal amounts of *two* different DNP derivatives of single amino acids actually were found. One was DNP.Phe; what could the other have been?

(g) What would have been obtained if that second amino acid had been N-terminal?

General

G. W. Wheland, *Advanced Organic Chemistry*, 2nd ed., Wiley, New York, 1955.

J. Hine, *Physical Organic Chemistry*, McGraw-Hill, New York, 1956.

C. K. Ingold, *Structure and Mechanism in Organic Chemistry*, Cornell University Press, Ithaca, 1953.

J. E. Leffler, *The Reactive Intermediates of Organic Chemistry*, Interscience, New York, 1956.

M. S. Newman, ed., *Steric Effects in Organic Chemistry*, Wiley, New York, 1956.

W. J. Hickinbottom, *Reactions of Organic Compounds*, 3rd ed., Longmans, Green, New York, 1957.

E. H. Rodd, ed., *Chemistry of Carbon Compounds*, Elsevier, Amsterdam and Houston; a series starting in 1951.

Organic Reactions, Wiley, New York; a series starting in 1942. Each chapter discusses one reaction ("The Clemmensen Reduction," "Periodic Acid Oxidation," etc.) with particular emphasis on its application to synthesis.

Note: Some of the above books will be referred to later by abbreviated names, e.g., O.R. III–2 for *Organic Reactions*, Vol. III, Ch. 2.

Molecular structure and intermolecular forces

G. W. Wheland, *Adv. Org. Chem.*, Ch. 1, 10.

C. K. Ingold, *Struct. and Mech.*, Ch. I, II, IV.

L. Pauling, *The Nature of the Chemical Bond*, 2nd ed., Cornell University Press, Ithaca, 1940.

G. W. Wheland, *Resonance in Organic Chemistry*, Wiley, New York, 1955.

C. A. Coulson, "The Meaning of Resonance in Quantum Chemistry," Endeavour, **6,** 42 (1947).

P. E. Verkade, "August Kekulé," Proc. Chem. Soc., 205 (1958).

W. Baker, "The Development of the Concept of Aromaticity," pp. 28–67 in *Perspectives in Organic Chemistry*, A. R. Todd, ed., Interscience, New York, 1956.

G. W. A. Fowles, "Lone Pair Electrons," J. Chem. Educ., **34,** 187 (1957).

M. Gorman, "The Evidence from Infrared Spectroscopy for Hydrogen Bonding," J. Chem. Educ., **34,** 304 (1957).

Isomerism and stereochemistry

G. W. Wheland, *Adv. Org. Chem.*, Ch. 4–8.

I. L. Finar, *Organic Chemistry*, Longmans, Green, New York, Vol. II, 1956, Ch. II–VI.

K. Mislow, "Optical Activity, Molecular Symmetry Elements, and Configuration in Biphenyl Series," Trans. N. Y. Acad. Sci., **19**, 298 (1957).

D. F. Mowery, Jr., "The Cause of Optical Inactivity," J. Chem. Educ., **29**, 138 (1952).

J. M. Bijvoet, "Determination of the Absolute Configuration of Optical Antipodes," Endeavour, **14**, 71 (1955).

M. L. Wolfrom, "Optical Activity and Configurational Relations in Carbon Compounds," Rec. Chem. Progr. (Kresge-Hooker Sci. Lib.), **16**, 121 (1955).

D. H. R. Barton and R. C. Cookson, "The Principles of Conformational Analysis," Quart. Revs. (London), **10**, 44 (1956).

W. G. Dauben and K. S. Pitzer, "Conformational Analysis," Ch. 1 in *Steric Effects*.

D. Y. Curtin, "Stereochemical Control of Organic Reactions — Differences in Behavior of Diastereomers," Rec. Chem. Progr. (Kresge-Hooker Sci. Lib.), **15**, 111 (1954).

Acids and bases

G. N. Lewis, "Acids and Bases," J. Franklin Inst., **226**, 293 (1938).

G. W. Wheland, *Adv. Org. Chem.*, Ch. 3.

R. P. Bell, "The Use of the Terms Acid and Base," Quart. Revs. (London), **1**, 113 (1947).

W. F. Luder, "Contemporary Acid-Base Theory," J. Chem. Educ., **25**, 555 (1948).

C. K. Ingold, *Struct. and Mech.*, Ch. XIII.

G. S. Hammond, "Steric Effects on Equilibrated Systems," pp. 426–460 in *Steric Effects*.

Nomenclature and pronunciation

A. M. Patterson, L. T. Capell, and M. A. Magill, "Nomenclature of Organic Compounds," Chem. Abs., **39**, 5875–5950 (1945).

E. J. Crane, "The Pronunciation of Chemical Words," Ind. Eng. Chem., News Ed., **12**, 202 (1934).

Free radicals

M. Gomberg, "An Instance of Trivalent Carbon: Triphenylmethyl," J. Am. Chem. Soc., **22**, 757 (1900).

G. W. Wheland, *Adv. Org. Chem.*, Ch. 15.

J. E. Leffler, *React. Int.*, Ch. I–II.

J. Hine, *Phys. Org. Chem.*, Ch. 18–23.

C. Walling, *Free Radicals in Solution*, Wiley, New York, 1957.

D. H. Whitten, "Electron Resonance Spectroscopy of Free Radicals," Quart. Revs. (London), **12**, 250 (1958).

Carbonium ions

F. C. Whitmore, "Alkylation and Related Processes of Modern Petroleum Practice," Chem. Eng. News, **26,** 668 (1948).

J. E. Leffler, *React. Int.*, Ch. V–VII.

C. K. Ingold, *Struct. and Mech.*, Ch. VII.

D. Bethell and V. Gold, "The Structure of Carbonium Ions," Quart. Revs. (London), **12,** 173 (1958).

Carbanions and tautomerism

J. E. Leffler, *React. Int.*, Ch. IX–X.

J. Hine, *Phys. Org. Chem.*, Ch. 10.

C. K. Ingold, *Struct. and Mech.*, Ch. X.

G. W. Wheland, *Adv. Org. Chem.*, Ch. 14.

G. S. Hammond, "Steric Effects on Equilibrated Systems," pp. 442–454, 460–470 in *Steric Effects*.

Substitution

J. Hine, *Phys. Org. Chem.*, Ch. 5, "Mechanisms for Nucleophilic Displacement on Carbon;" Ch. 6, "Reactivity in Nucleophilic Displacement on Carbon;" Ch. 16, "Electrophilic Aromatic Substitution."

J. F. Bunnett, "Mechanism and Reactivity in Aromatic Nucleophilic Substitution Reactions," Quart. Revs. (London), **12,** 1 (1958).

C. K. Ingold, *Struct. and Mech.*, Ch. VI, "Electrophilic Aromatic Substitution;" Ch. VII, "Nucleophilic Aromatic Substitution."

C. Walling, *Free Rads.*, Ch. 8, "Halogen Substitution Reactions."

G. Baddeley, "Modern Aspects of the Friedel-Crafts Reaction," Quart. Revs. (London), **8,** 355 (1954).

E. L. Eliel, "Substitution at Saturated Carbon Atoms," Ch. 2 in *Steric Effects*.

G. S. Hammond and M. F. Hawthorne, "Steric Effects in Aromatic Substitution," Ch. 3 in *Steric Effects*.

Addition to carbon–carbon multiple bonds

J. Hine, *Phys. Org. Chem.*, Ch. 9, "Addition to Carbon–Carbon Multiple Bonds."

C. K. Ingold, *Struct. and Mech.*, Ch. XII, "Additions and Their Retrogression."

J. I. G. Cadogan and D. H. Hey, "Free-radical Addition Reactions of Olefinic Systems," Quart. Revs. (London), **8,** 308 (1954).

M. S. Newman, "Additions to Unsaturated Functions," pp. 242–248 in *Steric Effects*.

Elimination

J. Hine, *Phys. Org. Chem.*, Ch. 7, "Elimination Reactions."

C. K. Ingold, *Struct. and Mech.*, Ch. VIII, "Olefin-forming Eliminations."

D. J. Cram, "Olefin-forming Elimination Reactions," Ch. 6 in *Steric Effects*.

Oxidation

O.R. VII–7, D. Swern, "Epoxidation and Hydroxylation of Ethylenic Compounds with Organic Peracids;" II–8, E. L. Jackson, "Periodic Acid Oxidation."

W. A. Waters, "Mechanisms of Oxidation by Compounds of Chromium and Manganese," Quart. Revs. (London), **12**, 277 (1958).

Reduction and hydrogenation

O.R. I–7, E. L. Martin, "The Clemmensen Reduction;" IV–8, D. Todd, "The Wolff-Kishner Reduction;" II–5, A. L. Wilds, "Reduction with Aluminum Alkoxides (the Meerwein-Ponndorf-Verley Reduction);" VI–10, W. G. Brown, "Reductions by Lithium Aluminum Hydride."

A. J. Birch, "Reduction of Organic Compounds," Quart. Revs. (London), **4**, 69 (1950).

G. C. Bond, "Mechanism of Catalytic Hydrogenation and Related Reactions," Quart. Revs. (London), **8**, 279 (1954).

Rearrangements

F. C. Whitmore, "The Common Basis of Intramolecular Rearrangements," J. Am. Chem. Soc., **54**, 3274 (1932).

R. T. Arnold, "The Rearrangement of Allyl and Aryl Groups as Anions," Rec. Chem. Progr. (Kresge-Hooker Sci. Lib.), **12**, 29 (1951).

G. W. Wheland, *Adv. Org. Chem.*, Ch. 12–13.

J. Hine, *Phys. Org. Chem.*, Ch. 14, 15, 23.

C. K. Ingold, *Struct. and Mech.*, Ch. IX–XI.

O.R. III–7, E. S. Wallis and J. F. Lane, "The Hofmann Reaction;" III–9, P. A. S. Smith, "The Curtius Reaction;" III–8, H. Wolff, "The Schmidt Reaction."

D. J. Cram, "Intramolecular Rearrangements," Ch. 5 in *Steric Effects*.

Acyl compounds

O.R. I–9, C. R. Hauser and B. E. Hudson, Jr., "The Acetoacetic Ester Condensation and Related Reactions;" IV–4, S. M. McElvain, "The Acyloins;" II–4, W. S. Johnson, "The Formation of Cyclic Ketones by Intramolecular Acylation;" VIII–2, D. A. Shirley, "The Synthesis of Ketones from Acid Chlorides and Organometallic Compounds of Magnesium, Zinc, and Cadmium."

C. K. Ingold, *Struct. and Mech.*, Ch. XIV.

J. Hine, *Phys. Org. Chem.*, Ch. 12–13.

A. G. Davies and J. Kenyon, "Alkyl–Oxygen Heterolysis in Carboxylic Esters and Related Compounds," Quart. Revs. (London), **9**, 203 (1955).

M. S. Newman, "Additions to Unsaturated Functions," pp. 204–233 in *Steric Effects*.

Carbonyl compounds

C. K. Ingold, *Struct. and Mech.*, pp. 676–690.

J. Hine, *Phys. Org. Chem.*, Ch. 11.

M. S. Newman, "Additions to Unsaturated Functions," pp. 233–248 in *Steric Effects*.

O.R. IV–5, W. S. Ide and J. S. Buck, "The Synthesis of Benzoins;" II–3, T. A. Geissman, "The Cannizzaro Reaction;" V–6, N. N. Crounse, "The Gattermann-Koch Reaction;" I–10, F. F. Blicke, "The Mannich Reaction."

α, β-Unsaturated carbonyl compounds

C. K. Ingold, *Struct. and Mech.*, pp. 690–699.

R. C. Fuson, *Advanced Organic Chemistry*, Wiley, New York, 1950. Ch. XIX, especially pp. 484–505.

O.R. IV–1, M. C. Kloetzel, "The Diels-Alder Reaction With Maleic Anhydride;" V–2, H. A. Bruson, "Cyanoethylation."

Nitrogen compounds

N. V. Sidgwick, T. W. J. Taylor, and W. Baker, *The Organic Chemistry of Nitrogen,* 2nd ed., Clarendon Press, Oxford, 1937.

R. H. Wiley, "Heterocyclic Chemistry," in *Organic Chemistry*, H. Gilman, ed., Vol. IV, Ch. 8, Wiley, New York, 1953.

E. Adams, "Barbiturates," Sci. American, Jan. 1958, p. 60.

W. A. Noyes, Jr., ed., *Science in World War II: Chemistry*, Little, Brown, Boston, 1948. Ch. 4 on explosives.

Polymers and polymerization

C. E. H. Bawn, "New Kinds of Macromolecules," Endeavour, **15,** 137 (1956).

G. Natta, "How Giant Molecules Are Made," Sci. American, Sept. 1957, p. 98.

A. V. Tobolsky, "Revolution in Polymer Chemistry," Am. Scientist, **45,** 34 (1957).

Natural products

C. S. Hudson, "Emil Fischer's Discovery of the Configuration of Glucose," J. Chem. Educ., **18,** 353 (1941).

E. J. V. Percival, *Structural Carbohydrate Chemistry*, Prentice-Hall, New York, 1950.

I. L. Finar, *Organic Chemistry*, Longmans, Green, New York, Vol. II, 1956, Ch. VII–XIX.

J. Simonsen, *The Terpenes*, Cambridge University Press. Vols. I–III, 2nd ed., 1947. Vols. IV–V, with W. C. J. Ross, 1957.

W. Klyne, *The Chemistry of the Steroids*, Wiley, New York, 1957.

Amino acids and proteins

L. Pauling, "The Configuration of Polypeptide Chains in Proteins," Rec. Chem. Progr. (Kresge-Hooker Sci. Lib.), **12,** 155 (1951).

P. Doty, "Proteins," Sci. American, Sept. 1957, p. 173.

L. Pauling, R. B. Corey, and R. Hayward, "Structure of Protein Molecules," Sci. American, Oct. 1954, p. 54.

F. Sanger and L. F. Smith, "The Structure of Insulin," Endeavour, **16,** 48 (1957).

F. Sanger, "The Chemistry of Insulin (Nobel lecture)," Chemistry and Industry, 104 (1959).

J. S. Fruton and S. Simmonds, *General Biochemistry*, 2nd ed., Wiley, New York, 1958, Ch. 2–7.

Chemistry of biological processes

W. G. Overend and A. R. Peacocke, "The Molecular Basis of Heredity," Endeavour, **16,** 90 (1957).

M. F. Perutz, "Some Recent Advances in Molecular Biology," Endeavour, **17,** 190 (1958).

J. H. Taylor, "The Duplication of Chromosomes," Sci. American, June 1958, p. 37.

F. H. C. Crick, "Nucleic Acids," Sci. American, Sept. 1957, p. 188.

G. Gamow, "Information Transfer in the Living Cell," Sci. American, Oct. 1955, p. 70.

D. E. Green, "Biological Oxidation," Sci. American, July 1958, p. 56.

J. B. Neilands and P. K. Stumpf, *Outlines of Enzyme Chemistry*, 2nd ed., Wiley, New York, 1958.

Use of isotopes

D. A. Semenow and J. D. Roberts, "Uses of Isotopes in Organic Chemistry," J. Chem. Educ., **33,** 2 (1956).

J. A. Bassham, A. A. Benson, and M. Calvin, "Isotope Studies in Photosynthesis," J. Chem. Educ., **30,** 274 (1953).

J. G. Burr, *Tracer Applications for the Study of Organic Reactions*, Interscience, New York, 1957.

W. F. Libby, *Radiocarbon Dating*, 2nd ed., University of Chicago Press, 1955.

Analysis

R. L. Shriner, R. C. Fuson, and D. Y. Curtin, *Systematic Identification of Organic Compounds*, 4th ed., Wiley, New York, 1956.

N. D. Cheronis and J. B. Entrikin, *Semimicro Qualitative Organic Analysis*, 2nd ed., Interscience, New York, 1957.

B. Crawford, Jr., "Chemical Analysis By Infrared," Sci. American, Oct. 1953, p. 42.

J. D. Roberts, *Nuclear Magnetic Resonance*, McGraw-Hill, New York, 1959.

W. H. Stein and S. Moore, "Chromatography," Sci. American, Mar. 1951, p. 35.

Special topics

R. A. Raphael, *Acetylenic Compounds in Organic Synthesis*, Academic Press, New York, 1955.

M. H. Bigelow, "Reppe's Acetylene Chemistry," Chem. Eng. News, **25,** 1038 (1947).

J. H. Simons, "Fluorocarbons," Sci. American, Nov. 1949, p. 44.

G. L. Jenkins *et al*, *The Chemistry of Organic Medicinal Products*, 4th ed., Wiley, New York, 1957.

H. E. Fierz-David and L. Blangey, *Fundamental Processes of Dye Chemistry*, Interscience, New York, 1949.

M. S. Kharasch and O. Reinmuth, *Grignard Reactions of Nonmetallic Substances*, Prentice-Hall, New York, 1954.

C. M. Suter, *Organic Chemistry of Sulfur*, Wiley, New York, 1944.

ANSWERS

TO PROBLEMS

Chapter 1

1.2 Tetrahedral. **1.3** Square. **1.4** CO_2 linear; BF_3 flat, 120° angles.
1.6 $CH_3SH > CH_3OH > CH_3NH_2$; $H_3O^+ > NH_4^+$. **1.7** (a) H_3O^+; (b) NH_4^+;
(c) H_2S; (d) H_2O. **1.8** (a) $CH_3^- > NH_2^- > OH^- > F^-$; (b) $NH_3 > H_2O > HF$;
(c) $SH^- > Cl^-$; (d) $F^- > Cl^- > Br^- > I^-$; (e) $OH^- > SH^- > SeH^-$.
1.9 $CH_3NH_2 > CH_3OH > CH_3F$. **1.10** (a) $OH^- > H_2O > H_3O^+$; (b) $NH_2^- > NH_3$;
(c) $S^{--} > HS^- > H_2S$.
1. Ionic: a, d, f, i, k. **12.** (a) H_3O^+; (b) HCl; (c) HCl in benzene.

Chapter 2

2.1 (a) -7 kcal; (b) $+11$ kcal; (c) -103 kcal. **2.2** (a) $+46$, $+14$, -21
kcal; (b) $+36$, $+30$, -19 kcal; (c) $+38$, -34, -69 kcal. **2.4** 2 (mirror images).
2.5 (a) 3; (b) 2; (c) 3 (2 are mirror images); (d) 1. **2.6** (a) (%C + %H) < 100%;
(b) 34.8%. **2.7** (a) 69.6% Cl; (b) 70.4% Cl; (c) 24.85 mg; (d) 26.49 mg;
(e) 27.44 mg. **2.8** (a) CH_3; (b) $C_3H_6Cl_2$. **2.9** (a) 79.8; (b) C_6H_6; (c) 78.
2.10 $C_4H_8O_2$.
1. A, 93.9% C, 6.3% H; B, 64.0% C, 4.5% H, 31.4% Cl; C, 62.0% C, 10.3% H,
27.7% O. **2.** (a) 45.9% C, 8.9% H, 45.2% Cl; (b) 52.1% C, 13.1% H, 34.8% O;
(c) 54.5% C, 9.1% H, 36.3% O; (d) 41.8% C, 4.7% H, 18.6% O, 16.3% N,
18.6% S; (e) 20.0% C, 6.7% H, 26.6% O, 46.7% N; (f) 55.6% C, 6.2% H,
10.8% O, 27.4% Cl. **3.** (a) CH_2; (b) CH; (c) CH_2O; (d) C_2H_5OCl;
(e) $C_3H_{10}N_2$; (f) $C_3H_4O_2Cl_2$. **4.** $C_{20}H_{21}O_4N$. **5.** $C_{14}H_{14}O_3N_3SNa$. **6.** (a) 85.8% C,
14.3% H; (b) CH_2; (c) C_6H_{12}. **7.** $C_2H_4O_2$. **8.** CH_2O. **9.** $C_{16}H_{10}O_2N_2$.
10. C_4H_{10}. **11.** (a) 941; (b) 6. **12.** (a) -129; (b) -45; (c) -25; (d) -3;
(e) -8; (f) -14; (g) -12; (h) 1st step $+46$; 2nd steps $+11$, -9, -10; 3rd
steps -19, -5, -2. **13.** (a) $+58$, $+21$, -45; (b) E_{act} of a chain-carrying
step ≥ 21 kcal.

Chapter 3

3.13 (a) 48% 1-Cl, 52% 2-Cl; (b) 67% 1-Cl, 33% 2-Cl; (c) 57.5% 1-Cl,
42.5% 2-Cl; (d) 23.5% 1-Cl, 51% 2-Cl, 25.5% 3-Cl; (e) 30% 1-Cl-2-Me (Me
= methyl), 22% 2-Cl-2-Me, 33% 3-Cl-2-Me, 15% 1-Cl-3-Me; (f) 46%
1-Cl-2,2,3-Me₃, 23% 3-Cl-2,2,3-Me₃, 31% 1-Cl-2,3,3-Me₃; (g) 35% 1-Cl-2,2,4-Me₃,
25% 3-Cl-2,2,4-Me₃, 17% 4-Cl-2,2,4-Me₃, 23% 1-Cl-2,4,4-Me₃. **3.16** 2,7-Dimethyl-
octane.
4. (e) 6. **6.** c, b, e, a, d. **10.** 2-Methylheptane, 50%; other two 25% each.
12. (a) 19% 1-Cl, 40.5% 2-Cl, 40.5% 3-Cl; (b) 23% 1-Cl-2-Me, 17% 2-Cl-2-Me,
24.5% 3-Cl-2-Me, 24.5% 4-Cl-2-Me, 11% 1-Cl-4-Me; (c) 23% 1-Cl, 49% 2-Cl,
17% 3-Cl, 11% 1-Cl-2-Et (Et = ethyl); (d) 49% 1-Cl-2,2-Me₂, 35% 3-Cl-2,2-Me₂,

897

16% 1-Cl-3,3-Me$_2$. **15.** (a) 2650 g; (b) 8710 kcal; (c) 170 g. **16.** Carius: mono, 45.3% Cl; di, 62.8% Cl. Mol. wt. by vapor density: mono, 78.5; di, 113.

Chapter 4

3. b, d, g, h, i, k (3 isomers). **4.** (b) 4 show geometric isomerism. **5.** Differ in all except (h); (k) dipole moment would tell.

Chapter 5

5.1 (c) 1-Butene 649.8, *cis*-2-butene 648.1, *trans*-2-butene 647.1; (d) 1-pentene 806.9, *cis*-2-pentene 805.3, *trans*-2-pentene 804.3. **5.5** (d) Steps (2) and (4) are too difficult with HCl. **5.8** A, alkane; B, 2° alcohol; C, alkyl halide; D, alkene; E, 3° alcohol.

7. 3° radical more stable than 2° radical, forms faster.

15. 2 *t*-C$_4$H$_9$Cl + Mg ⟶ MgCl$_2$ + *i*-C$_4$H$_{10}$ + *i*-C$_4$H$_8$.

Chapter 6

14. (a) −42.2 kcal/mole. **19.** Acid-catalyzed polymerization of alkene easily formed from 2° or 3° alcohol. **25.** (b) Myrcene, (CH$_3$)$_2$C=CHCH$_2$CH$_2$C(=CH$_2$)-CH=CH$_2$. **26.** (a) (CH$_3$)$_2$C=CHCH$_2$CH$_2$C(CH$_3$)=CHCH$_3$; (b) no; 1,4-addition.

Chapter 7

7.6 (e) For the same degree of unsaturation, there are two fewer hydrogens for each ring.

2. (r) 1-Cyclohexylcyclohexene; (s) cyclopentylcyclopentane. **7.** A, *cis*-dimethyl; B, *trans*-dimethyl. **8.** (c) Evidently electrostatic repulsion between highly negative atoms is more important than 1,3-interaction. **9.** (d) In the *trans*-isomer, both large substituents (the other ring) are equatorial; (e) high energy barrier (E_{act}) between decalins since bond must be broken. **10.** (a) *trans*-Addition. **12.** (a) 2; (b) 4; (c) 1; (d) 3; (e) 4.

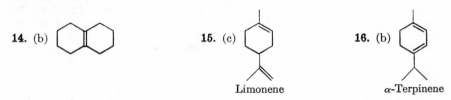

14. (b)   **15.** (c)   **16.** (b)

Limonene   α-Terpinene

Chapter 8

8.1 (a) +5.6 kcal; (b) −26.8 kcal. **8.2** (a) 824.1 kcal; (b) 35.0 kcal greater. **8.7** *ortho*, 103°; *meta*, 63°; *para*, 140°. **8.10** 26.0%. **8.11** 22.8%. **8.12** 18.5%. **8.13** 25.9%, 22.9%, 18.6%. **8.14** (a) 242, C$_6$H$_4$Br$_2$; (b) 153, C$_{12}$H$_{12}$; (c) 59, CH$_4$ON$_2$.

2. (a) 3; (b) 3; (c) 3; (d) 6; (e) 10; (f) 6. **3.** (a) 2, 3, 3, 1, 2; (b) 5, 5, 5, 2, 4 (neglecting stereoisomers); (c) none. **4.** (a) 2; (b) 3; (c) 1; (d) 4; (e) 4; (f) 2; (g) 4; (h) 4; (i) 2; (j) 1; (k) 3; (l) 2. **5.** (a) 1; (b) 1; (c) 2; (d) 1; (e) 2; (f) 3; (g) 2.

12. HO–NO$_2$ + H$_2$SO$_4$ ⇌ H$_2$Ö–NO$_2$ + HSO$_4^-$

H$_2$Ö–NO$_2$ ⟶ H$_2$O + NO$_2^+$ (*slow*)

H$_2$O + H$_2$SO$_4$ ⇌ H$_3$O$^+$ + HSO$_4^-$

14. (a) 33.6% C, 2.4% H, 63.7% Br; (b) $C_7H_6Br_2$; (c) $C_7H_6Br_2$; (d) 10 possibilities.

Chapter 9

9.9 (a) 17 at 25°; 12 at 80°.
6. ⁓CH₂C₆H₄CH₂C₆H₄CH₂C₆H₄⁓. **14.** 2-Methyl-2-butene. **20.** Ethylbenzene. **21.** *cis-* or *trans*-Stilbene. **23.**

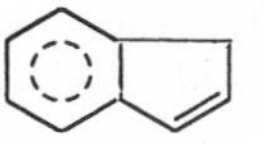

Indene 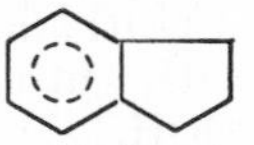   Indane

Chapter 11

12. (a) −300°; (b) −3.6°; (c) −0.9°. **15.** (a) 3; (b) 4; (c) 1; (d) 3; (e) 1; (f) 1; (g) 1; (h) 1; (i) 3; (j) 1; (k) 1; (l) 2; (m) 1; all fractions except (m) inactive as collected.

Chapter 12

1. (a) Two give iodoform; (c) one gives negative test. **13.** B, $HOCH_2CH_2OH$; D, $HOCH_2COOH$; G, $HOCH_2CHOHCH_2OH$; J, $CH_2=CHCOOH$; M, $HOCH_2C\equiv CH$; O, CH_3COCH_3; S, CH_3COONa; U, *cis*-1,2-cyclo-$C_6H_{10}(OOCCH_3)_2$; W, glyceryl triacetate; ZZ, 3-methylbiphenyl. **17.** A, $C_6H_5CH_2CHOHCH_3$; B, $C_6H_5CH(CH_3)CH_2OH$. **18.** (a) Geraniol, $(CH_3)_2C=CHCH_2CH_2C(CH_3)=CHCH_2OH$; (b) geometric isomers; (c) in geraniol, −H and −CH_3 are *trans*.

Chapter 13

13.4 (a) 1.9%; (b) 16.4%; (c) 66.2%; (d) 95.1%; (e) 99.0%.
14. (a) Complete inversion. **15.** (a) Inversion (57%) and racemization (43%). **22.** (a) C_4H_4Cl; (b) no; (c) 175. **23.** (a) C_2H_4Br; (b) at least $C_4H_8Br_2$; (c) C, 1,2-dibromobutane; D, 1-butene. **24.** (a) E 3 rings, F 3 rings; (b) E *p*-dibenzylbenzene, F 9,10-dihydroanthracene (see Sec. 31.17).

Chapter 14

1. No reaction: b, c, d, e, f, g, k, l, n, o. **5.** (o) Benzene + $HC\equiv CMgBr$ before H_2O treatment.

Chapter 15

15.4 (a) Complete inversion. **15.5** a, d, e. **15.22** 4.
8. Polyisobutylene. **12.** A, 3-bromo-4-methoxytoluene; B, *o*-methoxybenzyl bromide; C, *o*-bromophenetole. **19.** A, $ClCH_2CHOHCH_2OCH_3$; C, CH₂—CH—CH₂OCH₃; D, H₂C—CH₂ ;
   \O/ | |
                        H₂C—O

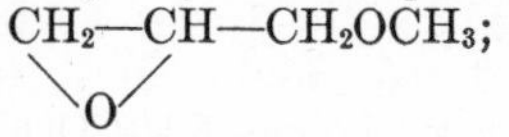

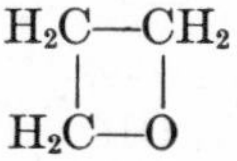

E, β-phenylethyl alcohol; F, acetaldehyde; J, p-$CH_3CH=CHC_6H_4OCH_3$; K, racemic *trans*-2-chlorocyclohexanol; L, racemic *trans*-1-methyl-1,2-cyclohexanediol; N, n-$C_4H_9OCH_2CHO$.

Chapter 16

16.1 91 at 110°, 71 at 156°; association occurs even in vapor phase, decreasing as temperature increases. **16.13** (a) 103. **16.14** (a) two, 83; (b) N.E. = mol. wt./number acidic H per molecule; (c) 70, 57. **16.15** Sodium carbonate.

11. C, n-$C_{16}H_{33}Br$; F, n-$C_{16}H_{33}COOH$. **26.** N.E. 165. **27.** Q, m-ethylbenzoic acid; U, 3,5-dimethylbenzoic acid. **28.** Nervonic acid, *cis*- or *trans*-$CH_3(CH_2)_7$-$CH{=}CH(CH_2)_{13}COOH$ (actually, the *trans*-isomer). **29.** Tropic acid, C_6H_5-$CH(CH_2OH)COOH$; atropic acid, $C_6H_5C({=}CH_2)COOH$; hydratropic acid, $C_6H_5CH(CH_3)COOH$.

Chapter 17

17.9 (a) two, 97; (b) S.E. = mol. wt./number ester groups per molecule; (c) 296.

15. (a) Spermaceti, n-hexadecyl n-hexadecanoate. **17.** (a) 5 —OH's; (b) 2 —COOH's; (c) 2 —OH's; (d) 3 —OH's; (e) one —COOH; gallic acid, 3,4,5-trihydroxybenzoic acid. **18.** M, indene (see page 453); P, $C_2H_5OCH_2$-$COOCH_2CH_2OOCCH_2OC_2H_5$; R, *trans*-2-methylcyclohexanol.

Chapter 18

18.4 Hydrogen is displaced from ring by another hydrogen ion (e.g., deuterium) in typical electrophilic substitution. **18.5** The —SO_3H group is displaced by an electrophilic reagent: bromonium ion or nitronium ion.

17. Saccharin, 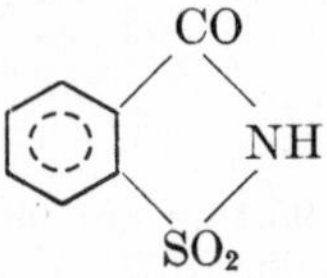 **18.** Chloramine T, $(p\text{-}CH_3C_6H_4SO_2NCl)^-Na^+$.

Chapter 19

6. (a) Putrescine, 1,4-diaminobutane; (b) cadaverine, 1,5-diaminopentane. **7.** Pair of enantiomers, a, c, d, f; one inactive compound, b; inactive *cis-trans* pair, e.

Chapter 20

20.2 Nitro group at *o*- or *p*-position stabilizes *amine* through structures like

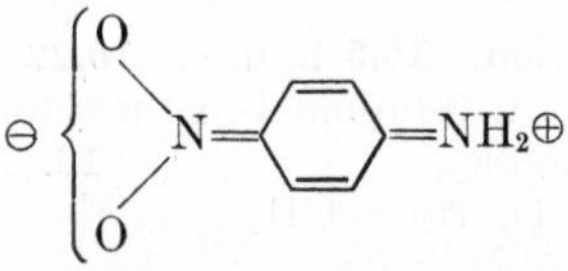

15. (a) Choline, $HOCH_2CH_2N(CH_3)_3{}^+OH^-$; (b) acetylcholine, CH_3COOCH_2-$CH_2N(CH_3)_3{}^+OH^-$. **16.** Novocaine, p-$H_2NC_6H_4COOCH_2CH_2N(C_2H_5)_2$. **17.** (a) $C_7H_6NBr_3$; (b) m-toluidine. **18.** F, N-methyl-N-phenyl-p-toluamide. **19.** S, 1,3,5,7-cyclooctatetraene. **20.** T, N-(p-bromophenyl)benzenesulfonamide. **21.** W, anilinium chloride.

Chapter 21

21.6 (a) $C_6H_5NHR + ArN_2^+ \rightarrow C_6H_5NR-N=N-Ar$;

(b) $C_6H_5NR-N=N-Ar + H^+ \rightleftarrows C_6H_5\overset{+}{N}HR-N=N-Ar$

$$p\text{-}Ar-N=N-C_6H_4NHR \leftarrow C_6H_5NH\overset{\downarrow}{R} + ArN_2^+$$

Chapter 22

22.12 (a) The —SO_3H group is displaced by electrophilic reagents, in this case by nitronium ion.
5. No reaction: b, c, f, h, n. **6.** Reaction only with c, p, r, s, t, u. **12.** *Ortho*; then *meta*; finally *para*. **13.** Phenacetin, $p\text{-}CH_3CONHC_6H_4OC_2H_5$;

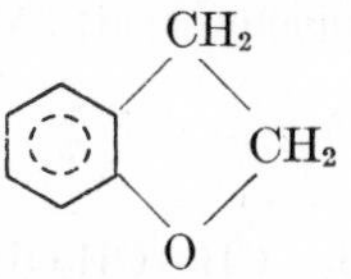

Coumarane 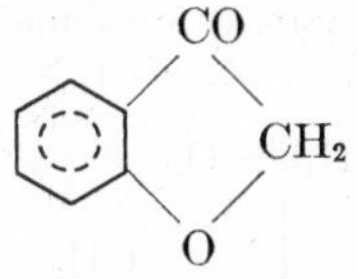   3-Cumaranone

carvacrol, 5-isopropyl-2-methylphenol; thymol, 2-isopropyl-5-methylphenol; hexestrol, 3,4-bis(*p*-hydroxyphenyl)hexane. **14.** N, *m*-cresol. **16.** O, *p*-allylanisole; P, *p*-propenylanisole. **17.** Q, isopropyl salicylate. **19.** Chavibetol, 2-methoxy-5-allylphenol. **20.** N-Phenylhydroxylamine, C_6H_5NHOH; W, $p\text{-}HOC_6H_4NH_2$. **21.** α-Terpineol, 2-(4-methyl-3-cyclohexenyl)-2-propanol. **22.** Coniferyl alcohol, 3-(4-hydroxy-3-methoxyphenyl)-2-propen-1-ol. **23.** (a) Hordinene, $p\text{-}HOC_6H_4\text{-}CH_2CH_2N(CH_3)_2$ or $p\text{-}HOC_6H_4CH(CH_3)N(CH_3)_2$ (actually, the former). **24.** LL, phenyl ether. **26.** PP, $5\text{-}(p\text{-}HOC_6H_4N=NC_6H_4\text{-}C_6H_4N=N)\text{-}2\text{-}hydroxybenzoic acid.

Chapter 23

23.6 Adipic acid, $HOOC(CH_2)_4COOH$. **15.** Beckmann rearrangement:

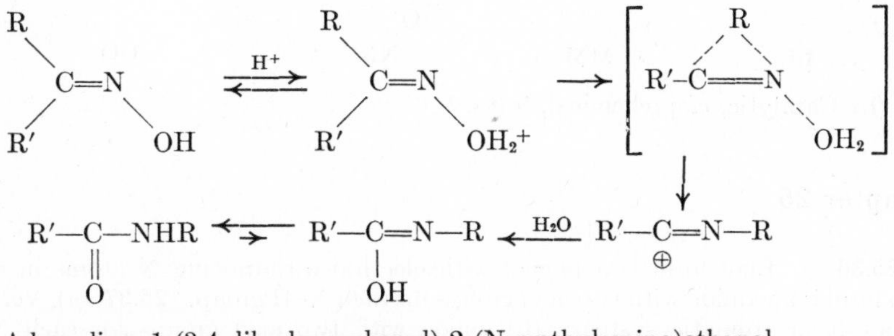

19. Adrenaline, 1-(3,4-dihydroxyphenyl)-2-(N-methylamino)ethanol.
20. $(CH_3)_2C=CHCH_2CH_2C(CH_3)=CHCHO$, citral *a* (–H and –$CH_3$ *trans*), citral *b* (–H and –CH_3 *cis*); dehydrocitral, $(CH_3)_2C=CHCH=CHC(CH_3)=CH\text{-}CHO$. **21.** Carvotanacetone, 5-isopropyl-2-methyl-2-cyclohexen-1-one. **22.** Phellandral, 4-isopropyl-3,4,5,6-tetrahydrobenzaldehyde. **23.** Piperine:

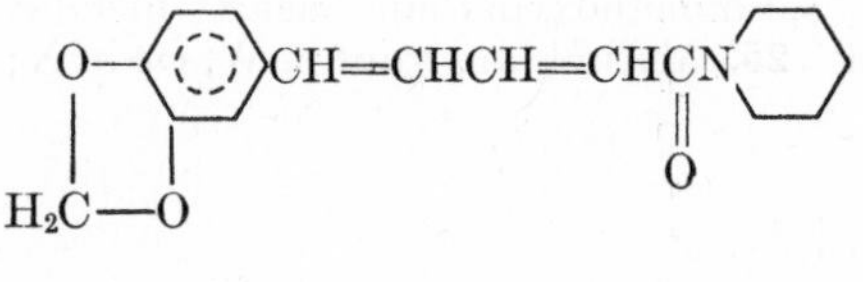

Chapter 24

24.5 Resolvable, b. **24.6** *Meso*, e, f. **24.7** One pair enant., a; two pairs enant., e, h, i; one pair enant. and one *meso*, b, c, d, f, g. **24.8** *cis* →*meso*; *trans* → racemate. **24.9** Racemate, a, c, d; *meso*, b. **24.15** A, $(CH_3)_2C(OH)CH_2OH$; B, *cis*-1,2-cyclohexanediol; C, 2-hydroxycyclohexanone; D, HOOCCHOHCH-OHCOOH; E, $HOCH_2CHOHCHOHCH_2OH$; F, $HOCH_2CHOHCOCHO$; G, $HOCH_2CHOHCHO$; H, $HOCH_2(CHOH)_3CHO$; I, $HOCH_2(CHOH)_4COOH$.

5. A, 1,10-decanediol; B, 2,5-hexanediol; C, 1,6-hexanediol; E, 1,5-pentanediol; F, glycerol; G, 3,4-hexanediol; H, 3-methyl-6-ethyl-3,6-octanediol; K, racemic *threo*-1-phenyl-1,2,3-propanetriol; L, 2,5-dimethyl-3-hexyne-2,5-diol; M, 1,4-bu-tynediol; N, 1,4-butanediol; O, 1,1,4,4-tetraphenyl-1,4-butanediol. **9.** P, 1,3-pro-panediol; Q, 1,2-propanediol; R, 2-methoxyethanol; S, dimethoxymethanol (dimethylacetal of formaldehyde); T, α-hydroxypropionaldehyde; U, hydroxy-acetone; V, β-hydroxypropionaldehyde; W, propionic acid; X, ethyl formate; Y, methyl acetate; Z, *cis*-1,2-cyclopropanediol;

AA   BB

10. CC, $C_6H_5COCHOHC_6H_5$ (benzoin); DD, $C_6H_5COCOC_6H_5$ (benzil); EE, cyclo-$(CHOH)_6$; FF, *cis*-9-octadecenoic acid; GG, 9,10-dihydroxyoctadec-anoic acid; HH, $C_6H_5COOCH_2CHOHCH_2OH$; II, glycerol; JJ, pinacol; KK, pinacolone. **12.** Here, any intermediate free radical with odd electron on asym-metric carbon loses configuration; it may be flat or an oscillating pyramid like NH_3. **14.** (b) 7 *meso*, one pair enantiomers.

17.

LL   MM   NN   OO

22. (b) Catalytic, *cis*; chemical, *trans*.

Chapter 25

25.36 (c) Enol form is a phenol with electron-withdrawing N atoms in ring; keto form is an amide with two acyl groups for each N–H group. **25.37** (a) Veronal cannot form aromatic system; (b) amide with two acyl groups for each N–H group. **25.46** (a) An amide; (b) n-valeranilide (N-phenyl-n-valeramide).

16. C, 1,3-cyclohexanedicarboxylic acid; F, 1,4-cyclohexanedicarboxylic acid; H, succinic acid; J, 1,2-cyclobutanedicarboxylic acid. **17.** K, 1,5-hexadiene; O, 2,5-dimethylcyclopentanecarboxylic acid. **18.** Q, $H_2NCONHNO_2$; R, semi-carbazide. **23.** T, hexamethylbenzene; U, $C_6(COOH)_6$; V, trianhydride of U. **24.** Hemipinic acid, 3,4-dimethoxyphthalic acid; metahemipinic acid, 4,5-di-methoxyphthalic acid. **25.** Methyls are *trans* in W, *cis* in X; (b) W is resolvable.

Chapter 26

26.4 (d) Ethyl 2,5-dioxocyclohexane-1,4-dicarboxylate.   **26.8** (a) ethyl benzoate + ethyl phenylacetate;   (b) ethyl oxalate + ethyl glutarate;   (c) ethyl phthalate + ethyl acetate.   **26.12** A, $C_2H_5OOCCOCH(CH_3)COOC_2H_5$. **26.16** 6.8% enol.

11. Nerolidol, $RCH_2C(CH_3)(OH)CH=CH_2$.   **12.** (c) Menthone, 2-isopropyl-5-methylcyclohexanone.

Chapter 27

27.5 $\sim\!\!\sim\!O(CH_2)_9COO(CH_2)_9COO(CH_2)_9CO\sim\!\!\sim$.   **27.7** (a) Diketopiperazine, 6-ring diamide;   (b) unsaturated acid;   (c) γ-lactam, 5-ring amide;   (d) δ-lactam, 6-ring amide.   **27.8** See Sec. 18.8.

5. C, citric acid, $(HOOCCH_2)_2C(OH)COOH$;   E, ϵ-hydroxycaproic acid;   F, $ClCH_2CHOHCH_2Cl$;   J, citric acid (see C);   M, coumarin (see Problem 23.30, page 643);   Q, 1-phenyl-3-nonanone.   **12.** MM, *meso*; NN, racemic.   **13.** Camphoronic acid, $HOOCCH_2C(CH_3)(COOH)C(CH_3)_2COOH$.   **14.** Pantothenic acid, $HOCH_2C(CH_3)_2CHOHCONHCH_2CH_2COOH$.

15.

Terebic acid

Terpenylic acid

Chapter 28

28.6 (b) Maleic→racemate, fumaric→*meso*;   (c) maleic→racemate, fumaric→ *meso*.   **28.12** B, $CH_3CH(CH_2COOH)_2$;   D, δ-ketocaproic acid;   E, CH_3COCH_2-$CH_2CH(COOC_2H_5)_2$;   F, $C_6H_5CH(CH_2COC_6H_5)_2$;   H, $CH_2=CHCH(COOH)CH_2$-CH_2COOH;   I, $C_2H_5OOCCH=C(COOC_2H_5)CH(COOC_2H_5)COCH_3$;   J, $HOOC$-$CH=C(COOH)CH_2COOH$.   **28.13** (a) K, $H_2C=C(COOC_2H_5)_2$;   (c) glutaric acid. **28.17** 1,4-Diphenyl-1,3-butadiene + maleic anhydride;   1,3-butadiene + 2-cyclopentenone;   1,3-butadiene (two moles).   **28.18** (a) 3-Ethoxy-1,3-pentadiene + *p*-benzoquinone;   (b) 5-methoxy-2-methyl-1,4-benzoquinone + 1,3-butadiene.

3. (a) $C_6H_5COCH_2CH(C_6H_5)CH(CN)COOC_2H_5$;   (f) $CH_3COCH_2C(CH_3)_2$-$CH(COOC_2H_5)COCH_3$;   (h) $(C_2H_5OOC)_2CHCH_2CH(COOC_2H_5)_2$;   (j) O_2NCH_2-$CH_2CH_2COOCH_3$;   (l) $O_2NC(CH_2CH_2CN)_3$;   (m) $Cl_3CCH_2CH_2CN$.   **5.** A, $(C_2H_5OOC)_2CHCH(C_6H_5)CH_2COCH_2CH(C_6H_5)CH(COOC_2H_5)_2$;   B, $(C_2H_5OOC)_2$-$CHCH(C_6H_5)CH_2COCH=CHC_6H_5$;   C, 4,4-dicarbethoxy-3,5-diphenylcyclohexanone.   **6.** (d) 4-Acetocyclohexene;   (g) 5-nitro-4-phenylcyclohexene;   (h) 1,4-dihydro-9,10-anthraquinone.   **7.** (a) 1,3,5-Hexatriene + maleic anhydride;   (b) 1-isopropyl-4-methyl-1,3-cyclohexadiene + maleic anhydride;   (c) 1,3-butadiene + benzalacetone;   (d) 1,3-butadiene + acetylenedicarboxylic acid;   (e) 1,3-cyclopentadiene + *p*-benzoquinone;   (f) 1,1'-bicyclohexenyl (see Problem 6(b)) + 1,4-naphthoquinone (see Problem 6(h));   (g) 1,3-cyclopentadiene + crotonaldehyde;   (h) 1,3-cyclohexadiene + methyl vinyl ketone.   **8.** *cis*-Addition. **9.** (a) Racemate;   (b) *meso*;   (c) 2 *meso*;   (d) *meso*.   **11.** N, glyceraldehyde; aconitic acid, $HOOCCH=C(COOH)CH_2COOH$;   tricarballylic acid, $HOOC$-$CH(CH_2COOH)_2$;   "tetracyclone," tetraphenylcyclopentadienone;   U, tetraphenylphthalic anhydride;   W, pentaphenylbenzene;   BB, $(CH_3)_2C(CH_2COOH)_2$;   DD, $CH_3CHOHC=CCH_3$;   EE, $CH_3COC=CCH_3$;   FF, acetylacetone;   GG, $(CH_3)_2C=CHCOOH$;   JJ, $HOOCCH=C(CH_3)CH_2COOH$.

Chapter 29

29.3 Glucose + 5HIO$_4$→5HCOOH + HCHO. **29.4** A, gluconic acid; B, glucitol; C, glucaric acid; D, glucuronic acid. **29.9** I, (+)-allose; II, (+)-altrose; VI, (−)-idose; VII, (+)-galactose; VIII, (+)-talose. **29.14** (a) 36.2% α, 63.8% β. **29.18** HCHO instead of HCOOH. **29.19** (a) Six-ring. **29.20** (a) Six-ring; (b) enantiomer. **29.21** (a) Five-ring; (b) optically active, L-family; (c) enantiomer.

4. E and E', allitol and galactitol; F, glucitol (or gulitol); H, glucitol (or gulitol)· I and I', allitol and galactitol; N, ribitol; O, arabitol (or lyxitol).

5. (a) P: (d)

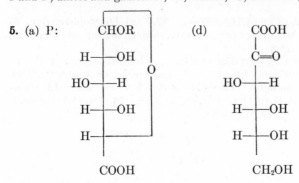

6. (a) 5 carbons, five-ring; (b) C–1 and C–4; (c) Q, methyl α-D-arabinofuranoside. **7.** Salicin, o-(hydroxymethyl)phenyl β-D-glucopyranoside. **8.** Indican, a β-D-glucopyranoside. **9.** Bio-inonose, the pentahydroxycyclohexanone in which alternating –OH groups are *trans* to each other. **11.** (a) T, D-ribose; U, D-arabinose; (b) 3-phosphate.

Chapter 30

30.10 C$_{12}$H$_{20}$O$_{10}$, non-reducing. **30.13** (a) 3 molecules of HCOOH per molecule of amylose. (b) Moles HCOOH/3 = moles amylose; wt. amylose/moles amylose = mol. wt. amylose; mol. wt. amylose/wt. per glucose unit (162) = glucose units per molecule of amylose. (c) 474. **30.14** (a) Largest group (another glucose unit) in axial position. **30.15** A poly-α-D-glucopyranoside; chain-forming unit, attachment at C–1 and C–6; chain-linking unit, attachment at C–1, C–3, and C–6; chain-terminating unit, attachment at C–1. **30.16** A poly-β-D-xylopyranoside; chain-forming unit, attachment at C–1 and C–4; chain-linking unit, attachment at C–1, C–3, and C–4; chain-terminating unit, attachment at C–1.

1. Gentiobiose, 6-O-(β-D-glucopyranosyl)-D-glucopyranose. **2.** (a) Trehalose, α-D-glucopyranosyl α-D-glucopyranoside; (b) isotrehalose, α-D-glucopyranosyl β-D-glucopyranoside; neotrehalose, β-D-glucopyranosyl β-D-glucopyranoside. **4.** Raffinose, α-D-galactosyl unit attached at C–6 of glucose unit of sucrose; melibiose, 6-O-(α-D-galactopyranosyl)-D-glucopyranose. **5.** (a) Melezitose, α-D-glucopyranosyl unit attached at C–3 of fructose unit of sucrose; turanose, 3-O-(α-D-glucopyranosyl)-D-fructofuranose. **6.** (b) D-Glucuronic acid; (c) D-xylose **11.** I, D-CH$_2$OHCHOHCHOHCOOH; J, HOOCCHO. **12.** (a) 3 molecules of HCOOH per molecule of cellulose; (c) 1390 glucose units.

Chapter 31

31.1 2; 10; 14. **31.3** (b) *trans*-Decalin; both large groups (the other ring) on each ring are equatorial. (c) *cis*-Addition, rate control; *trans*-addition, equilibrium control. **31.4** Benzylic substitution; elimination of HBr to give conjugated alkenylbenzene; benzylic-allylic substitution; elimination to give aromatic ring. **31.5** (a) Cadalene, 4-isopropyl-1,6-dimethylnaphthalene. **31.8** 1,2,4-Benzenetricarboxylic acid; 1,2,3-benzenetricarboxylic acid. **31.16** Deactivating acyl group transformed into activating alkyl group. **31.19** 23 kcal; 31 kcal. **31.21** (a) Most stable *tetra*hydro product; (b) reversible sulfonation yields more

stable product. **31.28** Pyrene,

6. F, phenanthrene. **8.** G, 1,2-benzanthracene; H, chrysene. **9.** α-Naphthol. **10.** (a) Diels-Alder; (c) J is *meso* compound, K is racemate. **11.** (d) Final product, β-tetralone (2-oxo-1,2,3,4-tetrahydronaphthalene). **12.** (a) 1,6-Cyclodecanedione; (b) bicyclic unsaturated ketone, one 7-ring and one 5-ring; (d) each ring has aromatic sextet. **13.** Eudalene, 7-isopropyl-1-methylnaphthalene. **14.** Y, 3,3'-dimethylbiphenyl; CC, 3,4'-dimethylbiphenyl; FF, hexaphenylethane; HH, tetraphenylmethane; II, 1,3,5-triphenylbenzene.

Chapter 32

32.1 B, CH₃COCH(COOC₂H₅)CH(COOC₂H₅)COCH₃. **32.3** —COOH deactivates ring. **32.4** Two units of starting material linked at the 5-positions through a —CH₂— group. **32.5** Cannizzaro reaction. **32.9** Hygrine, 2-acetonyl-N-methylpyrrolidine; hygrinic acid, N-methyl-2-pyrrolidinecarboxylic acid. **32.11** Hofmann degradation of nicotinamide. **32.12** Amine > imine > nitrile.

3. Pyrroline has double bond between C–3 and C–4. **4.** C, acetonylacetone. **5.** Porphin, with same ring skeleton as in hemin, page 876. **6.** D, 2–COOH; E, 3–COOH; F, 4–COOH. **7.** (a) 5- or 7-methylquinoline; (b) G, 7-methylquinoline. **9.** (e) Perkin reaction; (g) Reimer-Tiemann reaction. **10.** (See below for parent ring systems.) I, 2,4,6-Trihydroxy-1,3-diazine; K, 3,6-dimethyl-1,2-diazine; L, 3,5-dimethyl-1,2-diazole; M, 2,3-dimethyl-1,4-diazanaphthalene; N, 1,3-dioxolan-2-one (ethylene carbonate); P, 3-indolol (indoxyl, see Problem 8, page 779); R, 2,5-dimethyl-1,4-diazine; S, 1,3-diazolid-2-one (2-imidazolidone, ethyleneurea); T, 4,5-benzo-2-methyl-1,3-diazole (2-methylbenzimidazole); W, 2,4-dihydroxyquinoline; BB, 1,2-diazolid-3-one (3-pyrazolidone).

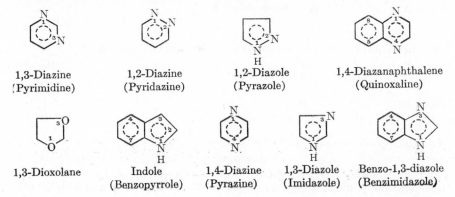

1,3-Diazine (Pyrimidine)   1,2-Diazine (Pyridazine)   1,2-Diazole (Pyrazole)   1,4-Diazanaphthalene (Quinoxaline)

1,3-Dioxolane   Indole (Benzopyrrole)   1,4-Diazine (Pyrazine)   1,3-Diazole (Imidazole)   Benzo-1,3-diazole (Benzimidazole)

11. II, 3,4-(CH₃O)₂C₆H₃CH₂CH₂NH₂; KK, 3,4-(CH₃O)₂C₆H₃CH₂COCl; LL, amide; MM, a 1-substituted-7,8-dimethoxy-3,4-dihydroisoquinoline; papaverine, the corresponding substituted isoquinoline. **12.** SS, (C₂H₅)₂NCH₂CH₂CH₂CHBr-CH₃; UU, 8-amino-6-methoxyquinoline; Plasmochin, 8-amino group of UU alkylated by SS. **13.** Nicotine, 2-(3-pyridyl)-N-methylpyrrolidine. **14.** AAA, *o*-hydroxybenzalacetophenone; (c) oxygen contributes a pair of electrons to complete an aromatic sextet. **15.** Tropinic acid, 2-COOH-5-CH₂COOH-N-methylpyrrolidine. **17.** (a) Guvacine, 1,2,5,6-tetrahydro-3-pyridinecarboxylic acid; arecaidine, N-methylguvacine. (b) Nicotinic acid.

Chapter 33

33.1 —NH₂ > —COO⁻; proton goes to —NH₂ to form ⁺H₃NCH₂COO⁻. **33.2** —COOH > —NH₃⁺; —COOH gives up proton to form ⁺H₃NCH₂COO⁻. **33.5** (a) On acid side; (b) on basic side; (c) more acidic and more basic than for glycine. **33.8** 4 isomers. **33.9** (a) CyS-SCy, Hylys, Hypro, Ileu; (b) CyS-SCy, *meso* and pair of enantiomers; others, two pairs of enantiomers. **33.11** Intermediate is CH₃CH(NH₂)CN. **33.12** A, (CH₃)₂CHCH(COOC₂H₅)COCOOC₂H₅; B, (CH₃)₂CHCH₂COCOOC₂H₅. **33.15** (a) 22.4 cc; (b) 44.8 cc; (c) no N₂. **33.16** Minimum mol. wt. = 114; could be valine. **33.18** Salmine, AlaArg₅₀-Gly₄IleuPro₆Ser₇Val₃. **33.19** Same as empirical formula (preceding problem). **33.20** Minimum mol. wt. = 70300. **33.21** (a) 16700; (b) 4. **33.22** (a) Phe.-Val.Asp.Glu.His; (b) His.Leu.CySH.Gly.Ser.His.Leu; (c) Tyr.Leu.Val.CySH.-Gly.Glu.Arg.Gly.Phe.Phe.

2. D, HOCH₂CH₂CH₂CH(NH₃⁺)COO⁻. **3.** (a) F, CH₃CONHC(COOC₂H₅)₂-CH₂CH₂CHO; J, CH₃CONHC(COOC₂H₅)₂CH₂(CH₂)₂CH₂NHCOCH₃. (b) K, NCCH₂CH₂CH(COOC₂H₅)₂; O, ⁺H₃NCH₂CH₂CH₂CHClCOO⁻. **4.** (a) Diketopiperazine, cyclic diamide; (b) unsaturated acid; (c) γ-lactam, 5-ring amide; (d) δ-lactam, 6-ring amide. **6.** (a) Betaine, ⁺(CH₃)₃NCH₂COO⁻; (b) trigonelline, N-methylpyridinium-3-carboxylate (dipolar ion). **7.** Q, C₂H₅OOCCH₂CH₂-NHCONH₂; R, a dihydroxydihydro-1,3-diazine (see page 905 for parent diazine ring system); S, a dihydroxydihydro-5-bromo-1,3-diazine; U, 2-chloro-4-amino-1,3-diazine; V, 4-chloro-2-amino-1,3-diazine. **9.** Minimum mol. wt. = 13000; minimum of one Fe atom and six S atoms. **10.** (a) Approx. 32 —CONH₂ groups; (b) 395–398 peptide links plus —CONH₂ groups; (c) 367–370 amino acid residues. **11.** Val.Orn.Leu.Phe

$$\text{·Pro·} \qquad \text{·Pro·}$$

Val.Orn.Leu.Phe

Gramicidin S
Cyclic decapeptide

12. Beef insulin:

Chain A:

Gly.Ileu.Val.Glu.Glu.Cy.Cy.Ala.Ser.Val.Cy.Ser.Leu.Tyr.Glu.Leu.Glu.Asp.⌐

⌐Tyr.Cy.Asp

Chain B:

Phe.Val.Asp.Glu.His.Leu.Cy.Gly.Ser.His.Leu.Val.Glu.Ala.Leu.Tyr.Leu.Val.Cy.⌐

⌐Gly.Glu.Arg.Gly.Phe.Phe.Tyr.Thr.Pro.Lys.Ala

(g) DNP.NH(CH₂)₄CH(NH₃⁺)COO⁻ from ε-amino group of Lys. If Lys had been terminal, would have gotten a double DNP derivative of it, and no DNP.Phe.

A

920

INDEX

O

P

R

R, symbol, 75
Racemates, **323–324**, 330–331
  resolution of, 548–552
Racemization, 377–378, 380
Radicals, free (*see* Free radicals)
(+)-Raffinose, 799–800
Rast method, 244
Rate-determining step, 375, 378
Rayon, 798–799
Reactivity, in electrophilic substitution,
  285–286, **290–293**
  and orientation, 92, 290–291
  relative, 33–34
  theory of, **291–293**
Rearrangement, to carbon, 256–259, 580–
  581, 600, 664–669
  to nitrogen, 535–538
  to oxygen, 590–591
  stereochemistry, 536–537, 667–669
Reducing sugars (*see* Sugars)
Reduction (*see* Hydrogenation; specific
  compound or family)
Reductive amination, 527, 528, **532–534**,
  865
Reformatsky reaction, 715–717
Reimer-Tiemann reaction, 596, **603–604**
  heterocyclic compounds, 840–841
Reppe, W., 165
Reserpine, 835
Resolution, of racemates, 331, 549–552
Resonance, **224**, 230–231
  benzene, 224–225, 226–230
  carboxylic acids, 451–453
  conjugated dienes, 231–233
  and electron release, 295–297
  and electron withdrawal, 404–405
  hyperconjugation, 270
Resonance energy, anthracene, 823
  benzene, 226
  conjugated dienes, 233
  definition, 224
  heterocyclic compounds, 837, 843
  naphthalene, 805
  phenanthrene, 823
  (*See also* Resonance stabilization)
Resonance stabilization, alkyl radical, 269–
  270
  allyl radical, 267–268
  amines, 546
  aryl and vinyl halides, 394
  benzyl carbonium ion, 277–278
  benzyl radical, 268–269
  phenols, 597–598
  triphenylmethyl radical, 274
Resorcinol, 595, **630**
Ribitol, 762
Ribonucleic acids (RNA), 884–886
(−)-Ribose, configuration, 761–762
  Kiliani-Fischer synthesis, 763
  in RNA, 884

Ring closure, **197–198**, 203
  anthracene derivatives, 826–828
  heterocyclic compounds, 839–840, 851–
  856
  isoquinoline derivatives, 853–854
  naphthalene derivatives, 820–822
  phenanthrene derivatives, 828–830
  quinoline derivatives, 851–852
Rosanoff, 764
Rotation, hindered, 102, 104, 105
  specific (*see* Specific rotation)
Rubber, "heavy," synthesis, 649
  natural, 187
  synthetic, 186–190, 696, 698
  vulcanized, 187
Ruberythric acid, 799
Ruff degradation, **755–756**, 762–763
Russell, Glen, 259

S

Saccharic acid, 748
Saccharin, preparation, 517
Safrole, 589
Salicin, 779
Salicylaldehyde, 596, **603**, 612
Salicylic acid, 603
Saligenin, 608
Salmine, 868
Sandmeyer reaction, 571–572, **574**
Sanger, Frederick, 869, 888
Saponification, 495
Saponification equivalent of esters, 499
Saran, 186
Sarett, Lewis, 740
Schiff test, aldehydes, 644
Schotten-Baumann technique, 476, 556
Schrödinger, Erwin, 4
Semicarbazide, 625, **633**
Semicarbazide hydrochloride, 633
Semicarbazones, 625, 633
Septanose ring, 800
Serine, *t* 860
Sheehan, John C., 888
1,2-Shifts, 258
  glycols, 667–670
    pinacol rearrangement, 665
  migration terminus, 667–669
  stereochemistry, 536–537, **667–670**
  synthesis of phenol, 590–591
σ (sigma) bonds, 9, 60
Silver acetylide, 169
Skraup synthesis, 851–852, 855
S_N1 reaction, 376
  mechanism and kinetics, 375–376
  reactivity, 378–379
  rearrangement, 379–380
  stereochemistry, 376–378
S_N2 reaction, 370–371
  compared with S_N1, 380–382
  reactivity, 373–375
  stereochemistry, 371–373

1a	2a	3b	4b	5b	6b	7b		8b
1 H 1.0080								
3 Li 6.940	4 Be 9.013							
11 Na 22.991	12 Mg 24.32							
19 K 39.100	20 Ca 40.08	21 Sc 44.96	22 Ti 47.90	23 V 50.95	24 Cr 52.01	25 Mn 54.94	26 Fe 55.85	27 Co 58.94
37 Rb 85.48	38 Sr 87.63	39 Y 88.92	40 Zr 91.22	41 Nb 92.91	42 Mo 95.95	43 Tc [99] **	44 Ru 101.1	45 Rh 102.91
55 Cs 132.91	56 Ba 137.36	a 57 La 138.92	72 Hf 178.50	73 Ta 180.95	74 W 183.86	75 Re 186.22	76 Os 190.2	77 Ir 192.2
87 Fr [223]	88 Ra 226.05	b 89 Ac [227]						

a Lanthanide series

58 Ce 140.13	59 Pr 140.92	60 Nd 144.27	61 Pm [145]	62 Sm 150.35

b Actinide series

90 Th 232.05	91 Pa 231	92 U 238.07	93 Np [237]	94 Pu [242]

*Symbol adopted officially in 1957 by the Commission on Inorganic
Nomenclature of the International Union of Pure and Applied Chemistry